PLANT PROPAGATION
by
TISSUE CULTURE
Part 2

In Practice

Edwin F. George Ph.D.

2nd Edition, 1993/1996

Exegetics Limited

© 1993, 1996 Copyright of the publishers:

Exegetics Ltd.,
Edington, Wilts.
BA13 4QG , England.

First published 1984
Second (revised) edition 1993/1996

A catalogue record for this book is available from the British Library

ISBN 0-9509325-5-8

Part 1
ISBN 0-9509325-4-X
Part 2
ISBN 0-9509325-5-8
Two volume Set
ISBN 0-9509325-6-6

Typeset by L.P. & T.S. Publishing Services, Somerton, Somerset.
Printed in Great Britain by Butler & Tanner Ltd., Frome, Somerset.

All sales and other enquiries should be sent to the publishers, Exegetics Ltd.

Preface

This book completes the second edition of *Plant Propagation by Tissue Culture* which now comprises two separate volumes. The author is grateful for favourable reviews of Part 1 of the series, and apologises that it has taken much longer than expected to prepare Part 2 for publication. He hopes that readers will appreciate the reasons for the delay when they survey the amount of information it contains.

There was a time, while the possiblities of propagating plants *in vitro* were first being explored, when it was thought that the new science would revolutionise horticulture and agriculture. Speculative money became available and new micro-propagtion laboratories were established at a rapid rate. That first flush of enthusiasm is over and it is now realised that, to be effective, micropropagation must serve a real need. Many commercial laboratories have closed and those that survive know that they must be capable of delivering plants reliably at a truly competitive price.

Interest in *in vitro* propagation continues in the academic world, but research effort is tending increasingly to be diverted towards the use of genetic manipulation and gene transfer for crop improvement. However, micropropagation, in its broadest sense, is essential to these objectives.

There is now a very large body of information on *in vitro* propagation of plant material and these books have attempted to give a detailed summary of current knowledge. That little attention has been given in these pages to topics such as anther culture; protoplast isolation, culture and fusion; and genetic transformation of plant material; results from a deliberate decision. To have included such details would have diverted from the primary objective.

The author and publishers wish to thank all those who have helped in any way in the preparation of this book. Our particular thanks go to Dr. P. K. Evans of Southampton University for his continued interest and advice, and for supplying several of the photographs in this volume. Other photographs were kindly provided by International Plant Laboratories Ltd., Baltonsborough, England and Mr. J. W. Spurr of Culture Consulting Services, who has also offered helpful suggestions. We wish to express our thanks to Mr. Andrew Brown of Plant Resources and Marketing, and Mr. John Ewing of John Ewing Orchids, Inc., for help and advice on commercial aspects of micropropagation.

Our appreciation and thanks go to Dr. J. J. Frett and Dr. J. M. Smagula and the Agricultural Institute of Canada, for permission to include two contour diagrams in Fig. 119; Dr. Ulla Gertsson and the Journal of Horticultural Science for allowing us to reproduce Table 128; Dr. P. C. G. van der Linde of Laboratorium voor Bloembollenonderzoek, for help with the diagram on page 887 (and together with the International Society for Horticultural Science, for granting permission to publish it); and the World Patents Index, Derwent Information Ltd., from whose data Table 136 was prepared.

Finally, I am grateful to Mrs. B. Fletcher for her sales expertise and design artwork and to my wife Heather, who has worked tirelessly on all aspects of preparation and without whose help the new edition would never have been completed.

Edwin F. George
November 1995.

Inoculation and transfer work in a large commercial micropropagation laboratory using laminar flow cabinets.

Contents

Table 73. Growth regulators used to induce direct shoot formation from mature organs of dicotyledons (where this is possible).
[Based on 55 protocols for 47 species in 46 papers].

Growth regulators	Use % protocols	Concentrations employed		
		Range μM	Average μM	Average mg/l
Auxins				
IAA	29.1	0.11–28.5	8.41	1.48
NAA	30.9	0.05–21.5	3.96	0.74
IBA	5.4	0.004–9.84	5.74	1.17
2,4-D	1.8	—	9.05	2.0
TEA ‡	1.8	—	38.14	10
> one auxin	1.8	—	—	—
No auxin	32.7	—	—	—
Cytokinins				
Kinetin	25.4	0..46–11.6	4.66	1.00
BAP	50.9	0.10–24.0	7.81	1.75
2-iP	5.4	4.92–24.1	17.88	3.63
Zeatin	10.9	0.09–22.8	4.22	0.92
Adenine sulphate	5.5	98.9–395.7	230.8	93.3
Thidiazuron	1.8	—	13.62	3.00
PBA	1.8	—	16.2	5.0
Coconut milk	1.8	20%	—	20.0%
> one cytokinin	10.9	—	—	—
No cytokinin	3.6	—	—	—
Gibberellins				
GA₃	5.4	0.08–1.4	0.99	0.34
No gibberellin	94.6	—	—	—
No PGRs at all	3.6	—	—	—

‡ 2(3,4-dichlorophenoxy)triethylamine (Dastoor et al., 1981; Smith, 1983)

Table 74. Growth regulators used to induce direct shoot formation from seedling-derived explants of dicotyledons.
[Based on 62 protocols for 50 species in 46 papers].

Growth regulators	Use % protocols	Concentrations employed		
		Range μM	Average μM	Average mg/l
Auxins				
IAA	11.3	0.14–10.96	6.31	1.12
NAA	24.2	0.54–5.37	4.91	0.92
IBA	6.5	0.12–24.6	1.89	0.39
NOA	9.7	0.25–4.95	1.11	0.23
2,4-D	6.5	0.45–9.05	3.85	0.85
Picloram	1.6	—	0.41	0.1
> one auxin	3.2	—	—	—
No auxin	45.2	—	—	—
Cytokinins				
Kinetin	17.7	0.34–27.9	8.37	1.80
BAP	64.5	0.22–221.9	16.16	3.64
2-iP	9.7	19.7–98.4	60.68	12.3
Zeatin	10.9	0.09–22.8	4.22	0.92
Thidiazuron	4.8	—	12.5	2.75
> one cytokinin	8.1	—	—	—
No cytokinin	6.5	—	—	—
Gibberellins				
GA₃	1.6	—	0.58	0.2
No gibberellin	98.4	—	—	—
Other regulants				
CCC	8.1	—	0.63	0.1
No PGRs at all	4.8	—	—	—

grown *in vitro* can sometimes provide a suitable alternative in woody species where the partial rejuvenation caused by *in vitro* culture appears to increase the probability of organogenesis.

As in the induction of indirect shoot formation from callus, direct shoot formation can almost always be induced by a range of concentrations of different regulants, although the optimum response may depend on the use of one or more specific compounds. However, their identity and the levels which are most effective, commonly vary from one experiment to another, between species, between varieties and cultivars of the same species, and

between one kind of explant and another taken from the same plant. The auxins and cytokinins listed in Tables 73 to 75 have been most commonly employed.

The growth regulator treatments summarised in the tables were, in nearly all cases, also used for Stages I and II. Only a few papers mentioned a special growth regulator regime for explant establishment. A comparison of Table 76 with the other tables shows that a higher concentration of auxin, and less cytokinin, has been used with mature explants than with immature ones, or with those derived from shoots or plants grown *in vitro*. In two cultivars of *Begonia × hiemalis*, a BA : NAA ratio of 1 : 10 was most

Table 75. Growth regulators used to obtain direct shoot regeneration from explants taken from *in vitro* shoots or plantlets. [Based on 32 protocols for 30 species in 29 papers].

Growth regulators	Use % protocols	Concentrations employed		
		Range µM	Average µM	Average mg/l
Auxins				
IAA	3.1	—	11.41	2.0
NAA	34.4	0.53–5.38	3.77	0.70
IBA	31.3	0.98–9.84	2.72	0.55
2,4-D	3.1	—	0.45	0.1
TIBA	3.1	—	1.00	0.5
More than one auxin	0	—	—	—
No auxin	25.0	—	—	—
Cytokinins				
Kinetin	6.3	9.29–18.59	13.94	3
BAP	68.8	0.44–15.09	5.78	1.30
2-iP	9.7	19.7–98.4	60.68	12.3
Zeatin	10.9	0.09–22.8	4.22	0.92
Thidiazuron	6.3	0.02–7.72	1.26	2.75
Adenine sulphate	3.1	—	197.8	80.0
Coconut milk	3.1	10.0%	—	10.0%
More than one cytokinin	6.3	—	—	—
No cytokinin	0	—	—	—
Gibberellins				
GA$_3$	6.3	0.29–4.91	2.60	0.9
No gibberellin	93.7	—	—	—
No PGRs at all	0	—	—	—

+ 0.01 mg/l BAP or 1 mg/l NAA + 0.1 mg/l BAP — Welander, 1977). In another cultivar the optimum ratio was 1 : 2. These ratios are unusual: as will be seen from Table 76, it is common to use more cytokinin than auxin. Very little auxin is necessary to induce shoots from immature explants.

Because the formation of callus prior to organogenesis is undesirable, the auxins IAA and NAA are most generally used for direct shoot initiation rather than 2,4–D. IBA has been used frequently to induce shoot formation on explants taken from *in vitro* cultures. BAP, and to a lesser extent, kinetin, have been commonly used as cytokinins. Thidiazuron was employed in comparatively few of the

examples in our samples, but has been shown to be effective in inducing direct shoot formation in several woody plants (Huetteman and Preece, 1993). Keeping *Taraxacum* explants on a medium containing thidiazuron and IAA for an extended period resulted in the formation of abnormal shoots and callus, instead of normal directly–initiated shoots (Song and Chua, 1991).

Precise concentrations of regulants to control morphogenesis can be demonstrated using explants composed of thin cell layers (*e.g.* the epidermis together with some subepidermal and cortical tissues). Tran Thanh Van (1973a,b) showed that the type of meristem formed directly on thin cell layer explants from the floral branches of tobacco, depended on the relative concentration of IAA, kinetin and sucrose. Thus floral buds could only be induced to form in the presence of 0.2 mg/l IAA and 0.2 mg/l kinetin and 30 g/l sucrose; vegetative buds were produced with 0.2 mg/l IAA, 2 mg/l kinetin and 10–30 g/l sucrose; and roots with 2–20 mg/l IAA, (or 0.2 mg/l IBA), 0.02 mg/l kinetin and 10 g/l sucrose.

Use of cytokinins only for induction

In some plants, direct shoot formation is induced by cytokinin alone, and the addition of auxin is inhibitory. The effect in *Physalis minima* can be seen in Fig. 120. Shoots were induced by 0.5–2 mg/l BAP, and the more IAA was added to the medium, the smaller was the number of shoots produced.

Where cytokinins alone induce the formation of shoots, their action may depend on the presence of endogenous auxin within the explant. Sections of cotyledons from *Lycopersicon esculentum* seedlings produced a small number of shoots when cultured with 0.7–1.4 µM zeatin riboside, but not if the explants had been pre–soaked in water (Branca *et al.*, 1991).

The effect of BAP in inducing direct shoot formation from *Pinus pinea* cotyledons, has been found to be dependent on the nitrogen content (probably the NH$_4^+$ level) in the medium. The regulant caused many more cotyledons to produce adventitious shoots, and was effective over a wider range of concentrations, when it was added to media containing Schenk and Hildebrandt (1972) or **Gamborg (1946) PRL–4–C** macronutrients, than to **MS** medium.

Shoot formation and elongation. Although bud formation may have been induced, sometimes shoots do not appear until explants have been transferred to a medium from which cytokinin is lacking. Shoot meristems formed on young leaves of the fern *Adiantum capillus–veneris* placed on **B5** medium containing 0.5 mg/l IBA and 0.01 mg/l BAP, but did not develop into shoots until explants were moved to a medium without regulants (Pais and

Casal, 1987). Similarly, adventitious shoots can be induced to form on parts of embryos or young seedlings of gymnosperms by treatment with cytokinin and/or auxin, but buds do not appear and grow into shoots until explants are moved onto a medium with no growth regulators (page 997).

The concentrations of growth regulators, particularly cytokinins, necessary to induce adventitious bud formation are often inhibitory to shoot elongation. Having placed explants on, or in, a medium which induces bud formation, it is therefore sometimes necessary to transfer them to a medium which has no growth regulators, or to one with a reduced concentration of cytokinin, to induce buds to grow into shoots (*e.g.* in soybean — Saka and Cheng, 1980). Adventitious shoots induced to form on the cotyledons of *Citrulus vulgaris* cotyledons by 5 mg/l BAP plus 0.5 mg/l IAA, were elongated by transferring explants to a medium containing 0.2 mg/l kinetin.

Cytokinin pre–treatment

Pretreating mother plants with cytokinin to improve subsequent *in vitro* morphogenesis has been described in Chapter 5. Somewhat similar results can also be obtained by treating just the explants (or the plant organ from which the explant is to be derived) with cytokinin solutions prior to *in vitro* culture. Examples of effective treatments are given in Table 77.

Harris and Hart (1964) obtained effective root and shoot regeneration from *Begonia* and *Streptocarpus* regardless of whether leaf disc explants were precultured with BAP or kinetin for 24h, or whether these cytokinins were included in the growth medium. By contrast, Economou and Read (1981) reported getting better growth and more distinct shoots

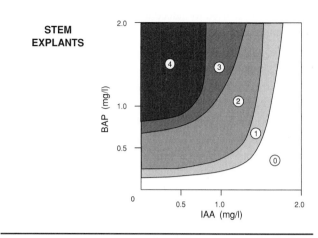

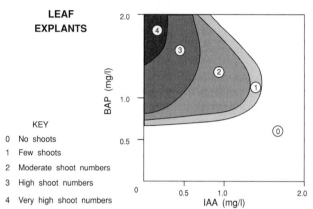

KEY

0 No shoots
1 Few shoots
2 Moderate shoot numbers
3 High shoot numbers
4 Very high shoot numbers

Fig. 120. The relative numbers of shoots formed directly on *Physalis minima* stem and leaf explants in response to exposure to combinations of IAA and BAP.
[Figure drawn from the data given by Bapat and Rao (1977)].

Table 76. The overall average concentrations of auxins and cytokinins used in the examples summarised in Tables 73, 74 and 75 with dicotyledonous explants from different sources.

Regulant	Mature explants	Immature explants	*In vitro* explants
	μM	μM	μM
Auxin	4.83	2.38	2.55
Cytokinin †	7.12	18.85	11.28
Cytokinin:auxin ratio	1.47	7.92	4.22

† Excluding adenine and coconut milk.

from *Petunia* leaf segments, if they were pretreated with a high concentration of BAP for 18 mins (and then transferred to a cytokinin–free medium) rather than being cultured on a medium containing BAP continuously. The number and weight of adventitious shoots was increased when auxin was added to the culture medium. An optimum concentration of NAA in the medium for explants derived from an 18 min leaf pretreatment in 400 mg/l BAP, was 0.1 mg/l (Economou and Read, 1982).

Mhatre *et al.* (1985) only obtained multiple shoots from nodal segments of *Morus indica*, if they had been pre–soaked for 48 h on **Kartha *et al.* (1974)** medium containing 0.5–2 mg/l BAP, before culture on the same medium containing agar.

Presoaking and germinating seeds of *Sesamum indicum* on a solution of 8 mg/l (35 μM) BAP or 2–iP, enhanced the formation of shoots, when shoot cultures were initiated from seedling shoot tips (George L. *et al.*, 1987). The pre–culture of seedlings on cytokinin preparations is similar to the technique used to induce multiple shoots from seeds (Chapter 2 and page 601).

Abscisic acid

It is usually unnecessary to add abscisic acid to the medium to induce direct shoot formation, but supplementing a medium containing 5 μM IAA and 5 μM BAP with 1–30 μM ABA, increased to 100% the proportion of *Cucumis* seedling explants which produced shoots (Niede *et al.*, 1989). A promotion of direct shoot formation has also been observed when 0.1 μM ABA was added for 2–4 weeks to the medium containing BAP and NAA on which *Pinus taeda* cotyledons were incubated. The area of the cotyledons which became morphogenic was increased by the ABA, and up to 56% more adventitious shoots were produced (Sen *et al.*, 1989).

Ethylene

Economou (1991) reviewed the effect of ethylene on shoot formation, but did not distinguish between shoot growth from pre–existing buds in shoot cultures and the induction, formation and growth of adventitious shoots formed directly or indirectly on explants. He concluded that the gas is promotive in some species, but may be inhibitory in others. As with other regulants, the promotive effect of ethylene is only seen at certain critical concentrations.

Ethylene often promotes direct adventitious shoot formation when it is present during the initial phase of culture.

For instance, the addition of 1–10 p.p.m. ethylene to vessels during the first 3–4 days of culture, enhanced adventitious shoot production from the bulb scales of lily (Van Aartrijk *et al.*, 1985). Kumar *et al.* (1986) found that the accumulation of ethylene and carbon dioxide in culture vessels during the first week of culture, promoted the formation of shoot buds on cotyledons of *Pinus radiata*. Thereafter, although excessive concentrations caused some dedifferentiation, if both CO_2 and C_2H_4 were eliminated, bud formation and growth were inhibited.

The number of adventitious shoots formed directly on leaf sections of *Petunia hybrida* was increased by adding 0.1–10 p.p.m. ethylene to the gas phase in vessels, being most effective when added at the beginning of the second week of culture. The inclusion of potassium permanganate solution in the jars (to adsorb ethylene), or the addition of Co^{2+} ions (to inhibit natural ethylene production) or Ag^+ ions (inhibiting ethylene action) reduced shoot formation (Economou, 1991; Dimasi–Theriou *et al.*, 1993).

However direct shoot formation of some plants has been stimulated by adding ethylene inhibitors to the culture medium (page 608).

Activated charcoal

After shoot formation has been induced on gymnosperm explants by cytokinin, activated charcoal is commonly added to Stage II or Stage III media to enhance shoot initiation and growth. Adding 5 g/l charcoal to an agar–

Table 77. Examples of cytokinin pretreatments which have increased adventitious, or lateral shoot formation.

Plant	Part treated	Treatment	Explant	Results	Reference
Dionaea muscipulata	Leaves	24 h in 2.1 mg/l 2iP solution	Leaves of *in vitro* cultured plants	Adventitious and then lateral shoots	Parliman *et al.* (1982b)
Gycine max	Seedlings	Grown with 0.2–20 μM BAP 4 weeks	Cotyledonary nodes	Adventitious shoots: numbers increased with higher levels of BAP pretreatment	Cheng *et al.* (1980) Saka and Cheng (1980)
Morus indica	Nodal segments	0.5–2 mg/l BAP, 48h	Nodal segments	Multiple shoots	Mhatre *et al.* (1985)
Petunia	Leaves	400–800 mg/l BAP for 18 minutes	Leaf segments	Increased numbers of adventitious shoots	Economou & Read (1981)
Philadelphus and *Dirca*	Shoots	BAP in forcing solution	Shoot tips	Improved shoot proliferation	Read & Yang (1987)

solidified **MS** medium enabled bulblets to be initiated more readily from twin scale bases of *Narcissus tazetta* (Steinitz and Yahel, 1982). The presence of activated charcoal in media will sometimes prevent unwanted callus formation on explants. Goncalves *et al.* (1979) reported that 8 g/l inhibited callus formation from explants of different organs of *Eucalyptus* spp. (including seeds, which germinated normally in the presence of charcoal, but otherwise formed callus). Presumably, in these cases, activated charcoal acts by adsorbing growth regulators or natural growth substances.

Gibberellic acid

Gibberellic acid is seldom added to media to induce direct shoot formation, but we note that in *Begonia* × *hiemalis*, 30–60 µM GA₃ enhanced the number of adventitious shoots formed per explant (Simmonds and Werry, 1987).

Root formation

Treatments to induce direct shoot formation sometimes result in simultaneous root initiation. More often shoots are rooted separately at Stage III or outside the culture vessel as described later in Chapter 14.

Growth conditions for direct shoot formation

Photon fluence

Although Table 78 shows that adventitious shoots can be formed under a wide range of light irradiances, where the effect of light on morphogenesis has been examined, an optimum flux density has often been discovered. A greater number of adventitious shoots differentiated from leaf discs or hypocotyl explants of *Brassica oleracea* incubated in a photon flux of 30 µmol m⁻² s⁻¹ than in 100 or 200 µmol m⁻² s⁻¹, but more shoots formed on root segments at the higher flux densities. Shoot production from all three types of explant was better under Grolux light at 32 µmol m⁻² s⁻¹ than under white light at 30 µmol m⁻² s⁻¹ (Lazzeri and Dunwell, 1986b). Similarly bud initiation was greatest on *Cucumis melo* cotyledon segments between 5 and 30 µmol m⁻² s⁻¹. No shoots were produced in darkness and less in 60–300 µmol m⁻² s⁻¹ photon fluence (Niede *et al.*, 1989).

Shoot regeneration from *Fragaria* leaf discs was not dependent on light, but more shoots were produced under low radiant flux (12.5 µmol m⁻² s⁻¹). The periphery of explants became brown and there was no regeneration when flux density was increased above 62.5 µmol m⁻² s⁻¹ (Nehra *et al.*, 1989). In *Rubus*, photon fluence did not influence the proportion of cotyledons which produced adventitious shoots, but more shoots were obtained in continuous light of 21 or 81 µmol m⁻² s⁻¹ than in darkness or in a 16 h day where the PPF was 30 µmol m⁻² s⁻¹. Leaf sections of this plant kept in darkness also produced less shoots than those placed in light of 30 µmol m⁻² s⁻¹ (Fiola *et al.*, 1990).

Daylength

In the examples shown in Table 78, direct shoot formation was induced on many plants in daylengths of 16 hours or more. Only in few plants was a shorter photoperiod employed. Short days or continuous darkness have been found to enhance adventitious bud formation of some species, (*e.g.* on *Crassula argentea* leaf sections — Paterson and Rost (1979); *Robinia* leaf and cotyledon sections — Arrillaga and Merkle, 1993). Such promotion could be a photoperiodic effect (Part 1, page 226) or could be due to there being less degradation of endogenous hormones in light of low total energy.

In some genera, experimental data on the most effective daylength has been inconsistent. Thus Heide (1964, 1965a) found that leaf cuttings of *Begonia* × *cheimantha* produced adventitious shoots more readily when kept in a daylength of 8–10 hours, but Welander (1977), and Simmonds and Nelson (1989), showed that petiole explants of *Begonia* × *hiemalis* (cultured in long days) produced adventitious shoots more readily if stock plants had been grown in a 15–16 hour day, rather than one of 7–8 hours. Possibly the stock plants were able to build up greater reserves of stored energy under the long day conditions.

Day lengths suitable for bud initiation may not always be optimal for shoot growth. For example, although adventitious buds formed on embryos of *Picea abies* regardless of daylength, their growth into shoots demanded a 16 hour day. If explants were kept in a 20 or 24 hour day at this time, 50% of the shoots were an abnormal pale green colour (Von Arnold, 1982).

Short day plants may produce flowers *in vitro* if cultures are maintained in short days (*e.g. Xanthium*, Jacobs and Suthers, 1971; *Glycine*, Dickens and Van Staden, 1985; *Streptocarpus nobilis*, Handro, 1977). Explants taken from plants which have received inductive short days, may produce shoots which flower in inductive (short) days or non–inductive (long) days, although in *Streptocarpus nobilis* the number of flower buds produced was greater in short (8 h) days (Simmonds, 1981).

Temperature

Explants are commonly incubated at 22–27°C to obtain direct shoot regeneration (Table 78). The numbers of

Table 78. Examples of environmental conditions used for direct shoot initiation.

Plant	Stage	Explant	Lighting level Irradiance $\mu mol\ m^{-2}\ s^{-1}$	Lighting level Illuminance lux	Photoperiod (h)	Temperature (°C)	References
Alhagi camelorum	I,II	Various *ex* seedlings.	[37] 8 W/m²		16	25	Bharal & Rashid (1981)
Averrhoa carambola	I,II	Root segments *ex i.v.* seedlings.	65		12	27±1	Rashid *et al.* (1992)
Begonia rex	I,II	Leaf fragments	[79] 17 W/m²		24	24	Chlyah (1972)
	I,II	Thin cell layers *ex* leaves	[79] 17 W/m²		9	25±2	Chlyah & Tran Thanh Van (1975)
	I,II	Leaf segments	(22.5)	1800	?	22	Bigot & Nitsch (1968)
Betula pendula	I,II	Leaf sections	36		16	25	Leege & Tripepi (1993)
Brassica campestris	II	Stem & leaf segs.	(16.1)	120 ft.c.	12	25±2	Cheema & Sood (1987)
	II	Cotyledon	30–40		16	24	Hachey *et al.* (1991)
Brassica napus	II	Internode	[140] 30 W/m²		16	26	Kartha *et al.* (1974a)
Brassica oleracea	I,II	Peduncle sections	80–100		16	25	Farnham & Nelson (1993)
Coleus parviflorus ➤	I	Leaf sections	Dark (5 weeks)		—	24	Asokan *et al.* (1984a)
	II		(18.8)	1500	16	24	
Chrysanthemum × *morifolium*	I,II	Stem and leaf	96		16	24±1	Lu *et al.* (1990)
Cucumis melo	I,II	Cotyledon & primary leaf	(31.2)	2500	16	24	Blackmon *et al.* (1981a)
Cyclamen persicum	I,II	Tuber tissue	Dark		—	24	Geier (1977)
Dianthus caryophyllus	I,II	Petals *ex* young buds	(50)	4000	15	25±1	Vainstein *et al.* (1992)
Fragaria × *ananassa*	I,II	Leaf discs *ex i.v.* plants	40–50		16	25/23(±1)	Sorvari *et al.* (1993)
	I,II	Young leaves	12.5		16	26	Nehra *et al.* (1988)
Freesia × *hybrida*	I	Young flower buds	Dark (8 weeks)		—	25	Pierik & Steegmans (1975a, 1976b)
	I		Light (8 weeks)		24	23	Pierik & Steegmans (1975a, 1976b)
➤	I	Flower buds with peduncle	Dark (8 weeks)		—	22	Darimont *et al.* (1982)
	II		(15)	1200	16	24	
Gloxinia hybrida	I	Floral peduncles	(12.5)	1000	18	26±1	Bigot (1974b)
Lavandula latifolia	I,II	Hypocotyl	[93] 20 W/m²		16	26	Calvo & Segura (1989)
Malus × *domestica* ➤	I	Leaf tissue	Darkness for 3 weeks (shoot formation)		—	23±2	Dufour (1990)
	II		40–60		16	23±2	
Matthiola incana	I,II	Sdlg. hypocots. & cotyls.	(6)	500	24	22±2	Gautam *et al.* (1983)
Nicotiana tabacum	I,II	Seedling cotyledons	(37.5)	3000	16	25	Everett (1982)
Psophocarpus tetragonolobus	I,II	Half primary leaf	(31.2)	2500	16	24	Bryan *et al.* (1981)
Rhododendron prinophyllum	I	Ovaries *ex* dormant flower buds	Dark (1 month)		—	25	Dai *et al.* (1987)
	II		35–50		16	25	
Robinia pseudoacacia	I	Immature leaf & cotyledon sections	Darkness		—	26±2	Arrillaga & Merkle (1993)
	II		100		16	26±2	
Rubus idaeus	I,II	Cotyledons *ex* embryos	70		16	24	Gingas & Stokes (1993)
Saintpaulia ionantha	I,II	Petiole sections	50		16	25	Bilkey *et al.* (1978)
	I,II	Petiole sections	(21.5)	1500	12	23	Harney & Knap (1979)
	I,II	Leaf sections	(25)	2000	12	26	Grunewaldt (1983)
Sinningia × *hybrida*	I,II	Floral peduncles	(12.5)	1000	18	26	Bigot (1974b)
Solanum laciniatum ➤	I,II	Leaf discs	(21)	1700	24	25	Davies & Dale (1979)
Vaccinium corymbosum	I	Leaf sections *ex i.v.* plants	Dark (10 days)		—	25–27	Billings *et al.* (1988)
	II		16–21		16	25–27	
	I	Leaves *ex i.v.* cultures	25–40		16	23±2	Callow *et al.* (1988,1989)

Abbreviations   * Found to be best by experimentation   20/15 Day/night temperatures   → =   Increasing to

( ) Approximate irradiances corresponding to illuminance measurements   [ ] conversion of W m^{-2} to $\mu mol\ m^{-2}\ s^{-1}$

† At explant level.   ➤ Adv. shoots directly & from callus

shoots obtained may be reduced if the temperature in the growth room is inappropriate. Shoot regeneration was significantly higher when *Cucumis melo* cotyledon segments were cultured at 25 or 29°C, rather that at 21°C (Niede *et al.*, 1989).

Multiple shoots from seeds

Exposing a germinating zygotic embryo to cytokinin can cause multiple shoots to be formed. Such shoots may have both an adventitious and an axillary origin (Part 1, page 52). Examples of successful treatments are shown in Table 79.

Although the technique is effective on many species, germinating seedlings of some plants do not proliferate in this way. Hisajima (1981) reported no response from *Solanum melongena* and *Lycopersicon esculentum*, and Fischer and Zimmer (1988) obtained typically high shoot proliferation with only *Mimulus luteus*, *Petunia hybrida*, *Sinningia speciosa*, and two *Vriesia* species. Seeds of other plants tested tended to blacken, to form callus, or to germinate without shoot multiplication. However, these authors used only 4.4 µM BAP which was combined with NAA. Hisajima (1982c) found that shoots were more reliably produced using BAP, rather than kinetin or 2–iP.

Because of poor penetration, as much as 25–50 µM BAP was usually required in the medium to induce multiple shoots from seeds, but only 2.5 µM was adequate for embryos dissected from seeds. *Withiana somnifera* seeds only produced multiple shoots when treated with 4.4 µM BAP; higher and lower concentrations of this cytokinin were ineffective (Sen and Sharma, 1991).

Shoot proliferation can also be induced from somatic embryos. Multiple shoots were formed from somatic embryos of *Citrus* cultured on **Murashige and Tucker (1969)** medium with 5 mg/l BAP (Grosser *et al.*, 1988). Although *Panax ginseng* somatic embryos germinated on $\frac{1}{2}$**MS** medium containing 1.4 µM GA$_3$, 2.2 µM BAP and 1.5% sucrose, they produced multiple shoots when the concentration of BAP was increased to 11.1 µM, especially if the sucrose level was also raised to 3%.

INDIRECT ORGANOGENESIS FROM CALLUS

The use of shoots which have been regenerated indirectly from callus is not recommended as a method to micropropagate plants because there is a high risk that regenerated plants will display somaclonal variation. However,

Table 79. Cytokinin treatments which have led to the production of multiple shoots.

Plant	Explant	Medium	Growth regulators	Reference
Anthurium scherzerianum	Seeds	**Knudson (1946) C**	4.4 µM BAP	Zimmer and Bahnemann (1982)
Almond	Seeds	mod. MS	25 µM BAP	Hisajima (1982a,b)
	Embryos	mod. MS	2.5 µM BAP	Hisajima (1982b)
Colocasia esculenta	Seeds	**LS**	5 mM OPE †	Jackson *et al.* (1977a)
Glycine max	Seeds	mod. **MS**	25 µM BAP	Hisajima and Church (1981)
	Zygotic embryos	mod. **MS**	1 µM BAP	Hisajima and Church (1981)
Mulberry	Seeds	**MS**	Either 40.4 µM 2Cl4PU or 44.4 µM BAP	Ohyama and Oka (1982)
Walnut	Seeds	mod. **Cheng (1975)**	40 µM BAP	Rodriguez (1982b)
Ten different plants	Seeds	mod. **MS**	Not given	Hisajima (1981)
Withania somnifera	Seeds	mod. **MS**	4.4 µM BAP	Sen and Sharma (1991)
Several different spp.	Seeds	**Knudson (1946) C**	4.4 µM BAP + 0.54 µM NAA	Fischer & Zimmer (1988)

† see Chapter 11.

the procedures used to obtain indirect shoot formation are summarised in this book for completeness, and because they have some application to the regeneration of plants after gene transfer.

The nature of indirect organogenesis

Although callus can be produced from appropriate tissues of most plants, it is not inevitable that indirect organogenesis will then be possible. Despite subculture to a range of growth regulator treatments, no organs may be produced at all, only a small proportion of cultures may show organogenesis, or roots may be produced and no shoots.

Adventitious shoots and roots can arise indirectly in two ways:

- on primary callus produced on the original explant;

   Indirect organogenesis which occurs during the formation of a small amount of primary callus can be difficult to distinguish from truly direct organogenesis (page 591).

- on callus in which a capacity for morphogenesis has been induced, but which shows no organ formation until it is excised and transferred to another medium.

Although it has come to be recognised that *embryogenic* determination can be induced during the formation of callus, there has been less agreement on whether a similar but different kind of determination occurs during the initiation of callus destined to give rise to shoots or roots. In early literature it was generally assumed that the media and regulants responsible for callus formation induced the formation of an undetermined tissue containing generalised organ primordia. The manner in which these primordia developed was thought to be decided when the callus was subcultured to a second medium (Halperin, 1966; Reinert *et al.* 1977). Organ primordia arise from meristematic nodules (which in another development pathway give rise to somatic embryos), or from nodules in which vascular elements are developed.

It is now thought that the exogenous regulants which induce callus formation are also often responsible for the kind of cytodifferentiation which takes place in the callus and the nature of the organogenesis which will follow at Stage II. Callus of *Medicago sativa* transferred from an induction medium containing a high level of 2,4–D (50 µM) and a low level (5 µM) of kinetin, to a regeneration medium lacking growth regulators, resulted in the formation of shoots and no roots on four different regeneration media (lacking PGRs). If the induction medium contained a low concentration of 2,4–D (5 µM) and a high concentra-

tion of kinetin (50 µM), roots and a smaller number of shoots were produced when **Linsmaier and Skoog (1965)** was used as the regeneration medium, but roots were accompanied by few shoots if the regeneration medium was **B5** or **Schenk and Hildebrandt (1972)** (Walker *et al.* 1978). This shows that although the type of morphogenesis is influenced by the Stage I medium, the nature of the organogenesis which occurs subsequently can be modified.

Callus produced at Stage I can usually be increased by subculture or by conversion to a suspension culture, without loss of morphogenic potential. However, the media and regulants used for this process can influence subsequent morphogenic capacity, and subculture on an unsuitable combination of nutrients and regulants may obliterate it. The caulogenic capacity of callus on a shoot–inducing medium generally rises during the first few weeks in culture on the Stage I medium and then declines during progressive subcultures. Possibly the number of meristematic primordia increases gradually during the initial Stage I culture?

It is unwise to regenerate plants from callus which has been maintained for long periods, because of the enhanced risk of somaclonal variation. Such genetic changes are usually thought to be responsible for the loss of regenerative capacity which often occurs in subcultured callus. An 8 week passage on Stage I medium caused *Arabidopsis* callus to have twice the frequency of adventitious shoot formation, than a 4 week one. However such callus showed a very low rate of shoot regeneration after 6 months in culture, and calli of one geographic race produced only roots after culture for this length of time (Negrutiu *et al.*, 1978a).

Each time shoots were formed from seed–derived callus of *Nicotiana tabacum*, Schiff and Bennici (1991) took leaf, stem, or petiole explants from them and reinitiated callus. A gradual increase in shoot regeneration during the first 2–3 generations of callus was followed by a loss in regenerative capacity. The explants died, gave rise to non–morphogenic callus or, in the case of stem explants, callus which produced teratomatous shoots.

Effective induction

As with direct organogenesis, the auxins and cytokinins best able to bring about shoot or root formation from callus, and the effective concentrations of these regulants, may vary from one species of plant to another, and even between cultures derived from different varieties of plants. Effective treatments may also depend on the nature and origin of the explant, its endogenous hormone content and the conditions used for *in vitro* culture. The most effective combinations of regulants to induce shoot–forming callus from *Albizia lebbeck* seedling explants (Varghese and Kaur, 1991) varied according to the kind of explant used in the following way:

Explant	BAP mg/l	NAA mg/l
Hypocotyl	2	1
Cotyledon	1	0.5
Root	2.5	1
Rachis	1	0.5
Leaf	3	1

The combinations of exogenous regulants necessary to induce adventitious shoot formation frequently differ from those which induce adventitious root formation. Usually adventitious shoots or roots can be induced to form by a range of growth regulator treatments, some being more effective than others.

Thus there is no absolute growth regulator treatment which must be used to obtain adventitious shoots and it is quite usual to observe authors recommending different treatments for the same plants. For example, adventitious shoots were produced on primary callus of *Episcia cupreata* leaf sections cultured on **MS** medium by using:

0.2 mg/l NAA + 0.2 mg/l kinetin	(Johnson, 1978b)
0.1 mg/l NAA + 0.5 mg/l BAP	(Bilkey and McCown, 1979)
0.9 mg/l NAA + 1.1 mg/l BAP	(Chin, 1980)

The results illustrated in the contour diagrams in Chapter 11 (page 446), are typical of those obtained when the effect of combinations of regulants is examined, demonstrating that it is only possible to discover the most advantageous treatments after testing several permutations. Only rarely, has it been suggested that *specific concentrations* of growth substances have been necessary for either root or shoot formation (*e.g.* by Padmanabhan *et al.*, 1974).

Note that there are two components of the number of adventitious shoots produced by auxin/cytokinin treatments. One is the number of shoots formed on each callus at Stage II, the other is the proportion of calluses which produce shoots. Both factors are influenced by the concentrations of regulants selected (usually in the same manner).

Adventitious root formation

The level of regulants present when generalised root/shoot primordia are formed, probably influences the subsequent pattern of development of these centres. The presence of an high endogenous auxin level appears to inhibit shoot formation and this is probably the situation in callus strains which are only capable or root formation. Possibly because tissues differ in their capacity to produce endogenous hormones, or to metabolise exogenous regulants, callus initiated from different explants has sometimes been shown to produce shoots and not roots, or roots and not shoots on identical media.

When morphogenesis is determined by exogenous growth regulators, adventitious root formation is usually promoted when the ratio of auxin to cytokinin is greater than one, or when there are equimolar concentrations of both regulants. The excess of auxin over cytokinin may be in the Stage I, or Stage II medium. Thus roots are likely to be produced when callus, induced with auxin and cytokinin, is subcultured to a medium supplemented only with auxin. Callus initiated in the presence of high concentrations of auxin may also give rise to roots when transferred to a medium in which auxin is absent, simply because there is still a high concentration of auxin within the tissues. For example, *Arabidopsis thaliana* callus, cultured on **MS** medium supplemented with 10 μM 2,4–D, 30 μM IAA and 7 μM kinetin, produced many roots when subcultured to **B5** medium containing 10–50 μM

Table 80. Examples of indirect adventitious root formation being induced by an excess of auxin in the Stage II medium.

Plant	Stage I Callus initiation	Stage I Callus maintenance	Stage II Root formation	Stage II Shoot formation	Reference
Aristida oligantha	9 mg/l 2,4-D	2 mg/l 2,4-D	1 mg/l 2,4-D	—	Lowe and Krul (1981)
	9 mg/l 2,4-D	2 mg/l 2,4-D	—	0.5 mg/l 2,4-D	
Bupleurum falcatum	2 mg/l 2,4-D	1 mg/l 2,4-D	3 mg/l NAA + 1 mg/l kinetin	—	Wang and Huang (1982)
	2 mg/l 2,4-D	1 mg/l 2,4-D	—	0.01 mg/l NAA + 6 mg/l kinetin	

kinetin. Shoots were produced on the second subculture to the same medium (Avetisov, 1976).

Two examples of where an excess of auxin in the final medium has induced root, rather than shoot formation are shown in Table 80. There is however no absolute rule whereby conditions leading to the formation of roots or shoots can be predicted and exceptions will be found to the above observations. For example, the conditions leading to the formation of roots and shoots in *Medicago*, given on page 602, are contradictory.

Effective growth regulator treatments

Dicotyledons

A one stage process. In some dicotyledons and monocotyledons it is possible, using highly competent explants, to induce the formation of callus which gives rise to adventitious shoots on the same medium without transfer. This occurs where the explants chosen have been, for example, shoot tips and axillary buds, stem pith, young petioles and leaves, segments of stems, parts of seedlings. These explants are no different from those which might be chosen to initiate callus from which shoots might be obtained in a second medium.

Table 81 summarises the growth regulators added to the medium in 100 protocols where caulogenesis occurred on the primary callus. The concentrations of auxins employed were less than those required in Stage I of a two–stage induction process (compare Table 81 with Table 82), while the level of cytokinin added to the medium was much higher.

A two–stage process. In many plants where it has been possible to obtain adventitious shoots from callus, two cultural stages have been employed:

1. **Stage I** involves obtaining callus from the explant by culture on an appropriate combination of media ingredients and growth regulators.

2. At **Stage II**, callus obtained from the original explant is transferred to another medium containing different growth regulators. If the treatment is successful, adventitious shoots are produced which may be excised and rooted.

The capacity for morphogenesis is largely determined by the growth regulators supplied at Stage I. The extent and nature of indirect morphogenesis may be modified by the medium and growth regulators supplied at Stage II, but generally at this stage one is seeking to provide the best environment for shoot (or root) formation and growth from meristematic centres which have been established at Stage I.

Frequently Stage I callus is subcultured to increase its volume, before the production of adventitious shoots is attempted. Alternatively it may be used to initiate suspension or protoplast cultures, which, when plated, give rise to callus colonies which can be transferred to Stage II.

Table 82 summarises the growth regulators used in some examples of the typical two–stage process in dicotyledons. The synergistic action of auxin and cytokinin on callus formation is especially pronounced in dicotyledons, and the table shows that morphogenic callus of broad–leafed plants is induced to grow with relatively low concentrations of auxins, usually, but not invariably, combined with a cytokinin. The stronger auxins 2,4–D and NAA are commonly employed at Stage I (in 97% of the protocols in Table 82). Adventitious shoots are induced to form from the callus cultures at Stage II by transfer to a medium containing the weaker (or more rapidly metabolised) auxin IAA, and/or a lower concentration of auxin than used at Stage I, or no auxin at all. Only rarely has it not been necessary to use a cytokinin at Stage II to induce shoot formation. Usually at this stage, a higher concentration of cytokinin is necessary than at Stage I.

Table 82 shows that several researchers have added more than one auxin to the Stage I medium, to induce the formation of callus capable of producing adventitious shoots. Saunders and Bingham (1975) found it advantageous to add 40 µM NAA to 2,4–D to the Stage I medium for *Medicago sativa* (Fig. 112 on Page 446 of Part 1).

A three–stage process. Callus can usually be subcultured before adventitious shoot initiation, although the risk of increasing somaclonal variation in the plants eventually regenerated will then be greater. Subcultured callus is usually maintained on the same medium used for initiation, with the same growth regulators or more commonly with similar regulants but a slightly lower concentration of auxin. A 3–stage process, in which the auxins used for callus initiation, are progressively decreased in concentration, and/or are replaced by less active compounds during callus subculture, can assist in subsequent shoot regeneration. Some examples of the effective use of this technique in dicotyledons are shown in Table 83.

Cytokinins. The effect of adenine in promoting adventitious shoot formation was noted in Chapter 11 (page 443), and so it is no surprise to find that it was used as a cytokinin in a comparatively large proportion of the Stage II protocols summarized in Table 82. Callus of *Trifolium pratense* and *T. incarnatum* induced to form on **B5** medium with 11 µM NAA and 10 µM each of 2,4–D and kinetin, formed shoot buds most effectively when transferred to the same medium (containing 20 mg/l thiamine),

Table 83. Examples of indirect adventitious shoot formation from callus after a 3–stage protocol in dicotyledonns, where callus has been subcultured before shoots are initiated.
Note the gradual reduction in auxin concentration at each stage and/or the replacement of 'active' auxins by weaker ones (see text).

Plant	Explant	Growth regulators used for:			References
		Callus induction	Callus subculture	Adventitious shoot initiation	
Brassica oleracea subspp.	Young hypocotyls	0.11 mg/l 2,4-D, 1.9 mg/l NAA, 4.3 mg/l kinetin	1.9 mg/l NAA, 4.3 mg/l kinetin	8 mg/l IBA, 0.04 mg/l kinetin, 15% CM	Dietert *et al.* (1982)
Cichorium endiva	Zygotic embryos	2.5 mg/l 2,4-D, 0.1 mg/l NAA, 15% CM	0.1 mg/l NAA, 15% CM	0.04 mg/l kinetin	Vasil and Hildebrandt (1966a)
Citrus spp.	Seedling stem or leaf	0.25 mg/l 2,4-D, 2.5 mg/l NAA, 0.25 mg/l kinetin	0.25 mg/l 2,4-D, 0.42 mg/l NAA, 0.25 mg/l kinetin	0.1 mg/l NAA, 0.25 mg/l BAP	Spiegel-Roy & Vardi (1984)
Digitalis purpurea	Seedlings and leaves	1 mg/l 2,4- D, 0.1 mg/l kinetin	1 mg/l IAA, 0.1 mg/l kinetin	1 mg/l IAA, 0.1 mg/l kinetin	Hirotani and Furuya (1977)
Lactuca sativa	Leaf and stem sections	6 mg/l 2,4-D, 0.1 mg/l NAA, 15% CM	0.1 mg/l NAA, 15% CM	10 mg/l IAA, 0.04 mg/l kinetin	Vasil and Hildebrandt (1966a)
Nigella sativa	Leaf segments	2 mg/l 2,4-D, 0.1 mg/l kinetin, 15% CM	0.1 mg/l IAA, 1 mg/l kinetin, 10% CM	No regulants	Chand and Roy (1981)

Cytokinins. In 1979, Bayliss and Dunn concluded that a requirement for cytokinin had not been established in cereals, either for callus initiation, or for the subsequent regeneration of shoots and roots. Although callus of many monocotyledon can be induced satisfactorily on a medium containing just an auxin growth regulator, cytokinins were added in approximately half of the experiments summarised in Table 84, and in several experiments these regulants have been shown to either have a beneficial effect on callus growth (Gamborg *et al.*, 1977; Bhojwani and Hayward, 1977) or, when added to the Stage I medium, to increase the frequency of shoot formation (Wei and Xu, 1990).

At Stage II, results have also shown that incorporation of cytokinin into the medium can sometimes assist morphogenesis or the growth of adventitious shoots and somatic embryos once they have been formed. Shoot initiation was promoted in various *Triticum* species when callus that had been induced and subcultured in the presence of 1–2 mg/l 2,4–D was transferred to a medium containing zeatin and IAA (1 mg/l of each) (Gosch–Wackerle *et al.*, 1979). A requirement for cytokinin was also demonstrated in another series of experiments on wheat by Zamora and Scott (1983). Callus initiated from immature leaves on **MS** medium (plus 50 mg/l arginine and 1 mg/l yeast extract) with 2.2. mg/l 2,4–D, gave rise to shoots

when transferred at Stage II to the same medium plus 0.2 mg/l 2,4–D and either 1 mg/l kinetin or 2iP. Only root regeneration and/or continued callus growth occurred in other combinations of these hormones.

Abscisic acid. Morphogenesis has also been enhanced when cytokinins have been applied to subcultured rice calluses. Rice callus initiated from various explants by 2,4–D, formed shoots when transferred at Stage II to a medium in which there was either 0.2 mg/l BAP or kinetin. The promotive effect of cytokinins at Stage II was greater if 100 mM (26.4) mg/l abscisic acid had also been added to the Stage I (preculture) medium (Nakano and Maeda, 1979; Inoue and Maeda, 1982; Maeda *et al.*, 1982a). Similar results were reported by Yan and Zhao (1982).

Ethylene

Ethylene. Ethylene can be inhibitory to callus growth and shoot morphogenesis, and there are several reports of silver nitrate increasing indirect shoot regeneration (Ag$^+$ ions inhibit ethylene action — Part 1, page 457).

Purnhauser *et al.* (1987) found that silver nitrate dramatically improved the regeneration of shoots from wheat callus and Purnhauser and Gyulai (1993) showed that supplementing the Stage II regeneration medium with 1 µM (0.17 mg/l) silver nitrate increased the number of

Table 84. A summary of the growth regulators used for <u>monocotyledons</u> to obtain adventitious shoot regeneration from callus in 2 steps [Based on 100 protocols in 81 papers covering 56 species].

Growth regulators	Stage 1				Stage 2			
	Use % protocols	Concentrations employed			Use % protocols	Concentrations employed		
		Range μM	Average μM	Average mg/l		Range μM	Average μM	Average mg/l
Auxins								
IAA	9.5	0.57–85.62	20.01	3.51	13.7	1.14–79.91	14.36	2.52
NAA	21.1	0.54–53.70	23.20	4.32	15.8	0.054–30.29	8.34	1.55
2,4-D	69.5	0.10–67.86	13.29	2.94	21.05	0.045–18.10	2.01	0.45
IBA	2.1	24.60–49.20	39.90	7.50	2.1	2.46–49.20	25.83	5.25
CPA	1.1	12.18	12.18	2.00	0	—	—	—
2,4,5-T	1.1	3.91	3.91	0	—	—	—	—
2,4,5-TP	0	—	—	—	2.1	18.55	18.55	5
More than one auxin	7.4	—	—	—	2.1	—	—	—
No auxin	2.1	—	—	—	44.2	—	—	—
Cytokinins								
Kinetin	18.95	0.47–23.23	6.52	1.40	28.4	0.47–50.18	8.68	1.87
BAP	8.42	0.44–8.88	3.97	0.90	14.7	0.44–22.20	5.39	1.21
2-iP	3.16	0.49–34.44	12.14	2.47	3.16	2.46–34.44	13.94	2.83
PBA	6.32	3.23–6.46	4.31	1.33	6.32	0.32–3.23	2.26	0.70
Zeatin	1.1	2.28	2.28	0.50	1.1	0.23	0.23	0.05
Adenine (sulphate)	0	—	—	—	2.1	300.0	300.0	121.3
Coconut milk	10.5	10–15%	—	11%	9.5	5–15%	—	10%
More than one cytokinin	1.1	—	—	—	8.4	—	—	—
No cytokinin	51.6	—	—	—	38.9	—	—	—
Gibberellins								
No gibberellin	100	—	—	—	100	—	—	—
No PGRs at all	0	—	—	—	25.3	—	—	—

wheat and triticale calluses which produced shoots, and also the average number of shoots produced per callus. A similar stimulation occurred when *Brassica napus* hypocotyl segments were cultured on a medium containing 10–100 μM AgNO₃

Adding 1 mg/l silver nitrate to the medium allowed the long–term culture of *Brassica oleracea* callus. Without it the callus died shortly after removal from the hypocotyl explants. Shoot regeneration from the callus was also enhanced by the presence of the Ag⁺ ions (Williams *et al.*, 1990). Direct shoot formation from explants of several *Brassica* species has similarly been found to be markedly enhanced by adding 1–10 μM AVG or 5–30 μM AgNO₃ (Chi *et al.*, 1990).

Copper ions. Two reports have indicated that increasing the concentration of copper ions in media, can enhance indirect morphogenesis. Garcia–Sogo *et al.* (1991) discovered that adding 0.1–5 mg/l $CuSO_4.5H_2O$ [1 mg/l (4 μM) was specially recommended] to the medium (containing **MS** salts) on which callus of *Cucumis melo* was initiated, increased the frequency with which organogenic calli were obtained from cotyledon explants. Also, more adventitious buds were produced per callus, and shoot growth was improved.

The second report is that of Purnhauser and Gyulai (1993) who, after initiating wheat and triticale callus on **Heinz and Mee (1969)** medium with 1 mg/l 2,4–D, transferred it the same medium in which the concentration of copper sulphate was increased from the 0.1 μM normally present in **MS** salts, to 1–100 μM. This had the effect of increasing the number of shoots produced and enhancing the root growth of the plantlets. In wheat anther cultures it was beneficial to increase the copper concentration in **MS** medium to 2 μM. Increasing the copper content of **MS** medium improved direct shoot regeneration from tobacco leaf discs, but did not increase shoot regeneration from *Brassica napus* hypocotyl segments.

Polyamines

Inhibitors of polyamine biosynthesis have been shown to reduce the formation of adventitious shoots and inhibit embryogenesis (Part 1, page 466). The results of Tiburcio *et al.* (1991), which showed that culture of maize callus for 3 months on medium containing 9 μM 2,4–D and 0.5 mM DFMA (an inhibitor of arginine decarboxylase) increased subsequent adventitious shoot formation, are however at variance with these findings. When the calli were transferred to a medium lacking auxin and DFMA, 64% produced shoots (*vs.* 24% of those untreated with DFMA) and the number of shoots per callus increased from 2.0 to 7.9.

Media for indirect shoot formation

A summary of the macronutrient and nitrogen contents of the media used in typical experiments leading to indirect adventitious shoot formation, is given in Table 85.

Dicotyledons. In our sample of experiments on dicotyledonous plants, media with a wide range of compositions had been used, especially for callus induction. They ranged from low salts media without ammonium ions, to media with very high salt concentrations. Callus was frequently subcultured onto a different medium for shoot formation which generally contained higher concentrations of NO_3^- and NH_4^+.

Monocotyledons. Perhaps because adventitious shoot regeneration is less easily obtained, the media selected for callus formation and shoot regeneration in monocotyledons are less variable in composition than those chosen for indirect shoot regeneration from dicotyledons. **MS**, or **Linsmaier and Skoog (1965)** media were used for callus induction in many species, and in most experiments shoot formation was achieved on the same medium as had been used at Stage I, it only being necessary to alter the growth regulators.

Although most workers have found that the concentrations of NO_3^- and NH_4^+ in **MS** have been optimal for callus initiation and shoot formation, it has been possible to obtain callus and shoot formation from monocotyledons on media with little or no NH_4^+ ions, and with no organic source of reduced nitrogen (*e.g* in *Saccharum* — Narayana and Srinivasan, 1971; *Triticum aestivum* — Chin and Scott, 1977). Shoot forming callus can also be obtained from monocotyledons by culture on **Gamborg *et al.* (1969) B5** medium, which contains only 2.0 mM NH_4^+. Lo *et al.* (1980) transferred the callus of *Agropyron, Alopecurus* and *Bromus*, initiated on **B5**, to **Linsmaier and Skoog (1965)** medium to obtain shoot formation, but Bhattacharya and Sen (1980) and Kaur–Sawhney and Galston (1984) were able to obtain shoot regeneration from *Oryza sativa* and *Avena sativa* explants, by culture on **B5** medium at both Stages I and II.

Torello and Symington (1984) initiated callus from mature caryopses of *Lolium perenne*, and also maintained the callus, on a medium containing **MS** salts, but subcultured it to a medium with only ½**B5** salts (contains 1 mM NH_4^+) for the regeneration of green shoots.

Use of amino acids

Adding amino acids, yeast extract, or casein hydrolysate to more dilute media with a low level of inorganic nitrogen, can improve callus growth (Carew and Schwarting, 1958; Green *et al.*, 1974; Larkin, 1982). Plantlets differentiated from *Nigella sativa* callus stopped growing on **MS** medium, unless after two months, 500 mg/l CH and 0.5 mg/l IAA were added (Chand and Roy, 1981). The presence of amino acids in the Stage II medium may also assist the formation of shoots. Negrutiu and Jacobs (1978a) found that shoot formation from *Arabidopsis thaliana* callus was improved if, in the last passage before regeneration at Stage II, all the inorganic nitrogen in **Gamborg (1966) PRL–4–C** medium was replaced with 0.36 g/l glutamine.

The advantages to be gained from supplementing the medium with amino acids are therefore probably the same as when embryogenic callus and somatic embryos are being cultured (see page 629). However, Table 85 shows that adventitious shoot formation can be obtained from many plants (dicots. and monocots.) on media which do not have special additions of organic nitrogen. Amino acids which would supply more than the equivalent of 0.1 mM NH_4^+ were added only to *ca.* 20% of media.

Reducing agents

As little as 1.8 mg/l ascorbic acid autoclaved with the medium on which *Solanum melongena* cell suspensions were cultured, induced an abnormally high frequency of

Table 85. A summary of the macronutrients[†], amino acids and total nitrogen of media used at Stages I and II for the formation of callus and indirect adventitious shoots in dicotyledons and monocotyledons.
[Based on 89 published experiments on dicotyledons and 100 published experiments on monocotyledons].

Stage	Statistic	NO_3^- mM[§] meq/l	PO_4^{3-} meq/l	SO_4^{2-} meq/l	Cl^- meq/l	K^+ meq/l	Ca^{2+} meq/l	Na^+ meq/l	Mg^{2+} meq/l	NH_4^+ mM[§] meq/l	H^+ meq/l	Total inorganic N mM[§] meq/l	Total ionic concentration mM	Amino acid N mM[‡]	Total NH_4^+ (ionic + organic) mM	Total N (ionic + organic) mM[‡]
Dicotyledons																
Callus initiation	Average	32.54	4.04	4.31	5.28	18.56	5.16	1.05	3.15	15.55	2.68	48.10	83.32	1.78	17.34	49.88
	Maximum	178.9	14.99	20.61	17.13	96.19	17.13	26.28	13.38	87.44	9.99	266.3	415.74	215.2	99.36	278.39
	Minimum	2.89	0.35	0.16	0.81	1.66	1.50	0	0.16	0	0.23	2.89	7.85	0	0	2.89
	% media with less than 0.1 mM	0	0	0	0	0	0	78.2	0	11.5	0	0	0	81.6	8.0	0
Shoot formation	Average	38.31	4.44	3.75	5.75	21.06	5.82	0.70	3.03	18.69	2.96	57.02	95.26	1.50	20.20	58.51
	Maximum	183.9	15.43	24.67	22.58	99.11	22.58	34.84	15.01	89.94	10.28	273.9	437.3	32.13	90.83	274.74
	Minimum	2.99	0.35	0.28	0.87	1.66	2.04	0	0.28	0	0.23	2.99	17.63	0	0.04	3.26
	% media with less than 0.1 mM	0	0	0	0	0	0	88.5	0	3.4	0	0	0	80.5	2.3	0
Monocotyledons																
Callus initiation	Average	34.49	4.24	3.03	5.25	19.39	5.16	0.19	2.81	16.62	2.82	51.11	85.70	2.20	18.82	53.31
	Maximum	45.34	20.06	8.79	20.12	30.0	10.06	4.01	6.0	20.61	13.37	65.95	109.98	32.68	53.29	92.69
	Minimum	0	0.35	0.58	0.87	1.66	1.21	0	0.58	0	0.23	0	6.8	0	0	2.03
	% media with less than 0.1 mM	0	0	0	0	0	0	88	0	4	0	0	0	79	2	0
Shoot formation	Average	34.96	3.88	2.92	5.24	18.85	5.24	0.13	2.72	17.47	2.59	52.44	86.60	2.07	19.55	54.51
	Maximum	45.34	9.3	9.59	12.18	30.0	8.90	4.01	3.0	20.61	6.2	65.95	109.98	32.68	53.29	92.69
	Minimum	2.0	0.82	0.58	0	1.66	0	0	0.58	0	0.55	2.0	6.8	0	0	2.03
	% media with less than 0.1 mM	0	0	0	0	0	0	91	0	2	0	0	0	79	2	0

‡ Assuming that all amino nitrogen present in organic additions is available as NH_4^+.

§ The molarity of an ion is obtained by dividing its equivalence by its valence. The molarity and equivalence of NO_3^- and NH_4^+ are thus the same.

† Weights of salts to prepare these macronutrients are given in the Appendix.

root and shoot formation. Fassuliotis *et al.* (1981) suggested that a degradation product of ascorbic acid might be responsible for this stimulation. Adding ascorbic acid to the medium can increase the number of shoots formed from *Nicotiana* (Part 1, page 201) and *Sorghum vulgare* (Wei and Xu, 1990) callus.

Some other antioxidants have been found to have a stimulative effect on rooting (see page 684) and somatic embryogenesis (see below). Cysteine has been shown to increase the frequency of pollen plant production from *Datura metel* anthers (Babbar and Gupta, 1982).

Conditions of culture

As Table 86 shows, callus from which adventitious shoots may be regenerated, has sometimes been initiated in the dark, or in light of weak photon fluence, but more usually has been initiated under the irradiance levels normally used in growth rooms.

The kind of treatment which is most favourable to subsequent morphogenesis is strongly influenced by genotype. For example, darkness was essential for callus induction and growth from stipule explants of *Fragaria* × *ananassa* (Rugini and Orlando, 1992), and necessary for

Table 86. Examples of environmental conditions used for the initiation of shoot–forming callus and subsequent morphogenesis.

Plant	Stage	Explant	Lighting level		Photoperiod (h)	Temperature (°C)	References
			Irradiance $\mu mol\ m^{-2} s^{-1}$	Illuminance lux			
Allium sativum	I,II	Shoot tips	(67.8)	5500	16	27/24	Abo El-Nil (1977)
Allium porrum	I	Basal plate	Dark (24 days)		—	24	Debergh & Standaert-de-Metsenaere (1976)
	II	Callus *ex* I	(50)	4000	17	22	
Anagallis arvensis	I,II	Hypocotyl segments	(25)	2000	14	27	Bajaj & Mader (1974)
Arabidopsis thaliana	I	Seeds, anthers leaves	(12.5)	1000	16	26	Negutiu *et al.* (1978b)
	II	[Callus *ex* I]	(50)	4000	16	25	
Averrhoa carambola	I,II	Basal part of sdlg. stem	65	—	12	27±1	Rashid *et al.* (1992)
Calotropis gigantea	I	Immature embryos	Darkness		—	27±2	Roy and De (1990)
	II	[Callus *ex* I]	60	—	16		
Camellia hybrids	I,II	Stem segments	(37.5)*	3000	16	22±1	Tosca *et al.* (1992)
Coryphantha macromeris	I,II	Seedling shoots	24	—	16	26±3	Smith R.H. et al. (1991)
Chrysanthemum morifolium	I	Shoot apical meristem	(62.5)	5000	10	27/22	Sangwan and Harada (1977)
	II	[Suspensions *ex* I]	62.5	5000	18	26	
	II	[Callus *ex* II]	62.5	5000	24	23	
Citrus grandis	I,II	Stem & leaf segs.	(37.5)	3000	14	26	Chaturvedi & Mitra (1974)
Cucumis melo	I,II	Cotyledon & primary leaf	(31.2)	2500	16	24	Blackmon *et al.* (1981a)
Fragaria × *ananassa*	I,II	Leaf stipules *ex* i.v. cultures	Darkness (essential) *		—	23±1	Rugini and Orlando (1992)
Freesia hybrida	I	Young ovaries	Darkness		—	25	Bach (1987)
	II	[Callus *ex* I]	(25)	2000	16	25	
(Some cvs.)	II	[Callus *ex* I]	Darkness		—	25	
Gebera spp.	I,II	Leaves *ex* i.v. cultures	60	—	16	25±1	Reynoird *et al.* (1993)
Hordeum marinum	I	Immature & mature embryos	Darkness		—	26	Rotem–Abarbanell and Breiman (1989)
	II	[Callus *ex* I]	60	—	16	26	
Indigofera enneaphylla	I,II	Sdlg. leaves & cotyledons	(18.8)	1500	24	25±2	Bharal and Rashid (1979)
Lagerstroemia indica	I,II	Cotyledon & hypocotyl	(31.2)	2500	16	24	Blackmon *et al.* (1981b)
Lathyrus sativus	I,II	Seedling stem segments	69	—	16	27±1/23±1	Sinha *et al.* (1983)
Lathyrus sativus	I,II	Seedling root segments	70	—	16	22	Roy *et al.* (1992)
Medicago sativa	I,II	Immature ovaries	70.3	5620	24	Not given	Saunders and Bingham (1975)
Otacanthus coeruleus	I,II	Various	50–70	—	16	27±3/20±1	Ronse and de Proft (1992)
Pelargonium hortorum	I,II	Stem pith	(61.3)	4900	24	26	Chen & Galston (1967)
Pelargonium hortorum	I	Petiole sections	Darkness (1–2 weeks)		—	25	Cassells(1979)
	II	Explants with callus *ex* I	[139.5]	(30 W/m²)	16	25	
Pisum sativum	I,II	Immature leaflets	(25)	2000	16	20/15	Rubluo *et al.* (1982)
Sansevieria trifsaciata	I,II	Leaf sections	41–75	—	16	25	Blazich and Novitzky (1984)
Setaria italica	I	Mature seeds	(12.5)	1000	24	25±2	Rao *et al.* (1988)
	II	[Callus *ex* I]	(25)	2000	24	25±2	
Solanum laciniatum	I,II	Leaf discs	(21.2)	1700	†	25	Davies & Dale (1979)
	I		Darkness equally effective			25	
Trifolium spp.	I,,II	Hypocotyl	35–45	—	16	25±4	Beach & Smith (1979)
Triticum aestivum	I,II	Various	(2.5)	200	24	23	Chin & Scott (1977)

Abbreviations   * Found to be best by experimentation   20/15 Day/night temperatures

          ( ) Approximate irradiances corresponding to illuminance measurements   [ ] Conversion of W m^{-2} to $\mu mol\ m^{-2} s^{-1}$

          † Not given, presumably continuous.

establishing callus of *Magnolia* (Biederman, 1987), but initiating callus of *Camellia* in the dark was found to inhibit later shoot regeneration and more shoots were produced when callus was initiated in a 16 hour day (3000 lux) (Tosca *et al.*, 1992). Ovaries of *Freesia hybrida* were incubated in the dark for 2 months to produce callus which was afterwards transferred to a 16 hour day (2000 lux). Callus of some cultivars initiated adventitious shoots in the dark but, in others, callus did not produce shoots until it was transferred to the light (Bach, 1987).

Davies and Dale (1979) found that in *Solanum lacianatum* it did not much matter whether callus was initiated in the dark or in the light. Callus developed from leaf discs in a different fashion in the dark than in the light but, providing dark–incubated explants with callus were moved to the light, the number of shoots produced and their rate of development was the same in both treatments. On the other hand, no shoots were produced from *Pisum sativum* callus if immature leaf explants were incubated in darkness, but the formation of roots was stimulated. The proportion of explants forming calli, and the proportion of calli which produced shoots was greatest when explants were incubated for 16 hours in light of 2000 lux at 20°C, and during the dark period kept at 15°C (Rubluo *et al.*, 1982).

Callus is often initiated in the dark or in light of low intensity. Negrutiu and Jacobs (1978) showed that *Arabidopsis thaliana* callus cultured in continuous low light (*ca.* 1000 lux), or transferred from the dark to continuous low light, showed a higher frequency of adventitious shoot formation than dark–grown callus. A 16 h photoperiod, or continuous light of higher illuminance (*ca.* 4000 lux) during callus initiation of proliferation, reduced the percentage of regenerating calluses.

EMBRYOGENESIS

Plant cells can be induced to give rise to somatic embryos directly. It has been said that direct embryogenesis is only initiated *in vitro* from cells which are predetermined to embryogenesis before excision (Part 1, page 29), but although it occurs most commonly on explants which could be assumed to be already committed (or to have retained a residual commitment) to form embryos (such as nucellus, ovule, ovary, embryo or seedling tissues), uncommitted tissues can also give rise to embryos directly. Tissues which were not committed to an embryogenic pathway can be induced to have embryogenic determination by exposure to an auxin. If the exposure has not been excessive, direct embryogenesis may result upon transfer of the tissue to media containing less auxin. Usually an embryogenic callus is formed in the medium containing the auxin and indirect embryogenesis is said to result when the callus is subjected to a lower auxin level.

Direct embryogenesis usually takes place when predetermined explants are cultured on media which are not supplemented with auxin, or which contain only a low concentration of auxin. Sometimes, if a predetermined explant is placed onto a medium containing a growth regulant (usually a relatively high concentration of auxin), a nodular tissue is produced by the proliferation of proembryonic structures, forming a callus–like growth. Embryos are then only produced if the tissue is transferred to a medium containing no growth regulators, or to one in which there is only a low level of auxin. For example, Nagmani and Bonga (1985) obtained callus by culturing the gametophytes dissected from immature ovules of *Larix decidua* on **Litvay et al. (1981)** medium supplemented with amino acids and a cytokinin. Subcultured to the same medium without cytokinin, this tissue produced somatic embryos. This pattern of development is not distinguishable from indirect embryogenesis.

These concepts are summarised in Fig. 121. Directly–formed and indirectly–formed embryos usually require to be moved to a medium with very little auxin before they will grow to a sufficient size to germinate and develop into plantlets. Embryos of both origins proliferate if left in the presence of auxin to form an embryogenic tissue or 'callus', and may give rise to secondary embryos in appropriate conditions.

How auxin may control determination

One hypothesis to explain how auxin may influence the the ability of cells to give rise to somatic embryos was put forward by Okkels (1988), who suggested that auxin brings about the demethylation of DNA in dividing cells, and that this is a requisite for proembryo formation. In contrast, embryo development was thought to require the methylation DNA, which becomes possible in pro–embryos when auxin is withdrawn.

If this hypothesis proves to be true, and if auxin is the only mediator of DNA demethylation, then a corollary is that tissues which are naturally embryogenically determined should be sites of high auxin concentration, possibly sites of auxin biosynthesis.

DIRECT EMBRYOGENESIS

Direct embryogenesis has been recorded in many plants, but has been less widely observed than indirect embryogenesis. There are probably two reasons for this:

- the conditions necessary to obtain direct embryogenesis can be more critical than those required to produce embryogenic callus;

- researchers usually require a means of producing large numbers of somatic embryos, for which purpose embryogenic callus or cell suspensions are more suitable. Less research effort has therefore been devoted to obtaining direct embryogenesis.

The globular structures which represent the first stage of directly formed embryos are produced on the surface of explants and, in the absence of high concentrations of auxin, they may grow to produce mature embryos and seedlings. Sometimes further separate maturation and germination media may be necessary.

Growth regulator treatments

Auxins

When explanted tissues are already embryogenically determined (PEDCs: Part 1, page 29), it may be unnecessary to add growth regulators to the medium to obtain direct embryogenesis. Sometimes however, competence, or the number of cells which become determined, is increased by treatment with a low concentration of auxin. Embryogenic determination, which is high in cells of the nucellus and ovule, can be less in explants taken from zygotic embryos, and less again in seedlings or more mature organs. It will be seen from Tables 87 to 89, that the need to expose explants to auxin to induce embryo formation, progressively increases as less determined tissues are cultured.

Nucellus explants. One of the tissues most highly committed to embryogenesis is the nucellus, that part of an ovule from which zygotic embryos arise. Nucellus explants of polyembryonic (*i.e.* plants which in nature commonly produce accessory asexual embryos within their ovules) and some monoembryonic *Citrus* cultivars have proved to be a particularly good source of directly regenerated somatic embryos (path **A** in Fig. 121), or of embryogenic callus (path **B**).

Culture of *Citrus* nucellus on growth regulator free–**MS** medium (Esan, 1973), or this medium supplemented only with malt extract (ME) (Rangan *et al.*, 1968; Navarro and Juarez, 1977), has been sufficient to induce direct embryogenesis *in vitro*. It is possible that ME favours the growth of embryos from pre–formed meristematic centres. The germination of embryos induced to form on media containing 1 g/l malt extract can, however, be poor (Moore, 1985). Some other reports of somatic embryos being produced from *Citrus* nucellus explants are given in Table 87.

Two authors listed in Table 87, found it necessary to add a low concentration of auxin to their medium to obtain direct embryogenesis from *Citrus* nucellus explants. However, the nucellus tissue of *Citrus sinensis* has been thought to be auxin–habituated (Button *et al.*, 1974), because adventitious embryogenesis is spontaneous; has been found to be *depressed* by the addition of auxins; and increased by treatments which reduce natural auxin levels (Button and Rijkenberg, 1977; Kochba and Spiegel–Roy in Button and Kochba, 1977; Kochba *et al.*, 1978b; Spiegel–Roy and Kochba, 1980). Moore (1985) found that adding 0.01 mg/l daminozide to the medium was more effective than 0.5 g/l malt extract for producing direct embryogenesis from the nucellus of polyembryonic varieties of *Citrus*. Possibly daminozide reduces the concentration of endogenous auxin or negates its effect?

Culture of polyembryonic *Citrus* nucellus usually results in the formation of pro–embryos or pseudobulbils (Part 1, page 33), which later develop into somatic embryos.

Direct embryogenesis can be obtained from the nucellus of other species. Nucellus tissue from several polyembryonic varieties of *Mangifera indica* formed somatic embryos directly in **MS** medium, modified to contain half the major salts and iron, 400 mg/l glutamine and 100 mg/l ascorbic acid. Embryogenesis did not depend on the addition of growth regulators, but was improved by adding 20% coconut water (Litz *et al.*, 1982). Similarly shoots were obtained from the nucellus of *Pyrus communis*, almost certainly *via* directly formed embryos (Yehia, 1985).

Explants of zygotic embryos or their component parts. It is apparent from Table 89 that direct embryogenesis has often been induced on embryo explants by culture without growth regulators, or in a medium containing only a cytokinin.

Where somatic embryos have been formed directly on zygotic embryos, it is presumed that the zygotic embryos, or those parts of them which gave rise to somatic embryos, were predetermined to embryogenesis (path **A** in Fig. 121).

Somatic embryos formed in the absence of auxin may grow to full size without transfer. In *Camellia japonica*, somatic embryos were produced without growth regulators on **MS** medium from cotyledon sections and from the embryonic axis excised from seeds, but were formed in

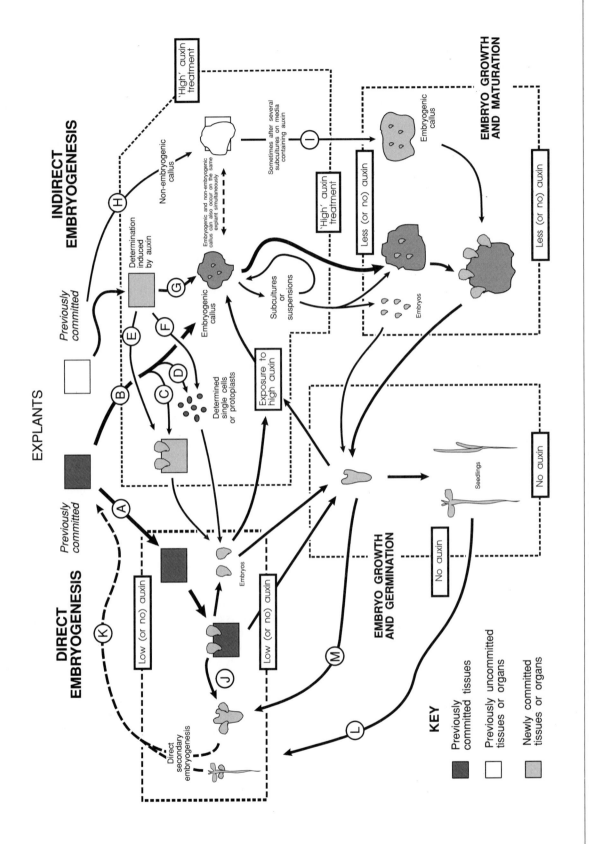

Fig. 121. Routes to direct and indirect embryogenesis and their regulation by auxin. The most common pathway to somatic embryo formation is shown by broad arrows. Shading shows the embryogenic determination of tissues and organs — see key.

Table 87. Examples of direct embryogenesis from nucellus and ovule (including the nucellus) explants of *Citrus*. Media and additions for embryo formation are shown. Embryos generally grow into seedlings without transfer to new conditions.

Plant	Explant	Medium	Sucrose %	Regulants	References
Citrus aurantifolia	Unpollinated ovules	Modified **MS**	3	0.1 mg/l NAA + 5mg/l adenine sulphate	Mitra and Chaturvedi (1972)
C. aurantifolia *Citrus paradisi* *C. paradisi* × *C. reticulata* *Citrus sinensis*	Undeveloped ovules	**Murashige and Tucker (1969)** + 500 mg/l malt extract	3	None	Gmitter and Moore (1986)
Citrus grandis	Nucellus	**MS** + malt extract	3	None	Rangan *et al.* (1968)
	Nucellus from young zygotic embryos	**MS** (mod. vitamins)	5	0.1 mg/l NAA + 0.3 mg/l BAP + 10 mg/l AdS	Huang *et al.* (1988)
Citrus limon	Nucellus	**MS** + malt extract	3	None	Rangan *et al.* (1968)
	Ovules	**MS**	3	None	Esan (1973)
Citrus medica,	Ovules	**MS**	3	None	Esan (1973)
Citrus microcarpa	Nucellus tissue	**Ranga Swamy (1961) I** + 400 mg/l CH	2	1 mg/l GA$_3$, 0.01 mg/l kinetin	Ranga Swamy (1958, 1959, 1961)
Citrus reticulata	Nucellus half of ovule	**Ranga Swamy (1961) I** + 400 mg/l CH	2	None, then :–	Sabharwal (1963)
		Ranga Swamy (1961) I	2	10% coconut milk	
Citrus reticulata × *C. sinensis*	Nucellus	**MS** + malt extract	3	None	Rangan *et al.* (1968)

greater numbers in the presence of 0.5–1 mg/l IBA (Plata and Viéitez, 1990). When culture with auxin has been necessary to induce direct embryo formation from embryogenically determined explants (paths **C** and **D**), or previously undetermined explants (paths **E** and **F**), embryos have formed in the induction medium, but have not progressed beyond an early cotyledonary stage until the concentration of auxin has been reduced.

Direct embryo formation after the treatment of *Glycine max* cotyledons with high concentrations of auxin (Table 89) is unusual. In most plants, this level of auxin would cause embryos to proliferate forming an embryogenic callus. Somatic embryos were found to arise *de novo* from single cells (or by folding of the scutellum) in *Sorghum bicolor* (Dunstan *et al.*, 1978).

Seedling and mature explants. Direct embryogenesis is also observed on explants taken from seedlings (paths **C** and **D** in Fig. 121), and from explants taken from even more mature organs (Table 88), in which embryogenic predetermination can be supposed to be minimal. Direct embryo formation from previously uncommitted cells is marked *via* paths **E** and **F** in Fig. 121.

In nearly all the examples shown in Table 88, auxin was required to initiate direct embryogenesis from the explants. Selection of the correct auxin may be important: somatic embryos were only formed on Manihot leaves

incubated on a medium containing 2,4–D. NAA was ineffective (Stamp and Henshaw, 1987). As in all other tissue cultures, the precise concentrations and combinations of growth regulators to induce the best results (the greatest number of explants to produce embryos, or the number of embryos produced per explant), varies between genotypes. Although in *Pelargonium* × *hortorum* (Zonal geranium) and *P.* × *domesticum* (Regal geranium)(Marsolais *et al.*, 1991a) the most effective overall treatment was 10 µM 2,4–D plus 2 µM BAP, the optimum for some genotypes was:

'Sprinter Scarlet'	10 µM 2,4–D plus 2 µM zeatin
'Ontario Two hundred'	10 µM 2,4–D plus 2 µM BAP
Tetraploid Regals	2 µM BAP (no auxin)

Transfer to a medium without auxin, or without any regulants, is usually necessary to ensure embryo development. Somatic embryos were formed directly in thin cell layers from the hypocotyl of *Helianthus annuus* cv. 'HA300B', when they were placed on **MS** medium (supplemented with 2000 mg/l casein hydrolysate and 30 g/l sucrose) containing 1 mg/l NAA, 1 mg/l BAP and 20% coconut milk. The embryos did not germinate on this medium and became vitreous, but development continued if explants were transferred to **B5** medium containing

Table 88. Some examples of direct embryogenesis being induced on explants derived from seedlings, or more mature explants. The media and growth regulators shown are those for the initial culture of explants, in which embryos appeared. Different media were employed to obtain embryo growth and germination.

Plant	Explant	Medium	Sucrose %	Regulants (mg/l)	References
Explants derived from young seedlings					
Apium graveolens	Petioles	MS	3	0.5 2,4-D	Zee and Wu (1979) Zee *et al.* (1979)
Brassica alboglabra	Petiole sections	MS	3	0.5 2,4-D	Zee and Wu (1979)
Corylus avellana	Cotyledonary node of 20-day old seedling	Cheng (1975) Basal	3	0.1–1 IBA + 0.11 BAP	Pérez *et al.* (1983, 1986)
Manihot esculenta	Cotyledons, apex, or young leaves	MS	2	2–12 2,4-D for 20 days ¶	Stamp (1987)
Pelargonium × *hortorum*	Petiole and hypocotyl	MS	3	2.2 2,4-D + 0.45 BAP	Marsolais *et al.* (1991a)
Pelargium × *domesticum* tetraploids	Petiole sections	MS	3	0.45 BAP (no auxin)	
Solanum melongena	Seedling cotyledons	Kartha *et al.* (1974a)	3	2.5–5 NAA	Fobert and Webb (1988)
Explants from mature organs					
Amaranthus hypochondriacus	Leaf discs	B5	3	2,4-D (rate not specified)	Flores *et al.* (1981)
Asparagus officinalis	Mechanically isolated mesophyll cells	MS but ½ NH$_4$NO$_3$ and KNO$_3$ + 500 mg/l glutamine	10.3	9.3 NAA + 0.22 BAP	Uragami *et al.* (1990)
Begonia semperflorens	Leaf segments	Rangaswamy (1961) I + 100 mg/l CH	2	1 kinetin	Sehgal (1975)
Chrysanthemum morifolium	Leaf midribs from stock plants	Heinz and Mee (1969)	9–18	1 2,4-D + 0.2 BAP	May and Trigiano (1991)
Manihot esculenta	Lobes of young leaves (4th and 5th from apex)	MS	2	2–12 2,4-D for 20 days	Stamp & Henshaw (1987)
Medicago sativa	Mesophyll protoplasts	Kao (1977) Protoplast	0.6 M glucose	None: treated with low electric fields (*e.g.* 0.02V for 20–44 h)	Dijak *et al.* (1986)
Smilax oldhami	Leaf segments from *in vitro* plants	½MS	3	1 BAP then 2 2,4-D	Yamamoto and Oda (1992)

¶ Subcultured on medium containing low auxin to get embryo formation

90 g/l sucrose, but no growth regulators (Pelissier *et al.*, 1990).

Separated cells. Wetherell (1984) suggested that the capacity of cells to regenerate is increased if they become isolated from their counterparts through the disruption of cytoplasmic plasmodesmata interconnections. He found that the number of embryos produced from suspension cultured cells of wild carrot was increased, and embryo development synchronised, if cells cultured in the presence of 5 mg/l 2,4–D, were plasmolysed for 45 minutes before being plated onto an auxin–free medium. The most effective plasmolysing solutions were 0.5–1 M sucrose or 1 M mannitol.

Support for this hypothesis is provided by several experimental results in which somatic embryos have been produced directly from single isolated plant cells or protoplasts. Dijak *et al.* (1986) obtained somatic embryos directly from protoplasts of *Medicago sativa* after treating them with an electric field and Song *et al.* (1990) obtained a similar result by the more conventional method of growth regulator treatment. Protoplasts cultured with 0.5 mg/l 2,4–D and 0.5 mg/l BAP formed proembryos, which were transferred to a medium lacking regulants to develop into plantlets when they had become green and were 2 mm in diameter.

Table 89. Media and growth regulators used in some examples of direct embryogenesis from zygotic embryos, or their component parts. The media and regulants shown are those for the initial culture of explants, in which embryos appeared. Different media were employed to obtain embryo growth and germination.

Plant	Explant	Medium	Sucrose %	Regulants	References
Acanthopanax senticosus	Mature zygotic embryos	**MS**	3	0.5 mg/l 2,4-D	Gui *et al.* (1991)
Brassica campestris	Immature zygotic embryos	**B5**	4	0.05 mg/l BAP	Williams and Maheswaran (1985)
Brassica napus	Immature zygotic embryos	**B5**	3	0.05 mg/l BAP	Pretova and Williams (1987)
Camellia japonica	Cotyledon sections and embryonic axis from seeds	Modified **MS**	3	None	Plata and Viéitez (1990)
Camellia japonica	Cotyledon segments from embryos	**MS**	3	2 mg/l IBA + 4 mg/l BAP, or 4 mg/l IBA + 2 mg/l BAP	Kato (1989)
Carica papaya	Immature zygotic embryos	½**MS** salts and inositol; full **MS** vitamins; 400 mg/l glutamine	6	5 mg/l 2,4-D	Fitch and Manshardt (1990)
Daucus carota	Mericarp of carrot seed coats	**MS**	3‡ (to 10)	None	Smith and Krikorian (1988).
Euterpe edulis	Mature or immature zygotic embryos	Modified **LS**	3	50–100 mg/l 2,4-D†	Guerra and Handro (1988)
Glycine max	Cotyledons from immature embryos	**Phillips and Collins (1979) L2**	1	0.55 mg/l 2,4-D	Lippmann and Lippmann (1984)
	Cotyledons from immature embryos	**Kartha *et al.* (1974a)**	3	2.5 mg/l 2,4-D	Hartweck *et al.* (1986)
		Kartha *et al.* (1974a)	1.5	10 mg/l NAA	
	Cotyledons from immature embryos	**Kartha *et al.* (1974a)**	6	40 mg/l 2,4-D	Finer (1988a)
	Cotyledons from immature embryos	**MS**	3	4.9 mg/l 2,4-D	Hepher *et al.* (1988)
	Cotyledons from immature embryos	**MS**	3	19.2 mg/l 2,4-D	Bucheim *et al.* (1989)
Helianthus annuus	Immature zygotic embryos	**Kartha *et al.* (1974a)**	6–12	1 mg/l 2,4-D or 3.3 mg/l dicamba	Finer (1987)
	Immature zygotic embryos (4–21 days after pollination)	**MS** supplemented with inositol and amino acids	9	No auxin; 0.5–1 ng/l BAP	Freyssinet and Freyssinet (1988)
Lotus corniculatus	Immature zygotic embryos	**Maheswaran and Williams (1984) EC6**	4	1–2 mg/l BAP	Williams and Maheswaran (1985)
Medicago sativa	Immature zygotic embryos	**Maheswaran and Williams (1984) EC6 + 1 g/l YE**	4	0.05 mg/l BAP	Williams and Maheswaran (1985)
Rubus sp.	Cotyledons of imbibed seeds	Modified **MS**.	3.08	1.1 mg/l TDZ	Fiola et al. (1990)
Sorghum bicolor	Scutellum of immature embryos	**MS**	3	2.5–5 mg/l 2,4-D	Thomas et al. (1977) Dunstan et al. (1978)
Thea sinensis	Segments of cotyledons from young seeds	**MS**	3	0.5mg/l 2,4-D + 0.05 mg/l kinetin	Bano *et al.* (1991)
Trifolium repens *T. pratense* *T. resupinatum*	Immature zygotic embryos	**Maheswaran and Williams (1984) EC6 + 1 g/l YE**	4	0.05 mg/l BAP	Williams and Maheswaran (1985); Maheswaran and Williams (1986)
Trifolium repens	Hypocotyl region of immature embryos	**Maheswaran and Williams (1984) EC6**	4	0.05 mg/l BAP	Maheswaran and Williams (1985)

† A high rate of 2,4-D was used to induce embryo formation because activated charcoal was added to the medium to prevent blackening (Part 1, page 471; pages 626 and 1157)   ‡ Preferred concentration.

Secondary adventitious embryos

Accessory somatic embryos arising directly from cultured zygotic embryos are often called secondary embryos (Part 1, page 56). Adventitious embryos commonly form in a similar fashion, directly on somatic embryos and upon parts (especially the shoot apex) of the young plants which are obtained when somatic embryos germinate (paths **J**, **L** and **M** in Fig. 121) (Part 1, pages 56 and 57). This indicates that direct embryogenesis is particularly a feature of embryogenically determined tissue. Often secondary embryos are produced on the same medium as that in which the growth of primary embryos occurred, but sometimes transferring primary embryos to another medium enhances repetitive embryogenesis. In *Camellia reticulata* (Table 89), secondary embryos were produced on the same medium as that in which embryo initiation occurred (Plata and Viéitez, 1990). However, to obtain secondary and tertiary embryos of *Camellia japonica* (Table 88), primary embryos needed to be transferred to **MS** medium containing 1 mg/l GA$_3$ (Kato, 1989). Secondary embryos are not produced in media containing high levels of auxin.

Adventitious embryos were induced to form on primary somatic embryos of *Helianthus annuus* by transferring them from **B5** medium with 90 g/l sucrose (no growth regulators), to **MS** medium with 120 g/l sucrose and 0.2 mg/l BAP (Pélissier *et al.*, 1990). The higher osmoticum allowed embryo proliferation to continue. By contrast, Smith and Krikorian (1988) obtained the formation of secondary embryos from directly formed *Daucus carota* somatic embryos by reducing the sucrose content of the medium from 3% to 1%. However, in this case, the cultures were not sustainable and embryos began to grow into plantlets.

Somatic embryos exposed to cytokinins can give rise to multiple adventitious and axillary shoots (see page 601).

Embryo multiplication

If directly formed somatic embryos are converted into plantlets, no further multiplication is possible. However, in some plants, secondary embryo formation has been seen to be highly repetitive. In *Glycine max*, for instance, Finer (1988a) observed numerous chains of up to 5 embryos as new embryos arose directly upon the apical surface of older ones. Besides the formation of typical bipolar embryos, the repetitive formation of just accessory cotyledons and root poles also occurs, and has been termed *embryo cleavage* by Pretova and Williams (1986). A complete spectrum of adventitious embryogenic structures is therefore possible, leading eventually to the formation of a proliferative embryogenic tissue, or 'callus'.

An embryogenic callus tissue can also be produced by inoculating directly formed embryos onto a medium similar to that used for their induction. This technique was used, for instance, by Ladyman and Girard (1991) to obtain an embryogenic tissue of *Cucumis sativus*, which could then be multiplied by 4–weekly subcultures.

Suitable media

Because a supply of reduced nitrogen is required for embryo growth (page 629), direct embryogenesis has been possible on media lacking ammonium ions, such as **Ranga Swamy (1961) I**, only where they have been supplemented with amino acids (casein hydrolysate supplying a mixture of amino acids has usually been sufficient). Embryo growth on modified **White** medium (Ranga Swamy, 1958 *et seq.*; Sabharwal, 1963) has been less satisfactory than on **MS** medium, which has been used most commonly. However, it seems that the total ionic concentration of the medium does not need to be high. **Maheswaran and Williams (1986) EC6** medium, which has a fairly low salt content (but provides NH$_4^+$), has been suitable, for example, to obtain direct embryogenesis in several legumes (Table 89). The addition of amino acids to media which also contain ammonium ions can have the same promotive effect on direct embryogenesis as it does on indirect embryogenesis (see below). The addition of yeast extract was necessary for direct embryo formation from immature zygotic embryos of several *Trifolium* species (Table 89). Without the extract, or with its concentration reduced to 0.5 g/l, the zygotic embryos germinated precociously and no somatic embryos were produced (Maheswaran and Williams, 1986).

Sucrose content of the medium

It will be seen from Tables 87, 88 and 89, that in many plants, direct embryogenesis occurs in media supplemented with 2–3% sucrose. In *Glycine max*, Hartweck *et al.* (1986) obtained more embryos on the cotyledons of immature zygotic embryos if they were cultured with 2.5 mg/l 2,4–D and 3% sucrose, than with 10 mg/l NAA and 1.5% sucrose, but embryos initiated by the latter were more normal in appearance. There is some evidence that higher concentrations of sucrose may assist embryo formation (Table 90). This is probably an osmotic effect (*c.f.* the osmotic effect on embryo formation in indirect embryogenesis, page 632).

In *Helianthus annuus*, direct formation of somatic embryos only occurred when zygotic embryos were cultured on **Kartha *et al.* (1974a)** medium supplemented with 6 or 12% sucrose. No embryos appeared in media containing 3% sucrose (Finer, 1987). Proembryos were formed di-

Table 90. Examples of direct embryogenesis being induced by the incorporation of high concentrations of sucrose into the Stage I medium

[The osmolalities given are estimated from the molarity of media ingredients].

Plant	Explant	Medium	Sucrose %	Estimated osmolality of medium		References
				Medium alone mOs/kg	Total (medium + sucrose etc) mOs/kg	
Chrysanthemum morifolium	Leaf midrib sections	**Heinz and Mee (1969)**	12–15	96	492–591	May and Trigiano (1991)
Daucus carota	Achene fruit tissue	**MS**	3–10	96	186–420	Smith and Krikorian (1988)
Daucus carota	Seedling cotyledons & apical tips	**MS**	25	96	926	Kurata *et al.* (1992)
Dendranthema grandifolia	Leaf midrib sections	**Heinz and Mee (1969)**	9–18	96	385–796	May and Trigiano (1991)

rectly on achene fruit tissue of *Daucus carota*, on **MS** medium supplemented with up to 10% sucrose, but embryogenesis was satisfactory when only 3% sucrose was provided (Smith and Krikorian, 1988). The formation of secondary embryos also occurred when the sucrose was reduced to 1%, but cultures were then not sustainable and embryos began to grow into plantlets (Smith and Krikorian, 1988).

INDIRECT EMBRYOGENESIS

Embryogenesis can now be induced and regulated in a large number of species, either directly on explants or indirectly, and once the embryogenic state is induced, there are close similarities between both processes (Mahaswaran and Williams, 1985).

Strictly speaking, the term *indirect embryogenesis* should only be used to describe that which occurs *via* routes **G** and **H + I** in Fig. 121, (*i.e.* embryogenesis which results from the induction of embryogenic determination in previously uncommitted tissue and the *de novo* formation of embryogenic callus). In practice however, explants used to initiate 'embryogenic callus' are commonly taken from organs such as zygotic ovules or embryos, or parts of young seedlings in which embryogenic determination may have persisted (path **B**). In these cases the embryogenic 'callus' which is obtained by culturing the tissue in auxin, often represents the proliferation of proembryonic tissue, so that embryos produced could be considered to have arisen *via* direct embryogenesis. The extension of route **J** through continued proliferation to **K** and **B**, can,

for example be argued for somatic polyembryogenesis from conifers (Part 1, page 32 and page 1007).

Whether path **B** represents direct or indirect embryogenesis is academic because treatment of explants is very similar. Paths **B, G** and **I** have all been considered to result in indirect embryogenesis in the pages which follow.

As mentioned in Part 1 (pages 82 ad 83), genetic variation has been found amongst some plants regenerated from somatic embryos, perhaps particularly where embryogenesis has arisen from previously undetermined cells or tissues. Micropropagation reliant on path **B** in Fig. 121) is therefore not to be preferred because any delay in the formation of somatic embryos occasioned through the formation and subculture of undifferentiated callus (path **H**) is likely to result in somaclonal variation in the population of regenerated plants. An extreme example of embryogenesis *via* path **I** was provided by Haccius and Lakshmanan (1965). Wound callus of *Nicotiana tabacum*, isolated in 1959 and subcultured on **White (1954)** medium plus 5% CM and 0.1 mg/l 2,4–D produced somatic embryos five years later when transferred to **Lin and Staba (1961)** medium containing 15% CM and 2 mg/l kinetin and cultured in high light (10 000–15 000 lux).

Genetic variation can also arise if, before embryos are regenerated, callus or suspension cultures which have arisen through path **G** (and to a lesser extent, through path **B**), are subjected to prolonged subculture. There are many examples of this practice leading to plants with atypical phenotypes (to quote but a few: in celery — Orton, 1985; in grapevine — Mullins and Srinivasan, 1976; Mullins, 1982; in *Angelica acutiloba* — Nakagawa *et al.*, 1982; in

Bromus inermis — Molnar and Grainger, 1982; in *Gossypium hirsutum* — Trolinder and Goodin, 1987).

Effect of auxins

The induction of embryogenesis

To bring about indirect embryogenesis, regulants are required which will both induce the embryogenic state and bring about embryo development. Although embryogenesis can be induced by other stimuli, such as an electric field or the pH of the medium, and even though the presence of other regulants, particularly cytokinins, may be required, it is usually considered to be controlled by auxin (either that produced endogenously within cultured tissues or that supplied from the culture medium) (page 612).

In both dicotyledons and monocotyledons, the culture of explants with auxin frequently results in the formation of more than one type of callus. One kind may be determined to produce somatic embryos, while other strains lack this potential and usually remain undifferentiated, however long they are subcultured. The usual explanation of this phenomenon is that tissues with different morphogenic capacities have arisen from cells of the explant with varying competence. The successful subculture and maintenance of embryogenic callus requires that it should be selected from other tissue at an early stage. Embryogenic callus is usually recognised by its nodular appearance.

It has been stressed several times above (page 612), that auxin at the concentrations necessary to initiate cells capable of forming somatic embryos and/or promote the formation of somatic embryos, is not essential for, and may be inhibitory to, continued somatic embryo development (Halperin, 1966; Jones, 1974a,b; Tisserat and Murashige, 1977a,c). The degree of embryo differentiation which takes place in the presence of auxin varies in different plants. In some species the early stages of somatic embryo development take place on the Stage I medium, and embryos are found within, or usually towards the surface of the tissue. The presence of auxin usually prevents these embryos ever developing much beyond the heart stage.

By electron microscopy and a study of the pattern of ionic currents accompanying the changes in shape and surface of cell clusters, Gorst *et al.* (1987) concluded that somatic embryo formation in carrot is arrested by auxin at the proembryonic stage. When 2,4–D is present in such cultures, proliferating cell clusters are formed which possess morphogenic determination. These have the capacity to form embryos, but embryogenesis cannot progress further until the auxin concentration is reduced (Kamada and Harada, 1979a; Gorst *et al.*, 1987).

When somatic embryo development is inhibited by auxin in this way, the division of pro–embryoidal cells usually continues, and this results in the production of a tissue whose appearance varies in different plants. It has been variously described as nodular callus, embryonic clumps, spherical meristems, nodules or pseudo–bulbils.

Some of the inhibitory effect of 2,4–D on embryo development may be relieved by increasing the concentration of Ca^{2+} ions in the medium (see page 632).

Effective synthetic auxins. The relative efficiency of synthetic auxins in promoting indirect embryogenesis is similar to their ability to induce callus formation and it has been said that those most effective for this purpose are compounds with an oxy–acetic side chain (*e.g.* 2,4–D, 2,4,5–T, MCPA, NOA and PCPA) (Kamada and Harada, 1979a). However, picloram and dicamba are very effective in inducing embryogenesis in certain plants and it may be that the capacity to embryogenesis is more related to the relative activities of these compounds in conventional tests for auxinic activities, or to their performance as herbicides.

Embryo formation

Typically, when embryogenic tissue is exposed to a medium lacking auxin (or to one containing only a low auxin concentration) numerous somatic embryos are formed superficially (Halperin, 1964; Rao *et al.*, 1973a,b). Together with embryos which may have been present in the tissue prior to transfer, these sometimes develop into plantlets, although sometimes a second transfer onto an auxin–free medium may be necessary. Somatic embryos formed in the absence of auxin, give rise to clumps of embryogenic cells if they are again exposed to high auxin concentrations (Fig. 121) (Halperin, 1966; Williams and Collin, 1976).

Assuming that the level within cultured tissues is in equilibrium with that in the medium, there are several ways in which the concentration of exogenously supplied auxin may be reduced to promote embryo formation:

- metabolism within the tissues (Part 1, page 428);

- breakdown of auxin in the medium;

- transfer of cultured tissues to a medium with a reduced auxin concentration.

Some auxins are more prone than others to breakdown in the medium (Part 1, page 424). The degree of metabolism will vary according to the nature of the auxin used and according to the plant species being cultured, and is the most likely cause of the variation in protocols to obtain successful embryo formation in different species. Auxins such as 2,4–D, which are particularly effective for promoting embryogenesis, are not usually metabolised or degraded in the medium. When such regulants are used, to obtain the continued differentiation and growth of embryos, it is commonly necessary to transfer embryogenic tissue and/or somatic embryos to a medium containing less auxin, a weaker auxin (*e.g.* IAA instead of 2,4–D), or no auxin at all. Thus indirect embryogenesis is usually brought about by using two, and sometimes three, media containing decreasing concentrations of auxin.

The concentration of auxin necessary to induce embryogenesis can vary considerably from one genotype to another. The numbers of embryos produced per explant or per unit weight of callus of suspension cultured cells is similarly genotype dependent. This is illustrated by the results of Raemakers *et al.* (1993) with *Manihot esculenta* using explants of young leaves.

Cultivar	Optimum 2,4–D to induce callus and embryogenesis mg/l	Explants producing embryos %	Somatic embryos (per explant) which germinated %
'Tjurug'	1	46	4.3
'M.Col 22'	8	81	22.1

Nevertheless, it has sometimes been possible to induce embryos to form and develop into well organised structures, or even plantlets, in a single medium. Particular examples of this kind are where it has been possible to obtain the formation of embryogenic callus by culture with only a cytokinin (page 613).

Habituated callus. Some highly embryogenic tissues (such as the highly embryogenic callus derived from the nucellus of polyembryonic *Citrus* varieties) are auxin habituated and in these tissues embryo formation may be stimulated by treatments which appear to reduce natural auxin levels. They have included:

— exposure of cells to X– or γ–radiation (Chourey *et al.*, 1973; Spiegel–Roy and Kochba, 1980); and

— reducing the rate of cell division in cultures.

> Two methods of reducing the growth rate of potentially embryogenic callus were effective in *Citrus*. One was to age the cultures by increasing the time during which they remain on the same medium before subculturing (Kochba and Button, 1974; Kochba and Spiegel–Roy, 1977). The other technique was to culture the callus for one passage on a medium devoid of sucrose (Kochba and Button, 1974).

Embryogenic callus cultures of other plants may also become habituated, for example, embryogenic cultures

of several cotton genotypes (Trolinder and Goodin, 1987; Finer, 1988b). Cultures of sugar beet (*Beta vulgaris*) are commonly habituated, and then callus formation, followed by shoot morphogenesis or embryogenesis, may occur on a medium devoid of regulants (Doley and Saunders, 1989).

Period of exposure to auxin

Embryogenic callus tissue of some species can be subcultured for a prolonged period on a medium containing auxin, but still retain the capacity to produce somatic embryos, which can develop into plantlets when the tissue is transferred to an auxin–free medium. Embryogenic callus derived from *Corylus avellana* zygotic embryos could, for example, be subcultured over two years without losing its morphogenic potential. In other cases prolonged culture on a medium containing growth regulator levels sufficient to induce the formation of embryogenic callus can result in the callus losing its capacity to produce embryos. This incapacity is hastened by exposure to high auxin levels. Nodular embryogenic callus of *Saccharum* began to lose its morphogenic potential after 12 weeks culture on the medium containing 7 mg/l 2,4–D used to induce its formation. After 20 weeks on such a medium the number of plants obtained per unit weight of callus had decreased to about one third of those obtained 8 weeks previously, and after a further 20 weeks, the ability of callus to produce plants had almost disappeared (Guiderdoni and Demarly, 1988).

Cytokinin treatments

In most dicotyledons, the addition of a low concentration of cytokinin (*e.g.* 0.1–1 μM BAP or kinetin) to media containing auxin tends to increase the growth rate of embryogenic callus. Only when the the concentration of these compounds is increased (*e.g.* to 5–10 μM), do they seem to negate the effect of auxin. Growth rate of the callus is then reduced and well formed embryos begin to appear. A low level of cytokinin was added to the primary medium in two–thirds of the reports in Table 12-23 where embryogenesis was induced in broad–leafed species. The cytokinin 2–iP is necessary (in conjunction with 2,4–D) to induce embryogenesis in some legumes (Arcioni and Mariotti, 1982) and a high kinetin to 2,4–D ratio has been reported to stimulate embryogenesis within tissue cultures of celery (Williams and Collin, 1976).

Nevertheless the incorporation of cytokinins into primary culture media together with auxins has been noted to retard or inhibit embryogenesis in several monocotyledonous and dicotyledonous plants (*e.g.* Vasil and Vasil,

1972; Rao *et al.*, 1973a,b; Bapat and Rao, 1979; Kamada and Harada, 1979a; Dale *et al.*, 1981; Ahloowalia, 1982).

In rare cases, embryogenesis has been induced by culturing explants with a cytokinin in the absence of an auxin, as in *Coffea arabica*. Embryogenic callus and somatic embryos arose from young leaf slices of this plant when the explants were cultured with only 5 µM BAP. Some of the embryos germinated on the original medium and the callus also proliferated. More embryos germinated when the callus was subcultured onto a second medium of the same composition (Yasuda *et al.*, 1985, 1986).

Embryogenic callus was produced from immature pre–cotyledonary zygotic embryos of *Abies nordmanniana* by culture with 5 µM BAP or 0.1 µM thidiazuron (Norgaard and Krogstrup, 1990). Direct embryogenesis has commonly been induced by cytokinins alone (Table 89).

Fujimura and Komamine (1975) showed that if they were added to a medium in which there was no auxin, cytokinins inhibited embryogenesis of carrot, except for 0.2 µg/l zeatin, which was promotive. When either IAA or 2,4–D was present in the medium, zeatin and the other cytokinins were inhibitory at all concentrations. Adding 0.5–1 µM of either BAP, kinetin or zeatin similarly inhibited the formation of embryogenic tissue of *Glycine max* (Lippmann and Lippmann, 1984).

Although cytokinins do seem to have some role in the induction of shoot formation in cereals and grasses (see Chapter 17), there is no firm indication that their addition is really beneficial to the induction of embryogenesis. They have sometimes been added to Stage I media (Table 93), but in many plants embryogenic callus has been obtained with media supplemented with auxin alone. Lu and Vasil (1981a) did find that it was essential to add 5–15% coconut milk to 2,4–D to induce embryogenic callus formation on *Panicum maximum* leaf segments, but some component other than cytokinin could have been responsible. However, in both dicotyledons and monocotyledons, cytokinins may promote the growth of preformed embryos enabling them to give rise to plantlets (see below and page 715, Chapter 14).

Growth regulator pretreatment

When cultured on a modified **MS** medium in which there were no growth regulators, zygotic embryos resulting from the cross of *Vigna glabrescens* × *V. radiata* produced some somatic embryos directly or *via* callus. The frequency of embryogenesis was increased however if embryos were harvested from pods, the peduncles of which had been treated daily during their development with a solution of 100 mg/l GA$_3$, 25 mg/l NAA and 5 mg/l kinetin. Embryogenesis, in this experiment, was partly

due to the interspecific nature of the zygotic embryos. No somatic embryos were obtained by culturing zygotic embryos of the reciprocal cross or from those resulting from selfs (Chen *et al.*, 1990).

Growth regulators used in practice

Dicotyledons

Two–stage procedure. In most dicotyledons, embryogenesis and subsequent embryo growth and development can be accomplished in two stages. In the first, an embryogenic callus is obtained; and at the second the callus, or sometimes recognisable somatic embryos, are transferred to a different medium, where embryos are allowed to form, grow and develop into plantlets. Table 91 summarises the growth regulator additions used in representative instances of the induction of somatic embryogenesis in a sample of dicotyledonous plants.

An auxin was incorporated into the primary culture medium in all the examples and a wide range of auxin concentrations was employed for different plant species. Table 91 shows that the average concentration of auxin applied in the primary cultures of broad–leafed species is generally 2–18 times greater than at the second cultural stage. Similarly, although 2,4–D was most commonly used at Stage I, this auxin has tended to have been used much less at the second stage, where IAA or NAA have been more commonly employed. On a significant number of occasions, no auxin at all was added.

Table 91 shows that cytokinins are often added with auxins to media for the induction of embryogenesis in dicotyledons. Kinetin has been frequently used for this purpose. Concentrations used at Stage II have been only slightly less than at Stage I. Cytokinin has often been omitted from media, and so is certainly not always required. However, is the presence of a cytokinin essential for the induction of embryogenesis in some species? Price and Smith (1979a) thought that they had obtained evidence for its importance in *Gossypium klotzschianum*, because no embryos were produced from the protocol A→E in Fig. 122, but were obtained in large numbers by following the procedures marked as A→B→C→F. However it would be expected that embryos would be produced from the protocol A→C→F, but this was not tried. A procedure such as A→C→F has been successful in other species (*e.g.* Walker and Sato, 1981; Stuart and Strickland, 1984a,b).

Embryogenesis using three (or more) stages. Some researchers have reported using a three or four stage procedure for obtaining embryogenesis in dicotyledons. Callus growth is obtained on a preliminary medium, the growth regulator content of which is likely to induce

Table 91. Growth regulators used for dicotyledons where a two-stage cultural process was sufficient to induce first indirect embryogenesis and then embryo growth and development.
[Based on 80 protocols for 53 species in 64 papers].

Growth regulators	Stage 1				Stage 2			
	Use % protocols	Concentrations employed			Use % protocols	Concentrations employed		
		Range μM	Average μM	Average mg/l		Range μM	Average μM	Average mg/l
Auxins								
IAA	6.25	1.43–22.83	8.28	1.45	12.5	0.06–11.42	4.03	0.71
NAA	20.0	0.11–26.85	12.34	2.30	18.8	0.11–10.74	2.78	0.52
2,4-D	66.3	0.45–99.53	14.24	3.15	16.3	0.001–22.62	2.80	0.62
IBA	6.3	0.05–78.72	31.50	8.00	5.0	1.23–4.92	2.15	0.44
CPA	1.25	12.18	12.18	2	0	—	—	—
2,4,5-T	0	—	—	—	1.25	0.39	0.39	0.1
NOA	0	—	—	—	1.25	9.89	9.89	2
Picloram	3.75	0.004–0.25	0.17	0.04	0	—	—	—
More than one auxin	5.0	—	—	—				
No auxin	0	—	—	—	43.8	—	—	—
Cytokinins								
Kinetin	63.75	0.09–23.23	5.66	1.22	30.0	0.47–41.82	6.32	1.36
BAP	18.8	0.44–38.18	6.94	1.56	15.0	0.44–8.88	4.45	1.00
2-iP	1.25	4.92	4.92	1	2.5	0.98–4.92	2.95	0.6
Zeatin	5.0	0.009–10.03	5.36	1.18	6.25	0.09–9.12	3.78	0.83
Adenine sulphate	2.5	4.95–74.19	38.57	16.0	7.5	4.95–98.92	51.11	20.67
Coconut milk	3.75	10–15	—	11.27%	3.75	10–20%	—	13.3%
More than one cytokinin	10.9	—	—	—				
No cytokinin	32.5	—	—	—	42.5	—	—	—
Gibberellins								
GA$_3$	2.5	1.44–2.89	1.44	0.5	2.5	0.28–2.89	1.59	0.55
No gibberellin	97.5	—	—	—	97.5	—	—	—
No PGRs at all	0	—	—	—	32.5	—	—	—

embryogenesis. Callus, usually without any obvious sign of embryogenesis, is then subcultured to a second or third medium each containing a progressively reduced concentration of auxin. Embryogenic callus, and/or small somatic embryos, are finally moved to a medium to encourage embryo growth and conversion to plantlets.

To obtain embryogenesis from *Nardostachys jatamansi* (Valerianaceae), Mathur (1993) initiated callus from the petioles of young leaves with 16.1 μM NAA and 1.16 μM kinetin. Embryogenesis only took place on sequential subcultures during a period of 7 months (possibly 5 subcultures of 6 weeks duration). The auxin:cytokinin ratio was gradually decreased during this period until the final concentrations of NAA and kinetin were 1.34 μM and 9.3 μM respectively.

Table 92 shows the regulants used in 20 examples where a three–stage procedure was adopted. The concentration of auxins used for subculture in these examples was, on

Table 92. Growth regulators used for dicotyledons where three separate cultural stages were used to induce indirect embryogenesis, embryo growth, and finally, embryo germination and plantlet growth.
[Based on 20 protocols for 15 species in 15 papers].

Growth regulators	Induction of embryogenesis				Embryo formation and growth				Germination			
	Use % protocols	Concentrations employed			Use % protocols	Concentrations employed			Use % protocols	Concentrations employed		
		Range μM	Average μM	Average mg/l		Range μM	Average μM	Average mg/l		Range μM	Average μM	Average mg/l
Auxins												
IAA	10.0	5.71	5.71	1.0	20.0	0.31–5.71	2.22	0.39	5.0	2.28	2.28	0.4
NAA	20.0	2.69–99.89	37.73	7.02	30.0	0.27–0.54	0.31	0.06	0	—	—	—
IBA	0	—	—	—	5.0	0.49	0.49	0.1	0	—	—	—
2,4-D	75.0	0.45–19.99	5.18	1.14	35.0	0.05–4.52	1.31	0.29	0	—	—	—
Picloram	5.0	2.48	2.48	0.6	0	—	—	—	5.0	0.004	0.004	0.001
> one auxin	10.0	—	—	—	5	—	—	—	0	—	—	—
No auxin	0	—	—	—	15	—	—	—	90	—	—	—
Cytokinins												
Kinetin	25.0	1.02–19.98	5.36	1.15	15.0	2.32–4.65	3.56	0.77	5.0	3.72	3.72	0.8
BAP	25.0	0.98–8.88	4.63	1.04	35.0	0.44–4.44	1.20	0.27	20	0.04–1.78	0.48	0.11
2-iP	0	—	—	—	5	4.92	4.92	1.0	0	—	—	—
Zeatin	10.0	0.009–4.56	2.29	0.50	10.0	0.91–1.00	0.96	0.21	5.0	0.09	0.09	0.02
Adenine sulphate	5.0	81.45	81.45	30.0	5.0	16.56	16.56	6.1	5.0	108.6	108.6	40
Coconut milk	0	—	—	—	0	—	—	—	0	—	—	—
> one cytokinin	0	—	—	—	5.0	—	—	—	5	—	—	—
No cytokinin	35.0	—	—	—	35.0	—	—	—	70	—	—	—
Gibberellins												
No gibberellin	100	—	—	—	100	—	—	—	100	—	—	—
No PGRs at all	0	—	—	—	15	—	—	—	65	—	—	—

average, less than that used at Stage 2 of the two–stage procedure (Table 91). For the final third stage where embryos are enabled to grow and germinate, auxin was nearly always omitted.

Callus maintenance. Embryogenic callus is usually maintained in a medium very similar to that used for initiation, containing 2–3% sucrose and less auxin than was added initially. Callus can be maintained and increased on a solid medium; often such cultures are kept in Petri dishes but need to be subcultured frequently. Embryogenic cultures can also be increased as suspensions in liquid medium.

Monocotyledons

In monocotyledons, embryogenic callus usually arises on the explants during the first passage on a medium containing auxin. The growth regulators used in 54 accounts of embryogenesis are summarised in Table 93. On aver-

age there were only small differences between the regulants used to induce embryogenesis in dicotyledons and monocotyledons. In monocotyledons, the 'more active' auxins 2,4–D, 2,4,5–T, picloram and dicamba were used more frequently than in dicotyledons, and a cytokinin in the Stage I medium was seldom included.

The majority of monocotyledon examples come from the the induction of embryogenesis in cereals and grasses. Embryogenic callus is commonly initiated from the scutellum of cereal embryos by culture on a medium such as **Linsmaier and Skoog (1965)**, **Murashige and Skoog (1965)** or **Chu et al. (1975) N6** to which a single auxin (*e.g.* 2,4–D or dicamba) is added. Only occasionally has a second auxin such as NAA or IAA been added. Siriwardana and Nabors (1983) found that adding 50–100 mg/l tryptophan (an IAA precursor) to **Linsmaier and Skoog (1965)** containing 1 mg/l 2,4–D, increased the formation of

Table 93. Growth regulators used for monocotyledons where a two-stage cultural process was used both to induce indirect embryogenesis and then to promote embryo growth and development.
[Based on 54 protocols for 27 species in 38 papers].

Growth regulators	Callus formation and induction of embryogenesis				Embryo growth and germination			
	Use	Concentrations employed			Use	Concentrations employed		
	%	Range	Average		%	Range	Average	
	protocols	µM	µM	mg/l	protocols	µM	µM	mg/l
Auxins								
IAA	5.5	5.7–9.99	8.56	1.5	13.0	1.14–17.12	5.54	0.97
NAA	9.3	0.27–5.37	3.80	0.71	11.1	2.69–26.85	7.38	1.38
2,4-D	75.9	0.62–45.24	11.33	2.51	18.5	0.045–4.52	1.14	0.25
2,4,5-T	11.1	3.91–39.14	12.39	3.17	1.85	0.78	0.78	0.2
2-CPA	1.85	10.74	10.74	2	0	—	—	—
Picloram	3.7	12.42	12.42	3	3.7	0.41	0.41	0.1
Dicamba	3.7	29.86	29.86	6.6	1.85	0.90	0.90	0.2
More than one auxin	11.1	—	—	—	1.85	—	—	—
No auxin	0	—	—	—	51.9	—	—	—
Cytokinins								
Kinetin	20.4	0.46–2.32	1.29	0.28	16.7	0.46–23.23	7.07	1.52
BAP	14.8	0.89–22.20	7.65	1.72	13.0	0.44–4.44	1.96	0.44
2-iP	1.25	4.92	4.92	1	2.5	0.98–4.92	2.95	0.6
Zeatin	1.9	7.98	7.98	1.75	0	—	—	—
Adenine sulphate	3.7	108.6	108.6	40.0	1.9	108.6	108.6	40
Coconut milk	14.8	5–10%	—	7.5%	5.6	5–10%	—	6.7%
More than one cytokinin	10.9	—	—	—	0	—	—	—
No cytokinin	51.9	—	—	—	59.3	—	—	—
Gibberellins								
GA3	0	—	—	—	5.6	0.29–2.89	1.15	0.4
No gibberellin	100	—	—	—	94.4	—	—	—
Abscisic acid	0	—	—	—	1.9	0.04	0.04	0.01
No ABA	100	—	—	—	98.1	—	—	—
No PGRs at all	0	—	—	—	38.9	—	—	—

embryogenic callus in 3 rice cultivars. The addition of 100 mg/l IAA had the same effect as tryptophan in one cultivar.

As in dicotyledons, three stage protocols have been used for some monocotyledonous species. For instance, callus formed by culturing mesocotyl tissue of *Aritida oligantha* on **MS** medium with 9 mg/l 2,4–D, was not obviously embryogenic, but a nodular callus was formed when the primary callus was moved to a medium containing 2 mg/l 2,4–D. Embryo formation only occurred when the nodular callus was moved onto regulant–free **Ben–Jaacov and Dax (1981)** medium.

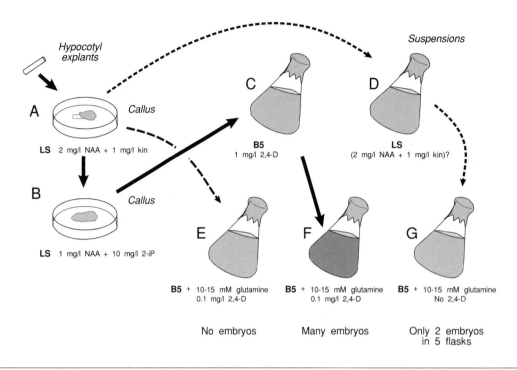

Fig. 122. Induction of embryogenesis in *Gossypium klotzschianum.*   [The experiment of Price and Smith 1979a].

In most cereals and grasses (*e.g. Pennisetum purpureum* — Haydu and Vasil, 1981; *Panicum maxicum* — Lu and Vasil, 1981a; *Lolium multiflorum* — Dale *et al.*, 1981; *Zea mays* — Lu *et al.*, 1982; *Bothriochloa caucasia* — Franklin *et al.*, 1990) embryos are formed and develop into well organised structures, or even plantlets, in a single medium, without the operative needing to subculture the callus to a medium with less auxin.

At Stage II, auxins were usually omitted, or 2,4–D (or 2,4,5–T) was replaced by NAA or IAA. The instances in Table 93 where 2,4–D was used again during embryo formation, include some experiments in which embryogenesis was induced and embryos clearly differentiated on the same medium. Nabors *et al.* (1983) reported that media containing IAA or tryptophan (an IAA precursor) together with 2,4–D or 2,4,5–T, markedly increased the formation of embryogenic callus in pearl millet, wheat and some cultivars of rice compared to occasions when the synthetic auxins were used on their own.

Palm trees are commonly propagated by embryogenesis, but because cultures are likely to exude polyphenols during culture, activated charcoal is usually added to the medium. The induction of callus growth and embryo-

genesis then requires abnormally high concentrations of auxin (Part 1, page 471 and page 1157).

Adventitious shoots *versus* somatic embryos

What is the difference between treatments which induce the formation of callus capable of giving rise to adventitious shoots and those which cause embryogenic callus to be initiated? As the growth regulatory compounds used to induce callus capable of forming adventitious shoots or somatic embryos are essentially the same, can one draw any general rules as to the methods of application and the concentrations most likely to produce each kind of organogenesis?

In some cases it seems that the occurrence of different kinds of morphogenesis can be controlled by the selection of particular exogenous regulants. For example, in callus cultures of *Petunia inflata* and *P. hybrida*, the addition of 2,4–D led to embryogenesis, the use of IAA/BAP led to the development of adventitious shoots with roots, and NAA/BAP to root development (Rao *et al.*, 1973a). This explanation is not altogether plausible because auxins apart from 2,4–D can induce embryogenesis if supplied in sufficient concentration and in circumstances where they are not rapidly metabolised.

Table 94. The average total concentrations of auxins and cytokinins used in 2–stage procedures to obtain indirect adventitious shoot formation, or indirect embryogenesis.
Averages for cytokinins which exclude adenine usage are given in brackets.

Class of plants	Type of growth regulator	Indirect adventitious shoot formation		Indirect embryogenesis	
		Stage I (Callus formation) µM	Stage 2 (Shoot formation) µM	Stage 1 (Callus formation) µM	Stage 2 (Embryo formation and/or growth) µM
Dicotyledons					
	Auxin	10.1	5.7	14.6	1.7
	Cytokinin	8.9 (5.8)	20.7 (9.3)	5.3 (4.3)	6.9 (3.1)
Monocotyledons					
	Auxin	17.0	4.6	12.8	1.8

In Table 94 we have averaged the total concentrations[†] of auxins and cytokinins which were employed in the experiments summarized in Tables 81, 82, 84 and 91. These figures are not a completely satisfactory comparison of the levels of regulants required, because compounds vary in their effectiveness; for example IAA is less effective than NAA or 2,4–D for inducing callus formation; adenine is a less effective cytokinin than BAP. Because relatively high levels of adenine have been added to some media, the concentration at which other cytokinins have been used is obscured. Concentrations of cytokinin are therefore given in the table with and without the inclusion of adenine.

Table 94 shows that in order to induce callus capable of producing adventitious shoots from dicotyledons, a lower concentration of auxin and a higher concentration of cytokinin is needed than for the induction of embryogenic callus. To allow morphogenesis at Stage 2, the level of auxin is invariable reduced, but needs on average to be reduced to 1.7–1.8 µM to obtain embryo formation and embryo growth. In monocotyledons, a slightly higher concentration of auxin has been used to obtain shoot–forming rather than embryo–forming callus.

Abscisic acid

In most experiments, there has been no need to add abscisic acid (ABA) to media to induce embryogenesis, or to obtain embryos, and its addition to Stage I media has been reported to be inhibitory (Fujimura and Komamine,

1975; Tisserat and Murashige 1977c). But although it was not added to the medium in any of the examples of indirect embryogenesis summarised in Tables 91, 92 and 93, low concentrations of ABA have been found to enhance the induction of embryogenesis in some plants (Chapter 11, page 454).

Adding ABA to Stage I cultures can increase subsequent adventitious shoot formation (see page 598) and possibly for the same reason, there was an advantage from incorporating 0.5–1 mg/l into the Stage I medium (containing 2 mg/l 2,4–D) for producing embryogenic callus from late–stage (21–25 days post anthesis) zygotic embryos of wheat (Qureshi et al., 1989). Here, precocious germination of the zygotic embryos was suppressed and embryogenic callus formation was promoted. Subsequent embryo conversion (page 635) was highest if only 0.5 mg/l ABA was employed. If ABA was added to the medium on which early stage zygotic embryos were cultured, the number producing embryogenic callus diminished, so that many less somatic embryos and plantlets were subsequently obtained.

By adding 0.5 µM ABA and 1.7 mM glutamine to the medium, embryogenic callus of Carya appeared to be changed to a non–embryogenic but much faster growing form. However, it was reconverted into a recognisably embryogenic form, by subculture on the medium lacking the two amendments. Yates (1988) thought this technique could be profitably used to increase the availability of somatic embryos of Carya.

[†] If more than one auxin or cytokinin were added to a medium, their concentrations were added together.

ABA can inhibit the development of secondary and abnormal embryos, but it was only added to the Stage II medium for one plant, *Triticum aestivum*, by one set of experimenters in the results represented by Tables 91, 92 and 93. The development of conifer embryos is dependent on the addition of ABA to the medium. *Pinus strobus* embryos grew most satisfactorily in **Gupta and Durzan (1985)** medium to which had been added 6% sucrose, 500 mg/l casein hydrolysate, 50 mM glutamine and 38 μM ABA (Finer *et al.*, 1989). In *Picea glauca*, structures resembling shoots were produced with 1–5 μM ABA, bipolar embryos with 10–20 μM, and when 30–40 μM ABA was present, precocious germination was inhibited and quiescent embryos with opaque cotyledonary structures, characteristic of mature zygotic embryos were produced. The latter were of a much better quality than the shoot–like ones, and produced elongated roots upon germination.

ABA inhibits polyembryony of *Picea abies* and causes pro–embryos to form individual embryos which elongate without precocious germination when grown for 2–3 subculture on a medium containing 0.1–0.5 NAA and 22.7 μM ABA. If a lower concentration of ABA (3.8 μM) was present, embryos did not reach an equivalent size until the 4th subculture (Boulay *et al.*, 1988).

The use of ABA for somatic embryo maturation is mentioned in Chapter 14.

Effects of ethylene

That ethylene can be inhibitory to embryogenesis has been suggested by the results of several investigations (Chapter 11, page 461). Roustan *et al.* (1989) found that adding cobalt chloride (10–50 μM) to the medium in which embryogenic carrot cell suspensions were subcultured, both reduced ethylene production and significantly increased the number of somatic embryos formed. The addition of ethephon negated the stimulation, which therefore appeared to be due to the lower level of ethylene rather than a direct stimulative effect of Co^{2+}.

Adding 5–10 mg/l silver nitrate to the Stage I medium, increased the proportion of immature zygotic embryos of *Zea mays* which produced 'type II' embryogenic callus (*cf.* 'type I' non–embryogenic callus), and furthermore increased the number of plants obtained at Stage II from 5 per gram (fresh weight) of callus, to 12 or more per gram (Vain *et al.*, 1989). Similar results have been obtained in *Hevea brasiliensis*. Auboiron *et al.* (1990) found that during Stage I callus formation there was a considerable release of CO_2 and ethylene in confined conditions. This was favourable for callus growth, but not for the formation of cells capable of developing into somatic embryos. Trapping the ethylene produced promoted embryogene-

sis as did adding 5–50 μM AOA (depending on the *Hevea* clone), or 5.9–58.8 μM $AgNO_3$. AOA [(amino–oxy) acetic acid] is another inhibitor of ethylene synthesis.

Although adding silver nitrate had no effect on the growth of *Pennisetum americanum* embryogenic callus grown on a maintenance medium, when 58.9 μM was added to the regeneration medium, it increased the number of plants obtained per vessel from 6–7 to 18. The antibiotic cefotaxime had a similar result (Pius *et al.*, 1993).

Gibberellic acid

Although there are some contrary reports (Part 1, page 449 and page 622), the addition of exogenous gibberellic acid has usually been found to suppress embryogenesis. This is consistent with the findings of Noma *et al.* (1982) that explants of carrot and *Pimpinella anisum* to which 2,4–D had been administered to induce embryogenesis, had high natural levels of polar gibberellins and a reduced ability to metabolise such compounds. In these plants, when the auxin was removed and somatic embryo development began, cultures metabolised GA_1 very quickly so that its level was much reduced (Part 1, page 449). GA_3 was however included in the medium used for embryo induction for two of the dicotyledonous species represented in Table 91: these were *Vigna aconitifolia* (callus derived from mesophyll protoplasts — Shekhawat and Galston, 1983a) and *Malus × domestica* (Mehra and Sachdeva 1984).

The addition of an antigibberellin compound to suspension cultures of *Glycine max* was found by Gamborg *et al.* (1983) to cause somatic embryos to be produced. Amo 1615, chlormequat, paclobutrazol and ancymidol were all effective. No embryos were formed without one of these compounds being present in the medium.

Exogenous gibberellic acid (*ca.* 1 mg/l) can sometimes assist the differentiation, growth and germination (see page 449 of Part 1 and page 716) of somatic embryos, when it is added to a medium in the absence of auxin.

Media for indirect embryogenesis

Nitrogen content

The presence of a supply of reduced nitrogen is not essential for the *induction* of embryogenesis (Kamada and Harada, 1979b) but, as in direct embryogenesis, is necessary for the formation of embryogenic callus and embryo growth. Kamada *et al.* (1982) found, for instance, that cells of carrot could be given the capacity to produce somatic embryos by culture in just a sucrose solution containing 2,4–D. However, the division of induced embryogenically determined cells (IEDCs — Part 1, page

30) to produce proembryos, and the growth and development of somatic embryos does require the presence of nitrogen in both its oxidised and reduced forms. Callus formed with auxin on a medium lacking NH_4^+, or amino acids, will not form embryos when transferred to an auxin–free medium.

Callus with the potential to form somatic embryos could be induced by adding 2,4–D and kinetin to **Schenk and Hildebrandt (1972)** medium containing only 2.6 mM NH_4^+ (NO_3^-/NH_4^+ ratio 90.5 : 9.5), but effective embryo regeneration did not take place on this medium in the absence of growth regulators until the NH_4^+ content had been increased to 12.5 mM (NO_3^-/NH_4^+ ratio then 66.4 : 33.6) (Walker and Sato, 1981). Embryogenesis of wild carrot will occur with as little as 5 mM NH_4^+ in the medium (NO_3^-/NH_4^+ ratio 92 : 8) (Halperin and Wetherell, 1965), but as explained in Part 1 (page 283), media in which the NO_3^-/NH_4^+ ratio is between 55 : 45 and 80 : 20, seem to be best.

As it is possible to induce embryogenesis *without* auxin by regulating the pH of culture media (see Chapter 9, page 301), and as the proportion of NH_4^+ to NO_3^- in a medium has a marked effect on final pH, part of the effect of the nitrate/ammonium ion content of a medium on embryogenesis may be due to pH control. Choice of an appropriate medium is important for this reason, and also because the effectiveness of auxin in regulating embryogenesis can be dependent on the medium with which it is used (Chapter 9, pages 282–284). Koetje *et al.* (1989) showed that at all concentrations between 0.5–3.0 mg/l, 2,4–D induced the formation of a greater number of rice embryos per embryogenic callus, capable of being regenerated into plants, when it was added to **Chu *et al.* (1975) N6** medium (supplemented with 1 g/l CH), than to **MS** (with an added 250 µM L–tryptophan). The NO_3^- : NH_4^+ ratio of **N6** medium is 80:20 (3.99), that of **MS** medium 66 : 34 (1.91). One mechanism whereby auxin may regulate embryogenesis, is by cell acidification (Chapter 11). Here it seems that 2,4–D was more effective in a medium which would have a more alkaline final pH.

With an NO_3^- : NH_4^+ ratio of 80 : 20, a medium containing 35 mM total nitrogen was found to be most effective for indirect embryogenesis in *Betula pendula* (Nuutila *et al.*, 1991), but for *Zea mays*, Suprasanna *et al.* (1991) reported that the best embryogenic response was achieved by increasing the concentration of both NO_3^- and NH_4^+ in **MS** medium from 39.4 and 20.61 mM to, respectively, 54 and 36 mM. This had the effect of decreasing the NO_3^- : NH_4^+ ratio from 66 : 34 to 60 : 40.

The nitrogen contents of the media employed to bring about indirect embryogenesis in the reports analysed for growth regulator usage (Tables 91 and 93) are summarised in Tables 95 and 96 respectively. In dicotyledons, although **MS** medium has been used in many experiments, embryogenesis has also been induced on media with a lower concentration of total salts, NO_3^- and NH_4^+. By contrast, embryogenesis in monocotyledons has nearly always been initiated in media with a high total concentration of macronutrient ions, **MS** medium being most often adopted.

Addition of amino acids

As mentioned above and on page 618, amino acids can provide the reduced nitrogen required for embryogenesis, so making the addition of ammonium ions unnecessary. In many instances amino acids have been shown to enhance, or even to be essential for embryogenesis, when the medium already contains NH_4^+ (page 289 of Part 1). This is especially true for dicotyledons. The need to add amino acids is less in monocotyledons, and where they have been used, they have more frequently been added to the Stage I medium (Table 96). This is probably because somatic embryos of monocotyledons usually form in the Stage I medium, where amino acids which favour their growth will have greatest benefit.

Possible reasons for the growth stimulation caused by amino acids when inorganic NH_4^+ is available, were listed in Part 1, page 290, the most cogent of which is that these compounds can be metabolised into other amino acids and proteins without the need for ATP synthesis. The benefit from adding individual amino acids, or the mixture of acids provided by casein hydrolysate, should be particularly noticeable in media deficient in phosphate. **Murashige and Skoog (1962)** medium does not have a high phosphate concentration.

Amino acids do not usually influence the·immediate formation of embryogenic callus, but once it has started to grow, the addition of amino acids, particularly glutamine (*ca.* 0.5–1 mM), glutamic acid (*ca.* 1–2 mM), or casein hydrolysate (500–1000 mg/l), often increases its rate of proliferation and enhances the growth of somatic embryos. Addition of amino acids to the Stage I medium can also improve the eventual conversion of somatic embryos to plantlets (see page 635). Indirect or direct embryogenesis has not been achieved in some species unless the medium has been supplemented with amino acids, casein hydrolysate, or yeast extract.

The improvement in somatic embryo growth and development caused by amino acids is exactly comparable to the requirements of immature zygotic embryos which have been isolated and cultured *in vitro*. Large zygotic embryos can usually be grown and enabled to germinate on a medium devoid of organic nitrogen, but immature ones require the presence of amino acids. Thus

Table 95. The nitrogen content of media used for <u>dicotyledons</u> to induce indirect embryogenesis at Stage I, and to encourage embryo growth at Stage 2.

Statistic		Stage I		Stage II	
		NO_3^- (meq/l)	NH_4^+ (meq/l)	NO_3^- (meq/l)	NH_4^+ (meq/l)
Basic media without amino acid additions					
Average concentrations		31.9	14.4	31.5	14.9
Range	High	55	35.9	55.0	35.9
	Low	2.5	0	2.5	0
NO_3^- / NH_4^+ ratio	Average	72.2 : 27.8		70.2 : 29.8	
Range	High	100 : 0		100 : 0	
	Low	6.5 : 93.5		6.5 : 93.5	
Amino acid additions					
Average concentrations		—	2.34	—	3.69
Range	High	—	21.5	—	100
	Low	—	0	—	0
Media containing amino acids		71.1%		76.3%	
Media containing amino acids contributing more than 0.05 meq/l NH_4^+		30.9%		41.2%	
Media as used (with amino acids when added)					
Average concentrations		31.9	16.8	31.5	18.5
Range	High	55	42.0	55	100
	Low	2.5	0.04	2.5	0.04
NO_3^- / NH_4^+ ratio	Average	66.7 : 33.3		63.3 : 36.7	
Range	High	98.8 : 1.2		98.8 : 1.2	
	Low	6.5 : 93.5		6.5 : 93.5	

embryo culture media have been supplemented with, for example, yeast extract (Islam, 1964; Gadwal *et al.*, 1968), glutamine (Pecket and Selim, 1965), asparagine and yeast extract (Anagnostakis, 1977), and a mixture of amino acids (Norstog, 1967; 1973). For the culture of *Glycine max* zygotic embryos, Lippmann and Lippmann (1993) replaced the $(NH_4)_2SO_4$ in **B5** medium with 10 mM glutamine. Somatic embryos of *Pinus strobus* grew satisfactorily when embryogenic callus was transferred to a medium containing glutamine (page 627), but in the absence of this amino acid only embryogenic callus was obtained.

Casein hydrolysate also has a stimulative effect on the *in vitro* growth of immature zygotic embryos (Sanders and Burkholder, 1948; Ziebur *et al.*, 1950; Kapoor, 1959; Mauney, 1961). Barley embryo growth was stimulated by adding 1% casein hydrolysate to **Randolph and Cox (1950)** medium, but germination was inhibited, because the water potential of the medium was decreased (Ziebur *et*

al. loc. cit.). Malt extract (ME), which typically contains little nitrogen, is able to induce direct embryogenesis in *Citrus* nucellus tissue (see page 613 above) and the addition of 1–1.5 g/l to **Murashige and Tucker (1969)** medium has also been shown to promote indirect embryo formation in the absence of growth regulants in *Citrus* and *Poncirus* callus which had been induced in the presence of 2,4–D. An alternative treatment was to add NAA and BAP to the medium (Beloualy, 1991). The basis of the ME stimulation of embryogenesis in these cases has not been determined.

The effects of amino acid additions on the nitrogen content of the media used in our sample of indirect embryogenesis (page 629) are summarised in Tables 95 and 96. **MS** media, and those based upon it, contain a nominal amount of glycine, which tends to exaggerate the proportion of media to which amino acid additions were made. The proportion of media in which amino acids contributed at least 0.05 meq/l (mM) NH_4^+ more

Table 96. The nitrogen content of media used for <u>monocotyledons</u> to induce indirect embryogenesis at Stage I, and to encourage embryo growth at Stage 2.

Statistic		Stage I		Stage II	
		NO_3^- (meq/l)	NH_4^+ (meq/l)	NO_3^- (meq/l)	NH_4^+ (meq/l)
Basic media without amino acid additions					
Average concentrations		38.1	18.8	37.8	18.6
Range	High	78.8	41.2	78.8	41.2
	Low	19.7	2.6	19.7	2.6
NO_3^- / NH_4^+ ratio	Average	68.0 : 32.0		68.0 : 32.0	
Range	High	90.5 : 9.5		90.5 : 9.5	
	Low	65.6 : 34.4		65.6 : 34.4	
Amino acid additions					
Average concentrations		—	1.02	—	0.59
Range	High	—	16.1	—	7.94
	Low	—	0	—	0
Media containing amino acids		67.2%		67.2%	
Media containing amino acids contributing more than 0.05 meq/l NH_4^+		14.8%		13.1%	
Media as used (with amino acids when added)					
Average concentrations		38.1	19.7	37.8	19.2
Range	High	78.8	49.2	78.8	49.2
	Low	19.7	2.6	19.7	2.6
NO_3^- / NH_4^+ ratio	Average	66.9 : 33.1		67.5 : 32.5	
Range	High	90.5 : 9.5		90.5 : 9.5	
	Low	55.7 : 44.3		60.1 : 39.9	

fairly represents a purposeful incorporation of organic nitrogen to influence embryogenesis. Although for dicotyledons, several workers added amino acids to the Stage I medium used for the induction of somatic embryogenesis, these compounds were more commonly added as a supplement at Stage II.

The presence of casein hydrolysate in the differentiation medium can suppress embryo formation after several subcultures (Banerjee and Gupta, 1976; Gupta *et al.*, 1987).

Effectiveness of different amino acids. The effectiveness of individual amino acids may depend on the capacity of a particular plant to effect their metabolism. IEDC cells produced by culture of *Gossypium klotzschianum* suspensions on **B5** medium plus 0.1 mg/l 2,4–D formed somatic embryos reproducibly when subcultured onto **B5** medium supplemented with 10–15 mM glutamine (Price and Smith, 1979a; Finer and Smith, 1984). Similarly, cell division, and the formation of embryos proceeded rapidly

when IEDC carrot cells were transferred to **MS** medium from which NH_4^+ had been removed and which had been supplemented with 10 mM glutamine or glutamic acid. α–Alanine was an equally effective source of nitrogen, probably because it was converted to glutamic acid by alanine amino transferase (Kamada *et al.*, 1982). Asparagine, aspartic acid, arginine and proline were also stimulative, but lysine, valine, histidine, leucine and methionine were found not to be effective (Kamada and Harada, 1979b) and L–tyrosine has been found to be inhibitory (Anderson, 1976). Although casein hydrolysate was stimulative, glutamine did not stimulate embryogenesis of *Triticum aestivum* (Ozias–Akins and Vasil, 1983b) and replacement of the inorganic nitrogen of **Schenk and Hildebrandt (1984)** medium with L–glutamine, resulted in the death of *Dactylis glomerata* cultures (Gray and Conger, 1985). Casein hydrolysate has often been found to be more effective than a corresponding mixture of amino acids (Part 1, page 287).

Proline (86.9 μM) and serine act to retard embryo differentiation of wild carrot if added to the auxin supplemented medium used to induce embryogenesis (Nuti Ronchi *et al.*, 1982). Thus when 100 mM proline (11.5 g/l) and serine were added to suspensions of carrot cells cultured on **B5** medium with 0.5 mg/l 2,4–D and 0.25 mg/l BAP, the rate of growth was decreased, although there was still active cell division. However, this resulted in the formation of many more cell clumps than normal, and when the suspension was filtered through nylon sieves and transferred to a medium lacking growth regulators, the capacity of the cultures to produce somatic embryos was greatly increased (Nuti Ronchi *et al.*, 1984).

Adding certain amino acids to **Schenk and Hildebrandt (1972)** (**SH**) medium, increases the number of embryos formed indirectly from *Medicago sativa*, callus, and hence the number of embryos available for conversion. Proline (100 mM), and alanine (30–100 mM) were found by Stuart and Strickland (1984a) to be most effective, but they were only stimulative if 2.6–25 mM NH_4^+ was present in the medium (*i.e.* the NH_4^+ in **SH** or an addition amount) (Stuart and Strickland, 1984b).

Without the addition of 2.2 mM proline to **MS** medium (containing 250 mg/l casein hydrolysate), only a white compact callus was formed from immature *Aesculus hippocastanum* embryos, and this became necrotic after 6 months. However when proline was incorporated, two kinds of callus arose simultaneously, one globular and the other embryogenic (Radojević, 1988). The formation of embryos in callus of *Rosa hybrida* was found by Rout *et al.* (1991a,b) to be dependent on the addition of 200–800 mg/l proline to the Stage II ½**MS** medium.

The presence of proline in media already containing NH_4^+ ions, also seems to enhance the formation of embryos in some monocotyledons (*e.g. Zea mays* — Armstrong and Green, 1985; Kamo *et al.*, 1985: *Bothriochloa caucasia* — Franklin *et al.*, 1990; *Oryza sativa* — Cho and Zapata, 1988), but to have no effect in others (Gray and Conger, 1985).

Divalent ions

Jansen *et al.* (1990) found that, in carrot, Ca^{2+} ions tend to overcome the inhibitory effect of 2 μM 2,4–D on embryo growth. Thus the number of embryos produced from a suspension culture was increased if, after the cells had been cultured on **B5** (1 mM Ca^{2+}) with 2,4–D, they were transferred to a hormone free medium with 10 mM Ca^{2+}, instead of normal **B5** medium. A change in calcium content seemed to be important, rather that the actual Ca^{2+} concentrations used during culture, because a similar improvement was noticed if cells were induced to become embryogenic on a medium with 0.1 mM Ca^{2+} and 2 μM 2,4–D and

were then moved to a regulant–free medium with 1 mM Ca^{2+}.

Gellan gum polymerises by binding divalent ions, particularly Mg^{2+}, and this may result in a reduction in growth if Mg^{2+} or Ca^{2+} become unavailable (Part 1, page 341). Embryogenic callus of *Larix × eurolepis* grew poorly on a medium gelled with 0.4% gellan gum until the content of $MgSO_4.7H_2O$ was increased from 185 to 925 mg/l (Klimaszewska, 1989).

Micronutrients

The proportion of wheat zygotic embryos which gave rise to embryogenic callus was reduced when microelements were not added to **MS** medium (He *et al.*, 1991). The omission of manganese caused the most noticeable decrease (21%). However, embryogenic callus of wheat is associated with the formation of white structures (putative embryos) and the number of these bodies produced was increased by the omission of zinc.

Redox potential

Conflicting evidence on whether embryogenesis is favoured by a reducing or an oxidative cellular environment was summarised in Part 1, page 200. Cells of *Selinum candolii*, obtained by culture on a medium enriched with 2,4–D, produced callus colonies from which 15–20 somatic embryos were obtained per gram fresh weight on a Stage II 2,4–D–free medium. If however the plated cells were covered with mineral oil, there was less callus growth, but a four–fold increase in the number of embryos per gram of callus (Mathur, 1991). These results are in agreement with the findings summarised on page 198, that embryogenesis is enhanced by a reduction in the partial pressure of oxygen during culture.

However, treatments to reduce the level of endogenous glutathione and increase the oxidising environment have also been reported to be effective. These have comprised the frequent addition of hydrogen peroxide to the medium (Kapik *et al.*, 1986), or the addition of 0.3 mM buthionine sulfoximine (an inhibitor of glutathione synthesis) (Earnshaw and Johnson, 1985).

Sugars and osmotic potential

Typically media used for Stage I or Stage II of direct or indirect embryogenesis have been supplemented with 2–3% sucrose, and in many cases this can be shown to be an optimal concentration. For example, using **Phillips and Collins (1979) L2** medium, Lippmann and Lippmann (1984) found that no somatic embryos were produced directly on *Glycine max* cotyledons if the medium contained 2% (or higher) sucrose or 1.5% (or higher) glucose. The largest number of embryos was obtained with 1%

sucrose; few embryos were produced with 1.5% sucrose in the medium. The optimum sucrose content for embryogenesis in *Betula* was found to be 20.8 g/l (Nuutila *et al.*, 1991).

However, as in the induction of direct embryogenesis (page 618), in a few species it has been found to be beneficial to add high concentrations of sucrose, which either enhances embryo formation or embryo growth (Table 97). There is, as yet, no clear understanding why high concentrations of sugar (or perhaps, more importantly, a low water potential) should be beneficial in some plants for the induction of embryogenesis and embryo formation, but not in others. The influence which the water potential of culture media may have on somatic embryogenesis was described in Part 1, page 335. Nadel *et al.* (1989) found that adding 3–4% mannitol to the Stage II (regeneration) medium (containing 3% sucrose) prevented cell lysis, improved normal embryo development and greatly increased the number of embryos which developed singly, and accelerated the formation of torpedo–stage embryos. Equimolar solutions of sucrose alone were not effective.

That there may be an interaction between the sucrose concentration of the medium and the auxin concentration necessary to induce embryogenesis was mentioned on page 426 of Part 1. Placing embryos on a medium of low water potential to assist embryo growth and maturation is described in Chapter 14.

Maltose. Using maltose instead of sucrose as a carbohydrate source has been found to enhance embryogenesis from anther explants of some cereals (Kuhlmann and Foroughi–Wehr, 1989; Orshinsky *et al.*, 1990; Scott and Lyne, 1994). It has been suggested that this is because its slow hydrolysis in the medium provides anthers with a source of glucose at a rate close to their normal utilisation (Roberts–Oehlschlager *et al.*, 1990) over a long period (Orshinsky *et al.*, 1990). Maltose promotes embryogenesis in anthers of some varieties of wheat but not others, which might be related to the sugars naturally present in anther walls (Trottier *et al.*, 1993). The slow hydrolysis of maltose means that media containing this sugar provide a more stable osmotic environment than those in which sucrose is included (Kuhlmann and Foroughi–Wehr, 1989).

pH

A medium pH of 4.0–5.0 has been shown to be associated with the induction of embryogenesis and the maintenance of pre–globular stage somatic embryos (Part 1, page 301). The low pH observed in such media probably results from the active uptake of NH_4^+ during the induction of embryogenesis, and/or the addition of auxin to the

medium, but may also actually contribute to the induction process. Marsolais *et al.* (1991a) found that direct embryogenesis of *Pelargonium* was most effectively induced when **MS** medium was adjusted to pH 4.5–5 before autoclaving.

Somatic embryo growth and development appears to be associated with a higher pH than that required for the induction of embryogenesis (*i.e.* 5.5 and above), which may partly account for the promotive effect of activated charcoal mentioned below. The addition of charcoal has sometimes been noted to elevate the pH of the medium (Chapter 11, page 471).

Activated charcoal

By adding 1 per cent charcoal to the medium, Fridborg and Eriksson (1975b) restored the capacity of a line of carrot callus to regenerate somatic embryos, which it had recently lost through aging. Omitting auxin from the medium was ineffective. It was thought that the charcoal adsorbed auxins added to the medium, auxin growth substances secreted by the tissues, or inhibitory phenolic molecules (Fridborg *et al.* 1978). Similar results with cell suspensions of carrot were acquired by Drew (1979) and Warren and Fowler (1981). In the work of Drew, subculture onto an auxin–free medium containing 1 per cent charcoal, 7 months after culture initiation, only resulted in somatic embryo formation where 1 ml of inoculum (and not 6 ml) had been added to each flask. This was taken to indicate that the charcoal used was insufficient to adsorb all the inhibitory metabolites from the larger quantity of cells. The promotion of embryogenesis by charcoal in these circumstances might alternatively be due to it acting as a sink for endogenously produced auxin, thereby depleting the effective concentration within cells.

The presence of 1 g/l charcoal was essential for embryogenesis in callus from mature *Hedera* stems and there was no morphogenesis without it. Once embryos were initiated however they would grow in a liquid medium without charcoal (Banks and Hackett, 1978; Banks, 1979a). In papaya callus, activated charcoal enhanced embryogenesis and enabled somatic embryos to develop more rapidly than otherwise (Litz and Conover, 1980a).

Androgenesis. Although the production of haploid plants from pollen is not analysed in any depth in this book, the occasional effectiveness of charcoal in promoting pollen embryogenesis and/or callus production from anthers, is relevant to our description of the induction of embryogenesis by growth regulants. Some examples of the successful use of charcoal for this purpose will be found in:

Table 97. Examples of the use of high sugar concentrations (high osmolality) to regulate indirect embryogenesis.
[The osmolalities given are estimated from the molarity of media ingredients].

Plant	Explant	Medium	Sucrose %	Estimated osmolality of medium		References
				Medium alone mOs/kg	Total (medium + sucrose etc.) mOs/kg	
Citrus sinensis	Callus formation	**Murashige and Tucker (1969)**	5	96	250	Kochba and Button (1974)
	Somatic embryo development	**Murashige and Tucker (1969)**	6	96	282	
Lycopersicon esculentum	Initiation of embryogenic callus	**MS**	12	96	492	Uddin and Berry (1988)
	Formation of embryogenic tissues	**MS**	3	96	186	
Pinus strobus	Formation of embryogenic callus	**Gupta and Durzan (1985) DCR**	3	37	127	Finer *et al.* (1989)
	Stage 2, embryo growth	**Gupta and Durzan (1985) DCR**	6	34	220	
Prunus persica	Formation of embryogenic callus	mod. **MS**	3	103	193	Raj Bhansali *et al.* (1991)
	Formation of globular embryos in callus	mod **MS** + 4.6 mM Ca(NO₃)₂	6	116	302	
Rumex acetosella †	Embryogenic callus	**MS**	6 §	96	282 ‡	Ćulafić *et al.* (1987b)
			2 + 21.3 g/l mannitol or sorbitol §	96	273 ‡	
	Embryos matured	**MS**	6	96	282	
Saccharum	Formation of embryogenic callus	**MS**	3	96	186	Ahloowalia and Maretzki (1983)
	Stage 2, embryo growth	**MS**	6	96	282	
Zea mays	Induction *and* embryo growth	**MS**	12	96	492	Lu *et al.* (1982)
	Embryo germination	**MS**	3	96	186	

† Adventitious shoot buds were produced when there was only 2% sucrose in the medium.   § These were alternative treatments

‡ Presumably the water potential was adjusted to the same osmolality in practice.

Nicotiana tabacum	Anagnostakis (1974)
Nicotiana spp.	Horner *et al* (1977)
	Johansson and Eriksson (1977)
	Reinert and Bajaj (1977b)
	Martineau *et al.* (1981)
	Heberle–Bors (1980)
Datura innoxia	Tyagi *et al.* (1980)
Lolium temulentum	Rose and Sunderland (1981)
Anemone virginiana	Johansson and Eriksson (1977)
Solanum tuberosum	Irikura (1975)

An effective concentration of charcoal has varied between species and between conditions of culture but its presence has been effective in anthers cultured on both semi–solid and liquid media (Rose and Sunderland, 1981).

Embryo growth and conversion

After somatic embryos have been formed in cultures, they may benefit by being separated from the tissue from which they were formed and placed on a medium which will favour their growth.

Subculturing. It may be necessary to subculture developing embryos at an appropriate stage to ensure their continued growth. Embryos of *Gossypium hirsutum* were more likely to complete their normal stages of development if they were transferred to fresh medium before they become longer than 1 mm. Embryos larger than this

Table 98. Examples of addition of amino acids to culture media to improve embryogenesis.

Plant	Medium	Macro-ions mM	NO_3^- mM	$\dfrac{NO_3^-}{NH_4^+}$ ratio	Amino acid supplement	Reference
Mangifera indica	**Litz et al. (1984a)**	47.9	19.7	1.91	400 mg/l glutamine	Litz *et al.* (1984)
Medicago sativa	**Saunders & Bingham (1972) B0i2Y**	60.0	25.3	2.03	2000 mg/l yeast extract	Lupotto (1983) Atanassov & Brown (1984)
Pelargonium × *hortorum* *Pelargonium* × *domesticum*	**MS**	95.75	39.4	1.91	10 mM glutamine or proline	Marsolais *et al.* (1991a)
Tylophora indica	**Rao et al. (1970) Suppl.**	44.7	18.4	2..16	200 mg/l yeast extract	Rao *et al.* (1970)

tended to become enlarged and vitreous upon transfer. If subculture was delayed, small embryos became white and translucent, while older ones (and the medium on which they were cultured) turned yellow. Transfer to a fresh medium did not then always ensure that the embryos continued to develop and proliferate (Trolinder and Goodin, 1987).

Nitrogen sources. The growth of *Gossypium* embryos has been found to be enhanced if they are transferred to **LS** or **MS** medium containing twice the normal concentration of KNO_3 (Davidonis and Hamilton, 1983; Trolinder and Goodin, 1987, 1988b; Umbeck *et al.*, 1987). Davidonis and Hamilton (1983) and Finer (1988b) also omitted NH_4NO_3 from these macronutrients. In this plant, a high concentration of NO_3^- and/or or a high ratio of NO_3^- to NH_4^+ therefore appear to be the most important criteria for embryo development.

In some, but by no means all plants, media containing amino acids may enhance the later stages of embryo growth (Table 98).

Embryo conversion. A somatic embryo is said to be converted when it develops into a plantlet growing in soil. Because, in many experiments, only a small proportion of the embryos produced in cultures do become plantlets, factors which influence the efficiency of conversion are of importance if embryogenesis is to be used as a method of plant propagation.

Embryo conversion can be influenced by treatments applied to callus *before* somatic embryo formation. The size of somatic embryos of alfalfa (and consequently the *proportion* of embryos which could be converted into plantlets) was however particularly increased when glutamine and arginine were added to the medium (Stuart and Strickland, 1984a).

Adding organic acids (especially 20 mM citrate) to the **Schenk and Hildebrandt (1972)** medium on which alfalfa petioles were cultured to produce callus, before embryogenesis was induced, both increased the number of somatic embryos eventually regenerated and caused the embryos to be of more normal appearance (Nichol *et al.*, 1991).

More embryogenic tissue was produced from *Cucumis sativus* cotyledons, and less hyperhydricity occurred, when the medium at the induction stage was gelled with 0.7% agar, rather than with 0.15% Gelrite. However, medium gelled with Gelrite was preferable at the next cultural stage, because the embryos obtained germinated more successfully (Ladyman and Girard, 1992).

Conditions for embryogenesis

Embryogenic callus is frequently induced to form when explants are cultured, and callus sub–cultured, in the dark, or in light of low irradiance (*e.g.* 1 μmol m^{-2} s$^-$). Embryo formation is promoted when callus is transferred to the light (typically 16h light of 20–50 μmol m^{-2} s$^-$) and placed on a medium lacking 2,4–D. The temperature used for incubation is usually 22–25°C.

Occasionally some variation in this protocol may be advantageous. May and Trigiano (1991) found that to obtain directly formed embryos of *Dendranthema grandiflorum* (*Chrysanthemum morifolium*), it was necessary to culture leaf midrib sections in the dark for 28 days, transfer them to light (16h of 25 μmol m^{-2} s$^-$ flux fluence) for 10 days, and then return them to the dark for 14 days. Embryogenesis did not occur in continuous darkness, or if the explants were incubated all the time in a 16 h photoperiod.

STAGE IIIa — SHOOT ELONGATION

Shoots harvested from shoot cultures need to be of a sufficient length to be handled and to provide suitable microcuttings for rooting. A separate elongation stage is usually only necessary for species which naturally have short stems, but may sometimes be required when relatively high cytokinin concentrations have been applied during Stage II to induce shoot regeneration or shoot proliferation in shoot cultures (see pages 583 and 596). Wherever possible, a separate shoot elongation stage should be avoided, especially in commercial micropropagation, as it adds to the cost of the plants eventually produced (Chapter16).

Growth regulators

Shoot elongation can often be achieved at a separate cultural stage by transferring shoot clusters for one or more passages onto a fresh medium containing no cytokinin, or one containing a reduced concentration of the cytokinin used at Stage II for shoot proliferation or shoot formation (*e.g.* where 0.5 mg/l BAP has been used for shoot multiplication, 0.02–0.05 mg/l may be sufficient for shoot elongation). In shoot cultures, an alternative is to substitute another 'less active' cytokinin for the one employed at Stage II (*e.g.* using 0.2–0.5 mg/l kinetin instead of 0.5 mg/l BAP). Although shoots should elongate once a cytokinin favouring shoot proliferation is omitted from the medium, shoot proliferation will slow down or cease. This may mean that although elongated shoots are suitable for rooting, continued shoot proliferation from residual material may be hindered.

Some examples of the changes in growth regulator treatments which have resulted in the elongation of shoots which were of insufficient length are shown in Table 99.

Inhibitors of ethylene action

Van Telgen *et al.* (1992) noticed that shoots of the rose cultivar 'Madelon' elongated more when grown in vessels with gas permeable closures, than when the vessels were closely sealed. This suggested an inhibitory effect on shoot growth due to accumulated ethylene (Part 1, page 462), a view substantiated when 0.8 mg/l silver thiosulphate (STS, an inhibitor of ethylene action) was added to the medium. In the presence of STS the length of rose shoots was increased, as was those of apple shoot cultures, providing the IBA concentration in the medium was kept to *ca.* 0.02 mg/l. Inhibiting ethylene biosynthesis with AVG did not have the same effect.

Gibberellic acid.

It is sometimes possible to elongate shoots on a medium with little or no cytokinin to which a low concentration of gibberellic acid has been added (see Table 99), but treatment is not always effective. In *Gymnocladus dioicus* shoot cultures, GA_3 was capable of elongating dominant juvenile shoots, but non–dominant juvenile ones, or short shoots formed on mature explants, were not affected.

Gibberellic acid must be used with caution at Stage IIIa because a high concentration produces long, weak shoots and the regulant also tends to prevent rooting at Stage IIIb.

Examples of successful elongation. Shoots of *Ficus lyrata*, formed adventitiously on young leaf sections cultured on a medium containing 24μM each of 2–iP, BAP and kinetin, were elongated on a medium containing 4 μM GA_3, 0.125 μM IBA and 0.24 μM each of 2–iP, BAP and kinetin. Shoots treated in this way could be rooted in one week on a low salts medium (Jona and Gribaudo, 1987)

To elongate *Eucalyptus* shoots, prior to rooting, Durand–Cresswell *et al.* (1982) added to the medium, 1 mg/l GA_3 plus 15 g/l activated charcoal. The gibberellin did not then prevent rooting of the shoots if they were incubated with 1 mg/l IBA in the dark until root emergence (one week).

Where rooting was inhibited. Attempts to elongate *Rubus idaeus* with GA_3 were not successful because it inhibited subsequent rooting (Welander, 1987). Shoot cultures of *Carica papaya* multiplied on a medium containing 0.5 mg/l BAP and 0.2 mg/l NAA were compact and had shortened internodes. Elongated shoots with larger leaves were produced upon transfer to a medium which also contained 1 mg/l GA_3, but the rate of shoot multiplication then fell off. Although GA_3–treated shoots were easily handled, the frequency with which they rooted was low (De Winnaar, 1988).

Alternative methods of application. Sohndahl *et al.* (1985) reported that adding gibberellic acid to the medium was not effective for elongating the shoots of *Coffea*, but that the regulant had the desired effect if a drop of a 25–50 mg/l solution was applied directly to the shoots at the time that they were excised for for rooting.

Small Stage II shoots can be difficult to separate and manipulate. An effective technique for elongating *Atriplex canescens* shoots was to pour sufficient of a 1.4 μM GA_3 solution into culture vessels to submerge the Stage II shoot clusters. The solution was tipped off after 3 seconds, but sufficient was left on the explants and the medium to induce shoot elongation. This treatment did not interfere with the induction of roots on a medium containing 11.4 µM IAA (Wochok and Sluis, 1980b).

Leaf removal

Scarpa *et al.* (1993) found that GA$_3$ was ineffective for shoot elongation of *Medicago sativa*. However, shoots did elongate satisfactorily if their basal leaves were removed manually so that each shoot possessed only 1–2 apical leaves.

The medium

Elongation is only necessary if Stage II shoots are too short to be excised and handled conveniently at Stage III. Although insufficient growth is frequently due to the cytokinin treatments used at Stage II, remember that it may also be due to the use of an inadequate medium. If shoot cultures of *Juglans nigra* were cultured on **Lloyd and McCown (1981) WPM** medium, axillary shoots needed to be etiolated (see below), but if they were grown instead on **Driver and Kuniyuki (1984) DKW** medium, etiolation was unnecessary because the shoots were longer and had much greater leaf development (Heile–Sudholt *et al.*, 1986).

Shoots of *Sapium sebiferum* induced to form directly on stem sections cultured on **MS** medium containing 100 mg/l casein hydrolysate (CH), did not elongate unless they were transferred to a medium without CH and with less cytokinin than used at Stage II (Mridula *et al.,* 1983).

To obtain shoots of *Prunus* rootstocks, Martinelli (1985) elongated shoots on a high salt liquid medium (see page 682). Elongation on an agar medium led to 'aging' (vitrescence?).

Etiolation

In some species shoots can be elongated prior to rooting through etiolation. Cultures are temporarily placed in the dark, or in light of a low PPF for a short period (Stimart, 1986). This can not only increase the length of shoots so that they are more readily handled, but may also increase the sensitivity of shoots to auxin

thus improving the frequency with which they may be rooted. A short dark treatment is alternatively used during the root initiation phase (Chapter 14), but this is no help in obtaining shoots which can be easily harvested.

In the absence of a convenient dark room, shoot cultures can be wrapped in aluminium foil (Zimmerman, 1983). Heile–Sudholt *et al.* (1986) kept Stage II shoot cultures of *Juglans*, which had been cultured on **Lloyd and McCown (1981) WPM** medium, in foil wrappings for 24 days. Axillary shoots which formerly had an average length of 5 mm, elongated to 5–10 mm in this period. The etiolated shoots were exposed to normal growth room lighting for 4 days before being excised for rooting studies. Shoots from *Eucalyptus* cultures were elongated by keeping cultures in the dark on a medium with only a low concentration (0.02–0.05 mg/l) BAP. After 20 days whitish, elongated shoots were put onto a rooting medium (Lubrano, 1988).

Etiolation does not invariably enhance root formation on cuttings and, if a dark (or low light intensity) treatment is too long, rooting may be impaired. This is often because, having had no capacity for photosynthesis, shoots will have low carbohydrate reserves. For instance, Maene (1985, *in* Debergh and Maene, 1987) found that shoots derived from shoot clusters incubated under a PPF of 20 µmol m^{-2} s^{-1} elongated uniformly but root formation and plantlet establishment *extra vitrum* were slow. By con-

Table 99. Examples of changes to the Stage II regulants which led to shoot elongation.

Plant	Regulants used for shoot multiplication (mg/l)	Regulants used for shoot elongation (mg/l)	References
Carya illinoiensis	1 IBA + 4 BAP	3 GA$_3$ + 0.1 BAP	Wood (1982)
Castanea sativa	0.1 BAP	0.01 BAP	San Jose *et al.* (1984)
Dracaena fragrans	0.1–1 BAP + 0.5–2 NAA	0.1 BAP + 1 NAA	Vinterhalter (1989) Vinterhalter *et al.* (1990)
Prunus amygdalus	0.1 NAA + 0.7 BAP	0.2 BAP	Rugini and Verma (1982;1983)
Prunus 'Pandora'	0.022 2,4-D + 1 BAP + 0.1 GA$_3$	0.1 GA$_3$	Boxus (1975)
Pyrus communis	2–4 BAP + 0.01 NAA	0.5 BAP + 0.01 NAA	Baviera *et al.* (1989)
Salix spp.	0.11–0.23 BAP	0–0.11	Bergman *et al.* (1985)
Vaccinium angustifolium	12 mg/l 2-iP	2.5 2-iP	Brissette *et al.* (1990)

trast, shoots from cultures kept under a flux density of 100 µmol m^{-2} s^{-1}, were short, but rooted readily. Further experiments (Maene and Debergh, 1987) showed that a satisfactory compromise could be reached by incubating cultures for just one or two weeks in low light, followed by 3 or 4 weeks lighting of higher 'intensity' (see Fig. 127 in Chapter 14).

A high level of lighting at Stage IIIa (*e.g.* 100–200 µmol m^{-2} s^{-1}) has the advantage that it causes some transpiration to occur (see page 661). Improvements in leaf quality and plant hardening are such that subsequent rooting is improved. A disadvantage of using high lighting levels in growth rooms is that energy costs (including the cost of cooling the rooms) are high. To further enhance shoot hardening, light of high PPF at Stage IIIa can be combined with cooling the base of the culture flask (see page 696).

Two–phase treatments

Adding liquid medium over the surface of exhausted Stage II cultures so that shoots are half submerged, can be an effective method of shoot elongation (Stimart, 1986). Maene and Debergh (1985, 1987) concluded that:

- The added liquid should have a high salt content;
- Using 40–60 g/l sucrose in the liquid causes shoots to have a high dry weight and enhances root formation and early plantlet growth when shoots are rooted *ex vitro*.

- If BAP was used for Stage II shoot multiplication, the liquid supplement should contain a lower level, or BAP should be replaced by kinetin (the necessary concentration of this cytokinin was greater than that which would have been used if the shoots had been subcultured to a separate Stage IIIa medium);
- If high rates of BAP were used at Stage II, it may be advantageous to add 0.3% charcoal to the supplement, together with kinetin;
- Addition of liquid should be made before shoots in Stage II clusters show apical dominance;
- Shoots should be allowed to stay on the supplemented medium for at least 4 weeks. If transferred earlier than this rooting may be severely inhibited.

Gibberellic acid can also be added to the liquid supplement (*e.g.* 1 mg/l, Antonelli and Druart, 1990).

If after the second subculture, a layer of liquid medium (**Ben–Jaacov and Dax (1981)**, 3% sucrose) was added above the solidified **MS** medium (containing 0.5 mg/l BAP and 3% sucrose) on which *Blandfordia grandiflora* shoot cultures had been multiplied, suppressed adventitious shoots were caused to elongate, thereby significantly increasing the effective rate of multiplication (Johnson, 1992).

A combined process involving etiolation, a two–phase medium, and high lighting for shoot elongation, hardening and root induction in *Cordyline* and *Dracaena* is illustrated in Chapter 14.

13

Problems in Initiating and Maintaining Cultures

BLACKENING OR BROWNING

BLACKENING AT STAGE I

The cut surfaces of many explants start to discolour soon after excision. The explants, or parts of them, frequently continue to darken when they are introduced into the culture vessel, where they may also exude dark coloured substances into the medium. This type of 'blackening' or 'browning' is associated with wounding. Not all the compounds produced are inhibitory, but it is frequently found that once discoloration occurs, growth is inhibited and tissues may die unless remedial steps are taken.

Explants may also produce pigments (pink, red, brown, reddish–brown, black, or blue) some time after excision, or cultures may give rise to them during subsequent growth. In some cases, formation at this stage is due to damage or senescence of some cells, caused by an unsuitable cultural environment. The secretion of substances by established cultures is less troublesome than the discoloration which occurs shortly after explant isolation but, when it occurs, growth is generally (but not invariably) prevented.

Explant discolouration and exudates

Damage resulting from the production of dark pigments is usually most severe during the initial stages of a culture, and ceases to be a problem once explants have commenced growth. Thus results obtained by Garton and Moses (1986) with shoots and lateral buds of *Alnus oregona* are typical. These explants exuded substances which resulted in the loss of four fifths of the cultures during the first 10 weeks. Only when shoot multiplication began after 22 weeks, did this cease to be a problem .

Effect of genotype

The extent of the blackening and growth inhibition which occurs in cultures is very genotype–dependent, being especially severe in genera that naturally contain high levels of tannins or other hydroxyphenols, such as *Castanea, Hamamelis, Juglans, Quercus, Paeonia, Rhododendron* and many conifers. Differences are also found between species of the same genus and cultivars within a species. For example, more phenolic exudate was produced by *Aconitum napellus* explants than by those of *A.*

noveboracense (Cervelli, 1987), and cultivars of *Sorghum bicolor*, selected for their high tannin content, surrendered such large quantities of pigmented phenolics, that the medium darkened and cultures readily became necrotic. Even here not all cultivars behaved in the same way because there were variations in the colour of the pigments and in the intensity with which they stained the medium (Cai and Butler, 1990).

Different genotypes not only differ in the amount of phenolic substances produced, the substances released also vary in their toxicity, or plants demonstrate different susceptibilities. Thus amongst the high tannin varieties of *Sorghum* mentioned above, differences in the tolerance to the dark pigments was observed (Cai and Butler, *loc. cit.*).

Source of explants

Young juvenile tissues are often less prone to browning on excision than older ones. This was the case with *Rosa* 'Paul's Scarlet' (Muhitch and Fletcher, 1984), but very young explants of coffee are *more* likely to show phenolic oxidation than those taken from older tissues (Duhem *et al.*, 1988). In oil palm, young leaves provided the best explants but the extent of browning was very sensitive to the presence of auxin in the medium (Rabechault and Martin, 1976). Whereas Haramaki (1971) could culture shoot tips of *Gloxinia*, axillary buds did not provide good explants because they oxidised too quickly.

Effect of rejuvenation. Tissues excised from heavily pruned and etiolated shoots of woody plants are often less liable to browning than those taken from adult parts of the plant. Explants excised from weak, shaded shoots of field–grown vines were less likely to suffer browning on isolation than others removed from normal shoots (Yu and Meredith, 1986). Browning occurred more frequently on *Pistacia* shoot tips taken from greenhouse–grown plants than on explants derived from aseptically–germinated seedlings (Alderson and Barghchi, 1982).

Time of year

A further factor influencing the extent of browning can be the time of year at which tissues are explanted. In *Hamamelis*, the browning intensity was greatest when, in the Northern hemisphere, explants were sampled in May, and lowest in July and August (Christiansen and Fonnesbech, 1975). Shoot tip explants of apple 'Northern Spy' were less likely to become brown if collected in mid–spring or summer (Hutchinson, 1982a). The proportion of cultures of *Quercus robur* 'Fastigiata' which showed phenolic oxidation increased many fold when explants were taken at the end of June, rather than early May (Howard and Marks, 1987), and phenolic secretion from

Acer rubrum shoot tips was especially marked when they were taken in July–August, as tree growth declined (Welsh *et al.*, 1979). However browning was observed on lateral shoot bud explants of *Acer saccharum* collected in spring, but not on those collected in winter (Kerns and Meyer, 1988) and a similar observation was made by Biederman (1987) who found that axillary bud explants of *Magnolia*, had a strong tendency to blacken if harvested before flowering (April) and during the subsequent growing season, but that this was much less of a problem when sampling was carried out during December to March.

Discolouration of established cultures

Discolouration can also occur in cultured tissues after a period of growth. Some plants (*e.g. Sorghum* — Davis and Kidd, 1980; *Parthenium hysterophorus* — Wickham *et al.*, 1980) produce callus that is especially liable to become discoloured and then necrotic after it has been cultured for some while. *Rosa hybrida* embryogenic callus turned brown when subcultured and then grew very slowly (De Wit *et al.*, 1990). The formation of phenolic compounds was associated with the decline of *Rosa* 'Paul's Scarlet' cell suspensions (Nash and Davies, 1972). *Pinus taeda* suspensions ceased to grow after several passages, turned brown as phenolic compounds were produced and died shortly afterwards (Heyser and Mott, 1980). The rate of decline was less pronounced if cell lines were subcultured at 2–3 week intervals.

Where browning is not detrimental

Phenols have an important natural function in regulating IAA oxidation (see Chapter 11). Those leached into water from guava explants promoted the growth of tobacco pith and carrot callus (possibly through synergism with auxin), only becoming toxic as the concentration increased (Casman *et al.*, 1978). Substances formed by the wound reaction can promote rooting.

Browning which results from the oxidation of simple phenols (see below) is therefore not necessarily detrimental to morphogenesis. Olive mesocarp tissue blackened within 1–2 weeks of planting on the medium, but nevertheless produced callus after 25 days (Lavee, 1977) and pieces of *Asplenium nidus–avis* tissue became completely brown after 2–3 days *in vitro* but still gave rise to new green clusters of cells within two months (Fernández *et al.*, 1991). Similarly the lamina of *Citrus mitis* leaves, with the midrib removed, was able to regenerate adventitious shoots even though explants turned brown and brittle (Sim *et al.*, 1989). Exudates from *Anigozanthos* and *Macropidia* explants do not impair *in vitro* growth (de Fossard, 1985). Saunders (1982) found that callus was three times more likely to arise on sugarbeet petiole segments which blackened, than on those which remained green.

Embryogenesis and somatic embryos have been noted to arise from brown tissue masses in some species, for example those of *Coffea* (Söndahl and Sharp, 1977; Söndahl *et al.*, 1979a,b), *Bambusa* (Mehta *et al.*, 1982), and *Juglans* (Tulecke and McGranahan, 1985). Krul and Worley (1977a) found that developing somatic embryos of *Vitis* were all adjacent to areas of necrotic callus cells and speculated that the embryos might induce cell lysis, or that a wound reaction stimulates embryogenesis.

THE CAUSES OF BROWNING

Tissue blackening occurs through the action of copper–containing oxidase enzymes (catechol oxidase), often called polyphenol oxidases, phenolase and tyrosinase (monophenol oxidase) (Lerch, 1981) which are released, synthesized or presented with suitable substrates and oxidative conditions when tissues are wounded or senescent. Substrates for these enzymes, which vary in different tissues, are commonly tyrosine or *o*–hydroxyphenols such as chlorogenic acid. Enzymes, normally latent on cell membranes and substrates retained within cell vacuoles, come together when cells are injured or become moribund.

The nature of exudates

The precise nature of the dark–coloured (usually brown or black) substances produced by plants has seldom been ascertained, although it is known that they are usually mixtures of complex phenolic substances. Toxicity is thought to occur by phenols becoming reversibly attached to proteins by hydrogen bonding, and by their oxidation to highly active quinones which then become cyclic or polymerised, and/or oxidise proteins to form increasingly melanic compounds (Harms *et al.*, 1983), which are sometimes termed 'polyphenols' in the literature. Quinones may also be produced from phenols through the action of peroxidase enzymes which can catalyse their oxidation in the presence of peroxide. This, and other free radicals, are released during the wounding process (Chapter 11).

Inhibitory phenolic substances produced by *Cattleya* orchid explants, which reddened the medium, were identified as eucomic acid and tyramine (Chapter 11, structure number **47**) (Ishii *et al.*, 1976).

Even though they may have the same appearance, the exudates produced by plants of different genera are not of the same chemical composition. This is shown by the fact that products released by shoot tips of *Rubus*, *Hibiscus* and *Rhododendron* had no effect on *Nicotiana tabacum* callus when it was grown on the exudate–containing medium, whereas the compounds released by shoot tips of *Juglans nigra* and *Euphorbia lathyris* were inhibitory. The degree of inhibition was not related to the extent to which the medium had been visibly stained by the previous explants (Compton and Preece, 1988a,b).

Phenolic compounds may inhibit the activity of enzymes. Carnation leaf extract inhibited the activity of β–glucuronidase (GUS) in transgenic tobacco plants, but the inhibition was abolished if the leaf extract was pre–treated with PVPP (see later) (Vainstein *et al.*, 1992).

PREVENTION OF BROWNING

If exudation from explants or cultures is accompanied by satisfactory growth or morphogenesis, there is no need to take precautions. Only when browning of tissues and the medium is associated with poor establishment (and this is the more usual situation), is it necessary to try to prevent it. Several different approaches are possible:

- minimising the damage caused to the explant;
- removing the phenolic compounds produced;
- modifying the physical environment so that conditions for the production of phenolics are not optimal;
- modifying the redox potential of the tissue;
- reducing phenolase activity and substrate availability;
- altering the composition of the medium and the growth regulators used.

The effectiveness of each of these remedies is considered in the paragraphs which follow.

Minimising damage

The extent of browning can be diminished by reducing the extent to which explants of susceptible subjects are wounded or damaged during excision and sterilisation.

In some species, the sterilants used to decontaminate explants can be responsible for accentuating the blackening of explants. Where blackening presents a severe problem, it can therefore be advisable to experiment with replacing one sterilant solution with another. Browning of *Strelitzia reginae* was less severe when 0.3% mercuric chloride was used as a sterilant instead of 9% calcium hypochlorite (Ziv and Halevy, 1983).

Removing phenolic substances

The presence of injurious phenolic substances often provokes explants to create further exudate, *i.e.* production can be autocatalytic. Removal or dispersal of the substances as they are formed is therefore found to be an effect method of control.

Leaching or dispersal

In species where black exudates can be a problem, pretreatment of plant material can help in obtaining viable explants. Firstly, care may need to be taken not to get exudate from surrounding tissue onto the explant during excision (Tulecke *et al.*, 1988). After that, washing to remove the products released from damaged cells is frequently effective. Explants should be rinsed or left in sterile water for 2–3 hours after isolation and before being transferred to culture (Cresswell and Nitsch, 1975; Lane, 1978; Vieitez and Vieitez, 1980b; Chevre *et al.*, 1983). For example, seeds of walnut and *Corylus* are often soaked in running water for 16–24 hours to remove phenolics before they are sterilised and germinated *in vitro* (Rodriguez, 1982b; Pérez *et al.*, 1985; Peñuela *et al.*, 1988).

Thorough rinsing after sterilisation is also necessary to wash away chemicals used for decontamination which, if they are not properly removed, may provoke the synthesis of phenolics. Rinsing of sterilised explants also removes any oxidised phenols which have started to accumulate.

Frequent transfers. As mentioned above, growth of explants can be limited by toxic metabolites even in the absence of obvious blackening. If explants do not show any sign of growth after 3–4 weeks, their chances of survival may be assisted by transfer to fresh medium. Rapid transfer is usually imperative if the medium around the explant begins to become discoloured or darkened. Browning or blackening is often particularly apparent on a solid medium where exudates are trapped by the agar and become concentrated in the vicinity of the explant. Probably the most widely used method of preventing tissue blackening is to subculture explants frequently, placing them on fresh medium after only a few days. The interval between transfers needs to be adjusted according to the severity of the problem. Often it is necessary to move explants every 1–7 days, but occasionally the period can be extended (*e.g.* to 20 days for *Vitis rotundifolia*, Sudarsono and Goldy, 1991).

Frequent transfers take up the time of laminar flow technicians and therefore constitute an expensive procedure which should not be undertaken in a commercial situation if other alternative techniques can be used. Nevertheless, it is usually only necessary for a short period with newly isolated explants and the number of culture vessels at this stage is usually small. The use of this frequent transfers to prevent injury is commonly described in research papers. Broome and Zimmerman (1978) found that it was successful with shoot tips of blackberry, where ascorbic acid, citric acid and cysteine hydrochloride (reducing agents — see below) were injurious. When the medium used for fig shoot tips turned brown after two days, explants were transferred to fresh medium, and again thereafter at weekly intervals to minimise possible inhibitory effects (Muriithi *et al.*, 1982).

The embryos of many cereals produce a brown pigment, deleterious to continued growth, within 3–4 days of being placed on an agar medium (Dunstan *et al.*, 1978). Production is more pronounced in media containing coconut milk (Vasil and Vasil, 1981a). Three to four transfers of embryos, and callus resulting from their culture, at 5–6 day intervals reduces, and eventually eliminates, pigment formation (Vasil and Vasil, *loc. cit.*). Usually 5–6 transfers at 2–3 day intervals are the most which are necessary before the production and/or oxidation of phenols ceases. However, explants of *Arachnis* species and *Aranthera* hybrids (orchids) exude phenolic compounds during the first six months of their culture and it is necessary to change the medium every few days for the whole of this period (Lim–Ho, 1982).

Browning of shoot tip explants generally ceases once shoot multiplication begins. Newly isolated nodal segments from juvenile *Juglans* shoots, needed to be moved to fresh medium once a week (sometimes cutting a 1 mm slice from the base), over a period of 2–3 months. After that, once shoot proliferation had started, subcultures were required only at 4 week intervals (Gruselle and Boxus, 1990). Even when it is established, callus of some species may turn brown and die if left on a medium without transfer. In *Elaeis*, subculturing at two–week intervals was adopted to safeguard against this eventuality (Nwankwo and Krikorian, 1983).

Trimming darkened tissue. In conjunction with moving explants to fresh media, it is advisable, at each transfer, to cut away any tissue which has started to become discoloured because, if left, the damage is likely to spread. Trimming brown explants and callus tissue from *Musa* cultures, prevented the spread of discolouration (Fichet, 1990b).

The use of liquid media. Explants are frequently less liable to browning if they are cultured initially on a liquid medium in which phenolics can readily diffuse away. It is therefore fairly common to find that Stage I of a cultural sequence has been conducted in liquid. Zepeda and Sagawa (1981) cultured pineapple shoot tips in the first instance in a rotated liquid medium composed of **MS** salts and 25% coconut milk.

Explants of orchids, which are especially liable to produce phenolic compounds, are generally placed into a shaken liquid medium in which exudates are diluted and dispersed (Lim–Ho, 1982). Even so, the medium may still become discoloured causing subculturing to be necessary (see above): Sarcanthine orchids turned a liquid medium brown and needed to be subcultured (Intuwong and Sagawa, 1973). Ichihashi and Kako (1977) found that *Cattleya* shoot tip explants survived better on a stationary liquid medium containing oxidase inhibitors than on a solidified medium of similar composition.

Effect of gelling agents. The rate of growth of newly–formed shoots can sometimes be improved if, after culture on an agar medium, they are moved to liquid shake culture. There could be several reasons why this should be, one of which is the possible dispersion of toxic metabolites in liquid, but their retention around the explant in a gelled medium (Simmonds and Werry, 1987). This is thought to be the most likely explanation; callus of *Parthenium argentatum* became brown on medium gelled with either agar or gelrite (Trautmann and Visser, 1989).

However, agar has sometimes been found to cause browning when another gelling agent has not. For instance, shoot tips of wild rice were less likely to become brown if they were cultured on a medium solidified with 0.4% agarose rather than 0.8% agar (Finch *et al.*, 1992). Only in rare cases has the addition of agar *reduced* browning; one such case is in *Ribes*, where increasing the agar concentration from 6 to 8–10 g/l helped to decrease the browning of cultures during storage (Gunning and Lagerstedt, 1986).

Culture on a porous substrate. Phenolics tended to be produced during the *in vitro* rooting of *Ephedra fragilis* on an agar medium. If however, shoots were cultured on Sorbarods® moistened with ½**MS** containing 1% sucrose, shoots grew more rapidly and phenolics seemed to diffuse away into the medium, rather than accumulating at the base of the explant (O'Dowd and Richardson, 1993). [†] Similarly, browning of *Dipterocarpus* zygotic embryos, which was troublesome on agar, could be prevented by culturing explants for the first 7 weeks on filter paper bridges (Linington, 1991).

In *Parthenium argentatum* where browning was very troublesome, Trautmann and Visser (1989) managed to reduce it by culturing callus on filter paper bridges, which being longer on one side than the other, caused medium to be syphoned. There was thus a gentle flow of fresh medium beneath the callus, as spent medium dripped to waste.

Adsorption with activated charcoal

The ability of activated charcoal (AC) to adsorb inhibitory compounds has been described in Chapter 11. By adding AC to tissue culture media it is sometimes possible to avoid the build–up of phenolic inhibitors, but because activated charcoal can also adsorb growth regulators and other components of the medium, it should be used with caution. Activated charcoal can be toxic to some tissues (*e.g.* to explants of *Pinus sylvestris* — Hohtola, 1988).

Bon *et al.* (1988) found that AC prevented the build up of polyphenols in the medium by stopping their steady synthesis within *Sequoiadendron giganteum* shoots during 6 weeks elongation *in vitro*. It was not clear whether this was because phenols were adsorbed from the stems before they could be polymerised, or because polyphenols were adsorbed after formation, or because some other compound essential to polyphenol formation (*e.g.* auxin) was removed.

Darkening of explants appears to be a universal problem in palms, but can be resolved by adding AC to the medium and using frequent transfers during the initial phase of culture. Other methods of preventing blackening appear not to be so successful (Tisserat, 1979). Some examples of the prevention of browning in Palmae by the addition of 0.45–3 g/l activated charcoal to the culture medium, are:

Date palm	Tisserat (1979)
	Reynolds and Murashige (1979)
Coconut	Fisher and Tsai (1978)
Oil palm	Nwankwo and Krikorian (1983)
Euterpe edulis	Guerra & Handro (1988)
Mascarena and *Caryota*	Wang and Huang (1976)

Charcoal is frequently added to orchid cultures; for example, 2 g/l improved the rooting of *Paphiopedilum* seedlings germinated *in vitro*, while 2 g/l was necessary

---

[†]   Sorbarods are radiation–sterilised cylinders of laminated cellulose, contained in a sleeve of perforated paper (Baumgartner Papiers, Lausanne CH–1001, Switzerland).

for the development of plantlets from *Phalaenopsis* protocorms (Fu, 1978). Van Waes (1987) found activated charcoal inappropriate for media used to germinate many species of European native orchids, because it resulted in lower germination and slower development. However, with most of the species (especially those which released polyphenols into the sowing medium), the addition of 0.02–0.3% AC to the *transplantation* medium caused growth to be stimulated.

The addition of 2.5 g/l charcoal to azalea shoot tip cultures after 40–45 days of culture, resulted in a greater number of well–developed plants. Without it, growth slowly stagnated (Preil and Engelhardt, 1977). Cultured shoots of raspberry were pale and chlorotic unless 5 g/l charcoal and a double dose of FeEDTA were added to the medium (Snir, 1981). The successful culture of *Zingiber* shoot tips was only obtained in media containing 3 g/l charcoal (Wang and Huang, 1976).

Adsorption by polyvinylpyrrolidone (PVP).

Biochemists have found that the extraction of active plant enzymes is, on occasions, prevented by the presence of polyphenols or tannins. Where this is the case, various compounds (particularly proteins, amides and polyamides) have been added to react with the phenols and restore enzyme activity. Caffeine is one amide that has been used successfully (Goldstein and Swain, 1965).

The most valuable polyamide for this purpose is PVP ('povidone') (Loomis and Battaile, 1966). PVPP (polyvinylpolypyrrolidone, cross linked PVP) which is also effective, is used as an adsorbent for the chromatographic separation of aromatic acids, aldehydes, and phenols; it has a high, usually unspecified, molecular weight). For biochemical enzyme isolations, soluble PVP is usually combined with a reducing agent such as mercaptoethanol. Phenols are adsorbed by PVP through hydrogen bonding, preventing their oxidation and polymerisation. PVP may also combine with oxidized (polymerized) phenolics, so preventing further oxidation by phenolase enzymes (Jones *et al.*, 1965). PVP preparations, including insoluble PVP (*e.g.* Polyclar AT — mol. wt. *ca.* 40 000), have been proposed as clarifying agents for beers and wines.

Various PVP products are available which vary in average molecular weights from 10 000–700 000. Several different kinds of PVP and PVPP have been used to prevent browning of plant tissue cultures, either as rinses for explants or by being incorporated into media, but not all have equivalent biological activity.

Blackening of seedling shoot tip explants of *Tectona grandis* was prevented by agitating the explants for 45 minutes in a 2% sucrose solution containing 0.7% of one of three different products:

- soluble PVP (average MW 360 000);
- an insoluble high molecular weight cross–linked PVP (Sigma Chemicals);
- Polyclar AT (see above).

before they were rinsed and inoculated onto solidified **MS** medium.

All three products prevented blackening, but only single shoots were produced from explants treated with 0.7% soluble PVP, whereas those treated with either of the insoluble PVP preparations gave rise to multiple shoots (Gupta *et al.*, 1980).

There are many reports of successful treatments with PVP, but it does not always stop the blackening of tissue cultured explants. Unlike activated charcoal, 0.1–3% (w/v) of two PVPs (MW *ca.* 10 000 and 40 000) did not have a beneficial effect on explant survival of date palm (Tisserat, 1979).

Rinses for explants. PVP (0.1 mM, no molecular wt. given) was used as a rinse for *Rosa hybrida* shoot fragments (Mederos and Rodríguez Enríquez, 1987). Fish and Jones (1988) dissected potato buds, and Hohtola (1988) *Pinus sylvestris* buds, in 1% soluble PVP.

Incorporation into the medium. PVP is usually added to the medium to counteract the browning of explants and/or the exudation of phenolic substances into the medium. Table 100 gives some examples of its successful use. Durand–Cresswell and Nitsch (1977) showed that after treatment with insoluble PVP (Polyclar), the brown exudate which came from cut tissues of *Eucalyptus grandis* during their first two days in culture, was no longer toxic.

The addition of PVP can improve the frequency of plant regeneration from anther cultures. Pollen embryos of *Datura innoxia* were produced in greater numbers when 0.5% PVP was included in the medium (Tyagi *et al.* 1981). Two per cent PVP also enhanced the plantlet yield from anther cultures of *Datura metel* (Babbar and Gupta, 1982) and improved survival and production of anther callus in *Saccharum* (Fitch and Hinchee, 1982). Jordan and Oyanedal (1992) found that the browning of small (5 mm) seedling shoot tips of *Pouteria lucuma* was prevented by adding 1–3 g/l PVP (MW 360 000) to the medium, while browning of larger explants was best prevented by using the same concentration of PVPP.

Inhibitory effects. There are few reports of growth inhibition resulting from PVP treatment, although Jones *et al.* (1965) have cautioned that high rates (2–4%) may inhibit the action of enzymes. Jorgensen (1988) noted that although anthers of *Quercus petraea* were prevented from turning brown by 1–2 g/l PVP 500, the amount of embryogenic callus was reduced. Some authors say that PVP can reduce the rate of *in vitro* shoot regeneration (Abdullah *et al.*, 1987; Hohtola, 1988).

Modifying the environment

The activity of enzymes concerned with both the biosynthesis (M.E. Davies, 1972a,b) and the oxidation of phenols, is increased by light (Creasy, 1968). Leaf extracts of *Eucalyptus* have been shown to have a much higher content of phenolic compounds, especially flavonoids when extracted in the light, rather than in the dark (Durand–Cresswell *et al.*, 1985).

Etiolated stock plants

Tissue blackening is less in explants taken from etiolated stock plants (Chapter 8) grown in darkness or very low light intensity, or in some cases, short days (Durand–Cresswell *et al.*, 1985). That of *Quercus robur*, *Acer platanoides* and *Garrya elliptica* was considerably reduced if explants were taken from plants grown in darkness or under plastic canopies in which there was only 1% of normal daylight: but initiation of *Hamamelis* shoot cultures was best if the soock plants had been kept in complete darkness (Marks *et al.*, 1987; Marks and Simpson, 1990).

These authors found that explants successfully isolated from etiolated stock plants of all plants except *Quercus robur* continued to grow without the appearance of oxidation products. In *Quercus* the benefit of etiolation was

of relatively short duration and a detrimental release of polyphenols occurred in over 70% of cultures initiated 56 days after the light covers were removed.

Nodal explants of *Protea obtusifolia* became brown and died unless the shoots from which they were excised had been covered previously with brown paper bags to reduce the natural light irradiance. Grown under these conditions, the shoots were partly etiolated when explants came to be excised (Watad *et al.*, 1992).

Culture in darkness or in light of low irradiance

Keeping newly isolated explants in the dark. Cultures are often initiated more readily if newly explanted tissues are kept in the dark for several weeks (Durand–Cresswell and Nitsch, 1977). For instance, shoot cultures of *Carya illinoinensis* were kept in the dark for an initial 2 weeks, thereafter in a 16 h photoperiod (Lazarte, 1984). *Mahonia* buds needed to be kept in the dark for 21 days on **MS** medium to which 1 g/l activated charcoal had been added (Daguin *et al.*, 1992).

Blackening is usually reduced or prevented by such dark treatment, and sometimes subsequent growth is improved even though tissue discolouration is not observed (Meyer, 1982). Explants may be transferred to normal light after a dark treatment, although transfer to light of low fluence (*e.g.* 7–15 μmol m^{-2} s^{-1}, *ca.* 500–1000 lux) may help to prevent browning. That of isolated *Phalaenopsis* nodes was controlled by culturing the explants for the first two weeks in the dark at 26°C. After this the cultures were

Table 100. Examples of the prevention of browning when PVP and PVPP were added to the medium.

Plant	Concentration	Type	Interval	Reference
Aconitum napellus	0.05% + 0.1 μM citric acid	Insoluble PVPP	Not specified	Cervelli (1987)
Castanea sativa	—	PVP	Callus initiation	Vestri *et al.* (1991)
Eucalyptus tereticornis	0.5 g/l	MW 360 000	Explant initiation	Subbaiah and Minocha (1990)
Hamamelis	1.0%	MW 40 000		Christiansen and Fonnesbech (1975)
Malus	0.5–2%	MW 44 000	First 4–6 weeks	Walkey (1972)
			First 4–8 weeks	McComb (1978)
Pinus brutia	0.0001%	Insoluble	Weeks 7–10 †	Abdullah *et al.* (1987)
Quercus (juvenile)	0.005–0.01%	MW 10 000	During initiation	Ahuja (1986)
Quercus spp.	0.5 g/l	—	Stage II cultures	Bellarosa (1988)

moved to the light and the temperature lowered to 22°C (Pieper and Zimmer, 1976a).

Ahuja (1986) reported that the blackening of *Quercus* cultures can also be lessened by placing them in light of low irradiance, but Marks and Simpson (1990) found that phenolic oxidation of several woody plants (see above) was not prevented by culturing explants in darkness during their establishment *in vitro*, although this treatment did enhance the suppression of blackening in *Hamamelis* and *Garrya* caused by etiolating stock plants.

Shoot formation from immature *Rhododendron* ovaries was improved if explants were kept for 2–4 weeks in the dark at 25°C. Many shoots formed under these conditions which greened later in light (16 h 35–50 μmol m^{-2} s^{-1}) (Meyer, 1982; Dai *et al.*, 1987).

Keeping more established cultures in darkness. Dark incubation can also be effective when black exudates are produced by a growing culture. The blackening of *Musa* callus (which was partially repressed by 50 mg/l ascorbic acid, 75 mg/l citric acid, 0.01% PVP and 0.5% activated charcoal — see below), was further reduced if the tissue was cultured in the dark (Drew, 1986). Callus of *Parthenium argentatum* (see page 643), initiated in a photon flux density of 0.5 μmol m^{-2} s^{-1}, continued to produce multiple shoots if kept in this irradiance, but quickly turned brown and died if moved to 25 μmol m^{-2} s^{-1} (Finnie *et al.*, 1989).

Callus from *Elaeis* tissues could be established in light or darkness, but most of the cultures grown in darkness had a tendency to turn brown and die if subsequently exposed to light for prolonged periods. This made it preferable to maintain routine cultures in the light (Nwankwo and Krikorian, 1983).

Low temperature treatments

Keeping newly–established explants at 2°C for a short period, helped to prevent blackening of coffee cultures (Duhem *et al.*,1988). Similarly, the production of brown exudate by *Eucalyptus* tissues was reduced if stock plants were submitted to a 5°C cold treatment for several days before explant dissection (Durand–Cresswell *et al.*, 1985).

Browning may also be prevented if it is possible to maintain plant material at a slightly lower temperature than normal, while still obtaining growth and/or morphogenesis. There was less exudation of brown–black substances from *Alstroemeria* rhizome segments incubated at 18°C, than from those maintained at 21°C or 24°C (Pierik *et al.*, 1988b), and browning which occurred during the rooting of *Vicia faba* shoots at 22°C, was limited if cultures were kept at 14–18°C during this

process. Activated charcoal was essential to prevent browning at 22°C, but was unnecessary at the lower temperatures (Selva *et al.*, 1989).

Composition of the medium

If attention to the way that explants are treated does not solve the problem of browning or blackening, attention should be given to the nature of the medium which is being used. Browning is often more pronounced on one medium than another, showing that it can be caused by inappropriate nutrients (Apavatjrut and Blake, 1977).

Browning is often less severe on a dilute medium than on a high salts medium such as **MS**. Uosukainen (1987) prevented the browning of shoot tip explants of several woody plants by establishing them on a medium containing only one tenth **MS** salts with no auxin. Only when the explants were established, were they moved to media containing higher salt levels. *Camellia japonica* shoot cultures grown on **MS** or $\frac{1}{2}$ **MS** medium showed progressive leaf browning and bud necrosis, but this did not occur on **Heller (1953; 1955)** medium supplemented with 1 mM ammonium sulphate (Samartin, 1989).

Several workers have found that culture on **Lloyd and McCown (1981) WPM** medium (total molarity of macronutrient ions, ΣI_m = 26.97 mM — see Part 1, page 329 and Table 49, page 398) has prevented browning, but the reason is not obvious, as some less suitable media contain equally low concentrations of macronutrients:

- Nodal explants of *Vaccinium* were less likely to turn brown on **WPM** medium than on **Lyrene (1980)** [Total ionic concentration (ΣI_m) = 26.21 mM), **MS** (ΣI_m = 95.75 mM), or **Zimmerman and Broome (1980) Z–2** (ΣI_m = 36.44 mM) or **Z–3** (ΣI_m = 18.22 mM) media.

- Two–node explants of *Berberis* were more liable to show exudation on **Anderson (1984) R** medium (ΣI_m = 10.61 mM) than on that of **WPM**.

- Adventitious shoots of *Cephaelis ipecacuanha* formed on **MS** medium turned brown and died, but browning and necrosis did not occur on **WPM** medium (Yoshimatsu and Shimimura, 1991).

Several media components have been thought to be responsible for browning.

Nitrogen and potassium. Anderson (1975) suggested that tissue browning of *Rhododendron* explants was accentuated by the high potassium levels in **MS** medium. No browning was experienced on a medium with half the normal concentration of KNO_3. A reduction in the concentration of nitrogen has been effective in preventing browning in other plants. In *Dioscorea opposita*, where it is normally a problem, browning did not occur if callus cultures were initiated on **MS** medium in which the concentrations of NH_4NO_3 and KNO_3 had both been reduced to 10 mM (Kuginuki and Nishimura, 1989). Similarly explants of *Pinus sylvestris* turned brown and died on **MS** medium, but grew satisfactorily when the concentrations of NH_4NO_3, KNO_3 and $CaCl_2$ were reduced by one half, and that of KH_2PO_4 was doubled (Hohtola, 1988). In this study, the explants would tolerate a 20–fold increase in the concentration of **MS** micronutrients without damage.

A reduction in the browning of *Ribes* cultures during storage was brought about by *increasing* the initial pH of the medium from 5.7 to 7.0–8.0 (Gunning and Lagerstedt, 1986). Under these conditions one would expect the uptake of nitrate ions to be reduced (page 296).

Other constituents. Browning of *Pistacia vera* cultures occurred when the composition of the medium was not suitable for rapid growth (Bargchi and Alderson, 1983). Barghchi (1986a) found that browning of meristem tip explants of this plant could be almost eliminated if $FeSO_4$ was initially omitted from the medium. The compound could be replaced at later stages without harmful effects. Similarly the temporary omission of copper from the micronutrients might be considered during one or more subcultures (see page 650). In *Pistacia atlantica* browning was directly proportional to the concentration of calcium nitrate in the medium and was thought to be related to the concentration of calcium ions. Best results were obtained in the presence of 1.7 meq/l Ca^{2+}, for although vigorous shoots with long internodes were produced in the presence of 3.4–10.2 meq/l, they were liable to become brown and suffer from apical necrosis (Mederos Molina and López Carreño, 1991).

Carbohydrate is required for the biosynthesis of phenolic compounds, and reducing the sucrose concentration to 1% can decrease polyphenols within tissues (M.E. Davies, 1972a). Hypocotyl callus of *Gossypium arboreum* grew satisfactorily on a modified **MS** medium with 3% glucose, but discoloured quickly if sucrose was used as a carbohydrate source (R.H. Smith *et al.*, 1976).

Growth regulators

Polyphenol formation from freshly excised explants can be influenced by growth regulators but results are not consistent, and compounds which have induced browning in one species are without effect in another.

Cytokinins. High kinetin levels were necessary for the growth of *Pelargonium* shoot tips, but the agar medium became dark coloured if more than 1 mg/l kinetin was present. The percentage of surviving explants was considerably increased by culturing them for the first week on basal medium without regulants, and then afterwards on a medium with cytokinin and auxin (Debergh and Maene, 1977). Browning of *Vitis rotundifolia* shoot cultures was thought to be associated with the addition of TDZ to the medium to promote shoot proliferation. Providing subcultures were carried out every 20 days, the problem could be kept under control (Sudarsono and Goldy, 1991).

Auxins. Browning is often associated with the use of 2,4–D, especially if high concentrations are added to the medium. Phenolic substances issued from callus of *Aconitum heterophyllum* initiated on a medium containing 1 mg/l 2,4–D, 0.5 mg/l kinetin and 10% coconut water, but browning was not a problem in callus initiated with 5 mg/l NAA and 1 mg/l BAP (Giri *et al.*, 1993). Cultures of *Borago officinalis* are susceptible to browning, so that although somatic embryogenesis was most effectively induced by 22.6 µM 2,4–D, it became necessary to use only 4.5–9 µM in subsequent investigations (Quinn *et al.*, 1989). Browning of coconut palm inflorescence tissue was induced by 100–500 µM 2,4–D (Ebert *et al.*, 1990). Browning also occurred when embryos of *Dioscorea* were cultured with high levels (181–362 µM; 40–80 mg/l) of 2,4–D which were necessary to induce callus formation in the presence of activated charcoal. It did not occur if 2–8 mg/l 2,4–D was added to the medium in the absence of charcoal (Viana and Mantell, 1989). However, for callus initiation from *Saccharum* stem tissue, 2,4–D was more effective than picloram, because callus formed more rapidly and the production of phenolic compounds was less (Fitch and Moore, 1990).

In *Chrysosplenium americanum* shoot cultures, browning took place if 2,4–D and/or BAP had been added to the medium, but not if IAA, NAA, kinetin or zeatin were added. Shoot proliferation was achieved with 0.5 mg/l NAA plus 1–5 mg/l zeatin (Brisson *et al.*, 1988). Root explants of *Comptonia peregrina* formed adventitious shoot buds in the presence of 0.5 µM BAP, but adding NAA to the medium caused the explants to become brown (Louis and Torrey, 1991).

Ethylene and carbon dioxide

Cell browning in lettuce has been thought to be due to the action of ethylene on the metabolism of phenolic compounds (Ke *et al.*, 1988). Suspension cultured cells of *Thalictrum minus* turned dark brown when they were moved from flasks to a bioreactor (Kobayashi *et al.*, 1991). Browning in this instance was shown to be caused by the removal of carbon dioxide from the bioreactor, because it could be reproduced in flasks by removing

CO_2. Kobayashi *et al.* conjectured that supplementary CO_2 prevented browning by counteracting the effect of ethylene (Part 1, page 458): cell browning was promoted by 200 p.p.m. ethephon, especially if CO_2 was removed.

Silver nitrate (an inhibitor of ethylene action — Part 1, page 457) at a concentration of 2–5 mg/l was used by de Block *et al.* (1989) to promote adventitious shoot formation from *Agrobacterium*–transformed explants of *Brassica*. However the silver ions were found to be toxic during prolonged use and *caused* the medium to turn brown. The browning could be prevented by adding 500 mg/l carbenicillin antibiotic together with the $AgNO_3$. Others have found that this combination of chemicals has induced vitrescence (see page 668).

Modifying redox potential

The tendency of dissolved compounds to be oxidised or reduced depends on the oxidation–reduction (redox) potential of the solution.

Antioxidants

Siegel and Porto (1961) defined an antioxidant as an electron donor which inhibits the oxidation of labile substrates with a high stoichiometric efficiency. Antioxidants include reducing agents, which remove oxygen from other molecules, and also compounds which act by alternative mechanisms, such as trapping or deactivating ions; reacting with intermediates in an oxidation–reduction equilibrium; reacting with an electron–transporting catalyst.

Reducing agents which lower the redox potential of solutions are effective in preventing the blackening of isolated plant tissues or plant extracts, and it is often assumed that they prevent the oxidation of phenols. According to Loomis and Battaile (1966) this is not so; rather they act by rapidly removing any quinone that is formed. The presence of reducing agents may even activate the *o*–hydroxylation of monophenols with harmful consequences.

Explants from plants whose tissues are liable to browning, are often washed in a solution of an anti–oxidant after sterilisation, excised on paper soaked with an anti–oxidant, and/or submerged in a solution of a anti–oxidant immediately after excision. Compounds which have been used for this purpose include ascorbic acid (*e.g.* 0.1%), citric acid, L–cysteine (Jarret *et al.*, 1985a; Visseur, 1987) or cysteine hydrochloride, dithiothreitol (0.4 g/l) (Ziv and Halevy, 1983; Han & Liu, 1990), mercaptoethanol and sodium thiosulphate (1 g/l) (Han and Liu, 1990). Haramaki (1971) kept shoot apices of gloxinia in an antioxidant solution until they were disinfected in bleach, after which they were rinsed in sterile antioxidant solution. Ziv (1983) dissected shoot tips of *Ruscus* on filter paper impregnated with 1% ascorbic acid. Rinsing explants in a solution of 50 mg/l cysteine prevented the browning of *Musa* shoot tips (Jarret *et al.*, 1985a).

Citric acid / ascorbic acid mixtures. A solution of ascorbic acid and citric acid is commonly used for rinsing freshly isolated explants to delay the browning process. Presumably citric acid acts as a chelating agent, sequestering metal ions which are needed to activate oxidative enzymes? It may therefore delay the breakdown of ascorbic acid, which has been shown to be oxidised to dehydro–ascorbic acid (Part 1, page 200) within 0.8–3 hours depending, most probably, on the concentration of copper and iron in the medium (Elmore *et al.*, 1990). Tartaric acid, which is both a reducing agent and a chelating agent for Cu^{2+} ions, should be more effective, but appears not to have been tried for this purpose. Some examples, of where explants have been rinsed in a mixture of citric and ascorbic acids before culture, are:

Plant	Citric acid mg/l	Ascorbic acid mg/l	Reference
Aechmea fasciata	100	150	Jones and Murashige (1974)
Musa textilis	1500	1000	Mante and Tepper (1983)
Phoenix dactylifera	150	150	Tisserat *et al.* (1979b)
Rhododendron	150	150	Anderson (1975)

Adding anti–oxidants to the medium. Anti–oxidants have also been incorporated into tissue culture media. Ascorbic acid is sometimes added to media for this purpose, but remember that it is heat labile (page 370) and should be filter sterilised, not autoclaved.

Including ascorbic acid in the medium used for isolating *Equisetum* shoot tips, prevented browning when the explants were transferred to a regular medium after 3 days (Wetmore and Morel, 1949). Adding 50 mg/l to the medium, helped to prevent the blackening of coffee cultures (Duhem *et al.*, 1988). Elmore *et al.* (1990) found that, in tissue culture media, ascorbic acid is oxidised very rapidly to dehyro–ascorbic acid, which also disappeared from media during an 11 hour period. When browning is prevented by adding ascorbic acid to a medium, it must therefore act through: —

- an immediate effect of the intact molecule;

- the compound (or dehydro–ascorbic acid) being taken up rapidly by tissues; or

- a product of ascorbic acid oxidation being responsible for the observed effects.

NECROSIS

Necrosis strictly describes the death of part of a living organism. Its occurrence on parts of plant tissues in enclosed vessels can readily lead to death of the whole culture. Callus of *Lonicera* spp. initiated from leaf tissue on medium containing 2,4–D became necrotic and could not survive subculture, even if cultures were transferred to darkness. Callus initiated in the presence of NAA did not behave in this way (Georges *et al.*, 1992).

Callus of oil palm became brown and necrotic, possible due to an accumulation of phenolic substances, unless it was transferred to a fresh medium at approximately 14–day intervals (Nwankwo and Krikorian, 1983).

Leaf browning during culture

Attempts to root *Coronopus navasii* (Brassicaceae) resulted in leaf browning on **MS** medium without regulants unless shoot clusters containing at least 10 leaves were cultured (Iriondo and Pérez, 1990).

SHOOT NECROSIS

Apical necrosis

Calcium deficiency

Apical necrosis occurs particularly in shoot cultures, especially those of woody plants. Although there may be other causes, the most common reason is calcium deficiency in the apices of cultured shoots due to the ion either having been inadequately absorbed from the medium, or not having been translocated (Part 1, page 294). In culture vessels, high humidity limits transpiration and hence the movement of xylem–translocated ions and compounds, so that calcium may not reach apical tissues. In greenhouses, tip necrosis may occur if calcium is leached from shoot apices by excessive watering (Chapter 14, page 728).

Growth substances

Apical senescence and leaf drop occurred on some shoots during shoot culture of *Eucalyptus* spp. when callus grew at their nodes. The problem was avoided by not subculturing the affected shoots (Le Roux and Van Staden, 1991).

Kataeva *et al.* (1991) found that many shoots of *Malus* × *domestica* and *Camellia sinensis* developed apical necrosis and had leaves which turned brown and tended to drop if, after 3 subcultures on a medium containing cytokinin, they were moved to a cytokinin–free medium for 2–3 passages to promote rooting. An ELISA analysis of the endogenous growth substances in the affected shoots, led to the conclusion that necrosis was, in this case, caused by a deficiency of natural hormones.

Subculture interval

Leaf yellowing and necrosis both increase when shoot cultures are not subcultured sufficiently frequently. If these symptoms are detected the interval between subcultures should be reduced; this practice will assist in the maintenance of a high rate of shoot proliferation. The interval between subcultures often has to be adjusted between one cultivar and another.

Rapid water less

Shoot apices may sometimes die if plants lose water rapidly during *in vitro* hardening. *Rosa hybrida* shoot apices became necrotic during this stage in vessels fitted with perforated lids plugged with cellulose fibre (Ghashghaie *et al.*, 1992).

Gaseous pollutants

Righetti (1990) showed that gas or alcohol burners, operated with a limited air supply, emit large quantities of gases such as methane, butane, ethane, propane, ethylene, methanol and ethanol. If such burners are used for sterilising instruments, or for flaming the mouths of vessels, the concentration of gases within laminar flow hoods and within vessels can be unacceptably high.

Bud necrosis can be caused by the presence of such volatile carbon compounds within culture vessels. In the experiments of Righetti (*loc. cit.*), if cultures of a cherry rootstock (*Prunus avium* × *P. pseudocerasus*) were established in a laminar flow hood where instruments were dipped in ethanol for sterilisation and then flamed with a gas burner set to have a yellow flame, 95% of the apical buds on shoots became necrotic after 6 days of incubation, followed a few days later by leaf degreening and partial leaf abscission.

Remedies

Making calcium more available. As mentioned in Part 1, tip necrosis can often be cured by increasing the concentration of calcium in the medium, or by changing the physical environment in which the cultures are grown so that transpiration is increased. Leaf yellowing and meristem necrosis of *Populus trichocarpa* shoots was significantly reduced by growing them on $\frac{1}{2}$**Gresshoof and Doy (1974)** medium supplemented with 3 mM calcium gluconate and 0.5 g/l MES (Nadel *et al.*, 1992). The authors thought that the absence of Cl^- and the lower level SO_4^{2-} ions in **Gresshoff and Doy** medium compared to **MS**, might also have been contributory.

Increasing the calcium concentration in **MS** medium by adding calcium nitrate and adjusting the concentrations of other salts, was found to reduce the incidence of apical necrosis in *Cydonia oblonga*. Unfortunately the medium was then unsatisfactory because the altered concentrations of nitrate and ammonium ions supported poor shoot growth (Singha *et al.*, 1990).

Apical necrosis of olive, which occurred on **B5** medium, was attributed by Fiorino and Leva (1986) to a low ratio of Ca^{2+} to total nitrogen. In **B5** macronutrients, the molar ratio of Ca / N is 1:26.2, and in **MS** medium it is 1 : 20. By modifying **MS** medium so that the ratio was 1 : 7.6-9.0, Fiorino and Leva found that no necrosis occurred.

By contrast with the above results, the presence of high concentrations of Ca^{2+} has been associated with the *occurrence* of apical necrosis in *Pistacia atlantica* (see page 647)

Reducing gaseous pollutants. Gas burners should never be allowed to burn with a yellow flame within laminar flow hoods. Although burners adjusted to give a blue flame still emit high concentrations of carbon dioxide, the proportion of incompletely–combusted volatiles produced is negligible. Gas emissions are eliminated if an electric bunsen, or oven, is employed to sterilise instruments.

Use of a two–phased medium. Apical necrosis was a severe problem during the multiplication and rooting of *Cydonia oblonga*. It was partially overcome by the use of a double phase medium. A layer of liquid medium of the same composition as the underlying layer (but lacking agar), was poured onto the surface of the semi–solid medium directly after subculture and was renewed several times during the subculture period of 4 weeks (Vinterhalter and Nešković, 1992).

A practical application

Shoot tip necrosis is usually detrimental, but has been used to practical advantage to devise a large scale method of producing potato microtubers in a bioreactor (McCown and Joyce, 1991). As potato shoots do not produce axillary shoots in response to cytokinin, branching was stimulated in a bioreactor by feeding shoots with a medium which caused the shoot tips to die. The multiple shoots so produced were used as sites for microtuber production (see page 813).

Apparent aging

An unusual abrupt transition of shoots from a juvenile to a mature phenotype occurred after shoot cultures of *Coriandrum sativum* had been subcultured for approximately 9 months. After a further 6–8 months of subculture the production of normal axillary and adventitious shoots from the mature phenotype decreased and was followed by necrosis, apparently caused by the physiological aging of the cultured material (Kataeva and Popowich, 1993).

HYPERHYDRICITY (Vitrification)

THE SYMPTOMS

Compared to the characteristics of plants growing *in vivo*, tissues and organs formed *in vitro* can have an atypical anatomy, morphology and physiology. Some authorities consider that these changes are an implicit feature of cultured shoots and that they commence as soon as there is new shoot growth *in vitro*, progressively increasing in extent and severity the longer cultures are maintained (Debergh *et al.*, 1992). According to this hypothesis, the changes in leaf structure and function found in plants cultured in closed vessels (described in Chapter 14, page 720) are but early symptoms of a complex syndrome of abnormal characteristics (Ziv, 1991).

Under some cultural conditions, highly abnormal tissues and organs may be detected after a period of culture: shoots or plantlets become difficult to propagate *in vitro*: their capacity for survival may be severely reduced and many may perish either in the culture vessel, or upon transfer to the external environment. Losses of up to 60% of cultured shoots or plantlets have been known to occur during commercial micropropa–gation (Pâques, 1991).

Mild symptoms

The 'glassy shoot syndrome' can occur with various degrees of severity and is not always accompanied by changes in the phenotypic characters described above.

Initially, part of the shoot, or just one or two leaves (especially those touching the medium) may be affected. The shoots of cultures demonstrating mild symptoms often grow more rapidly than normal and may show abnormally high rates of axillary shoot formation. Any such advantage is lost if the condition becomes more severe.

Severe symptoms

In the most extreme circumstances, hyperhydric shoots have short internodes and their shoot apices appear fasciated (see page 740). Affected shoots are often swollen and pale green and their leaves have a translucent, watery, or glass–like appearance; leaves may be elongated or strap–like, and are frequently also turgid and brittle, and have a greyish–blue colour. Sometimes the leaves of affected shoots become thickened, wrinkled, or curled, and then they may appear to be a darker green than normal because layers of tissues are superimposed one upon another. When shoots in this condition do not elongate in a normal fashion, there is a reduction of apical dominance, causing bushy clumps of shoots to be formed. This has been noted, for example, in *Dianthus caryophyllus* (Leshem and Sachs, 1985), in *Picea sitchensis* (John, 1986) and *Gypsophila paniculata* (Dillen and Buysens, 1989).

Highly abnormal shoots do not normally produce adventitious roots, or only root poorly. This is not always the case: for example 'wet' shoots of *Pinus radiata* rooted well *extra vitrum* after initial losses ceased, but the plantlets were not as sturdy as those obtained from normal waxy shoots (Aitken–Christie *et al.*, 1985).

Definitions

When an extreme 'glassy–shoot' condition was first recognised, its occurrence was described as *vitrification*. Although this term, has been used very widely in the literature, it is no longer recommended. Choice of the word 'vitrification' to describe glass–like shoots was an etymologically incorrect description of the symptoms observed. The verb 'to vitrify' means to convert into glass or a glass–like substance, whereas water–soaked cultures have not become composed of glass, but only have a glassy appearance; *i.e.* they are *not* vitrified but are *vitreous*. The state of appearing to be like glass (vitreous) is *vitreosity* or *vitrescence*. Water can correctly be described as becoming vitrified when it is converted directly from a liquid into a solid (glass–like) phase during freezing (Fahy *et al.*, 1984). Vitrification has been used in its correct sense in cryobiology (Part 1, page 174), so that

we have a term which has two different meanings in closely related technologies.

For such reasons, a panel of eminent research workers, each of whom has specialised in the occurrence and nature of the glassy shoot syndrome, has recommended that 'vitrification' should no longer be used to describe abnormalities in tissue cultures. Instead the term *hyperhydricity* has been proposed (Debergh *et al.*, 1992), and should now be adopted. The associated adjective is 'hyperhydric'.

Various other terms are found in the literature to describe abnormalities which are now recognised as hyperhydricity: affected shoots or plants have been said to be wet, waterlogged, humid, hyper–hydrated, glassy, vitreous, translucent or succulent. Hyperhydricity has also been termed waterlogging, hyperhydric transformation and translucency.

Occurrence

Hyperhydricity may be found in shoot and node cultures, and in shoots regenerated from callus of all kinds of plants, but its extent and frequency varies widely between different genotypes. It is most often encountered in the mass propagation of woody species, but is also especially liable to occur in certain families of herbaceous plants. Plants in the family Caryophyllaceae, for example, are particularly vulnerable (Evans *et al.*, 1986; Stimart, 1986; Mii *et al.*, 1990; Ault, 1992).

The degree of susceptibility and the precise appearance of affected shoots not only varies according to the kind of plant being cultured but also depends on the nature of the culture. Shoots showing varying degrees of vitrescence are frequently found within the same culture vessel and within different vessels of the same culture. In carnation, Leshem (1983) defined three types of shoots, each having a different internal structure:

i). *normal*;

ii). *translucent*, the leaves of which were light green, non–glaucous and lacking epicuticular wax;

iii). *succulent*, with thick, dark green leaves on clusters of stunted shoots.

This categorisation was supported by Pâques and Boxus (1987b), who called hyperhydric shoots 'non–succulent' if they possessed abnormal leaves which were twisted to reveal only the lower epidermis, and 'succulent' if the leaves were thicker than normal (with or without some leaf curling).

Pâques (1991) suggests that there may be two kinds of hyperhydricity, one resulting from the passive diffusion of water into tissues, the other from an active phenomenon relating to a disturbance in metabolic processes. Whether this is indeed the case, or whether excessive water uptake leads ultimately to more severe symptoms, is unclear. 'Wet' shoots of *Pinus radiata* are intermediate between normal waxy ones and highly abnormal translucent shoots (Aitken–Christie *et al.*, 1985).

THE NATURE OF HYPERHYDRICITY

The hyperhydric condition can affect all tissues and organs cultured *in vitro*. It is brought on by the manner in which a culture has been treated and so is a physiological disorder, and not a pathological one, and neither is it contagious. Although many factors have been identified which may induce it, hyperhydricity is not entirely predictable. When it occurs, tissues are found to have undergone a change in their metabolic processes and this leads to an alteration to their normal structure and appearance.

Hyperhydric tissues generally exhibit reduced lignification (they are *hypolignified*) and this causes vessels and tracheids to be missing, or to possess an abnormal form, in stems, buds and leaves. As cells also have relatively decreased levels of cellulose, the plastic properties of their walls are changed causing them to be defective and deformed. Plant cells deficient in both cellulose and lignin have reduced wall pressure and so take up more water, causing tissues to assume the characteristic water-soaked and enlarged appearance.

Cells in hyperhydric tissues lose a clear axis of elongation and those in the developed parts of shoots remain meristematic for shorter intervals than normal. Vitrescent plants also have lower calcium, inositol, and soluble protein levels, but greater than normal amounts of potassium, phosphorus, glucose and sucrose (Zimmerman *et al.*, 1988b).

Shoots. The leaves of hyperhydric shoots have a thin cuticle, a thin–walled epidermis and abnormal stomata. In normal carnation leaves, the cell walls bordering stomata are thickened and form ridges so that the pores are protruding and elliptical. On hyperhydric leaves the walls of border cells were found to be thin and often damaged, so that the pores were rounded and non–protruding (Ziv and Ariel, 1992). Hyperhydric leaves of *Datura insignis* have a high proportion of abnormal stomata, characterised by deformed guard cells (Miguens *et al.*, 1993). There is abundant parenchymatous tissue in hyperhydric leaves and the spongy mesophyll is composed of large cells. Differentiated palisade cells are reduced in number (Brainerd *et al.*, 1981) and in many cases are completely absent; chloroplasts have an abnormal structure and a low chlorophyll content. The lack of normal internal organisation results in a reduction of both growth and the capacity for photosynthesis (Werker and Leshem, 1987).

Such structural changes are found in some measure in practically all plants cultured *in vitro*; it is their extreme expression which leads to recognisable hyperhydricity.

Hyperhydric shoots do not survive very well if they are moved from the culture vessel into the external environment, and so are difficult to acclimatize or transport between locations. This is due to a variety of morphological and physiological defects. Water loss will be exaggerated because leaves have an incomplete epidermis, have stomata which are abnormally developed, and/or have no epicuticular wax.

Callus. Callus can also become hyperhydric. It is then brittle, does not differentiate vascular elements, and is non–organogenic. Cell walls have a low cellulose content and no lignin (Le Dily *et al.*, 1993).

Biosynthetic processes

Several metabolic processes are altered in hyperhydric plants. Shoots come to contain less protein and chlorophyll than normal, and, as mentioned on page 666, lignin biosynthesis is disrupted. Hyperhydric stomata of *Dianthus* contained callose, a polysaccharide normally found in callus and wounded tissues, which is not present in the stomata of normal leaves (Ziv and Ariel, 1992). In *Petunia*, inositol levels in vitreous leaves were found by Zimmerman and Cobb (1989) to be below those in normal leaves, although there was no shortage of the reducing sugars which normally act as a substrate for the biosynthesis of this compound.

A rise in hydrogen peroxide levels may be responsible for many of the observed metabolic changes in hyperhydric tissues. In vitreous habituated callus of *Beta vulgaris*, Le Dily *et al.* (1993) found there to be an increase in the production of polyamines (see page 662) and a blockage in the porphyrin pathway, resulting in reduced catalase and peroxidase activities. They suggested that the absence of these enzymes to detoxify hydrogen peroxide, and its high concentration due to the increased activity of diamine and polyamine oxidase enzymes, would lead to an accumulation of the toxic OH· radical. This could explain the observed lipoperoxidation of cellular structures.

Stability of the hyperhydric condition

The most extreme symptoms of abnormality are usually found to be non–reversible. In some cases, shoots or plantlets showing symptoms can resume normal growth once they are placed in a favourable environment, although this usually means that new normal leaves are formed in response to the improved conditions, while the atypical morphology of the previously–formed organs is unchanged. Hyperhydric shoots, formed from *Gaillardia pulchella* in the dark, turned green and became healthy within a few days of the cultures being transferred to the light (Bourque *et al.*, 1989). Leonhardt and Kandeler (1987) caused vitrescent shoots of *Pediocactus* to revert to a normal appearance by grafting them onto normal plants.

Although hyperhydricity can sometimes be reversed, it is unwise ever to subculture abnormal shoots because the hyperhydric condition is usually maintained during transfer and persists in any new cultures which are established. Le Roux and Van Staden (1991) found that 1–5% of *Eucalyptus* shoots became hyperhydric during shoot culture. This and other abnormalities were avoided by not subculturing affected shoots. In commercial micropropagation, hyperhydric shoots and cultures are discarded.

Leshem (1986) subcultured the apical 2–3 mm of vitrescent shoots of carnation at monthly intervals for 20 months. Normal–looking shoots did appear during this period, but were thought not to originate from the direct growth of tips which had already produced abnormal tissues. They were often found in cultures which had not been subcultured for 6–9 weeks, but their occurrence and origin were unpredictable. Healthy looking plants were produced if the 'normal' shoots were rooted, but these were later found to produce flowers of variable colours (see page 743).

FACTORS WHICH INFLUENCE HYPERHYDRICITY

Many different factors have been identified which contribute to the induction of hyperhydricity. They are not all of equivalent importance, and some may only induce characteristic symptoms of vitreosity when cultures are grown in unfavourable environments.

Environmental factors

1. The cultural environment

Less than optimal growth conditions. Hyperhydricity occurs in both herbaceous and woody species and young shoots are most likely to become affected. Symptoms are less likely to occur when cultures are growing rapidly. Searching for ideal growing conditions is therefore likely to minimize its incidence (Rugini *et al.*, 1987), while the use of environmental conditions which limit growth will make its occurrence more likely. Shoot cultures of *Prunus armeniaca* grow more rapidly if supplied with sorbitol than if provided with sucrose. Shoots were often hyperhydric when 8.8 µM BAP (see page 665) was added to a sucrose medium, but the frequency of the disorder caused by this concentration of regulant was much less when sorbitol was the carbon source (Marino *et al.*, 1991).

Temperature and light. Hyperhydricity tends to be promoted by high temperature, low light irradiance, or by placing cultures in the dark. Shoots of a peach × almond hybrid became aged and water–soaked when cultured at 25°C, but not at 20°C (Martinelli, 1985) and shoot cultures of *Aster* and *Chrysanthemum* produced few axillary shoots, all of which were vitrescent and succulent if grown under low irradiance (Stimart, 1986).

The maximum regeneration of shoots from petal callus of *Dianthus* occurred in a medium containing 60g/l sucrose and 1 g/l casein hydrolysate (CH), maintained at a temperature of 30°C. Hyperhydricity, which was a problem under these conditions, could be lessened (without altering the concentrations of auxin and cytokinin) by reducing sucrose and CH to 30 g/l and 0–0.5 g/l respectively, and the incubation temperature to 15–20°C (Frey and Janick, 1991).

Taji and Williams (1989) found that the hyperhydricity of shoots regenerated from hypocotyl and cotyledon segments of *Clianthus formosus* could be reduced by keeping the cultures at 5°C for 10 days, before returning them to room temperature. Similarly, the extent of hyperhydricity in *Olearia microdisca* node culture was reduced when vessels were placed in a temperature of 5°C, but at this temperature the rate of shoot multiplication was very low (Williams and Taji, 1991).

2. High relative humidity around shoots

Shoot growth in conditions of continuously high relative humidity is probably the most important environmental factor causing the onset of hyperhydricity.

Shoots cultured in liquid media, including those supported over a liquid medium on filter paper bridges, are more liable to become vitrescent than those grown on solid media, but the extent of abnormality varies very much with genotype. *Dianthus caryophyllus* (carnation) (Davis *et al.*, 1977) and *Citrullus lanatus* (watermelon) (Hale *et al.*, 1992) are, for instance, very likely to become hyperhydric in liquid media, whereas *Begonia rex* and

Nicotiana tabacum cultured in the same conditions are relatively unaffected (Hale *et al.*, *loc. cit.*).

What it is about a liquid medium that causes hyperhydricity is unclear. It could be the absence of oxygen or gaseous exchange (Part 1, page 195), that leaves and shoots become waterlogged during prolonged immersion, or that, as in completely saturated atmospheres, transpiration is suppressed. Shoot cultures of *Amelanchier* × *grandiflora* became hyperhydric if cultured in continuous contact with liquid medium and if placed in a 7 litre vessel and immersed with liquid for 5 minutes every 30 minutes. There was no hyperhydricity, however, if the frequency of immersion was decreased to 5 minutes in every hour (Krueger *et al.*, 1991).

Even on solidified media, shoots are usually enclosed in an atmosphere which is almost completely saturated with water vapour. This prevents normal transpiration within shoots. The leaves of plantlets or shoots growing on a solid medium sometimes become glassy if they grow into the medium or grow along its surface (Pâques and Boxus, 1987b), or touch the side of the culture vessel, but of a normal appearance if they grow upright. Hyperhydricity can therefore sometimes be avoided by changing the position of explants. Hyperhydricity in *Cynara scolymus* shoot cultures was reduced by ensuring that axillary buds did not come into contact with the medium (Lauzer and Vieth, 1990).

When hyperhydricity occurs in erect shoots, lowering the humidity in the upper part of the culture vessel invariably prevents it developing in new shoots, but may not cure symptoms which have already developed. Shoots and organs also become hyperhydric if they are covered in condensation. The shoots and roots forming on somatic embryos of *Sorghum* became necrotic and died if they were covered by condensation (Wernicke *et al.*, 1982).

A reduction of humidity around growing shoots or plantlets can be brought about in various ways:

• by deliberately aerating cultures.

Ventilating or aerating cultures with dry air has the effect of reducing the humidity around cultured shoots and plantlets. It is very effective in reducing or eliminating hyperhydricity, but there are many difficulties in its implementation.

Air admitted to axenic cultures must be contaminant–free and so there are two ways in which it can be admitted to cultures:

① As a stream of air, which has been bacteriologically filtered, supplied under positive pressure;

② By diffusion through a suitable porous membrane fitted to each container.

Forced ventilation is not practical for plant cultures growing in small closed vessels and to culture them in open vessels, in axenic growth rooms, would present considerable difficulties. It has, therefore, usually only been attempted when cultures are grown in large containers.

• by covering the tops of vessels so that some water vapour can escape.

Diffusion in and out of the vessel must be arranged in such a way that contaminants cannot enter. It has been done in the past by plugging tubes with cotton wool, using paper instead of metal or plastic stoppers, by arranging that screw caps are not tightly turned down. More recently research papers have reported fitting small bacteriological filters into the caps of vessels or the use of vessels made from, or fitted with, a selectively permeable membrane, capable of letting water out but allowing CO_2 to enter to maintain photomixotrophic and photoautotrophic growth. Plastic films with these properties include polymethylpentene, microporous polypropylene (Kozai, 1991), microperforated polyethylene (Debergh, 1991) and some fluorocarbon polymers. Some of these films are commercially available .

The major disadvantage to increasing aeration, by whatever method, is that water is lost from the medium. The concentration of salts and agar in the medium then increases and this inevitably leads to poor growth, toxicity and shoots which root poorly when they are moved to the external environment. The problem is most extreme when the entire cap of the vessel is made of porous material. Free access of air can be used for a few days just before transfer, but for more prolonged ventilation it is necessary to insert small bacteriological filters into each vessel or its closure, or to arrange for air to diffuse through small paper–covered holes (Fig. 123).

Agar–solidified media become hardened if water is lost from a vessel. Dry agar reabsorbs little water without being reheated, so that adding water to a vessel does not restore the medium to its condition at the start of the culture. When Majada *et al.* (1992), reduced humidity in cultures by fitting vessels with bacteriological filters, they found that it was preferable to grow carnation shoot cultures on Sorbarods® moistened with liquid medium, rather than on an agar–solidified medium. Serious growth inhibition could then be prevented, by periodically supplying water to the cultures. Although shoot and internode lengths were less than in normally aerated cultures, hyperhydricity was largely avoided, multiplication rates were comparable to those in traditional shoot cultures, and shoots needed little acclimatization. A disadvantage of such a technique in commercial micropropa–gation where numerous small vessels are employed, is that cultures need frequent attention.

• by using water–absorbing materials.

The relative humidity within culture vessels can be reduced by using water–absorbing chemicals. Ziv *et al.* (1981, 1983) reduced the proportion of vitrescent carnation shoots, by placing uncapped culture tubes into a desiccator contain-

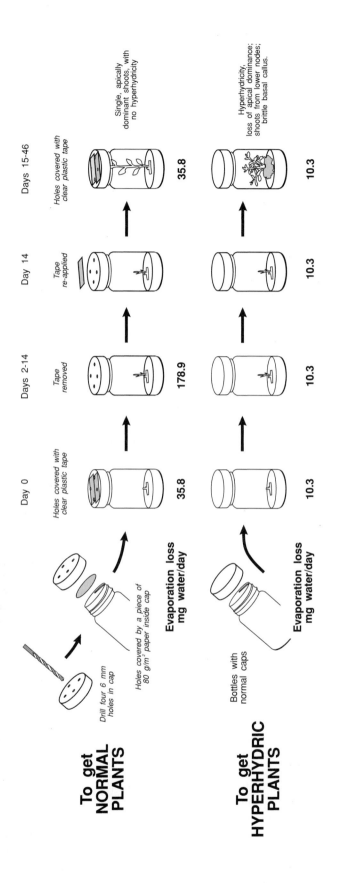

Fig. 123. The experiment of Dillen and Buysens (1989) in which hyperhydricity was prevented in *Gypsophila* cultures. Hyperhydricity did not occur when the interior of vessels was ventilated during the early stages of culture, before active growth began.

ing anhydrous calcium chloride for 6–12 days. The relative humidity within the tubes was thereby reduced to 85%.

Although this technique has been found to be effective in reducing hyperhydricity under experimental conditions, it is not practical for large–scale micropropa–gation: prolonged application would again result in the desiccation of the medium.

- **by growing cultures on agar slants.**

Water does not collect around cultured shoots to the same extent if they are grown at the top of agar slants rather than in conventionally filled tubes. Ziv *et al.* (1983; 1987) reported that this was an effective method of reducing the proportion of carnation shoot cultures which became vitrescent: shoot tips at the bottom of the slopes became hyperhydric.

- **by controlling the condensation of water.**

Water will condense at the coolest place within a culture vessel. In many growth rooms the top of the culture vessel is cooler than the base and this results in water droplets forming on the lid. Air at the top of the vessel is then fully saturated. In small containers of growing shoots, the leaves developing in this region are liable to become hyperhydric and of poor quality. By cooling the bottom of culture vessels, so that their bases are at a slightly lower temperature than the top, water can be caused to condense into the medium. Relative humidity around the shoots is then reduced and hyperhydricity prevented (Part 1, page 212).

Maene and Debergh (1987) list several advantages of using this method: the medium does not dry out; only a relatively small amount of energy is required to operate the basal cooling system; transpiration occurs from leaves, thereby improving the quality of shoots; and shoot growth and subsequent rooting are markedly improved. These authors warn that in consequence of the improved sap flow within shoots, media of lower than normal salt concentrations may need to be employed: however, if this kind of treatment is applied after 3–4 weeks of Stage IIIa culture, the salt levels within the medium will already have been reduced.

Importance of the lag phase. Dillen and Buysens (1989) prevented the development of hyperhydricity in shoots arising on *Gypsophila paniculata* node cultures, by partially reducing the relative humidity within culture vessels. These were covered with caps through which holes had been drilled and pieces of 80 g/m^2 uncoated paper inserted beneath each closure to prevent the entry of contaminants (Fig. 123). By covering holes at various times it was discovered that hyperhydricity could be prevented without severe growth inhibition, by exposing the newly–initiated cultures to more freely ventilated conditions 2–14 days after cultures had been newly initiated. Cultures exposed continuously to the lower humidity shown in Fig. 123 were also non–vitrescent, but shoot length was considerably reduced.

Hyperhydricity thus appeared to be induced *during the lag phase* of the cultures, and once shoots became vitrescent, conditions which favoured normal growth, such as increased ventilation or an high agar concentration, did not restore normal growth. Similarly, high humidity was not damaging to the cultures once 2–3 normal leaves had formed. The longer the lag phase lasted, the greater were the chances of hyperhydric growth. Shoot tip explants, which grew rapidly after transfer, rarely produced vitrescent shoots, even in conditions of high humidity, and if 2–node explants were employed, the shoots which grew (quickly) from upper nodes were normal, whilst those from lower nodes, which were slow to start growth, were always hyperhydric.

These findings suggest that hyperhydricity results from a change in cell determination (see page 668).

3. Two-phased media

Pierik (1987) pointed out that among the several advantages of adding a layer of liquid medium above the semi–solid layer in culture flasks (see Part 1, page 193), was the fact that it sometimes lessens or completely prevents vitreosity. Other reports (*e.g.* John, 1986; Viseur, 1987; Jones *et al.*, 1988) have tended to agree with this observation: hyperhydricity in cultures of Sitka spruce, *Pyrus communis* and one variety of strawberry was cured by adding a small amount of sterile distilled water to the surface of a semisolid medium. Proliferation of *Pyrus communis* shoot cultures (which are normally very liable to hyperhydricity) was avoided indefinitely by culture on a modified **MS** (see page 662) medium in two layers (40 ml containing 0.7% Difco Bacto agar below 10 ml liquid medium. Both layers contained 6.7 μM BAP (Rodriguez *et al.*, 1991).

Exposing shoots to a layer of liquid medium will increase the relative humidity around shoots and, according to the observations in section 2 above (page 657 onwards), might be expected to *increase*, rather than decrease the tendency of shoots to become hyperhydric. Possibly the absorption of nutrients and growth regulators into tissues is enhanced when shoots are bathed in a surface layer of liquid, and that hyperhydricity is avoided because shoot growth is more vigorous? There are some reports of hyperhydricity being magnified by culture on a 2–phase medium. Bach and Cecot (1988) found that *Hyacinthus orientalis* shoots were more liable to become glassy than when grown on a conventionally–solidified medium.

4. Poor transpiration

That methods to improve transpiration can help to reduce hyperhydricity has been mentioned above. Transpiration within cultured shoots is also improved by using high light levels. An illuminance of between 3000–10 000 lux (corresponding to a photon flux density of *ca.* 37.5–125

μmol m^{-2} sec^{-1}) has frequently been recommended for Stage III cultures (see Part 1, page 228), but Maene and Debergh (1987) report that levels of up to 17000 lux [roughly equivalent to a flux density of 187.5 μmol m^{-2} sec^{-1} (*sic.*)] may be effective for some plants at this stage. Under this irradiance, *Ficus benjamina* cultures at Stage IIIa develop high quality leaves. The authors point out that this is because leaf temperatures increase in accord with lighting levels and in consequence, leaves and stomatal pores contain more water than the surrounding air, even if the relative humidity throughout the vessel is 100%. At high irradiances there is a sufficient water gradient between the inside and outside of leaves for transpiration to occur during the period in which the cultures are illuminated each day. As the movement of solutes within shoots is increased, media with a low salt content may once again need to be used.

The cost of extra light will be excessive if it is only used to cure vitrescence. Much more energy is required than to cool the base of culture flasks. Remember that high lighting levels will usually also necessitate increased cooling of the growth room. The situation may be different if high irradiance is combined with CO_2 supplementation to stimulate autotrophic growth (see Part 1, page 205; page 722 this volume).

Note that gaseous exchange into and out of vessels is enhanced if the temperature of the growth room is varied during the day (typically between the photoperiod and the dark period).

5. The water potential of the medium

The water potential of a medium, and particularly the matric potential component, has an effect on hyperhydricity, which is frequently induced, or made worse, in submerged liquid culture (*e.g.* in carnation, Davis *et al.*, 1977; Ziv and Ariel, 1992) and where shoots fall into, or become submerged in a semi–solid medium containing a low concentration of agar (Singha 1982c). In some plants (*e.g. Betula pendula* × *B. pubescens*), normal shoots become completely vitrescent over a period of several weeks when moved from an agar medium to a liquid one, but revert to normal when moved back to agar.

In some species, (*e.g. Dianthus chinensis* and *Cynara scolymus*), where the hyperhydric state is more stable (Böttcher *et al.*, 1988), adding extra agar to media is one of the more reliable ways of preventing or curing hyperhydricity. Such treatment is, however, not an effective preventative method. The concentration may have to be increased from 0.6–0.8% to 1.1% or 1.8% to cause shoots to have a normal appearance, and this causes the growth of cultures to be slowed, the rate of multiplication in shoot

cultures to be reduced, and can make the agar difficult to remove from explants.

> Note however, that although these effects are often ascribed to the effect of agar in reducing the water potential of the medium, there may often be another explanation. This is that the rate of uptake of cytokinin into tissues is less on an agar–solidified medium than from a liquid one — see page 665.

Hyperhydricity also occurs on media gelled with other materials. Cultures grown on low concentrations of gellan gum as the only gelling agent are particularly liable to become hyperhydric, but the tendency can be reduced or eliminated if the concentration is increased, or some agar is added to the medium as well. In a modified **MS** medium without ammonium ions, the water potential with 0.12% Gelrite was –0.263 MPa, and with 0.5% Gelrite, –0.299 MPa. On these media, all the shoots regenerated from *Agave tequilana* stem segments were hyperhydric. Only when 2% Gelrite was added to the medium (water potential –0.441 MPa), were 82% of shoots non–vitrified (Castro–Concha *et al.,* 1990). A mixture of gelling agents found suitable for apple shoot tips was 1–1.5 g/l Gelrite plus 2–4 g/l agar (Pasqualetto *et al.*, 1986). Hyperhydricity of almond shoots was eliminated by culture on 0.7% agar plus 0.5% pectin (Rugini and Verma, 1983).

Effect of sugars. Increasing the sugar concentration (*e.g.* from 3% to 8%) in a medium solidified with 1% agar (Ziv *et al.* 1981, 1983) had the same effect as increasing agar concentration. Similarly Langford and Wainwright (1988) reported that glassiness was rare in rose shoot tip cultures grown in **MS** medium with 40 g/l sucrose, but increased as the concentration of sucrose decreased.

A somewhat contrary result was obtained by Zimmerman and Cobb (1989) with *Petunia hybrida* shoots, which were much more liable to hyperhydricity on a medium containing **MS** salts containing 1g/l Gelrite and 30 g/l sucrose (80% shoots affected) than one containing 3 g/l Gelrite and 15 g/l sucrose (10% shoots affected).

Possible effect on humidity. As mentioned in Chapter 9, the osmotic potential of a solidified plant culture medium has two negative components, one contributed by the dissolved salts and organic components of the medium (ψ_s), the other by any gelling agents, such as pectin and agar, which are included (the 'matric potential', ψ_m). Thus one possible explanation of the curative effect of high concentrations of sugars and gelling agents is that they have caused the total water potential of the medium (Ψ_{tcm}) to be decreased.

$$\Psi_{tcm} = \psi_s + \psi_m$$

A decrease in the water potential of the medium would cause the relative humidity with culture vessels to fall slightly (Chapter 9), thereby allowing some transpiration from cultured shoots (see 2. and 3. above).

Adding extra sugar to the medium will slightly reduce the relative humidity in culture vessels (Chapter 9). From Table 36 (page 336, Part 1) it can be seen that adding 8% sucrose, instead of 3% sucrose, to **MS** medium would reduce the theoretical relative humidity in vessels from 99.6% to 99.2%.

6. The macronutrient and micronutrient composition of the medium

The hyperhydric condition often occurs on full strength **MS** salts, but not on media with less concentrated macronutrients. For example, in experiments of Beauchesne (1981), shoots of *Salix babylonica* became hyperhydric on **MS** salts, had few vascular bundles and died if they were transferred to the same strength medium for a second passage. By contrast, shoots cultured on $1/3$ **MS** had more xylem vessels, while those on Knop's macronutrients had an even greater number and were always normal in appearance. *Malus* and *Prunus* shoot cultures are less liable to become vitrescent if they are grown on the medium of Lepoivre, rather than **MS** medium (Pierik, 1987). Unfortunately the rate of shoot multiplication on dilute macronutrient solutions is usually considerably less than that on more concentrated alternatives so that their use is not an ideal way to overcome hyperhydricity.

However, it seems that hyperhydricity is less influenced by the osmotic (water) potential of macronutrient solutions, than by the concentration of ammonium and nitrate ions. Thus Kevers *et al.* (1984) and Ziv *et al.* (1987) have shown that normal plants of *Salix babylonica* and *Dianthus caryophyllus* can be obtained on **MS** macronutrients providing the ammonium ion is omitted. Gradually increasing ammonium to the normal level in **MS** medium induces a parallel development of glassiness and hypolignification (Daguin and Letouzé, 1985).

Plants grown with ammonium nutrition produce abnormally high levels of ethylene (see below) and also come to have considerably higher levels of polyamines (Chapter 11) than those grown with nitrate nitrogen.

Le Dily *et al.* (1993) have suggested that the deficient structure of cell walls in hyperhydric tissues may permit uncontrolled uptake of NH_4^+ ions. However NH_4^+ is taken up rapidly, even by normal tissues, and can lead to changes in the way other ions are absorbed. The greater amounts of nitrogen in grape vine tissues as increasing quantities of ammonium sulphate were added to the medium, was parallelled by an increase in Fe, and P and a decrease in K. The levels of these elements was not markedly changed when the medium was supplemented

with increasing amounts of sodium nitrate (Villegas *et al.*, 1991).

Certainly, under conditions of poor transpiration, levels of the ammonium ion in many media are often too high for the growth of normal shoots. When hyperhydricity appears on **MS** salts containing 20.6 mM ammonium ion, it can usually be prevented by lowering the concentration of the ammonium ion to 0–10.3 mM (in effect eliminating ammonium nitrate, or reducing its concentration by up to one half). The best growth of *Dianthus caryophyllus* shoots occurred on **MS** salts when the levels of nitrogenous compounds were adjusted to provide 40 mM NO_3^- (very slightly more than the normal concentration) but only 6 mM NH_4^+ (Ziv and Ariel, 1992). The frequency of vitrescent shoots in *Allium sativum* shoot cultures was reduced when the total nitrogen in a modified **Linsmaier and Skoog (1965)** medium was maintained at 60 mM, but the proportion of nitrate to ammonium ions increased from 40/20 to 56.5/3.5 (Nagakubo *et al.*, 1993).

Hyperhydricity of chestnut which occurred on **MS** medium was prevented by using macronutrients which contained only half the **MS** level of nitrates (Chauvin and Salesses, 1988). This approach (in combination with 2–phased layers of medium) was also successful with *Pyrus communis*: Rodriguez *et al.* (1991) added only one half of the weight of nitrates specified for **MS** medium to each litre of medium, while the weights of calcium chloride and magnesium sulphate were doubled. The change this makes to the ionic composition of **MS** macronutrients is shown in Table 101. In this case, reducing the *absolute concentration* of both nitrate and ammonium ions was effective; the ratio of nitrate to ammonium ions remained the same as in **MS** medium.

Organic nitrogen sources. Organic media additions, which also supply reduced nitrogen, cannot be used as a substitute for ammonium in media causing hyperhydricity. For example, the addition of 3 g/l casein hydrolysate to a medium containing **MS** salts, contributed to the hyperhydricity of carnation shoots in rotated liquid culture (Davis *et al.*, 1977). The numbers of turgid and thickened shoots could be decreased by removing the organic nitrogen source and by reducing the kinetin concentration (see later).

The effect of other ions. There are some reports that an inappropriate concentration of other ions can induce the hyperhydricity syndrome, for example a deficiency in calcium ions (Kreutmeier *et al.*, 1984) or potassium ions (Pasqualetto *et al.*, 1988b). Ziv *et al.* (1987) thought that hyperhydricity might be induced by inappropriate ratio between Ca^{2+} and NH_4^+ ions: the proportion of hyperhydric *Dianthus* cultures was decreased if all **MS** macronu-

Table 101. A comparison of the macronutrients of 'MS2' medium, used by Rodriguez *et al.* (1991) to prevent vitrescence of pear shoot cultures, with those of MS medium.

Ions	Equivalence (meq/l)	
	'MS2' medium	MS medium
NO_3^-	19.70	39.4
PO_4^{3-}	3.75	3.75
SO_4^{2-}	6.0	3.0
Cl^-	11.97	5.98
K^+	10.65	20.04
Ca^{2+}	11.97	5.98
Na^+	0	0
Mg^{2+}	6.00	3.00
NH_4^+	10.30	20.61
$[H^+]$	2.50	2.50
Sum of I^+ or I^-	41.42	52.12
Total N	30.00	60.01
Nitrogen ratios		
NH_4^+/N	0.34	0.34
NO_3^-/NH_4^+	1.91	1.91

Weights of salts from which these macronutrients can be prepared
will be found in the Appendix

trients except calcium chloride were decreased to half their normal concentration.

Quoirin and Lepoivre (1977) developed a medium for *Prunus* shoot tip culture which gave a high proliferation rate without the formation of succulent leaves. The new macronutrients did not contain chloride ions and this was thought to be a possible reason for the absence of vitrescence in the cultures. Shoots arising from sugarbeet callus cultures were vitrified on media containing high levels of sodium chloride, but green and healthy if 70 mM sodium sulphate was added instead (Chandler *et al.*, 1988). However, the medium of **Quoirin and Lepoivre** differs from MS medium in other respects: for example it contains much less ammonium and a smaller ratio of NH_4^+ to total nitrogen. Decreasing the concentration of all MS micronutrients (except Fe) to one tenth, reduced the incidence of glassy shoots in carnation cultures (Dencso, 1987).

Cobalt ions. Bartolo and Macey (1989) experimented with omitting cobalt ions from several different media on which *Brassica oleracea*, *Passiflora mollissima* and *Saintpaulia ionantha* cultures were grown for shoot multiplication. Growth and shoot proliferation of *Saintpaulia* was greater in the absence of Co^{2+}, than in the presence 0.1 µM (the concentration of Co^{2+} normally present in MS medium). *Brassica* and *Passiflora* shoots were however stunted and unhealthy in the absence of Co^{2+} and *Passiflora* shoots showed symptoms of senescence.

Gaspar and Kevers (1985) had previously reported that hyperhydricity of carnation shoots could be prevented by using 1 µM cobalt chloride in MS medium (instead of the 0.1 µM which is normally present). An excess of cobalt can be toxic however. When 250 mg/l cobalt chloride (1.05 mM Co^{2+}) was added to the MS medium on which 'M 26' apple shoots were cultured, there was less hyperhydricity, but shoot growth and multiplication rate were severely reduced (Standardi and Micheli, 1988).

What then is the physiological activity of Co^{2+}? Cobalt ions have a protective action against metal chelate toxicity (Albert, 1958), can prevent injury caused by uncontrolled oxidative processes (page 307), and in high concentration can inhibit ethylene biosynthesis (page 456). Whether any of these properties are involved in the control of hyperhydricity, is uncertain.

7. Lack of oxygen.

The possibility that a lack of oxygen in the medium is one cause of hyperhydricity in shoot cultures, is raised by the findings of Woodward *et al.* (1991), but contradicted by other results. In *Cephalotus follicularis* vitrescence was overcome by transferring shoot cultures from an agar–solidified medium to the top of rockwool wetted with the same solution. On this substrate, the poor vigour, yellowing and dark green glassy appearance, which occurred on agar, disappeared and a high rate of shoot multiplication was achieved. However, *Pinus radiata* shoots were more vitrescent in a shaken liquid medium than in static liquid (Aitken–Christie *et al.*, 1988).

8. The pH of the medium.

A pH effect on hyperhydricity was recorded by Berghoef and Bruinsma (1979a). Flower buds of *Begonia* became glassy if they were grown on a medium containing 10 mM NO_3^- and 5 mM NH_4^+, adjusted to pH 4, but the symptoms did not occur if the medium was adjusted to pH 5. It is interesting that low pH had an immediate effect, because regardless of the initial acidity level, the pH of the medium was 4.8–5.0 after 3 weeks.

Additional factors

Several other factors have been found to affect the onset of hyperhydricity:

1. Further properties of gelling agents

Although there is a strong connection between matric potential and the occurrence of hyperhydricity, matric potential may not fully account for the observed effect of agar. Apart from increasing the water potential of the medium, the addition of extra agar to the medium causes contact with the cultured plant material to decrease. This may decrease the tendency of cultures to become hyperhydric by causing there to be a reduced uptake of nutrients and growth regulators (Debergh, 1983; Bornman and Vogelmann, 1984), including materials likely to cause a physiological disturbance. However, this hypothesis does not explain why a medium gelled with 1.5 g/l Gelrite consistently gives rise to vitreosity, even though it has the same apparent firmness as that to which 7 g/l Difco Bacto agar has been added and where the symptoms do not arise (Pasqualetto *et al.*, 1986, 1988b).

Some commercial agars are more liable than others to promote hyperhydricity. When the same amount of agar is added to a medium, the extent of hyperhydricity varies according to the brand (Part 1, page 340) and sometimes, even the lot number of agar of one particular kind. For example, apple shoots which were hyperhydric on Phytagar, had a normal appearance on Difco Bacto agar (Loreti and Pasqualetto, 1986).

This effect may be related to the matric potentials of the different products (Owens and Wozniak, 1991), but as the effect on hyperhydricity often seems to be separate from the firmness of the gel produced, it has been suggested that agar may contain substances which are able to prevent, or partially prevent, the syndrome (see Part 1, page 339), but there has been no indication of which chemical characteristic might be involved (Pâques, 1991). However, the capacity for agars to prevent vitreosity may be related to the degree with which they are hydrolysed when autoclaved together with other components of culture media. It is well known that agar does not polymerise and solidify completely at an acid pH (page 299, Part 1). Pâques and Boxus (1987b) reported that if the solid and liquid phases of agar which had been autoclaved at pH 3.5 were mixed, explants did not become 'vitreous' in the presence of BAP, and shoot proliferation was promoted. They conjectured that agar prepared in this way might adsorb substances in the medium which normally promote hyperhydricity, or that it might release an anti–hyperhydricity substance which is absorbed into plant tissues. A patent on the beneficial properties of the supernatant water soluble fraction of acid–hydrolysed agar was filed by Boxus and Pâques (1986) (page 817). The fraction, called the "anti–vitrifying complex", has been found to prevent hyperhydricity of several species in the presence of BAP (Pâques and Boxus ,1987b; Pâques, 1991), including that normally experienced by cultures grown in liquid media (Scherer, 1988; Pâques, 1991).

Two anti–vitrescent agents 'EM1' and 'EM2' are marketed by Pronatec S.A.[†]

2. A changed redox potential.

Rugini *et al.* (1987) found that hyperhydricity of almond shoots was reduced or eliminated if they were cultured on a medium containing 4.5% fructose (which is a reducing sugar, *i.e.* a reducing agent), instead of sucrose. Placing cultures on medium gelled with M–Gel® (which contains grape wine sugars) was also effective. Similarly glassiness was prevented from developing in shoots of some *Prunus* and *Pyrus* species, and cured in shoots which had already been affected, when they were incubated on 1% galactose (also a reducing sugar). This sugar also slowed the development of symptoms in *Malus* (Druart, 1988).

How reducing sugars may act to control hyperhydricity is as yet unclear: Druart suggested that they might decrease the high oxidative potential which is found in vitrified leaves. This hypothesis receives support from the findings of Standardi and Micheli (1988), who discovered that adding 500 mg/l reduced glutathione (a biological reducing agent in thiol–dependent enzyme reactions, see Chapter 7) to shoot cultures of 'M.26' apple rootstock, diminished the proportion of hyperhydric shoots and increased the multiplication rate. Caffeic acid (200 mg/l) had a similar, but less marked effect.

3. The action of sterilants

Hyperhydricity may be induced in some plants by prolonged sterilisation procedures (Pierik, 1987). For example, because shoot tip explants from field–grown material of *Prunus tenella* needed to be sterilised for a longer period than material from glasshouse–grown mother plants, the resulting cultures had an abnormally high proportion of hyperhydric shoots. Alderson *et al.* (1987) thought that this might have been due to stress induced by the chlorine treatment.

---

† 62, rue du Lonsg Pot, 59800 Lille, France.   See also page 1236.

4. The growth regulators added to the medium.

Cytokinins. In shoot cultures, the induction of hyperhydricity can be influenced by the type and concentration of the growth regulators used. In many species, it is especially likely to be induced by high levels of cytokinin, while lower rates induce the proliferation of normal shoots. This was the case with *Gerbera aurantiaca* (Meyer and Van Staden, 1988). Where there is a beneficial increase in shoot multiplication, it is sometimes possible to use a high cytokinin concentration for a few subcultures. Shoots would then be transferred to a medium containing a lower rate, to prevent deterioration (Clemente *et al.*, 1991). Shoot cultures of *Sequoia sempervirens*, which become hyperhydric when kept continuously on a medium containing BAP, have been kept healthy and capable of proliferation for at least 13 years, by placing them alternately, at monthly intervals, on a medium containing BAP, and then on a medium without cytokinin to which activated charcoal has been added (Franclet, 1991).

Cytokinins are particularly liable to induce the glassy shoot syndrome when they are added to cultures in which there is another sub–optimal factor (such as when an inappropriate gelling agent has been used, or where cultures have been subjected to high humidity or some other stress). The cytokinin BAP has been especially noted to induce hyperhydricity when used at high concentration . This may mean that the concentration of BAP which produces the highest number of axillary shoots in a shoot culture cannot be used. The following levels of hyperhydricity were observed in *Salvia leucantha* shoot cultures:

BAP concentration (mg/l)	Proportion of hyperhydric shoots %
0	5
0.1	10.7
1	47

This meant that the optimum concentration for shoot multiplication was 0.1 mg/l (Hosoki and Tahara, 1993).

The sensitivity of plants to BAP depends on their genotype and on the other environmental conditions to which cultures are subjected. *Camellia sinensis* is very resistant to vitrescence and in experiments of Kataeva *et al.* (1991) only 5% of shoots showed symptoms when they were cultured on a medium containing 5 mg/l ($22.4 \mu M$). Even 0.01 mg/l resulted in all the melon shoots placed in a liquid medium becoming hyperhydric, whereas on an agar–solidified medium, vitrescence only became a problem when the cytokinin level was raised from 0.1 to 0.7 mg/l (Leshem *et al.*, 1988a). Hyperhydricity of *Narcissus* cv. 'Bridal Crown' shoots, was overcome by reducing the BAP concentration in the medium while at the same time increasing the agar concentration from 6 to 8 g/l (Squires and Langton, 1990). An explanation for these results is provided by work of Debergh *et al.* (1981) and Bornman and Vogelmann (1984) who have shown that cytokinin uptake is inversely proportional to the agar content of the medium.

Symptoms of hyperhydricity can sometimes be prevented by culture on, or transfer to, a medium containing a cytokinin other than BAP (*e.g.* 2–iP, Werner and Boe, 1980; Bunn and Dixon, 1992b,c — but this cytokinin can also cause vitrescence, see below). There were many glassy shoots in *Gerbera jamesonii* cultures when 1–10 mg/l BAP was added to encourage shoot proliferation, but very few if 1 mg/l kinetin was used instead (Dencso, 1987). Cytokinin–induced development of hyperhydricity is dependent on genotype. Some varieties or species of plants within any given genus are likely to be more tolerant of BAP than others.

The induction of hyperhydricity is not confined to BAP alone, and high rates of other cytokinin compounds may also induce the symptoms, although results depend greatly on the kind of plant which is treated. Thus, 10 mg/l zeatin (plus other regulants) caused shoots of jojoba cv. 'California' to become translucent with large basal calluses, although they could be multiplied satisfactorily using 2 mg/l (Jacoboni and Standardi, 1987); more than 3 mg/l 2–iP caused severe vitrescence of papaya shoots (Kataoka and Inoue, 1992); reducing the concentrations of adenine sulphate and kinetin lowered the incidence of hyperhydricity in carnation shoot tip cultures (Davis *et al.*, 1977).

Thidiazuron ($4.5 \mu M$) induced hyperhydric shoots of *Vitis vinifera* 'Barbara' (Gribaudo and Fronda, 1991) but, unlike BAP, was not damaging to apple (Kataeva *et al.*, 1991). Huetteman and Preece (1993) found hyperhydric shoots in cultures of some clones of *Acer saccharinum* grown on a medium containing thidiazuron. These shoots were difficult to root, but if cultures were maintained, or shoots moved to a medium lacking cytokinin, vitreous shoots frequently elongated and regained a normal appearance. They could then be rooted and acclimatized more readily.

Cytokinin habituation. Although in most plants cytokinins are the growth regulants most likely to cause hyperhydricity, Leshem and Sachs (1985) and Leshem *et al.* (1988b) have shown that high auxin levels induce translucent shoots in some carnation cultures. In these experiments, high concentrations of NAA increased, and BAP decreased, the proportion of carnation shoot tips which developed abnormally. However the growth habit of the hyperhydric shoots (an absence of apical dominance and no root formation) suggested that cytokinins might be involved. They therefore conjectured that the vitrescent condition, although induced by high auxin, could be due to abnormally high endogenous cytokinin levels caused by cytokinin habituation.

The proportion of hyperhydric carnation shoots was determined during the first week of axillary bud culture and was unchanged thereafter, as though it were permanently fixed. Normal shoots did occasionally appear on hyperhydric ones and these could be raised as normal plants. Leshem *et al.* (*loc. cit.*) noted that a cytokinin–habituated sugarbeet callus was reported by Crevecour *et al.* (1987) to look rather like vitrescent tissue.

The hypothesis that cytokinin habituation can be responsible for hyperhydricity receives some support from the results of Kataeva *et al.* (1991), who induced vitrescence in apple by culturing shoots on a medium containing BAP in high humidity. When they examined the concentration of growth substances within the vitrescent shoots, they found that the level of natural cytokinins was several times greater than in normal shoots.

Callus of *Phaseolus lunatus* (Capelle *et al.*, 1983) and *Juglans nigra* (Neuman *et al.*, 1993) has been found to become cytokinin autonomous after initial culture on media containing thidiazuron.

Cold temperature storage. Shoots of deciduous azaleas multiplied in the presence of 4.5 µM thidiazuron were compact and hyperhydric, with strap–like leaves. If after 3 transfers the cultures were stored for 3 months at 3°C, Briggs *et al.* (1988a,b) found that shoots regained a normal phenotype and elongated. Hypotheses which might explain this result, are:

 — the cytokinin was metabolised during storage, so that its concentration was reduced;

 — cold reversed the cytokinin effect of thidiazuron;

 — cold storage overcame cytokinin habituation caused by thidiazuron.

Auxins. That auxins can sometimes induce hyperhydricity has been mentioned above. It is, however, an unusual observation, although the addition of auxins to media containing cytokinins does often increase the proportion of vitrescent shoots observed: for example, shoots from shoot tip cultures of *Brassica campestris* only became vitrescent if an auxin was added to the medium together with 2–iP cytokinin (Paek *et al.*, 1987), and the extent of hyperhydricity in apple cultures increased when 5.7 µM IAA or 5.3 µM NAA was added to a medium containing 4.4–22.2 µM BAP (Kataeva *et al.*, 1991).

Hyperhydricity during rooting. Shoots regenerated from protoplast culture of *Brassica oleracea* rooted readily on **Pelletier *et al.* (1983) G** medium (contains ½**MS**

macronutrients and 0.01 mg/l NAA), but were often hyperhydric even after the roots formed. To enable these plantlets to withstand transfer *extra vitrum*, Robertson and Earle (1986) found that *in vitro* culture without growth regulators was necessary until a normal phenotype developed. This was obtained by hardening the shoots on sterile vermiculite moistened with **G** medium salts.

Hyperhydricity and the formation of callus were associated with the use of NAA for inducing *in vitro* rooting of *Ephedra fragilis* shoots. These problems were much reduced by substituting IAA as the auxin (O'Dowd and Richardson, 1993).

Gibberellic acid. Shoots of *Brachycome iberidifolia* regenerated from protoplast–derived callus on **MS** medium containing 0.5 mg/l NAA and 4 mg/l BAP, all became hyperhydric when rooted on the same medium, this time containing 0.3 mg/l IAA. Malaure *et al.* (1990) solved the problem by also adding 0.5 mg/l GA$_3$ to the rooting medium.

Activated charcoal

Vitrescent shoots were formed when semi–organised callus of *Pinus radiata* which had been cultured with 5 mg/l BAP, was moved to a medium containing 0.5% activated charcoal, but no growth regulators. To obtain normal shoots the charcoal had to be eliminated from the medium (Aitken–Christie *et al.*, 1988).

POSSIBLE CAUSES OF HYPERHYDRICITY

The failure of lignin biosynthesis.

The activity of certain enzymes has found to be changed in hyperhydric tissues (Gaspar *et al.*, 1987) and the vessels and tracheids of vitrescent shoots are deficient in lignin. Hegedus and Phan (1983a,b; 1987) showed that if low concentrations of phloridzin (and its derivative/precursors, phloroglucinol and *p*–coumaric acid) were added to vitrescent cultures of apple, shoots resumed a normal appearance. A similar observation has been reported with callus cultures of an *Helianthus* interspecific hybrid (Witzens *et al.*, 1988), where the occurrence of hyperhydricity in one third of the regenerated shoots was prevented by adding either phloridzin (30–100 mM), naringenin (30 mM), or esculin hydrate (30 mM) to the culture medium. Phan and Hegedus (1986) showed that addition of phloridzin to the medium increased the activities of enzymes involved in lignin synthesis. The compound was taken up and converted to *p*–coumaryl–CoA

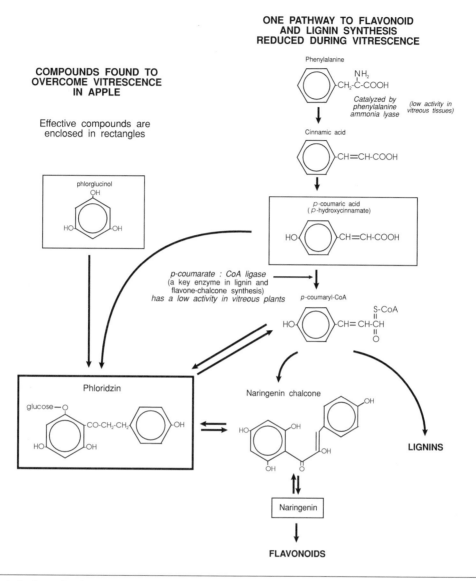

Fig. 123. Pathways to lignin synthesis.
Synthesis is suppressed during vitrescence but can be re-activated in apple and sunflower shoots by the addition of phloridzin (or its derivatives/precursors)
[Based on Phan and Hegedus, 1986; Witrzens *et al.*, 1988]

(a precursor of lignin formation). Its presence also re–activated the entire set of enzymes involved in lignin biosynthesis (Fig. 124).

Hyperhydric shoots have been reported to be returned to normality by being stored at low temperature. This treatment was effective on almond cultures (kept at 4°C for 15 days — Rugini and Verma, 1983) and with *Clianthus formosus* (kept for 10 days at 5°C, then at room temperature for 30 days —Taji and Williams, 1989). Phan and Hegedus (1986) also found that storage of their apple cultures at 4°C for 4 weeks in the dark, resulted in an increase in the natural phloridzin level within shoots, a stimulation of enzymes of the lignin pathway, and the elimination of hyperhydricity. Unfortunately, in this case, the curative effect was short–lived because, unlike cultures to which phloridzin had been added exogenously, the 'cured' plants became hyperhydric again in the next subculture.

Ethylene and growth regulators

Hyperhydricity is more likely to occur in tightly sealed tubes (*e.g.* those covered with Parafilm or aluminium foil) than in those covered more loosely (*e.g.* with cotton wool or a metal cap) (Hakkaart and Versluijs, 1983; Zimmerman *et al.,* 1988a). Ethylene production (and the conversion of the precursor ACC to ethylene) has been found to be greater in hyperhydric tissues than normal ones, especially when healthy tissues are first moved onto media which induce hyperhydricity. These findings suggest that ethylene might be a trigger in the development of the 'glassy shoot syndrome' because, at physiologically active levels, the gas is known to alter the activity of phenylalanine ammonia–lyase in plants, an enzyme in the lignin synthesis pathway (Letouzé and Daguin, 1987). The use of vessels or closures which are gas permeable and so prevent the build up of gases such as ethylene and carbon dioxide in the head space above cultures, can help to prevent hyperhydricity (Debergh *et al.,* 1992).

Kevers *et al.* (1984) suggested that hyperhydricity might be induced when an initial stress (*e.g.* excess cytokinin or ammonium ion) modifies the phenol level in tissues and thereby enhances the activity of both soluble and membrane–bound peroxidase enzymes. This in turn would be expected to cause the observed burst of ethylene biosynthesis. The hypothesis then goes on to suggest that an excess of ethylene in the culture vessel might inhibit further biosynthesis of the gas, causing the activities of PAL and acidic peroxidases to decrease, so that lignification is hindered. Hyperhydricity is more likely to be a problem when media contain ammonium ions (page 662 and below) and plants grown in soil or hydroponically with ammonium nutrition evolve much greater amounts of ethylene than those supplied with nitrate nitrogen (Barker and Corey, 1987). In sand culture, the increased ethylene evolution could be prevented by buffering the medium, and also by adding potassium ions (Corey and Barker, 1987). The above observations suggest that hyperhydricity might be prevented if ethylene biosynthesis could be arrested. High levels of Co^{2+} ions (page 663) and anti–oxidant treatments (page 664), which have been noted to prevent hyperhydricity in some circumstances, *are* treatments also known to inhibit ethylene biosynthesis (Chapter 11). But unfortunately other inhibitors of ethylene biosynthesis have not been found to prevent vitreosity (Phan, 1991) and adding ethylene to the atmosphere in which cultures are growing does not induce glassiness (Kevers and Gaspar, 1985b). Adding both silver nitrate and carbenicillin (see page 648) to the medium caused the proportion of hyperhydric shoots regenerated from *Brassica* cotyledons to be *increased* (Hachey *et al.,* 1991).

Leshem and co–workers (1985, 1988) have proposed that hyperhydricity is caused by an auxin/cytokinin imbalance. They suggest that this occurs because isolated shoot tips are capable of producing auxins in their leaves, but

have no roots to supply cytokinin. It is often noted that the symptoms of hyperhydricity get less if it is possible to root the affected shoots.

Cytokinins are known to increase natural ethylene biosynthesis, while at the same time inhibiting some of the effects of ethylene on plant growth (Burg and Burg, 1968). As ethylene is implicated in the induction of hyperhydricity, it is tempting to speculate that the tendency of cytokinins to induce this syndrome might be related to their inducing abnormally high ethylene production by plant tissues.

Ammonium detoxification processes

Ammonium ions are normally taken up rapidly from plant culture media, and this may result in plant tissues coming to possess physiologically damaging endogenous concentrations. The excess of NH_4^+ may induce a 'detoxification process' which diverts carbohydrates away from other biosynthetic pathways by increasing the activity of glutamate dehydrogenase enzymes. The ion is then preferentially incorporated into glutamic acid, the first stage in the conversion of ammonium into organic nitrogen compounds (see Fig. 93, Chapter 9, page 277). The presence of high levels of glutamate probably induces glutamate dehydrogenase enzyme, the activity of which has been noted to be at a high level in vitrescent tissues (Letouzé and Daguin, 1983). Instead of entering into cellulose and lignin synthesis, sugars are then utilised in the production of amino acids (Daguin and Letouzé, 1986). Under these conditions, the normal process, whereby L–phenylalanine is de–aminated, ceases to operate properly. This leads to a deficiency of cinnamic acid (and hence *p*–coumaric acid) from which lignins are made (Fig. 124). Vitreous tissues have been noted to be deficient in phenylalanine ammonia lyase enzyme (Kevers and Gaspar, 1985a; Letouzé and Daguin, 1987)

It is possible that adding one or more organic acid to media in which hyperhydricity is initiated, would facilitate the detoxification of NH_4^+ without draining carbohydrates away from other essential metabolic processes (Part 1, page 277).

Hyperhydricity — a determined cellular condition?

Leshem *et al.* (Leshem, 1983a; Leshem and Sachs, 1985) suggested that hyperhydricity could be a stable teratomatous condition, determined in the initial stages of a culture, and thereafter capable of stable unlimited development.

Arguments in favour of this hypothesis are that:

- frequently only a proportion of shoots in a culture becomes hyperhydric;

If the condition is caused by straightforward toxicity, why are not all shoots affected in the same way?

- there is evidence that affected shoots are cytokinin habituated (page 666);

- the onset of hyperhydricity can be influenced by environmental conditions existing during the lag phase of a culture and similar adverse conditions applied at a later stage of shoot development are without effect (page 660).

PREVENTING HYPERHYDRICITY

To summarise, hyperhydricity may be prevented or reduced by one or more measures. The following are those which have been found to be most successful:

1. Reducing the relative humidity in the culture vessel.

   The use of a less tightly fitting closure may sometimes solve the problem. A particularly effective technique is to arrange for the base of culture vessels to be cooled, particularly during the period just before root induction and transfer to the external environment. Reduction in RH shortly after establishment of a culture may be most effective.

2. Increasing the concentration of agar or Gelrite in a semi–solid medium, or increasing the concentration of sucrose. This will result in a reduced rate of proliferation in shoot cultures.

3. Using a 2–phase culture technique instead of the conventional single–phase agar method.

4. Culturing shoots on a porous support wetted with liquid medium, rather than on a semi–solid medium.

5. Where shoots or organs are to be grown on a liquid medium, ensuring that they are immersed only periodically and not continuously.

6. Decreasing the concentration of ammonium ions in the medium.

7. Adjusting the the initial pH of the medium.

8. Adding one or more organic acids such as citrate, succinate or malate to the medium to assist with NH_4^+ assimilation.

9. Decreasing the concentration of micronutrients in the medium.

10. Replacing sucrose with fructose or galactose, or adding reduced glutathione to the medium.

11. Transferring cultures to a medium without regulants. This may permit the formation of new shoots without hyperhydricity.

12. Decreasing the concentration of cytokinin used and/or changing from the use of a particular cytokinin, particularly BAP, to another compound with similar activity for one or more subcultures.

13. Culturing tissues with an auxin/cytokinin ratio more appropriate to the plant species.

14. Adding phloridzin or one of its precursors to the medium.

15. Growing shoots or plantlets under light of higher irradiance. As explained above, this is likely to be a more expensive option than the use of basal cooling.

14

Rooting and Establishment

This chapter deals with establishing the products of micropropagation as plants which are capable of growing in the harsh environment that exists outside the culture flask. Rooted plants are required for this purpose that are capable of withstanding contact with contaminating organisms, dry atmospheres, fluctuating temperatures and high irradiance light. Culture of plant material within the abnormal closed environment within a culture vessel, produces delicate shoots and plantlets which must be weaned through a transitional period, during which they are said to be *hardened* or *acclimatized* for survival in the greenhouse or out–of–doors.

STAGE IIIb — ROOTING MICROCUTTINGS

All methods of micropropagation, apart from embryogenesis, result in single shoots, or clumps of shoots, and to obtain plantlets, these must usually be treated as cuttings (which are frequently called *microcuttings*) and rooted at a separate stage of the micropropagation process. Adventitious shoots, or axillary shoots produced during node or shoot culture, occasionally produce roots spontaneously during micropropagation. A defined rooting stage is then unnecessary and the rooted plantlets can be moved directly from Stage II vessels into the external environment for hardening.

Just as is found when rooting conventional cuttings, those of some species root easily *in vitro* and often produce roots spontaneously, for example, some orchids and *Asparagus*, (Chin, 1982), *Begonia* (Thakur, 1975),

Cryptanthus and *Philodendron* (Debergh and Maene, 1981), *Solanum tuberosum* (Hussey and Stacey, 1981a), and in *Digitalis thapsi* (Herrera *et al.,* 1990). Shoots of *Sesbania aculeata* produced directly on seedling hypocotyl sections, often rooted on the shoot induction medium (Bansal and Pandey, 1993).

A separate rooting stage is unnecessary for plants which produce storage organs *in vitro*, because bulbs, tubers or corms produced *in vitro*, can be planted directly into the greenhouse or field.

In most instances, the treatments used to produce shoots *in vitro*, do not encourage root formation, so that shoots must be harvested and then treated as cuttings to be rooted separately. Two methods may be adopted:

- shoots may be rooted *in vitro* during a separate rooting stage, and then transferred to the exterior environment;
- shoots can be moved out of culture and rooted as small conventional cuttings.

Although in the early days of micropropagation, *in vitro* rooting was practically the only method used for obtaining plantlets, *ex vitro* rooting is now used in commercial laboratories wherever possible, because it eliminates a cultural stage and reduces the overall cost of micropropagation. *In vitro* rooting is, however, still commonly utilised and sometimes it is the only practical method of rooting plants (Alderson *et al.*, 1988). It also offers the greatest degree of control over the rooting process.

Certain plants, especially some herbaceous species, root more readily and survive better and/or have a higher growth rate and produce more axillary shoots if they have been rooted in vitro, rather than directly rooted extra vitrum. This was the case with Kalanchoë blossfeldiana (even though shoots of this plant are easy to root) (Tymoszuk and Hempel, 1987) and many species of *Lycopersicon* (Turner *et al.*, 1987). *In vitro* rooting was essential for *Stevia rebaudiana*, the shoots of which are very sensitive to drought (Ferreira and Handro, 1988a). In such instances, the extra cost of an *in vitro* rooting stage may be justified if it results in plantlets of better final quality, or if losses during the acclimatization stage can be reduced.

Disadvantages of *in vitro* rooting

A major disadvantage of *in vitro* rooting is the difficulty of inducing a root system which will be fully effective when the plants are transferred to soil. As explained later in this chapter, roots produced *in vitro* frequently lack root hairs and vascular connections, and may not begin to develop a secondary cambium until removed from the culture vessel. Debergh and Maene (1981) found that when plants were examined about two weeks after planting out, roots produced in culture had, in most cases, died and new ones had started to develop. Roots which grow *in vitro* are also likely to be damaged as plantlets are removed from culture (particularly if they need to be washed to remove agar), or as they are planted out, and this increases the chances of infection with fungal or bacterial diseases.

Quality requirements

Although the direct formation of roots from small isolated explants is rare (Part 1, page 28), it commonly occurs on the stems of large shoots, particularly if they are wounded, or severed from the plant. On small pieces of severed stem used as cuttings, root formation occurs at the base, where it is desirable, wherever possible, to induce direct adventitious root formation. If shoots produce a basal callus from which roots develop later, vascular connections between shoot and root are liable to be incomplete. Although functional connections may eventually be formed, establishment of an autonomous plantlet will be delayed and the chances of successful transfer reduced. Indirectly formed roots are often incapable of supporting a shoot: the roots and the whole plant may die, or new roots may need to grow before the plantlet can sustain itself. In only a few papers (*e.g.* for *Eucalyptus* — de Fossard *et al.*, 1978), has the prior growth of callus been described as essential to *in vitro* rooting.

If callus is produced on shoot bases in response to auxin treatment it is advisable to experiment with the use of a different regulant or an alternative support system. Callus formed on *Ephedra* shoots placed on an agar–solidified medium containing either IAA, NAA or IBA, but was reduced to a minimum by supporting the shoots on Sorbarods wetted with liquid medium containing IAA. The other two auxins were still prone to induce callus formation on these supports (O'Dowd and Richardson, 1993).

In spite of the comments in the preceding paragraphs, it is rare to find root formation on cuttings without the appearance of some associated callus. The trick in obtaining well rooted plants is to keep callus growth to a minimum.

Types of roots. Roots formed *in vitro* can be of different kinds, depending on the treatment under which they were produced. Certain auxins cause the production of a few unbranched roots, while others cause fine, highly branched roots to be produced. Not all kinds of roots are of equal value for ensuring plant survival. Those produced in the presence of high levels of auxin have an abnormal morphology and function (see page 675). On microcuttings of *Penstemon serrulatus*, adding IBA or IAA to the medium caused long, thin roots to be formed. Short fat roots were promoted by NAA which also induced the formation of secondary roots. The highest percentage of rooted plantlets with an average of 4.4 roots each, resulted from using 4.4 µM IBA (Wysokinska, 1993)

In *Asparagus* it is necessary to obtain the production of a single tap root on plantlets, because plants so possessed develop a crown, and are the only ones to survive *ex vitro*. *Asparagus* shoots on which several unbranched roots are slowly formed, die during acclimatization (Javouhey and Marionnet, 1990).

For satisfactory growth in the field, rubber trees should ideally possess a tap root (Chapter 17). Unlike rubber trees on seedling rootstocks, those derived from conventional cuttings tend to have a spreading root system, and micropropagated trees are liable to have similar characteristics (Sobhana *et al.*, 1986).

Roots formed *in vitro* often have a different appearance to those formed on microcuttings in the external environment: for example, Rogers and Smith (1992) found that roots of *Rosa chinensis* formed *in vitro* were short, brittle, dark and unbranched, while those formed *ex vitro* were thinner than the *in vitro* roots, long, white, flexible and branched, and possessed root hairs. McClelland *et al.* (1990) noticed that plants of *Acer, Betula* and *Malus* rooted *in vitro*, developed roots which tended to grow horizontally, and so could be distinguished from plants which had been rooted *ex vitro* even during later stages of production.

Secondary thickening. Some researchers have said that roots formed *in vitro* do not become sufficiently developed to support the growth of woody plants with the result that at the acclimatization stage, a high proportion of plantlets may die, or the growth of plantlets may suffer a setback.

McClelland *et al.* (1990) found that a vascular cambium was not produced in adventitious roots formed *in vitro* on shoots of *Acer, Betula* and *Malus*. The roots were therefore unlike those produced on shoots *ex vitro*, in which secondary growth occurred at an early stage. When shoots rooted *in vitro* were transplanted *extra vitrum*, many roots died immediately, and others persisted during acclimatization without further growth. Further papers from the University of Illinois (Rogers and Smith, 1992; Smith *et al.*, 1992) have extended these findings to other woody plants. The authors of the latter paper concluded that any advantage of *in vitro* rooting is negated in woody plants because of the arrested growth of secondary xylem and that roots developed on an agar–solidified medium do not begin to form a secondary cambium until they have been moved out of the culture vessel. *Ex vitro* rooting was therefore thought to be the preferred method for woody plants, in which secondary thickening is important, but not so essential for herbaceous species and monocotyledons where root secondary thickening does not take place.

By contrast, some other researchers have found that microcuttings of woody plants rooted *in vitro* have required a shorter period of acclimatization and have produced plantlets of a better quality than cuttings of the same kind rooted *extra vitrum*, e.g.:—

Apple, pear   Kunneman and Albers (1992)

Leucospermum   Tal *et al.* (1992a,b)
cordifolium

Alnus oregona   Garton and Moses (1986)

Shoot quality. To root satisfactorily and continues growth when transferred from culture, shoots produced during micropropagation must themselves be of good quality and must not deteriorate appreciably during root induction and initiation. Shoot deterioration has been thought to be the cause of erratic rooting sometimes reported for *Vitis* (Chée and Pool, 1988).

Alternative techniques

The principal methods which are employed for rooting microcuttings *in vitro* and *extra vitrum* are summarized in Fig. 125, and discussed in detail on the pages which follow.

IN VITRO ROOTING

Stages in the rooting process

A few plants are suitable for rooting as shoot clusters but in most species, shoots to be rooted *in vitro* are excised singly and, after the basal leaves have been trimmed off, are planted in a suitable medium until roots have formed. Many factors influence the success of this operation, as will be shown below. Some are very simple, such as observing that rooting only takes place effectively when explants have reached a minimum size; others are more complex.

It is generally found that four phases can be distinguished in the rooting process (Moncousin, 1986):

- an *induction* phase, when the capacity for root formation is determined;

- an *initiation* phase, when visible cytological changes occur;

- an *organisation* phase, when root primordia can be seen to be produced histologically;

- a *growth* (root elongation) phase, when primordia develop into roots.

Treatments which promote one of these activities may not be optimal for those which precede or follow. The initiation phase is readily observed, but how can one determine whether root induction has taken place? Some authors have assumed that auxin induces the necessary cell determination, while others (*e.g.* Druart *et al.*, 1982) have suggested that it can be induced by a dark treatment, with auxin necessary for subsequent root initiation.

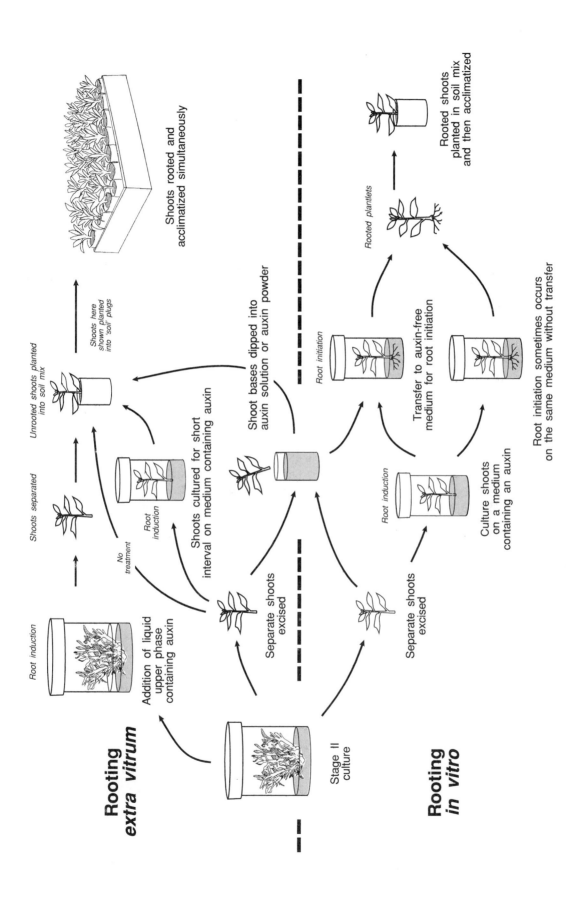

Fig. 125. The principal methods for rooting shoots derived from shoot tip cultures.
Many subsidiary factors, by which rooting may be enhanced, have been omitted for simplicity (see text).

Growth regulators

Rooting without regulants. Generally treatment with a growth regulator considerably speeds the process of rooting and causes cuttings to produce more roots than they otherwise would. However, in some species it is simply necessary to transfer shoots or shoot clusters to a hormone–free medium and roots will form.

Axillary buds of *Acacia aldiba* all produced rooted plantlets on a dilute medium without growth regulators (Duhoux and Davies, 1985), and Horn *et al.* (1988b) found that some varieties of rose similarly rooted satisfactorily with no auxin treatment. Microcuttings of *Brassica oleracea* Capitata group rooted readily on a growth regulator–free medium (Lillo and Shahin, 1986). IBA did not assist the rooting of *Elaeagnus angustifolia* shoots: only 37.5% rooted in its presence, whereas 95% of shoots rooted on a medium devoid of regulants (Economou and Spanoudaki (1988).

The origin of a shoot, and the growth regulators used during its production, influence the requirement for auxin. This can be illustrated from experiments of Ferreira and Handro (1988a,b): shoots of *Stevia rebaudiana* regenerated directly from leaves in the presence of 2 mg/l BAP, required to be placed on a medium containing 0.1 mg/l IBA for root induction; shoots which arose from leaf–derived callus, formed callus and roots at their basal ends without auxin treatment.

> Callus was induced on leaf discs by placing them on a medium containing 0.5 mg/l 2,4–D + 0.5 mg/l BAP + 1 mg/l GA$_3$. Shoot formation occurred when the callus was moved to the same medium to which 0.02 mg/l NAA and 2 mg/l kinetin had been added.

The effect of cytokinins

Inhibitory action. Root formation is generally inhibited by the high concentration of cytokinins used to induce shoot multiplication or shoot formation at Stage II. Therefore, in most cases, shoots must be transferred to a different Stage III environment for root formation to occur. For *in vitro* rooting this means placing shoots or shoot clusters onto a medium lacking cytokinin, that is to say, on a regulant–free medium (see above), or on one containing auxin alone.

Plants which can be micropropagated without cytokinin often root into the Stage II medium. Examples are node cultures of chrysanthemum and potato (Levy, 1985) and shoot cultures of several insectivorous plants (Woodward *et al.*, 1991). The shoots of some species may also root spontaneously when they are moved to a Stage IIIa elongation medium lacking cytokinin, or when the cytokinin in the Stage II medium becomes depleted. This may occur in shoot cultures towards the end of the normal Stage II sequence, or when Stage II cultures have been left longer than usual before harvesting and subculture.

Cytokinin carry–over. Occasionally sufficient cytokinin may be carried over from Stage II to inhibit rooting at Stage IIIb. Shoots of *Alberta magna* rooted in three weeks on a medium containing NAA providing there had been no cytokinin in the medium used during the previous subculture. If 1 mg/l BAP had been included, 8 weeks culture on the root–inducing medium was required before rooting commenced (Ben–Jaacov *et al.*, 1991). The number of microcuttings of *Gerbera jamesonii* which produced roots was significantly smaller if 20 mg/l BAP[†] had been included in the proliferation medium, than if 1.25 mg/l had been used: there was however no difference in the length of the roots which were formed after either treatment (Hempel *et al.*, 1985). Shoots of *Vitis rotundifolia* which had previously been cultured with 5 μM BAP rooted significantly better than those which had been in contact with 10 μM of this cytokinin (Lee and Wetzstein, 1990).

Steps may therefore need to be taken, in advance of the rooting stage, to reduce the level of cytokinins in shoots. The cytokinin in *Gerbera* and *Rosa* cultures may need to be reduced during the 1–2 subcultures which precede Stage IIIb (Stimart, 1986). *Lavandula angustifolia* (= *L. spica*) shoot clusters were subcultured from **LS** medium containing 0.3 mg/l BAP or kinetin, to the same medium with 0.1 mg/l cytokinin one month before rooting (Oliphant, 1988) and *Kalanchoë blossfeldiana* shoot cultures were given one passage without BAP (formerly 2 mg/l) before rooting (Tymoszuk and Hempel, 1987). Improved rooting of several *Albizia* species was obtained by transferring shoot clumps from **Gamborg *et al.* (1968) B5** medium containing BAP, to the same medium with 0.18 mg/l IAA. After 30 days incubation, single shoots were excised and planted on IAA again for root initiation (Tomar and Gupta, 1986).

Syringa vulgaris shoots, propagated by single node culture with 0.8 mg/l 2–iP in the medium, root more readily than those multiplied by shoot culture (requiring 5 mg/l BAP plus 0.1 mg/l IAA). Waldenmaier and Bünemann (1991) therefore proposed that in a micropropagation programme, shoot culture should be followed by one cycle of single node culture before shoots are to be rooted.

---

†   Prolonged culture with 20 mg/l BAP would lead to hyperhydricity and loss of the stock.

Rooting of some plants has been reported to be difficult if thidiazuron has been used to promote Stage II shoot proliferation (Meyer and Kerns, 1986; Gray and Benton, 1991).

Positive effects. In many plants, a small amount of cytokinin can be present at Stage III without preventing rooting, and may have beneficial effects. Martinelli (1985) found it advantageous to add 0.003 mg/l kinetin to the rooting medium (containing 1 mg/l IBA) for *Prunus* rootstocks, finding that at this concentration the cytokinin did not inhibit rooting, but helped to prevent yellowing of the shoot tips. Shoots of the leguminous tree *Dalbergia sissoo* could be rooted on a medium containing 0.5 mg/l IAA and 1 mg/l kinetin (Datta *et al.*, 1983), and other legumes, *Lupinus luteus* and *Sesbania aculeata*, respectively rooted best on medium supplemented with 0.5 µM NAA and 0.05 µM 2–iP (Daza and Chamber, 1993), and 2.5 µM IBA and 0.4–2.2 µM BAP (Bansal and Pandey, 1993).

Cytokinins used to induce shoot proliferation of shoot cultures impede the growth of cryptic bacteria, which may only become virulent once plant material is moved to a rooting medium (Part 1 page 441).

Stimulation of rooting. In just a few plants rooting has been reported to be positively *induced* by cytokinin treatment. Mehra–Palta *et al.* (1978) reported that root induction on loblolly pine shoots required both 0.1 mg/l NAA and 0.1 mg/l BAP. Abdullah *et al.* (1989) increased the proportion of *Pinus brutia* shoots which rooted *in vitro* by adding 0.05 mg/l BAP to NAA, or NAA plus IBA, treatments. Higher concentrations of BAP had a negative effect. Valles and Boxus (1987a) found that most cultivars of *Rosa hybrida* could be rooted with 3 mg/l IBA in the rooting medium, but cv. 'White Dream' needed 1 mg/l IBA +1 mg/l BAP for the induction and growth of roots.

In lowbush blueberry the percentage of shoots (arising from shoot tip culture) which rooted *extra vitrum* without auxin, was positively correlated with the concentration of 2–iP added to the medium at Stage II (Frett and Smagula, 1981b), suggesting that rooting was stimulated by the presence of of residual cytokinin.

There are also examples of rooting being induced by cytokinins alone: thus Nemeth (1979) could root shoots of *Prunus* and *Cydonia* by culturing them with BAP and no auxin (other cytokinins were ineffective), and Williams *et al.* (1985) rooted *Eremophila lanii* on **MS** medium with 1 µM kinetin and 1 µM BAP. *In vitro* root formation on *Hosta sieboldiana* shoots was significantly enhanced by adding 80 mg/l adenine sulphate to otherwise growth regulant free ½**MS** medium (Hill *et al.*, 1989). Shoots of sugar beet can be rooted without auxin on **MS** medium containing 0.5 mg/l kinetin (Konwar and Coutts, 1990).

The stimulative effect of cytokinin on root formation may be temperature dependent: Fanizza *et al.* (1988) found that shoot tips of *Vitis vinifera* formed roots on **LS** medium containing 0.4–0.8 mg/l BAP when cultures were maintained at 32°C, and noted that callus of this plant also formed roots when cultured with these concentrations of cytokinin at 32–35°C.

Auxin treatments

In the vast majority of species, the formation of adventitious roots on isolated shoots is promoted by auxin but in a few plants (*e.g.* those mentioned above and *Anthurium scherzerianum* — Geier, 1986: *Euphorbia fulgens* — Zhang *et al.*, 1987), exogenous auxins seem to have little effect.

The number of roots formed on each shoot often increases in proportion to the concentration of auxin applied, but when the concentration becomes supra–optimal, callus formation is promoted, and roots have an abnormal appearance and their average length, and subsequent shoot growth may be decreased. The addition of high levels of IBA to the rooting medium sometimes causes shoot tip necrosis. An optimal intermediate level of auxin must therefore be selected for rooting microcuttings: the most appropriate compound and concentration is very genotype–dependent.

The proportion of *Acer* shoots which rooted *in vitro* was greater as IBA was increased from 0.1 to 7.4 µM, but at the higher concentrations roots were often abnormally thick, fleshy and fused, and their ability to survive when the plantlets were acclimatized was reduced (McClelland *et al.*, 1990). Similarly an average of 2.9 roots per shoot of *Eugenia smithii* were formed *in vitro* when 1 mg/l NAA was included in ¼ or ⅕**MS** medium, but the roots were short and fleshy. Although the number of roots was slightly less when NAA was reduced to 0.5 mg/l, root quality was improved (Toussaint *et al.*, 1992).

Root induction. The presence of auxin seems to be especially necessary for the *induction* of rooting (Haissig, 1986), which is thought to occur within a few hours of auxin application (Collett, 1988). In those plants and those situations where exogenous auxin is unnecessary, endogenous auxin levels are presumably adequate. The wounding caused during the preparation of a cutting, causes the concentration of phenolic compounds (which probably act as auxin protectors) to increase. Perhaps in consequence, free IAA levels also increase at the base of the shoot at this time (Moncousin, 1991b).

Peroxidase activity, which is low in tissues prior to rooting, increases sharply as root initiation commences (Chandra *et al.*, 1971; Quoirin *et al.*, 1974; Van Hoof and Gaspar, 1976; Thorpe *et al.*, 1978; Ranjit *et al.*, 1988b) and rooting is promoted by treatments which cause there to be a high capability for the oxidation of endogenous IAA at, or just before this time, and a relatively lower capability immediately thereafter (Moncousin and Gaspar, 1983; Haissig, 1986). Free IAA in the rooting zone decreases at this time.

Root initiation. Where exogenous auxin is required, the levels used for induction often need to be decreased for root initiation and elongation.

Methods of auxin treatment

Where shoots are to be rooted *in vitro*, exogenous auxins can be applied in two ways. Shoot can be:

- cultured for a prolonged period on a medium containing auxin;

- treated with an auxin for a short period prior to culture on an auxin–free medium.

Auxin concentrations for pre–treatments need to be higher than when auxin is included in the medium. Lane and McDougald (1982) termed the exposure of shoots to a large amount of auxin for a brief period, an *acute* application, and the presence of a lower level for a prolonged period, a *chronic* application. Application of a growth regulator for just a short while is also termed, by some workers, a single *pulse treatment*.

Prolonged (chronic) auxin applications

Shoots can often be rooted satisfactorily on a medium into which auxin has been incorporated in sufficient quantity for the concentration within explanted shoots to become adequate for root induction. Presumably endogenous levels afterwards decline sufficiently during the culture period through metabolism and conjugation to permit root initiation and growth.

Choosing the correct concentration. Note that the auxin treatment which produces the highest number of roots per shoot may not necessarily be the most appropriate. This is because plantlet growth *extra vitrum* can be affected. In *Blandfordia grandiflora*, the greatest number of roots per shoot was produced by culture on a basal medium containing 8 μM IBA or 32 μM IAA (*ca.* 7.5 and *ca.* 6 roots per shoot respectively), but the highest proportion of surviving plantlets resulted from using only 2 μM IBA or 0.5 μM IAA (which gave only *ca.* 5.6 or 4.1 roots per shoot respectively) (Johnson and Burchett, 1991).

Genotypic effects. The auxins most frequently incorporated into media to induce rooting are IAA (0.1–10 mg/l), NAA (0.05–1 mg/l) or IBA (0.5–3 mg/l). These compounds can sometimes be treated as alternatives, but often root formation is much better with one auxin than another. NAA, for instance, was superior to IAA or IBA for the rooting of olive shoots (Rugini and Fontanazza, 1981), better than IBA for *Prunus avium* (Snir, 1982a), better than IAA for *Beta vulgaris* (Owens and Eberts (1992), and better than all other auxins for *Duboisia myoporoides* (Kukreja and Mathur, 1985). However, IBA is the preferred auxin treatment for many plants; it was, for example, superior to NAA for rooting *Carica papaya* (Drew, 1987), *Castanea sativa* (Vieitez and Vieitez, 1983), and *Gypsophila paniculata* (Kusey *et al.*, 1980). IAA produced better rooting than IBA or NAA in *Prunus cerasifera* (Hammerschlag, 1982b) and *Pyrus communis* (Baviera *et al.*, 1989). NAA or NOA caused apple microcuttings to produce basal callus: for this reason only IAA or IBA could be used.

Selection of the most appropriate auxin depends not only on its ability to induce rooting, but also on the quality of the roots it produces, and whether it tends to induce callus on the stem (an adverse feature). NAA (0.5 mg/l), or NAA plus IBA (0.5–1 mg of each compound) gave rise to swollen roots and stem callusing on *Prunus tenella* shoots while IBA (0.5 mg/l) produced normal thin roots and little callus (Alderson *et al.*, 1987).

Auxin uptake and metabolism. Genotypic differences in the capacity of compounds to induce root formation may be caused by the comparative ability of tissues to take up and/or metabolise synthetic auxins. James (1983b) found marked differences in the ease with which shoots of two apple rootstocks would form roots *in vitro* in response to IAA, and suggested that this might reflect the rate at which the auxin was metabolised by the two different genotypes. Shoots of the pear cultivar 'Conference', produce roots readily in the presence of IBA, whereas 'Doyenné d'Hiver' is difficult to root. Baraldi *et al.* (1993) were able to show that 'Conference' shoots took up more IBA than 'Doyenné d'Hiver' and had an ability to convert some of this auxin into IAA during root induction, whereas 'Doyenné d'Hiver' did not possess this capacity.

There are reports of 2,4–D being used for root induction, but they are rare, and in most plants the compound is ineffective in inducing root formation, or is toxic. Possibly this is related to the rate and method of metabolism of the compound in most tissues. Unlike NAA and IBA, 2,4–D did not induce any root formation on shoots of *Anigozanthos fulginosa*, and even at concentrations less than 10 μM, the compound inhibited rooting of *Malus* × *domestica* 'Granny Smith', causing both shoots and medium to discolour within a few days (Sriskandarajah and Mullins, 1981). Three examples of the successful use of 2,4–D which we have noted are:

Plant	Source of shoots	2,4–D (mg/l)	Reference
Birch	Callus	0.1	Huhtinen (1976)
Salpiglossis	Shoot cultures	0.1–1.0 (better than NAA)	Boyes and Sink (1981a)
Leptospermum flavescens	Shoot cultures	1.1	Shipton and Jackes (1986)

2,4–D is especially liable to induce callus formation at the base of cuttings (Lazarz *et al.*, 1982); in other cases the compound inhibits rooting (*e.g.* in apple — Sriskandarajah and Mullins, 1981).

Plants requiring high levels of auxins. Bouza *et al.* (1992) found that root induction in *Paeonia suffruticosa* 'Madame de Vatry' required shoots to be exposed to a high level of auxin. Unfortunately, this treatment harmed terminal buds, and rooted plantlets did not grow properly *ex vitro*. To solve the problem, after shoots had been incubated for 10 days on **MS** medium containing 75 μM (15.2 mg/l) IBA, they were placed on growth regulant–free medium containing 0.3% activated charcoal to promote root growth. Rooted plantlets were then stored at 4°C for two months before being transferred to pots.

Another approach to such a problem might be to use a mixture of auxins.

Mixtures of auxins. Adventitious root formation in some plants has been found to be more effectively induced by a mixture of auxins than by a single compound. Some reports of such usage are given in Table 102.

Shoots of *Bougainvillea* proved difficult to root *in vitro*. Chaturvedi *et al.* (1978) at first grew some on an NAA medium and then transferred them to a medium containing 2,4,5–T. Although this treatment resulted in 60% rooting, formation was preceded by undesirable callusing. A higher proportion of rooted shoots has been obtained by placing shoots onto a medium containing both 0.1 mg/l IBA and 0.1 mg/l 2,4,5–T. Using this treatment, there was no callus formation (Sharma *et al.*, 1981a).

A mixture of 0.001 mg/l NAA and 0.005 mg/l IBA resulted in significantly better rooting of *Vitis labrusca* microcuttings than NAA (0–0.01 mg/l) or IBA (0–0.05 mg/l) alone. In combination the two auxins had an additive effect (Lewandowski, 1991).

Short (acute) auxin treatments

Roots initiated by an auxin (particularly NAA) may sometimes fail to grow until the regulant is reduced in concentration, and shoot growth may be similarly suppressed. Prolonged exposure to auxin also increases the chances of callus formation. To counteract these problems, some workers prefer to administer auxin for only a short time. Lane and McDougald (1982) found that an acute treatment was effective on 'M9' apple rootstock in which, unlike other cultivars, shoots formed callus (which prevented rooting) when NAA was presented at a low level over a long period.

There are two ways to apply acute doses of auxin:

- shoots can be cultured in a solution or on a medium containing concentrated auxin for a short period;
- shoots may be simply dipped into a concentrated auxin powder or placed briefly into a concentrated solution.

The pre–culture technique. Placing shoots on an auxin–containing medium (often one containing an abnormally high auxin concentration) for just a short interval can be an effective method of root induction. Roots develop and grow when the cuttings are moved to an auxin–free medium. It is supposed that, through this sequence, the concentration of endogenous auxin is more effectively reduced to permit root growth.

The procedure was followed, for example, by Mascarenhas and co–workers (Table 102) with several tree species, and with the plants shown in Table 103. The duration of the pre–treatment may be critical. Mridula *et al.* (1983) found that extending auxin treatment of *Sapium* from 48 to 72 hours reduced the percentage of rooted shoots from 70 to 0, but a higher proportion of *Prunus cerasus* microcuttings produced roots after 30 days when kept for 11 (rather than 8) days on **MS** medium with 1 mg/l IBA before transfer to a regulant–free medium. In the latter experiment, the highest number of roots per cutting occurred when the auxin treatment extended over the whole of the 30 day period (Marín and Gella (1987).

As an alternative to culturing shoots on an auxin–containing medium for a short period, it can be sufficient simply to place their cut ends into a solution of auxin. Apple shoots which would not form roots when 0.1–10.0 mg/l IBA, NAA or IAA were incorporated into a medium, did so if separated and immersed in an aqueous solution of 1 mg/l IBA for 15 minutes. Roots then formed on an unamended solidified or liquid medium with filter paper supports, particularly if the shoots were inverted (Abbott and Whiteley, 1976). Collett (1988) found that the best treatment for rooting cuttings from shoot cultures of *Malus* and *Cydonia*, was to dip them overnight in 0.3–3.0 μM (0.05–0.53 mg/l) IAA (depending on genotype), and then plant them on a weak medium without regulants.

Table 102. Examples of the use of auxin mixtures added to media to induce rooting.

Plant	Mixture of auxins				Length of exposure	Reference
	IAA (mg/l)	NAA (mg/l)	IBA (mg/l)	IPA (mg/l)		
Eucalyptus glubulosus	2.0	2.0	—	—	48–72 h	Mascarenhas *et al.* (1982a)
Eucalyptus tereticornis	2.0	2.0	2.0	2.0	48–72 h	Mascarenhas *et al.* (1982a)
Hevea brasiliensis	10.0	10.0	10.0	10.0	48–72 h	Mascarenhas *et al.* (1982a)
Mitragyna parvifolia	5.7	5.37	4.9	—	Continuously	Roy *et al.* (1988)
Punica granatum ex mature source	2.0	—	2.0	2.0	72 h (dark)	Mascarenhas *et al.* (1982a)
Rosa hybrida (1 cv. out of 14)	—	0.1	0.05	—	Continuously	Horn *et al.* (1988b)
Sapium sebiferum	1.0		1.0	1.0	48 h †	Mridula *et al.* (1983)
Tamarindus indica ex juvenile source	1.0	1.0	1.0	1.0	72 h	Mascarenhas *et al.* (1982a)
ex mature source	2.0	2.0	2.0	2.0	72 h †	
Tectona grandis ex juvenile source	0.1	—	0.1	0.1	48 h	Mascarenhas *et al.* (1982a)
ex mature source	2.5	—	2.5	2.0	48 h	
Vitis labrusca	—	0.001 0.01‡	0.005 0.05‡	—	Continuously (1 cm roots in 10 days)	Lewandowski (1991)

† Subsequent transfer to an auxin-free medium containing 0.25% activated charcoal was necessary.

‡ An alternative combination.

This was more effective than culturing the explants in the same medium containing 1 µM IBA, possibly because IAA is rapidly metabolized. If a relatively high rate of auxin has been used for induction, it may improve root formation if activated charcoal is added to the auxin–free medium (see below). Charcoal adsorbs excess auxin as it is leached into the medium, so that the endogenous level is gradually reduced.

Dips into concentrated solutions or powders. *In vitro* rooting can often be induced by dipping cultured shoots into a concentrated auxin solution for a short period (before placing them on an auxin–free medium). This can be a more effective and time saving way of inducing root formation than more protracted pre–treatments, especially those involving a separate cultural stage. Once again it can be necessary to discover the most effective compound.

Fiorino and Leva (1983) found that dipping the basal 5 mm of apple microcuttings for 1 hour into 2 mM IBA dissolved in 95% ethanol (and then placing the shoots on an auxin–free medium), was more effective for inducing root formation than culturing the shoots in a medium containing 15 µM IBA. Some other examples of acute treatments are given in Table 104.

Deleterious effects of auxin treatment

We have mentioned that application of auxin at a concentration which is too high can affect subsequent plant survival. A deleterious effect has also been noted even when the auxin has had no effect on rooting. This was the case with *Mahonia repens*, where 1–30 mg/l had no affect on rooting, but diminished the proportion of surviving plants with increasing concentrations (Garton and Moses, 1986). An IBA dip decreased the survival of *Vitis* (Faulks and Mudge, 1988). Treating *Rosa hybrida* cv. 'Alexander' with a mixture of NAA and IBA resulted in a lower rate of establishment: in two other cultivars, 0.1 mg/l NAA with 0.05–0.1 IAA had the same effect (Horn W. *et al.*, 1988b).

Table 103. Examples of plants in which a short pulse of auxin was successful in inducing root formation on cuttings.

Plant	Pre-treatment			Transfer medium	References
	Auxin (mg/l)	Medium	Duration (days)		
Castanea	75 IBA	½WPM, 4% sucrose	5	Same medium, no PGRs	Serres (1988)
Coffea arabica	2.0 IBA	B5 with mod. organics	10	Same medium, solid or paper bridge, no PGRs	Sondahl *et al.* (1985)
Olea europaea	4 NAA	**Ben-Jaacov and Dax (1981)**	7	**Ben-Jaacov and Dax (1981)**	Rugini and Fontanazza (1981)
Malus × domestica	1–5 BA or 5 IAA	MS	4–6	½MS	James & Thurbon (1979)
	1 IBA	½MS	6–8	½MS + 0.25% AC	Snir & Erez (1980)
Prunus amygdalus	1 NAA	½**Bougin & Nitsch (1967) H** macros (rest as **H** medium)	4 (in dark)	Same medium on vermiculite	Rugini and Verma (1983)
Persea americana	25 IBA	⅓MS salts, LS vits.	3	Same medium + 1% AC	Pliego-Alfaro (1988)
Sapium sebiferum	1 mg/l of each of IAA, IBA & IPA	**White (1963)** + 0.25 mg/l each of Na_2SO_4, $CoCl_2.6H_2O$	2 (in dark)	MS + 0.25% AC	Mridula *et al.* (1983)

Other substances affecting rooting

Auxin synergists

Several unusual chemicals (*e.g.* sub–lethal doses of sul-phuric acid or magnesium chloride) have been noted to promote rooting (Soekarjo, 1966), while other com-pounds act synergistically with auxins (Gorter, 1962). Such treatments may make cells more sensitive to auxin (Gorter, 1969) or may protect natural auxins from rapid metabolism (Chapter 11).

Various phenolic compounds (including phloroglucinol and phloridzin) are sometimes found to promote rooting (see Part 1, page 429 *et seq.*) and there is a considerable literature on their possible roles in stimulating IAA syn-thesis, liberating bound auxin, modulating IAA oxidase and forming IAA–conjugates (see papers and reviews by Haissig, 1986; Jarvis, 1986; Mato and Vieitez, 1986; Gaspar and Coumans, 1987; Moncousin, 1988).

Recent experiments have shown that phloroglucinol only seems to promote the rooting of apple shoots taken from early subcultures *i.e.* its effect is related to the degree of rejuvenation of the shoots (Webster and Jones, 1989).

Gibberellic acid

As explained in Chapter 11, gibberellic acid (GA_3) is usually observed to inhibit rooting. However there are reports of the compound having had the opposite effect (Nanda *et al.*, 1972; Hansen, 1976, 1978; Coleman and Greyson, 1977a,b). Nanda *et al.* (1967) found that GA_3 stimulated root formation on *Kalanchoë* cuttings under short day conditions, but (unlike auxin) it failed to in-duce rooting in long days. Gibberellic acid (30 µM) and IAA (30 µM) had an additive effect on promoting the number of roots formed on *Pisum sativum* epicotyl cut-tings, and synergistically enhanced the rate at which roots appeared (Adhikari and Bajracharya, 1978). Bhat-taracharya *et al.* (1978) also reported synergy between these compounds in the rooting of *Abelmoschus esculen-tus* shoots.

Low concentrations of GA_3, applied during a previous cultural stage, may improve subsequent root formation, providing the compound is not also present in the rooting medium (Leroux, 1968). However, exogenous GA_3 ap-plied during Stage II, is frequently carried–over in the tissues to Stage III where it inhibits later root formation (de Fossard and de Fossard, 1988b).

Shoot growth and eventual rooting of the cherry rootstock '46–1 Mazzard' on a gibberellin–free medium, was increased during 6 consecutive subcultures when it was co–cultured with the variety 'Colt' (which is easy to root). Ranjit and Kester (1988) thought that this resulted from the exudation by 'Colt' of gibberellin into the medium, because similar results could be obtained by culturing '46–1' Mazzard' shoots with 0.1–0.25 mg/l GA₃. Rooting was inhibited if the level of exogenous GA₃ was increased to 0.5–1 mg/l or above .

Antigibberellins. The normal inhibitory effect of gibberellins on rooting is emphasized by the root promoting activity of 'antigibberellin' growth retardants, on some plants. Davis *et al.* (1985, 1986) found that cuttings gathered *in vivo* from plants of *Coleus, Phaseolus, Plectranthus, Prunus laurocerasus, Salix discolor* and *Vitis labrusca* rooted more readily after being soaked for 24–72 h in 3–25 mg/l paclobutrazol. Shoot growth was initially inhibited, but usually returned to normal 2–3 months after the cuttings had been planted in soil.

Root formation on explants *in vitro*, or the rooting *extra vitrum* of microcuttings, can also be promoted by 'anti–gibberellins', and the effect is additional to that produced by auxin. *Rubus* (blackberry) shoots dipped into 10 mg/l paclobutrazol subsequently produced greater numbers of roots *in vitro*, while *Euonymus kiautschovica* cuttings dipped into 50 or 200 mg/l paclobutrazol solutions, produced more roots than the controls when placed in mist sprays (El–Sherbini *et al.*, 1988). Rooting of asparagus was enhanced by the inclusion of 5 µM ancymidol and 7% sucrose in the medium (Desjardins *et al.*, 1987a). Triadimefon (0.34 µM) promoted adventitious root formation on *Phaseolus* hypocotyls (Fletcher *et al.*, 1988).

Unusual regulants

Chapter 11 describes several unusual regulants, but few are reported to be used routinely for root induction on micropropagated plants.

Polyamines. Exogenous applications of polyamines tend to mimic some of the effects of auxins and it is thought that polyamine synthesis precedes adventitious root formation (Tiburcio *et al.*, 1989).

Polyamines have a stimulative effect on rooting (see Part 1, page 466) but, being generally less effective promoters than synthetic auxins, are not commonly used in practical micropropagation. There are a few indications of their value as additives to media which have been mentioned

Table 104. Examples of the use of acute auxin treatments to induce *in vitro* rooting.

Plant	Pre-treatment	Reference
Castanea mollissima	1 sec dip in 9.8–14.8µM IBA in 70% ethanol	Yang *et al.* (1986)
Daphne × *burkwoodii* D. odora	Short dip into 100 mg/l NAA in 50% ethanol, or transfer to agar medium containing 200 mg/l NAA for 1–2 hours	Cohen & Le Gal (1976) Cohen (1977)
Dicentra spectabilis	20 seconds in 1500–2000 mg/l filter-sterilised IBA solution	Lazarz and Sink (1980) Lazarz *et al* (1982
Diospyros kaki	250 mg/l IBA in 50% ethanol, 30 sec	Sugiura *et al.* (1986)
Gypsophila paniculata	50 seconds in 25 mg/l NAA in 20% ethanol	Kusey *et al.* (1980)
Lonicera periclymenum	1 second dip into 2 mg/l IBA	Boonnour *et al.* (1988)
Malus × *domestica* 'M9'	100–300 mg/l NAA in 50% ethanol, 2 min†	Lane and McDougald (1982)
Petunia hybrida	Dip into 50 mg/l aqueous NAA	Economou and Read (1981)
Prunus cerasus	18 hours in 50 mg/l IBA solution	Popov *et al.* (1976)
Telopea speciosissima	Few seconds in 500–1000 mg/l IBA	Seelye (1985)

† allowed to dry before shoots were placed on a solid medium.

in Chapter 11. Putrescine was found to increase the proportion of olive cuttings which formed roots if it was added to an IBA–containing talc in which the base of the cuttings was dipped (Rugini *et al.*, 1990). Roots could be induced on shoots of *Juglans* hybrids, by adding 10 mg/l serotonine (an aromatic polyamine) in conjunction with 1 mg/l juglone (a naphthaquinone). Used alone, neither compound was effective (Jay–Allemand *et al.*, 1993).

The application of auxins to cuttings has been found to enhance polyamine synthesis during the formation of root primordia and again during root growth (Friedman *et al.*, 1985).

Coumarin. Coumarin stimulated root formation on plumules of *Pinus sylvestris* when used alone at 10 μM or if succeeded by an IAA treatment (Bornman and Janson, 1980). The improvement in rooting brought about by the combination of 68 μM (10 mg/l) coumarin and 6 or 10 μ IAA, in a medium gelled with Gelrite, was sufficient for the compound to be used on a routine basis for *Bambusa tulda*. Not only was a high proportion of shoots induced to form roots when coumarin was added to the medium, but also, roots showed markedly improved growth (Saxena, 1990).

Vessel capacity

De Fossard and de Fossard (1988b) reported an effect of vessel size on the rooting of *Verticodia* and many other species in their laboratory. The proportion of rooted shoots and the growth of shoots during the rooting process, were consistently improved by placing shoots into vessels of 250 ml capacity, rather than into 39 ml tubes. Very similar results were obtained by McClelland and Smith (1990) who found that microcuttings of several woody plants produced more roots *in vitro* if they were cultured in 200 or 300 ml vessels, rather than in 60 ml tubes. The proportion of *Camellia reticulata* shoots which rooted was much higher if multiplication had been carried out in 500 ml jars rather than in closed test tubes (San–Jose *et al.*, 1991). In larger vessels the intra–vessel concentration of ethylene might be less, or the concentration of oxygen or other gases in the vessel, greater.

Effects of ethylene on root formation have been mentioned in Chapter 11. Since those paragraphs were prepared we have noticed that Dimasi–Theriou *et al.* (1993) have found that the addition of at least 10 p.p.m. ethylene to culture vessels considerably promoted the rooting of *Petunia hybrida* shoots. Lower concentrations (0.01–1 p.p.m.) had no effect.

Root elongation seems to be promoted by endogenous ethylene, because it has been shown to be inhibited by AVG (Part 1, page 455) (Chi *et al.*, 1990).

Media effects

Macronutrients

Ionic concentration. Satisfactory rooting can take place on full strength culture media but it is a very common practice to transfer shoots to be rooted from high strength media (such as **MS**) to less concentrated solutions, or to a dilution of the same medium used at Stage II (or Stage IIIa). There is then also less likelihood of plantlets becoming hyperhydric. In a random sample of 54 papers describing *in vitro* rooting, we found that full strength **MS** macronutrients were used at Stage IIIb in only 44% of cases, whereas they had been used in 91% of the preceding Stage II cultures. Just occasionally high salt media have been reported to be more promotive to rooting than less concentrated formulations: **MS** medium was better than ½**MS** for *Trifolium* (Singha *et al.*, 1988).

Dilute media formulations commonly used for root initiation are ⅕ to ½ **MS**, media based on **Knop's** macronutrients, or **White (1954)** medium. The total molarity of macronutrient ions (ΣI_m) (see Part 1, page 329 and Table 49, page 398) in these media is:

⅕**MS**	19.2 mM
½**MS**	47.9 mM
Knop (1865)	27.0mM
White (1954)	17.7 mM

Rooting in the complete absence of minerals proved to be the best stratagem for *Leucospermum obtectus*. With this plant, although Bunn *et al.* (1989) obtained satisfactory rooting on ¼**MS** medium, there was a tendency for basal callus to be formed, and no rooted shoots survived upon transfer to soil. Shoots rooted in water agar containing auxin did not produce callus, and most survived when transferred *extra vitrum*.

Nitrogen content of the medium. In most plants, the favourable effect of reduced macronutrient concentration on *in vitro* rooting may be less due to total ionic concentration than the fact that the optimum concentration of nitrogen ions for root formation is much lower than for adventitious shoot formation and growth.

Hyndman *et al.* (1982a) showed that the improved root initiation on rose shoots obtained by lowering the concentration of **MS** salts in the nutrient medium, was particularly due to the provision of a total nitrogen concentration closer to the optimum of 7.5 mM (instead of the 60 mM present in full strength **MS**). When they maintained 7.5 mM nitrogen, it was possible to reduce the remaining salts by as much as 16–fold without deleterious effects.

The optimum nitrogen concentration for rooting has been found to differ between species and even between plant cultivars. The effect is shown by comparing the above results with those of Geier (1986): shoots resulting from micropropagation of *Anthurium scherzerianum* rooted on **Bourgin and Nitsch (1967) H** medium (ΣI_m = 44.7 mM) which contains 720 mg/l ammonium nitrate,

[27.4 mM nitrogen; ratio of NO_3^- to NH_4^+, 67:33 (2.0)]

but took almost twice as long to achieve consistent rooting if the concentration of this salt was reduced to 200 mg/l:

[ΣI_m then 31.8 mM; total nitrogen concentration 14.4 mM; ratio of NO_3^- to NH_4^+, 83 : 17 (4.8)].

Apple shoots took much longer to form roots if inorganic nitrogen was omitted from **Lloyd and McCown (1981) WPM** medium (Orlikowska, 1992b).

In some plants, the presence of ammonium ions favours the growth of roots, while in others it may be inhibitory. However, even where NH_4^+ is required, its concentration should be less than that of NO_3^- and Moncousin (1982, reported in 1991a) concluded that it should only represent 15–20% of the total inorganic nitrogen provided in rooting media. Three cultivars of *Malus* × *domestica* rooted most satisfactorily *in vitro* when NH_4NO_3 (the only source of NH_4^+ ions) was omitted from a rooting medium containing ½**MS** salts (Sriskandarajah *et al.*, 1990a). However, ammonium nitrogen was shown to be necessary for normal root growth of *Carica* which rooted best on **De Fossard *et al.* (1974) MEDIUM** preparation (total nitrogen 30 mM). With only nitrate nitrogen, roots were abnormally thickened and had few laterals (Drew, 1987).

Calcium ions. Several authors have stressed the importance of Ca^{2+} for rooting. De Fossard *et al.* (1978) found that high Ca^{2+} was desirable for rooting *Eucalyptus* cuttings, and this was confirmed by McComb and Bennett (1982) who obtained better rooting of plants in this genus in ¼**MS** macronutrients than in full strength solution, providing $CaCl_2$ was kept at half the **MS** level. Grosser *et al.*, (1988) rooted *Citrus* and *Poncirus* microcuttings on ½**Murashige and Tucker (1969)** medium with full strength iron and calcium, and extra calcium helped to prevent yellowing of *Prunus* shoot tips during rooting and resulted in better acclimatization in the greenhouse (Martinelli, 1985 — see below).

By contrast, 4.5 mM Ca^{2+} (**MS** medium contains 3.0 mM) has been reported to adversely affect root induction on *Berberis thunbergii* shoots (Karhu and Hakala, 1991).

Other macronutrient ions. Tripathi (1968) discovered macronutrients to be particularly important for the organisation of Jerusalem artichoke root meristems, but that potassium (or possibly magnesium) was not essential. Rooting did not occur on Nitsch and Nitsch (1956) medium but was satisfactory on a newly–devised medium without potassium.

Moncousin (1982 reported in 1991a) found the presence of sodium or chloride ions detrimental to rhizogenesis in several plants, and according to Reinert *et al.* (1977), raising the phosphate concentration of the medium can suppress or weaken the root–promoting effect of auxin. When plants are multiplied at Stage II on media (*e.g.* **MS**) containing supplementary phosphate, the concentration of phosphate is reduced during *in vitro* rooting (Paek *et al.*, 1984).

Pre–culture on a high salts medium

Although high salt levels are usually disadvantageous to adventitious root formation, an adequate salt concentration is necessary. A very dilute medium was not favourable to the formation of roots on leaf discs of *Streptocarpus*. In the presence of 2 mg/l NAA there was a gradual increase in the number of roots (and a decrease in the number of adventitious shoots) formed on explants floated on **Schott and Schraudolf (1967)** mineral solution (ΣI_m = 11.41 mM) as the concentration was raised to four times this level (Appelgren and Heide, 1972). Martinelli (1985) found that pre-culture of micropropagated *Prunus* rootstocks in an abnormally high concentration of salts improved subsequent rooting. Shoots were elongated on a double strength **MS** medium containing an extra 1 g/l $Ca(NO_3)_2.4H_2O$ and before rooting on a more dilute agitated liquid medium, again supplemented with extra calcium nitrate.

The preculture of shoots on a medium more concentrated than that to be used for rooting, was also employed by Morini and Concetti (1985) for shoots from cultures of *Prunus* rootstocks. These had been multiplied on **Lloyd and McCown (1981) WPM** medium, but rooted much better if they were elongated on **MS** medium (no cytokinin) before being rooted on **WPM** medium. Similarly, Kataoka and Inoue (1992) reported that the composition of the Stage II medium had an effect on the rooting of *Carica* shoots *extra vitrum*. Most roots were obtained from shoots which had been multiplied on 1.5 × **MS** medium containing 3% sucrose and 1.2% agar.

Effects of pH on *in vitro* rooting have been discussed on page 300 of Part 1.

Micronutrients

As mentioned in Chapter 9, boron is important for root formation and is an essential element for the growth of excised roots in culture (Neales, 1959). It has been shown to be beneficial to *in vitro* rooting when shoots or explants have been cultured only on macro–element solutions (Hemberg, 1951; Gorter, 1965).

Boron is essential to auxin action and a supply of exogenous boric acid in the rooting medium is usually beneficial (see Chapter 9). Boron appears to be particularly required for root initiation and growth (Middleton *et al.*, 1978; Haissig, 1986) but may also be necessary for root induction in the light. Dark–grown seedlings can develop root primordia in the absence of boron, but subsequent root growth is limited (Middleton *et al.*, 1978). Less boron is required for root formation when cuttings are kept in low light, or short days (Warrington, 1933; MacVicar and Struckmeyer, 1946). However there is evidence that high concentrations of the element can militate against root formation. In *Berberis thunbergii* adventitious root induction on shoots was inhibited in the dark by 0.15 mM H_3BO_3 (**MS** medium contains 0.1 mM) and in the light by 0.2 mM (Karhu and Hakala, 1991).

Vitamins

Vitamins are generally thought to be inessential additives to media in which shoots are to be rooted. Full strength **MS** or **Staba** vitamins (Part 1, page 414) have been noted to inhibit root formation of *Peperomia* and *Prunus* respectively (Berry, 1978; Skirvin *et al.*, 1981b). In both cases the percentage of shoots forming roots was increased (20% *vs.* 70% for *Prunus*) when low vitamin levels were used.

However, there may be exceptions to this generalisation. Although when there was no sugar in the medium, a mixture of vitamins (mg/l), *viz*:

> 0.5 nicotinic acid; 0.5 pyridoxine HCl; 0.5 Ca pantothenate; 0.5 thiamine HCl; 0.005 biotin; 10 adenine; 50 *myo*–inositol [this is ½**Morel and Wetmore (1951b)** vitamin mixture]

decreased the proportion of *Camellia* shoots which rooted in a half–strength salt mixture especially devised for this genus (Beretta and Eccher, 1987); if 30 g/l glucose was added, the vitamin mixture *increased* the rooting of var. 'Elsie Jury'. Another variety, Debbie' rooted best without vitamins (Beretta *et al.*, 1988).

Riboflavin. Riboflavin (Vit. B_2) has been found to inhibit the formation of callus at the base of shoots which occurs either with or without the addition of auxins to the medium. The absence of callus may then have either a promotive or inhibitory effect on adventitious root formation, depending on the plant species.

Miller *et al.* (1982) found that **Staba's** mixture of vitamins prevented the rooting of a peach rootstock: riboflavin was particularly responsible. Rooting of *Eucalyptus ficifolia* shoots was prevented by 10 μM (3.8 mg/l) riboflavin because it stopped IBA–induced basal callus formation which was an essential requisite for rooting (de Fossard *et al.*, 1978; Gorst *et al.*, 1982).

Riboflavin *increases* the frequency of root initiation on *Carica papaya* shoots in both light and darkness, promotes root and shoot growth and decreases the formation

of callus so that roots are more likely to be formed directly (Drew, 1987; Drew *et al.*, 1993). Drew *et al.* (1993) found that the benefit from riboflavin treatment of *Carica* shoots could be obtained by administering the compound in one of three ways:

> Shoots could be kept for 2 days on medium containing 10 μM IBA and then transferred to auxin–free medium containing 10 μM riboflavin;
>
> Shoots could be cultured for two days in darkness on medium containing 10 μM and 31 μM riboflavin, and then transferred to the light;
>
> Shoots kept in the light on an agar medium containing 10 μM IBA could then be supplied with a 300 μM solution introduced as a layer onto the surface of the medium (1 ml on 10 ml of medium).

Riboflavin was especially promotive with *Chamaecyparis obtusa* treated with greater than 5 μM IBA. This concentration of auxin normally induced callus formation but callus growth was suppressed by 2.66 μM riboflavin. In the presence of the vitamin there was also more vigorous root elongation so that roots became like tap roots; and a greater proportion of shoots formed roots at low auxin concentrations (Ishii, 1986).

The mode of action of riboflavin is not fully elucidated. Gorst *et al.* (1982) noticed that it had no effect on cultures incubated in the dark and thought that the promotion of rooting might be due to riboflavin gaining an oxidising potential in visible light. The oxidised form of the compound can sensitise the degradation of IAA and certain synthetic auxins. According to this hypothesis, the addition of riboflavin to light–grown cultures would negate the effect of added auxin. However as riboflavin can promote root initiation during both light and dark incubation, its inhibition of callus growth may be more important (Drew, 1987).

Vitamin D_2 (calciferol) and its analogue, dihydrotachysterol, were reported to stimulate the rooting of *Populus* and *Phaseolus* cuttings in combination with IBA (Buchala and Schmid, 1979), but have not featured in much subsequent experimentation.

Amino acids

Although organic components are sometimes included in rooting media, they are usually inessential. However, Novák and Juvova (1983) found that shoots of *Vitis* did not form roots on **White (1943)** minerals alone, but only on the complete medium with organic supplements.

The effect of amino acids will, of course, depend on the inorganic sources of nitrogen in the medium. Kamada and Harada (1979c) found that amino acids could either stimulate or interfere with direct root formation from internode explants of *Torenia*, depending on which other ingredients were supplied. On **MS** medium without

NH_4NO_3 and with only 20 mM KNO_3 (+ 0.1 mg/l NAA and 1 mg/l BAP), all amino acids except aspartic and glutamic acids inhibited root formation. When other organic compounds except inositol and benzyl adenine were also absent, several amino acids stimulated root formation.

Rooting of *Prunus cerasus* shoots was hastened and enhanced by adding 250–500 mg/l proline to the rooting medium containing 1 mg/l IBA. Proline had no effect in the absence of the auxin (Baraldi *et al.*, 1988). Using a *Malus* rootstock, Orlikowska (1992b) showed that adding 200 mg/l arginine to **Lloyd and McCown (1981) WPM** medium containing IBA, increased the number of roots per shoot and induced a large proportion of shoots to form roots even in low auxin concentrations.

Antioxidants. Standardi and Romani (1990) found that the percentage of apple shoots which rooted was increased by adding 1.3 mM reduced glutathione and 1.05 mM citric acid to the weak mixture of salts used for root initiation and elongation. Rooting was reduced if these compounds were introduced into the 'initiation medium' containing IBA, into which shoots had been placed previously for one week in the dark. Ascorbic acid has been found to stimulate root growth of *Allium cepa* (Part 1, page 200).

Sugars

Root formation is an energy–demanding process and carbohydrate must be provided through photosynthesis or from exogenously supplied sugars. The presence of sugar has indeed been found essential for *in vitro* rooting of many species although, as mentioned in Chapter 9 (pages 334 and 691), the optimum endogenous concentration is easily exceeded, especially when cultured shoots are capable of photosynthesis. This means that the best concentration of sugar in a rooting medium, may differ according to the environmental conditions in which shoots are, or have been, grown. In early work, Gautheret (1969) showed glucose to be more stimulative than fructose or sucrose for root formation in *Helianthus* tuber pieces (the optimum concentration being 40 g/l, the minimum 6 g/l), and Pierik showed that sugar was required for root formation on segments of *Rhododendron* stems (Pierik, 1969) or *Lunaria* petioles (Pierik, 1972).

Most species root satisfactorily with the addition of 20–30 g/l sucrose to a rooting medium: for example, *Dendranthema* (chrysanthemum) shoots propagated on **MS** medium rooted best in 20 g/l sucrose, although higher concentrations had proved optimal for shoot multiplication (Roest and Bokelmann, 1975). However, there are some examples of abnormally high sucrose levels stimulating root formation. They were essential for the rooting

of olive shoot segments cultured in Knop's solution (Scaramuzzi and de Gaetano, 1974) and 'mini-crowns' of *Asparagus* rooted best when 60 g/l sucrose was added to **MS** medium (Conner and Falloon, 1990). The best rooting of *Gentiana kurroo* (propagated on **MS** medium with 30 g/l sucrose), occurred when the concentration of sucrose was increased to 60 g/l (Sharma *et al.*, 1993).

The rooting of apple shoots was sucrose–dependent within a broad range of concentrations and was decreased only if the concentration was below 20 g/l or above 52 g/l (Lane, 1978). In avocado the proportion of rooted cutting was unaffected by sucrose in the range 0–60 g/l and the same number of roots per cutting occurred with 15–60 g/l sucrose. Only at 90 g/l did sucrose become inhibitory (Pliego–Alfaro, 1988).

The importance of a supply of sugar to the rooting process makes it preferable to root some species *in vitro* rather than *ex vitro* (Gebhardt, 1985). However rooting in the external environment can sometimes be improved if shoots are kept on a high sucrose medium for a short period before transfer. The rooting of walnut shoots *extra vitrum* was improved if the shoots had previously been placed for a short while in a medium containing a high level of sucrose. The shorter the pre–exposure to sucrose, the greater the concentration required: 52.6 g/l for 7 days was better than 40.2 g/l for 14 days (Driver and Suttle, 1987).

Sugar × nitrogen interaction. Welander (1976) discovered that, providing a high concentration of auxin (10 mg/l IAA) was present, rooting of sugar beet hypocotyls depended on a balance between the sucrose and total nitrogen in the medium. The maximum numbers of roots was produced in 16 mM nitrogen and 58.4 mM (2%) sucrose, or 5 mM nitrogen and 116.9 mM (4%) sucrose. Similar results have been obtained with cultured rose shoots by Hyndman *et al.* (1981; 1982a,b). In a medium containing ½**MS** salts, it was possible to increase the number of roots formed per shoot by progressively raising the sucrose level from 1 to 7%. Nine per cent was supra–optimal. The maximum number of roots per explant was obtained with a molar ratio of sucrose to total nitrogen (mixed nitrate and ammonium ions) above 5. High numbers of roots were produced on 87.6 mM (3%) sucrose for example, if only 7.5 mM of total nitrogen was made available in an **MS** salt formulation. From this work, it seems probable that the optimum level of sucrose (or other sugar) for root formation will vary according to the medium used. The best treatment will also undoubtedly differ from one species to another.

Sugar × auxin interaction. For rooting *Begonia* shoots, there was an interaction between sucrose and auxin concentrations. The greatest number of roots per shoot oc-

Table 105. Examples of dark treatments given to microcuttings to improve their rooting.

Plant	Dark treatment (days)	Growth regulator treatment	Subsequent treatment	Reference
Aesculus hippocastanum	10	2 mg/l IBA	Same medium in light	Radojević *et al.* (1987)
Camellia japonica	9–18	1g/l IBA dip	30 μmol m^{-2} sec^{-1}, 12h day, 25°/18°C	Samartin *et al.* (1986)
Camellia japonica	12	1 g/l IBA, 15 min dip	30 μmol m^{-2} sec^{-1}, 16h day	Vieitez *et al* (1989a)
Eucalyptus spp.	2–3	Various (dep. on sp.)	To hormone-free medium + 2.5 g/l AC	Mascarenhas *et al.* (1982)
	10–14	1 mg/l IBA	To hormone-free medium + 10 g/l AC; light 4500 lux 16h	Lubrano (1988)
	3	2 mg/l IBA	Same medium, 10–14 d at 5 μmol m^{-2} s^{-1}, 25°C	Le Roux & Van Staden (1991)
Hevea brasiliensis	2–3	10 mg/l each of IAA, IBA, IPA, NAA	To hormone-free medium + 2.5 g/l AC	Mascarenhas *et al.* (1982)
Juglans regia	7–10	2 mg/l IBA	Same medium in light	Gruselle *et al.* (1987)
Malus × *domestica* 'Supreme Red', 'Wellspur'	Multiplication medium 14 in dark	Originally 0.1 mg/l IBA +1 mg/l BAP	Moved to rooting medium with 0.1 mg/l IBA	Anderson (1982)
'McIntosh', 'Mutsu'	3–7 at 25–30°C	3 mg/l IBA in medium + sucrose	Shoots then moved to peat plugs in light	Zimmerman & Fordham (1985)
'Ougnoe', 'Chernomorskoe letneyy'	First 7 at 25°C	3–8 h dip in 100 mg/l IAA or IBA, or 1 mg/l IAA or IBA in medium	No regulants, light 3000-5000 lux	Kataeva & Butenko (1987)
'Redspur', 'Goldspur'	21	0.3 mg/l IBA in 1.5% sucrose solution	Shoots with root initials to peat plugs in light	Jones *et al.* (1985)
Paeonia lactiflora	14 at 15°C	0.1 mg/l IBA or IAA	15°C 16 h (30 μmol m^{-2} s^{-1})	Albers & Kunneman (1992)
Prunus amygdalus	4	1 mg/l NAA	Same medium in light	Rugini & Verma (1982)
Prunus dulcis 'M55', 'Tuno'	10	1.0 mg/l NAA	Same agar medium, 16 h day	Rugini *et al.* (1988)
Prunus persica nectarina cv. 'May Fair'	7 at 5°C	2.5 mg/l IAA	Same agar medium with auxin	Antonelli & Chariotti (1988)
Pseudotsuga menziesii	First 15 at 22°C	0.2 mg/l NAA + 0.2 mg/l IBA	Medium with no regulants in light	Gupta & Durzan (1987a)
Rubus idaeus	5	0.01 mg/l IBA	Medium with no regulants in light	Welander M. (1987)
Santalum acuminatum *Santalum lanceolatum*	28	1 mg/l IBA	Cultures transferred to light once roots had formed	Barlass *et al.* (1980)

is denied light by being placed into a rooting substrate composed of opaque materials.

The amount of light passing through a solidified medium is reduced by suspending finely divided charcoal, lamp-black, or graphite in it. Proskauer and Berman (1970) found that the addition of charcoal allowed rhizoids of a moss to grow in the medium and green filaments to develop on the surface. *Cymbidium* shoot tip cultures produced green roots in the light, but terrestrial roots covered with root hairs were observed to penetrate the medium when culture tubes were wrapped in opaque paper, or 2–4 g/l charcoal was dispersed in the agar (Werckmeister, 1971). Thurston *et al.* (1979) found that growth of *Cattleya* and *Stanhopea* orchid seedlings was better on **Knudson (1946) C** medium containing 0.2% graphite. Unlike charcoal, graphite does not adsorb toxic substances so that its beneficial effect was almost certainly due to its darkening the medium. Spencer *et al.* (1980) recommended the addition of graphite to a medium for orchid mericloning that included light sensitive antibiotics.

These above results also make it probable that where charcoal has been reported to improve root growth, part of its effect has been due to the decrease or elimination of light in the root zone. Adding lampblack (but in this case, not charcoal — see above) to the medium, improved the rooting of *Cinchona* by stimulating lateral root development (Krikorian *et al.*, 1982b).

The *in vitro* rooting of *Rosa × hybrida* shoots was improved when the lower part of the culture vessels was shaded with black tape (Khosh–Khui and Sink, 1982b), and this technique has since been used successfully in other genera. Rugini *et al.* (1988) discovered that cultivars of *Prunus dulcis* (almond), which only rooted in the dark, rooted most satisfactorily when shoots were placed into a semi–solid medium within jars painted black at the base, and the surface of the medium covered with sterile black polycarbonate granules. The cultures were incubated with the upper portion of the shoots in light (60 μmol m^{-2} s^{-1}, 16 h, 23°C). Compared to dark treatment of the whole cutting, basal etiolation resulted in a higher proportion of explants becoming rooted, more roots per explant, greener shoots and a higher survival rate subsequently. Basal etiolation (with the upper part of the shoot in high light — 21 W m^{-2}, 16h) was also found to be highly effective for rooting micropropagated olive shoots (Rugini *et al.* 1988, 1990; Cañas and Benbadis, 1988).

Photon fluence and daylength

The irradiance and daylength in which stock plants have been grown, can affect the potential of explants to form roots directly (Part 1, page 256). This is of little practical significance to micropropagation, except that the daylength to which Stage II cultures have been subjected, could be expected to influence the subsequent rooting of shoots.

Low irradiance and short days. Short days and low irradiance generally promote root induction in a similar fashion to darkness. For instance, de Fossard *et al.* (1978) noted that a low light level (10 μmol m^{-2} s^{-1}) was conducive to the rooting of *Eucalyptus* in a similar way to darkness, whereas 300 μmol m^{-2} s^{-1} was clearly inhibitory. *Alstroemeria* rhizomes were best rooted in light of 7 W m^{-2} and rooting was less at lower (1.2–2.2 W m^{-2}) or higher (15.4 W m^{-2}) irradiances. In *Prunus cerasifera*, the percentage of microcuttings which rooted was reduced by shortening the photoperiod from 16 h to 8 h, but the length of roots produced was greatest in a 12 h day. The number of roots per shoot was not affected by photoperiod (Morini *et al.*, 1991a). The proportion of *Carica papaya* shoots which rooted was greater when shoots were kept in a 12 h, rather than a 16 h or 24 h day, however in continuous light less callus was produced and the roots were fine and well branched (Drew and Miller, 1989).

Interaction with auxin. Possibly because etiolation affects auxin metabolism, it is often found that treatments which cause etiolation interact with the exogenous auxin requirement for rooting. Less boron is needed for rooting in low light or short days (see above). A low photon fluence acted synergistically with auxin to promote root formation from artichoke tissue (Saussay and Gautheret, 1971), and several rosaceous species required lower IBA concentrations for root induction after cuttings had been kept for 1 week in the dark than if kept in continuous illumination: some kinds *only* rooted after dark treatment (Norton and Boe, 1982).

Auxin treatment could substitute for the promoting effect of short days on the rooting of *Kalanchoë* cuttings. Roots were even initiated in long days on cuttings taken from plants which had been kept in long days, providing the cuttings were treated with IAA or IBA (Nanda *et al.*, 1967). In shoot apices from the adult phase of *Hedera helix*, root formation was practically zero in light of 4300–5400 lux, but could be promoted by 10 mg/l IAA when the illumination was only 540 lux. Juvenile phase apices, on the other hand, could be rooted in the higher illuminance providing they were treated with 5–10 mg/l NAA (Hackett, 1970).

High irradiance and long days. There may be some plants where rooting will be promoted by keeping cultured shoots in long days. Hansen (1987) described the effect of keeping stock plants in various daylengths on the subsequent ability to root cuttings taken from them. Long day treatments were said to promote rooting of some species of *Salix*, a clone of *Begonia × cheimantha*, *Vigna radiata* and *Rhododendron*.

Although darkness usually promotes root induction, the initiation and growth of roots is promoted by light incident on the foliage, and is usually improved as irradiation is increased. Shoots of *Leucospermum*, for instance, rooted more satisfactorily *in vitro*, under 210 μmol m^{-2} s^{-1} than when cultured under 110 or 150 μmol m^{-2} s^{-1} (Tal *et al.*, 1992a).

Carbohydrate requirement

Experiments with whole plants and cuttings have shown that the etiolation effect on rooting is enhanced by a substance (probably sugar) produced by leaves in the light which is translocated in the phloem proximally to the etiolation zone (Bassuk and Maynard, 1987). It is known that plant tissues need to be supplied with carbohydrate before they will produce adventitious roots, and it is often found that roots form most rapidly in light of high photon fluence.

Possible carbohydrate optimum. There can be an optimum concentration of internal carbon reserves above and below which the formation of adventitious roots is inhibited (see above and page 684). During *in vitro* rooting, the necessary supply of carbon energy can be provided both by sugar in the medium and, in green tissues, through photosynthesis. If the combined source is too great, rhizogenesis may be inhibited (Part 1, page 335).

Light quality

Effects of the wavelength of incident light on rooting were mentioned in Chapter 7. Confirming the results on *Vitis* and *Prunus* obtained by Chée and Pool, and Baraldi *et al.* (page 223), Rossi *et al.* (1993) have shown that rooting of *Prunus insititia* is promoted by red light. The proportion of shoots which rooted in light of different colours is shown in Table 106. Although all the shoots rooted in the absence of auxin in red light, the authors noted that the largest number of roots per shoot occurred where auxin was supplied during red light treatment.

Lighting during root elongation

Vinterhalter *et al.* (1990) have shown that in *Dracaena fragrans*, the rate of root elongation increases in a 16 h photoperiod as light irradiation is increased from 1 to 17 μmol m^{-2} s^{-1}. *Dracaena* is capable of photosynthesis at low irradiances and so the effect of light here was thought to be due to the production, through photosynthesis, of a product necessary for root growth, but probably not a carbohydrate as root elongation was not dependent on the presence of sucrose in the medium.

Temperature

In vivo rooting is usually favoured when the temperature in the rooting zone is higher than that of the air. Root induction *in vitro* is generally promoted by culturing shoots in relatively high temperatures and even shoots of species adapted to cool climates are induced to form roots most rapidly at temperatures several degrees above normal soil temperatures (but there are exceptions, see below). The optimum for subsequent root growth may be somewhat less. Gautheret (1969) noted that roots were formed most effectively on *Helianthus* tuber segments at 26°C, but, once initiated, the roots could grow at lower temperatures. If the temperature fluctuated around the optimum, root initiation was stimulated.

Shoots of apple resulting from micropropagation, rooted best at 28°C day/22°C night, and if culture temperatures were reduced to 23°/17°C or 18°/12°C, there were progressive reductions in the number of roots formed (Lane, 1978). The induction or rooting of 'Myrobalan' plum shoots during an initial 2–week dark treatment occurred more rapidly at 26°C than at 21°C (Hammerschlag,

1981b, 1982b). Roots formed at the higher temperature were also longer than those formed at 21°C, although the percentage of shoots producing roots was similar (Hammerschlag, 1982b). Roots were induced to form *in vitro* on *Phlox paniculata* shoots at 30°C but, for root elongation, the cultures were moved to 22°C (Schnabelrauch and Sink, 1979). *Carica papaya* shoots kept at a night temperature of 25°C were found to root more effectively as the daytime temperature was increased from 22, to 27, or 29°C. The roots produced at 29°C were finer and had more lateral branches than those produced at other temperatures (Drew and Miller, 1989).

Pierik (1972) discovered that petiole segments of *Lunaria annua* formed few roots at 25°C but rooted well at this temperature in the presence of auxin if they had been previously kept for 20 weeks at 5°C. The cold treatment had the same effect as keeping the explants in darkness at 25°C.

Rooting at lower temperatures. Despite the previous remarks, there are reports of various plants forming roots *more* satisfactorily at lower temperatures than those used for micropropagation. Shoots of *Digitalis lanata* multiplied at 24°C were rooted in the presence of 10 μM IBA at 19°C (day) and 14°C (night) (Schöner and Reinhard, 1986), while *Aconitum carmichaeli* shoots produced more roots at 20°C than at 25°C (Hatano *et al.*, 1988). Comparatively low temperatures seem to be preferred for the rooting of some conifers. Douglas fir shoots rooted best at 19°C; less roots but much callus were produced at 24°C (Cheng and Voqui, 1977); relatively few shoots of *Pseudotsuga menziesii* rooted at 24°C, but many more rooted at 19°C and were afterwards also more successfully established in soil (Cheng, 1979); spruce shoots rooted best when cultured at 20°C during the day and at 18°C in the night, rather than at 24/18°C, 20/15°C, or 25/25°C (Rumary and Thorpe, 1984).

Table 106. The proportion of shoots (%) of *Prunus insititia* which rooted when cultured in light of varying spectral quality.
[Data from the paper of Rossi *et al.*, 1993].

Spectral quality of light	Photon fluence μmol m^{-2}s^{-1}	Auxin treatment	
		0.5 μM NAA	None
White	36	100	81
Far red	12	93	10
Red	36	100	100
Blue	36	69	71
Darkness	0	100	5

A strong interaction between genotype and the optimum temperature for rooting has sometimes been demonstrated. W. Horn *et al.* (1988b) found that the best temperature for rooting the shoots of rose hybrids, varied between cultivars: the best overall results were obtained when cultures were kept at 18°C, but the rooting of some varieties was better at 12°C while other 'thermopositive' cultivars required 24°C. Although the most rapid shoot multiplication of the *Prunus* rootstock 'GF 677' (*P. persica* × *P. amygdalus*) occurred when cultures were maintained at a constant 22°C day and night, *in vitro* rooting occurred best if shoots were then kept at 22°C/18°C (16h day/8h dark). However the rooting of *P. insititia* 'GF 655/2' was the same in a constant 22°C as in 22°C/18°C (Loreti *et al.*, 1988).

Promotion of rooting by activated charcoal

Shoots of a number of different species root more readily *in vitro* when activated charcoal (AC) has been added to the medium, sometimes together with auxin (Table 107). Charcoal has also been reported to improve root growth where roots have already been initiated.

Possible modes of action. Stimulation of root growth has been severally ascribed to charcoal:

- adsorbing inhibitory substances (and/or preventing tissue blackening);
- slowly adsorbing auxins and thus improving the milieu for root initiation; or
- darkening the culture medium (see above).

Observed stimulation. Activated charcoal adsorbs auxin so that detrimental effects on root growth are relieved, but it does not do so until the regulant has had time to initiate root formation. This is shown by the results of Krikorian and Kann (1987) with *Sapium sebiferum*. Microcuttings formed roots on **Lloyd and McCown (1981) WPM** medium supplemented with 0.54 μM NAA, but the roots were short and thickened. Normal roots appeared when 0.01% activated charcoal was also added and although charcoal alone had some effect in initiating roots, their extent and quality was much improved by the presence of auxin. Aziz *et al.* (1992) found that shoots of *Musa acuminata* formed roots more rapidly with 0.1 mg/l IBA and 0.025 g/l AC than with AC alone.

Lilien–Kipnis and Kochba (1987) discovered that if 5 g/l activated charcoal was added to the rooting medium, shoots of *Gladiolus* resulting from shoot cultures, produced long fine roots with many more secondary branches than if cultured with auxin alone. Charcoal also had a beneficial effect on shoot growth, and plantlets rooted on AC survived better when planted out and produced more and heavier cormlets. These results seemed not to be explicable by immediate inactivation of auxin, as there was a response to increasing NAA (from 0.1 to 10 μM, 0.02 to 1.86 mg/l). Rooting of the variety 'Kinneret', for example, was best with 3 μM NAA and 5 g/l AC.

More hypocotyl cuttings of *Pinus sylvestris* rooted *in vitro* if activated charcoal (0.01–20 g/l) was added to an agar medium without regulants. This was presumed to have been due to the absorption of inhibitory substances and not to the interception of light, because the medium with only 0.01% AC was translucent (Grönroos and Von Arnold, 1985).

Ernst (1974, 1975) noted that charcoal improved the germination and growth of *Paphiopedilum* and *Phalaenopsis* orchid seedlings *in vitro*. The growth of aerial roots was inhibited, while that of geotropic ground roots was improved in the presence of charcoal. This was thought to be partly due to its ability to darken the medium and partly due to its capacity to adsorb inhibitory substances, including ethylene.

For root induction on *Eucalyptus*, *Hevea* and *Sapium*, Mascarenhas *et al.* (1982) and Mridula *et al.* (1983) first cultured shoots with auxins and then on ½MS medium with 0.25% charcoal. In *Sapium* this procedure considerably reduced the time required for root initiation. Plant varieties may differ significantly in their response to charcoal. A novel treatment was devised by Sondahl *et al.* (1985) for *Coffea* cuttings: they were planted in a two–layered medium where there was 10 μM IBA in the top layer, and 2.5 g/l activated charcoal in the basal layer.

Inhibitory effects. Activated charcoal does not always promote rooting. Bressan *et al.* (1982) discovered that 0.3–1.0 g/l activated charcoal (added to a medium containing ¼MS salts and 1 mg/l IAA) promoted root formation in just one of six rose cultivars. More than 3 g/l charcoal completely prevented rooting. The charcoal was more effective if it had been rinsed successively in acid, base and an organic solvent, rather than as directly supplied[†]. Norton and Norton (1988a) found that 2 g/l charcoal increased the number of roots formed by *Prunus* shoots, but decreased the number in *Spiraea*, and had no

---

[†]   3–volumes each of water, diethyl ether, 2% NH4OH in 50% ethanol, water, 6N HCl and water.

Table 107. Examples of the addition of activated charcoal to the rooting medium.

Species	Activated charcoal (g/l)	Growth regulators		References
		Auxin (mg/l)	Cytokinin (mg/l)	
Arabidopsis	5.0	0.03 IAA	1 kinetin	Scholl *et al.* (1981)
Dianthus caryophyllus	0.2	None	None	Dencso (1987)
Ficus	1–3	None	None	Makino *et al.* (1977)
Fragaria × *ananassa*	0.5–4.0	1 IBA	None	Damiano (1978)
Malus × *domestica*	20.0	1 IBA	None	Whiteley and Abbott (1977)
Rhododendron	2.5	2 IAA	None	Preil & Engelhardt (1977)
	0.6–0.8	5 IBA or none	None	Kyte and Briggs (1979)
	1.0	None	None	Meyer (1981)

effect in *Arctostaphylos* and *Rhododendron*. Rooting of *Digitalis lanata* shoots was strongly inhibited if 1 g/l activated charcoal was added together with 10 μM IBA (Schöner and Reinhard, 1986).

When activated charcoal (3 g/l) was added with 4.1, 10.2 or 20.4 mg/l IBA, it inhibited the rooting of *Cinchona* shoots (Krikorian *et al.* 1982b). Inhibition in these instances was probably due to auxin absorption by the charcoal. Some roots were formed in its presence at the cut ends of the *Cinchona* shoots at the highest IBA level.

Electromagnetic fields

An unusual treatment which increased the proportion of *Prunus cerasifera* shoots which rooted *in vitro* was reported by Lucchesini *et al.* (1992). Stage II shoot cultures growing on multiplication medium were exposed to varying magnetic fields generated by coils electrically connected in series which were placed on either side of a vessel. Shoots from treated containers rooted as well as those which had been grown for a further passage on an elongation medium without cytokinin. Shoot length and shoot fresh and dry weight were increased by the magnetic treatment and although roots were shorter than normal they were well suited to *ex vitro* hardening. If similar results can be obtained with other plants, the authors suggested that magnetic field treatment could be used to shorten the sequence of cultures necessary for micropropagation, by removing the need for an elongation stage.

Tissue dependent factors

Shoot size

Shoots often only root properly once they have reached an adequate size. With *Artemisia dracunculus*, Mackay and Kitto (1988) showed that compared to small cuttings, a greater proportion of those larger than 10 mm formed roots, and the plants produced survived better when transplanted, and had more shoots. The best *in vitro* rooting of various rose cultivars was obtained by choosing shoots which were at least 2 cm in length (Douglas *et al.*, 1989). Rooting of the adventitious shoots arising from *Lavandula* callus was similarly found to be dependent on their size and vigour (Panizza and Tognoni, 1988).

The presence of nodes

Cuttings of some plants root best if excised through an internode, while the rooting of others is more successful if they are cut through a node. The presence of a node at the base of microcuttings of *Stevia rebaudiana* delayed root formation and decreased the number of rooted shoots (Ferriera and Handro, 1988a).

Wounding

Removing a strip of bark from *Rhododendron* stem sections was found by Pierik and Steegmans (1975e) to greatly increase the proportion which formed roots *in vitro*, the speed at which roots were produced, and their final weight. These authors point out that the uptake of auxin from the medium would have been improved by this treatment. Extensive wounding of mung bean cuttings increased their rooting (Robbins *et al.*, 1981). In addition, if shoots obtained from shoot tip cultures of apple (Snir and Erez, 1980; Sriskandarajah and Mullins, 1981), *Simmondsia chinensis* (a 2mm deep vertical incision — Rost and Hinchee, 1980), or sweet cherry (cut both sides with a scalpel — Snir, 1982a,b), were wounded and then treated with auxin, they rooted more readily.

Juvenility

The marked effect of the physiological age of cultured plant material on root formation, and the possible 'rejuvenating' effect of etiolation, have been discussed in Chapter 8. Shoots produced from cultures, particularly those of mature woody plants, are generally difficult to root at first, but root more easily with progressive subcultures. The necessity to acquire juvenility is usually not apparent in herbaceous species, but is occasionally recorded. After 3–7 subcultures, the rate of bud formation in shoot cultures of *Asparagus* suddenly increases and at the same time shoots become capable of being rooted (Doré, 1990). In woody plants an improved rooting capacity sometimes only becomes apparent after many subcultures. The results reported by Amin and Jaiswal (1988) shown in Table 108 are typical of those often obtained.

Persistence of juvenility. The capacity of shoots to root easily is frequently maintained in micropropagated plants after they have been planted in the field (see Chapter 15). This can mean that once micropropagated stock plants have been established, they can be used as a source of cuttings for renewed propagation *without the need to resort to further micropropagation.*

Hairy root disease

At the site where the bacterium *Agrobacterium rhizogenes* infects plants, tissues are typically induced to produce a profusion of roots covered with root hairs ('hairy

roots'). The effect is caused by the transfer of a root–inducing (pRi) plasmid from the bacterium to the host. The plasmid then inserts a part of its DNA (t–DNA) into the plant genome where the t–DNA becomes stabilised and expressed. Root promotion is due to just a few t–DNA loci (*rol*A, B and C, particularly *rol*B) (Rugini and Mariotti, 1991). These genes have also been transferred into engineered plasmids from *Agrobacterium tumefaciens* of the kind commonly used for genetic manipulation experiments (Zhi–Ming Wei *et al.*, 1986).

Excised hairy roots can be used to initiate isolated root cultures. These usually have a high rate of growth *in vitro* and may be used for various research purposes (Mugnier, 1988) and for the production of plant secondary products (Knopp *et al.*, 1988; Mano *et al.*, 1989; Parr *et al.*, 1988). Cells transformed by the root–inducing plasmid (pRi) t–DNA and plasmids carrying only *rol* genes, can give rise to callus cultures, which produce many hairy roots, and to transgenic plants.

Several workers have investigated whether the *Agrobacterium rhizogenes* root–inducing genes could be used to induce root formation on shoots resulting from micropropagation of woody plants where roots are not produced readily. Two methods by which this might be attempted are:

- Shoots obtained from micropropagation could be inoculated with wild–type *Agrobacterium rhizogenes* or with engineered *Agrobacterium tumefaciens* plasmids containing one or more of the *rol* genes. Cells in the root–producing zone might then be transformed, but not those in the rest of the shoot.

- Transgenic plants could be regenerated from transformed tissues in which *rol* genes had been integrated. When micropropagated, the shoots of such plants should root readily.

When *A. rhizogenes* or *A. tumefaciens* have been used to introduce plasmids, bacterial infection of the host plant tissues is controlled by treatment with an antibiotic: carbenicillin is often applied 2–3 days after culture initiation.

Patena *et al.* (1988) investigated whether *A. rhizogenes* could be used to induce root formation on species which are difficult to root after micropropagation. Inoculation of certain strains onto the cut surface of apple shoots did lead to the formation of thick fleshy roots. The paper does not say whether the roots were functional although, according to Tanaka *et al.* (1985), transformed roots can fully support the growth of plants. Rugini and Mariotti (1991) found that inoculation with wild–type *A. rhizogenes* caused a significant proportion of olive,

Table 108. The improvement in rooting of *Psidium guajava* shoots with increasing subcultures [results of Amin and Jaiswal, 1988].

Subculture number	% shoots forming roots	
	Without auxin	With 0.2 mg/l IBA + 0.2 mg/l NAA
0	0	33 ± 6.4
5	30 ± 7.2	70 ± 4.8
10	72 ± 8.1	90 ± 5.3

apple, almond and pistachio shoots to form roots. No roots were formed by untreated shoots. In olive, the survival of shoots rooted in this way was similar to that of shoots rooted with auxin, but only a low proportion of the inoculated shoots of the other species survived. When shoots of the same woody plants were inoculated with *A. tumefaciens* containing plasmids carrying one or more *rol* genes, only a small percentage rooted. This was thought to be due to low plasmid virulence.

Using the second of the two approaches above, Rugini and Mariotti (1991) found that *Actinidia deliciosa* shoots, regenerated from leaf discs transformed with a plasmid engineered to have *rol* A, B and C genes, rooted readily on an auxin free medium. However the transgenic plants were shorter than normal and had smaller leaves. Transgenic plants carrying DNA from the pRi plasmid can have abnormal phenotypes (Tepfer, 1984) depending on the segments of t–DNA which have been transferred (Taylor *et al.*, 1985), although Wei *et al.* (1986) and Hamill and Rhodes (1988) reported obtaining normal plants of *Nicotiana hesperis* and *Solanum nigrum*, from shoots directly regenerated from transformed hairy root cultures.

Conclusion. Root induction which depends on transformation by the *A. rhizogenes* plasmid or its genes would only be useful if it were able to improve the rooting and survival of difficult subjects. Results obtained so far suggest that auxin treatments are more reliable.

PRE–TRANSFER TREATMENTS WHICH AFFECT ESTABLISHMENT

This section describes manipulations which can be applied to cultures *before shoots or plantlets are transferred to the external environment* which may improve survival *ex vitro*, or modify the development of the plants obtained. Many of these procedures can be applied equally well to Stage II cultures, to Stage III cultures during elongation rooting, to microcuttings already rooted *in vitro*, or to cultures bearing shoots which are shortly to be harvested for rooting *extra vitrum*. Some workers call treatments which can enhance survival 'in vitro hardening'.

In vitro **hardening**

Shoots or plantlets can be hardened in the culture flask before they are moved *extra vitrum*, but because suitable treatments involve additional manipulations, they are seldom employed.

The adaptation of leaves so that they can control water loss in conditions of low humidity appears to be brought about when the cytoplasm of the constituent cells has a low (more negative) water potential. The water potential of leaf cells can be decreased by loss of water through transpiration, or by the plant being grown in a medium of low osmotic potential.

In vitro hardening can therefore be achieved by

- Decreasing the water potential of the medium;
- Reducing the humidity in the culture vessel.

Both kinds of treatment cause plantlets to develop functional stomata and epicuticular wax, but if applied in excess, can result in a reduction in the rate of plantlet growth (Short *et al.*, 1987).

Decreasing water potential

Chapter 9 explains how the water potential of the medium can be decreased by:

- increasing the salt content of the medium;
- adding a non–toxic osmoticum such as mannitol or polyethylene glycol;
- increasing the sucrose content;
- increasing the concentration of agar in the medium.

Each of these methods can prevent the occurrence of hyperhydric shoots, which are very susceptible to damage outside the culture flask, and also enhance the formation of wax deposits on leaves of cultured shoots. Zilis *et al.* (1979) found that by increasing the agar concentration from the 8–10 g/l used at Stage II, to 10–14 g/l, they were able to harden shoots at Stage III and enable them to withstand desiccation *ex vitro*.

However increasing agar content at Stage III is not generally considered to be a practical measure because:

- agar is an expensive ingredient of tissue culture media;
- high agar levels in the rooting medium can damage roots (Rahman and Blake, 1988b);
- removal of agar from plant roots before transplanting is more difficult when the concentration is high.

The effect of sucrose. The requirement of shoots for sugar during the rooting process was described on page 684. Sugars decrease the water potential of the medium, so does the presence of a high concentration during the rooting process enhance plant survival? The answer seems to be yes, providing root formation is not inhibited, because not only will shoots have been exposed to a greater stress *in vitro*, they will also have greater reserves of carbohydrate to resource future growth. However, once roots have formed *in vitro*, it can be advantageous to transfer plantlets to a medium with less sucrose, and at the same time place the cultures under light of relatively high irradiance. This can have the effect of starting plantlets on the path towards autotrophy and beginning the hardening process.

Reuther (1991) advocated reducing the sucrose concentration in the rooting medium for *Pelargonium* and *Vitis* to 5 or 10 g/l finding that in light of 60–65 μmol m^{-2} s^{-1}, photoautotrophy and vegetative development were favoured and this contributed to a higher survival rate and accelerated growth upon transfer of the plants to soil.

It is generally found that the easiest and most generally applicable way of ensuring the survival of plantlets *extra vitrum* is to maintain at least 30 g/l sucrose in the final Stage III medium. Wainwright and Scrace (1989) found that the survival and quality of *Ficus* and *Potentilla* plantlets at Stage IV was improved by so doing, and suggested that a high concentration of sucrose increases the amount of carbohydrate stored in shoots. Plantlets then have a high reserve of energy with which to initiate the new leaf growth necessary for acclimatization (see below).

Using high salts media. Although increasing the concentration of salts in the rooting medium will decrease water potential and might be expected to harden plants before their removal from culture, the practice is not generally beneficial for *in vitro* rooting (page 681). Williams *et al.* (1992) found that high mineral levels reduced the survival of *Lechenaultia formosa* plantlets *ex vitro*, probably because *in vitro* root formation had been inhibited.

Reducing relative humidity

Plantlets or unrooted shoots are much more readily acclimatized to an external environment if they have been cultured *in vitro* at less than 100% relative humidity (RH) (Short *et al.*, 1987) and, where it has been possible to grow plantlets *in vitro* in 80% humidity, they have been transferred directly to soil without acclimatization (Short *et al.*, 1987; Majada *et al.*, 1992).

Chrysanthemum plantlets grown in 94% RH showed little signs of wilting when transplanted; compared to plants grown in 100% RH, the hardened plants had thicker leaves, improved stomatal closure and a thicker cuticle. Tanaka *et al.* (1992) found that the rate of net photosynthesis per unit leaf area was decreased by reducing relative humidity *in vitro*, but thought that plants would suffer little loss in dry weight and be more able to withstand water stress after transplanting if, while still within the vessel, they were exposed to relative humidities of 85–90%.

Cooling the bottom of culture vessels. Most methods of reducing humidity described in Chapter 7 (page 212), are impractical for routine work. Cooling the base of the culture vessel is an exception and results in a humidity gradient in the vessel. In these conditions, shoots begin transpiration which results in the accumulation of salts in the leaves and assists in *in vitro* hardening. The method can only be used for a short while using a medium containing a low concentration of salts (or a medium where salts have been already largely exhausted) (Maene and Debergh, 1987).

The use of special closures. The humidity within flasks can be reduced by sealing vessels with closures which allow evaporation. These might be proprietary closures which allow gas exchange, or lids which have been drilled and lined with paper (see Fig. 123, Chapter 13). Placed onto vessels during an *in vitro* hardening stage, such closures allow the relative humidity within vessels to be reduced, and also permit the entry of carbon dioxide so that photoautotrophy becomes possible under appropriate conditions (page 698). Care should be taken to avoid an excessive drop in humidity or plants will be damaged or apical necrosis occur (see page 653).

Opening the tops of vessels. Even though it may not be practical to reduce relative humidity within vessels while cultures are growing, it can be a sensible precaution to gradually remove the closures on imperviously sealed culture vessels before transfer is to be effected. If cultures are placed in a room with a relative humidity of *ca.* 80%, closures can be removed completely several days before planting is anticipated. These measures should be used with caution because, although cultures contained in narrow tubes can be exposed to fairly dry air without too much damage, those in large diameter containers wilt rapidly and will be severely injured if treated in the same way (Zimmerman, 1984a). Therefore the covers of wide–mouthed jars should only be partially opened at first.

Some laboratories remove covers from culture vessels within the humidity tent in the greenhouse to which plantlets or shoots are to be transferred. Franklin *et al.* (1990) moved Magenta® boxes containing plantlets of *Bothriochloa caucasia*, raised from somatic embryos, to the greenhouse once their shoots were 3 cm high. The lids were opened after 2–3 days, and 7–10 days later surviving plantlets were transferred to soil. Media used for rooting seldom contain organic supplements, apart from sucrose, and contamination does not seem to be a problem for up to 7 days before final transfer, although difficulties may arise should shoots or plantlets be left uncovered for a longer period.

Humidity reduction at Stages II and III. The effectiveness of growing cultures in ventilated vessels for preventing vitrescence and inducing *in vitro* acclimatization, has been mentioned in Chapter 13 (pages 660 and 658).

Whish *et al.* (1992) cultured the shoots of *Ptilotus* in reduced humidity which was intermittently applied during Stage IIIb, while they were rooted *in vitro*. The reduced humidity was found to enhance auxin–stimulated root formation and subsequent survival of plantlets during acclimatization. It was essential to ensure that the reduced humidity did not dehydrate the medium to the point that salts became toxic, or the agar dried so that it was unsuitable for root formation.

The leaves of Stage IIIa cultures of *Rosa multiflora* which had been kept at 75% RH for 3 weeks showed adaptations to a dry atmosphere in their position of stomata, and the robustness of their epidermis and guard cells (Capellades *et al.*, 1990).

Adjusting *in vitro* lighting and temperature

Enhanced transpiration and hardening

When cultured plants are exposed to high photon fluence, their leaf temperature is increased above that of the container. Air within the leaf can therefore hold more water per unit volume than that outside (even though both have a relative humidity of 100%), and so transpiration occurs as long as the lights are on (Reuther, 1988b). Enhanced transpiration under a PPF of 150–200 μmol m^{-2} s^{-1} can be accompanied by improved leaf quality (Maene and Debergh, 1987) and a reduced likelihood of hyperhydricity (page 661).

Murashige (1974) pointed out that establishment is facilitated by maintaining plants in light of high irradiance before, during, or after *in vitro* rooting. Sweet gum plants grown under high irradiances (50–315 μmol m^{-2} s^{-1} from metal halide lamps) either *in vivo* or *in vitro*, were found to have larger cells and a more compact mesophyll than those grown in low light. But all *in vitro* plants had smaller, thinner leaves and smaller mesophyll cells than *in vivo* plants, and except at 315 μmol m^{-2} s^{-1}, significantly greater stomatal densities (Lee N. *et al.*, 1988).

Plants which are rooted *in vitro* in high light are therefore partly conditioned for transfer *extra vitrum*. Their acclimatization may be further increased if they are supplied with supplementary carbon dioxide (see page 722). Doi *et al.* (1992) found that *Freesia* plantlets cultured in 0.1%

CO_2 during the rooting stage, were more easily acclimatized than those rooted in ambient CO_2.

Driver and Suttle (1987) pre–conditioned shoots of walnut and peach which were suitable for rooting, by keeping them, before the rooting stage for up to 15 days on a basal medium (with high sucrose) in light of an increased irradiance but shorter daylength (66 μmol m^{-2} s^{-1} for 17 h daily, *c.f.* 55 μmol m^{-2} s^{-1} for 24 h which was used for shoot multiplication). At the same time the temperature was reduced from 29 to 19°C. The treatment encouraged stem lignification and profoundly improved the percentage of shoots which rooted and survived as plants, when plantlets were placed directly into the field (see below). Using light of high irradiance at normal growth room temperatures can reduce survival when plantlets are transferred *extra vitrum*. Williams *et al.* (1992) found that *Lechenaultia* plantlets survived less well after such treatment, probably because they had been subjected to temperature stress in the culture vessels.

Root quality

For successful establishment, shoots of *Morus laevigata* (propagated and rooted with IBA at 25°C) needed to be kept at 30°C for 7–10 days with a constant photoperiod, until the roots became brown. Plantlet survival *ex vitro* following this extra treatment was 80%; without it 95% of the plantlets died (Islam *et al.*, 1993b).

Encouraging autotrophic growth

Stage II cultures. Provided that light of high irradiance is present and there is sufficient CO_2, the development of a functional photosynthetic apparatus can be enhanced in some plants by decreasing or eliminating sucrose from the medium. In strawberry, leaves formed in the presence of sucrose cannot become autotrophic, and consequently they die when sucrose is removed. If however the existing leaves are removed from plantlets before they are moved onto a medium lacking sucrose, new leaves are formed which are capable of producing a positive carbon balance through photosynthesis (Grout and Price, 1987).

Stage III cultures. Carbon dioxide enrichment of the environment in which shoots are rooted *in vitro* can assist hardening. When Deng and Donnelly (1993) rooted *Rubus idaeus* shoots in the light in 1500 p.p.m. CO_2, they found that root number and length, plantlet fresh weight and photosynthetic capacity were increased, especially if the sucrose in the medium was reduced below 30 g/l, or eliminated altogether. Sucrose promoted plantlet growth but depressed photosynthesis and reduced *in vitro* hardening. Plantlets became autotrophic on sucrose–free media if kept in either ambient (*ca.* 340 p.p.m.) or enriched CO_2 conditions and in consequence were more effectively hardened *in vitro* than if grown before transfer with sucrose in the medium.

Using high irradiances available in the greenhouse. Burr (1976) placed vessels containing fern shoot cultures into a greenhouse for two weeks before planting out, so that they finished their *in vitro* development under a higher light intensity. This technique was tried by Roberts *et al.* (1992) for Stage IIIb cultures of chrysanthemum and rose grown on Sorbarods moistened with liquid rooting medium. When the cultures were contained in vessels fitted with selectively permeable membranes which allowed the entry of carbon dioxide, there was more shoot and root growth in vessels placed in the greenhouse in irradiances which varied from 16 to 189 W m^{-2} than in vessels kept in a growth room (16 W m^{-2}). In the greenhouse it was possible to omit sucrose from the medium to obtain photoautotrophic growth even without CO_2 supplementation. The authors were so encouraged by their results that they suggested that, using their technique, Stage IV acclimatization might become unnecessary for some plants. Rooted plants could be transplanted, still in the Sorbarods, directly into soil.

Growth regulants and subculturing techniques

Hyperhydricity and cytokinins. Hyperhydric shoots survive very poorly in the outside environment. The degree of hyperhydricity in shoot cultures can be influenced by the choice of cytokinin for Stage II multiplication (Chapter 13). A deleterious effect of BAP on survival, without obvious outward symptoms of hyperhydricity, has been noted for *Liriope, Schefflera* and *Philodendron*. In these plants, where BAP had been employed to stimulate axillary shoot formation, only 10% of shoots survived Stage IV establishment, whereas 90% survived where kinetin or 2–iP had been used at Stage II (Griffis *et al.*, 1984). The improved survival in *Liriope* occurred even though there was no apparent difference in the manner with which roots were produced (Stimart, 1986).

Establishment is improved by frequent and regular subculturing during the shoot multiplication stage of shoot and node cultures; delaying Stage II subculture is deleterious (Stimart, *loc. cit.*).

The use of growth retardants. Smith *et al.* (1990a) found that chrysanthemum plantlets rooted in a medium containing 0.5–2 mg/l paclobutrazol were less liable than controls to wilt on being transplanted to soil. This was attributed to the treated plants having leaves with more epicuticular wax and chlorophyll, and smaller stomata with an improved capacity for closure; roots with an increased thickness; and, if 1–2 mg/l paclobutrazol had been used, a reduced stem length, root length and leaf area. Results obtained subsequently, by adding a number of other growth retardants to the liquid rooting medium with which Sorbarods were soaked, were compatible with the hypothesis that resistance to wilting derives from the inhibited synthesis of gibberellins (Smith E.F.*et al.*, 1991; Roberts *et al.*, 1992). Novello *et al.* (1992) observed that 1 mg/l paclobutrazol applied in the same way to cultured shoots of *Vitis vinifera*, caused plantlets to have leaves with a reduced area, bearing smaller stomata than usual. Stem length was also reduced, and when roots were formed they were thicker and more numerous than those on the control shoots. The conductance of water from the paclobutrazol–treated plants was less than that from untreated plantlets, and similar to that in plantlets grown in 94% relative humidity. It therefore appeared that paclobutrazol treatment would make plantlets better able to withstand acclimatization.

Practical utilisation of *in vitro* hardening

At present, few laboratories seem to use special pre–transfer treatments, and microcuttings or rooted plantlets are moved directly to the nursery for acclimatization. Even though growth can be promoted and plants more readily acclimatized if Stage II cultures are supplied with supplementary CO_2 in light of high photosynthetic photon flux (100–200 μmol m^{-2} s^{-1} (Part 1, page 205), the use of artificial lighting of this 'intensity' in growth rooms requires high power consumption and is not economic. In most climates, provision of the requisite photon fluence by admitting natural light would lead to high cooling costs.

Cooling the base of culture vessels (above) is a more effective way of improving transpiration and has a much smaller energy requirement, but there is little evidence to show that even this technique is widely employed.

Storage and vernalisation

Plantlets which have been rooted *in vitro* can often be stored in the culture vessel before being planted out and acclimatized. Cold treatment of rooted plantlets can also be used to induce the capacity to flower in plants which have a cold requirement — a technique likely to be of especial use to plant breeders. For example, the requirements for bolting and seed set of sugar beet can be fulfilled by storing rooted plantlets in their culture vessels for 3 months at 4–5°C (Catlin, 1990).

EXTRA–CULTURAL ROOTING

As explained at the beginning of this chapter, *ex vitro* rooting is now commonly used in micropropagation establishments. Unrooted shoots are also sold to growers for rooting *ex vitro* on their own premises. Debergh and Maene (1981) estimated that the labour involved in rooting individual shoots *in vitro* can cause this stage of micropropagation to account for 35–75 per cent of the total cost of plants propagated through tissue culture, depending on species. Rooting microcuttings *extra vitrum* eliminates one set of labour costs and overheads, as rooting and acclimatization are effectively combined into a single stage of the micropropagation process and expensive growth room space is released for other purposes.

Ex vitro rooting can be used for many plants, although losses are sometimes less if shoots have been rooted *in vitro* before being planted out. The technique is particularly suitable for species which root easily and it has been said to have especial advantages for woody plants in which secondary thickening is important for proper root function (page 672). In many of these plants, the absence of a vascular cambium may mean that roots formed *in vitro* are incapable of proper water movement. Hildebrandt and Harney (1983) observed that only a few roots were lost when *Syringa* plants, rooted *ex vitro*, were potted, whereas many were lost when plantlets rooted *in vitro* were transferred to the outside environment and shoots had effectively to be re–rooted.

When shoots are rooted outside the culture vessel, they are treated as normal (delicate) cuttings and are set into a porous rooting substrate after they have been removed from *in vitro* culture.

Further advantages

Although there are many instances where the reverse is true (page 671), shoots can often be rooted more effectively *ex vitro* than in a culture vessel. Williams and McHughen (1986) could not root indirectly–formed shoots of *Lens culinaris in vitro*, but managed to root 11% in a sand bed within a mist chamber. This advantage applies especially to woody plants. For example, Marks *et al.* (19867) could root 70% of the shoots of *Tilia cordata* and *Tilia platyphyllos* in culture vessels, but no lateral roots were formed and leaf fall and tip necrosis were prevalent. Much better results were obtained by rooting the cuttings directly *ex vitro*. These workers also found that shoots of *Magnolia* × *soulangiana* rooted *in vitro* gave smaller plants with shorter internodes than those rooted directly into compost. Similarly Schwarz *et al.* (1988) could not root *Pinus strobus* shoots *in vitro*, but 28% rooted in an artificial soil mixture. Troncoso *et*

al. (1988) rooted and established a greater proportion of *Vitis* microcuttings *ex vitro* under mist, than *in vitro* using an agar medium.

Disadvantages

In species where the technique is effective, there are few disadvantages to *ex vitro* rooting. Although *ex vitro* rooting is cheaper, it can occasionally result in herbaceous plants of smaller initial size and quality than if they had been rooted *in vitro*. However *ex vitro* rooting is still likely to be the most cost–effective method unless there are significant differences in the rate of plantlet growth. Usually early size differences soon disappear. This was the case with pineapple (De Wald *et al.*, 1988).

In many woody species, plantlets rooted outside the culture vessel become established *more* rapidly than those which have been first rooted *in vitro* and then acclimatized. For example, plantlets of *Syringa vulgaris* rooted *ex vitro* could be potted 4–6 weeks earlier than those rooted *in vitro* (Hildebrandt and Harney, 1983). In addition a higher proportion of rooted plantlets may survive after *ex vitro* rooting, than if shoots had been rooted in a culture vessel.

Methods employed

Shoot cultures are usually subcultured as shoot clumps until the rooting stage. Clumps are removed from the culture vessels and shoots are excised, which are of a suitable, fairly uniform size. Small shoots are difficult to handle and may not root well. If they do root, they usually provide plantlets which grow away slowly. Maene and Debergh (1983) found that shoots of *Cordyline terminalis* should be 2.5–5.0 cm in length. Few shoots smaller than this were able to form roots, while those which were larger died, apparently because they were liable to rapid water loss. Similarly *Euphorbia* shoots needed to be at least 31 mm in length ; few shorter than this survived (Zhang *et al.*, 1986; Zhang and Stoltz, 1989).

Usually discrete shoots are used but in some species, especially those with short prostrate shoots, it can be better to root shoot clusters. Inserting clumps of shoots into the rooting medium, to be divided once roots have formed, can minimise the shock of transplantation (Metcalfe, 1984). For this reason commercial laboratories also sometimes supply clumps of shoots to customers. Damiano (1977) reported that good transplants of strawberry could be obtained at lower cost and at an earlier stage if shoots were transferred to a sand/peat mixture as incompletely separated clumps rather than as individual plantlets. Stapfer and Heuser (1986) rooted shoot clusters of *Heuchera sanguinea*

Table 109. Mixtures of materials used to support microcuttings during rooting *extra vitrum.*

Plant	Rooting mixture		Reference
	Materials	Proportions	
Alnus glutinosa	Jiffy® mix		Garton *et al.* (1981a)
Amelanchier, Daphne (require a dry mix)	Perlite, peat	4:1	Hill (1988)
Chrysanthemum cinerariae-folium	Sand	—	Grewal and Sharma (1978)
Gardenia jasminoides	Sphagnum peat	—	Economou and Spanoudaki (1985)
	Sphagnum peat, perlite	1:1	Economou and Spanoudaki (1986)
Hydrangea macrophylla	Sphagnum peat, vermiculite, perlite	1:1:1	Bailey *et al.* (1986)
Populus spp.	Sterilized soil, peat, perlite	3:1:1	Chalupa (1974)
Malus × domestica	Peat, sand	2:1	Boxus (1987)
Prunus 'Hally Jolivette'	Peat, perlite	1:1	Lineberger (1982)
Rhododendron 'P.J.M. hybrids'	Sphagnum peat, coarse sand	1:2	Ettinger and Preece (1985)
Syringa vulgaris	Vermiculite	—	Hildebrandt and Harney (1983)
Tiarella cordifolia	Redi-Earth ®	—	Kitto (1986)
Vaccinium vitis-idaea	Sphagnum peat, vermiculite, perlite	2:1:1	Hosier *et al.* (1985)
Various plants e.g.*Rhododendron*, *Vaccinium*	Fine peat, fine perlite, sawdust	1:1:1	Hill (1988)
Veronica 'Red Fox'	Sphagnum peat, vermiculite	1:1	Stapfer *et al.* (1985)
Vinca minor	Sphagnum peat, vermiculite	1:1	Stapfer and Heuser (1985)

directly and only then divided them to provide suitable plantlets for growing on. However, single gerbera shoots were more prone to initiate roots than undivided shoot clusters (Murashige *et al.* 1974).

Usually shoots form roots *extra vitrum* in 2–5 weeks; the time required may vary according to genotype even within a single species.

***In vitro* hardening.** The techniques which help to harden rooted plantlets before they are moved out of culture can equally well be applied to shoot cultures, before shoots are harvested for rooting *extra vitrum*. The combination of methods used by Debergh and Maene (1990) is illustrated in Fig. 126.

Planting substrates

Explants taken from *in vitro* cultures are often treated with a fungicide (see below), and dipped in auxin (although this may not be necessary), before being planted (set or stuck) into a suitable porous substrate (compost).

Mixtures of peat, pumice, sand, vermiculite or perlite contained in trays or flats have been used for this purpose (Table 109), although planting into plugs of various kinds is now more common (see below). Sterilized soil can be a component of rooting substrates, but is seldom used on account of variability, cost and inconvenience.

It is most important to select a substrate with the correct characteristics, for there can be marked differences in root formation in different materials and this affects the quality of the plantlets obtained (Altman and Freudenberg, 1983). A 1:1 mixture of fine peat and sand resulted in slightly better rooting and survival of *Camellia* plantlets than 1:1 coarse sand and peat, or 2:1:1 perlite, peat and shredded bark (Samartin, 1992). Peat can be too acid a substrate for root formation in some species, and some kinds of vermiculite are too alkaline (Hutchinson, 1982a). Apart from having a neutral, or only slightly acid pH, composts or substrates need to have a high water–holding capacity, but yet provide good aeration. If cuttings are sprayed with mist, peat mixtures may not pro-

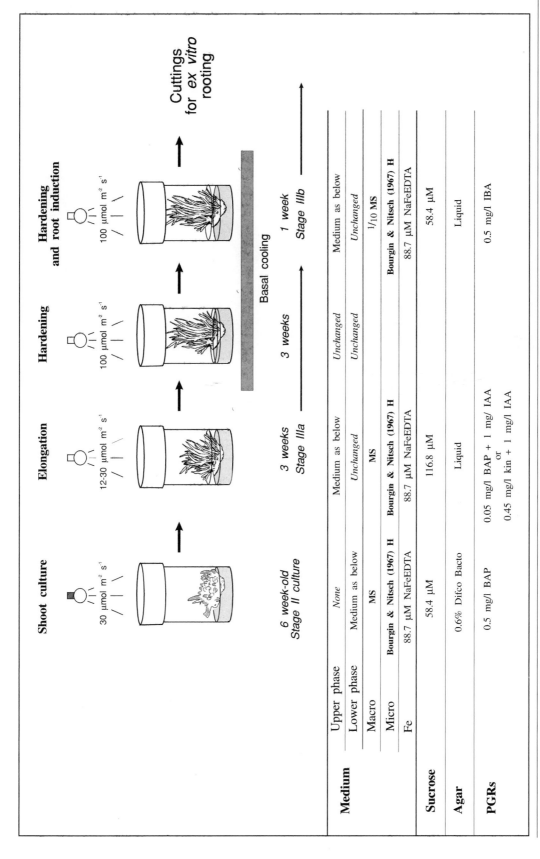

Fig. 126. A series of integrated steps which are effective in elongating, hardening and inducing root formation in shoot cultures of *Cordyline*. It will be seen that the use of a two–phased medium is coupled with varied lighting and cooling the base of the culture vessels [from Maeene and Debergh, 1987; Debergh and Maene, 1990].

The figure shows stages: **Shoot culture** → **Elongation** → **Hardening** → **Hardening and root induction** → Cuttings for *ex vitro* rooting.

		Shoot culture	Elongation	Hardening	Hardening and root induction
		30 μmol m² s⁻¹	12–30 μmol m² s⁻¹	100 μmol m² s⁻¹	100 μmol m² s⁻¹
		6 week-old Stage II culture	3 weeks Stage IIIa	3 weeks	1 week Stage IIIb
				Basal cooling	
Medium	Upper phase	*None*	Medium as below	*Unchanged*	Medium as below
	Lower phase	Medium as below	*Unchanged*	*Unchanged*	*Unchanged*
	Macro	**MS**	**MS**		¹/₁₀ **MS**
	Micro	**Bourgin & Nitsch (1967) H**	**Bourgin & Nitsch (1967) H**		**Bourgin & Nitsch (1967) H**
	Fe	88.7 μM NaFeEDTA	88.7 μM NaFeEDTA		88.7 μM NaFeEDTA
Sucrose		58.4 μM	116.8 μM		58.4 μM
Agar		0.6% Difco Bacto	Liquid		Liquid
PGRs		0.5 mg/l BAP	0.05 mg/l BAP + 1 mg/ IAA or 0.45 mg/l kin + 1 mg/l IAA		0.5 mg/l IBA

Fig. 127. *Dracaena* cuttings rooted directly into plugs.

vide adequate drainage (Hutchinson, 1985b). The suitability of a rooting substrate for *Telopea speciosissima* (a 1:2 mixture of peat and perlite) was thought by Offord and Campbell (1992) to be related to its air–filled porosity (greater than 20%) after saturation and drainage for 24 h.

The mixture used will need to be varied according to the kind of plant being grown. Hill (1988) records that *Daphne* and *Amelanchier* require a 'dry mix', while azaleas and blueberries rooted and grew better in one which held more moisture. On vermiculite, 94% of *Carica papaya* shoots rooted and there was an average of 6.6 roots per shoot, but on peat the proportion of rooted shoots was only 32%, and there were only 1.1 roots per shoot (Kataoka and Inoue, 1992).

Microcuttings are very susceptible to pests and pathogens, and so the rooting medium should be sterilised by steam or λ– (gamma) irradiation whenever there is any risk of infection, and the cuttings or compost should be treated with fungicide (see below).

As with *in vitro* rooting, it can be beneficial to move shoot clusters for a short period to a medium without regulants before they are planted as cuttings. This improved the rooting and survival of *Telopea speciosissima* (Seelye, 1985).

Nutrient salts. It is usual to incorporate nutrient salts into the rooting substrate, or to moisten it with a weak nutrient solution such **Hoagland and Snyder (1933)** or $\frac{1}{2}$**MS** salts.

Plug systems

The handling of rooted plantlets and the facility with which they can be moved on to larger containers is improved if microcuttings are rooted directly into some kind of discrete container of compost, or into 'plugs' (Fig. 127), rather than into trays or boxes of rooting medium. Each plantlet then becomes a separate unit. Plugs are also suitable for plantlets obtained from *in vitro* rooting (see page 724). Cuttings or plantlets in plugs are usually packed into trays or flats which are placed onto capillary matting.

McCown (1986) has discussed the suitability of some of the available kinds of plug for the rooting of microcuttings. Clearly any commercially–available product must be of a reproducibly similar composition from one batch to another and free from weeds, pests and pathogens. To encourage rooting, the wetted plug should permit oxygen diffusion. An ideal product might even contain nutrient salts so that irrigation with a nutrient medium is unnecessary. Relative cost is clearly an important consideration in selecting an appropriate product.

The simplest kind of plug is a rigid tube which is filled with a suitable rooting preparation, usually a mixture of

Table 110. Reports of *ex vitro* rooting without the aid of auxins.

Plant	Reference
Aechmea fasciata	Jones & Murashige (1974)
Alnus glutinosa	Garton *et al.* (1981a)
Artemesia granatensis	Clemente *et al.* (1991)
Begonia rex	Cassells & Morrish (1985)
Brassica napus	Kartha *et al.* (1974a)
Carya illinoinensis	Hansen & Lazarte (1984)
Chrysanthemum cinerariaefolium	Grewal & Sharma (1978)
Dianthus caryophyllus	Davis *et al.* (1977)
Euphorbia fulgens	Zhang *et al.* (1986)
Exacum affine	Torres & Natarella (1984)
Gardenia jasminoides	Economou & Spanoudaki (1985;1986)
Halesia carolina	Brand *et al.* (1985)
Heuchera sanguinea	Stapfer & Heuser (1986)
Hydrangea macrophylla	Bailey *et al.* (1986)
Lythrum virgatum	Heuser (1983)
Mammillaria elongata	Johnson & Emino (1979)
Prunus 'Hally Jolivette'	Lineberger (1982)
Rhododendron chapmanii	Barnes (1985)
Rhododendron yakushimanum hybrids	Marks (1991a)
Rhododendron 'PJM hybrids'	Ettinger & Preece (1985)
Rhododendron spp.	Economou *et al.* (1981)
	Economou & Read (1984; 1986a)
Rhododendron spp.	McCown & Lloyd (1983)
Rorippa nasturtium aquaticum	Wainwright & Marsh (1986)
Rubus allegheniensis & sp.	Gupton (1986)
Rubus idaeus	Snir (1981)
Tiarella cordifolia	Kitto (1986)
Vaccinium angustifolium	Frett & Smagula (1983)
Vaccinium spp.	Smagula & Lyrene (1984)
Vaccinium vitis-idaea	Hosier *et al.* (1985)
Veronica 'Red Fox'	Stapfer *et al.* (1985)
Vinca minor	Stapfer & Heuser (1985)

peat, sand, vermiculite or perlite. Other types of ready–made plug comprise peat pellets (Jiffy–7®, Techniculture plugs®) (McCown, 1986; Bennett, 1987), and phenol–resin foam cubes (Oasis Horticubes® — see page 686). Rockwool (stonewool) plugs (Grodan–Rockwool, The Netherlands) can also be used (Maene and Debergh, 1983). Microcuttings of *Dracaena* which have been rooted directly into Jiffy plugs are shown in Fig. 127. Plugs are not suitable unless cuttings can be easily inserted into them.

Pierik (1991b), reviewing the use of Rockwool plugs, said that before use they should be saturated with a weak nutrient solution, normally with a pH of 5.2, and the excess allowed to drain away.

Shoots should be washed free of residual organic compounds before insertion into plugs, to minimise the risk of infection. Alderson *et al.* (1988) found that micro-cuttings of rose could be rooted non–aseptically in Sorbarods (see above) soaked with **Lloyd and McCown (1981) WPM** medium containing 1 µM IBA, providing fungicides were also present. Tilt MBC (a mixture of propiconozole and carbendazim — Ciba Geigy) at 0.005 or 0.01% was best, effectively preventing the growth of fungi and algae. Roots formed relatively slowly in the rods but plantlets could be transplanted without root disturbance. Disadvantages of using cellulose cylinders in this way were that concentrations of fungicide needed to be modified for different rose varieties, and because the cylinders were liable to shrink when dry, they required careful watering.

Auxin treatments

Cuttings of many plants root more readily if they are exposed to auxin before they are planted into a rooting substrate, but, as is the case with *in vitro* rooting, treatment with auxin does not necessarily ensure good root formation. In fact microcuttings of many species can be rooted by being inserted into a soil mixture without any further treatment. Examples of plants in which transfer without auxin pre–treatment has been reported to have led to successful rooting, are given in Table 110.

Sometimes auxin may increase the number of roots formed on each shoot without altering the proportion of rooted shoots. However, in most plants, dipping shoots into auxin solutions or auxin/talc powder mixtures before planting, also spectacularly increases the proportion which forms roots and survives acclimatization. For example, without auxin treatment only 20% of *Camellia* shoots produced roots *extra vitrum*, but of those dipped into an IBA solution, 95% were rooted (Samartin, 1992). Commercial rooting powders or solutions are frequently used to treat shoots: they often contain both auxin and fungicide. There seems to be little difference in the effectiveness of powders or liquids, although some would argue that auxin solutions permit a better control over the amount of compound administered. Solutions have often been prepared by dissolving auxin in ethanol, although horticulturists have found propylene glycol (50% aqueous v/v) to be an alternative solvent for IBA.

Table 111 gives some example of the treatments used by different authors. Where auxins were found to be necessary, NAA or IBA have been used most frequently [although it will be seen that Roest and Bokelman (1973) had considerable success with a 1% IAA talc]. The commercial rooting powder, 'Rootone F1' ™ used by Gray

Table 111. Examples of the use of auxin dips or short-interval soaks, as pre-treatments to promote rooting *ex vitro*.

Plant	Pre-treatments		Reference
	Auxin powders	Auxin solutions	
Actinidia chinensis		500 mg/l IBA	Monette (1986a)
		750 mg/l IBA dip	Barbieri & Morini (1987)
Anthemis arvensis	1% IAA talc		Roest & Bokelmann (1973)
Begonia × *hiemalis*	0.4% IBA		Simmonds (1984)
Begonia × *tuberhybrida*		2 mg/l aqueous IBA	Peck & Cumming (1984a)
Calendula officinalis	1% IAA talc		Roest & Bokelmann (1973)
Calocedrus decurrens		Shoot bases for 24 h in solution of 25 mg/l NAA + 25 mg/l IBA	Jelaska & Libby (1988)
Camellia sasanqua		1 g/l IBA, 20 min dip	Samartin (1992)
Chrysanthemum leucanthemum	1% IAA talc		Roest & Bokelmann (1973)
Chrysanthemum parthenium	1% IAA talc		Roest & Bokelmann (1973)
Chrysanthemum segetum	1% IAA talc		Roest & Bokelmann (1973)
Helenium autumnale	1% IAA talc		Roest & Bokelmann (1973)
Hypericum perforatum	1% IAA talc		Roest & Bokelmann (1973)
Hypochoeris radicata	1% IAA talc		Roest & Bokelmann (1973)
Juglans hindsii × *J. regia*		1016 mg/l (5 mM) IBA	Driver & Kuniyuki (1984)
Lagerstroemia indica		15 sec 0–1 mg/l IBA	Zhang & Davies (1986)
Leontodon autumnalis	1% IAA talc		Roest & Bokelmann (1973)
Matricaria maritima	1% IAA talc		Roest & Bokelmann (1973)
Picea abies		127 mg/l IBA overnight	Bornman (1983)
Populus spp.		100 mg/l IBA, 24 h	Chalupa (1979)
Quercus spp.		15 min, 500 mg/l IBA	Bennett & Davies (1986) Bennett (1987)
Rosa cvs.		1 mg/l NAA + 1 mg/l Vit. D_2 (liquid, shaken for 1 h)	Pittet & Moncousin (1982)
Syringa vulgaris	0.1% IBA talc		Hildebrandt & Harney (1983)
Ulmus spp.		100 mg/l IBA, 24 h	Chalupa (1979)
Vaccinium ashei		300 mg/l IBA dip	Lyrene (1980)
Vaccinium corymbosum	0.1% IBA talc		Wolfe *et al.* (1983)
Vaccinium corymbosum	0.3% IBA		Cohen & Elliott (1979)
Vaccinium sp.		Briefly in 1 g/l IBA in 50% ethanol	Zimmerman & Broome (1980)
Vitis rotundifolia	'Rootone F'		Gray & Benton (1991)

and Benton (1991), contains a mixture of four different auxins:

Compound	Concentration % w/w
NAA	0.033
1–naphthaleneacetamide	0.067
2–methylnaphthaleneacetamide	0.013
IBA	0.057

Seelye (1985) reported that many *Telopea speciosissima* microcuttings died if they were dipped into auxin immediately before they were planted. A high proportion rooted and survived if they were dipped into an IBA solution (500–1000 mg/l) 2 weeks *after* they were originally set into a soil mix. Could this observation have been related to the presence of GA_3 in the shoot proliferation medium?

Using 50% ethanol solutions of NAA (537, 2685 or 5370 µM) or IBA (490, 2450, or 4900 µM), Mackay and Kitto (1988) showed that the number of roots on *Artemisia* cuttings increased with auxin concentration, but the length of roots decreased. The concentration of auxin in powders can also be important. Rooting of *Telopea speciosissima* was better when shoots were dipped in a powder containing 3 mg/g, rather than 1 mg/g IBA. Shoots dipped into an 8 mg/g IBA powder rooted, but did not survive (Offord *et al.*, 1990).

Table 112. Pre-cultural *in vitro* treatments to induce roots before *ex vitro* root formation.

Plant	Treatment time	Medium		Sugar g/l	Auxin mg/l	Reference
		Type	Nature			
Begonia × tuberhybrida	10 days	Stationary liquid	Distilled water	None	2 IBA	Debergh and Maene (1981) Peck and Cumming(1984a)
Carya illinoinensis	6 days	Liquid, supported	**Lloyd and McCown (1981) WPM**	20 glucose	10 IBA	Hansen and Lazarte (1984).
Cyphomandra betaceae	2 weeks	Agar	¼ **MS** salts (plus **LS** vitamins)	30 sucrose	IBA	Cohen and Elliott (1979)
Malus × domestica	3–7 days	Liquid	½ **MS**	15 sucrose	0.3 IBA	Zimmerman and Fordham (1985)
Rosa cvs.	5 days	Shaken liquid	Mineral salts	60 sucrose	0.5 NAA	Avramis *et al.* (1982b)
Rhododendron	10 days	Agar	Modified **Anderson (1975)**	30 sucrose	5–15 IBA	Douglas (1984)

Saturating the rooting substrate. An alternative technique for enhancing root formation, which has not been widely adopted, is to saturate the rooting substrate with an auxin. To root *Tsuga heterophylla*, Cheng (1976b) watered mica peat with an NAA solution (2.8 mg/l) every two days, while for *Cordyline, Dieffenbachia, Dracaena, Ficus, Spathiphyllum* and *Manihot utilissima*, Debergh and Maene (1981; Maene and Debergh, 1983) saturated Rockwool blocks with 2 mg/l IBA at planting, washing the auxin away after 6 days, or allowing the auxin to be slowly reduced in concentration by subsequent leaching.

Auxin pre–treatments *in vitro*. There is a half–way position between *in vitro* and normal *ex vitro* rooting. It is to incubate microcuttings in a special medium until roots have been induced, or (using a slightly longer incubation period) until roots have just begun to be initiated, and only then to plant them *extra vitrum*. Root induction and final shoot quality is improved by the presence of sugar. The number of shoots producing roots is usually increased by the addition of an auxin. Although the use of a liquid medium for *in vitro* rooting often leads to vitrescence and poor shoot quality (see above), the much shorter incubation required for root induction means that it can be employed for most plants.

This technique can result in a high proportion of rooted shoots and is especially valuable for subjects which are difficult to root. The additional *in vitro* treatment adds to costs, but the improved rooting and survival of cuttings once they are planted out, recommend consideration for some plants. Examples of successful treatments of this kind are shown in Table 112. Murashige *et al.* (1974) obtained no improvement in the rooting of *Gerbera* shoots by dipping them in IAA, IBA or NAA solutions, whereas pre–culture of microcuttings in a medium con-

taining 10 mg/l IAA for at least 10 days, significantly enhanced subsequent root formation.

Two–phase supplements. Less effort is required for *in vitro* root *induction* if a liquid medium is added to the semi–solid medium previously used for shoot multiplication. Marks *et al.* (1987) found that adding a superficial layer of liquid medium at the shoot multiplication stage not only increased the numbers of shoots formed, but also improved the later direct rooting of *Magnolia* and *Rhododendron*. Liquid medium alone had some benefit, but in the case of *Rhododendron*, best results were obtained by the addition of IBA to the liquid phase. Root induction in *Cordyline* and *Dracaena* can be achieved by adding a liquid layer of 0.5 mg/l IBA in ¹⁄₁₀**MS** macronutrients [plus **Bourgin and Nitsch (1967) H** micronutrients] to the top of the agar–solidified multiplication medium.

Fig. 126 illustrates how, in an integrated procedure, this technique was preceded with the use of a liquid phase supplement and low light, for shoot elongation, and then high fluence light combined with basal cooling of culture vessels for *in vitro* hardening. After one week of incubation with auxin for root induction, shoots are separated from the shoot clusters and transferred to a peat–based rooting compost *ex vitro* (Maene and Debergh, 1987; Debergh and Maene, 1990). However, to justify the extra cost of incorporating such a system into the routine of a commercial laboratory, there would need to be marked improvements in the proportion of cuttings rooted, plantlet survival and plant quality. Druart (1991) reported that using a two–phase medium for the plum × peach rootstock 'Citation', caused problems. Even though elongation and rooting occurred perfectly satisfactorily, growth was frequently checked when plantlets were being acclimatized at Stage IV.

Fungicides

Treating cuttings with fungicides before they are planted in a rooting medium helps to prevent damping off, and increases the proportion which survives and becomes adjusted to greenhouse conditions. A fungicide dip usually precedes treatment with auxin, and many products can be employed (see page 725). A fungicide is often incorporated into commercial rooting powders. Ahuja and Muhs (1982) found that poplar shoots were advantageously dipped into antibiotics before being placed in a rooting compost. Root formation was usually hastened, but one genotype was sensitive to the (undisclosed) compounds used.

As an alternative to dipping cuttings or plantlets, the potting compost into which shoots or plantlets have been newly transferred can be watered with fungicide solution. This treatment is sometimes used in addition to dipping the plant material. A suitable dose for drenches is half the manufacturer's recommended concentration. Zimmer *et al*. (1981) watered *Anthurium* plantlets with Previcur–N fungicide.

The environment for *ex vitro* rooting

Rooting small batches of cuttings

Newly–planted cuttings must be kept in high humidity. This can be achieved by covering small batches of microcuttings planted into individual containers with glass or transparent plastic vessels, with plastic bags, or with larger sheets of film. Flats can be individually covered with rigid plastic lids or light plastic domes, or placed into plastic tents. To maintain humidity the cuttings will probably need to be syringed with water 2–3 times a day, beginning immediately after they are planted. As roots begin to develop, the frequency may be reduced to a single spray on alternate days.

Small covered containers are very liable to become overheated in greenhouses and need to be shaded in hot weather. Recent research papers frequently refer to the use of specially constructed high humidity chambers within growth rooms for *ex vitro* rooting. Within such chambers the temperature is usually maintained at *ca*. 25°C and relative humidity at 90%, and cuttings are given 16–24 h light per day from cool white tubes supplying 40 μmol m^{-2} s^{-1}.

After 3–4 weeks, when roots have formed, microcuttings can be gradually acclimatized to the normal environment (see page 722).

Rooting larger batches of shoots

Humidity. When large numbers of shoots are to be rooted simultaneously, it is necessary either to provide growth rooms especially devoted to *extra vitrum* rooting (an expensive solution), or to carry out the rooting process in a specially adapted area of a greenhouse. A means of keeping a high relative humidity around the cuttings is again essential and, depending on the ambient PPD, some shading may need to be applied. The methods used to maintain high humidity, and control temperature and exposure to light, are the same as those used during the acclimatization of plantlets which have been rooted *in vitro* (see page 725). Although misting is commonly used to increase the humidity for rooting conventional cuttings, and is also used for microcuttings, high humidity tents, or fogging tend to be preferred. Comparative results between mist and fog systems often show that disease problems are reduced in fog, a higher proportion of cuttings produce roots, or shoot and root growth are improved (Howard and Marks, 1987).

Relative humidity can be decreased and the light irradiance gradually increased once roots have formed, usually in 20–30 days, to allow the plantlets to acclimatize.

Bottom heating. Providing the ambient temperature is not excessive, rooting is improved by keeping the temperature in the rooting zone higher than that of the ambient air. This also helps to maintain a high humidity around the cuttings. Basal warming is always possible in growth rooms, but may not be feasible in greenhouses during summer months. It can be discontinued once a root system has formed. One convenient method of providing basal heat is with electrically heated soil warming cables or blankets. Wong (1982), for example, kept shoots of *Rhododendron* planted in flats in a humidity tent where the ambient temperature was 21–24°C day and 18°C night, but the 'soil' temperature was maintained at 24–27°C. Providing bottom heating makes it imperative that humidity around the shoots is closely monitored (page 727).

Selecting an appropriate time of year. Because in temperate climates, environmental conditions in glasshouses differ markedly at different times of the year, it can be advantageous to give some thought to the most opportune time to micropropagate certain species, so that microcuttings are available for direct rooting at a time of year which will be most suitable for their establishment. In Washington State, U.S.A., the seasons indicated in Table 113 were most suitable for rooting various woody subjects (Hill, 1988).

Table 113. Seasons of the year which, in the U.S.A., Hill (1988) found to be most suitable for rooting various plants *ex vitro.*

Type of plant	Examples	Season
Deciduous subjects	*Amelanchier, Syringa, Magnolia, Betula*	From March onwards
Slow growing evergreens	*Cornus canadensis, Kalmia*	July through to September
Other evergreens	*Pieris, Rhododendron*	September through to March

Supplementary lighting. Although shading is often necessary to prevent cuttings being damaged by solar radiation, *ex vitro* rooting is inhibited in poor light. It was decreased in *Vaccinium macrocarpon*, for instance, by placing shoots in trays covered with translucent lids. The proportion of rooted shoots and the dry weight of the plantlets after acclimatization was much greater when the lids were of clear plastic (Marcotrigiano and McGlew, 1991).

When shoots are to be rooted in greenhouses during the winter, supplementary lighting will probably be required in temperate climates. High pressure sodium vapour lamps are frequently used for this purpose. Wong (1982) reported supplying *Rhododendron* shoots with 4500 lux from such lights for 16 h per day. The lights were even kept on under shade during the summer, as by this means it was possible to maintain high irradiance while diminishing the adverse effects of too much heat.

Carbon dioxide supplementation

The leaves on shoots or plantlets that have grown *in vitro* are often capable of very limited photosynthesis *extra vitrum* and it is only new leaves formed in the external environment which are capable of normal carbon assimilation. An enhancement of photosynthesis can be brought about by enriching the atmosphere with additional carbon dioxide. Lakso *et al.* (1986a,b) obtained a striking improvement in the root and shoot growth of unrooted *Vitis* shoots directly after transfer from culture, when they were placed under a PPF of 150 μmol m^{-2} s^{-1} (18 h, 26°C) and the air enriched to contain 1200 p.p.m. CO_2. Enrichment is not effective until some days after shoots or plantlets have been transferred (*i.e.* until new leaves have started to grow) and may be ineffective unless photon fluence is increased with supplementary lighting (Desjardins *et al.*, 1987a,b). Twenty and 30 days after culture of the vine shoots with extra CO_2, the plants were 2 and 4 times greater in dry weight than controls. By 30 days, root growth was 6 times greater than that of untreated plants (Lakso *et al., loc. cit.*.).

Similar results have been obtained with other plants (see page 729).

THE GERMINATION AND DEVELOPMENT OF SOMATIC EMBRYOS

EMBRYO CONVERSION

Somatic embryos formed at Stage II must normally be induced to grow and 'germinate' into plantlets (somatic seedlings) at Stage III before they are transferred to the external environment and grown as plants, a possible exception being if they are to be planted directly into the soil in a protective coating, or by fluid drilling. The regeneration of somatic embryos into plantlets is called *conversion*. Numerous embryos can be produced during somatic embryogenesis but when, for example, they develop asynchronously and precociously, and some have an atypical morphology, only a proportion can be finally *converted* into plantlets. Progression from embryo initiation to final seedling germination requires a series of cultural operations, and with present techniques it is only possible at each step to carry forward a proportion of the embryos initially obtained. This is because many are of an unsuitable quality or fail to grow further. Descriptions of the 'germination' of somatic embryos should be examined carefully. Sometimes they refer only to the first stages of embryo growth and do not necessarily imply that plants were (or could have been) obtained.

Plantlets obtained from somatic embryos germinated *in vitro* need to be acclimatized in the same way as rooted cuttings, before being planted in the external environment. Somatic embryos cannot be considered to have germinated satisfactorily until they have grown sufficiently for continued survival.

Embryo quality

When immature zygotic embryos are excised and cultured, they usually germinate *precociously* and develop into seedlings prematurely. Instead of mature resting embryos being formed, the shoot apex, the radical and/or the hypocotyl or epicotyl of an embryo start to elongate and turn green, before the embryo has grown to a full size, and before the cotyledons have grown to a normal size. Somatic embryos are also said to germinate precociously when pro–embryos do not form shoot and root primordia simultaneously, or do so without passing through the characteristic phases of development. Precocious germination of wheat somatic embryos was more of a problem in media where embryogenesis had been induced by adding 2,4–D to the medium, than when dicamba had been used. It could be prevented by transferring embryos to a medium containing double the normal concentration of **MS** salts and adding 0.4–1.9 μM ABA (Carman *et al.*, 1988b). The concentration of abscisic acid increases in seeds during the latter stages of their natural development, preventing precocious embryo germination (Kermode, 1990).

In the experiment described above, the water potential of the medium was decreased by doubling the concentration of salts in the medium. Decreasing water potential in other ways has a similar effect. Precocious germination of wheat somatic embryos on a medium containing **MS** salts, could be prevented by adding potassium or sodium chloride to lower the water potential of the medium from *ca.* –387 kPa to *ca.* –486 kPa (Part 1, page 336). Adding a high concentration of casein hydrolysate to the medium has this effect. Precocious germination of *Medicago sativa* embryos was prevented by increasing the sucrose concentration in the medium from 30 to 60 g/l (Anandarajah and McKersie, 1990).

Precocious germination usually prevents embryo proliferation. In certain genotypes of wheat, somatic embryos were found to produce scutelli and multiple shoots and roots while still on **MS** medium containing 2,4–D. Once they had germinated, the embryos could not proliferate to give rise to secondary embryogenic tissue, so that the morphogenic potential of the cultures was limited (Bapat *et al.*, 1988).

Maturation. The inhibition of precocious germination improves the quality of somatic embryos and allows embryos to mature. To obtain well formed plantlets, the embryos form characteristically mature structures. Processes encouraging such development, in which embryos grow towards a size typical of that found in seeds, accompanied by the storage of reserves of carbohydrates and amino acids, are called embryo *maturation*. Deliberate maturation steps have not been found to be essential, but are highly desirable and enhance germination and *in vitro* embryo conversion. Maturation becomes essential if embryos are to be germinated directly in soil.

When a culture containing a mixed population of embryos is transferred to a maturation medium it is usual for only a proportion to grow and mature to a stage of development and size to be suitable for subsequent germination. Only 6–8% of *Picea* embryos derived from suspension culture reached this stage (Attree *et al.*, 1990b)

Selection. The quality of somatic embryos produced by many early protocols was often far from that of fully developed zygotic embryos in seeds; hypocotyls and radicals were often abnormally elongated while cotyledons were small. One important criterion for successful conversion is that embryos should approach zygotic embryos in appearance and internal characteristics (Gupta *et al.*, 1991). When large numbers of embryos are available, it can be desirable to select individuals of a uniform size for germination. Common methods of separating embryos from callus, non–embryogenic cells, and fused embryos, involve the use of screens, sieves or glass beads (Warren and Fowler, 1977); the use of density separation on Percoll (Lutz *et al.*, 1985) or sucrose (Kim and Janick, 1990) gradients; or differential sedimentation in a centrifuge (Lo Schiavo, 1984). Note, however, that embryos need to be handled cautiously at this stage. Boulay *et al.* (1988) found that it was best to separate embryos of *Picea abies* from spent medium by sedimentation. Centrifuging, even at $100 \times g$ for 10 min caused embryos to grow abnormally and fail to develop. It is often necessary to pick normal embryos from such mixed tissue masses. After globular embryos of *Euphorbia pulcherrima* had been removed from a suspension by sieving and filtration, and placed on filter paper, they were cultured on the paper for 3 weeks. Normal embryos were then picked out by hand and this separation had a strong stimulating effect on their germination (Preil, 1991).

Effect of genotype. Using existing protocols, it is noticeable that with some plants considerable difficulty is experienced in obtaining somatic embryo conversion. Variation in conversion frequency can even be found within cell lines of the same species; for example, Becwar *et al.* (1986) discovered considerable variation in the maturation and germination of *Picea abies* somatic embryos among cell lines isolated from different whole plants.

Nature of the medium

It seems that for effective maturation, the embryos of most plants require to be exposed to a high partial pressure of oxygen, because embryos grown on semi–solid media usually have a higher conversion rate than those grown in liquid media. Stuart *et al.* (1987) described the following conversion rate for *Medicago sativa* embryos:

Type of culture	Conversion %
Semi–solid	70–90
Suspensions in flasks	<30
Suspensions in bioreactors	2–3

Ammirato (1982) needed to transfer somatic embryos of yams (*Dioscorea* spp.) from a liquid to a semi–solid medium to obtain plantlet development. The formation and maturation of *Picea abies* somatic embryos from embryogenic callus is only possible if tissues are capable of free gas exchange. Embryogenic cells grown in suspension in liquid medium needed to be transferred to a semi–solid medium, or placed onto a filter paper support on the surface of a semi–solid medium to facilitate subsequent transfer (Attree *et al.*, 1990a). An alternative is to immobilise a suspension on polyurethane foam bathed with liquid maturation medium (Pâques *et al.*, 1992).

However, when direct measurements were made on *Picea abies* embryos, the effect of the gas phase varied between different lines, but the general tendency was for partial pressures of 5 kPa oxygen, and 6 kPa carbon dioxide, to stimulate maturation (Kvaalen and Von Arnold, 1991). In a medium fully saturated with oxygen and carbon dioxide from air, the respective partial pressures of these gases at 760 mm Hg would have been, respectively, 20.3 kPa and 0.034 kPa[†]. Thus in Kvaalen and Von Arnold's experiment, a high oxygen tension was *not* required, but CO_2 supplementation was beneficial.

The conversion of *Apium graveolens* embryos (naked or encapsulated) was improved by germinating them in an atmosphere enriched with 2% carbon dioxide (Onishi *et al.*, 1992).

Culture in liquid medium. In some species it is possible to provide sufficient oxygen to developing embryos in a liquid medium if it is vigorously agitated. The continued development of somatic embryos formed adventitiously on the axes and cotyledons of immature zygotic embryos of *Theobroma*, was enhanced by culture in a shaken liquid medium (gyratory shaker 50 r.p.m.). The cotyledons of the developing somatic embryos were larger and thicker than those of somatic embryos grown on a solid medium and appeared to be more equivalent to mature seed embryos *in vivo* (Pence *et al.*, 1979, 1980a). The growth and maturation of *Freesia hybrida* somatic embryos was accelerated by transferring embryogenic callus together with differentiating embryos to liquid medium subjected to gyratory shaking (Bach, 1992).

Preconditioning and maturation

Culture density

Halperin (1967) showed that the further growth of somatic embryos formed in suspension cultures of wild carrot, was proportional to the density at which they were plated onto a fresh medium. In the most low density cultures, the embryos were very reduced in size and did not show distinctive root and shoot poles. Warren and Fowler (1981) concluded that there was an 'embryo factor' which needed to be present at a critical level to co–ordinate cell division and morphogenesis. The presence of cytokinin (see below) and amino acids may be all that is required: *Dioscorea* embryos subcultured in groups of five, developed shoots and roots on unsupplemented medium, but if transferred singly they would only grow if the medium was fortified with 0.02 mg/l zeatin and 500 mg/l glutamine.

Darkness

Maturation can often be conducted in the dark, but somatic embryos must normally be exposed to light before they will germinate. However, embryos of *Ilex* first required a period in darkness (Hu and Sussex, 1972). An inhibitory effect of light on the growth of late stage zygotic embryos has also been observed in this genus (Ferreira and Hu, 1989). Norway spruce embryos germinated best when they were placed in the dark for 7 days before being kept in continuous light (Gupta *et al.*, 1991b) and many more *Cyclamen persicum* somatic embryos germinated in the dark than in the light (Kiviharju *et al.*, 1992).

Chilling

A factor or factors which originate in cotyledons (Abou–Zeid and Neumann, 1973; Thevenot and Côme, 1973), causes the seeds of many plants, especially woody species, to require chilling before they will germinate, or before seedlings will grow actively after germination. Somatic embryos of many plants are found to behave in a similar fashion and although dormancy is mainly found in woody species, embryos of some herbaceous species may also germinate more readily after a cold treatment. *Eschscholzia* somatic embryos required 4–8 weeks chill-

---

† $pCO_2 = (0.035\% \times 760) - (23.736 \times 0.0035) = 0.2577$ mm Hg or 0.034 kPa: see page 195, Part 1. The abnormally high partial pressure of CO_2 was obtained by using a forced flow gas supply.

ing at 6°C to induce germination (Kavathekar *et al.*, 1977). Chilling carrot somatic embryos at 4°C for 3–4 days, together with ABA treatment, helped to increase their survival when desiccated during encapsulation (see below) in a synthetic resin (Kitto and Janick, 1983; 1985b).

Both zygotic and somatic embryos of *Vitis* exhibit dormancy. That of grape seeds can be overcome by chilling at 5–10°C for up to 3 months, while to overcome the dormancy of somatic embryos of this plant, 2–8 weeks at 4°C has been found to be effective by some workers (Rajasekaran and Mullins, 1979, 1982; Rajasekaran *et al.*, 1982; Martinelli *et al.*, 1991). Somatic embryos of other species may need to be treated in the same way: embryos of *Juglans* are placed on a medium without regulants for 2 months at 2–6°C (McGranahan *et al.*, 1987), while *Aesculus hippocastanum* somatic embryos did not germinate unless they were kept in the dark at 6°C for 6 months (Profumo *et al.*, 1991).

Chilling can stimulate the germination of somatic embryos in the same fashion as desiccation (see below). Kott and Beversdorf (1990) found that it was a preferable technique for *Brassica napus* embryos (kept at 4°C for 9–12 days in light or dark), because less manipulations were involved and there was a reduced risk of contamination.

Treatment with abscisic acid

The use of abscisic acid (ABA) to assist somatic embryos to reach maturity has been mentioned in Chapters 11 and 12. This growth substance also regulates the maturation of embryos, preventing precocious germination, increasing tolerance of desiccation, and allowing embryos to store reserves of carbohydrates (Fujii *et al.*, 1989; Gupta *et al.*, 1991). The process may be enhanced if additional sucrose, or unusual sugars such as lactose or maltose (see below) are present in the medium (Schuller and Reuther, 1993), or especially if a non–permeating osmoticum such as polyethylene glycol (PEG) or dextrans are employed (see below).

Picea embryos were effectively matured during 28 days of incubation on paper supports wetted with ½**Von Arnold and Eriksson (1981)** medium containing 2% sucrose and 16 μM ABA (see below). This concentration of ABA was more effective than 32 μM for a shorter period. Maturation did not take place however if the cultured embryos were wet. It was therefore necessary to remove the lids from vessels for 2–3 days in a laminar flow cabinet prior to the commencing the ABA treatment (Attree *et al.*, 1990b).

Regenerated somatic embryos of *Medicago sativa* have been found to mature if cultured for 3 weeks in **Schenk**

and Hildebrandt (1972) medium supplemented with 5 μM ABA (Fujii *et al.*, 1989). In carrot 1–5 μM ABA, and in celery 50 μM ABA, is effective in enhancing maturation if applied either during the embryo induction phase, or after embryo formation (Kitto and Janick, 1983, 1985a; Redenbaugh, 1991).

The period during which embryos are cultured on a maturation medium may influence the success with which they can afterwards be germinated. The highest proportion of *Larix × decidua* embryos germinated after 3 weeks of culture in a maturation medium containing 40–60 μM ABA (Lelu *et al.*, 1994b). *Picea* embryos were matured with 16 μM ABA for 28 days (Attree *et al.*, 1990b)

Desiccation tolerance. Somatic embryos which have been treated with ABA have been found to resist desiccation (see below) more effectively. *Medicago sativa* were able to resist damage by desiccation after exposure to 5–10 μM ABA (Senaratna *et al.*, 1989a). The time at which embryos were exposed to ABA was critical: they were responsive for only a few days and required to be treated with the growth substance at *ca.* 14 days after embryo development had commenced on a hormone free medium.

Takahata *et al.* (1992) found that 10–100 μM ABA increased the desiccation tolerance of *Brassica* embryos. Treatment was best applied at the cotyledon stage and exposure to the regulant for 1 or 7 days was equally effective (Takahata *et al.*, 1993). Embryos of *Brassica* dried without having first been supplied with ABA, or those treated with only 1 μM, were inviable, but desiccation tolerance of celery somatic embryos was improved by only 1 μM ABA plus proline [100 mg/l —Park *et al.*, 1988; 115.1 mg/l (1 mM) Kim and Janick, 1990; 1991].

Germination and growth. In most species, embryo germination and growth seems to be promoted by a reduction of the ABA concentration used to promote maturation. It can also be important to keep the concentration used for maturation to a minimum, or a residue may adversely affect germination (Attree *et al.*, 1990a,b). Transfer to a medium without ABA, or incorporation of activated charcoal into the germination medium, has been effective in conifers (Durzan and Gupta, 1987; Pullman and Gupta, 1991). It has also been suggested that desiccation may assist germination by reducing ABA levels.

Water potential

Finkelstein and Crouch (1986) proposed that ABA may inhibit water uptake by embryos, because both ABA and culture on a medium of high osmolality (*ca.* 970–1180 mOsm/kg) (low water potential), acted in a similar way to prevent rapeseed embryo germination. Decreasing the osmotic potential of the medium on which conifer somatic embryos are grown has similarly been found significantly to reduce their tendency to germinate, and to improve their vigour and morphology. Moisture stress also seems to trigger a switch from the accumulation of starch to the accumulation of protein.

Effective maturation of conifer embryos has occurred when embryos were first cultured on a medium with an osmolality of *ca*. 450 mOsm/kg, followed by transfer to another medium containing activated charcoal and a high concentration of ABA (Gupta and Pullman, 1991; Pullman and Gupta, 1991). *Helianthus annuus* embryos induced to form on a modified **MS** medium with 30 g/l sucrose (osmolarity *ca*. 186 mOs/kg) required to be transferred to **B5** medium with 90 g/l sucrose (osmolarity *ca*. 351 mOsm/kg). The lower water potential of the second medium allowed embryo development to continue. Similarly, *Glycine* somatic embryos initiated on a medium containing **MS** salts and 5 g/l sucrose, were matured on media with, firstly **MS** salts plus 30g/l sucrose (2 weeks), and then **MS** salts plus 60 g/l sucrose (5 weeks). Germination occurred afterwards on a medium with $\frac{1}{2}$**MS** salts plus 10 g/l sucrose (Komatsuda *et al.*, 1992).

Non–permeating osmotica. Attree *et al.* (1991) (Attree and Fowke, 1993) have found that white spruce embryos can be matured effectively by treatment with abscisic acid combined with 5–10% polyethylene glycol (PEG). They propose that maturation is enhanced by water stress, but that when this is brought about by a low molecular weight solute such as sucrose, water stress is only temporary. Sucrose is able to cross the cell wall where, if its concentration is high, it causes plasmolysis. Soon, however, the sugar is taken up into the cell which then recovers. By contrast, placing a non–permeating high molecular weight solute, such as PEG, in the medium, causes the pressure potential of cells to be increased (to become less negative) causing water to be withdrawn from cells without causing plasmolysis. Cells may then only equilibrate their water potential with that of the medium by increasing the internal concentrations of solutes. The uptake of sucrose, for example, may then stimulate the deposition of storage reserves.

Adding PEG to media reduces the availability of oxygen to cells in non–agitated media by decreasing both the partial pressure of dissolved oxygen in solution and the rate at which the gas can diffuse (Mexal *et al.*, 1975). Maturation (which requires the availability of a high oxygen concentration, see above) with PEG is therefore not practicable if embryos are suspended in liquid media.

For osmotica to be unable to cross the walls of conifer somatic embryos, their molecular diameter must be greater than 3.0–3.5 nm (Attree and Fowke, 1993). Attree

et al. (1991) have used PEG 4000, Cornu and Geoffrion (1990) PEG 6000 for larch embryos, and Gupta and Pullman (1991) PEG 8000 for Douglas fir and Norway spruce embryos. The combination of 3% sucrose and 7.5% PEG 4000 provides an osmotic potential approximately equal to that of 9% sucrose.

Desiccation

Desiccation is a process to which most zygotic embryos are subjected and which may have a natural physiological role in the transition of embryos from a developmental state into a state in which they have the capacity to germinate (Kermode *et al.*, 1986). Desiccation has been found to promote maturation and induce a state of quiescence in somatic embryos (Gray 1987a). It is thought that drying redirects embryo metabolism. Under its influence, the formation of proteins associated with development and storage products gives way to the synthesis of proteins and enzymes characteristic of those found in germinating seedlings (Kermode *et al.*, 1986).

Desiccation helps to overcome dormancy, and in some plants the rate of growth of the plantlets obtained from desiccated somatic embryos has been found to be greater than that of hydrated ones (Parrott *et al.*, 1988; Senaratna *et al.*, 1989b).

In *Medicago sativa*, embryos were found not to survive desiccation satisfactorily unless they had been matured first of all on a medium containing ABA (see above). Plantlets were obtained from *ca*. 60% of desiccated embryos (and from a higher proportion if embryos had been pre–selected according to size and uniformity) and were more vigorous than those from embryos which had not been dried (but even so less vigorous than seedlings from zygotic embryos) (Senarata *et al.*, 1989a,b; 1990).

To enhance conversion, somatic embryos are therefore often dried, and for this purpose, all authorities agree that slow drying over several days at a comparatively high humidity, is preferable to rapid drying in air at ambient room humidity (Kim and Janick, 1989a; Roberts *et al.*, 1989a; Senaratna *et al.*, 1989a). Drying is usually carried out in progressively dry atmospheres in desiccators, using atmospheres of known relative humidities above saturated salt solutions. A comparison of some published values for the humidities obtainable over various salts is given in Table 114: salts to provide many other controlled humidities are also listed in the three references given in the table. Embryos are often dried down to a water content of 10–13%, and desiccation routines from which embryos have recovered and germinated have been continued for periods from 1–21 days. Gray (1989) found that the water content of *Vitis longii* embryos was reduced by 21 days exposure to reduced humidity in the following way:

Table 114. The relative humidity above saturated salt solutions.

Saturated salt solution	Relative humidity (%)		Reference
	20°C	25°C	
CuSO$_4$.5H$_2$O	98	—	Hodgman et al. (1962)
K$_2$SO$_4$	98	97.5	Winston and Bates (1960)
NaCO$_3$.10H$_2$O	93	87*	Hodgman et al. (1962) Lide (1991)
	92	87	Winston and Bates (1960)
NH$_4$Cl	79.5	78	Winston and Bates (1960)
	79.5	79.3	Hodgman et al. (1962) Lide (1991)
NaCl	76	75.5	Winston and Bates (1960)
NaCl plus KCl	70	71.5	Winston and Bates (1960)
NH$_4$NO$_3$	65.5	62.5	Winston and Bates (1960)
Ca(NO$_3$)$_2$.4H$_2$O	55.5	50.5	Winston and Bates (1960)
	—	51*	Hodgman et al. (1962) Lide (1991)
K$_2$CO$_3$.2H$_2$O†	44	43	Winston and Bates (1960)
CaCl$_2$.6H$_2$O‡	32.3	31*	Hodgman et al. (1962) Lide (1991)
	32.5	28.5	Winston and Bates (1960)

* At 24.5°C

The following footnotes are provided in Winston and Bates (1960):

† Should be granulated, then moistened; powdered form unstable.

‡ May be unstable around 20°C.

Relative humidity	Water content of somatic embryos after 21 days
%	%
95	30
85	14
75	12

Each of these treatments was sufficient to improve conversion from zero (non–desiccated), to 34%.

A mild drying treatment may be all that is required for somatic embryos of some plants. Roberts et al. (1989a) found that desiccation at high humidity was preferable for *Picea glauca* embryos, exposure to 97% RH being sufficient to enhance and synchronise germination.

Some other reports in which a greater proportion of embryos has germinated after desiccation, are as follows:

Glycine max	Hammatt & Davey (1987)
	Parrott et al. (1988)
Medicago sativa	Redenbaugh et al. (1991)
	McKersie et al. (1989)

A procedure which reduced the tissue moisture of wheat somatic embryos to *ca.* 10%, increased the proportion which subsequently germinated. The method consisted of maintaining the embryos at 10°C and at 92% R.H. for 14 days, followed by 32% R.H. for 23 days. Germination was then on a low salts (osmolality of 47.9 mOs/kg) medium (Carman, 1988).

Storage of desiccated embryos. If somatic embryos are to be used for large scale plant propagation, it will often be necessary to store them until the time is right for germination. Some techniques whereby this might be done were mentioned on page 165 of Part 1. Desiccation also enables somatic embryos to be stored before germination. A degree of quiescence was induced in orchard grass embryos by drying them in 70% relative humidity at 23°C (Gray, 1987b). The dried embryos contained 13% water compared to the 70% in fresh ones. Despite being yellow and brittle, 18% of the embryos germinated in **MS** medium after 7 days, and 4% after 14 days storage.

Better results were obtained with grape embryos, where plants were obtained from 28% of embryos stored for 7 days and from 20% stored for 21 days. However, treated embryos are thought not to become dormant, because they are capable of germination immediately upon re–hydration (Gray, 1989), and in fact they usually germinate more readily than non–desiccated embryos.

Desiccated *Medicago sativa* embryos have been stored without loss of viability for 12 months at room temperature and humidity (Senaratna *et al*, 1990). Takahata *et al.* (1992) managed to store dried microspore–derived somatic embryos of several *Brassica* spp. at room temperature for 6 months with no loss of conversion. Desiccation was accomplished in this case by slow drying after ABA treatment, followed by storage at 80°C for 2 days.

Germination. Like their non–desiccated counterparts, desiccated embryos are usually germinated on a low salts medium, without growth regulators, which contains 2–3% sucrose. They may also be germinated with advantage on a porous substrate such as sterile vermiculite wetted with a similar medium (see page 715). Approximately 45% of *Juglans* embryos germinated on a cotton compress wetted with liquid medium, whereas only 10% germinated on agar (Deng and Cornu, 1992).

Ideally, desiccated somatic embryos should take up water slowly, because rapid imbibition leads to leakage of cytoplasmic contents (Senarata *et al.*, 1989b). In the absence of a seed coat, this is difficult to regulate.

The proportion of *Apium graveolens* embryos which germinated after desiccation, could be improved by centrifuging samples on a sucrose density gradient. The highest frequency of mature embryos was found at the 9–12% interface (Kim and Janick, 1990).

Sugars

Maltose. Maltose may maintain a fairly stable osmoticum for cultured tissues, while slowly providing a source of glucose (see page 633) or may break down to yield glucose during autoclaving (Redenbaugh K.*et al.*, 1987b). A mixture of 0.3% maltose and 2.5% PEG 6000 was added to **B5** medium by Denchev *et al.* (1993) for the development of *Medicago sativa* embryos. In the presence of maltose, embryos grow larger, their morphology is more typical, and they become more viable so that the frequency with which they can be converted into plantlets is increased. The stimulative effect of maltose is dependent on the presence of 15 mM NH_4^+ (Strickland *et al.*, 1986; 1987: Stuart *et al.*, 1986; 1987; 1988). Glucose has a similar effect to maltose (Redenbaugh K. *et al.*, 1987b).

Sucrose. Sucrose is usually necessary for *in vitro* embryo germination. The conversion of somatic embryos, especially those germinated in soil (see below) can be improved if they are pre–cultured on a medium with a high concentration of sucrose. Culture on **MS** medium with 10% (0.28 mM) sucrose increased the frequency with which *Glycine max* embryos could be converted (Bucheim *et al.*, 1989); keeping *Medicago sativa* embryos for 4–6 weeks on 1.5 times **Schenk and Hildebrandt (1972)** medium with 4.5–6% sucrose, had a similar effect (Redenbaugh, 1991).

Culture media for germination

Composition

Somatic embryos of very many plant species germinate satisfactorily on the same medium, containing the same concentration of sugars, as was used to induce embryogenesis. In these cases it is only necessary to transfer the embryos to fresh medium with less auxin than was used to induce embryogenesis, or to a medium where regulants have been omitted (Tables 91, 92 & 93 in Chapter 12). Ammirato and Steward (1971) concluded that the effectiveness of **MS** medium for embryogenesis *in vitro* was due to its promotion of the later stages of embryo development, rather than embryo initiation. They found coty-

ledon growth of somatic embryos to be particularly responsive to a greater availability of nitrogen. By adding extra nitrogen sources to White's medium (especially ammonium nitrate), the same rate of embryo growth was obtained as occurred on **MS** medium. *Anethum* embryos germinated only where 1 g/l yeast extract had been added to **MS** medium (Sehgal, 1978).

Amino acids. The addition of amino acids to culture media has been noticed to enhance the growth of somatic embryos of several different species of plants. Some workers have also found that germination of somatic embryos requires, or is improved by, the addition of amino acids to the medium. *Aesculus hippocastanum* embryos did not germinate unless 400 mg/l glutamine was added to **MS** medium containing 1 mg/l IAA and 1 mg/l GA_3 (Radojević 1988). Germination media for conifer somatic embryos usually contain half strength salts, 1–2% sucrose, vitamins, a low concentration of one or more amino acids, and activated charcoal (Gupta *et al.*, 1991b). The germination of *Mangifera indica* somatic embryos was increased from 35% on a modified **Gamborg *et al.* (1968)** B5 medium containing ½ strength salts, to 63% on the same medium incorporating 20% coconut milk and 0.025% casein hydrolysate (Dewald *et al.*, 1989).

Water potential

Some comparisons between media used to obtain somatic embryos and media used for embryo germination are given in Table 115. It will be seen that, in most of the experiments listed, embryos were germinated on a medium of higher (less negative) water potential (ψ_{tcm}) than that on which they were initiated, or matured (page 711). The media used for embryo germination at Stage III usually contain less concentrated macronutrients and/or sugars than are used at Stage II.

Somatic embryos formed from endosperm callus of sandalwood were subcultured from **MS** medium onto **White (1963)** medium to obtain plantlet development. If they were left on **MS** medium the embryos did not develop a tap root and shoots grew only to the second leaf stage (Lakshmi Sita *et al.*, 1980). Dale *et al.* (1981) found that large embryos of *Lolium multiflorum* would germinate if individually transferred to full strength or half strength **MS** medium without growth regulators, but that the less well developed ones needed to be moved to half strength **MS** with 0.5 mg/l 2,4–D, 3 mg/l IAA and 1 mg/l kinetin.

Even when a high salts medium (of low water potential) has been used for somatic embryo germination, young embryo–derived plantlets are usually transferred to one of lower ionic concentration to enable them to grow to a sufficient size for transfer *extra vitrum*. Once germination

Table 115. Characteristics of media used for embryogenesis and somatic embryo germination.

Plant	Medium for embryogenesis			Medium for germination			Reference
	Macro-nutrient ions	Sucrose	Water potential at 25°C	Macro-nutrient ions	Sucrose	Water potential at 25°C	
	mM	g/l	MPa	mM	g/l	MPa	
Asclepias syriaca	95.8	60	–0.70	64.5	58.2	–0.47	Singh (1984)
Asparagus officinalis	95.8	30	–0.46	33.9	30	–0.31	Willmar & Hellendoorn (1968)
Carica candamarcensis	95.8	30	–0.46	47.9	20	–0.27	Jordan *et al.* 1983)
Carica hybrids	47.9	60	–0.58	18.0	60	–0.51	Moore & Litz (1984) Litz & Conover (1982; 1983)
Dendranthema grandiflorum	95.8	120–150	–1.21 → –1.50	95.8	30	–0.46	May & Trigiano (1991)
Glycine canescens	95.8	30	–0.58	47.9	30	–0.34	Grant (1984)
Gossypium hirsutum	95.8	30	–0.58	47.9	15	–0.23	Shoemaker *et al.* (1986)
Hibiscus acetosella	52.0	40G	–0.72	61.89	20	–0.30	Reynolds *et al.* (1980) Reynolds & Blackmon (1983)
Plantlet growth				44.7	10	–0.19	
Ipomoea batatas	95.8	30	–0.46	95.8	16	–0.36	Cheé *et al.* (1990)
Juglans spp.	104.1	30	–0.48	104.1	30	–0.48	Driver & Suttle (1987)
Root growth of seedlings on:				6.1	5	–0.05	
Lolium multiflorum	85.8	30	–0.44	47.9	30	–0.34	Dale *et al.* (1981)
Medicago sativa	59.8	30	–0.37	16.5	15→30	–0.15 Ä0.26	Johnson *et al.* (1981)
Medicago sativa	60.0	30	–0.37	67.2	10	–0.24	Atanassov & Brown (1984)
Medicago spp.	60.0	30	–0.37	67.2	10	–0.24	Brown & Atanassov (1985)
Panax ginseng	95.8	30	–0.46	47.9	15	–0.23	Shoyama *et al.* (1988)
Pennisetum americanum & *Pennisetum* hybrid	95.8	60	–0.70	95.8	30	–0.46	Vasil & Vasil (1981a)
Picea abies	84.2	34.2	–0.46	95.8	20	–0.39	Hakman & Von Arnold (1985)
Pisum arvense *Pisum sativum*	95.8	30	–0.46	95.8	15	–0.35	Jacobsen & Kysely (1984)
Saccharum officinarum	95.8	30	–0.46	95.8	30	–0.46	Ho & Vasil (1983)
Plantlet growth on:				47.9	60	–0.58	
Santalum album	95.8	20	–0.39	18.0	20	–0.19	Lakshmi Sita *et al.* (1979; 1980)
Trifolium rubens	83.0	25	–0.39	83.0	25	–0.39	Grosser & Collins (1984)
Embryos with shoots rooted on:				51.9	15	–0.24	
Trifolium sarosiense hybrid	83.0	25	–0.39	51.9	15	–0.24	Phillips *et al.* (1982)
Embryos with shoots rooted on:				51.9	15	–0.24	
Vigna aconitifolia	94.9	30	–0.46	47.5	10	–0.19	Shekhawat & Galston (1983a)
Vitis vinifera	13.5	50	–0.41	17.7	20	–0.19	Mullins & Srinivasan (1976)
Zea mays	75.1→95.8	120	–1.17→ –1.22	95.8	20	–0.38	Rapela (1985)
	95.8	120	–1.22	62.2	20	–0.30	Truong-Andre & Demarly (1984)
Zea mays	95.8	20	–0.386	83.1	60	–0.67	Green (1982)
Plantlet growth on:				83.1	20	–0.36	
Zea mays	95.8	120	–1.22	95.8	30	–0.46	Lu *et al.* (1982)
Plantlet growth on:				47.9	15	–0.23	

has taken place, it is usually found that the roots of somatic seedlings do not grow properly on media of high concentration (*e.g. Juglans* and *Trifolium* in Table 115). When grass and cereal somatic embryos have germinated *in vitro*, Vasil and co–workers transferred the plantlets to a medium containing only ½**MS** inorganics before finally planting them *extra vitrum* (Lu and Vasil, 1981a; Lu *et al.*, 1982; Vasil and Vasil, 1981a,b).

Methods of support

Germination of somatic embryos and subsequent plantlet growth may be improved if, instead of being placed on a semi–solid medium, embryos are placed on vermiculite, or some other porous substrate, which is wetted with a nutrient solution. They may be planted on such a porous support before germination, or they may be moved to it once germination has commenced on agar or filter paper.

Asparagus somatic embryos grew into small plantlets when they were layered onto a Whatman No. 1 filter paper wetted with a modified **MS** medium containing 0.2 mg/l IAA and 1 mg/l zeatin (Levi *et al.*, 1986). Carrot embryos grew more normally on polyester, or ceramic wool than they did on agar (Tsuji *et al.*, 1992). Cotton embryos 3–10 mm in length were planted directly on sterile vermiculite fed with **Stewart and Hsu (1977) E** medium (ionic concentration 24.4 mM) containing 0.1 mg/l IAA, and if the embryos were small, 0.1 mg/l GA_3 (Umbeck *et al.*, 1987; Trolinder and Goodin, 1987, 1988b). *Picea* embryos were moved to a perlite : peat : vermiculite (1:1:1) mixture, watered with a salts solution, once germination had commenced (Boulay *et al.*, 1988).

Cultural conditions

The growth and acclimatization of germinating somatic embryos can, of course, be accelerated by conditions which are promotive to shoots cultured *in vitro*. Tsuji *et al.* (1992) showed, for example, that the growth of young plantlets growing from the somatic embryos of carrot was promoted by culture in a carbon dioxide concentration of 2000 p.p.m. Acclimatization was promoted if the humidity in vessels was maintained at 80%.

Transplanting somatic seedlings

The plantlets produced from embryos germinated on a nutrient medium must eventually be moved into a solid planting substrate and there carefully weaned (see below) until they are capable of growth as plantlets in the external environment. Sterilised soil may be suitable for some plants but usually a free draining compost is used.

Juglans and *Pterocarya* somatic embryos, initially germinated on **White (1940)** medium containing 0.5% sucrose and 0.5% activated charcoal, were moved for further growth to peat plugs contained in vials, which were wetted with the same medium (McGranahan *et al.*, 1987). *Eleusine coracana* plantlets with small roots, obtained by germinating embryos on **MS** medium, were planted in an autoclaved mixture of soil (3 parts) and vermiculite (1 part). This was watered with 1% NH_4NO_3 and 1% KNO_3 (Sivadas *et al.*, 1990).

Sugars

Embryo growth. Jones (1974b) showed that sucrose was essential for the growth and germination of carrot embryos. Those plated onto a basal **MS** agar medium without sucrose, failed to grow but remained viable for up to two years when kept in a growth room illuminated with less than 400 lux. Within three weeks of injecting sucrose into culture flasks stored for 1 or 2 years, spherical and heart shaped embryos formed green cotyledons. Some of these embryos germinated normally but most proliferated to give fresh groups of adventitious somatic embryos.

Embryo growth is arrested by very high sucrose levels (in cocoa it was reduced to zero by incorporating 21% sucrose into the medium — Pence *et al.*, 1980b, 1981) and in carrot, small embryos produced in the presence of 120–200 g/l sucrose, give rise to numerous adventitious secondary embryos (Ammirato and Steward, 1971). These develop into abnormal plants when they are germinated (Liyanage and Kurata, 1992).

Embryo germination. A supply of sugar is essential for initial germination and plantlet growth but the requisite concentration is generally less than that necessary for embryo development (Table 115). Somatic embryos of carrot and *Sium suave* grew into plantlets with leafy cotyledons and actively growing roots on **MS** medium with 30 g/l sucrose. If instead, 120 g/l sucrose was added to the medium, smaller embryos were formed which had fore–shortened radicles and smaller but fleshy cotyledons, rather like zygotic embryos found in seeds (Ammirato and Steward, 1971).

Growth regulator effects

Auxins

In the majority of cases, to induce the formation of somatic embryos from embryogenic callus, it is necessary to transfer the callus from a medium containing a relatively high concentration of auxin, to a similar medium which contains none, or to one in which there is a reduced auxin concentration. Embryo germination frequently occurs on the same secondary medium, especially if any auxin supplements are further reduced in concentration.

Embryos induced to form in the presence of 2,4– D, sometimes grow more satisfactorily on a medium containing a small concentration of IAA, IBA or NAA. The presence of a low concentration of one of these compounds in the differentiation medium can promote the root growth of embryos. A low level has sometimes been added to a medium containing ABA at the maturation stage (see below), for instance 0.1–0.5 µM NAA together with ABA enhanced the growth of *Picea abies* embryos (Boulay *et al.*, 1988).

Cytokinins

The presence of a cytokinin in the medium is often beneficial to the germination of somatic embryos of dicotyledons (Tables 91 and 92, Chapter 12) and can promote embryo germination of monocotyledonous plants (Table 93). Vasil and Vasil (1981b) reported that embryos of *Pennisetum americanum* developed into robust plantlets when they were transferred to **MS** medium plus 1 mg/l 2–iP or zeatin. Dale *et al.* (1981) germinated Italian ryegrass embryos on **MS** medium containing 0.2 mg/l kinetin and the germination of wheat embryos was promoted if they had been grown on a medium containing coconut water (Carman *et al.*, 1988a). However, Wernick and Brettell (1980) said that 0.1 mg/l kinetin was only an optional addition to **MS** medium to obtain the germination of *Sorghum bicolor* embryos; the most important thing was to transfer them to a medium without 2,4–D.

Gibberellins. In several papers gibberellic acid (GA$_3$) has been reported to promote embryo germination, stimulating either shoot or root growth (see page 449 of Part 1). 1.4–2.9 µM (0.5–1 mg/l) is typically added to the medium for this purpose, often in conjunction with IAA (*ca* 1 mg/l) or a cytokinin for dicotyledons, or as the only regulant for monocotyledons.

Growth inhibitors

Some asexual embryos may be prevented from germinating by inhibitors naturally occurring within the embryo itself or within the tissue on which embryogenesis took place. *Theobroma cacao* somatic embryos germinated only if they were first leached in water. This leachate inhibited the germination of lettuce seeds and was thought likely to contain *p*–coumaric acid (Wang Y. *et al.* 1981). The somatic embryos formed directly on the cotyledons of *Ilex* seed embryos, would not germinate until they were removed separately, or in clusters, and planted on the same medium (Hu and Sussex, 1972). Similarly, in *Albizia lebbek*, somatic embryos developed only as shoots if they were left on the original explant, but if these shoots were excised and subcultured onto the same me-

dium, they formed roots and grew into complete plants (Gharyal and Maheshwari, 1981).

Transfer to a regulant–free medium. Where germination occurs on a medium containing low concentrations of growth regulators, it may afterwards be necessary to move the very small plantlets to a regulant–free medium with a low salt content (see above) for continued growth.

PLACEMENT IN SOIL

There are several approaches to obtaining a regular stand of well–spaced plants in the field. Seed can be sowed thickly and seedlings thinned to the required density; seed can be sown with a precision drill so that seedlings emerge at the correct spacings; or cuttings or seedlings can be grown in a greenhouse or nursery, and planted into the field when well established. The latter technique is well suited to crops whose seed is expensive, where establishment from directly sown seed is difficult or erratic, or where the young seedling requires protection. Planting plug–grown plants is common practice for many ornamentals, vegetable crops and forest trees and the process can be automated when plantlet numbers are large (page 814).

Transplanting established plants

Pre–germination of somatic embryos and establishment of the resulting plantlets in a soil plug, or some other kind of miniaturised container is a perfectly acceptable way of transferring to the field plants which have been propagated through somatic embryogenesis. It is the technique which has been used for oil and date palms raised from somatic embryos.

Direct field planting

Instead of germinating somatic embryos *in vitro*, transferring them as plantlets to a nursery, and then establishing the plants in the field, a great deal of recent research has been applied to devising methods for direct planting before germination has taken place. Much of this work is hampered by the poor quality of somatic embryos produced by existing technology, and their lack of storage tissues, such as swollen cotyledons or endosperm, to sustain embryo growth, and the protective outer coatings of the normal seed. To be able to germinate after direct field planting, somatic embryos must be able to tolerate some degree of desiccation.

In this case vascular connections between roots and shoots may be inadequate at the time of transfer, so that there is an adequate upward flow of water and nutrients, and/or an insufficient downward passage of carbohydrates to the roots (see page 671).

— that in woody plants, adventitious roots produced *in vitro* only form a primary vascular system which has poor conductance.

The consequences of an incomplete vascular system in roots of woody plants formed *in vitro* has been discussed on page 672 but, as mentioned there, woody plants have been rooted *in vitro* and later acclimatized satisfactorily. Water conduction in roots of *Juglans regia* produced *in vitro* was adequate to maintain the plantlets during acclimatization without the development of secondary xylem. Berros *et al.* (1993) found that roots arose from cells close to the metaphloem so that vessels were well connected to the main vasculature of the stem.

— that the presence of roots on shoots which are not yet capable of autotrophic carbon assimilation, will also mean that roots are not sufficiently supplied with carbohydrate during the early days after transfer *extra vitrum*.

Using rate of water loss to assess hardening

As plantlets are progressively acclimatized, the rate of water loss from their leaves decreases. The relative degree of plantlet acclimatization can therefore be measured very simply by a method first used by Brainerd and Fuchigami (1981). Leaves are removed from sample plants, and are weighed and left to dry at *ca.* 40% relative humidity (see page 712), The leaves are weighed again and then finally oven dried and weighed once more. The percent water loss (*L*) during this period:

$$L = \frac{(\text{Fresh weight} - \text{Weight after controlled drying})}{(\text{ Fresh weight} - \text{Oven dried weight})} \times 100$$

decreases the longer plantlets are acclimatized, until it reaches a constant value and is thus inversely proportional to the degree of hardening of the plantlets.

Using this method, Lewandowski (1991) obtained the following relative hardening of *Vitis labrusca* plantlets. Leaves were stored for 20 minutes at 40% relative humidity. Under these conditions leaves from:

— non–hardened plants lost *ca.* 82% of their water;

— plantlets gradually hardened for 15 days, lost 46% of their water (these were capable of surviving in a greenhouse at 44–66% relative humidity);

— but plantlets grown in the greenhouse for a further 6 days (14 days gradual hardening plus 7 days in the glasshouse), lost only 6% of their water.

In a slight variation of this method Debergh (1991) weighed small samples of leaf tissue at regular 5 minute intervals for one hour as they dried at *ca.*45% relative humidity (before they were finally oven dried to determine dry weight). The graphs of water loss obtained show that leaves of Stage II and Stage III plants are much more liable to water loss than Stage II plants which have been hardened *in vitro* in 75% relative humidity.

Photosynthesis

Leaf structure

Shoots or plantlets growing on a sugar–supplemented medium *in vitro* produce only a small amount of their carbohydrate requirement through CO_2 fixation and have to change to fully autotrophic nutrition when they are removed from culture. Photosynthetic competence takes some time to be instituted because the internal anatomy and ultrastructure of shoots and leaves propagated *in vitro* is often different to that of greenhouse or field grown plants (Dunston and Sutter, 1982; Wetzstein *et al.*, 1981; Wetzstein and Sommer, 1981). The leaves of strawberry plants formed *in vitro* were, for example, lacking in palisade cells and mesophyll air space. Although the latter increased during acclimatization and the leaves thickened, the leaves never gained the hidden stomata or the same photosynthetic apparatus as the leaves newly produced after transfer (Sutter *et al.*, 1985). The depth of palisade cells in *Prunus insititia* 'Pixy' was significantly less in the leaves of aseptically–grown shoots than in those which had grown on plantlets transferred to the greenhouse, or grown on plants in the field (Brainerd *et al.*, 1981)

Chloroplasts of *Liquidambar* shoots cultured in low light were poorly developed and had disorganised grana (Wetzstein and Sommer, 1982).

Carbon assimilation

In many species, leaves present on shoots in culture vessels, and sometimes even those initiated in culture but expanded *extra vitrum* (Donnelly and Vidaver, 1984), are incapable of the transpiration and the photosynthesis required for survival outside. The photosynthetic apparatus of newly transferred cauliflower plantlets was insufficient to produce a net positive carbon balance, mainly because there were lower levels of chlorophyll and a lower ribulose biphosphate (RubP) carboxylase enzyme activity than normal (Grout and Donkin, 1987).

Grout and Aston (1978) demonstrated that 7 days after transplanting, cauliflower plantlets had begun fixing CO_2 more actively than *in vitro*, but were still releasing more CO_2 than they were assimilating through photosynthesis. Dark respiration was higher than in seedlings of comparable age, suggesting that the plants had a high energy requirement for adaptation to their new environment.

Only after 14 days was a positive carbon balance a-chieved. The growth of new leaves occurred at this time. Similar observations have been made with other plants (Donnelly *et al.*, 1984) and it is clear that in many species, leaves formed *in vitro* may serve as little more than storage organs (Wardle *et al.*, 1979, 1983). They do not increase in size after transplanting, have a low rate of photosynthesis which never recovers to normal, and gradually die back. By contrast, leaves newly formed *extra vitrum* grow rapidly, and have a normal appearance and photosynthetic function (Deng and Donnelly, 1993). However, salts and organic substances stored in older non–functional leaves are translocated to assist the growth and development of new organs during acclimatization (Grout and Millam, 1985).

In other species, leaves formed *in vitro* can become adapted and contribute to carbon fixation (Donnelly *et al.*, 1985; Desjardins *et al.*, 1988; Grout, 1988). Reuther (1988b) found, for instance, that the rate of photosynthesis of *in vitro Pelargonium* plantlets increased when they were exposed to high irradiance light (80–260 μmol m^{-2} s^{-1}) for one week in a CO_2–enriched atmosphere.

For those species in which photosynthesis can be shown to increase during *in vitro* preconditioning (page 695), Reuther (*loc. cit.*) suggested the following treatments should precede transfer to the external environment:

- a slight increase in photon fluence;

- gas exchange with the ambient atmosphere (loosening or removing closures (page 696);

- enriching the carbon dioxide in the growth room and in the first period after transfer to the greenhouse (page 707).

The photosynthetic capacity of shoots cultured *in vitro* can be increased by lowering the sucrose in the medium or omitting it altogether (Short *et al.*, 1987: Part 1, page 204), but survival of plantlets during their first two weeks *in vivo* is precarious if they do not have reserves of starch in their leaves accumulated during culture (Wardle *et al.*, 1979).

In conventional micropropagation, carbohydrate reserves are built up by maintaining sucrose in the Stage II or Stage III medium prior to acclimatization (see page 696). This practice also helps to improve *in vitro* hardening, because the water potential of the medium is then decreased (Part 1, page 330). The presence of sugar in an *in vitro* rooting medium assists both these processes, as well as being beneficial to root growth. Carbohydrate reserves are also accumulated if photoautotrophic growth has been possible *in vitro*.

ACCLIMATIZATION

The process of acclimatization has been termed 'acclimation' in some papers. The latter term is not recommended in connection with the adjustment of tissue cultured plants to conditions *ex vitro*, as acclimation strictly denotes the adaptation of an organism in the wild to a natural climatic environment. The process whereby plants adjust to new man–made environments should be called acclimatization (Conover and Poole, 1984).

Acclimatizing plantlets
rooted *extra vitrum*

Where shoots obtained from tissue culture are rooted in the external environment, rooting and hardening can take place consecutively, so that plantlets can be practically fully hardened *before* they are replanted. As explained on page 706, microcuttings need to be kept in high humidity and partial shade when they are initially removed from the culture flask until root initiation has occurred. After that acclimatization through a gradual reduction in shading and relative humidity can conveniently take place at the same time as the shoots become rooted. Coverings are therefore gradually removed, and syringing, misting or fogging with water, is gradually reduced and finally discontinued as soon as roots have grown (unless there are signs of stress). Where cuttings have been covered with plastic film, the process of acclimatization can be assisted by progressively making holes in it, to allow the gradual ingress of drier air.

Once microcuttings have formed roots, any planted into trays can be transplanted into pots or liners and returned to a humidity chamber for a further week. Plantlets in plugs are treated in the same way (page 730) or sold to customers for replanting.

Plantlets rooted in a growth room would be transferred to a greenhouse and placed in partial (*e.g.* 20–50%) shade if the weather was hot and sunny. Water misting is sometimes applied for *ca.* 2 weeks at this stage, after which shading is removed, or plantlets are moved to lighter shading (*e.g.* 20%) without mist.

Quality requirements

Micropropagated shoots need to attain a minimum size before they are suitable for rooting. When small shoots are pre–rooted *in vitro*, it is often found that their survival during the acclimatization is less satisfactory than where large shoots had been selected.

Fig. 129. A chrysanthemum shoot, rooted *in vitro* on an agar medium, which is ready to be transplanted.

Acclimatizing plantlets rooted *in vitro*

Prior to hardening, plantlets rooted *in vitro* should have well–proportioned shoots and roots that are capable of supporting each other (Sommer and Caldas, 1981). They are then ready for transplanting (Fig. 129). Some rooted plantlets are acclimatized by micropropagation laboratories for sale as hardened plants growing in soil: most are sold to nurseries as they come from the culture vessel to be acclimatized by the purchaser.

High humidity is essential for successful acclimatization. Once deflasked, plantlets should be treated carefully and moved to a protected environment as quickly as possible, because they can desiccate within a few minutes in a hot dry atmosphere (Zimmerman, 1984a). Plantlets dispatched from a propagation laboratory should be planted as soon as they are received. To minimize delay, many nurseries and laboratories carry out de–flasking in the growth room or greenhouse where acclimatization is to take place (Metcalfe, 1984). Deflasking may have been preceded by previously opening the tops of culture vessels (page 696). Hygiene should not be relaxed when

plants are removed and it is wise to ensure that benches are cleaned with an antiseptic, and that operators wash their hands and sterilise instruments before handling plant material.

Removing agar. It is generally recommended that when plantlets have been rooted, or somatic embryos germinated in agar, the gel should be gently washed away from the roots in luke–warm water. The need to remove agar has been associated with the gel trapping sucrose and other organic compounds in the proximity of roots, causing plantlets to be infected by disease–causing organisms or damaged by toxic microbial metabolites. It is probably unnecessary to remove agar if the rooting medium did not contain sugar. Where shoots of *Begonia* had rooted into an agar mineral salts medium (no sucrose), plantlets grew satisfactorily into compost, whether agar was washed from the roots, or not (Bowes, 1990).

Some authors advocate washing agar away in a dilute fungicide solution (Metcalfe, 1984), or dipping or soaking the roots of newly–isolated plantlets in a fungicidal or bactericidal solution (see later).

Porous substrates. The advantage from *in vitro* rooting of microcuttings on porous substrates such as sand, perlite, foam or Sorbarods becomes apparent at this stage, because there is then no agar to be removed, and plantlets can be transferred from the culture flask with little root disturbance. This means that such plants can usually be established readily in the external environment. For example, raspberry plantlets rooted in a phenol resin foam could be removed from culture tubes with the roots intact inside the foam cylinder. The foam was simply washed to remove the nutrient solution, dipped in fungicide and the plantlets potted in a peat : sand mixture so that the foam was covered (Gebhardt, 1985). When *Chrysanthemum* plantlets, complete with the Sorbarods into which they had been rooted, were planted into compost, they transpired more than plants which had been transplanted bare rooted from agar, but wilted less (Roberts and Smith, 1990).

Planting composts

Rooted plantlets need to be transferred to plugs, or a suitable free–draining 'compost' with a high proportion of air space. The materials from which compost is prepared should have been sanitized or pasteurized to eliminate bacterial or fungal infections. Boxus (1987) cautioned against using freshly–sterilized planting mixture because fungal infections have often been found to grow on their surface.

Planting composts may not necessarily be the same as the mixtures best suited to *ex vitro* root initiation and the one chosen may need to reflect the environment under which plantlets are to be hardened. Suitable mixtures of repro-

Table 117. Some mixtures used for setting out plantlets rooted *in vitro*.

Plant/s	Mixture	Ratio	Reference
Woody plants	Peat, vermiculite	2:1	Druart and Boxus (Boxus
Conifers	Peat, perlite, pine bark Peat, perlite, vermiculite	—	Mohammed and Vidaver (1988).
Ornamental foliage plants	Peat, perlite	1:1	Lazarte and Foberg (1986)
Ribes nigrum	Vermiculite, fine sand	7:3	Ma *et al*. (1992)
Rosa chinensis	Peat, perlite, soil	1:1:1	Hayward *et al*. (1988)
Various plants	Peat, sand	3:1	Metcalfe (1984)
Zantedeschia	Peat, pumice sand, perlite	2:2:1	Pocock (1984)

ducible composition, can be prepared from the materials used for *ex vitro* rooting, as well as bark and polystyrene. Woody plants often require a more open compost than herbaceous species. Mixtures which have been found to be acceptable are listed in Table 117, but these may not be universally suitable and some plants may have special preferences. For certain plants, attention may need to given to the pH of the planting material. High salinity and inappropriate pH can readily damage tissue cultured plants and lead to high losses through damping off (Cooper A., 1987).

Daza and Chamber (1993) found that plantlets of *Lupinus luteus* were acclimatized best if they were transplanted to perlite irrigated with nutrient solution containing 0.5 µM NAA and 0.05 µM 2–iP (the same regulants as had been used for *in vitro* rooting). This encouraged the further growth of roots, but for satisfactory plantlet growth, it was necessary to replant into peat after 4 weeks.

Most species benefit from the addition of nutrient salts, either through the compost being watered with a simple nutrient solution [such as the half or full strength macronutrients of **Hoagland and Snyder (1933)** plus micronutrients], or by adding $\frac{1}{3}$ to $\frac{1}{2}$ the quantity of a complete slow release fertilizer mixture that would be used when potting up vigorous plants which had been raised *in vivo*. For example, the addition of a proprietary nutrient mix to the compost significantly improved the growth of *Vitis labrusca* plantlets during acclimatization (Lewandowski, 1991). The concentration of nutrients can be critical. Baviera *et al*. (1989) found that *Pyrus communis* plantlets grew faster and had a better root system when watered with a low concentration of nutrient salts, than with a high level.

A few species are better acclimatized in compost without nutrients. For instance, Rahman (1988) found that *Arto-*

carpus heterophyllus plantlets survived much better if they were grown for the first 20 days in compost containing only a low level of nutrients or none at all. The presence of NH_4^+ was particularly inhibitive. Feeding with inorganic ions was commenced once new roots and leaves had formed.

Containers

Plantlets are inserted into boxes, trays, or pots of compost. All containers and pots should be new, or if previously used, should have been scrupulously cleaned and soaked in bleach. The kind of plant container selected will depend on the nature of the plant and its ultimate market. Woody plants are usually established singly in separate pots which will ultimately allow roots to be air pruned. Planting plugs are also suitable for many species and have the advantage that plantlets can be readily handled (see page 702).

Fungicide treatments

As newly rooted plantlets, like microcuttings which are to be rooted *extra vitrum* (page 706), are very susceptible to fungal damage, they are usually dipped or soaked in a preparation of a broad spectrum fungicide before planting (Metcalfe, 1984). Fichet (1990a) soaked pineapple plantlets overnight in a 2 g/l benomyl solution. Rooted plantlets which are to be sent to a grower before hardening should be treated in a similar manner.

Some laboratories may alternatively (or additionally) drench or spray plantlets with a fungicide immediately they have been set out, so that both plants and compost are treated. The literature shows that several different chemicals have been successfully employed: benomyl, dichlofluanid, propamocarb (Previcur), captan, iprodione (Rovral), thiram, metalaxyl (Ridomil), mancozeb, etridiazole (Terrazole), and zineb. Application rates are usually lower than the manufacturer's recommended dosage, as young plantlets with an ill–formed cuticle are easily damaged.

A further fungicide spray is often applied 10–14 days after the first treatment (often with a different compound to that used originally). Boxus (1987) suggested local repeat sprays on any flats (boxes) which show signs of infection, or where fungal mycelium is seen growing on the surface of the compost. Regular sprays during the hardening period may be a necessary safeguard for some plants. Species which are liable to bacterial attack (*e.g. Zantedeschia*) are best soaked in antibacterial solution before planting and the compost drenched with a fungicide plus an antibacterial agent, after planting (Pocock, 1984). Plantlets derived from somatic embryos may also need to be sprayed or watered with fungicide when they are planted into soil.

Pesticide damage. Pesticides can be damaging to foliage of plantlets during the early stages of weaning, but should the need for spraying arise, fungicides or insecticides can probably be applied safely after 2–3 weeks. However, in the absence of previous experience, all chemical applications should be preceded by preliminary tests, because in some plants a heightened sensitivity can persist over several months (see page 746).

Environments for hardening plantlets

The high humidity and protection necessary during the rooting of plants *ex vitro* (page 706), are also essential during the early stages of the acclimatization process. A minimum of 85% relative humidity should be maintained during the first few weeks. At the same time it is necessary to prevent plantlets from becoming overheated, or from receiving very high levels of solar radiation. When acclimatization is carried out in greenhouses, shading is therefore frequently required (page 722).

Methods for hardening small numbers of plants

Suitable environments for hardening small batches of plantlets are similar to those which can be used for rooting small batches of microcuttings *ex vitro* (see page 706). In very small numbers, individual plantlets or somatic seedlings can be covered with a glass or plastic beaker which is gradually raised to allow the ingress of air.

> Trolinder and Goodin (1987) had the novel idea of covering somatic seedlings of cotton firstly with a 10 ml beaker, then progressively with others of 30, 50, 100 and 150 ml capacity. A change to a beaker of larger volume was made every 3 days. Three days after being placed under a 150 ml beaker, the plantlets could be taken into the greenhouse.

The most common method of hardening small batches of plantlets is to place them in flats (either planted directly, or planted in pots or plugs) which are covered with clear rigid plastic lids or with plastic domes made of thin film. One way to do this is to slide a flat into a length of polyethylene tubing of an appropriate diameter. Two metal hoops keep the plastic film off the plantlets. The ends of the tubing are closed with rubber bands or wire twists (Fig. 130). Holes can be cut in the plastic film at a later stage to reduce the relative humidity within the enclosure.

Rooted plantlets of *Vitis labrusca* were hardened underneath a shade cloth by being covered by plastic domes. After the seventh day, domes with perforations of increasing size were substituted every two days, until the covers could be dispensed with at day 14 (Lewandowski, 1991). The relative humidities to which the plants were exposed by these treatments were as follows:

Covering	Exposure	Relative humidity (%)	
		Summer	Winter
Plastic dome	Days 0–6	98–99	98–99
Lightly perforated dome	Days 7–8	92	82
Moderately perforated dome	Days 9–10	86	68
Heavily perforated dome	Days 11–13	75	53
Covering removed	Day 14 onwards	66	46
		(greenhouse humidity)	

Methods for hardening large numbers of plants

When plants are being produced commercially in large numbers, they are usually hardened in the greenhouse. The available techniques are listed in Table 118, together with advantages and disadvantages of each system.

Humidity tents. Plastic tents and/or fogging are now most widely employed by large micropropagation laboratories for acclimatizing plants. Depending on the conditions, transparent or translucent plastic film is used and is usually stretched over metal arches. Plastic humidity tents are the least expensive, but can readily become overheated and need to be shaded in hot weather (*e.g.* using 50% shade cloth) and the temperature and humidity monitored frequently.

Humidity within tents depends on the ambient environmental conditions and whether bottom heating is supplied. It almost always needs to be supplemented. In small plastic tents its level can be kept up by manually spraying water through a fine hand mister. As this needs to be done

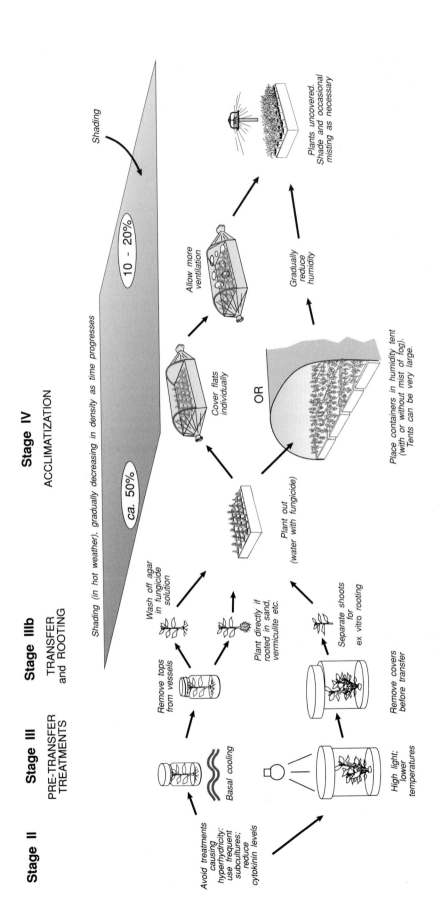

Fig. 130. Steps in hardening and acclimatizing plants which have been propagated *in vitro*.
Some alternative pre-treatments have been omitted for simplicity.

frequently, high humidity is usually maintained by placing trays or individual containers on capillary matting. Alternative devices which can be automatically set to maintain a predetermined humidity level are: an humidifier, intermittent water mists, or a fog of fine water particles (see below). Frequent misting has disadvantages (see below).

The wet tent system. A method for covering cuttings to be rooted with a continuously wetted fabric was devised by Whitomb (1983) after an idea of Francelet (Fig. 131). Cuttings of several species have been found to root as well in the tent as under mist; a few species root more readily. The system was found to give better results for the acclimatization of *Euphorbia* microcuttings than shade or intermittent mist (Zhang and Stoltz, 1989b).

Automatic misting. Automatic water mists are usually applied to plantlets placed inside humidity tents, but sometimes plants are also sprayed with mist just after they have been removed to the open greenhouse bench. The aim should be to maintain a fine film of water on leaves without causing the rooting 'compost' to become over watered. Survival of most plants is adversely affected in very wet environments.

The frequency of spraying (which is best regulated with a timer, rather than leaf controller — Bowden, 1985), therefore needs to be varied according to the prevailing environmental conditions. Some routines which have been reported are:

Length of spray (seconds)	Repeat interval (minutes)	Temp. or environment	Reference
6	8	18°C	Hill (1988)
5	6 (1 week) 12 (2 weeks)	—	Glendening and Sjolund (1988)
1–2	3–6	Greenhouse	Zimmerman (1984a)
5	15	Greenhouse	Hutchinson (1984b)

Many propagators do not favour automatic misting during the initial hardening of tissue cultured material. It makes plantlets very wet and has several disadvantages:

 — algal growth is likely to develop and plants are liable to be attacked by fungi and bacteria;

 — nutrients may be leached from both plants and compost;

 — the compost may be made too wet for healthy root growth.

 — plants may suffer from tip necrosis. This sometimes occurs on cuttings weaned in mist, and is caused by calcium in the plant being leached away by water (Griesbach *et al*., 1988) (see Part 1, page 294). It is therefore not advisable to use misting

Table 118. Alternative methods of acclimatizing large numbers of micropropagated plants [after Griffis *el al*., 1984].

Method	Advantages	Disadvantages
Plastic covers over single flats (polyethylene or rigid plastic).	Low cost flexible system; flats individually maintained , so easy to separate requirements for individual crops. Easy to use and portable. Good humidity maintenance	Considerable heat build up under covers. Requires storage of many small items. Much effort required to look at each tray several times each day. Need to gradually lift or perforate existing covers, or change to perforated ones to gradually reduce humidity.
Clear or shaded plastic tent (with or without mist)	Inexpensive and easily made. Relative humidity can be kept to high levels	Can be build-up of heat, so shading may also be required. Temperature difficult to control. If no automatic mist, frequent monitoring necessary to see when watering or increase in humidity required.
Wet tent cover	Good control of humidity and temperature. Humidity can be reduced as plants harden	More elaborate structure to set up and run.
Automatic mist (with or without a cover)	Reliable systems which need little monitoring. Frequency and duration of misting can be varied as hardening proceeds	Moderate investment costs. Planting compost often becomes too wet and there can be fungal or algal growth. Mist leaches nutrients from plants and potting composts.
High pressure fog	Gives 100% R.H. but does not leach nutrients. Excellent in hot weather: heat significantly reduced giving pleasant working conditions	Expensive investment and has high maintenace cost if water supply not pure.

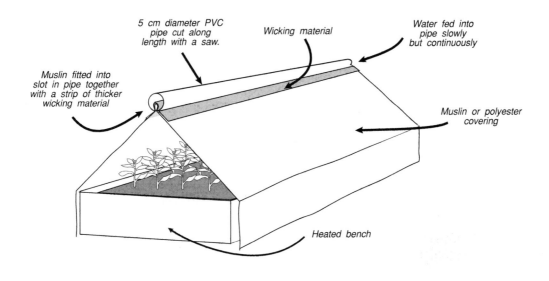

Fig.131. The wet tent devised by Whitomb (1983) for rooting cuttings or for acclimatizing ready-rooted plantlets.

treatment during acclimatization of susceptible species.

Fogging. Fogging systems have been developed as an alternative to water mists for rooting cuttings and for hardening plantlets. Fogs which contain relatively big water particles are suitable for large–sized conventional cuttings, but for micropropagated material, a 'dry' fog produced by a device operating at high pressure, and which consists of water particles of less than 10 μm diameter, has the advantage that it reduces transpiration without greatly wetting leaves or the growing medium. Fungal disease problems are therefore reduced and there is adequate oxygen in the root zone. Problems of over-heating in the greenhouse are greatly reduced by fogging and the environment is pleasant to work in. Foliar feeds, and fungicide and pesticide treatments can be administered in the fog particles. Fogging is now preferred for *ex vitro* rooting and the establishment of tissue cultured material (Broome *et al.* 1986) and is used by many micropropagation laboratories (Fig. 132). Its chief disadvantage is the cost of installing the necessary high pressure equipment (Spear, 1986). Maintenance can also be expensive in hard water areas. Stimart (1986) found that plants grown in fogs can develop very soft succulent foliage, not fully adapted to a final *in vivo* environment.

A low cost fogging chamber developed by Okada *et al.* (1992) consisted of a long tunnel greenhouse fitted with ventilating fans and fogging nozzles. A gradient of fog particles was created by having the nozzles at just one end of the house. Plantlets were placed in dense fog just after deflasking and moved every 5–7 days into a less wetted environment.

Light and shade. Plantlets need to be exposed to high light to begin photosynthesis but, because they have been grown in comparatively low light *in vitro*, are unable to withstand full sunlight. Survival will be adversely affected in too low a photon flux: survival of *Grevillea* and *Leucospermum* was much reduced, for example, if light 'intensity' was reduced from 14000 to 7000 lux (Tal *et al.*, 1992c).

Plants acclimatized in a growth room can be exposed to artificial light of relatively high irradiance (*e.g.* 70–100 μmol m^{-2} s^{-1}), but those kept in a greenhouse must be shaded from direct sunlight in hot climates. Depending on the ambient conditions, light availability in the greenhouse will then probably have to be reduced initially by the provision of 50–90% shade to provide a PPF similar to, or slightly above that suggested for establishment growth rooms. A lower density shading is required when fogging is used, as fog itself reflects some of the incident light. Reduced lighting is especially important for some subjects *e.g. Syringa* (Pierik *et al.*, 1986). Where shading has been necessary, it can be reduced once roots have been formed.

To continue growing healthy plants during the winter in temperate climates, it is necessary to employ supplementary lighting (*e.g.* from high pressure sodium lamps) during an appropriate photoperiod. The marked effect

Fig. 132. Acclimatizing micropropagated plants in fog within a commercial greenhouse.

extra lighting can have on the growth and even the later field performance of plants was shown by Desjardins *et al.* (1990). *Asparagus* cloned *in vitro* grew much more rapidly in the greenhouse when provided with an irradiance of 80 μmol m^{-2} s^{-1} in addition to ambient solar radiation, and this resulted in plants which were equal in size to seedlings after two years in the field. Tissue cultured plants not originally given supplementary lighting were much smaller and less vigorous at this time.

Temperature. The temperature most suitable for acclimatization will depend on the plant species. A recommended range is 15–25°C, but temperatures above and below these limits may be unavoidable or desirable in some circumstances. In greenhouses, cooling will usually be necessary during summer months. When the air temperature is not excessive, bottom heating is advocated, because, as with *ex vitro* rooting, it gives rise to improved root growth, and assists in maintaining a humid micro–climate around the plantlets. It can be turned off once new leaves have begun to form.

Carbon dioxide enrichment

Just as carbon dioxide enrichment can assist the rooting and growth of plants if applied during an *ex vitro* procedure (page 707), if applied during acclimatization it can improve the survival and growth of plants rooted *in vitro*. The growth of strawberry plantlets was increased and the length of the necessary acclimatization period probably shortened by increasing the CO_2 concentration to *ca.* 750 p.p.m. when solar radiation was above 58 W m^{-2} (Hayashi and Kozai, 1987). Rooted plants of *Asparagus* were kept in the greenhouse for 10 days under 95% relative humidity until one extra spear had appeared. They were then given CO_2 supplementation and supplementary lighting of 80 μmol m^{-2} s^{-1} during daylight hours (the latter when solar irradiation fell below 250 μmol m^{-2} s^{-1}). Using a combination of these treatments it was possible to obtain plants of a suitable size to move from the nursery, 3 weeks earlier than normal. The provision of extra carbon dioxide was ineffective without supplementary light, which also modified leaf anatomy leading to improved photosynthetic ability.

An automated acclimatization unit

An automated acclimatization room was built experimentally by Hayashi and Kozai (1987). Plantlets in Rockwool blocks were supplied with liquid medium and were subjected to an environment in which temperature, humidity, lighting level, carbon dioxide concentration and the rate of air flow could be controlled through a computer program. A high proportion of plants survived acclimatization in the apparatus, and growth was more rapid when carbon dioxide supplementation was used. However the results obtained do not seem to justify the considerable extra expense of such a system.

Anti–transpirant films

Spraying plantlets with anti–transpirant coatings has been advocated as a method of reducing water loss from newly–planted material, but has not been widely practised. Some anti–transpirant materials can be toxic to micropropagated plantlets which have just been removed from the culture flask.

Wardle et al. (1979) demonstrated that cauliflower plantlets sprayed with a polyvinyl resin had a 2–3 times greater cuticular resistance to water loss and did not need a preliminary hardening. McComb and Newton (1981) obtained a 95% survival rate when their Kangaroo Paws plantlets were sprayed with 'Acropol' (a polyvinyl acetate) and directly placed in the glasshouse. Gradually reducing the humidity of a chamber over one week was less efficient and involved more work. Snir (1983) applied 1% Folicote™ to sour cherry microcuttings after they had formed roots in closed boxes; and Hutchinson (1985b) established apple plantlets without misting, after treating them twice with 5% Folicote, once at transfer and again 5 days later.

Although some other experiments have been less successful (Preece and Sutter, 1991), establishment *can* be improved by coating leaves, as is shown by the experiment of Selvapandiyan et al. (1988). No establishment phase was necessary for several species raised *in vitro*, if the leaves of plantlets were smeared with impermeable materials (50% aqueous glycerol, low melting point paraffin or petroleum grease, dissolved in diethyl ether). Plantlets so treated could be transferred directly into pots.

The final stages of the hardening process

Plants are finally hardened off by gradually reducing the humidity and increasing the PPFD to which they are exposed. The air flow through tents is gradually increased and plants are sometimes moved from there to mist on uncovered benches for a short period; light misting at this stage is not so deleterious. Exposure to light should be increased as plants become established, by removing shading, or reducing it in one or more stages. In hot climates many species benefit from being retained in a partially shaded area. Griffis et al. (1984) retained *Spathiphyllum* in 73–80% shade; *Gerbera* daisies were retained in 30% shade for several weeks.

Factors which influence the re–establishment of transplants have been reviewed by McKee (1981), Conner and Thomas (1982) and Preece and Sutter (1991).

PLANTING OUT

Plantlets acclimatized in small containers or plugs are usually transplanted into pots or liners of soil or compost for further growth. Plants are not withdrawn from plugs at this stage, plug and associated root system being transferred intact to the new medium. Because soil readily withdraws water from highly porous materials, where plantlets have been rooted and acclimatized in plugs, it is necessary to be especially careful to water adequately during the first few days (Pierik, 1991b).

Direct field planting

There are a few plants which need very little hardening, or even no hardening at all. Rooted plantlets of *Glehnia littoralis* could be potted without any acclimatization, probably because they formed a well–developed cuticle *in vitro* and possessed leaves with a relatively small surface area in proportion to their weight (Hiraoka and Oyanagi, 1988). Experiments have shown that it is possible to transplant some plants to the field directly from the culture flask, or immediately after the initiation of roots. Some temporary protection is required for rooted cuttings. Driver and Suttle (1987) have planted microcuttings of walnut (pre–hardened *in vitro*, see page 697) directly into the field, because rooted walnuts have been difficult to transplant from pots (McGranahan et al., 1987). Cuttings were given only a 1–2 weeks root induction treatment and, when the roots were just beginning to develop, planted directly into watered soil in the field when soil temperatures ranged from 5–40°C. The shoots were then protected with a series of plastic cups; the first being translucent and having a 266 ml capacity. Over this was placed a 296 ml styrofoam cup, and over this again another 473 ml styrofoam container. The three containers together sufficiently regulated light, temperature and humidity within the internal air space. Plants were irrigated by a short duration sprinkler or by drip feed. Root and shoot growth occurred under the cups so that these covers could be removed in 8–10 weeks and re–used. The method has also been used successfully with *Prunus persica* (nectarine).

Levy (1985; 1988) reported that it was possible to transplant self–rooted shoots of potato directly from the culture container into the field. About 40% of the plantlets survived when they were protected by screen shields and given sprinkler irrigation. Established plants went on to produce tubers.

Small tubers, cormlets or bulbs formed *in vitro* can be planted directly into the greenhouse or into the open field without any preliminary hardening. With bulbs it may, however, be necessary to break an assumed dormancy before growth will resume. Bulbous subjects bearing leaves and a storage organ also seem to be resistant to environmental change. For example, provided that bulblets of *Narcissus* were of a sufficient size (more than *ca.* 1 cm diameter) and had been stimulated to form 2 leaves and a good root system, they could be moved directly from culture to soil in open fields (Steinitz and Yahel, 1982).

Field treatment. The increased susceptibility of tissue cultured plantlets to certain pesticide treatments, may extend to field situations, where herbicide treatments suitable for normal crops have been found to cause damage (see page 746).

NITROGEN–FIXING BACTERIA

Legumes, and plants of a few other families, develop a symbiotic association with specific nitrogen–fixing bacteria. The bacteria are enabled to grow in nodules on the roots of infected plants where they utilise translocated carbohydrates; in return the plant is able to metabolise some of the nitrogenous compounds produced by the bacteria through reduction of atmospheric nitrogen, and in consequence they usually exhibit a greatly improved rate of growth. Legumes are infected by nitrogen–fixing bacteria of the genus *Rhizobium* and artificial inoculation of seeds or plants is often practised in crop plants to ensure a consistent increase in yield without the application of nitrogenous fertilizers.

Where leguminous plants have been micropropagated, a symbiotic association with *Rhizobium* will have been lost. It can therefore be advantageous to inoculate the roots of plantlets with a suspension of *Rhizobium* during the acclimatization stage. Dhawan and Bhojwani (1986) found that, although micropropagated *Leucaena leucocephala* plantlets took 3 weeks longer to develop

root nodules than comparable seedlings, 80% did become nodulated if they were inoculated with *Rhizobium* during hardening. A greater proportion of the nodulated plants survived transplanting to the field than their non–nodulated counterparts.

MYCORRHIZAL FUNGI

As mentioned in Chapter 4, beneficial mycorrhizae develop from fungi forming endotrophic and ectotrophic associations with plant roots. Mycorrhizae are important in improving the inorganic nutrition of plants, particularly by enhancing the uptake of phosphorus and nitrogen from the soil. As the fungi responsible for mycorrhizae are lost during micropropagation, several workers have tried to discover effective methods of re–infection.

Fungal culture and inoculation

Endomycorrhizae

Certain woody species, especially members of the Pinaceae, grow very poorly without the presence of ectomycorrhizae, and have been known to die when planted in locations where the the requisite fungus is not endemic. Inoculating the roots of seedlings with selected fungi has sometimes dramatically altered the survival and growth of pine seedlings planted on previously unforested soils. Various kinds of ectomycorrhizal fungi are produced commercially.

Although some fungi which are ectotrophic on plant roots can form mycorrhizae with plants of several different genera, others are host specific. Methods of screening ectotrophic fungi for the ability to synthesize mycorrhizae with the roots of a particular species, were described by Mason (1983). In one of these, a pure culture of the fungus is first of all obtained by inoculating a suitable medium with internal segments of fruiting bodies. Seedlings of the host plant are then germinated aseptically and transferred to the surface of an agar slope of a special low phosphate medium, and an inoculum of cultured fungal hyphae is placed close to the root tip. The presence of mycorrhizae is observed after the seedlings have been incubated for 4–6 weeks in continuous light.

Endomycorrhizae

Unlike ectotrophic fungi, vesicular–arbuscular (VA) mycorrhizal fungi show very little host specificity and each of the many species described is capable of infecting a wide range of plants. VA fungi are obligate symbionts and cannot be grown in isolated axenic culture. Inocula are most reliably obtained from infected host species grown in sterilised soil, but the fungi may also be grown on cultures of isolated plant roots (Rhodes, 1983). Schubert and Martinelli (1988) used an integrated sample of soil, spores and infected roots from infected pot cultures of *Trifolium pratense* when they wished to introduce *Glomus caledonium* and *G. occultum* fungi to the roots of *Pistacia integerrima*.

Inoculating micropropagated plants

In vitro inoculations

Cuttings from *Betula pendula* seedlings were placed on an agar medium specially chosen because it permitted root formation without the addition of plant growth regulators, and did not induce basal callus. When the medium was inoculated as above with the ectotrophic fungus *Paxillus involutus*, mycorrhizae were formed and the growth of the plants was stimulated (Grellier *et al*.., 1984). The same fungus was used to infect cuttings taken from the apex of axenic *Castanea sativa* seedlings. These were placed on a special agar medium (Chapter 9) which had been inoculated with a suspension of the fungus. As roots formed on the microcuttings, mycorrhizae developed which led to a considerable increase in plant growth. The existence of mycorrhizae could be confirmed by the presence of a fungal mantle surrounding secondary roots, and stimulated plant growth (Strullu *et al.*, 1986).

Vesicular–arbuscular fungi

An *in vitro* method for infecting plants with VA fungi has been described by Hepper and Mosse (1980). Resting spores are sieved from infested soils and can be further separated by centrifuging in a sucrose gradient. Spores are surface sterilized with a solution containing a wetting agent and 20 µg/ml Chloramine T together with 200 µg/ml streptomycin, if necessary after dissection from the

sporocarp. They are then pre–germinated on 1% water agar and used to inoculate root cultures. *Trifolium* is often used as a host genus. At this stage, roots which have been grown on a modified **White (1963)** medium are moved to a similar formulation with a modified phosphate supply ($NaH_2PO_4.2H_2O$ replaced by equimolar KH_2PO_4, or alternatively ten times this concentration of insoluble calcium phytate, a slow release phosphate source). Further cultures can be initiated by using pieces of axenically–infected roots as inocula.

For practical purposes, plants are probably best infected with VA endophytes after they have been transplanted to pots. Reliable infection of micropropagated strawberries (Kiernan *et al.*, 1984) and grapevines has been achieved in this way and has resulted in growth enhancement or an increase in crop yield, although the best fungal strain for each cultivar may vary (Chávez and Ferrera–Cerrato, 1990). In the latter case, a steam sterilized mixture of 50:50 w/w sand and soil was inoculated with 40–50 spores per pot just before the rooted cuttings were planted in it. At the same time, attempts to infect micropropagated grapevine cuttings on an agar–based root elongation medium with VA spores (pre–germinated or otherwise) placed close to the roots by the method described above, were not successful (Schubert *et al.*, 1987). Several other woody plants have been successfully inoculated during establishment at Stage IV (Mohammed and Vidaver, 1988). Pots containing micropropagated plantlets of *Pistacia integerrima* were each treated with 50 grams of the inoculum mentioned above.

REVIEWS

Reviews of acclimatization procedures will be found in articles by: Conover and Poole (1984); Preece and Sutter (1991); and Sutter *et al.* (1992).

15

The Phenotype of Micropropagated Material

This chapter describes anomalous structures observed in tissue cultures and changes in the characteristics and performance of plants micropropagated by methods thought not to engender genetic variation, *i.e.* in plants multiplied by shoot or node culture, by direct organogenesis and by somatic embryogenesis. Most changes noted are physiological and impermanent, but some do persist and affect the manner in which plants grow, flower and fruit, and so modify economic and aesthetic value. Because such changes *do* occur, it is most important to study the attributes of micropropagated plants as they grow to maturity in greenhouse, garden or field. Woody plants, which mature slowly, need more careful study than herbaceous species.

Genetic variation (see Chapter 3) is chiefly found in plants originating from tissues which were previously dedifferentiated, *i.e.* in plants which have been regenerated from previously unorganised callus or suspension cultures. This means that when unusual features are noticed in plants produced indirectly from callus or suspension cultures, it is usually impossible, without careful analysis, to say whether they have had a genetic, or a physiological, origin. Thus when plants of *Gynura aurantiaca,* regenerated from callus cultures, were found to be larger, more uniform in growth and time of flowering, to produce more flowers per plant, to be more apically

dominant, and to have different leaf shapes, the cause was initially obscure. The characteristics were retained during subsequent asexual propagation (Myerson and Krul, 1982) suggesting that they may have had a genetic origin. A further study of the plants and their sexual offspring would have been necessary to ascertain the validity of this hypothesis.

Many abnormalities were found amongst *Dendranthema* plants regenerated from leaf callus which had been maintained nine years. The observed effects could have been due to genetic instability, chimeral rearrangement, induced juvenility, or residual growth regulator effects (Sutter and Langhans, 1981).

Minimising phenotypic variation

Abnormalities in tissue cultures, and in the plants produced from them, often increase in frequency the longer cultures are maintained. It is therefore a wise policy to discard shoot cultures if there is a reduction in the size and vigour of shoots, or if atypical plants are produced, for example with leaves which fail to unfold or are misshapen. Thereafter, cultures of the same plant should be renewed from stock plants at more frequent intervals, before such deterioration might be expected.

Some of the changes observed in cultures and micropropagated plants may be avoided by the use of a different protocol, but it may be difficult or impossible not to encounter others which are a direct consequence of procedures which are current best practice. There is no incentive in trying to eliminate those alterations to the phenotype which are perceived to be advantageous.

ABNORMAL ORGANS

ABNORMAL GROWTHS RESULTING FROM ORGANOGENESIS

Most organs which are produced adventitiously from explants, or from callus cultures, have a recognisable form, *i.e.* they are shoots, roots or somatic embryos. Occasionally the signals necessary for organ formation appear to be incomplete, interrupted, or inaccurate, so that correct determination (Part 1, page 26 *et seq*.) is not achieved. This leads to the development of incompletely formed, or even grossly abnormal structures which in the past have been called 'teratomas' or 'organoids'. Such organ–like growths are a feature of many calluses infected with crown gall disease (Braun, 1959, 1969) and often arise from habituated callus (Fox, 1963; Lutz, 1966). However they are also liable to arise during any sequence of direct or indirect (Bowes, 1971; Favre, 1977) morphogenesis conducted *in vitro*.

Abnormalities which have been found during morphogenesis are categorised and listed in Fig. 133. They have usually been classified into:

- **Leaf–like structures**.

    These include leaf–like protuberances with little or no vascular tissue (phylloids — Bornman, 1985, 1987); and stunted abnormal leaves. An unusual kind of leaf development was occasionally noted in *Brachycome* cultures, arising from calluses which had an uncharacteristic shape. The leaves were covered in hairs and had an abnormal stunted appearance (Gould, 1978) and the meristems from which they developed rarely gave rise to shoots with normal phyllotaxy.

    Occasionally normal–looking leaves appear to be formed from calluses or explants without the clear existence of an associated shoot meristem. Bowes (1976b) found that leaf–like organs could arise in *Taraxacum* cultures, and Wainwright and Harwood (1985) and Hawkes and Wainwright (1987) noted the appearance of 'adventitious leaves' from seedling tissues of *Cyclamen persicum*. It has never been settled whether in such circumstances leaves have arisen *de novo*, or from shoot meristems which have been unable to give rise to stem tissue.

- **Abnormal roots and rhizoids**

    The development and morphology of roots produced *in vitro* is influenced by cultural conditions, and by the type and concentration of auxin used for inducton. Abnormal roots, not fully capable of supporting plantlet growth, may be produced on shoots if the concentration of auxin used is too high, or if the auxin chosen is unsuitable for the plant in question (see page 671). Root–like teratomas or abnormally shaped roots may also be formed in inappropriate conditions, *e.g.* in unsuitable media (Part 1, pages 281 and 282). Such structures may remain undeveloped, or may subsequently give rise to normal roots.

    Roots of abnormal appearance regenerated from callus cultures have sometimes been called *rhizoids* (Cellárová *et al.*, 1992).

- **Floral organoids**

    Tissue excised from floral organs is often observed to give rise *in vitro* to flowers, or parts of flowers (Part 1, page 243). Sometimes clearly defined organs are produced, but on other occasions structures are incomplete and only resemble sepals, petals, stigmas, carpels or stamens.

- **Pseudobuds**.

    Pseudobuds are extended bud like structures which often have damaged or retarded apical meristems and short distended leaf–like appendages. They are frequently hyperhydric (Bornman, 1985, 1987).

- **Meristematic nodules** (see page 806).

- **Tuber–like structures**.

    An organised tuber–like 'neoplasm' tended to be formed at the basal end of red beet shoot tip explants (Harms *et al.*, 1983). After a few subcultures, cutting off such structures at each transfer, the tuber–forming tendency diminished and the shoots proliferated normally.

- **Phymas**.

    Phymas are pustular nodules of undifferentiated cells, up to 3 mm or more in diameter (Bornman, 1985, 1987). They seem to represent the formation of structures with the minimum of organisation from otherwise undifferentiated cells.

- **Pseudobulbils**

    The term 'pseudobulbil' has been used to decribe adventitious bulbous structures formed in tissue cultures. They seem to arise when morphogenesis is

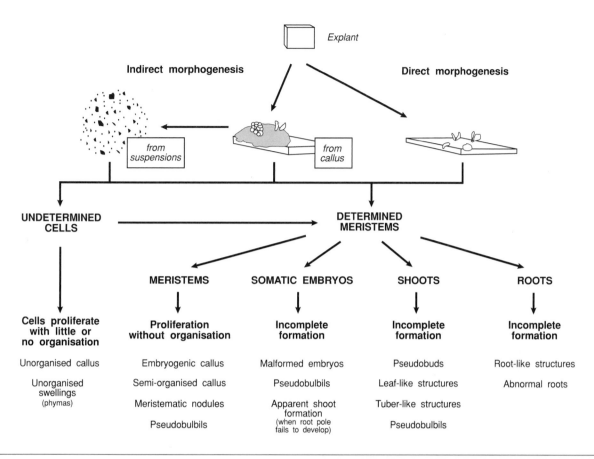

Fig. 133. Abnormalities which can arise *in vitro* as a result of incomplete, or inaccurately determined, morphogenesis.

arrested. Bulbils which arose on *Picea* cotyledons apparently represent a stage of partial shoot development because they can eventually give rise to shoot buds (Bornman, 1985, 1987). In *Citrus*, the term pseudobulbil has been used to denote a bulbous structure formed in embryogenic callus. These pseudobulbils have been thought to represent an arrested stage of embryogenesis (Ranga Swamy, 1961; Button *et al.*, 1974).

- **Abnormal somatic embryos**

A proportion of somatic embryos formed *in vitro* frequently develops abnormally (Part1, page 62). This seems to be due to the artificial uncontrolled stimulation of embryogenesis by auxin growth regulators. Where embryo genesis occurs without the addition of auxin, unusual forms of embryos occur less frequently. In *Rubus occidentalis* embryogenesis on cotyledonary explants occurred slightly more rapidly with the addition of 2,4–D to the medium, but the frequency of abnormalities such as polycotyledony and the formation of 'rooty masses' increased (Gingas and Stokes, 1993).

Some measures which have been found to increase the uniformity of populations of somatic embryos were mentioned in Part 1, pages 63 and 454. The incidence of abnormal embryos was reduced in *Prunus persica* by shortening the interval between subcultures to 20 days (Raj Bhansali *et al.*, 1990). Abnormal embryos may give rise to normal plantlets, but some imperfections lead to distorted seedlings while others prevent embryos developing further.

Examples of abnormally developed organs are the elongated structures which differentiated from leaf discs of *Solanum laciniatum* cultured in the dark (these occasionally developed into sprout–like shoots) (Davies and Dale, 1979), and the shoot–like structures produced directly on the perianth and bracts of immature onion inflorescences, which only rarely grew into shoots (Dunstan and Short, 1979a). Seckinger *et al.* (1979) recorded the occurrence of 'organoids' in red oak callus. The latter were thought to be either shoot initials lacking a well–developed apical meristem, or structures akin to the 'pseudobulbils' formed in nucellar callus of *Citrus*.

More than one kind of abnormal structure may be observed in a culture at the same time. For example, Bowes (1976a) reported nodular outgrowths, root–like structures and abnormal somatic embryos in *Crambe maritima* cultures. Normal organs can sometimes grow out of initial malformations.

Effect of cultural conditions

When genetically normal tissues give rise to abnormal adventitious structures, it must be assumed that the conditions, media or growth regulators which have been provided are not optimal for morphogenesis. For example, the proportion *Picea abies* cotyledons from which buds are directly regenerated decreases as the concentration of cytokinin is increased above an optimum, while the number of abnormal bud–like structures, such as pseudobuds and phylloids, increases. The same effect is achieved by decreasing the matrix potential of the gelled medium: cytokinin uptake from the medium is presumed to be increased under these conditions (Bornman, 1987).

Floral buds of *Nicotiana tabacum* with sepal primordia continued normal organ production on unsupplemented **LS** medium (40 g/l sucrose). However, if 10 mg/l kinetin was added to the medium, buds produced a large number of structures having some characteristics of sepals and some characteristics of petals, and then continued with the initiation of fairly normal stamens, and then carpels (McHughen, 1982).

Effect of genotype

Abnormal organs also develop from tissues in which there is an imperfect genotype. Thus callus which has become highly aneuploid usually becomes incapable of producing normal adventitious shoots; that derived from tobacco pith with 70–100 chromosomes per cell (the normal is $2n = 48$) produced only occasional anomalous shoots which did not develop further in culture (Fox, 1963). Shoots or somatic embryos which are abnormal, or which fail to develop in a normal way, have sometimes been regenerated from the callus which has been derived from the fusion of protoplasts from unrelated genera (Krumbiegel and Schieder, 1979; Schieder and Krumbiegel, 1980; Gleba and Evans, 1983).

Hyperhydric shoots have been considered to be teratomatous (see Chapter 13).

Unusual growth forms

In a strict sense, unorganised callus and embryogenic callus are abnormal growths. The former occurs when undifferentiated cells proliferate in an unorganised fashion; the latter, when cells which are embryogenically determined grow and divide, instead of producing a single somatic embryo. A semi–organised callus and abnormal nodular structures can arise when determined cells, committed to form apical meristems, proliferate, instead of actually producing shoots or roots. The failure of organogenesis to follow a normal sequence or to be properly completed leads to some of the abnormalities seen in somatic embryos and to the continued proliferation of somatic embryos (Chapter 2, page 56).

ABNORMALITIES IN SHOOTS AND PLANTLETS

The atypical structures described so far are those which have resulted during morphogenesis. The techniques used for micropropagation can also produce changes in the growth and development of shoots and plants produced from pre–formed apical meristems. The most common of the resulting abnormalities in form and function, which appear to result from changes initiated *in vitro*, are listed in Fig. 134, and discussed below and in the section which follows on page 746. Malformations, if they occur, are less gross than those which result from imperfect morphogenesis, and abnormal organs still have a recognisable appearance.

Some altered characteristics can be observed in the culture vessel. Others become apparent after acclimatization, when micropropagated plants are grown *ex vitro*.

Shoot growth

Stunted growth

In shoot cultures of some plants, the occasional shoot may remain small and stunted, and fail to revert to normal growth. Isolated shoots of this kind should be discarded, but if a significant proportion of shoots is affected in this

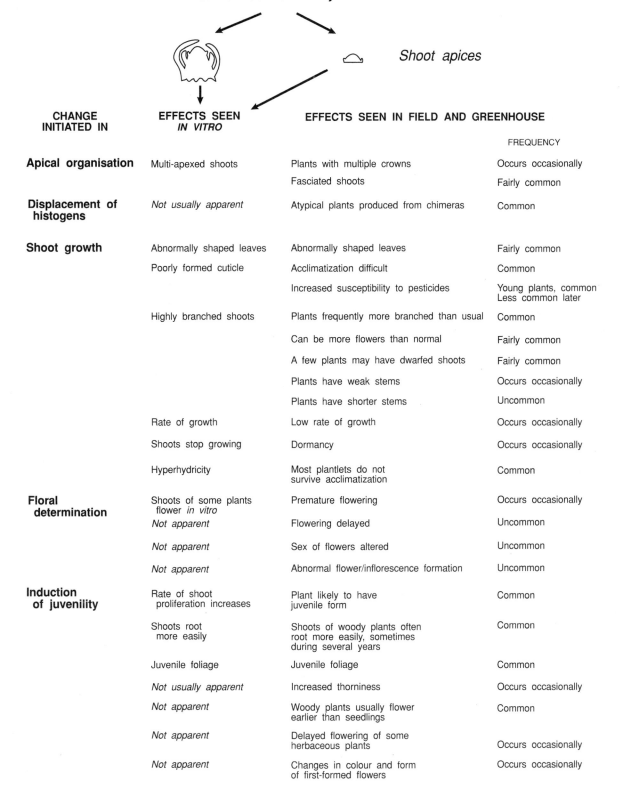

Organised shoots *in vitro* originating from explants with buds, from primordia formed by direct or indirect morphogenesis, or from somatic embryos

Shoot apices

CHANGE INITIATED IN	EFFECTS SEEN *IN VITRO*	EFFECTS SEEN IN FIELD AND GREENHOUSE	FREQUENCY
Apical organisation	Multi-apexed shoots	Plants with multiple crowns	Occurs occasionally
		Fasciated shoots	Fairly common
Displacement of histogens	*Not usually apparent*	Atypical plants produced from chimeras	Common
Shoot growth	Abnormally shaped leaves	Abnormally shaped leaves	Fairly common
	Poorly formed cuticle	Acclimatization difficult	Common
		Increased susceptibility to pesticides	Young plants, common Less common later
	Highly branched shoots	Plants frequently more branched than usual	Common
		Can be more flowers than normal	Fairly common
		A few plants may have dwarfed shoots	Fairly common
		Plants have weak stems	Occurs occasionally
		Plants have shorter stems	Uncommon
	Rate of growth	Low rate of growth	Occurs occasionally
	Shoots stop growing	Dormancy	Occurs occasionally
	Hyperhydricity	Most plantlets do not survive acclimatization	Common
Floral determination	Shoots of some plants flower *in vitro*	Premature flowering	Occurs occasionally
	Not apparent	Flowering delayed	Uncommon
	Not apparent	Sex of flowers altered	Uncommon
	Not apparent	Abnormal flower/inflorescence formation	Uncommon
Induction of juvenility	Rate of shoot proliferation increases	Plant likely to have juvenile form	Common
	Shoots root more easily	Shoots of woody plants often root more easily, sometimes during several years	Common
	Juvenile foliage	Juvenile foliage	Common
	Not usually apparent	Increased thorniness	Occurs occasionally
	Not apparent	Woody plants usually flower earlier than seedlings	Common
	Not apparent	Delayed flowering of some herbaceous plants	Occurs occasionally
	Not apparent	Changes in colour and form of first-formed flowers	Occurs occasionally

Fig. 134. How changes initiated in growth and development *in vitro* affect the form and behaviour of shoots and plants in the culture vessel, and later in greenhouse or field.

way, the concentration of cytokinin should be reduced (page 584), or the medium should be supplemented with gibberellic acid (Chapter 11, page 450). Gibberellic acid is usually added to media for apple shoot cultures. When only auxin and cytokinin are used as growth regulators for *Malus*, shoots are often produced with short internodes and small, unopened, curled leaves. Normal growth occurs when gibberellic acid is supplied (Pua *et al.*, 1983).

Abnormal seedling growth is sometimes found when zygotic embryos are grown *in vitro*. For example, a proportion of the plants obtained from culturing *Juglans regia* embryos had disturbed polarisation, abnormal anatomy and unusual rates of development. Kornova and Stephanova (1993) thought that these effects were related to embryo age. The dormancy which often follows seedling growth from cultured embryos is discussed below.

Precocious germination

The abnormal, or precocious germination of somatic embryos has been described on page 708.

Leaf abnormalities

Shape or arrangement

Many plants have leaves with unusual shapes both during and after micropropagation, either caused by direct effects of growth regulators, or by the rejuvenation of the plant during culture. Growth regulators may induce twisted or lanceolate leaves on young plants, but leaves formed later are of a normal shape. Those of micropropagated *Gerbera* plants are sometimes reflexed and cupped (Stimart, 1986). The occurrence of elongated, strap–shaped leaves is a symptom of hyperhydricity (page 655). The leaves of *Alnus crispa* produced on shoots cultured on **MS** medium with 30g/l (87.5 mM) sucrose were large and distorted and had a curled surface. To correct this condition Tremblay *et al.* (1984) found it necessary to increase the sucrose concentration for one clone to 60 g/l (175 mM), and in another clone to substitute sucrose with 31.5 g/l (175 mM) glucose.

A dramatic change of leaf form was instanced by Thakur *et al.* (1976). In 5–8% of their cultures of leaf or internode segments of *Bacopa monnieri*, some directly regenerated shoots had alternate leaves on the lower nodes, as opposed to the normal opposite and decussate arrangement which is typical in this species. The effect was only transitory; normal shoots were produced from the lateral buds of abnormal shoots released from dormancy by decapitation, and the alternate leaf arrangement did not persist if the abnormal shoots were re–cultured.

Differences between seedling–derived and tissue culture–derived plants of Brussels sprout, which were not related to abnormal chromosome number, were discovered by Clare and Collin (1974). Initially, plants regenerated from tissue culture had the appearance of young adults with thickened stems; when mature, the plants of the two groups were more similar but callus–derived plants were significantly taller, had a tendency to have fasciated tops (see below) and to have flat rather than cup–shaped leaves. More extreme abnormalities in leaf shape and position found on plants regenerated from callus kept in culture for over one year, were likely to have been due to somaclonal variation.

Juvenile leaf form. The juvenile leaf form found on plants immediately derived from tissue cultures depends on the degree of rejuvenation which has been induced by *in vitro* culture. Usually plants soon revert to producing adult foliage, but sometimes a juvenile leaf shape persists for a long while (see Part 1, page 240). Plantlets of apple produced from shoot–tip cultures were identical to shoots grown *in vivo* except that they lacked trichomes (Lane, 1978).

Loss of chlorophyll

Sometimes a proportion of the plants regenerated from tissue cultures are without chlorophyll. Such plants may be complete or partial *albinos*, the latter having white sectors in their leaves. The leaves of affected plants are found to contain plastids, which fail to develop into chloroplasts (Haskins *et al.*, 1971). Fully albino shoots and plantlets are able to survive *in vitro* because they are supplied with a carbohydrate energy source (Lassocinski, 1985), but, even so, are often found to grow more slowly than their green counterparts (Chin, 1979).

Albinos are occasionally found in broad–leafed genera (*e.g.* in *Pyrus*; Mehra and Jaidka, 1979: *Citrus limettoides*; Raj Bhansali and Arya, 1979: *Populus tremuloides;* Noh and Minocha, 1990), but occur with regularity in Gramineae amongst the plants obtained *via* indirect organogenesis from callus (including plants derived from protoplast culture), or from somatic embryogenesis. Some albino plants are almost invariably found in batches of plantlets derived from cereal anther culture.

The inability of plants to produce chlorophyll is now usually thought to have a genetic cause. Changes to both nuclear and chloroplast genes, and changes in ploidy (Park and Walton, 1989) may be involved. Albino plants derived from the anther culture of barley have been found to possess DNA within their plastids from which sections have been deleted (Chapter 3, page 75 *et seq.*). The frequency with which albino plants occur is influenced by the conditions in which the culture has been grown, and has been shown in various circumstances to be affected by:

- the genotype of the stock plant (Jackson and Dale, 1988; Heszky *et al.*, 1989);

- the environment in which the stock plant was grown (Anderson *et al.*, 1987; Creemers–Molenaar *et al.*, 1988; Ouyang *et al.*, 1987);

- temperature (Part 1, page 76);

- the nature of the medium used, specially the concentration of KNO3 it contains (Feng and Ouyang, 1988; Binh *et al.*, 1989);

- the age of the culture (Dale *et al.*, 1981);

- the type of growth regulators added to the medium.

> Increasing the concentration of 2,4–D in the medium to induce embryogenesis and organogenesis from *Lolium perenne* inflorescence explants, resulted in a higher frequency of albino shoots (Creemers–Molenaar *et al.*, 1988). Adding 7 mg/l dicamba to the medium used to induce callus from *Oryza sativa* root tips, caused all the plants eventually regenerated from the callus to be albino. Green shoots were obtained if 1–4 mg/l dicamba or 1 mg/l picloram were used (Zimny and Lörz, 1986). Oard and Rutger (1988) noted that adding 0.1 mg/l BAP to the medium used for regenerating plants from embryogenic callus, seemed to induce the formation of some albino plants. In other circumstances, cytokinins stimulate chlorophyll formation (see below).

Albino shoots and plants can result from the culture of explants from chimeras (see below).

Evidence for a physiological cause. Despite the general assumption that albino plants result from genetic changes, there are indications that sometimes loss of chlorophyll is due to a temporary physiological condition induced by *in vitro* culture. Besides persistent albinos, 10 per cent of the plants produced from *Hordeum marinum* callus expressed a transient chlorophyll deficiency. The plantlets became green when transferred to soil (Rotem–Abarbanell and Breiman, 1989). Albino foliage occurred in shoot cultures of *Aconitum* (a dicotyledon) when they were grown on a medium gelled by agar. Moving shoots to a medium gelled with Gelrite alleviated the problem (Cervelli, 1987).

The proportion of albino plantlets obtained from callus of forage grasses was reduced by the addition of 1 mg/l kinetin to the regeneration medium, possibly because it assisted in plastid formation (Lo *et al.*, 1980). Albino

shoots of *Brassica oleracea* regenerated from protoplast–derived callus, rapidly produced chlorophyll when cultured on **Linsmaier and Skoog (1965)** medium containing 1 mg/l IAA and 10 mg/l BAP. This particular cytokinin was necessary for chlorophyll production (Robertson and Earle, 1986).

Leaf variegation

Loss of variegation. Plants with variegated leaves are sometimes chimeras and therefore difficult to propagate by tissue culture without losing their distinctive markings (see Part 1, page 88 and page 743 in this chapter).

Variegated foliage does not always indicate that a plant is a chimera. *Hosta decorata* can lose its white leaf margin during shoot tip propagation even when plantlets are derived from axillary shoots. However, in this plant variegation seems to be determined physiologically. Its loss is often only a temporary phenomenon, and characteristic leaf markings can reappear. Papachatzi *et al.* (1981) restored them by keeping potted plants at 3–6°C for 5 months. Stimart (1986) found that variegation was regained with time, but that this delayed the marketing of micropropagated plants.

Occurrence of streaking or mottling. A proportion of micropropagated strawberry plants is sometimes found to have white or yellow leaf streaking or mottling (Schaeffer *et al.*, 1980; Swartz *et al.*, 1981; Boxus *et al.*, 1984). These malformations have been thought to be due to the occurrence of chimeral albino sectors (Schaeffer *et al.*, 1980), or to have a non–genetic origin: they are possibly related to the rejuvenated condition of the plants (Boxus, 1989). Leaf streaking is only seen at the planting out stage: plants die if the condition is severe; those with mild symptoms may revert to being completely green.

Formation of multiple shoot apices

Cytokinin treatments occasionally cause shoots to develop more than one meristem at their growing point. This leads to the formation of deformed shoots which are sometimes apparent in the culture vessel, but on other occasions do not develop until plantlets have been transferred to greenhouse or field. In one form of this abnormality, leaves may grow around the apex in the fashion of a rosette. Sometimes striations on an affected stem indicate the tissue produced by each meristem. Anderson *et al.* (1982) have shown that shoot tip propagation of some varieties of strawberry can result in plants with two kinds of abnormality:

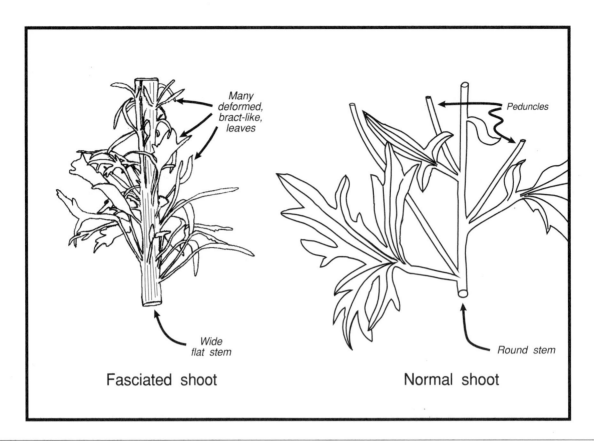

Fig. 135. Parts of a fasciated and a normal shoot of *Delphinium*, each cut just below the inflorescence.
In this genus, shoots often begin fasciated growth when 20–30 cm high. Flattened stems grow to the normal height of approximately one metre and then produce an unusually large and flattened inflorescence.

- plants with multiple crowns, each having a single growing point.

    If plants were split, each individual crown gave rise to a normal single–crowned plant, and if left alone, one crown in the cluster eventually became dominant over the rest.

- plants with multiple apices.

    Shoots produced many apices, usually in a linear fashion, but sometimes in a circular arrangement.

Such abnormalities have been detected *ex vitro* in plants micropropagated with very high rates of shoot proliferation. The prevalence of the abnormalities in micropropagated strawberries has varied between the cultivars tested. In the experiments of Anderson *et al.* (*loc. cit.*) 'Cambridge Favourite' showed no multi–apexing , while a high proportion of 'Cambridge Vigour' plants were affected. In susceptible varieties, the prevalence of the abnormality was generally related to the concentration and nature of the growth regulators used. In the presence of IBA, the complexity of multi–apexed buds increased as the concentration of BAP was raised from 0.023 mg/l (no multi–apexing) up to 2.3 mg/l (together with 0.2–2 mg/l IBA). The further addition of GA_3 to the medium decreased the proportion of affected plants.

Shoot fasciation

Occasionally the meristem at the apex of a shoot divides or proliferates to produce several separate shoot apices which do not merge, but grow side by side and continue to differentiate new tissues simultaneously. The resulting shoot, which is said to be *fasciated*, is wider than usual and is generally flattened (see Figs. 135 and 136).

Shoot fasciation is relatively common in nature, where it may sometimes be induced by mild injury, but often seems to occur completely fortuitously. The presence of more than one apex in flattened stems, prevents normal phyllotaxy and the number of leaves per unit length of stem is often greatly increased. In some cases, leaf shape is little altered, but on other occasions small atypical appendages are produced (Fig. 135). A fasciated shoot may arise from an axillary bud, or from the main growing point of a shoot. There is no genetic abnormality in the cells of a fasciated shoot, and normal growth may resume if a shoot arises from one part of the meristem complex.

Fig. 136. A fasciated shoot of *Forsythia* from a garden–grown bush.
Some leaves have been removed from the front of the fasciated stem to show its form. The flattened stem resulted from the growth of many fused apices, one of which finally reverted to a normal growth habit.

phyllotaxis; this is followed by the formation of a flattened apex and stem.

Hackett and Anderson (1967) noted some fasciated shoots among those which were regenerated from shoot apex callus of carnation. Apices of these shoots produced fan–shaped structures with two ranks of leaves. Davis *et al.* (1977) found that shoot fasciation occurred in carnation if meristems were damaged during excision of shoot tip explants.

Driss–Ecole (1981) reported obtaining flattened and fasciated shoots from meristem cultures established from normal *Celosia cristata* seedlings. The abnormality occurred on shoots cultured on **MS** medium containing IAA and kinetin, but only when cultures were kept in a 16 h day; shoots which grew in an 8 h photoperiod were unaffected.

The multi–apexing in strawberry, described above, did not result in flattened fasciated stems, but caused plants to produce small single–apexed crowns at intervals, giving them a bushy appearance with may small competing crowns. Leaves were arranged abnormally and two or more typically emerged simultaneously. Multi–apexing persisted in some plants for at least two years.

Somatic embryos. Fasciation of the shoot apex is also one kind malformation seen in somatic embryos (Sanders, 1950). Most embryos with this kind of deformity do not grow to maturity, but fasciation has been observed occasionally on the plantlets derived from somatic embryos. Litz and Conover (1983) obtained a few fasciated plantlets from somatic embryos of a *Carica* hybrid. Plants which survived grew out of the abnormal morphology.

Growth regulator effects

In most cases, the occurrence of fasciated shoots *in vitro* has been associated with growth regulator treatments. Aberrant phyllotaxis and fasciation were induced in *Kalanchoë blossfeldiana* by increasing the concentration of IAA and zeatin in the medium above 1 µM (Varga *et al.*, 1988). However multi–apexing, leading to shoot fasciation, is particularly related to cytokinin treatment *in vitro*.

Hempel (1985) found that carnation apices were more likely to become fasciated when shoots were cultured in the presence of BAP, zeatin, or 2–iP, than when kinetin was added to the medium. Shoots of carnation with wide deformed leaf blades which grew together and became chlorotic, were obtained by Weryszko and Hempel (1979) when carnation shoot tips were cultured on a medium with **MS** salts and BAP, but none occurred when BAP was replaced by kinetin.

In *Delphinium* plants (Fig. 135), shoots often begin fasciated growth when 20–30 cm high and produce a flattened stem which grows to a normal height of over one metre before producing an abnormally large and flattened inflorescence. In other plants, *e.g. Osteospermum*, a flattened stem may be terminated by an enlarged and unusually shaped flower or capitulum.

Shoot fasciation *in vitro*

Shoots. Multiple apexing and shoot fasciation occur more frequently during *in vitro* culture than *in vivo*. Fasciation, which is the most common manifestation of the formation of multiple growing points, has been frequently observed amongst adventitious shoots (Fig. 137) and on axillary shoots produced in shoot cultures. Fasciated shoots arising from micropropagation generally have the same flattened appearance as those found *in vivo*. The first symptom of fasciation is usually an altered

Fig. 137. A fasciated shoot of *Petunia* formed *in vitro*.

Fused or fasciated shoots of *Telopea speciosissima* occurred with increasing frequency in **Adams *et al*. (1979a)** medium (containing 0.05 mg/l IBA), as the concentration of BAP was increased from 0.3 to 2 mg/l. Abnormal shoots could be avoided by the use of low levels of BAP together with 1–3 mg/l GA₃ (Seelye, 1985).

Normal shoots often emerge from fasciated ones if the latter are subcultured onto a medium lacking cytokinin, but most commercial laboratories would rogue all abnormal shoots during subculturing, or when selecting shoots for rooting and acclimatization. Single, normal–looking shoots emerged from fasciated *Acer saccharinum* shoots which had been rooted on a medium lacking cytokinin (Huetteman and Preece, 1993).

Srivastava and Glock (1987) induced the formation of fasciated adventitious shoots, by treating *Betula* callus with *p*–fluorophenyl alanine during 3–4 subcultures.

Thidiazuron. Thidiazuron, which is a particularly effective cytokinin for woody plants, has been especially noted to induce shoot fasciation. The abnormality has been found, for example, in *Acer saccharinum* (Preece *et al*., 1991a); *Cercis canadensis* var. *alba* (Yusnita *et al*. 1990a); *Malus × domestica* (Van Nieuwkerk *et al*., 1986); and *Fraxinus americana* (Huetteman and Preece, 1993).

Fasciated *Acer saccharinum* shoots were particularly liable to arise on a medium containing thidiazuron when shoots had proliferated to the extent that culture vessels were very crowded and also when shoot apices measuring less than 5 mm were used to initiate new subcultures (Huetteman and Preece, 1993).

Effect of genotype. The propensity of some varieties of plant to be more prone to shoot fasciation than others suggests that susceptibility is genetically controlled. The occurrence of fasciated shoots during carnation shoot culture is, for example, related to the variety which is propagated (Hempel, 1985). Varieties of *Kalanchoë blossfeldiana* have also been found to vary in their susceptibility to *in vitro* shoot fasciation (Varga *et al*., 1988), as have clones of *Acer saccharinum* (Huetteman and Preece, 1993).

Fasciated shoots on micropropagated plants

Shoot fasciation may only appear after plants have been acclimatized. A high proportion of plants with fasciated shoots was discovered by Knuttel and Benoit (1988) in plants of *Rhododendron* 'Molly Fordham' which had been micropropagated. These plants did not thrive, but plants of the variety 'Anglo' which showed the same symptoms, appeared to grow out of them. Although shoot fasciation was not uncommon in cultures of *Acer saccharinum* supplied with thidiazuron, Huetteman and Preece (1993) observed the phenomenon in only one field planted tree. This produced a fasciated stem during the end of its first growing season, but stem growth during the second year returned to normal.

Chimeral rearrangement

The breakdown in the orderly arrangement of the histogenic cell layers in shoot apices which can result from tissue culture, can cause some ramets produced from chimeras to be phenotypically different to the stock plant. Examples of the kind of variation which can be engendered, even by using shoot culture, have been given in Part 1, pages 87 *et seq.*

The possible chimeral status of a stock plant should be suspected if micropropagated plants display variations in leaf variegation, flower colour or vigour. Note however, that such changes can also result from plants being freed from virus diseases (Chapter 5).

Production of albino plants

Leaves having white segments are often found on chimeras with chlorophyll–deficient cells in one of their histogenic layers. Tissue culture of such plants can result in the production of albino plants if the cell layers become displaced. Chin (1979) was able to obtain green and albino plants of *Episcia* by culturing appropriate segments of leaves and inducing the formation of adventitious shoots. Albino plants can also be obtained from variegated *Sanseveria zelonica* and *Pelargonium zonale* chimeras.

Changes in flower colour and form

When variation in flower colour occurs as a result of micropropagation there must either have been a mutation (probably as a result of somaclonal alteration of the genome), or the stock plant was a chimera and rearrangement of the histogenic layers has occurred *in vitro*. The latter is more likely if the plant has been propagated by shoot culture, or another technique likely to preserve genetic integrity.

Leshem (1983b) noticed that in hyperhydric shoots of carnation, cells of the corpus (Part 1, page 86) were unusually large and vacuolated, leading to apices tending to be of the 'mantle over core' type. This led Leshem (1986) to suggest that the variable flower colours in carnation plants produced from hyperhydric shoots (page 659) were caused by some plants having rearranged cell layers, the mother plant having been a chimera.

Chimeral rearrangement is known to lead to the appearance of new flower colours and forms (Skirvin and Janick, 1974, 1976a; Dommergues and Gillot, 1973; Sutter and Langhans, 1981).

Reduced plant vigour

There have been suggestions that some plants derived by direct regeneration from epidermal tissues might be lacking in vigour. Bush *et al.* (1976) found that plants of chrysanthemum, regenerated from petal explants, differed in vigour from those derived from shoot tip culture.

This was attributed to the original chimeral state of the mother plants and the possibility that the plants were composed of cells with different growth capacities. Variation thought to be due to the rearrangement of the cell layers of chimeras was discovered when plants were regenerated directly (or after the brief appearance of intermediary callus) from ray florets of four selections of the chrysanthemum variety 'Early Charm' (Khalid *et al.*, 1989).

A mutation in the L3 layer of *Pelargonium* chimeras, which resulted in dwarfed growth, was thought to have a higher stability than cells in the L1 and L2 layers responsible for leaf variegation in the chimeras. Displacement of the layers in the apex during tissue culture propagation resulted in the appearance of dwarfed plants (Reuther, 1988c).

Reduction in the vigour of tissue cultured plants, not apparently associated with chimeral separation, is mentioned on page 753.

Leaf shape and seasonal growth

Using axillary shoot proliferation for the commercial micropropagation of globe artichoke (*Cynara scolymus*) cultivars from the early Mediterranean group, has resulted in a series of different stable phenotypes. Shoots all appear to be similar *in vitro*, but in the field, plants are found vary in leaf shape and pattern of growth. Pécaut and Martin (1991) confirmed these results and found that shoot culture of four such cultivars resulted in the occurrence of three off–types:

— **Pastel variant.** Leaves are more divided and curled than the norm, bracts in the head are more convex, and head development and harvest in both spring and autumn are much later than usual;

This variant occurs naturally in plants propagated from offsets with a frequency of about 1 plant in 1000.

— **Bull variant.** Leaves are less pinnate, and the head more globular than normal. Heads are ready for harvest at the normal time, but the number of heads per stem is very low;

— **Pastel–bull variant.** Leaves are highly divided but larger than those of pastel plants. Bracts of the head are short, the number of heads per stem low, and harvest is late.

In early subcultures, pastel variants were more likely to arise from cultures initiated from small (less than 0.3 mm) than from large (*ca.* 3 mm) shoot apices. They were detected with the following frequencies in the four cultivars:

Cultivar	Size of shoot tip explant	Frequency of pastel variants
'Violet de Provence'	<0.3 mm	23% after 3–4 subcultures 62% after 9–10 subcultures 100% after 10–15 subcultures
	3.0 mm	9% after 3–4 subcultures 40% after 9–10 subcultures 100% after 10–15 subcultures
'Tudela'	—	52% after 16 subcultures
'Niscemese'	—	9% after 6 subcultures
'Lisco sardo'	—	100% after 25 subcultures

Bull and pastel–bull variants also occurred with a much lower frequency.

The cause of the increase in these variants through micropropagation is unknown. It has been suggested that the original plants are chimeras but this is not well established.

CAUSES AND CURES

Growth regulators

The use of auxins and cytokinins in media can result in regenerated plants being morphologically different from normal, especially if the concentrations of these regulants have been excessive.

Cytokinins

Leaf shape. Cytokinins used to promote axillary or adventitious shoot formation in Stage II cultures can cause leaves to have an abnormal shape and to be thicker than normal. Spathe–shaped leaves are liable to be produced on shoots of *Chrysanthemum* grown on media with high cytokinin–auxin ratios (Sutter and Langhans, 1981).

Branching. Cytokinin treatment also frequently induces an atypically compact or branched habit in regenerated plants and an inhibition of the formation of adventitious roots (Chapter 14). Increased branchiness often persists in micropropagated plants when they are transferred to the greenhouse or field (see page 747). It is commercially desirable in some species, but undesirable in others.

Abnormal growth. Fonnesbech *et al.* (1977a) record that abnormal shoots were regenerated from shoot tip cultures of *Asparagus plumosus* if too high a concentration (2–10 mg/l) of any one of 5 cytokinins was incorporated into the growth medium. Shoots induced to form under these conditions were compact with long cladodes and had callus–like clusters of shoots around the nodes, whereas those produced by 0.2 mg/l cytokinin appeared

normal. Plantlets of potato obtained through shoot tip culture showed teratomatous shoot development and had an inhibited root system if high kinetin levels had been added to the medium (Novák *et al.*, 1980).

Malformations seem particularly likely to occur when BAP is used as a cytokinin, but their common occurrence may simply reflect the frequent use of this compound. Lane (1979a) records that shoots formed directly on flax hypocotyls were normal if induced by 0.02 mg/l BAP but were fasciated and poorly defined when formed in the presence of 0.1–0.2 mg/l. Callus was produced by 1.1 mg/l BAP. Shoots regenerated from potato tuber discs had slender stems and leaves that were not fully expanded, if they were induced by BAP at a concentration above 1 mg/l. Adding more than 30 mg/l adenine sulphate to the medium caused similar effects (Jarret *et al.*, 1980a). Shoots formed on nodal stem sections of *Dioscorea bulbifera* were malformed if supra–optimal levels of either BAP or kinetin were used (Forsyth and Van Staden, 1982) and Song and Chua (1991) found that abnormal shoot development occurred in *Taraxacum mongoliam* cultures if explants were kept for an extended period on media containing thidiazuron.

High levels (1.8 mg/l) of BAP employed during shoot culture of *Anigozanthos*, caused many shoots to be produced, but these weres stunted, crowded and tubular. Following transfer to medium with 0.1 mg/l BAP, the shoots became normal in appearance (McComb and Newton, 1981). Stunted shoots and somatic embryos of *Saintpaulia* were produced by 0.5 mg/l BAP (Bilkey *et al.*, 1978), and Vieitez and Vieitez (1980a) obtained short rosetted shoots of chestnut with 5 mg/l BAP (but not with 1–2 mg/l). Singha (1982b) reported that 5–10% of *Malus × purpurea* cv. 'Eleyi' shoots came to have thickened and cup–shaped leaves, and failed to proliferate during routine shoot tip subcultures on a medium with 1 mg/l BAP.

Cytokinins, and particularly BAP are partly responsible for hyperhydricity of cultured shoots and regenerated organs (Chapter 13). The toxicity caused in apple shoot tip cultures by the continuous use of BAP, was reduced or eliminated by Werner and Boe (1980) when they periodically substituted 2–iP for BAP during subcultures.

The application of 0.1–1 mg/l of three cytokinins to *Cymbidium* cultures increased the formation of protocorms but retarded their growth and root formation. When 10–50 mg/l of the compounds was added to the medium, marked stimulation of protocorm initiation was accompanied by toxic and teratogenic effects, disturbed chlorophyll synthesis and abnormal mitotic cell division (Rucker, 1974). All these abnormalities disappeared if protocorms were transplanted onto a cytokinin–free medium.

Auxins

Abnormalities in regenerated plants have been less frequently attributed to auxins used in media. Most reports have been associated with the use of these regulants in rooting media.

The fertility of flowers produced on plants of *Arabidopsis thaliana* regenerated from leaf callus, depended on the concentration of auxin added to the rooting medium. High concentrations were inhibitory (Avetisov *et al.* 1976). Abnormalities such as modification of petal shape and number, shoot fasciation and the development of ovular zones on what are normally sterile flowers, were noted by Bigot (1982) as becoming more common in plants of *Begonia* × *hiemalis* when shoots had been kept more than one month on a rooting medium containing 0.2 mg/l IBA and 0.5 mg/l 2–iP. Gerbera shoots separated from shoot clusters were kept for 10 days by Murashige *et al.* (1974) on a medium containing 10 mg/l IAA before being planted in the greenhouse. The IAA treatment increased the number of roots which formed *extra vitrum*. If 100 mg/l IAA was used instead of 10 mg/l, the shoots rooted to the same extent, but plants afterwards grew much more slowly.

Krul and Worley (1977a) thought that the occurrence of grape somatic embryos with malformed primary leaves might have been due to the use of 2,4–D in early cultural procedures.

Gibberellic acid

As mentioned in Chapter 11 (page 450), GA$_3$ can help to produce normal plantlets from shoot tip cultures where shoots are stunted and deformed. Used injudiciously however, gibberellic acid can cause shoots grown *in vitro* to be elongated. In *Limnophila chinensis* where GA$_3$ unusually induced direct caulogenesis, the shoots formed were pale green and spindly at all concentrations, and had few narrow leaves, or no leaves at all (Sangwan *et al.*, 1976). In tobacco this effect was counteracted by the cytokinin 2–iP, which on its own promoted the formation of short shoots bearing broad round leaves (Engelke *et al.*, 1973). Shoots of normal appearance occurred with a combination of 2–iP and GA$_3$, when the concentration of each growth regulator was optimised.

Ethylene

Ethylene accumulated in tightly sealed vessels can have both promotive and inhibitory effects on growth and morphogenesis (Part 1, pages 459 *et seq.*). The presence of ethylene can cause shoots to grow abnormally. Potato shoots in vessels covered with tightly screwed metal caps tended to produce stolon–like shoots with small leaves. If the vessels were further sealed with PVC tape of Parafilm, shoots were short and swollen and had only small scale–like leaves. These effects were eliminated by placing a vial within each vessel containing a solution of the ethylene absorbent, mercuric perchlorate (Hussey and Stacey, 1981a).

When 0.5–2 mg/l BAP was added to the medium, cultured shoots of *Ceratonia siliqua*, became covered with white proliferations which were confirmed to be hypertrophied lenticels. The symptoms persisted during 42 subcultures (Vinterhalter *et al.*, 1992) and were probably caused by the cytokinin provoking a high rate of ethylene biosynthesis, and the gas becoming trapped within the culture vessels. The formation of intumescences around the lenticels of shoots kept in ethylene has been recorded by Wallace (1928), Crocker (1948) and Jackson *et al.* (1987b).

Media effects

Abnormal shoots may arise if cultures are grown on media with an incorrect balance of ions. Abnormal leaves arose in *Adiantum* cultures if the concentrations of ammonium or nitrate ions in **Gamborg *et al.* (1968) B5** medium were increased above the customary levels (Pais and Casal, 1987).

Temperature

The effect of temperature on the subsequent growth and development of cultures was mentioned in Chapter 7 (pages 208 *et seq.*), where it will be seen that conditions *in vitro* sometimes exert a carry–over effect and influence the growth of plants after they have been established in the external environment. One commercial micropropagation laboratory obtained many aberrant plants from shoot tip cultures when the temperature control in their growth room broke down, causing the room to overheat during a single night (personal communication). The effectiveness of cytokinins is found to decrease as temperatures rise, but that of auxins to increase (Part 1, page 442). Possibly the abnormal leaf shapes observed were therefore due to auxin toxicity?

UNUSUAL CHARACTERISTICS OF PLANTS AFTER MICROPROPAGATION.

Although most species can be propagated *in vitro* by a method which, under normal circumstances, will introduce very little additional genetic variation, changes are often encountered in the growth and physiology of plants finally obtained from tissue cultures, even amongst plants which are multiplied by meristem, shoot, or node culture. Experience has indicated which abnormalities are likely to be caused by temporary epigenetic or environmental effects.

Some of the temporary changes which occur as a result of *in vitro* culture are disadvantageous, but others are advantageous and add to the value of the micro–propagated product. For example, an improved rate of growth frequently results from the elimination of pathogens: increased branchiness (see below) is a valuable characteristic in some ornamentals. Virus tested yams (*Dioscorea alata*) propagated by tissue culture have consistently out yielded diseased material in many countries (Chandler and Haque, 1984).

SHORT–LIVED EFFECTS

Effects of cultural conditions

It should always be remembered that the manner in which plants have been cultured can influence their early growth in greenhouse or field. Saebø *et al.* (1992) found that even though the highest rate of photosynthesis *in vitro* occurred in light with high irradiance in the blue wavebands, plants of *Betula pendula*, which had been micropropagated in light containing both blue and red components, performed best in the field. Plants cultured in lighting provided by incandescent lamps grew very slowly out–of–doors.

Micropropagation in closed containers almost invariably results in the formation of leaves with an abnormal structure and function. There is an absence of epicuticular wax, a change in the location, morphology and function of stomata, and an altered photosynthetic capacity. Shoots may also show symptoms of vitrescence: if severe, these will prevent the plant surviving in the external environment. These effects persist when shoots or plantlets are moved to the *in vivo* environment but their significance is progressively reduced as new leaves are formed and the plantlets commence autotrophic growth (Chapter 14).

Pesticide tolerance

In several trials, the tolerance of micropropagated plants to pesticides has been found to be less than that of those which were multiplied conventionally. Possibly this is because young plants derived from tissue culture lack a well–formed cuticle, despite their having been through a period of acclimatization. Many fungicide sprays, and chemicals normally used to control liverworts and mosses, can be toxic (Smith W.A., 1982). This can make disease control in the nursery a problem.

An increased susceptibility to the pre–emergence herbicides simazine, oryzalin, and diphenamide persisted in tissue cultured brambles after they were planted in the field, but plants were unaffected by the maximum recommended rate during their second year (Mudge *et al.*, 1986). Similar results were obtained with red raspberry plants (Meador, 1985; Mudge *et al.*, 1986; Neal *et al.*, 1990). Micropropagated plants in both the greenhouse and field were injured by simazine and oryzalin, but injury was reduced if application was delayed until 2–4 weeks after planting. A napropamide wettable powder caused some foliar injury, but plants were not harmed by a granular form of this compound.

Dormancy

The dormancy which often overtakes micropropagated plants was discussed in Chapter 7 (Part 1, page 211): that which affects cultures of bulbous species is discussed on page 883.

Culture of excised embryos. The seeds of plants, particularly those of plants native to temperate zones, may need to be vernalised (given a cold treatment), or be treated with gibberellic acid, before zygotic embryos will grow normally *in vitro*. Dormancy of some other seeds is overcome if they are immersed in a weak solution of hydrogen peroxide. In some cases (*e.g.* in *Fraxinus ornus*, Arrillaga *et al.* 1992), the dormancy of embryos is overcome when they are excised from the seed and cultured *in vitro*. The addition of gibberellic acid to the medium may then be effective (*e.g.* in *Comptonia peregrina*, Del Tredici and Torrey, 1976).

Even after treatments such as these, some of the seedlings obtained from germinating embryos may not grow normally. A proportion of seedlings from excised peach embryos became rosetted and did not elongate: normal

Table 119. Examples of plants in which the increased branching of micropropagated plants is an advantage.

Plant	Advantage	References
Begonia × hiemalis	Plants more marketable	Stimart (1986)
Hydrangea	More attractive as a pot plants	J.B. Jones (1979)
Kalanchoë	More attractive as a pot plants	Smith and Nightingale (1979)
Rosa hybrida	Dwarf roses more attractive as pot plants	Stimart (1986) Dubois *et al.* (1988) Dubois & De Vries (1988)
Vaccinium	Increased yields in consequence	Read *et al.* (1988)

growth could then usually be obtained from axillary buds after cold storing the plants at 4°C for 3 weeks (Brooks and Hough, 1958).

Somatic embryos of the plants whose zygotic embryos require a cold treatment before growth, often behave in the same way. Their treatment is described on page 709.

SEMI–PERMANENT CHANGES

Shoot growth

Branching habit

Micropropagated plants often show increased branching. This is often put down to the residual action of the cytokinin used to induce shoot proliferation *in vitro*, but may also be due to rejuvenation, or to the origin of explants. In many plants, particularly those sold in pots as ornamentals, increased branching is a desirable feature and makes the plants more attractive, but in others it is not required (Capellades Queralt *et al.*, 1991). Some examples of plants in which increased branching is an advantage are listed in Table 119.

When micropropagated, strawberry plants of most varieties produce many more runners than normal during their first 1–2 years in the field, making them generally unsuitable for direct cropping, but valuable as a source of future planting material (see below). Increasing the amount of BAP used in strawberry micropropagation from 0.5 mg/l to 3 mg/l had no effect on the increase in observed

runnering (Marcotrigiano *et al.*, 1984). By contrast, in *Senecio × hybridus*, where the cytokinin BAP used during shoot culture had a particularly noticeable effect on subsequent branching, as the concentration in the medium was raised from 0 to 0.1 or 1.0 mg/l, the plants eventually obtained became more branched with additional leaves (although individual leaves were smaller in size) (Gertsson, 1988b). The time to develop flowers was consequently increased, plants flowered later, and their inflorescences were taller than those on seedlings. Adding 5 mg/l BAP to cultures resulted in plants with stunted foliage and few leaves and flowers.

Gerbera plants multiplied with BAP in the Stage II medium branched more freely than normal plants, but the degree of branching was reduced in proportion to the period of time during which plants stayed on an *in vitro* rooting medium (Meynet, 1983). Gerberas, micropropagated by Hempel (1985) and stored at low temperature before planting, were also noted to branch more freely than controls.

Zhola *et al.* (1992) noticed that some micropropagated Asiatic *Lilium* plants uncharacteristically produced, when adult, bulbils in their leaf axils. This feature seemed to be associated with the addition of cytokinin to the medium in which the bulblets, from which the mature plants were derived, had been regenerated.

Woody plants. Increased branchiness in field or greenhouse also occurs in some woody plants as a result of micropropagation. In those which grow as shrubs, instead of branches arising at some distance above ground level, micropropagated plants have been found to produce branches from the base. Micropropagated roses initially produce more flowering shoots per plant than newly grafted roses when planted *ex vitro* (Stimart, 1986): blue-berries have been found to produce many more canes (see page 757). Tamarind trees, which originated as adventitious shoots on seedling hypocotyls, have been found to have profuse branching and to grow as bushes rarely exceeding 3–4 m in height. Trees of this species grown from seeds are moderately branched and may reach a height of 25 m (Mascarenhas *et al.*, 1987).

Although micropropagated rhododendron plantlets have been found to grow without the rest cycles which occur in rooted cuttings, some kinds (possibly due to the micropropagation protocol), have produced just one vertical shoot; the lack of branching here is a disadvantage because plants have had to be pinched to induce them to develop an acceptable growth habit (Smith W.A.,1982). According to Capellades Queralt *et al.* (1991), the quality of micropropagated rhododendrons has been criticised by growers. Plants have weak stems, and losses during the acclimatization period are often followed by a period of dormancy. Slow growth has resulted in micropropagated plants not flowering as rapidly as those initiated from normal cuttings. By contrast, others have reported that micropropagated rhododendrons, particularly 'PJM' hybrids, had satisfactory (McCown and Lloyd ,1983; Ettinger and Preece, 1985; and Preece,1991), or increased basal branching (Wong, 1982).

Explant origin. The origin of buds used to initiate shoot cultures can affect growth *in vitro* and in rare cases the behaviour of micropropagated plants when they are established *ex vitro*. Marks and Myers (1992b) found that plants of *Daphne odora* grown from explanted apical shoot buds, branched while still in the vegetative phase, whereas those which had originated from lateral shoot buds failed to branch before flowering, even if the tips of the plants were pinched.

Shoot quality

Stem length and stem diameter of some plants is affected by their being propagated in tissue cultures. Often this is related to the increased branchiness of the plants, but this is not always the case. Plants of *Ficus lyrata* and *Kalanchoë* produced by micropropagation, may have shorter internodes (Smith and Nightingale, 1979). *Saintpaulia* plants resulting from *in vitro* propagation are usually more uniform and have a more pronounced rosette appearance, with smaller leaves than plants produced from cuttings. As their flowering is unaltered, they are more attractive as pot plants (Cassells and Plunkett, 1984).

The stem diameter of some micropropagated plants has been found to be less than that of normal plants. Stimart (1986) reported that in *Dendranthema* (chrysanthemum),

Dianthus and *Kalanchoë*, this inadequacy led to lodging: micropropagated *Gypsophila* grown in the field was liable to break off at the soil line. Stimart (*loc. cit.*) said that the problem could be partly overcome by adopting a slower rate of shoot multiplication and by culturing plants in light of high irradiance.

Root growth

Hardy deciduous azaleas from tissue cultures have been found to produce larger root systems than plants derived from conventional stock plants (Read *et al.*, 1988). This contrasts with the weaker root systems produced by some other woody plants which have been micropropagated (see page 750).

Flowering

Ripeness to flower

The induction of flowering *in vitro* and the proclivity of micropropagated plants to flower when they have been planted in the greenhouse or out–of–doors, were discussed in Part 1, pages 243 to 245, and the following comments serve only to reinforce what was said there. Micropropagated carnations have been found to flower prematurely (see page 848).

Accelerated flowering. Although woody plants cloned by tissue culture techniques show many juvenile characteristics, they frequently come into flower before true seedlings planted in the field at the same time, which indicates that they had not undergone full rejuvenation. Thus plants of *Eucalyptus tereticornis* and *E. torelliana*, propagated by shoot culture from buds of mature trees, flowered during their second year in the field: seedlings first flowered 2–3 years later (Gupta and Mascarenhas, 1987; Mascarenhas *et al..*, 1988). Similar results were obtained with micropropagated teak and tamarind (Mascarenhas *et al.*, 1987). The former began to flower in their second year in the field (seedlings flowered in years 4–5), while micropropagated tamarind began flowering $3\frac{1}{2}$–$4\frac{1}{2}$ after planting, a useful attribute where fruits have an economic value; tamarind trees raised from seed normally take 13–14 years to reach the flowering stage (Mascarenhas *et al..*, 1988).

When plants are required to be sold as flowering ornamentals, any delay in flowering is a commercial disadvantage. Micropropagated *Metrosideros* plants began to return to adult foliage 6 months after they were planted in pots (Oliphant, 1988) and flowered after 2–3 years. Although the interval to flowering was much shorter than that required by seedlings, which have a 5–10 year juve-

fungi, or viruses, or because of a changed physiology. The attribute is particularly valuable in the nursery where a saleable plant can often be obtained in a shorter time than from conventionally–rooted cuttings (Smith W.A., 1982).

Differences in vigour have been reported between plants of *Saintpaulia* regenerated directly from the epidermis or the internal pith tissues of leaf petioles (Bilkey and Cocking, 1981). Plants from the internal tissues grew larger than those that were of epidermal origin. As the original plants were presumed to be non–chimeral, no satisfactory explanation for this difference could be given. Possibly the larger plants were tetraploid? The authors of the paper thought this was unlikely and speculated whether their results were due to the 'inherently' (meaning epigenetically determined) low vigour of the epidermal cells.

Plants lacking in vigour

Cassells and Minas (1983b) obtained between 4 and 13% aberrant types amongst many species and varieties of *Pelargonium* propagated by meristem and shoot culture. These had reduced height and width and a smaller leaf area, but at least 80% of the abnormal plants reverted to a normal habit after they had been grown in a greenhouse for 6–12 months.

Plants regenerated from leaf callus of strawberry cv. 'Redcoat' had reduced plant vigour, shorter petioles, smaller leaf laminae, but more leaves and runners than normal. The frequency of such variants was greatest (10%) amongst plants regenerated from callus which had been initiated with the highest experimental levels of BAP and 2,4–D (20 µM each). The dwarf phenotype was maintained in runner plants taken from the primary variants. Its cause was thought to be due to the physiological effect of growth regulators: attempts to demonstrate the existence of different isozyme patterns or chromosome numbers, which would have demonstrated the occurrence of somaclonal variation, were not successful (Nehra *et al.*, 1992).

Secondary products

Many plants which contain substances of industrial or pharmaceutical interest have been subjected to tissue culture. Usually there has been an interest in producing such secondary products *in vitro*, but sometimes plants have been micropropagated with a view to extracting the compounds from field grown material. Sometimes yields have been higher than in conventionally propagated plants, on other occasions, less.

On a dry weight basis, the roots of micropropagated *Bupleurum falcatum* plants had a similar saponin content to those of seedlings, but the amount of saikosaponins *c* and *d* were significantly larger (Hiraoka *et al.*, 1986). However, compared to plants propagated by division of the rhizome, the contents of two sesquiterpenes and a polyacetylenic acid, were low during the first 2–3 years of growth in plants of *Attractylodes lancea* propagated by tissue culture. The contents only reached normal levels after 3–4 years in the field (Hiraoka and Tomita, 1990).

The leaves of *Eucalyptus citriodora* are harvested for the extraction of oil, yielding citronellal and citronellol. When select trees with an high leaf oil content were micropropagated their leaves had the same oil content as those of the stock plant 6 months after being planted in the field. Leaves of seedlings cannot be harvested until the plants are at least three years old, because it is not until then that the oil concentration in the leaves reaches a stable level (Gupta and Mascarenhas, 1987; Mascarenhas *et al.*, 1988)

FIELD PERFORMANCE

With a few exceptions, some of which have been mentioned above, micropropagation results in uniform batches of plants which grow, flower and fruit normally. The performance of herbaceous plants which grow to maturity in one or two years is easily monitored, but the behaviour of tissue–cultured woody plants, which reach maturity after many years, takes much longer to assess. For this reason, there are relatively few published accounts of the long term field performance of micropropagated woody plants.

Although it can be expected that eventually (providing they have not been increased by techniques which lead to genetic variation), plants multiplied *in vitro* will be equivalent or superior to those propagated by traditional techniques, it cannot be assumed that their growth and behaviour in the short term will necessarily be the same. Moreover, the characteristics of different cultivars of a species *in vitro* are not necessarily an indication of the field performance of those cultivars (Preece *et al.*, 1991b).

TREE FRUITS

Fruit trees were amongst the first woody plants to be micropropagated on a large scale, and there is consequently more information about their performance in the field than for other woody plants.

Apple and pear

Self–rooted trees

Most trials with apple have shown that self–rooted micropropagated trees produce more vegetative growth and behave more like trees budded onto seedling rootstocks, than trees budded onto known dwarfing rootstocks, but results do vary between cultivars and different trial locations. In many climates nearly all cultivars are too vigorous for high density orchards or for planting in gardens.

Unlike true seedlings, microcuttings of apple produce trees which often flower during their third year in the field (Mullins, 1985), although flowering has occurred 1–2 years after planting (Zimmerman, 1983). Generally micropropagated trees flower later than scions grafted onto accredited rootstocks (Zimmerman, 1983) and the crop is borne in the upper part of the canopy, as occurs in seedlings at the end of the juvenile phase (Rosati and Gaggioli, 1987). Self–rooted micropropagated 'Bartlett' pear was found to behave in a similar way.

In Italy, three micropropagated apple varieties had smaller trunks and a more upright canopy than grafted trees during their first years in the field (Cobianchi *et al.*, 1988), and similarly Webster *et al.* (1985) found micropropagated apple trees grew slowly on their own roots in their first year and were comparatively small in years 2 and 3, and slow to develop a branched structure. However, many self–rooted apple cultivars eventually produce much vegetative growth. 'Cox' was too vigorous and flowered and cropped poorly. The fruits of 'Golden Delicious' were russeted (as they are when grown on their own roots from non–tissue cultured stock) and fruit production relative to wood growth was less than where the cultivar had been grafted onto 'M.9' or 'MM.106' rootstocks (Webster *et al.*, *loc. cit.*). Self–rooted micropropagated apple trees of the cultivars 'Northern Spy', 'Ozark Gold', 'Stayman' and 'Rome Beauty' produced more vegetative growth and yielded less than trees budded onto 'MM.106' or 'M.26' (Zimmerman and Miller, 1991). Similarly Rosati and Gaggioli (1987) found that tissue cultured 'Golden Delicious' trees were more vigorous than those grafted onto 'MM.106' and 'M.111' rootstocks and were as productive as scions grafted onto 'MM.106', even though they came into bearing one year afterwards. The experience of Druart and Boxus (1987)

with 'Golden Delicious' was that after 7 years in the field, micropropagated self–rooted trees had thicker trunks and higher vigour than trees grafted onto 'M.9', but less fruit and smaller yields.

However, the growth and fruiting of some micropropagated fruit trees may be acceptable. 'Malling Greensleeves' and 'James Grieve' growing on their own roots are two apple cultivars where this could be the case (Webster *et al.*, *loc. cit.*). The cultivar 'Gala' may also produce an acceptable tree in England from a self–rooted microcutting (Jones, 1991). After the fourth year in the field, the yield of micropropagated pear trees and those grafted onto dwarfing quince rootstocks were similar (Neri *et al.*, 1989).

Grafted trees

Self–rooted apple trees might be expected to be more vigorous than their counterparts grafted onto dwarfing rootstocks, and so the results of trials where micropropagated scions have been grafted, are of interest. When the variety 'Malling Greensleeves' was grafted onto the dwarfing rootstocks 'M.27' and 'M.9', or the invigorating rootstock 'M.25', tree vigour followed a pattern which would have been expected from the rootstock. However shoot growth was more vigorous than that of conventionally grafted trees and this characteristic was maintained for at least five years. Cropping was also delayed for one year and the trees grafted onto 'M.9' and 'M.25' produced an abnormally large number of suckers, which would be disadvantageous in practical fruit production (Jones and Hadlow, 1989). Increased sucker production has also been noted when apple scion wood has been grafted onto micropropagated apple rootstocks (Navatel *et al.*, 1988: reported in Jones, 1991).

Peach, nectarine, plum and cherry

In a trial in Italy, the peach cultivars 'Maycrest' and 'Roza' and the nectarine 'Firebrite' obtained on their own roots from micropropagation, were much smaller at planting than trees budded on 'PSB2' peach seedling rootstocks, but the difference in trunk size and tree height diminished with time. By the end of the third year, in each cultivar the growth habit and fruit yield of the trees from the two sources were very similar.

Hammerschlag and Scorza (1991) concluded that, based on yield and growth, peach trees propagated by shoot culture should be acceptable for commercial fruit orchards. At two sites in the U.S.A., fruit production from tissue cultured trees was initially higher than from budded trees, but differences disappeared during the following 1–3 years. Differences in productivity were probably related to the size of the trees at planting: the budded trees were smaller than the tissue cultured trees at this time, but continued to increase in size and trunk diameter more rapidly. In Europe, the preference is still for grafted trees. Approximately 10 million plants of a peach almond hybrid are produced by shoot culture each year in Italy as rootstocks for peach orchards (Pierik, 1991a).

Micropropagated plum trees of the variety 'Bluefire' were slower to bear fruit than grafted trees (Cobianchi *et al.*, 1988), and micropropagated 'Independence' nectarine trees and sour cherry trees grew less rapidly than grafted trees and had a lower fruit yield or began to bear later (Cobianchi *et al.*, 1988; Liverani *et al.*, 1989; Rosati and Gaggioli, 1987). In Poland, however, self rooted sour cherry plants propagated by shoot culture were found to be satisfactory. The young trees survived a severe winter in their second year, and bloomed freely in the fourth and fifth years *ex vitro*: all were true to type (Borkowska and Szczerba, 1990).

Grapevine

Grapevines are particularly liable to become juvenile during *in vitro* culture (page 750). When three clones of the grape vine 'Corvinia Veronese' were multiplied by shoot culture, the plants produced had altered 'juvenile' characteristics. Leaves produced during *in vitro* growth were elongated and lacked their typical lobing. No tendrils were formed. During their first year in the field the *in vitro* propagated plantlets had apices and young shoots which contained anthocyanin, and leaves which were smaller than normal with less lobes of a modified shape: there were fewer serrations, but those which were present were pronounced. The leaves also had a thicker lamina and were bristly, particularly on the lower side. Like plants propagated by embryogenesis (see above), shoots and the first–formed leaves, had an unusual coppery tinge and stems were a reddish green due to an increased anthocyanin content. The first fruit clusters formed were atypical and small–fruited. All abnormalities decreased as years passed, but even after 3 years, sprouts at the base of the main stem still had the same characteristics.

Juvenility not only affects the appearance of plants when they are established out of doors, but causes them to start cropping later than conventionally propagated material, and to have reduced yields during the early years in the field. Cancellier and Cossio (1988) reported that six years after being planted, the average weight of fruit per bunch on a clone of 'Corvina Veronese' was half that on conventionally propagated bushes, and the weight of fruit per plant only 63%. Cancellier and Cossio (1987, 1988) said that the combination of these features precluded the use

of plants obtained by *in vitro* multiplication from commercial planting.

Kiwifruit

Juvenile traits are also found in micropropagated *Actinidia* plants (Cancellier and Cossio, 1988). Leaf petioles and shoot tips of young plants have a reddish colour and the plants are intensely hairy. Massai *et al.* (1991) found that 2–year old micropropagated vines were less susceptible to frost than vines which had been raised from cuttings, and when the plants were pruned in the spring, the new leaves on the micropropagated stock contained more chlorophyll and had a higher rate of assimilation than the controls.

Self rooted micropropagated plants (ST) of cv. 'Hayward' and plants of this cultivar grafted onto 'D1' rootstock (GD), initially were more vigorous and had a larger leaf area than plants grown from hardwood cuttings (HC). Increased vigour seemed to be associated with the larger root systems which the ST and GD plants possessed (Piccotino *et al.*, 1991), but such differences may only have been a characteristic of the plants used in this trial, because in another experiment (Monastra and Testoni, 1991) micropropagated plants and cuttings grew more rapidly than plants grafted onto either 'Bruno' or 'D1' rootstocks.

In both trials, the self–rooted plants gave the highest fruit yields after 2–3 years growth: there was a slight delay in fruiting during the early years. However, Monastra and Testoni (1991) concluded that although self–rooted *Actinidia* plants had a high growth rate, scions grafted onto micropropagated 'D1' rootstock gave plants with the highest productivity and fruit quality.

Papaya

Micropropagated papaya trees have a shorter juvenile stage than seedling trees. This has the advantage that less nodes have to be produced on the stem before flowering and fruiting commences. Fruits therefore begin to be produced earlier in the life of the tree at only 30–40 cm from the ground (which makes harvesting easier). In seedlings, the main stem usually has to reach 1.5–2 metres before flowering commences (although in Australia the length of unproductive stem can be reduced by ensuring that juvenile growth occurs during the winter, when shorter internodes are formed) (Drew, 1988).

SOFT FRUITS

Blackberry

When they were field planted, thornless blackberries of several different cultivars propagated by tissue culture generally performed as well as, or were more vigorous than, plants propagated by tip layers or stem cuttings, but the average fruit size of the tissue cultured plants was smaller during the first year (Swartz *et al.*, 1981a; Swartz *et al.*, 1983): leaf shape was unaltered and only one off–type plant was discovered possessing sectorial leaf chlorosis (Swartz *et al.*, 1983).

Strawberry

Effects of tissue culture

Micropropagation can profoundly alter the physiology of the micropropagated strawberry plants. Many of the observed changes are related to rejuvenation; the causes of others is not yet understood.

For a period of up to four months after planting in the field, Mohamed *et al.* (1991b) found that micropropagated plants of the cultivar 'Fern' had reduced net photosynthesis, and sometimes, delayed flowering but, in general, compared to plants which are propagated by conventional means, strawberries multiplied in tissue cultures have been especially noted to have increased vigour in the field (Damiano, 1980a; Swartz *et al.*, 1981b). Heightened lateral bud activity alters source/sink relationships: leaf area per crown tends to be reduced, and dry matter is re–allocated to either fruits or crowns and flower trusses (Cameron *et al.*, 1989).

Because of these tendencies, plantings of micropropagated strawberries often result in higher plant densities and a greater number of trusses per crown and and hence more flowers when grown in matted rows (Swartz *et al.*, 1981b). In some cases, yield in the first year has been found to be slightly increased (Cameron *et al.*, 1989), but when there are more fruits, they are usually smaller in size, and their average weight is reduced. The proportion of large fruits of marketable size may then be much less than normal. In other trials the total crop has been smaller than usual, and sometimes born on shorter stems (especially in the variety 'Gorella') (Damiano, 1980a).

In two trials (Damiano *et al.*, 1983; Theiler–Hedtrich and Wolfensberger, 1987), increased runners and smaller fruits occurred in the cultivars 'Gorella' and 'Redgauntlet', but 'Belrubi' produced more small fruits only if plants had been cold stored before planting; plants behaved normally and produced large fruits if plantlets were set out directly. Small yields were recorded from tissue cultured 'Gorella' and 'Senga Sengana' plants, but micropropagated plants of certain varieties have yielded more fruits than normal plants in the second season (*e.g.* in cvs. 'Guardian' and 'Redchief' — Zimmerman, 1982; in cv. 'Pocahontas' — Damiano *et al.*, 1983).

Flowering

The tendency of strawberry plants to produce an excessive number of flowers per inflorescence when they have been derived from prolonged micropropagation has been mentioned in Part 1, page 245. To avoid this problem, European micropropagation laboratories are said not to carry shoot cultures beyond ten subcultures (Boxus, 1989).

Runnering

Strawberry plants obtained from shoot cultures propagated with a cytokinin and/or gibberellic acid in the medium, almost always produce more stolon runners and more runner plants than plants derived from field–grown runners, and their crown number is usually larger (Damiano, 1980a; Damiano *et al.*, 1983). Leaf area and crown diameter of the runners tend to be smaller than normal. The French cultivar 'Bordurella' which normally does not form runners, produces 5–7 per plant after being micropropagated (Boxus, 1989).

The consequence of excessive runnering. Because of the tendency of most varieties to produce many runners, (especially during their first year in the field), micropropagated strawberries have not usually been recommended for direct cropping, despite their increased vigour. They have, however, been particularly suitable for the production of planting stock for nurseries.

However it is possible that micropropagated plants of some varieties might be suitable for direct field cropping. Theiler–Hedtrich and Wolfensberger (1987) found that tissue cultured plants of the cv. 'Belrubi' behave liked normal runner plants in the field and suggested that it should be possible to utilise other varieties for direct fruit production by a careful evaluation of the best cultural environment and planting time for each. They pointed out that there was some evidence that fruiting ability was influenced by cultural conditions during the *in vitro* phase.

The enhanced vigour conveyed by tissue culture wears off slowly with time (Swartz *et al.*, 1981b, Damiano *et al.*, 1983), but it can be transferred in some measure to primary, secondary or tertiary runners (Cameron and Hancock, 1986). Damiano *et al.* (1983) found that second generation plants still had a tendency to produce more runners: the plants were intermediate between first generation and normal plants. Runners taken from micro-propagated mother plants gave plants with heavier crops from both fresh runners and those which had been cold stored (Damiano *et al.*, 1980).

Correcting excessive runnering. Increased lateral bud activity may be induced by the medium and the cytokin-ins added to it, to increase shoot multiplication. The number of crowns per plant was influenced in the variety 'Cambridge Favourite' by BAP and the medium: field–grown plants obtained from shoots multiplied without BAP, or multiplied on **Gamborg** *et al.* **(1968) B5** medium (instead of **MS**) had a very low number of crowns per plant (and a lower yield) (Atkinson *et al.*, 1986). Mo-hamed *et al.* (1991a,b) attributed the rejuvenation of strawberry during micropropagation to BAP and GA$_3$. In the cultivars 'Fern' and 'Tribute', plants obtained from tissue cultures had more vegetative growth (runners and branched crowns) than those originating from runners: true seedlings were even more vegetative. Adding 5 µM ABA to the **MS** medium used for propagating the plants had an anti–rejuvenating effect: it reduced the numbers of crowns and increased the number of inflorescences produced by plants in the field. The addition of 10 µM paclobutrazol had a similar effect. Plants resulting from ABA or paclobutrazol treatments had flattened apical meristems (typical of meristems at the pre–floral stage) and a greater proportion of adult trifoliate leaves. It remains to be seen whether plants propagated with ABA or a growth retardant in the medium will be more suitable for field planting.

Susceptibility to pathogens

Micropropagated plants of some varieties of strawberries have been found to be more susceptible to fungi for a short period after they have been transferred to the field. This may be related to the changed nature of the plant cuticle or to the rejuvenating effect of tissue culture. Seedlings of the cultivar 'Raritan' and tissue cultured plants of this cultivar are liable to be infected with *Phytophthora* dur-ing their early growth (Shoemaker and Swartz, 1985). Some cultivars have similarly been shown to have a temporarily increased susceptibility to mildew (Rancillac *et al.* 1987 reported in Boxus, 1989). Rancillac and Nour-isseau (1989) said that field plantings of the strawberries 'Gorella' and 'Belrubi' originating from beyond 18–30 subcultures, have shown an increased susceptibility to pathogens, and 'Gorella' to early senescence.

Blueberries

The micropropagation of blueberries has been outstand-ingly successful because field trials have shown that

plants produced by this means are more vigorous than plants produced from conventional cuttings (Smagula and Lyrene, 1984), and consistently yield more fruit during the first 3 seasons after field establishment (Read *et al.*, 1988, 1989). These improved yields are due to the high numbers of branches formed on micropropagated plants. Grout *et al.* (1986) described how, in the field, *Vaccinium corymbosum* plants propagated by tissue cul-ture formed many more lateral and basal branches, which grew more rapidly than those on plants derived from normal cuttings. In consequence of having more branches, tissue cultured plants produced more flower buds per plant. Micropropagated plants also suffered less winter injury (Read *et al., loc.cit.*).

FOREST TREES

As is explained on page 970, the aim of forest tree micropropagation is to produce clones of elite trees which have been selected from populations of genetically vari-able siblings. When selection is made on the basis of exceptional growth rate, leading to a high rate of increase in timber volume, cloned trees would be expected to grow more rapidly than unselected seedlings, providing selec-tion has been successful, and vegetatively propagated plants have the same inherent vigour as seedlings in their early years.

There has not been a great number of published reports on the field performance of forest trees propagated by tissue culture. The results which are available only relate to growth characteristics measured from 1–6 years after planting, and observations need to be continued over a longer period. This is especially important where tissue cultured trees have made a slow start.

Broad leafed trees

Some micropropagated broad–leafed trees have been found to be more vigorous than seedlings during their first years in the field. Micropropagated *Eucalyptus tereti-cornis* and *E. torelliana* plants, derived from elite trees, were more vigorous than seedlings during their first 3 years in the field: the rate of increase became comparable with that of the seedlings after this (Gupta and Mascaren-has, 1987; Mascarenhas *et al.*, 1988).

Micropropagated selections of *Betula platyphylla* have been found to grow more rapidly than unselected seed-lings in the field. Those of var. *szechuanica* obtained from micropropagating three fast growing seedlings from a variable seedling population, grew to a greater height in the greenhouse and had a larger number of nodes, than plants derived from three slow growing seedlings from the same population (McCown and McCown, 1987). Similarly, selected plants of *B. platyphylla* var. *japonica* were 1.5 times greater in height and more than 3 times greater in volume after 3 growth periods than seedling controls (Ishii and Kanazashi, 1992)

Micropropagated seedling and elite trees of teak grew more rapidly than true seedlings of 'plus' trees during their first four years in the field, resulting in their having greater height and trunk diameter (Mascarenhas *et al.*, 1987).

Coniferous trees

Field results so far available for the growth of coniferous trees, relate to plants derived from axillary buds or adventitious shoots; trees propagated through embryogenesis have not reached the same stage due to the late discovery of this method of regeneration in gymnosperms.

Many micropropagated coniferous trees have tended to be less vigorous initially than true seedlings. *Pinus taeda* plantlets at first showed a lag in growth compared to seedlings, but their rate of growth became comparable after 4 years (Amerson *et al.*, 1988). The growth of micropropagated *Pinus taeda* trees was retarded during their first 2 years in the field, although their subsequent rate of growth was similar to seedling controls (Mott *et al.*, 1986). After one year of growth *extra vitrum*, tissue cultured plantlets of *Pinus pinaster* had grown poorly compared to normal seedlings and showed rhythmic growth and the early appearance of secondary needles (Boulay, 1987a).

However, in field trials conducted by the Weyerhauser Corporation, micropropagated plantlets and seedlings of *Pseudotsuga menziesii* grew at the same rate. The fact that the average height of plants which originated from tissue culture was still less than that of seedlings at the end of 5 years, probably reflected the different size of the two kinds of plant at the time of planting (Ritchie and Long, 1986). In France, little difference was observed over a five year period in the field in the growth of *Sequoia sempervirens* trees established from rooted cuttings, seedlings, or tissue cultures, although in California, rooted cuttings suffered from prolonged plagiotropism from which they could only be cured by pruning (Boulay, 1987a).

Pinus radiata plants derived *in vitro* from seedling cotyledons grew at a similar rate to seedlings when planted in the field, although their maturation state was more like that of 3–4 year–old trees (Smith D.R. *et al.*, 1982). Micropropagated *Pinus radiata* trees have been planted on a large scale in New Zealand since 1985 and, considering the relatively high cost of the product, must clearly have been found to grow satisfactorily.

GENETIC VARIATION IN MICROPROPAGATED PLANTS

The high risk of engendering genetic variation makes some methods of tissue culture multiplication unsuitable for routine micropropagation. The techniques used for commercial micropropagation, chiefly shoot and node culture, but sometimes direct shoot or embryo formation, have been chosen because genetic variation is a rare event. When variation appears amongst plants which have been propagated from organised tissues, by one of the methods recommended in Chapters 2 and 3, some exceptional event must be postulated to have occurred during the micropropagation process. In particular, have shoots arisen from cells which at some time has been in a phase of unorganised growth?

Variation in plants from shoot cultures

In shoot cultures, somaclonal variation can arise when adventitious shoots arise from callus which has formed at the base of shoot clumps. A less likely cause is when adventitious shoots arise directly from the explanted tissues.

Where an unexpectedly high frequency of mutation is found amongst plants propagated by shoot culture, the cause is usually one of the following:

- the occurrence of adventitious shoots from unorganised tissue;

- the occurrence of directly formed adventitious shoots (a less likely cause);

   Shoots having this origin can be difficult to separate from those which have originated from axillary buds.

- the plant was a chimera and displacement of the distinct histogenic layers has occurred.

   Variation resulting from the propagation of chimeras was discussed in Part 1, page 85 *et seq.*

In shoot cultures where multiplication can be strictly confined to the formation of new shoots from axillary buds, the occurrence of mutations is no higher than would be expected from random genetic change in conventionally propagated plants.

Basal callus was frequently observed in shoot cultures of *Digitalis thapsi* from which more than 50% of regenerated shoots were found to be phenotypically abnormal (Herrera *et al.*, 1990).

Strawberry variants. In strawberry shoot cultures, Jemmali *et al.* (1992) found that adventitious buds often arose between the leaf stipules, particularly on media with high rates (5 mg/l) of BAP, and thought that the origin of these buds could be a possible source of variant plants. Unusual plants (some apparently chimeras) have been discovered amongst strawberry plants grown from meristem/shoot cultures (Swartz *et al.*, 1981; Zimmerman, 1981):

- in the variety 'Earliglow' plants derived from a single meristem tip had a narrow sectorial white streak in some leaves and rarely on fruit trusses and fruits;

- an irregular sectorial yellow chlorosis was found in a few plants of the varieties 'Earliglow', 'Redchief', 'Tristor' and 'Tribute'. This is occasionally found in strawberry seedlings.

   Yellow or white chimeric leaf streaks were also reported by Schaeffer *et al.* (1980) in the varieties 'Aliso', and 'Belrubi'. The abnormal markings could spread until leaflets were half yellow and half green (when the plant would die), or disappear so that plants reverted to being entirely green.

- a low–yielding dwarf variant.

Chrysanthemum. Clones with conspicuously different characteristics from their parent were obtained by Machin, (1978) and Votruba and Kodytek (1988) by meristem culture of several varieties of *Dendranthema × grandiflora (C. × morifolium)*. Amongst the changes found were alterations in the shape of leaves, florets and flowers, and differences in flowering date, plant height, the number of flowering shoots after pinching, and flower diameter. The reasons for the changes were not defined, but it has been suggested that the original varieties might have been chimeras.

Banana and pineapple. Mutations in the field amongst banana plants propagated by tissue culture have been reported frequently. Gavinlertvatana (1992) said that variation was marked in some trials, but absent in others, suggesting that particular cultivars were more susceptible to change than others, or that poor *in vitro* techniques had sometimes been employed. Mutations or physiologically induced variations have also been reported in micropropagated pineapple plants. Antoni *et al.* (1986) found

that occasion variation in plants propagated through the culture of axillary buds, was not sustained during continued growth. Gavinlertvatana (1992), who obtained plants with leaf spines and multiple crowns, discarded such abnormal ramets at transplanting.

Boston fern

The Boston fern (*Nephrolepis exaltata 'Bostoniensis'*) may yield up to 25% aberrant plants from shoot cultures initiated from runner tips. Fern plants tends to multiply rapidly *in vitro* and besides axillary shoots, many adventitious shoots can be produced, which are more likely than axillary shoots to display genetic variability. Zimmerman (1982) thought that *N. exaltata* might be genetically unstable in tissue culture and recommended that the number of subcultures should be strictly limited, new ones being initiated regularly from clean stock plants. However Leffring and Soede (1982) found that variations in ferns micropropagated on **MS** medium were only temporary, and if runner tips of the abnormal plants were propagated in the normal way, the new plants were normal. Plants which did not show phenotypic variation could be obtained by micropropagating plants on a medium containing half (rather than full–strength) **MS** salts, the concentration of vitamins and growth regulators remaining unchanged.

That the correct salt strength is important if phenotypic variation is to be avoided, has subsequently been confirmed by Borgan and Naess (1987). However in these experiments a high proportion of variable plants were produced if *Nephrolepis* was *multiplied* on **Soede (1981)** medium with half–strength, rather than full–strength, macronutrients. The unusual plants had a hanging habit of growth, but later grew out of this. There was also an incidence of dwarfed plants when cultures were *initiated* on half strength salts.

Plants regenerated *via* direct morphogenesis

As mentioned on pages 83 and 84 of Part 1, plants regenerated from directly formed shoots are normally without genetic change. Note however, that in some species, even the occurrence of a brief callus phase can result in the formation of abnormal plants. In *Lycopersicon esculentum*, adventitious shoots formed 15 days after hypocotyl segments had begun to be incubated. They arose mainly in the callus which had been produced at the cut ends of the explants, although a few were formed directly from the subepidermis. Even though there was only a very short phase of unorganised growth, about 10% of the plants obtained were morphologically abnormal (Ohki *et al.*, 1978).

However *Begonia* × *hiemalis* plants, which originated directly from leaf segments or flower pedicels, showed an increasing amount of phenotypic variation if they had been produced after the continuation of *in vitro* propagation for 1 or more further cycles. 'Schwabeland Red' showed many variations in leaf shape, leaf colouring, shoot size, branchiness and floral attributes. Westerhof *et al.* (1984) were unable to ascertain whether the changes resulted from mutation or were epigenetic effects induced by the medium ($\frac{1}{2}$**MS** plus 2 mg/l IBA and 0.2 mg/l BAP).

Variation obtained from embryogenic callus

As explained in Chapter 3, plants obtained from somatic embryos formed directly on explants, or from directly initiated embryogenic callus are usually found to be genetically homogeneous.

There are exceptions, especially where embryogenic callus has been maintained over a long period. Somatic embryos induced to form in callus or suspension cultures after a period of unorganised growth are more likely to give rise to variants (Part 1, page 83). The phenotypic abnormalities of most of the plants of *Carica papaya* produced indirectly from callus by somatic embryogenesis, appeared to be due only to a transient disruption of the normal development pattern, and not genetic variation, because they eventually grew out of their abnormal morphology.

Over one quarter of the plants obtained through somatic embryogenesis of nucellus tissue of *Citrus clementina* had abnormal phenotypic characters which were maintained for 7 years in the greenhouse or by budwood propagation (Navarro *et al.*, 1985).

De Buyser *et al.* (1988) obtained a high proportion of abnormal chromosome numbers, alterations in the structure of mitochondrial DNA and morphological abnormalities and a gradual decline in fertility amongst wheat plants regenerated from embryogenic callus maintained for several years.

16

Commercial Micropropagation

THE ECONOMICS OF PRODUCTION

The technology of commercial micropropagation has not altered in any major way since the first edition of this book appeared in 1984. Although there is much research into possible methods of large scale production involving techniques such as the automation of existing procedures, and the production of somatic embryos, the use of these technologies for commercial plant propagation is not widespread, and so far they have not had an impact on the multiplication of many species. The most reliable method of micropropagation for the majority of plants is still by the division of axillary shoots. In most species, this requires a high input of manual labour at all stages, and particularly for the handling, division and reflasking of Stage II shoots.

The economics of micropropagation have not therefore changed radically during recent years and although knowledge of how to propagate plants has increased considerably, the number of species to which tissue culture technology can be profitably applied remains restricted. Micropropagated plants have many advantages (see Part 1, page 39 and page 787), but it is still much cheaper to multiply many plant types from seeds or to multiply them vegetatively using 'macropropagation' (conventional) methods *in vivo*.

Ways of facilitating vegetative propagation by these so–called 'conventional' techniques continue to be found, and challenge the economics of *in vitro* methods. For example, in recent years it has been shown that axillary shoot formation can often be stimulated on stock plants growing *in vivo* by using cytokinin sprays. Cuttings from such plants can then be rooted by using the same methods which are used to root microcuttings *ex vitro* (Norton and Norton, 1988). Woody plants can be grown in severely pruned hedges and/or given etiolating treatments to provide cuttings which can be readily rooted *in vivo* (Part 1, page 234).

Can the cost of continued micropropagation be justified for those plants where recently micropropagated stock can provide cuttings with excellent rooting capacity (see page 752).

THE COST OF MICROPROPAGATION

The extent to which micropropagation can be practised commercially is limited by the cost of production. If the uses, and the crops to which the science can be applied, are to be greatly extended, it is vital that production costs should be decreased. One estimate suggested that a 50% reduction in average cost would allow the market to be expanded to more than 10 times its current size, and that by decreasing production costs by 90%, the potential market would become 1000 times larger than at present (Kozai, 1991).

It is probable that lower costs would allow tissue culture techniques to be employed for the vegetative propagation of forestry planting stock, fruit trees, plantation crops, and many varieties of vegetables. Opportunities already exist for the vegetative multiplication of hybrids which are expensive to reproduce from seeds, and as time progresses, micropropagation might be expected to extend to genetically modified plants in which a desirable phenotype would be lost during sexual reproduction (Levin and Vasil, 1989).

COSTS INVOLVED IN CURRENT TECHNIQUES

The comments in this section largely apply to present techniques of shoot and node culture, but other methods of propagation are capable of a similar method of analysis.

The cost of micropropagation is influenced by a number of factors, many of which are dependent on genotype:

- The capital and overhead costs of the laboratory;

- The cost of labour;

- Material costs;

- The *in vitro* characteristics of the plant to be propagated, *e.g.*:

  - How easy it is to establish a culture capable of sustained multiplication — in woody plants this includes the time it takes to obtain a partially 'rejuvenated' culture capable of rapid growth and multiplication;

  - How rapidly and quickly a plant can be multiplied: in shoot or node culture, this depends on the number of new shoots produced for subculture or rooting, and the interval between subcultures;

  - Whether shoots need to be rooted in culture, or whether they can be rooted *extra vitrum*.

- The losses incurred at each stage of the micropropagation process, *e.g.*:

  - the proportion of cultures lost through contamination;

  - the proportion of shoots affected by hyperhydricity;

  - the proportion of shoots which fail to become rooted and do not form plantlets;

  - the proportion of plantlets which do not survive acclimatization.

- The final number of plants required and whether production is a single event, or part of a continuing process.

Each of these factors is examined in the sections which follow.

Allocating laboratory costs

Table 120 demonstrates the way in which money might need to be spent in setting up and running a commercial micropropagation laboratory capable of producing 2–3 million plants annually. Costs have been entered into the table as weekly expenditures and to facilitate conversions to local currencies which are independent of inflation, they have been entered in arbitrary currency units. The value of one such unit can be deduced against labour and material costs in the table: it is equivalent to the cost of employing an operative to work at a laminar flow bench for 40 minutes (in 1995 about UK£3.00 or US$5.00). The table represents a probable cost allocation in a country where labour costs are high: the comparative cost of labour and materials will be different where wage costs are low. In Table 120, laboratory and greenhouse costs have been grouped together. In a large micropropagation enterprise, the greenhouse facility might well be separately costed.

Capital cost

The capital cost of running a commercial micropropagation laboratory comprises the cost of renting or purchasing suitable buildings and equipment.

Costs will depend on:

- The number of plants to be propagated annually;

- The standard of hygiene to be used in the laboratory; and,

- The quality of the building which is to be erected.

A building of sufficient size to accommodate the staff and equipment necessary to produce 3 million plants per year might need to cover 800 to 1400 m^2, depending on the standard required and the nature of the work to be carried out. A smaller building would have space for few facilities. It might contain, for example, just a simple air

Table 120. An hypothetical analysis of the weekly cost of operating a micropropagation laboratory capable of producing *ca.* 3 million ramets per year.

It has been assumed there are 30 laminar flow hoods each operated during a single shift of 8 hours per day, during a 5 day week .

Costs are given in arbitrary currency units (one unit being equivalent to tho cost of employing a technician to work at a laminar flow cabinet for 40 minutes).

Costs can also be apportioned as indicated in Column 2 viz.: Overheads (O); Direct costs (D); Materials costs (M); and Sales costs (S) — see text.

Breakdown of expenditure	Type of cost	LABOUR COSTS				TOTAL COSTS	
		Hours worked per week	Cost per hour	Costs per week		Actual costs per week	%
		Units	Units	Units	%	Units	
Capital cost							
Depreciation & borrowing costs on buildings and equipment (see text).	O					1635	27.3
Wage costs							
Laboratory work							
Subcultures for plant production	D	1080	1.5	1620	42.4		
Culture initiation	D	120	2.0	240	6.3		
R and D transfers etc.	O	80	2.5	200	5.2		
Media preparation and sterilisation	D	80	2.0	160	4.2		
Quality assurance	D	40	2.5	100	2.6		
Washing up, cleaning	D	80	1.0	80	2.1		
Transport around laboratory	D	80	1.5	120	3.1		
Growth room work	D	80	1.5	120	3.1		
Greenhouse and shipment							
Planting	D	40	1.5	60	1.6		
Plant management							
Quality control	D	40	2.0	80.0	2.1		
Greenhouse controls	D	5	1.5	7.5	0.2		
Watering and feeding	D	25	1.5	37.5	1.0		
Acclimatization	D	10	1.5	15	0.4		
Dispatch	S	400	1.5	600	15.7		
Office work							
Management							
Production/Planning	O	8	3.0	24	0.6		
Accountancy	O	20	3.0	60	1.6		
Other	O	12	3.0	36	0.9		
Office routine (Typing, computer, telephone)	O	40	1.5	60	1,6		
Marketing and sales	S	80	2.5	200	5.2		
TOTALS				3820	100	3820	63.8
Running costs							
Chemicals and consumables							
Media, sterilants, fungicides etc.	M			71			
Minor equipment replacements and maintenance	O			25			
Fuel and Utilities							
Electricity	M			140.0			
Gas, water	M			50.0			
Packaging (assume here that delivery charged to customer)	S			20			
Maintenance of buildings	O			50			
Travel; books; journals; software	O			60			
Taxes	O			33			
Commercial fees and expenses	O			35			
Contingencies	O			50			
TOTALS				534		534	8.9
GRAND TOTAL						**5989**	100

filtration system, and staff would probably only be expected to change into laboratory coats before entering the laboratory: there would be no space for changing rooms so that more elaborate protective clothing could be worn. A larger and more expensive facility would thus provide for better standards of hygiene, and could house a wider range of equipment which might, for example, allow virus–testing to be carried out.

Costs also depend on the quality of the building materials used. A cheap laboratory can be constructed from prefabricated rooms joined together, but this type of building can be expected to have a limited life. Purpose–built concrete or brick buildings are more expensive, but longer lasting. Construction costs for a laboratory built to average standards might amount to 250 currency units per square metre. This would include mechanical and sanitary services, electricity and plumbing and a ducted air filtration system. The cost would be increased, perhaps to 265 currency units per square metre of building, when the purchase of land and the provision of external services and car parking are included.

Assuming that buildings and equipment are purchased new, we might arrive at a figure for Table 120 from:

Purchase of land and construction
of a laboratory building　　　　= 300 000 currency units

Construction of a greenhouse = 20 000 units

Purchase of laboratory equipment = 125 000 units

A simple way of calculating the annual capital cost of the laboratory might then be:

Borrowing cost on 300 000 units at 15% = 45 000 units

Depreciation on buildings over 20 years = 15 000 units

Depreciation on equipment over 5 years = 25 000 units

The yearly total is equal to 85 000 units. The weekly capital cost which has been entered into the table is therefore $\frac{85000}{52} = 1635$ units.

Labour costs

The results of many studies have shown that, in developed countries, the cost of employing staff for commercial micropropagation work accounts for a very significant proportion of the running costs of an entire laboratory. The ways in which the weekly wage bill may need to be divided are shown in Table 120. Wage costs depend on the efficiency of a laboratory, upon the kinds of plants being grown and the methods of micropropagation employed. Shoot culture, which requires the meticulous division of axillary shoots from shoot clumps, is very labour intensive.

Production factor. A term called the *production factor* is used by some laboratory consultants to assess the efficiency and cost of micropropagation and in deciding

the time and facilities necessary for propagation. It is obtained by dividing the number of cultures (*i.e.* units of production: explant, shoot, shoot cluster — *NOT* the number of vessels) handled by operators during an assessment period (usually one year of laboratory operation) by the number of ramets (shoots and/or plants) actually produced during that period. The production factor is clearly related to proportion of the growth room space occupied by the subcultures from which saleable product (shoots or plantlets) will be obtained.

The commercial propagation of most kinds of plants requires more cultural operations than the number of plants produced by the laboratory. This is because non–productive transfers are necessary while stocks of a plant are being built up before production can begin, and because non–productive work is required on stock cultures. An average production factor for ornamental species in commercial laboratories is often about 2.5; figures for individual species obviously vary. Production is efficient when the factor is low; high factors indicate inefficient and costly production. The production factor is high when plants are rooted *in vitro*.

An expected production factor can be used to calculate how many laminar flow operations (or operators, or laminar flow cabinets) are required to produce a given number of plants. Thus a laboratory, such as the one in our example, aiming to produce 3 million ornamental plants per year, might need to allow for:

2.5 (production factor) × 3 = 7.5 million

transfers, or subcultures, per year (assuming there is no wastage of plants). Normally however, at least 20% of the shoots or plantlets produced are lost or unavoidably wasted, so that $7.5 \times 1.2 = 9$ million transfer operations would be necessary to achieve our target. If we assume that, on average, a technician completes 1200–1500 subcultures or transfers during an 8 hour working day, it becomes clear that our hypothetical laboratory requires about 30 technicians to work at laminar flow hoods. If there is one 8 hour shift per day, 30 working positions would be required; only 15 positions if two 8 hour shifts are operated.

In Table 120, the wage cost of operating laminar flow benches has been set at *ca.* 30% of the total cost of running the entire laboratory; the overall wage bill to 63% of the total. Published estimates of micropropagation labour costs for the U.S.A. and Western Europe vary between 39 and 85% of the total cost of production; the average is near 70%. Kurtz *et al.* (1991) said that in 1989, 64% of the production costs of a Twyford International, Inc. laboratory producing 7.5 million units per year, were due to labour costs; the labour directly required for transfers accounted for 34%, and the rest was equally divided between media preparation, culture initiation etc. and supervision.

At the time of writing, the cost of labour is much less in Eastern Europe, Africa and many Asian countries. It is no surprise that laboratories are being set up in these areas to supply plants for European and North American markets, the cost of air freight being much less than the extra costs of home production. In consequence, some European micropropagation laboratories have closed during the last few years or have relocated their operation. Orchid laboratories in the U.S.A. are facing severe competition from imports of Asian origin.

Moving production to areas of lower labour costs is only a short term solution to the problem of making micropropagation more cost effective, for labour costs will gradually increase worldwide.

Reducing handling time. As the greatest proportion of costs in propagating plants using shoot or node culture is involved in labour required for transfers, wage costs can be reduced by:

- shortening the time taken for an operator to deal with each container;

It takes longer (and is therefore more expensive) to dissect out separate small shoots, than it does to cut shoots randomly, or to divide a mass of shoots into two or more pieces, or to move clumps of multiplying shoots to fresh media without division. Instead of dissecting out individual shoots to serve as explants for subcultures, it is sometimes possible to cut off shoots quickly, pass on those shoots of a sufficient size to Stage III, and then chop the remaining basal shoot mass into two or more crude pieces to initiate new cultures. This technique has been reported to be effective, for example, for Boston fern (Oki, 1981).

- reducing or simplifying the stages required for micropropagation.

A good example is the use of two–phased media supplements (see below).

- Ensuring that vessels are of such a nature that they can be quickly opened and closed and that explants can be easily inserted and removed.

Two–phased media additions. Avoiding the need for transfer by adding liquid medium to the top of spent agar medium (Part 1, page 193) is particularly effective when there is no need to harvest shoots for multiplication or transfer to Stage III. It is thus suitable when shoots would otherwise need to be moved to another medium for elongation or to induce root formation. Subculture is avoided by pouring a layer of liquid medium containing appropriate growth regulators onto the surface of the semi–solid medium which is already in the vessel (Maene and Debergh, 1985).

The procedure whereby root induction is brought about by pouring a root–inducing medium onto a spent Stage II

medium has been described on page 705 of this volume. Roots may be produced in this two–phased medium, or shoots can be harvested after a brief period of exposure to be rooted *extra vitrum*. Use of a two–phased medium replaces the transfers necessary for a separate rooting stage, and so requires less time and resources than conventional transfer, especially if it is done by an automated injection system. As with manual transfer, the timing of liquid phase additions can be critical.

A large increase in the number of harvestable shoots in *Blandfordia grandiflora* shoot cultures was obtained by pouring a layer of liquid medium onto shoot clusters 8 weeks after the first transfer. The cultures had been grown on semi–solid **MS** medium with 0.5 µM BAP. The liquid supplement was ½**MS** salts (plus full organics and 3% sucrose) without regulants. Because suppressed shoots were stimulated to elongate by this treatment, a transfer involving cutting was avoided (Johnson, 1992).

San–Jose *et al.* (1991) cultured *Camellia reticulata* shoots on an agar solidified medium containing 8.9 µM BAP, 9.1 µM zeatin, 9.8 µM 2–iP and 0.05 µM IBA, for 4 weeks. Each vessel was then topped up with liquid medium in which the cytokinin concentration had been halved. Shoots were harvested after a further 4 weeks of growth.

The cost of washing and cleaning. The cost of washing vessels can be reduced by using cheap disposable plastic containers. If re–usable glass or plastic vessels are used, the considerable time which is spent melting and removing agar can be avoided when it is possible to grow cultures in a liquid medium. Vessels which have contained liquid media can go straight to the dishwasher without pre–treatment. Oki (1981) thought that the slightly slower rate of multiplication which occurred when Boston fern was propagated in liquid medium, was worth accepting, because of the saving in washing up time.

Laboratory design. As labour comprises such a large proportion of the total production cost of micropropagated plants, it is wise to try to facilitate rapid and efficient movement throughout the laboratory complex by efficient laboratory design. Time and motion studies can help in this respect (Strode and Abner, 1986). Solutions may sometimes have to be compromises: for instance, although wide aisles and wide shelf spacings can make it much easier and quicker to place and retrieve cultures from growth rooms, extra non–productive space is required in an environment which is expensive to build and operate.

Equipment. Automated cutting and handling devices have not yet been devised to replace the manual labour involved in producing plants from shoot cultures. How-

Fig. 138. Large sized vessel used for micropropagation in a commercial laboratory.

ever, apparatus to save time in media preparation and dispensing is now widely available (page 794).

Care in the selection of equipment should go right down to the choice of an appropriate culture vessel and type of closure. Laboratories differ in their choice of container, some preferring to place many cultures in one large box (Fig. 138), others using smaller vessels containing just a few explants. Large plastic boxes have several advantages: less vessels are required for a given number of plants, less effort is necessary to insert medium and clean vessels after use, explants are easily inserted, cultures easily taken out, and less vessels have to be dealt with if a liquid supplement is added during culture. However lid removal can be time consuming and will require the use of both hands, but once the vessel is opened, many cultures can be dealt with before it has to be resealed. The atmosphere in very large vessels may be less likely to cause hyperhydricity, but may also be less likely to allow sufficient ethylene to accumulate to promote shoot proliferation of some species (Part 1, page 207). The greatest disadvantage from using large vessels is that if there is contamination, many cultures may have to be discarded.

Small vessels take longer to load with medium, but it has been said that they can bring a saving in labour costs because they can be opened and closed quickly. A technician can hold a small vessel in one hand and use the other to remove the closure. Vessels which are not sealed with film can be opened and closed much more rapidly than sealed ones.

In making a choice between vessels, the number of cultures which can be accommodated per unit area of growth room is perhaps the most important consideration (see page 776). If the same rate of shoot multiplication and the

same quality of shoots can be obtained from a vessel containing 3 cultures occupying 20 cm^2 of bench space (6.7 cm^2 per culture) as in a box containing 20 cultures occupying 180 cm^2 (9 cm^2 per culture), serious thought should be given to using the smaller vessels. If however, only 2 cultures can be grown satisfactorily in the small vessels, the larger boxes might be preferred.

The use of trays to transport vessels around, prevents many loading and unloading operations (Strode and Abner, 1986) and accidents through vessels being dropped or knocked.

Preparation for planting and dispatch. It will be seen from Table 120 that preparing shoots for planting, and preparing and packing shoots and plants for dispatch to customers, can take a considerable amount of manual labour: in our example 10% of all laboratory costs. All techniques which lessen the amount of handling which is necessary will therefore greatly assist in reducing a laboratory's running costs. The saving resulting from rooting plants *extra vitrum* has been mentioned in Chapter 14.

Shoots rooted *in vitro* in an agar medium are particularly difficult to deal with as usually they must be washed free of agar before planting (page 723). Considerable savings in labour costs can be made by rooting shoots in liquid media, or even better, in porous materials. Shoots rooted *in vitro* in plugs can be packed for dispatch to customers with the minimum of preparation.

Greenhouse work. Ensuring that a high proportion of shoots become rooted and successfully acclimatized is of great significance to the success of commercial micropropagation (see below). The effective management of these operations by greenhouse staff is therefore of vital importance to the total efficiency of a laboratory. Reduction of losses during rooting and acclimatization are discussed below.

The time necessary to plant tissue cultured plantlets or shoots into 'soil' can vary greatly between plants, depending on the separation and preparation necessary before planting, and the nature of the material to be handled. *Prunus insititia* microcuttings could be prepared for rooting at the rate of 400 per hour, but only 150 microcuttings of *Actinidia* 'Hayward' could be prepared in the same time, because all but apical leaves had to be removed to prevent rotting. Once they were ready, 800 microcuttings of either kind could be planted in one hour (Fasolo Fabbri Malavasi and Predieri, 1988). Wong (1982) mentioned that only 380 *Rhododendron* shoots (75 mm in length) could be planted into flats for *ex vitro* rooting during one hour.

The cost of materials

Media. Media costs form only a small proportion of the total cost of running a micropropagation laboratory. Costs can be reduced if agar or chemicals are ordered in bulk (Strode and Abner, 1986), but this practice does have disadvantages (Part 1, page 362). The cost of any single ingredient of a medium (even that of a solidifying agent) is small compared to the cost of labour required for micropropagation. This means that even though research into simplified media does contribute towards a reduction of production costs (Soczek and Hempel, 1988), it is less important than work directed towards more efficient production techniques.

Most studies on costing have therefore concluded that, rather than economise on media ingredients, it is better to expend a little more money on a medium to ensure getting the best quality of plants that is possible, or to obtain the most rapid multiplication rate (Standaert–de–Metsenaere, 1991). Thus in shoot culture it might be better to purchase an expensive cytokinin which ensured rapid multiplication, than to use a cheaper, but less effective compound, which gave a lower rate of proliferation. Zeatin, priced at *ca*. 300 currency units per gram, might be an exception but, even with this compound, where there is a real advantage, the extra cost may be small in comparison to the benefit gained. Assume, for example, that culture with 1 mg/l zeatin allows Stage IIIa shoots to be elongated exceptionally well. If each shoot requires 20 ml of medium, the additional cost of elongating 10 000 shoots would be 6 currency units, or only 0.006 units per shoot.

The use of liquid, instead of semi–solid media, not only saves the cost of adding a gelling agent, but also reduces the cost of washing and cleaning — see above. Media costs can also be reduced by culturing more shoots per culture vessel (de Fossard, 1977). However, even where this is possible, the extra labour cost of placing, separating and dissecting crowded plant material, may not always make the practice desirable.

Power supplies. The cost of electricity to power heating, cooling and lighting within a laboratory is significant, so that any measures which can help to reduce consumption are worthy of serious examination. In many countries electricity can be purchased more cheaply during the night than during the day. In these circumstances, commercial laboratories using a 12 or 16 hour photoperiod usually arrange for part of it to coincide with the 7 or 8 hour period of cheap supply. For a 16 hour photoperiod, full lighting might therefore be timed to come on between 1400 and 0600 in each 24 hours. Low power lights mounted on the ceiling are turned on to gain access to rooms at other times.

Standaert–de–Metsenaere (1991) mentions that the extra cost of installing electronic ballasts for controlling fluorescent lighting tubes has proved cost effective in his laboratory. Such ballasts consume 30% less electricity than traditional ones and also produce far less heat.

The possibility of reducing the number of lighting tubes in a growth room by arranging them in vertical, rather than horizontal banks, is mentioned on page 778.

The cost of losses

The cost of production increases if cultures or propagules have to be discarded during micropropagation. Typical causes of rejection are that cultures are diseased or contaminated, that shoots or plantlets are atypical, or have an abnormal physiology, or that shoots or plantlets have been produced in excess of requirements. Each of these factors can be thought of as having a direct cost.

Contamination costs. Contamination is an obvious source of extra cost to the micropropagation laboratory, and if the loss of cultures is not rigorously monitored and controlled, it will add considerably to the cost of each ramet produced.

As explained in Chapters 1 and 5, contaminated cultures can arise from:

- the carry over of superficial contaminations from improperly disinfested stock plant material;

- the appearance of 'cryptic' organisms which were located within plant tissues and which were not eliminated by surface sterilisation;

- the entry of organisms (which may be airborne or be carried on tools) due to faulty transfer techniques;

1. SINGLE PRODUCTION RUN. A theoretical example — no losses predicted

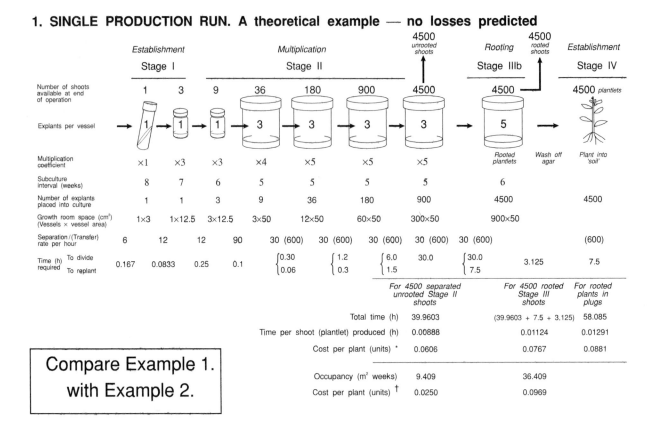

	For 4500 separated unrooted Stage II shoots	For 4500 rooted Stage III shoots	For rooted plants in plugs
Total time (h)	39.9603	(39.9603 + 7.5 + 3.125)	58.085
Time per shoot (plantlet) produced (h)	0.00888	0.01124	0.01291
Cost per plant (units) *	0.0606	0.0767	0.0881
Occupancy (m² weeks)	9.409	36.409	
Cost per plant (units) †	0.0250	0.0969	

Compare Example 1.
with Example 2.

2. SINGLE PRODUCTION RUN. As it might happen in practice — losses incurred

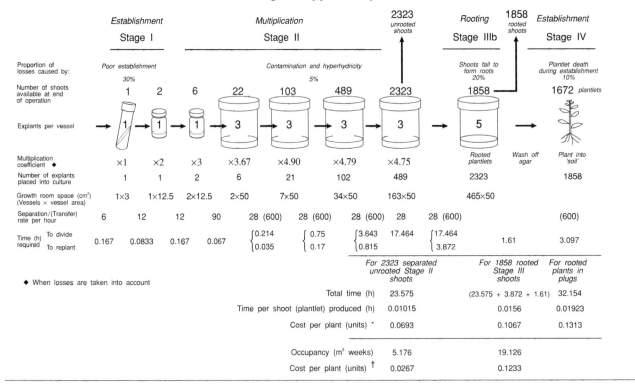

♦ When losses are taken into account

	For 2323 separated unrooted Stage II shoots	For 1858 rooted Stage III shoots	For rooted plants in plugs
Total time (h)	23.575	(23.575 + 3.872 + 1.61)	32.154
Time per shoot (plantlet) produced (h)	0.01015	0.0156	0.01923
Cost per plant (units) *	0.0693	0.1067	0.1313
Occupancy (m² weeks)	5.176	19.126	
Cost per plant (units) †	0.0267	0.1233	

Fig. 139. Shoot and plantlet production from an hypothetical shoot culture which is terminated after the sixth subculture. The cost of producing shoots or plantlets is calculated in each case from a) the time spent on transfers, and from b) growth room occupancy.

* Based on a cost of 6.825 currency units per hour of directly productive transfer work (see page 779);

† Based on a cost of 11.978 currency units per m² week of growth room occupancy (see page 777).

3. REPEATED SUBCULTURING. A theoretical example — no losses predicted

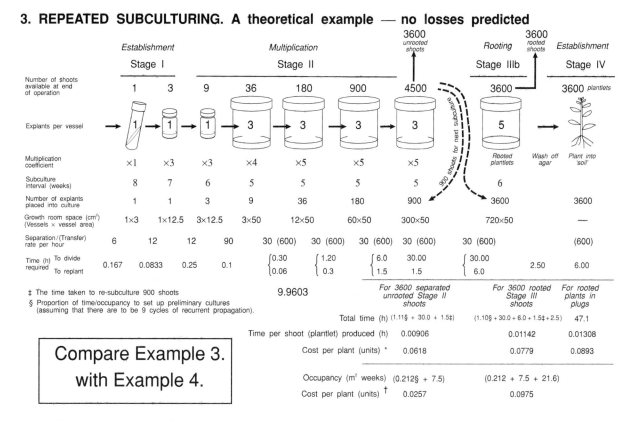

> Compare Example 3. with Example 4.

4. REPEATED SUBCULTURING. As it might happen in practice — losses incurred

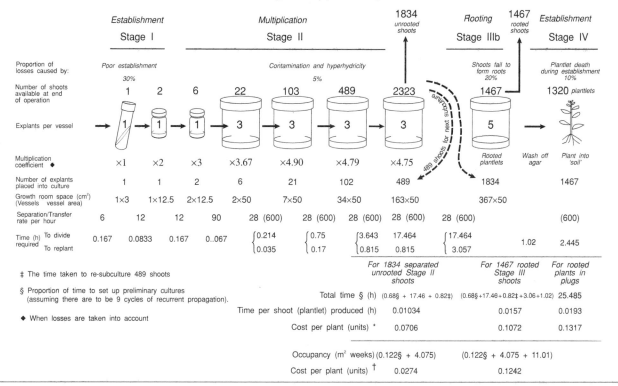

Fig. 140. Shoot and plantlet production from an hypothetical shoot culture where the size of the sixth subculture is maintained by recurrent propagation.
The cost of producing shoots or plantlets is calculated in each case from a) the time spent on transfers, and from
b) growth room occupancy.

* Based on a cost of 6.825 currency units per hour of directly productive transfer work (see page 779);

† Based on a cost of 11.978 currency units per m^2 week of growth room occupancy (see page 777).

- the entry of insect infestations;
- the cross contamination of cultures during transfers by poor technique and the failure to recognise contamination in the vessels being opened.

For these various reasons, a proportion of cultures may become contaminated at any stage from culture initiation through to routine multiplication and elongation at Stage III. Fortunately the occurrence of contamination during *in vitro* rooting is less likely. As subculture and division of explants proceeds, failure to eliminate infected cultures would lead to a spread of contamination through division and transfer, and a gradual increase in the proportion of affected vessels. Control therefore involves checking vessels on a regular basis. Using a mathematical approach, Korhonen *et al.* (1988) calculated that in an hypothetical micropropagation routine involving 4 cycles, the most critical time to monitor and remove contamination would be in the second cycle.

Illustrated examples. The effect of a series of progressive losses in each of Stages I through IV is shown in Figs. 139 and 140. The first diagram on page 768 shows how losses could affect the numbers of plants obtained from a single production run, and the second on page 769, how losses can affect routine production maintained by regular repeated subcultures. In the upper half of these diagrams, shoot cultures have been assumed to have been multiplied without loss. In the lower part of the figures, the progress of the production run is plotted with the occurrence of losses at each stage, the proportion of which is typical of those commonly found in laboratories.

Fig. 139 supposes that an order has been obtained for 4500 units (unrooted shoots, rooted but unacclimatized shoots, or rooted acclimatized shoots in plugs) and it is decided to provide one of these products as a 'one–off' operation and not to maintain subcultures for repeat orders. For the sake of simplicity it has been assumed that the cultures were started from a single explant (although this would seldom be the case in practice).

Whereas, without loss, 4500 shoots could have been available for sale after the sixth subculture, repeated losses cause only 2323 shoots to be available. If subculturing was stopped at this stage, subsequent losses would mean that only 1672 plantlets rooted in plugs were obtained. These numbers would be unlikely to satisfy the customer, so that one further subculture would have to be carried out to obtain the necessary quantity.

Losses of a similar magnitude which occur when production is based on continued subculturing are shown in Fig. 140. It will be seen that, in order to obtain the numbers of rooted or unrooted shoots available in the absence of

losses, there would need to be a considerable increase in the number of final Stage II cultures.

A discussion of methods which can be used to evaluate the effect of losses on the cost of producing shoots or plantlets is provided in following sections of this chapter.

Overproduction. Gearing production so that the number of plants obtained at the end of a micropropagation sequence is as close as possible to that required at a given time, for a given market, is one of the most important factors in reducing production costs. For reasons which are discussed later (page 785), it is a difficult task, and the closeness with which targets are reached without there being a large excess or under availability, reflects on the skill of the laboratory management. Costs are reduced by culling unwanted cultures or plants at the earliest possible stage in the production sequence: elimination of unwanted Stage II cultures will reduce the cost due to unnecessary transfers and rooting procedures at Stage III; discarding excess *in vitro* cultures eliminates the cost of rooting and maintaining plants in the greenhouse.

Research

Research is usually directed towards improving techniques at all stages, so that production becomes cost effective. It may sometimes be required to bring a new plant into production. Usually there is some published work which can be copied to set up a tentative method of propagation, but investigative work will need to be carried out at least to confirm the effectiveness of the technique before commercial production is commenced. When Poonsapaya *et al.* (1989) compared two published methods for obtaining somatic embryogenesis in the same rice cultivar, they obtained the best results by combining the techniques, *i.e.* using the initiation medium and regeneration method described by one laboratory, but the vessels and regeneration medium of the other.

In the absence of any previous work, a suitable method would have to be worked out from first principles starting, perhaps, with a method which has been applied to a plant of the same family. However, as all results *in vitro* are highly dependent on genotype, even when there is a great deal of information on the culture of a plant, some research will almost certainly need to be devoted to finding the best conditions for new varieties and cultivars. At the minimum this may mean finding the optimum concentrations of growth regulators.

Research utilises management time, the time of operatives at laminar flow benches, and space for vessels within growth rooms, none of which can be used for propagation leading directly to sales. In this sense it can be regarded as an unavoidable overhead. According to

Barnhill Jones and Sluis (1991), micropropagation laboratories typically devote about 5% of their annual research budget towards discovering the best medium and protocol for new plants and new cultivars. This kind of work only extends the use of present technology and does not lead to the improvement or development of new techniques. Most laboratories rely on the discoveries of academic institutions to make progress in these fields, as they are unable to afford more far reaching investigations: at best less than 1% of the total budget of a large laboratory is devoted to these aims.

Reducing costs using altered techniques

Where wage costs are high and laboratories compete with others overseas who can employ much cheaper labour, research must always be directed towards ways of reducing costs, through rationalization of the working system, and ensuring that the maximum number of non–infected cultures is produced per unit time. There has consequently been much interest in mechanising existing techniques and devising alternative ones which would require less manual effort (page 794 *et seq.*).

In the absence of radically different techniques, where labour is required for each transfer and treatment to which cultures are subjected, the greatest cost savings are to be made by devising methods which eliminate or simplify cultural operations or cultural stages, in particular avoiding or simplifying cultural steps which do not lead to plant multiplication (Schulze, 1988). One of the most effective cost–reducing steps which has been generally introduced during recent years is to dispense with, wherever possible, the rooting shoots *in vitro*. By transferring shoots directly from Stage II to be rooted and, at the same time, acclimatized in 'soil', a whole *in vitro* cultural stage is dispensed with. Rooting single shoots *in vitro* is very expensive; in cases where there is no alternative, this stage can limit the economic success of a propagation method. The way that it can increase handling and packing costs has been mentioned on page 766.

PRODUCTION FACTORS INFLUENCING COST

Comments on costing in this chapter refer principally to expenditure on propagation using shoot or node culture. Similar observations will apply where adventitious shoots are used as propagules and repeated transfers are involved; the economics of producing plants from somatic embryos, or from shoots or storage organs multiplied by large scale methods, will be somewhat different.

Multiplication rates

One important factor influencing the cost of micropropagation, is how quickly plant numbers can be increased (page 783). The rate at which plants can be produced per unit time from shoot or node cultures, is dependent on:

- the increase in the number of shoots (or propagules) of a suitable size or stage of development during the course of a subculture;

> This is the *multiplication coefficient* (sometimes called the multiplication factor) and is obtained by dividing the numbers of shoots or propagules at the end of a subculture (N) by number of shoots or propagules at the beginning (N_0).

- the interval between subcultures.

> The greater the multiplication coefficient and the shorter the interval between subcultures, the cheaper will be the cost of a plant resulting from the protocol (see page 783).

Rates of multiplication by shoot or node culture differ markedly from one kind of plant to another, and according to the medium and growth regulators used. Because cultures are handled rapidly, there is a need to select only well–formed shoots, but short intervals between subcultures are preferred. Micropropagation laboratories often employ only modest rates of multiplication, and are satisfied with an increase of only 2–3 shoots per subculture at 3–4 week intervals (Blakesley and Lenton, 1987). Published multiplication rates resulting from academic studies, tend generally to be greater than those achieved in commercial practice.

> Note that in many papers on micropropagation, the multiplication coefficient is called the multiplication rate. This is incorrect because 'rate' implies a quantity per unit time. Use of the term *multiplication rate* should be reserved for the number of propagules obtained per unit of time (*e.g.* 6 shoots per 5 weeks from each explant).

A small sample of published rates of multiplication from shoot and node cultures is given in Table 121. The marked variation from one type of plant to another is typical. Even within a single genus or species, multiplication rates nearly always vary between different genotypes. Newbury (1986) found that in shoot cultures of different varieties of *Antirrhinum*, one could be increased 5.9 times every 22 days, while, over the same interval, the rate of increase of another was only 2.1–fold. Shoot cultures of *Mahonia aquifolium* 'Apollo' produced 1.7 shoots every 50 days; over the same interval cv. 'Undulata' gave 1.3 shoots and *M. japonica* 'Wintersun', 2.9 shoots (Daguin *et al.*, 1992). In *Potentilla fructicosa*, the high rate of proliferation of cv. 'Snowbird' was due to it producing

Table 121. The rates at which various plants have been propagated during Stage II of shoot or node cultures.

Plant	Multiplication coefficient†	Subculture interval (weeks)	Authors
Actinidia deliciosa	2	3	Fiorino and Loreti (1987)
Caladium × hortulanum	*ca.* 6	4	Cooper and Cohen (1983)
Chrysanthemum cinerariaefolium	5	4	Levy (1981)
Ferrocactus acanthodes	6.6	8–10	Ault and Blackmon (1987)
Halesia carolina	5.5	9	Brand (1993)
Malus × domestica	3	3	Fiorino and Loreti (1987)
	22	9	Brand (1993)
Nephrolepis exaltata	5	6	Burr (1975)
	4	5	Theiler-Hedtrich & Theiler-Hedtrich (1979)
Prunus insititia 'Pixy'	5	3	Fiorino and Loreti (1987)
Rhododendron	5–20	8	McCown and Lloyd (1983)
Rosa hybrids	1.6–2.8	8	Horn W. *et al.* (1988b)
Rubus idaeus	4	4–6	Mudge *et al.* (1986)
Ribes nigrum	1.5–4.0‡	3	Brennan *et al.* (1989)
Solanum tuberosum	8–10	4	Hussey and Stacey (1981a)
	8	8	Goodwin and Adisarwanto (1980c)
Zingiber officinale	15–18	4	Bhagyalakshmi and Singh (1988)

† See text   ‡ Depending on cultivar

up to 5 orders of branching. Another cultivar, 'Pink Whisper', only produced 3 orders of branching (Remphrey *et al.*, 1993).

Actual proliferation rates depend on the protocols used and may vary according to the time of year at which the primary explants were gathered (Norton and Norton, 1988f), although this effect tends to disappear during subsequent subcultures.

Optimising the rate of increase

In some plants the rate of shoot multiplication is highest soon after a shoot culture has been established, but declines and remains relatively steady over progressive subcultures. An example was provided by Compton *et al.* (1993): in most genotypes of *Citrullus lanatus*, the number of shoots obtained per explant was 2.7–4 during the first 4–weekly period of culture, peaked to 5.3–12.5 during the first and second subcultures, but had declined to 3.7—7.7 after 6 months. In such situations it may be

possible to modify the rate of shoot production by temporarily altering the concentrations of growth regulators in the medium, but as mentioned on page 784, this should be done with caution if a proportion of shoots is being harvested as subculturing proceeds.

Theoretical rates of increase

Assuming that the rate of increase of shoots in successive subcultures continues at the same pace (*i.e.* in an exponential fashion), the theoretical number of plants which could be obtained in a single year by continuing to multiply any one of the species listed in Table 123 in the manner indicated, is equal to the multiplication coefficient k ($= N/N_0$) raised to the power T/t, where T is the number of weeks in the time interval of interest (*i.e.* 52); t is the interval in weeks between subcultures; N_0 is the number of propagules at the beginning of a subculture; and N is the number of shoots or plants at the end. Thus, from a culture where shoot number increased by a factor of 5 every 6.5 weeks, one could theoretically expect to

Table 122. The effect of subculture duration on the rate of propagation of a tree paeony [data of Harris and Mantell, 1991].

Culture characteristics	Subculture duration (weeks)		
	3	4	5
Average multiplication coefficient	2.03	2.28	2.50
Shoot doubling time (days) ‡	21.7	24.8	27.0
Estimated number of propagules produced in 1 year from 1 shoot	150 000	30 500	13 700

‡ See page 774.

get 5^8, or 390 625 shoots per year. A shoot culture in which the increase in shoot number was 3–fold every 4 weeks could, in theory, yield 4^{13}, or 1 594 323 shoots per year.

Both the multiplication coefficient *and* requisite subculture intervals are important in determining productivity. Harris and Mantell (1991) found that the shortest shoot doubling time (page 774) — and hence the fastest rate of shoot multiplication — in *Paeonia suffruticosa* shoot cultures occurred if shoots were subcultured every 3 weeks, even though the multiplication coefficient was lowest at this interval (Table 122).

Composite multiplication coefficients. Where the multiplication coefficient varies at successive steps in the process of propagation, then the effective increase in shoot number over several stages is equal to:

$$k_1 \times k_2 \times k_3 \ldots \ldots \times k_n = K.$$

Thus at the establishment phase of a shoot culture, where some of the explants fail to grow, the multiplication coefficient, k_1 might equal 0.7; During the first Stage II culture, k_2 might equal 2; at the subsequent subculture, k_3 might equal 4; and if the shoots obtained were then rooted, but 20% failed to root, k_4 would equal 0.8. The composite multiplication coefficient (K) from this series of cultures would then be 4.48.

Marin and Duran–Vila (1991) used this concept when investigating a scheme for the *in vitro* conservation of various kinds of *Citrus* germplasm. Here rapid multiplication was not required, but the value of K at both a primary establishment, and a secondary maintenance cycle, needed to be reliably greater than 1 so that genetic lines were maintained.

Extravagant estimates. Some published estimates of the theoretical rates at which various plants could be increased by tissue culture techniques are given in Table 123. The suggestion from this table that extraordinarily large numbers of some species can be produced in a short while, is not accurate, because the reports have not indicated the numbers of plants which can actually be propagated in a given time by a tissue culture laboratory where facilities (especially growth room space) and labour are finite, and where there are occasional mishaps. Published estimates of rates of increase have usually also assumed that cultures could be continued indefinitely without re–initiation and that there would be no losses due to contamination.

Similar reasoning shows that commercial laboratories will usually not be able to deliver very large numbers of plants of one kind on a single date. Customers placing large orders must be prepared to accept successive deliveries.

Table 123. Some published theoretical annual rates of micropropagation.

Plant	Propagation method	Rate of multiplication	Reference
Allium cepa	Axill & adv. shoots	7500–60 000 shoots or bulbs	Hussey (1978a)
Alnus glutinosa	Shoot culture	1000×10^6 plants	Garton *et al.* (1981a)
Cephaelis ipecacuanha	Shoot culture	100 plants per shoot tip	Ideda *et al.* (1988)
Curcuma zedoaria	Shoot culture	9.8×10^6 shoots	Yasuda *et al.* (1988)
Eucalyptus spp.	Shoot culture	7.5×10^{13} plants	Gonçalves *et al.* (1986)
Salix viminalis	Shoot culture	10×10^6 plantlets	Read *et al.* (1982)
Vitis spp.	Shoot culture	3×10^6 microcuttings	Nozeran and Bancilhon (1972)
	Shoot culture	10×10^6 microcuttings	Rajasekaran and Mullins (1982)

Doubling time in shoot or node cultures.

As an accurate way of compounding the rate of increase of shoot number in shoot or node cultures, with the interval which is necessary before shoots can be subcultured or harvested, Flegmann and Wainwright (1981) suggested the calculation of a *shoot doubling time*, which is analogous to the cell generation (or doubling) time used in studies of cultured cell populations (King and Street, 1977; Gilissen *et al.*, 1983). The appropriate figure is obtained by scoring the numbers of shoots at the beginning (N_0) and end (N) of several successive subcultures. On each occasion the natural logarithm ($\ln_e$) of the ratio N/N_0 is taken, and then added to the previous total. The sums of the logarithms $\Sigma \ln_e N/N_0$ are then plotted against the time (t) which has elapsed from the start of the culture (i.e. excision and first explant transfer) to the end of the particular subculture period. If the resulting plot (ignoring an initial lag period) is a straight line, the increase in shoot number has been exponential, and then:

$$N = N_0 \, e^{\,bt}, \quad \text{(where b is the slope of the line).}$$

Shoot doubling time (in days, t_d, or in weeks, t_w) is obtained from the equation:

$$t_d = \frac{(\ln_e 2)}{b_y} = \frac{0.6931}{b_y}$$

The slope of the line is accurately determined by regression analysis, but a line of best fit can be drawn by eye and b_y estimated from the graph, because:

$$b_y = \frac{y}{x},$$

where

> $x =$ the time (in days or weeks) between two points on the linear section of the graph, and
>
> $y =$ the units on the logarithmic axis which correspond to this time interval.

These calculations can be illustrated from Table 124, which gives observations on the progress of shoot multiplication in an hypothetical culture. A plot of the resulting $\Sigma \ln_e N/N_0$ against elapsed time (t) is shown in Fig. 141. Shoot doubling time (t_w) in the example is $0.6931/0.34 = 2.04$ weeks (14.26 days).

Shoot doubling times depend on the environmental conditions to which the culture is subjected. They will therefore be influenced by factors such as temperature and cytokinin concentration. Research should try to minimise the doubling time while at the same time ensuring that shoots of suitable size and quality are produced for transfer. Shoot doubling times given by Flegmann and Wainwright for blackcurrant and apple shoot cultures, are shown in Table 125.

Using morphogenesis or embryogenesis

Rapid rates of propagation are not confined to shoot and node culture and even faster multiplication is possible from some plants using direct shoot formation or embryogenesis. The production of new bulblets from bulb scale segments can be rather slow *e.g.* 400–600 bulblets from one bulb of *Bowiea* in 16–20 weeks (Jha and Sen, 1985), but in some cases shoot and bulb formation can be carried

---

Table 124. Hypothetical records of the rate of shoot multiplication in a shoot culture, from which a shoot doubling time is calculated. Shoot doubling time in this experiment was 14.26 days (see Fig 141).

Shoot number at start of passage N_0	Shoot number at end of passage N	Subculture interval (weeks)	Time elapsed from initiation of culture (weeks)	Multiplication coefficient $\dfrac{N}{N_0}$	$\ln_e \dfrac{N}{N_0}$	$\Sigma \ln_e \dfrac{N}{N_0}$
1	1	6	6	1	0	0
1	3	5	11	3	1.0986	1.0986
3	12	4	15	4	1.3863	2.4849
12	58	4	19	4.8 †	1.5686	4.0535
58	290	4	23	5 †	1.6094	5.6629
290	1421	4	27	4.†	1.5892	7.2521
1421	7389	4	31	5.2 †	1.6487	8.9008

† Note that the average multiplication factor at each subculture is rarely exactly the same.

out in liquid media (see page 813) and scaled up to give high rates of multiplication.

The formation of adventitious organs in other plants can sometimes be very rapid *e.g.* 160 000 plantlets could be obtained from green globular bodies of *Asplenium* in 6 months (Higuchi and Amaki, 1989); the direct formation of multiple shoot primordia on *Stevia rebaudiana* shoot tip domes could provide one million shoot primordia from one initial shoot tip in 3 months (Miyagawa *et al.*, 1986).

The importance of timing

Production planning forms an important part of the management skills in a micropropagation laboratory. Efficient and low cost working requires that growth room space is kept continuously filled, because if new cultures do not immediately replace those which have been removed, the laboratory is losing money. It is also important to have plants ready at the exact time they are required by customers. New orders will not be forthcoming if a laboratory fails to deliver plants at agreed times.

Table 125. Shoot doubling rates recorded by Flegmann and Wainwright (1981) for apple and blackcurrant shoot cultures grown with one of three concentrations of BAP.

Plant	Concentration of BAP		
	0.24 µM (0.05 mg/l)	1.2 µM (0.27 mg/l)	6 µM (1.35 mg/l)
Apple	18.4 weeks	2.5 weeks	2.3 weeks
Blackcurrant	16.4 weeks	3.1 weeks	2.0 weeks

It is easier to avoid slack periods in a production schedule if a large variety of plants is cultured, each having a peak of demand at a different time of the year (Pierik, 1988). Accepting the correct mix of contracts is therefore another important management skill. Autumn is a poor time for sales of foliage plants in temperate climates (Donnan, 1986). A change to the production of other kinds of plants is required at such times.

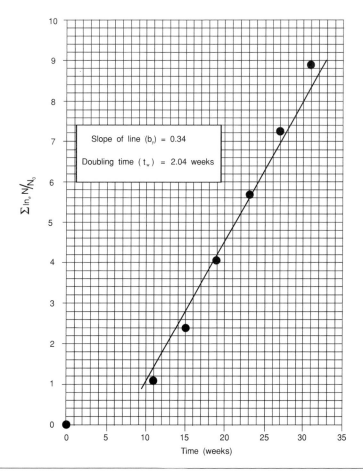

Fig. 141. A plot of logarithmic shoot proliferation in the hypothetical example set out in Table 124.

Storage techniques (Part 1, page 163 *et seq.*) can be used to even out peaks and troughs in production, but holding large numbers of shoots or plantlets in controlled environment rooms adds significantly to production costs.

CALCULATING PRODUCTION COSTS

An effectively managed plant tissue culture laboratory will have a detailed analysis of the costs of each stage of production as they relate to different crops.

The average cost of each plant produced is equivalent to the total cost of running the laboratory for a given period of time, plus, in a commercial operation, an expected profit from the operation; the total then divided by the number of plants produced over that period. Thus if a laboratory produces 2 million plants per year (n), and the laboratory were to cost $400 000 (C) to operate for one year, then the average cost of each plant produced ($\bar{e}$) would be $400 000/2 000 000, or 20 cents.

Although this is an accurate figure, some other approach is needed when trying to improve laboratory efficiency, or when trying to calculate a cost price (and hence a suitable selling price) for a particular kind of plant. Accurate costings must take into account the labour and facilities expended at each stage of production. Two useful methods of calculating comparative costs with some measure of accuracy have been described in the literature:

- Costings based on the utilisation of growth room space (Strain, 1980; Zimberoff, 1985; Donnan, 1986);
- Costings based on the time necessary at the laminar flow bench for isolations and transfers (Donnan, 1986; Chu and Kurtz, 1990).

Costings based on each of these techniques are considered below.

GROWTH ROOM UTILISATION

Costing on growth room space is based on the concept that the laboratory is working to full efficiency when shelving is:

a) fully occupied all the time; and

b) vessels are kept on growth room shelves for the minimum possible interval.

Occupancy

Several workers have pointed out that the cost of producing plants by micropropagation techniques can be calculated from the cost of growth room space per unit time, C_{at} (*i.e.* cost averaged over area and time — the cost per square metre of growth room shelf space per week). A decision to produce a defined number of shoots or plants typically necessitates carrying out a series of subcultures, each producing a larger number of propagules than the last, until the production target is reached. The vessels employed at each subculture occupy an area of growth room bench space, usually for several weeks, *i.e.* they occupy both space and time, the product of which, necessary to produce a given batch of plants, can be defined as vessel *occupancy*. The total occupancy which is necessary [O], comprises the area (square metres) and time (weeks, months or years) which have been taken up by the vessels during the series of subcultures necessary during production. The occupancy of the containers shown in the first example in Fig. 139, was calculated from:

$$(1 \text{ vessel} \times 3 \text{ cm}^2 \times 8 \text{ weeks}) + (1 \times 12.5 \times 7) + \ldots (900 \times 50 \times 6)$$
$$= 364086.5 \text{ cm}^2 \text{ weeks} = 36.409 \text{ m}^2 \text{ weeks}$$

The occupancy required to produce a given number of shoots or plantlets will differ from one variety of plant to another, depending on the multiplication coefficient; the size of the vessel necessary for its culture; the intervals between subcultures; and the number of explants available to launch the propagation process.

Examples of occupancy

Estimates are given in the literature of the number of plants which could be produced in one year from 1 square metre of growth room space (*i.e.* from an occupancy of 1 m^2 year). Thus producing an average of 40 shoots every eight weeks from *Rhododendron* shoot cultures contained in 100–150 ml vessels, yielded approximately 75 000 shoots from an occupancy of one square metre of culture space per year (McCown and Lloyd, 1983). Other published figures are 35 000 plants of woody species and 150 000 strawberry plants per square metre per year [Boxus, reported by Barlass (1989)].

The above examples give the numbers of shoots which would be expected from stabilised shoot cultures. Total occupancy for the given numbers of plants would therefore be higher than 1 m² year if the space and time necessary to initiate the respective cultures were taken into account. The average occupancy per shoot (O_s), or per plant (O_p), produced in the above examples is:

Rhododendron $\quad \frac{1}{75000} = 0.000013$ m² years, or

$\quad\quad\quad\quad\quad\quad \frac{52}{75000} = 0.00069$ m² weeks

$\quad\quad\quad\quad\quad\quad\quad\quad = 6.9$ cm² weeks

Strawberry $\quad \frac{1}{150000} = 0.0000066$ m² years, or

$\quad\quad\quad\quad\quad\quad \frac{52}{150000} = 0.00035$ m² weeks

$\quad\quad\quad\quad\quad\quad\quad\quad = 3.5$ cm² weeks

These occupancies are lower than would be expected in practice because they do not allow for a production factor.

Costings based on occupancy

The entire output of a micropropagation laboratory passes through the growth room. The cost of producing plants during a period of one week is equivalent to the total cost of running the laboratory for one year (Table 120), divided by the shelf area of the growth room and by the number of working weeks per year. The cost of propagating a given number of plants (n) is thus equivalent to C_{at}, multiplied by occupancy. The cost of one plant of that batch is:

$$\text{Cost per plant} = \frac{C_{at} \times O}{n}.$$

Suppose that the laboratory whose costs are summarised in Table 120 has 250 m² of shelf space in the growth room but, on average, manages to place two layers of vessels on each shelf. If one costs the laboratory on a weekly basis there is then an effective 500 m² of shelf space available per week, and if the growth rooms are available for a full 52 working weeks per year, their total available occupancy is $250 \times 2 \times 52$, or 26 000 m² weeks. The total cost of operating one square metre of space for one week is equal to the weekly cost or running the entire laboratory divided by the total number of square metres of growth room space available. In our example this can be represented as $\frac{5989}{500} = 11.978$ currency units .

Assuming that the growth room area is always filled to capacity, O_s (the occupancy per shoot) for a batch of 2323 unrooted shoots (the lower half of Fig. 139) which required a total occupancy of 5.176 m² weeks, would be:

$$\frac{5.176}{2323} \times 10000 = 22.28 \text{ cm}^2 \text{ weeks}$$

while O_p (occupancy per plant) for 1858 rooted plantlets equals:

$$\frac{19.126 \text{ m}^2 \text{ weeks}}{1858} \times 10000 = 102.94 \text{ cm}^2 \text{ weeks}$$

The occupancy per shoot above is much higher than the occupancies calculated for *Rhododendron* and strawberry on the opposite side of this page.

The costs of producing one *in vitro* shoot or rooted plantlet in our examples is, respectively:

$$5.176 \text{ m}^2 \text{ weeks} \times \frac{11.978}{2323} = 0.0267 \text{ currency units, and}$$

$$19.126 \text{ m}^2 \text{ weeks} \times \frac{11.978}{1858} = 0.1233 \text{ currency units.}$$

Notice how, in the examples shown in Figs. 139 and 140, occupancy per shoot or per plant, increases as losses are incurred during a production run, and also increases sharply when an *in vitro* rooting stage is required.

Laboratories in which the cost of growth room occupancy is high must work with high value plants or have a large throughput of plants, to make money (Donnan, 1986).

Incompletely filled growth rooms

Plant costs are greater if growth room space is not fully occupied. Should the growth room area be under–utilised, the cost of producing each plant rises, but not strictly in proportion to occupancy if compensatory measures are taken. For example, under–production of plants will mean that less labour has been required and less materials used. Costs are reduced if less direct labour has been employed, but overhead costs must still be carried. Zimberoff (1985) reckoned that the cost of production increased by 1.5 times if a crop occupied only half the available growth room space and cultures were not immediately put back to refill vacant areas.

Mobile shelving

Growth room utilisation can be increased if mobile racks of shelving are installed, because it is then possible to eliminate all but one passage way. To gain access to a stack of shelves, racks are pushed to one side until there is sufficient space for entry. Such a system is similar to that used for the storage of little used reference books in some large libraries. Its utilisation in a growth room makes full use of the constant environment space, but increases the cost of fitting out a room: more shelving units are required and racks must be mounted in such a way that they can be moved from side to side with the minimum of effort. Close spacing of lighted racks requires that attention be paid to air circulation around vessels to ensure that local overheating does not occur, and the additional number of lighting tubes within the growth room will increase the demand on its cooling facilities.

Stacking vessels

Production costs can be reduced if more than one layer of vessels is placed on growth room benches. This can be achieved by containing vessels in light wire mesh trays, one on top of another (Part 1, page 105). Because light penetration into vessels is often poor when lighting sources are placed above growth room benches (especially if vessels are stacked one on top of another and have opaque closures), Hayashi *et al.* (1992) and Kozai *et al.* (1992) investigated the provision of sideways lighting. When fluorescent tubes were arranged in vertical banks and stacks of vessels placed against them, the dry and fresh weights and leaf area of potato shoots were much greater than those of shoots in conventionally lighted vessels where shoot length was reduced. The authors suggested that either less lighting would be necessary using this system, or that, using light of high flux density, space utilisation could be reduced by shortening the interval between subcultures.

Growth room size

Of the space–time taken up by the series of subcultures necessary to produce a given number of plants, by far the greatest proportion (from 50% to over 80%, depending on the nature of the plant and the number of subcultures necessary) is taken up by the last (*i.e.* the subculture from which the final number of plants or shoots is obtained). Let us assume again that we have a growth room which provides a total occupancy of 26 000 m^2 weeks per year, and that on average in our laboratory 55% of the space and time is taken up by the final stages of propagation. This means that if the space is always fully occupied, approximately 14 300 m^2 weeks each year is devoted to final subcultures. If they stay on the shelf for an average of 5 weeks, there is one culture per vessel, and an average of 3 shoots are obtained from each, the approximate number of shoots or plantlets which can be obtained from the growth room area is:

1. Using vessels which occupy an area of 42.25 cm^2 [†]

$$\frac{14300 \times 10000}{5 \times 42.25} \times 3 = 2.03 \times 10^6$$

2. Using vessels which occupy an area of 84.5 cm^2

$$\frac{14300 \times 10000}{5 \times 84.5} \times 3 = 1.02 \times 10^6$$

The number of plantlets which might be obtained from the room if boxes of 240 cm^2 area were used (each containing 12 cultures), is:

$$\frac{14300 \times 10000}{5 \times 240} \times 12 = 1.43 \times 10^6$$

Although growth rooms, ideally, should be fully occupied, this is generally an unrealisable objective because there will always need to be a small reserve of space. Cultures may not be produced according to plan, and demand is likely to fluctuate. Some laboratories seem to carry a large number of stock cultures which, by permanently occupying bench space, reduces the effective throughput of newly propagated plants.

TIME SPENT ON STERILE TRANSFERS

An alternative method of estimating the cost of production is to assess the labour involved in the sterile transfers necessary in propagation. Assuming that plants are only obtained by the use of laminar flow cabinets, the cost of producing a batch of plants can be estimated from the cost of operating the laboratory for one hour, multiplied by the number of hours in which the cabinets were used to carry out the necessary subcultures. Calculations are usually based on the time in which cabinets were *directly used* for propagation. The time during which cabinets were used for research purposes, for maintaining stock cultures, or for dispensing media is excluded. Some laboratories distinguish between routine multiplication and the initiation of cultures, staff with greater skill and experience being used for the latter work.

Records should allow for such distinctions, but if they do not, it is possible to multiply the total time during which laminar flow cabinets have been operated by a productive work factor, which takes into account the time generally spent on research oriented transfers and other work; but this approach is not preferred.

Accurate costings based on the time spent on transfers require careful records of the time spent on each of the subcultures necessary to produce a batch of plants, and knowledge of the final number of shoots or plantlets produced. To keep the kind of records described by Kurtz *et al.* (1991), for every Stage II subculture, each transfer technician would need to note:

a) the number of vessels containing shoots opened per day;

b) the specified number of explants per vessel;

c) the losses discovered due to poor growth or contamination;

d) the number of new vessels to which plant material has been transferred;

e) the specified number of explants in each new vessel;

---

†   A vessel with a circular base of 6.5 cm diameter can be assumed to occupy an area of 6.5 cm^2.

f) losses due to other factors;

Records are simplified for routine subculturing to vessels of the same size. Some laboratories employ one person to label cultures as they are prepared who also makes the appropriate records, thus relieving laminar flow technicians from this responsibility.

Entered onto a computer, data can be used to monitor the performance of each employee and to predict product availability. If a detailed record is not kept for each subculture, an approximate estimate of the total time taken to produce a batch of plants can be made by recording just the time taken to carry out the last subculture, providing it is known what proportion of the total work it represents.

Average costs are more easily calculated. Thus in any one week, the following situation might occur:

Cost of running the entire laboratory for one week (C_w)	5989 units (Table 120)
Hours of directly productive transfer work in one week (h_p)	$1080 \times {}^{6.5}\!/_8 = 877.5$ †
Cost per hour of directly productive transfer work in week (C_p) = (C_w/h_p)	${}^{5989}\!/_{877.5}$ ™ = $6.825\,units$‡
Total number of transfers of all kinds	173 076
Transfers per hour of productive work (including maintenance transfers)	197.2
Average cost of each transfer	${}^{6.825}\!/_{197.2} = 0.0346$ units
Total number of shoots transferred to Stage III	57 692
Number of shoots transferred to Stage III per hour of productive work	${}^{57692}\!/_{877.5} = 65.7$
Average production cost of each shoot =	${}^{6.825}\!/_{65.7} = 0.104$ units

† Allowing for breaks during the day

‡ Note this is ${}^{6.825}\!/_{1.5} = 4.5$ times greater than the cost (1.5 units) of employing a technician for one hour.

Improving on the rate of transfer

Costings based on the time spent on transfer work, draw particular attention to the importance of obtaining the rapid manipulation of cultures without accident or cross contamination. Several methods of motivating the work force to a continued level of high performance have been discussed in the literature.

Length of the working day. Those running laboratories have described how working efficiency declines when workers spend long periods at laminar flow cabinets. In the laboratory exemplified in Table 120, a single 8 hour shift has been allowed for, with workers having a 15 minute break morning and afternoon, and a 1 hour break for lunch. Some laboratories employ staff to work only 4 hour shifts, of which there might be 4 during the day. A paid meal break is then avoided but the difficulty of

training and motivating a large number of operatives becomes a problem. To avoid having too many employees, laboratories have been known to ask those working the first 4 hour shift to return for the third, and those who work the second shift to return for the fourth.

Incentive plans. Donnan (1986) mentioned three incentive plans which have been tried in various laboratories:

1. All technicians are placed in a common pool and payment is on the basis of the performance of the whole laboratory. This has the disadvantage that it penalises fast workers and over–rewards slow ones.

2. A bonus is paid for propagules transferred or harvested above a minimum standard. Using this method of payment it is necessary to share work on different plants equitably, for some species can be dealt with at a much faster rate than others.

Disadvantages with both these schemes are that they can easily result in careless work, leading to damage to cultured material and to high levels of contamination. Laboratories have coped with this problem by imposing financial penalties when levels of contamination exceed the average. A loss of bonus applied to all operatives for the mistakes of one or two, will soon prove to be highly unpopular; the alternative requires an extremely efficient recording system where the history of each vessel is known in detail.

Donnan (*loc. cit.*) comments that an incentive system of this kind needs to be set up on a long–term basis, or some workers will prefer to take time off once they have met the minimum standard, instead of receiving a productivity bonus. Scheme 3 (below) was therefore tried and found to be most successful.

3. To pay for the number of vessels actually handled through a points system. To operate the scheme it is necessary to set a standard rate of working for each crop and each stage of manipulation. Thus where it is thought that 60 vessels per hour is the norm, 1 point is given for each vessel handled. In a different crop, or at a different stage where only 30 vessels might normally be dealt with each hour, the points allocation would be 2 per vessel.

Comparative costings

Choice of method

Costings based on the cost of transfers and on the cost of growth room occupancy are clearly related, because the number of vessels to be placed in the growth room each week depends on the number of technicians employed in transfer work, and upon the rate at which manipulations are carried out. However they will not give precisely the same results.   This can be seen from the hypothetical examples shown in Fig. 139. When calculating production costs, the two methods can therefore be thought of as alternatives. However a comparison between the results obtained by both methods can provide useful information, because wide divergence in results can indicate that the laboratory is over– or under–staffed in comparison with the available shelf area of the growth rooms.

Comparisons between protocols

Costings are necessary to make accurate comparisons between protocols, and there may be occasions when the two methods of calculating the production costs of individual plants may not give sufficiently accurate figures. Two alternative methods described by Schulze (1988) for micropropagating 10 000 plants of *Saintpaulia ionantha* 'Kimi' are shown in Fig. 142. In method **A**, clumps of shoots obtained *in vitro* (which have naturally produced adventitious roots) are divided and planted directly in soil for acclimatization. In method **B**, *in vitro* shoot clumps are planted into soil where they are allowed to acclimatize and grow before they are divided and planted as single plants. Method **B** plants were of a high quality, and more closely matched growers' requirements.

In Fig. 142 we have entered estimates of how long it might take to perform the necessary operations, and in Table 126 some hypothetical costs have been applied. According to these calculations, especially when the cost of productive transfer work in the laboratory (page 779) is greater than the hourly cost of greenhouse work, Method **B** not only results in better quality plants, they are also cheaper. However, Schulze (*loc. cit.*) thought that Method **B** plants would cost more than those produced by Method **A**. Whatever you decide, we hope the example will illustrate the importance of accurate costings.

PRODUCTION PLANNING

An evaluation of growth room occupancy shows that even within a single laboratory, when the same protocol is used throughout, the cost of producing plants can still differ markedly according to the subculturing strategy employed.

Suppose that 10 000 rooted plantlets are required of a cultivar not in regular production but, to allow for possible losses during rooting *ex vitro*, it is estimated that 10500 shoots should be produced. Suppose too that cultures are initiated by placing one shoot as an explant in each vessel; shoots harvested from one subculture are used to initiate the next; and previous experience has taught that shoot culture can be relied upon to give 5–fold multiplication every 3 weeks. Propagation is carried out

Table 126. Calculating the relative cost of propagating *Saintpaulia* by the two methods shown in Fig. 142.

Method	Location	Cost per hour (units)	Hours worked	Total cost (currency units)
A	Laboratory	6.825 †	101.75	694.44
	Greenhouse	5.0‡	27.78	138.90
Total				833.34
B	Laboratory	6.825 †	53.92	368.00
	Greenhouse	5.0‡	38.89	194.45
Total				562.45

† From page 763.

‡ The cost per hour for planting in Table 120 has been increased to allow for other greenhouse overheads.

in vessels of 6.5 cm external diameter, and sufficient material is available to set up 3 vessels initially. Table 127 shows five different strategies for tackling the problem.

1. Shoots can be multiplied without any pre–planning until the end of the fifth subculture, when 9375 shoots can be expected to be available.

   a) 9375 is close to the required number, so you might decide to stop propagation at this point and inform the customer that this is all the plants you could provide on this occasion. This is not a professional approach, but the total area time to produce one shoot is as low as it can be using this protocol viz. 0.00317 m^2 weeks.

   b) You might decide that the customer will not be happy with the number of plantlets produced from 9375 shoots, and so subculture them all, ending up at the end of the sixth passage with 46 875 shoots. You can then supply 10 500 shoots for rooting, but what of the rest? If they can be sold or reused in some other way, occupancy per shoot (Os) remains low at 0.00317 m^2 weeks; but if the remainder is discarded, Os leaps up to 0.0141 m^2 weeks (i.e. the plantlets have cost 4.4 times as much to produce).

2. An alternative strategy is available at the end of subculture 5: subculture 6 can be set up in 2100 vessels so that only 10 500 shoots will be obtained in 3 weeks time, and there will be no waste. The occupancy per plant is reduced thereby to 0.00536 m^2 weeks.

3. The cultured plants normally produce 5 new shoots every three weeks. In our example, if an average of 5.6 shoots could be produced during subculture 4 (instead of the 5 normally expected), it would be possible to set up 2100 vessels for subculture 5 to produce the 10 500 plants required. The requisite average of 5.6 shoots per vessel

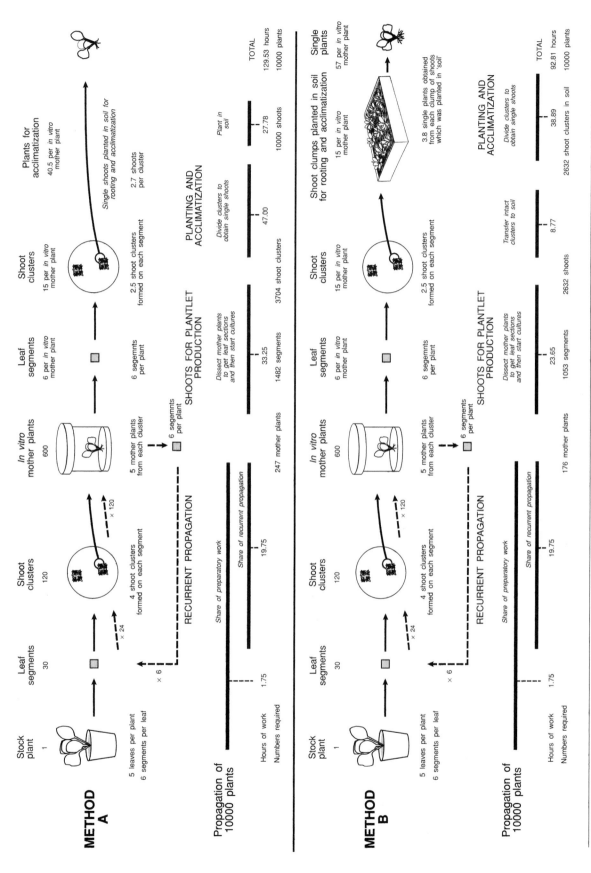

Fig. 142. The comparative costs of micropropagating *Saintpaulia* by two alternative methods [after Schulze, 1988]. See text for detailed explanation.

Table 127. The space and time occupied in a growth room by an hypothetical series of subculture aimed at producing 10 500 plants. It has been assumed that shoots multiply by a factor of 5 at each subculture, there is normally 3 weeks between subcultures, cultures are grown in vessels which each occupy 42.25 cm² of bench space, and that there is one layer of vessels on the bench.

Options		Subculture number 1	2	3	4	5	6	Total occupancy (m² weeks)	Occupancy per shoot sold (cm² weeks)
1. No pre-planning	Vessels (explants)	3	15	75	375	1875	9375	**A** Sell 9375 and omit subculture 6	**A** *Discard remainder* → 141.45
	Subculture interval (weeks)	3	3	3	3	3	3	29.698	*Use remainder* → 31.69
	Shoot yield	15	75	375	1875	(9375)	(46875)	**B** Sell 10500	31.68
	Occupancy (weeks)	0.038	0.190	0.951	4.753	23.766	118.828	148.526	
2. Adjust size of last subculture	Vessels (explants)	3	15	75	375	1875	2100		
	Subculture interval (weeks)	3	3	3	3	3	3	Use only 2100 shoots for subculture 6. Discard the rest.	
	Shoot yield	15	75	375	1875	(9375)	10500	56.316	53.63
	Occupancy (weeks)	0.038	0.190	0.951	4.753	23.766	26.618		
3. Adjust size of subculture '5'	Vessels (explants)	3	15	75	375	2100			
	Subculture interval (weeks)	3	3	3	4	3			
	Shoot yield	15	75	375	2100	10500		34.135	32.51
	Occupancy (weeks)	0.038	0.190	0.951	6.338	26.618			
4. Adjust size of all subcultures **A. Starting with 3 vessels**	Vessels (explants)	3	17	84	420	2100			
	Subculture interval (weeks)	4	3	3	3	3			
	Shoot yield	17	85	420	2100	10500		33.317	31.73
	Occupancy (weeks)	0.051	0.215	1.065	5.324	26.662			
B. Starting with 1 vessel	Vessels (explants)	1	4	17	84	420	2100		
	Subculture interval (weeks)	3	3	3	3	3	3		
	Shoot yield	5	20	85	420	2100	10500	33.330	31.74
	Occupancy (weeks)	0.013	0.051	0.215	1.065	5.324	26.662		

might be obtained from subculture 4 by keeping the vessels in the growth room for 4 weeks instead of 3. This option reduces the occupancy per shoot, O_s to 0.00325 m² weeks, but is not always available: it would be impossible, for example, to adopt it if a multiplication coefficient of 18 were required from a culture where shoots normally increase 5–fold at each subculture.

4. Growth room utilisation is kept to a minimum by calculating the size of each subculture starting from the final number of plants required, and working backwards to find the number of vessels required at each step. Option 4 in Table 127 shows that by obtaining 17 shoots from subculture 1, instead of 15, in theory it is possible to obtain 10 500 shoots from subculture 5 at minimum cost. For the calculations it has been assumed that the vessels comprising Passage 1, would have to be retained for 4 weeks instead of the customary 3 to obtain the extra number.

Certain conclusions can be drawn from the above example. Assuming that growth room space is always kept fully occupied, the cost of production can be reduced by:

- **Placing as many explants into a vessel as is possible without causing a decrease in the rate of shoot production.**

- **Allowing each culture the optimum amount of space.** In many cases this will mean placing explants as closely as possible without sacrificing shoot number or shoot quality. There may be an interaction between multiplication rate and vessel volume, but unless the multiplication coefficient is greatly increased, using large vessels each containing only a few explants will result in higher occupancy;

- **Placing more than one layer of culture vessels upon the shelf in growth rooms.**

- **Increasing the multiplication coefficient;**

- **Reducing the time between subcultures;**

- **Producing very close to the exact final number of shoots required in the minimum number of subcultures.** The most economical way to do this is to adjust the requisite number of vessels for each subculture as soon as possible in the production period. At each subculture thereafter the number of vessels to be inoculated should be very close to that required to achieve the final target.

> In practice, because the number of explants produced will not be as theoretically predicted, but vary at each subculture (see Fig. 139), the number of cultures to be carried forward should be reviewed at each subculture *before* transfer work is completed, so that operators do not waste time and materials setting up unnecessary vessels.

- **Minimising losses due to contamination**

Multiplication rate

The time to produce a given number of plants (and hence growth room occupancy and costs) is reduced if the rate of multiplication of a culture can be increased, by increasing the multiplication coefficient or decreasing the interval between subcultures. The rate of multiplication of shoot cultures is mainly controlled by growth regulators added to the medium, but other factors can be influential (*e.g.* the nature of the medium used, the volume of the culture vessel and the orientation of explants). The multiplication coefficient of *Camellia* shoot cultures was greater when shoots were placed horizontally on the medium, rather than when they were inserted in a vertical position.

Effective techniques for increasing the rate of shoot proliferation may vary between closely related cultivars: Douglas *et al.* (1989) found that they could more than double the rate of proliferation of one *Rosa* cultivar by removing the shoot apex when shoots were subcultured; in another cultivar, the rate of multiplication was increased by only using shoots of at least 2 cm as explants, and by reculturing shoots to fresh medium every 3 weeks.

Size of the initial culture

Beginning shoot production with the largest possible number of culture flasks might seem to be another cost saving practice. Certainly it does reduce the time needed to produce the necessary number of shoots or plants, but in terms of costs based on growth room occupancy, any saving is negligible. It can be seen from example 4B in Table 127, that there would have been only an extremely small reduction in growth room occupancy (*O*) by starting the production cycle with 1, 3 or 24 initial vessels (in the latter case, 7 would have had to be discarded). When the cost of maintaining the starter cultures in the growth room is taken into account, any benefit is eliminated.

Investigating explant density and vessel size

In our example (Table 127) it has been assumed that one explant placed into a cylindrical vessel of 6.5 cm diameter (occupying 42.25 cm²) will give rise to 5 new shoots every 3 weeks. Occupancy would clearly be decreased if the same multiplication coefficient were obtained when more than one explant was place into the same sized vessel, showing that, to decrease costs, it is important to allot only the minimum area of bench space to each explant (culture). Bond and Alderson (1993) investigated the optimum number of nodal rhizome sections of hybrid

Table 128. The effect of varying the concentration of BAP on the number and quality of shoots produced by *Senecio* × *hybridus* cultures.

The average number of shoots obtained at each subculture is shown for three production strategies: ① represented by rectangles with rounded corners; ② represented by circles; ③ represented by squares [data from Gertsson, 1988a].

BAP level	Subculture number						Shoots per original explant ($\times 10^3$) §	Shoot quality
	0	1	2	3	4	5		
0.1 mg/l		7.8	6.4	4.9	4.1	4.3	4.3	Easy to root
					7.1	7.2	31.1	Easy to root
1 mg/l	Pretreatment (before culture)			9.1	9.5	7.8	33.7	Difficult to root

§   This is the number of shoots theoretically produced after 5 subcultures.

Alstroemeria which should be placed into 140 ml jars. The number of shoots per explant remained between 4.1 and 4.6 in the presence of 1–5 explants per jar, and only began to decrease (*ca.* 3.4) when 6 explants were present.

If the area of growth room space per explant is kept to a minimum, then the size of vessel used does not greatly alter occupancy. It is theoretically always slightly less if small vessels are used, each containing a small number of explants, because of the greater flexibility which is possible in adjusting the number of explants to be set up at each subculture to produce a given number of plants. However, advantages from using large vessels (page 766) may outweigh this small disadvantage, and preparing and filling a large number of small vessels with medium is obviously costly. Optimum explant density and vessel size can only be determined through experimentation and experience.

Changing the growth regulator treatment

From the examples given so far in this chapter, it might be assumed that once established, shoot cultures can be subcultured to give an optimum rate of increase by using the same growth regulators at each transfer. This is not necessarily so, and an experiment of Gertsson, summarised in Table 128 shows that if the rate of increase is starting to decline, changing the concentration of regulants for one or two subcultures can markedly alter the number of plants produced in a given time. The results also reveal the compromise which must be made between obtaining a large number of shoots and ensuring that they

are of a suitable quality. Culturing *Senecio* shoots with 1 mg/l BAP for 3 subcultures instead of 2, resulted in a greater final number of shoots but, as the shoots were difficult to root, the number of plants obtained would have been reduced. Any temporary increase in cytokinin level is acceptable during the build up of a stock of cultures, but should be in advance of a final, or a continuing shoot harvest.

The optimum interval between subcultures

Optimisation of the multiplication coefficient and subculture interval is important if the cost of shoot cultures is to be minimised. Most would agree that increase in shoot number and the length of time necessary between subcultures can only be determined by experiment and experience with propagating each particular genotype. A method of mathematical solution proposed by Hara and Kozai (1992) may be useful to those wishing to prepare computer simulations, or computer–based predictions which can assist practical micropropagation.

The rate of increase in shoot number is determined by the cultural environment and by the nature and previous cultural history of the plant, but particularly by the concentration of cytokinin (and sometimes also that of other growth regulators) added to the culture medium. High concentrations of cytokinins may lead to the production of many shoots, but a proportion may become hyperhydric and unusable, or shoots may fail to elongate satisfactorily, and so may need to be given an additional elongation treatment, or cultures may need to be retained

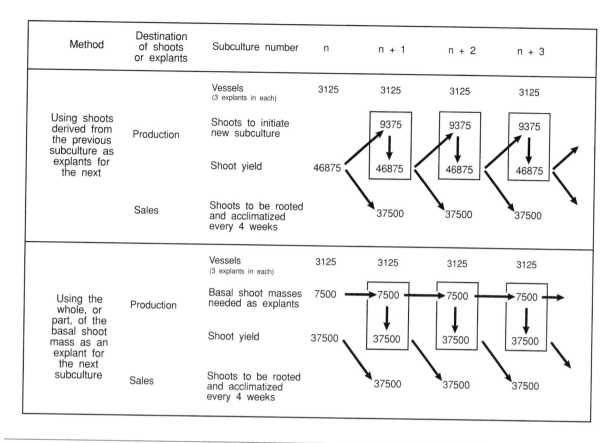

Fig. 143. Examples of the allocation of propagules between sales and production when continued micropropagation of a plant is needed. Two alternative methods of obtaining 37500 shoots per subculture are shown, but division of the basal shoot mass is not always possible or wise.. Regular production in this fashion is only possible once a sufficiently large number of stabilised shoot cultures has been obtained.

in the growth room for an extended period before they are of a sufficient size to harvest.

Arnold *et al.* (1992) experimented with a range of different concentrations of auxin and cytokinin on shoot cultures of four *Rosa hybrida* cultivars which were then subcultured at either 6, 8, or 10 week intervals. The growth regulators which gave the optimum shoot proliferation over each of these time periods were then selected and used to carry forward cultures of each cultivar for one year. This resulted in three treatments in which there were either 8, 6, or 5 subcultures. The efficacy of each protocol was assessed by scoring the product of the proportion of vessels containing healthy shoots, with the number of harvestable shoots in such vessels. Very clear differences were found between the cultivars, with the optimum culture period for two of them being 6 weeks, for another 6 or 8 weeks, and the fourth 8 weeks.

Implications of planning

Although plants are usually required in batches of a defined size, production is often difficult without wast-

age. This is especially the case when a customer requires a defined number of shoots or plantlets on a particular date. In these circumstances, even if the optimum size of each subculture can be readily calculated from prior knowledge of the characteristics of the plant, it is impossible to predict that the necessary rate of shoot multiplication will always be obtained, and that there will not be unforeseen losses (*e.g.* due to contamination). Over–production at each stage of the subculturing process is therefore inevitable and this will unavoidably increase the cost of production (see page 770).

Figs. 139 and 140 illustrate how the time required for subculture increases greatly during the final stages of plant propagation. This means that large batches of shoots, which may take laboratory technicians several days to separate at the final stage, should not be produced until it has been planned how they are to be handled as they emerge from culture. If the customer requires a large number of unrooted shoots, it may be necessary to send several consignments on a daily basis to complete the order.

Avoiding slack periods. The cost of production increases if a micropropagation laboratory is not busy all the time. Production therefore needs to be carefully planned to make best use of available space in growth rooms and greenhouses and, as mentioned on page 775, the capability to propagate a wide range of plants is the best way of avoiding there being insufficient work at certain periods of the year. Short–term storage techniques mentioned in Chapter 6 can sometimes avoid the otherwise inevitable disposal of temporary surpluses.

The best use of micropropagation. Although it is not apparent from the calculations shown in Fig. 140, shoots or plants are usually supplied in an economical fashion, when demand is being satisfied from a continuing production line, without wastage. This fact is appreciated by large production companies who realise that present methods of micropropagation are best suited to providing customers with a steady stream of plant material (Hartman, 1985), rather than the production of batches of plants in response to exceptional orders, or supplying customers for just part of the year when there is a seasonal demand (Kurtz *et al.*, 1991).

Even with herbaceous plants, to initiate a production run from explants freshly excised from mother plants introduces an extended lead time. In woody plants, which frequently require many months before they produce axillary shoots at a stabilised and predictable rate (Part 1, page 240), this practice is even more slow and costly. Here it is definitely a wise policy to propagate plants continuously, or at least to maintain a nucleus of stabilised cultures from which intermittent orders can be initiated.

Where new cultures are initiated from some of the organs harvested from the previous subculture, continuous production of many plants becomes possible once a critical number of shoots is available. Part of the total number of shoots or plants is then diverted to sales, while part is retained to initiate the next subculture (Figs. 140 and 143). This procedure is sometimes called *recurrent propagation*. In practice some over–production will usually be necessary to ensure that an adequate number of shoots continues to be available for both purposes.

Production is somewhat simpler, and less vessels are required to obtain the same number of shoots, if the basal shoot mass is re–used as an explant for the next subculture, especially if it can be subdivided first.

> Propagation from a basal shoot mass often results in the formation of associated callus from which adventitious shoots may arise. Many laboratories are therefore wary of using this technique lest they produce genetically variable plants.

Although recurrent propagation is convenient, it is often not possible, or is thought to be unwise, to continue production endlessly. This is because the rate of multiplication sometimes declines after several subcultures, and because the occurrence of a mutation would result in large numbers of aberrant plants. Usually therefore new cultures are re–initiated periodically. Recurrent propagation of the *Saintpaulia* cultures represented in Fig. 142 was continued until one initial culture had contributed to the formation of 50 000 new plants.

Because suitable multiplication protocols take time to work out, and it may take several months to establish plant material and obtain Stage II cultures capable of rapid proliferation, micropropagation is not suited to producing plants for which there is a sudden demand. Micropropagation is also not suitable (without extremely careful planning) for producing those kinds of plants which would be required for field or garden planting (or to attract customer interest) during just a few weeks of the whole year. In many parts of North America and Europe, for example, *Pelargonium* plants are purchased by gardeners during just a few weeks in the spring, but then are required in large numbers.

Contracts. To ensure continuity of production without wastage, micropropagation laboratories encourage customers to enter into contracts which stipulate that plants will be purchased regularly during a defined period. The length of the contracted period will be governed by the size of the order. In normal circumstances a laboratory would expect a customer to take a proportion of the plants required at regular intervals over a prolonged period (ideally over 12–18 months). It is then agreed that cancellation of either supply or demand cannot be made without several months prior notice by either party.

MARKETING MICROPROPAGATED PLANTS

Available products

Regardless of the multiplication method employed, micropropagation is at present able to offer plant material of four main saleable catagories or types:

1. unrooted shoots or shoot clusters which the purchaser can use as cuttings (or occasionally as scions);
2. shoots which have been rooted *in vitro*, but not yet hardened or acclimatized;
3. rooted, hardened and substrate–adapted, plantlets;
4. storage organs which can be directly planted into soil in greenhouse or field.

The first two of these forms are specialised products which can only be sold to skilled nurserymen. Those of the remaining two classes are more robust, can be held back without damage for longer periods before sale, and are suitable for sale to a wider range of customers.

In addition to our four main categories, one could add micro–grafted trees and orchid seedlings germinated *in vitro*, but sales of each of these products are comparatively small. In the future it may be possible to add encapsulated somatic embryos, or shoots which can be planted in soil to yield plantlets, to the kinds of plant material available from tissue culture. At the moment, the technology is not sufficiently advanced to permit this to be done reliably.

Marketing strengths

It will be obvious from the earlier sections of this chapter that the cost of micropropagation varies greatly from one species or cultivar to another. Although in many instances present methods cannot provide plants which compete in price with those which have been conventionally propagated, there are some advantages over traditional techniques. These were discussed in Part 1, pages 39 and 40.

Perhaps the chief advantages from a marketing point of view are that micropropagation provides a method of cloning which:

> – may not be otherwise possible;
>> Or may be possible by conventional methods, but only at a slow pace, perhaps through the use of a specialised technique.
>
> – can be carried out rapidly;

> Micropropagation can often be used to multiply stock of new plant varieties very quickly.

> – may provide plants which have advantages in form, uniformity, or yielding capacity over plants which have been propagated by conventional methods.

Sales are most easily achieved where the benefits of these advantages are apparent and the market can stand the costs involved. Laboratories can then considerably increase the availability of plant material, where it would otherwise be absent, or in short supply. Many foliage plants which are commonly purchased for home and office decoration were not grown commercially as ornamental pot plants before the advent of micropropagation.

Other advantages which may help to promote a micropropagated product are:

> – the ability to produce plants all the year round; and,

> – the ability to produce plants which are free from disease;

Micro–propagated plants are readily transported, and can usually meet exacting phytosanitary standards so that an international market can be considered.

Health status

All plants resulting from *in vitro* propagation can be produced with a certified health status. Making sure that plants are free from disease and contamination should be an integral part of controlling the quality of propagated material. It helps to prevent loss of cultures during production, ensures that the customer has no problems with the crop, and becomes essential when material is to be exported and requires a phytosanitary inspection. Cassells (1991) suggested that, because it is so difficult to confirm that plant material is totally free of contaminants, micropropagated plants could be sold on the basis of the following health grading system:

Class 1	Free of all cultivatable micro–organisms; free of all major diseases of the crop.
Class 2	Free of all cultivatable micro–organisms; free of all specified diseases of the crop.
Class 3	Free of all cultivatable bacteria.
Class 4	Untested.

Although a disease–free status is perceived by customers to be an advantage in micropropagated plants, Barnhill Jones and Sluis (1991) found that it added less to the value of a product than has been suggested in the past.

Marketing weaknesses

Markets for products for which there is a very large potential demand are chiefly denied to the micropropagation industry by the high cost of production. The cost of micropropagated material is often 2–5 times that of plants grown from rooted cuttings. But in many instances, competition is not with other methods of vegetative multiplication, but with plants grown from seed which can be produced even more cheaply. One of the best examples is the potential for clones of elite trees in afforestation programmes. Genetically variable trees grown cheaply from seed are still largely preferred to genetically superior trees cloned at high cost. Lowering the cost of micropropagation would create a large new market opportunity, but general confidence has not yet been established that micropropagated elite trees will give superior yields (page 972).

The cost and difficulty of producing small batches of plants, discussed in the previous section, has precluded their production from large laboratories and has presented difficulties to the smaller ones, becoming a hindrance to expanding the product range. Added difficulties are that protocols which allow reliable micropropagation, take time to develop. Even when production problems are resolved, it can often take a considerable time from the receipt of a stock plant to the availability of sufficient Stage II cultures to guarantee consistent production. One answer to these problems has been the setting up of laboratories specialising in distinctive product lines: examples are the success of small laboratories propagating ferns or orchids, and those concentrating on the multiplication of certain woody ornamentals.

Customer acceptance of micropropagated material has tended to restrict sales in the past, but has been helped during recent years by resolving the inconsistent quality of material delivered to nurseries. This has largely been achieved through a better knowledge of methods of establishment. The sale of rooted plants in liners has also enabled unskilled and ill–equipped customers to be untroubled by acclimatization procedures.

Problems with genetic variability in shoot and node culture can be avoided or minimised by ensuring that indirectly formed adventitious shoots are not produced (Part 1, Chapter 3). The occurrence of somaclonal variants has however proved to be a major restraint to the use of tissue culture for plant propagation and has precluded several potential methods for rapid *in vitro* multiplication. The field performance of some crop plants resulting from temporary physiological changes induced during culture has also occasionally restricted usage, although in many cases observed changes are advantageous (Chapter 15).

Persistent rejuvenation. The discovery that cuttings taken from many woody plants form roots much more readily than adult plants for months or years after the stock plant has been micropropagated (page 752), has removed the need to have these plants multiplied *in vitro* in large numbers because *in vivo* rooting of cuttings taken from a few stock plants will be much less costly.

Selling for profit

Many commercial laboratories have participated in the multiplication of ornamental pot plants and species grown to produce cut flowers. Demand for such plants continues over many months of the year. However, the strong competition between laboratories results in there being little opportunity to increase prices above the accepted 'going' rate. Profit margins on these products are therefore low, and inefficient laboratories are readily put out of business. There is more profit in multiplying unusual plants but this is only possible where a laboratory is in possession of methodology which is not readily copied by others or where it is in close contact with specialised customers.

In practice, the selling price for micropropagated material is often governed by the price charged for equivalent plants which have been grown from seeds or multiplied vegetatively by conventional methods. Cuttings of many common plants mass produced by conventional methods are still much cheaper than micropropagated material. For example, the prices for chrysanthemum plantlets in Table 129, compare unfavourably with the price of cuttings produced in the Canary Islands and imported into mainland Europe. This is currently *ca.* UK£0.05 per plant (0.017 currency units; US$0.083), making the cheapest tissue cultured product about 3 times as expensive and therefore uneconomic to produce.

Franclet and Boulay (1982) estimated that micropropagated *Eucalyptus* plants would cost twice as much to produce as seedlings of the same size, and Bornman (1987) that *an in vitro*–grown plantlet of *Picea abies* cost 25 times more a seedling and 2.5 times more than a rooted cutting. To set against these cost disadvantages is the fact that clones of elite trees have greater intrinsic worth because of their superior growth attributes, resistance factors and superior final yield. Here it is a matter of convincing foresters that the product is worth an initial high investment because of the substantial long–term gain.

The stage at which plants are sold

Selling non–rooted cuttings (Type 1, on page 787) or plantlets which have just been rooted *in vitro* (Type 2) is generally not so profitable as selling plants which are well established in plugs or liners (Type 3). Knuttel and Benoit (1988) found that it cost 62% of the possible sale price to produce material of *Rhododendron* to the levels of category 1 or category 2, but only 46% of the price which it was possible to charge for plants prepared and acclimatized to the level of category 3. The cost of rooting and growing a cutting to liner size was thus less than the difference in price between the two kinds of saleable product.

Pricing plants

Examples of the manner in which the costs of producing shoots or rooted plantlets by micropropagation are built up, are illustrated in Figs. 139 and 140 (pages 768 and 769). A mark–up (of 35–40%) must be added to production costs to find a profitable selling price. At the time of writing (1995), the currency unit in Table 120 is equivalent to *ca.* £3.00 Stirling or *ca.* U.S.$ 5.00. In order to make a profit, the unrooted shoots produced by the propagation schedule described in the lower half of Fig. 139 would therefore have to sell for:

$$0.0267 \text{ to } 0.0693 \times \frac{135}{100} = 0.036 \text{ to } 0.096 \text{ currency units}$$

(UK£0.11–0.29 or US$0.18–0.48)

and unacclimatized rooted plantlets for:

$$0.1067 \text{ to } 0.1233 \times \frac{135}{100} = 0.144 \text{ to } 0.164 \text{ currency units}$$

(UK£0.42–0.49 or US$0.72–0.82)

Cost per plant may decrease as the scale of production is increased, particularly if production techniques can be adapted and/or some degree of automation introduced.

Theiler–Hedtrich and Theiler–Hedtrich (1979) gave a detailed evaluation of the space and time needed to propagate Boston ferns and *Saintpaulia ionantha* by tissue

Table 129. Ex laboratory prices of some kinds of micropropagated herbaceous and woody plants.
Approximate conversions between currencies shown in brackets.
One 'currency unit' taken to be equivalent to UK£3.00 or US$5.00.

Plant	Type	Current average prices per plant *ex* laboratory		
		Currency units	UK£ (1995)	US$ (1995)
Herbaceous plants				
Nephrolepis		(0.04–0.06)	0.12–0.18†	(019–0.29)
Anthurium	Types grown in pots	(0.067)	0.20†	(0.32)
	Types grown for cut flower production	(0.18)	0.55†	(0.88)
Lilium longiflorum	Plantlets or bulblets	(0.03)	0.09†	(0.14)
Lilium	Asiatic types	(0.04)	0.12†	(0.19)
Dendranthema grandiflorum	Virus–free chrysanthemums (large numbers)	(0.05)	0.15†	(0.24)
	Virus–free plants (small numbers *i.e.* 100–200)	(0.167)	0.50†	(0.80)
Orchids	Small numbers of flask-grown seedlings (6–10 cm leaf span)	(0.833)	(2.50)	4.00‡
Cymbidium	Mericloned (depending on variety stage etc.)	(0.17–0.40)	0.50–1.20†	(0.80–1.92)
Woody plants				
Rosa	Rose plantlets depending on size, variety and stage	(0.093–0.12)	0.28–0.35†	(0.45–0.56)
Rhododendron	From agar	(0.073–0.12)	0.22–0.30†	(0.35–0.48)
	Weaned in plugs (depending on variety)	(0.15–0.33)	0.45–0.65†	(0.72–1.04)
Prunus	Weaned in plugs	(0.24)	0.73†	(1.17)
Pyrus communis	Weaned in plugs	(0.27)	0.80†	(1.28)

† Estimates kindly provided by Mr. A.C. Brown of Plant Resources and Marketing.

‡ Kindly provided by John Ewing Orchids.

Table 130. A comparison of the occupancy and labour requirement for propagating 10 000 Boston ferns or *Saintpaulia* plants *in vitro*, or conventionally in a greenhouse.
[After Theiler-Hedtrich and Theiler-Hedtrich, 1979.]

Plant	Occupancy		Labour	
	Conventional propagation (greenhouse)	Tissue culture (growth room and greenhouse)	Conventional propagation (greenhouse)	Tissue culture (growth room and greenhouse)
	m^2 weeks	m^2 weeks	hours	hours
Boston fern	434.6	14.7	2 120	170.8
Saintpaulia‡	120.9	54.6	13.2	137.8

‡ Compare the cost per plant of *Saintpaulia* with that indicated in Table 126.

culture or by conventional methods. Boston ferns can only be multiplied slowly without tissue culture, and the necessary manual labour and greenhouse occupancy makes plants much more expensive than those produced by micropropagation (Table 130). As can be seen from the table, with *Saintpaulia* the situation is more problematic: although greenhouse occupancy is greater than growth room utilisation, very little time needs to be spent on multiplication, whereas tissue cultured plants are only produced by time–consuming manipulations.

Swartz and Lindstrom (1986) calculated that strawberry plants cost 2–7 times more to produce by micropropagation than plants obtained from runners but, despite this, plants derived from tissue cultures continue to be sold where new varieties need to be rapidly multiplied rapidly, or where disease free foundation stock is required.

Current prices

Examples of the prices quoted in 1995 for some micropropagated plants are given in Table 129 (the conversion to 'currency units' being intended to make the figures have a wider and more lasting value). In some cases, where the cultivar being propagated is new and been

registered under Plant Breeders' Rights, a royalty is payable on top of the prices shown. The price per plant depends on its genus (*i.e.* how easily and at at what effort it can be micropropagated), the number of plantlets ordered and, to a lesser extent, the value of the product to the purchaser. The prices shown in Table 129 correspond with the average cost of micropropagated plants in Europe, which was estimated in 1990 to be *ca.* 0.08 currency units (page 793).

It is interesting to compare the prices in the table with the cost of pre–germinated seedlings of garden flowers which have begun to be offered by mail order by certain seed companies in the United Kingdom during recent years (Table 131). The similarity in prices suggests there should be an opportunity for selling finished micropropagated plants by mail order, but Barnhill Jones and Sluis (1991) reported that an attempt to sell small rose plants by this means in the U.S.A. was not successful.

Plants from somatic embryos

In considering the use of somatic embryos as an economic vehicle for vegetative propagation, one is often making

Table 131. The 1994 mail-order retail per plant prices to gardeners of pre-germinated seedlings and plug–grown plants of popular ornamentals.

Plant	Seedlings in trays				Larger plants in plugs		
	Size	Currency units (see Table 120)	UK£ pence	US$ cents equivalent	Currency units (see Table 120)	UK£ pence	US$ cents equivalent
Begonia semperflorens F$_1$	Small sized	0.0139	4.17	6.95	0.0640–0.07095*	19.2–21.3*	32.0–35.5*
	Large sized	0.0355	10.65	17.75			
Impatiens F$_1$	Small sized	0.0355	10.65	17.75	0.0676–0.0748*	20.3–22.4	33.8–37.4
Petunia F$_1$		0.0288	8.64	14.40	0.0640–0.0710*	19.2–21.3*	32.0–35.5*

* Depending on the quantity ordered

comparisons with the cost of plants raised from seed or, in the case of encapsulated somatic embryos, with the cost of seeds themselves. The seeds of plants are not only well designed to produce new seedlings, they usually do so reliably. Most can be stored without loss of viability for long periods, and those of very many species, are produced in large numbers and can be harvested at low cost. Some examples of the prices of individual seeds are given in Table 132.

Providing there is no genetic variation amongst the offspring, many researchers have proposed that the cost of micropropagated plants could be most effectively reduced if they were raised from somatic embryos instead of axillary shoots. This has been especially suggested as a method for multiplying forest trees where large numbers of plants are required, but where seedlings cost very little. However, those plants at present produced *via* embryogenesis are not necessarily obtained more cheaply than their equivalents produced from seed. In 1984, Wooi estimated that the cost of producing an individual oil palm plantlet at the 3–4 leaf stage by tissue culture, was about 5 Malaysian dollars, and therefore about 5 times the price asked for a seedling of comparable size. At that time the potential benefit from planting clones of selected plants *was* thought to make the extra cost worthwhile.

Encapsulated somatic embryos

If somatic embryos are to be used as replacements for true seeds, the reliability with which new plants are obtained and the price of those plantlets, must be similar. An estimate of the probable cost of producing encapsulated somatic embryos which could be used as an alternative to true seeds, was given by Redenbaugh *et al.* (1987b). In that year, true seeds of alfalfa were found to be priced at U.S.$ 0.00066 cents each, while encapsulated somatic embryos of this crop plant would have cost U.S.$ 0.026 cents each (*i.e.* 39 times as much).

Although the technology has not progressed sufficiently to provide a means of multiplying such field crops, it could be competitive for seeds which are more difficult to produce and which consequently have a high value, where a superior genotype can only be reproduced vegetatively, and where a clone is of greater economic value than sexually produced genotypes. Seeds of F_1 hybrid vegetables are the most obvious example (Table 132). Gardeners are willing to pay as much as 18 U.S. cents (1995) for a single F_1 *Capsicum* seed (which suggests a production cost of about U.S.$ 5–6 cents per seed).

Table 132. The cost of individual seeds of some field crops, vegetables and garden ornamentals.

Plant		Cost per seed	
Latin name	Common name	Currency units (see Table 120)	US cents 1994
Capsicum F_1 (retail packet of seed)	Sweet pepper	0.04	18.0
Daucus carota (retail packet of seed)	Carrot	0.00022	0.10
Hordeum sativum	Barley	0.0000044	0.002
Impatiens F_1	Busy Lizzie	0.039	17.7
Lactuca sativa (retail packet of seed)	Lettuce	0.000083	0.038
Medicago sativa	Alfalfa	0.0000024	0.0008–0.0011
Triticum aestivum	Wheat	0.0000024	0.0011
Zea mays	Corn	0.00024	0.11
Glycine max	Soybean	0.000018	0.008

MICROPROPAGATION BUSINESS

Spectrum of business activity

Micropropagation techniques are used primarily by businesses offering plants for general sale. Such businesses are of several kinds. There are firstly those concentrating solely on micropropagation and the sale of plant material or small plants to nurseries and growers:

- **Businesses selling the immediate products of the laboratory only.** There are no greenhouse facilities for transferring plants to soil and cultures are sold in vessels at any stage, together with unrooted microcuttings and plantlets which have been rooted *in vitro*.

  Small micropropagation businesses of this kind have little capacity to hold plants in reserve and are therefore dependent on a continuous succession of orders. Some larger laboratories have been set up to multiply plants of a single kind, *e.g.* date palms, oil palms, woody ornamentals.

- **Businesses with a laboratory and associated greenhouse facilities.** Products can be the same as those sold by laboratories without greenhouse facilities, but it is common to concentrate on the sale of rooted acclimatized plants.

  The larger micropropagation laboratories are often of this kind, and concentrate wherever possible on *ex vitro* rooting and the sale of acclimatized plants in plugs and liners.

Micropropagation laboratories have also been established by businesses which primarily use the plants produced internally:

- **Existing nursery businesses.** The laboratory may sell some plant material to customers, but the majority is passed to the nursery side of the business where it is sold later at any stage of growth from plugs to mature plants.

- **Plant breeders.** Some large plant breeding companies have tissue culture facilities, which are used to propagate specific lines used in breeding programmes. These laboratories often also use pollen and anther culture as a step towards producing homozygous parental lines. Companies engaged in genetic engineering of plants (which nowadays includes many plant breeding companies), apply micropropagation techniques in the regeneration and multiplication of genetically transformed material.

Total size of the business

It is very difficult to keep track of commercial laboratories on a worldwide basis, so no really accurate estimates are available of the number of plants produced each year through micropropagation. In the 1970's and 1980's many new laboratories were set up in the U.S.A. and Western Europe. Laboratories propagating orchids then became established in Asia, and now the micropropagation of a wide range of plants has been started in Eastern Europe and Asia, while the number of businesses operating in Western Europe and the U.S.A. has declined.

Some idea of the number of plants thought to be produced annually from *in vitro* cultures is given in Table 133.

The figures published in the table are not up to date and so the total of micropropagated plants now sold worldwide each year is likely to have increased in the interim. Perhaps a 25% increase in the numbers of plants produced in the U.S.A. and Western Europe might be conjectured between 1988 and 1994? There are two reasons for a cautious projection for these geographical regions: firstly there has been an economic recession on both continents during the period, and secondly a proportion of production has moved to countries with lower wage costs.

An extensive analysis of the extent and nature of micropropagation in Europe was published by Pierik (1990). The survey which relates to the year 1988 suggests that the figures given by Chu and Kurtz (1990) (in Table 133) for the size of the European micropropagation business may have been considerably underestimated. Pierik's survey showed that 212 million plants were produced in Europe in 1988 from a total of 248 laboratories, including plant breeding companies which normally propagate a small number of plants each year. The COST 87 (a European co–operative programme, Ó Ríordáin, 1992) 1990 survey showed 181.2 million plants from 180 laboratories. Out of the total, most of the laboratories surveyed were small, but 37 (Pierik), and 39 (Ó Ríordáin) acknowledged producing 1 million or more plants annually. The possible decline in the number of Western European laboratories is reflected in the 1993 COST Directory (which has omitted some businesses which were in existence at that time), where only 170 commercial laboratories are recorded (Ó Ríordáin, 1994).

Table 133. The extent of world business in commercial micropropagation (largely based on surveys carried out in 1988).

World region	No. commercial laboratories	Annual production (millions)	Principal crops	References
North America		84.7	Pot plants	Chu and Kurtz (1990)
	ca. 100	*ca.*75	Foliage pot plants, woody plants	Zimmerman and Barnhill Jones (1991)
Western Europe	248	212.5	Pot plants, Plants grown for cut flowers	Pierik (1991a)
		66.5		Chu and Kurtz (1990)
		181.2	Ornamentals, *Prunus*, fruit trees (1990)	Ó Ríordáin (1992)
Eastern Europe	162*	15–23*	Foliage plants, cut flowers	Hempel and Debergh (1991)
Asia		55.7		Chu and Kurtz (1990)
	105	76	Orchids, plants grown for cut flowers	Gavinlertvatana & Prutpongse (1991)
Australia and New Zealand	20–25	*ca.* 82	Ornamentals, foliage plants and plants grown for cut flowers.	Barlass (1991)
Latin America	15–20†	—	Largely ornamentals ?	Handro and Chaverra (1991)
TOTALS	650–660	299.2–482.7		

* Information imprecise. Many small laboratories were previously government supported.

† Only imprecise information available.

Accurate data on the output of commercial micropropagation laboratories is difficult to obtain and compile, because when invited to give details of the actual numbers of plants produced, some laboratories decline to answer. Others present an optimistic picture, suggesting that they are larger and more productive than really is the case; or giving production capacity, rather than the actual numbers of plants actually sold in the market place.

Zimmerman and Barnhill Jones (1991) estimated that in 1989–1990 there were probably no more than 100 laboratories (including orchid laboratories) in the U.S.A. but these had a total production capacity of more than 150 million plants. Less than half the capacity appeared to be realised so that the total annual output was probably *ca.* 70–75 million plants. Out of all the laboratories, 5 were responsible for the half of the plants produced annually by micropropagation in the U.S.A., while another 8–10 were responsible for 25–30%. The remaining 80–85 laboratories were therefore quite small.

In 1988 in the U.S.A., the most widely micropropagated plants were those which would be grown for sale as pot ornamentals; *e.g. Sygonium*, ferns and *Spathiphyllum* (Chu and Kurtz, 1990). Most of the plants produced through micropropagation in Europe are also destined to be sold eventually as pot plants. This category includes (in approximate order of numbers produced each year) such plants as ferns (*Nephrolepis, Davallia*), *Saintpaulia, Ficus, Anthurium, Spathiphyllum, Syngonium* and orchids. Plants which will be grown in nurseries to provide cut flowers are also produced in large numbers, especially *Gerbera* daisies.

Of the Eastern European countries, Poland has been most to the fore in supplying micropropagated plants; *ca.* 15 million were produced in 1988 (Hempel and Debergh, 1991).

Turnover. The total turnover of the micropropagation industry worldwide can be estimated by multiplying the number of plants produced annually, by an average price per plant. In 1990, Ó Ríordáin (1992) placed the mean price per plant at 0.3 ECU (*ca.* 0.08 currency units — see page 762), making the worth of total sales of plants micropropagated in Europe to be more than 54 million ECU. Using a mean selling price of 0.08–0.09 currency units, the total turnover of micropropagation businesses worldwide can be estimated to be in the region of 40 million currency units (presently equal to *ca.* UK£m120 or U.S.$m200).

REDUCING THE COST OF MICROPROPAGATION

As mentioned on page 762, the opportunities for micropropagation would increase many-fold if it were possible to provide clones at less cost than is presently possible. The high cost of labour associated with shoot and node culture has led research workers to automate some of the necessary operations and to search for less labour–intensive solutions, for it is only by improving existing techniques or designing new methods of multiplication, that production costs can be reduced. Although the problem has been appreciated for many years now (Stokes, 1981) and some experimental systems have been developed, as far as we know none has been fully successful.

Costs could be reduced in several ways:

- systems used at present might be improved so that plantlets can be produced at less cost;

    This might be achieved by increasing the rate at which material can be multiplied, and/or reducing the labour costs. Some cultural steps which are necessary at present might be eliminated or operations which are carried out by hand, might be automated.

- new large scale techniques might be developed;

    The objective would be to find new approaches to micropropagation, capable of delivering high rates of multiplication from facilities which were less costly per unit of production.

IMPROVING PRESENT TECHNIQUES

Photoautotrophic growth

Photoautotrophic growth has been discussed in Part 1 (page 204 *et seq.*) and on page 697. As the addition of sugar to the medium is unnecessary when cultures are photoautotrophic, problems of contamination are much reduced or eliminated. This should permit the use of large vessels, facilitating mechanical handling and automation. The use of photoautotrophic cultures should therefore assist large scale micropropagation. Techniques seem to be only applicable to cultures at Stages II and III, bearing shoots with green leaves. The growth of small explants, morphogenesis and embryogenesis are best conducted in the presence of sugar.

To achieve photoautotrophic growth, cultures must be subjected to light of high photon fluence. This means that running costs are high if the light is provided from artificial sources. Natural daylight can be used, but then control of other aspects of the environment can be difficult. Maintaining vessels at an acceptable temperature also presents particular problems and is a source of additional cost.

Using autotrophic growth in micropropagation

Work is progressing at several laboratories to investigate the possibility of propagating plants *in vitro* on media devoid of sucrose.

For this purpose, CO_2 in the atmosphere is usually increased so that it is at least double the normal ambient level (*ca.* 350 v.p.m.; 350 μmol mol^{-1} — Part 1, page 203). Aitken–Christie *et al.* (1992) found that it was beneficial to add activated charcoal to the sugar–free medium on which *Pinus radiata* shoots were grown. The growth rate of shoots decreases within tightly sealed vessels as carbon dioxide is utilized during photosynthesis, and so it essential to employ vessels in which gases can be freely exchanged: for example, vessels may be made from a gas permeable material; covered with a microporous film (Kozai *et al.*, 1991); or have a microporous membrane incorporated into the lid (Davies *et al.*, 1992).

Although it has been suggested that production costs could be significantly reduced by adopting autotrophic growth techniques for micropropagation (Kozai, 1989), work on photoautotrophic growth *in vitro* is still at the experimental stage. Fujiwara *et al.* (1988) designed an apparatus for growing shoots and plantlets autotrophically at the rooting and acclimatization stages with which enhanced growth of strawberry plantlets could be demonstrated. Kozai and co–workers (Kozai 1989, 1991a,b; Kozai *et al.*, 1991) have obtained rapid growth of *Cymbidium*, potato, carnation and strawberry by culturing these plants in media without sucrose, by providing CO_2 enrichment and light of high PPF. *Theobroma cacao* shoots do not grow and proliferate readily in culture, but Figueira *et al.* (1991) found that CO_2 enrichment (20 000 p.p.m.) and high PPF (150–200 μmol m^{-2} s^{-1}) encouraged shoot elongation and leaf development of shoots and microcuttings, and enhanced rooting, so that a system for rapid micropropagation became feasible.

Mechanisation and automation

The preparation and dispensing of media

Chapter 10 of Part 1 describes only the preparation of small quantities of medium and has been criticised by one

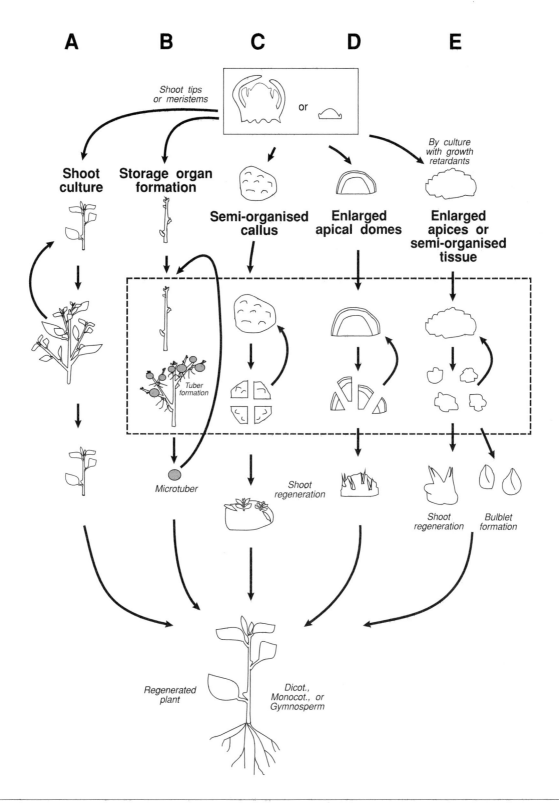

Fig.146. Possible routes to mass propagation — 1. Methods based on preserving the integrity of meristems, and therefore least likely to result in genetic variation.
Stages enclosed within dotted lines might be carried out in liquid media.

used for shoot cultures or the direct regeneration of shoots.

However, there are many reports of Stage II shoot cultures being carried out in a liquid medium, either in a thin layer of static medium, or in a shaken flask. Examples of the latter are given in Table 134, and illustrate that liquid culture of many species is possible using intermittent immersion. When explants are grown in small flasks of liquid media which are shaken, or in vessels placed on an apparatus which causes them to be intermittently immersed, growth and the rate of shoot proliferation can be more rapid than on a semi–solid substrate (Part 1, page 191). Lal and Ahuja (1993) found that, compared to propagating shoots of *Rheum emodi* on a semi–solid medium, agitated liquid culture required 50% less medium and caused there to be a 1.5–2.2 fold increase in the rate of shoot growth and multiplication. The time required to handle cultures was also reduced by 38%. With such advantages, the use of liquid medium for large scale shoot culture should perhaps be more carefully considered. Perhaps its employment requires the development of different apparatus?

Directly formed shoots and storage organs

Direct shoot formation. Adventitious shoots, formed directly from explants, are used for the micropropagation of plants from which this type of regeneration occurs readily. In some of these species, shoot multiplication can be carried out in an agitated liquid medium (Table 135). High rates of shoot formation in shaken liquid medium were described by Takayama and Misawa for *Begonia ×hiemalis* (1981; 1982b,c), *Saintpaulia* and *Gloxinia* (1982c). Leaf segments bearing newly–initiated shoots were transferred to flasks of liquid medium maintained on a rotary shaker at 180 r.p.m. to induce rapid shoot growth. Shoots were moved to an agar medium for rooting. According to Takayama (1990), liquid culture is most useful in *Begonia* to enhance the growth of pre–formed buds. The lack of polarity in agitated liquid medium causes many more buds to grow than would normally develop, and the liquid medium, with high aeration, causes the rate of shoot growth to be much greater than it would have been on agar.

Problems which might be experienced by using direct shoot regeneration in a liquid medium are similar to those experienced with shoot tip cultures. In addition, it can be difficult to prevent some shoots arising from callus and thus being liable to display somaclonal variation. Where

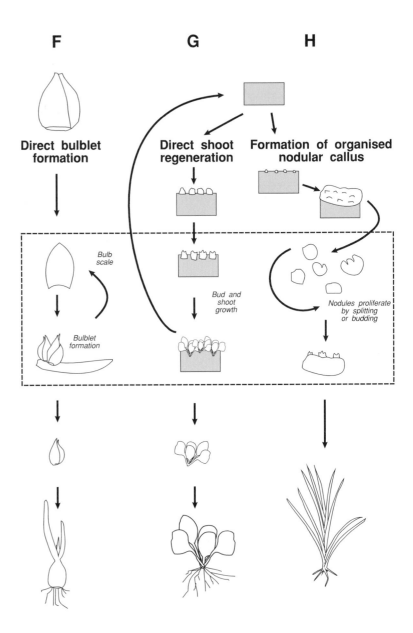

Fig. 147. Possible routes to mass propagation
— 2. Using direct adventitious shoot formation.
Stages enclosed within dotted lines might be carried out in liquid media.

hyperhydricity is a problem, a liquid culture phase can be reserved for the multiplication of shoot buds: shoot and leaf growth should then be carried out in conditions where vitrescence is less likely to occur. As with shoot cultures, excellent shoot regeneration and growth can be obtained where explants are bathed in a liquid medium intermittently (Stevenson *et al.*, 1982).

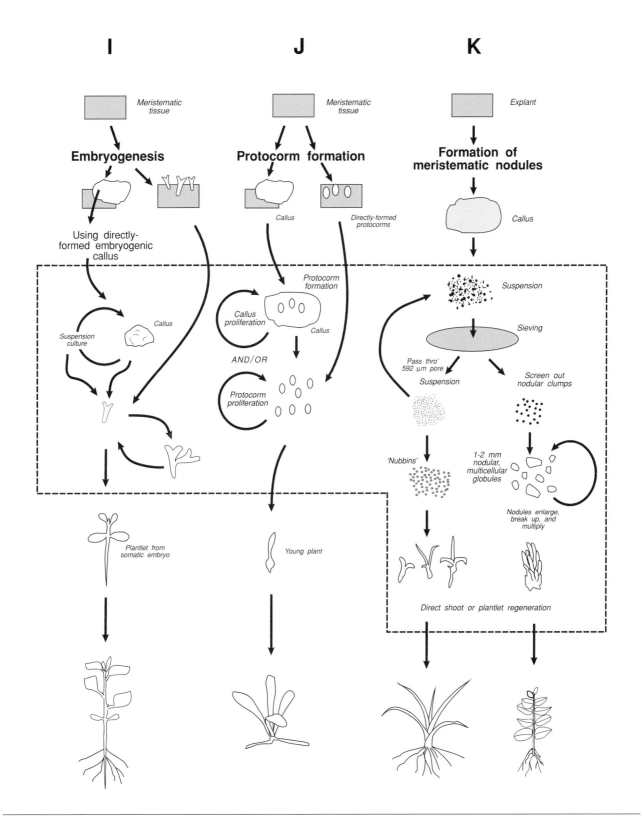

Fig. 148. Possible routes to mass propagation — 3. Using embryogenesis, protocorms (in orchids), and meristematic nodules.
Genetic variation is most likely to occur where the growth of unorganised cells or tissues precedes morphogenesis. For this reason indirect embryogenesis has been omitted as a recommended method: for the same reason, the indirect formation of meristematic nodules illustrated here, could give problems.
Stages enclosed within dotted lines might be carried out in liquid media.

Table 134. Examples of shoot cultures carried out in liquid media.

Plant	Stage	Results	Type of culture	Reference
Amelanchier alnifolia	II	Shoot proliferation	Rocked vessels, with little medium	Harris and Mason (1983)
Amorphophallus rivieri	II	Axillary shoot proliferation	Shake culture	Asokan *et al.* (1984c)
Arctostaphylos uva ursi	II	Shoot proliferation	Rocked vessels, with little medium	Stevenson *et al.* (1982) Harris and Mason (1983)
Chrysanthemum morifolium	II	Axillary shoot growth	Rotary shaker 180 r.p.m.	Takayama and Misawa (1982c)
Colocasia esculenta	I, II	Axillary shoot proliferation	Reciprocating shaker 60 r.p.m.	Jackson *et al.* (1977a)
Dianthus caryophyllus	II	Axillary shoot growth	Rotary shaker 180 r.p.m.	Takayama and Misawa (1982c)
Aechmea fasciata	I	Establishment	1 r.p.m.	Jones and Murashige (1974) Murashige (1974)
	II	Shoot proliferation	Stationary liquid	
Elettaria cardamomum	II	Formation of axillary shoots	Agitated	Priyadarshan and Zachariah (1986)
Eucalyptus spp.	II	Shoot proliferation	Rotary shaker, 120 r.p.m.	Gupta *et al.* (1981) Mascarenhas *et al.* (1982a,b)
	IIIa	Shoot elongation	Rotary shaker	Gupta *et al.* (1983)
Fuchsia hybrida	II	Multiple shoots	Flasks tilted to 35° every 30 seconds	Stevenson and Harris (1980)
		Shoot proliferation	Rocked vessels, with little medium	Harris and Mason (1983)
Myrtus communis	II	Shoots from shoot tips	Agitated	Uhring (1983)
Oxalis tuberosa	II	Multiple shoots	Shaken 60 r.p.m.	Estrada *et al.* (1986b)
Photinia serrulata	II	Shoot proliferation	Flasks tilted to 35° every 30 seconds	Harris and Stevenson (1979, 1982)
Pieris japonica	II	Shoot proliferation	Flasks tilted to 35° every 30 seconds	Harris and Stevenson (1979, 1982)
Prunus persica	II	Shoot multipliation	Roller drum	Hammerschlag (1981a)
Rheum emodi	II	Multiple shoots	Agitated (80)–120 r.p.m.	Lal and Ahuja (1989; 1993)
Schlumbergera spp.	II	Shoot proliferation	Rotated	Johnson *et al.* (1976)
Solanum tuberosum	II	Axillary shoot growth	Shaken 60 r.p.m.	Estrada *et al.* (1986a)
Tropaeolum tuberosum	II	Multiple shoots	Shaken 60 r.p.m.	Estrada *et al.* (1986)
Ullucus tuberosus	II	Multiple shoots	Shaken 60 r.p.m.	Estrada *et al.* (1986)
Vitis hybrid	II	Shoot proliferation	Rocked vessels, with little medium	Harris and Mason (1983)
Vitis vinifera	II	Shoot proliferation	Flasks tilted to 35° every 30 seconds	Harris and Stevenson (1979, 1982)

suspension as 1–5 mm cell clumps which increased in number by breakage, due to agitation. Each group of cells possessed an epidermis–like layer, and when transferred to a solidified medium, produced shoot buds which could be grown into fully developed plants (Nagasawa and Finer, 1988).

Enlarged apical domes

Enlarged apical domes may be of greater potential for large scale culture than nodules. Wakizuka and Yamaguchi (1987) obtained such structures by culturing shoot meristems from germinating caryopses of *Eleusine coracana*. Whereas normal shoot meristems have a diameter of 70–80 μm, those obtained grew to 5–10 mm and could be cut into pieces and subcultured. The abnormal apices, which had an organised structure, could be divided and subcultured or induced to form numerous buds.

The use of growth retardants. Methods for inducing the formation of the type of domes observed by Wakizuka and Yamaguchi (1987) have not been reported for other plants, but a technique has been published by which similar structures can be produced predictably. Hyperhydricity is caused by the culture of leafy tissue in liquid media, and Ziv (1989, 1990, 1992) has found that the addition of growth retardants to a culture medium can reduce or prevent leaf development, and cause the induction of compact bud aggregates or meristemoids which do not become vitrescent.

Ziv (1992) has also discovered that adding paclobutrazol to liquid media to induce the proliferation of compact bud clusters or meristemoids, results in the plantlets ultimately obtained having enhanced wax formation and normal stomatal function during the hardening stage.

By culturing buds of *Gladiolus*, *Nerine* and *Brodiaea* or *Philodendron* in a liquid medium containing a growth retardant, the explants proliferated and produced large bud aggregates, protocorm–like bodies, or organogenic cell clusters, without leaves. Subculture to media without retardants resulted in further proliferation of the bud aggregates, or production of plantlets or cormlets or bulblets.

The preferred growth retardants in these experiments were 1–2.5 mg/l paclobutrazol or 0.5–2 mg/l ancymidol, but similar results were obtained by Ziv (1989) with 2.5 mg/l daminozide or 1 mg/l uniconazole. Leaf development from the apical buds of *Crocus sativus* was suppressed if the corms from which buds were excised had been pre–treated with ethylene, or immersed in 1000 mg/l ethephon for one hour. This resulted in the formation of many small axillary buds which developed into corms (Plessner *et al.*, 1990).

Embryogenic callus

Embryogenic tissue is readily cultured suspended in liquid media and is therefore highly suitable for large–scale plant propagation. Relatively little genetic variation seems to occur amongst plants produced from somatic embryos if they have originated from directly initiated embryogenic callus, or suspensions derived therefrom. The production of embryos from previously 'unorganised' callus is not preferred, as regenerated plants are more likely to show genetic variation.

Direct embryo formation and proliferation

We know of no examples where the proliferation of secondary embryos in liquid medium having been used as a method for routine propagation. However, the orchid protocorm is a type of meristematic nodule (usually considered as a pro–embryo — Part 1, page 56) which proliferates *in vitro* and gives rise to populations of plantlets which, in the main, are genetically homogeneous.

There are many examples of protocorm formation and proliferation in liquid media (page 924) and propagation can be conducted on a large scale by this means. Pieper and Zimmer (1976b) described an apparatus for multiplying *Cymbidium* protocorms: Cheng and Chua (1980, 1982) cultured *Anthera* and *Dendrobium* in a bubble column bioreactor in which rates of callus and protocorm proliferation were much greater than on a static medium.

Orchid shoot tips were grown satisfactorily in an intermittent immersion bioreactor by Tisserat and Vandercook (1985, 1986) (see below) and produced a greater amount of tissue or axillary shoots than on agar medium.

Higuchi *et al.* (1987) have obtained the production of 'green globular bodies' from several fern genera by culturing runner tips or rhizome sections on medium containing BAP as the only regulant (see page 913). It has been proposed that these structures represent aggregates of shoot primordia (Higuchi *et al.*, 1987), or are similar to orchid protocorms (the fern equivalent of somatic embryos?) (Higuchi and Amaki, 1989). The nodular appearance of green globular bodies and their possession of an epidermal layer suggest that they can be included under our heading of 'calloid' tissues.

Green globular bodies of ferns proliferate in the presence of BAP, but shoot development is inhibited until the tissue is subcultured onto medium without growth regulators, or one containing a low concentration of auxin. The rate of multiplication of green globular bodies has been found to vary in different fern genera, but in *Nephrolepis* it is suitable for commercial propagation (Amak and Higuchi, 1991).

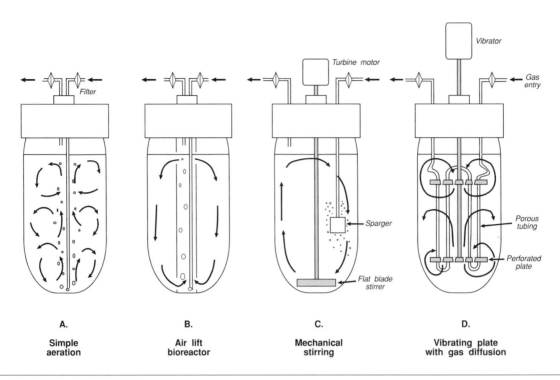

Fig. 149. Four kinds of bioreactor which might be used for micropropagtion.

Bioreactors

The vessels used for culturing plant cells, tissues or organs in liquid medium on a large scale are termed *bioreactors*, and sometimes fermentors (Goldstein *et al.*, 1980; Martin, 1980), or fermenters (King and Street, 1977) by analogy with the large vessels used for the growth of bacteria (Street, 1977a). Many descriptions relate to apparatus for the culture of plant cell suspensions, usually for the production of secondary metabolites of economic value; bioreactors intended for plant propagation are usually smaller (1–5 litres, but occasionally up to 50 litres). If an effective protocol has been developed, it should be possible to produce at least 0.2–0.4 million somatic embryos in a 2 litre vessel. Lutz *et al.* (1985) obtained 5000 carrot embryos per ml of suspension.

The larger the size of a bioreactor and its associated components, the more complex will be the sterilisation routine. Hale *et al.* (1992) thought the following criteria were important in plant bioreactor design:

– All components should be fully autoclavable;

– the growth chamber should be transparent for adequate light transmission and visibility;

– materials should ideally be more breakage resistant than glass;

– components should be easily assembled and disassembled for cleaning;

– there should be the minimum number of openings to avoid contamination.

In all cases a major factor in design is the need to supply the cultures with adequate oxygen in such a way that cells, tissues or organs are not damaged. When the plant material is to be totally immersed in liquid medium, the culture is usually agitated by mechanical means or by the upward passage of air, or oxygen. Mechanical agitation can be provided by magnetic stir bars; by turbines with propeller blades, or flat blades set at an angle; or by vibrating perforated plates (Fig. 149, **C** and **D**).

Most bioreactor chambers are constructed from glass or rigid plastic. If they are to be filled with liquid medium, they must be strong enough to withstand the weight, pressure and turbulence of their contents. Where thin layers of liquid are used to replace a semi–solid medium, containers can be less robust. Pâques *et al.* (1992) describe using a large translucent plastic bag which is cheaper than conventional vessels.

Reactors giving complete submersion.

Several different types of bioreactor have been devised in which plant cells or tissues are completely submersed in liquid medium: four kinds are illustrated in Fig. 149. These apparatus have been principally used for the culture of cell suspensions, for which each has advantages and disadvantages. All four designs may be suitable for producing somatic embryos in suspension, but culture of nodular aggregates and plant organs presents a more difficult problem, because large structures are easily damaged by inappropriate agitation and may also accumulate in one part of the apparatus or clump together and impede efficient circulation.

Most accounts in the literature of large scale organ culture in liquid media, describe nothing beyond the use of small flasks which have been agitated on an orbital shaker. Bubble or airlift reactors (**A** and **B** in Fig. 149) may be suitable alternatives for large–scale production. However the design of suitable apparatus to scale–up the culture of large fragments of plant tissue is no easy task; each kind of organ, and each kind of plant may require a different approach.

Oxygen supply. Compressed air, oxygen, or a controlled mixture of gases, is bubbled into the base of air lift bioreactors and many mechanically agitated ones. Air is normally supplied at the rate of 0.025–2 v.v.m. (volume of air supplied per volume of medium per minute). When cell suspensions are aerated by this means, particularly if a rapid rate of agitation is also employed, foam may accumulate on the top of the culture as bubbles bring cellular material to the surface. Cells then aggregate in the foam layer, forming an undesirable callus–like crust, and also adhere to the sides of the vessel above the medium. These cells do not receive an adequate supply of nutrients.

There have been numerous approaches to overcoming the problem of foaming (Taticek *et al.*, 1991). They include modifying the air supply so that bubble size is changed; sieving and rinsing the inoculum before beginning the culture to remove single cells, cell debris and the contents of broken cells (Teng *et al.*, 1993); isolating the aeration area from the inoculum (Teng *et al.*, 1993); adding a non–toxic anti–foaming agent; or introducing oxygen by diffusion through gas–porous tubing suspended in the medium (Bioreactor **D** in Fig. 149)(Preil, 1991).

As organs, or organ fragments, grow and proliferate in a bubble or airlift bioreactor, it is necessary to increase the rate of air flow to ensure continued circulation. This can cause problems. In *Gladiolus*, Ziv (1990) and co–workers found that bud and calloid aggregates became necrotic when the aeration rate was increased to 1 v.v.m., probably because of the vigorous agitation. That it can be important to provide supplementary carbon dioxide in the air stream, has been mentioned on page 647.

Reviews of bioreactor design. The design of bioreactors for plant cell and organ culture has been discussed by Martin (1980), Cazzulino *et al.* (1991), Preil (1991), Preil and Beck (1991), Styer (1985) and Veliky and Martin (1970). Ritterhaus *et al.* (1990) describe pilot plant tests of fermentor tanks with up to 75 000 litres capacity, intended for culturing plant cells for the extraction of secondary products. Engineering considerations for the construction of bioreactors have been reviewed by Taticek *et al.* (1991).

Reactors mimicking normal culture vessels

A layer of liquid medium can be used where it is desired closely to reproduce the conditions existing inside small culture vessels filled with semi–solid medium. The medium can be replenished at intervals, or circulated continuously. To anchor explants and stop them being submerged they can be placed on porous materials. Pâques *et al.*(1992) positioned *Pinus pinaster* cuttings on floating polycarbonate discs. To obtain embryogenesis from *Picea*, suspension cultured cells were immobilised on polyurethane foam. Embryo maturation in this plant does not normally occur until callus is placed on a semi–solid medium where there is good gas exchange. On the foam, 18 globular embryos were obtained per cm^2 compared to only 11 per cm^2 on agar.

Conifer embryos can be cultured in liquid suspensions but require a solution having a high partial pressure of oxygen during maturation. Because adding polyethylene glycol to the medium to induce moisture stress reduces the concentration of oxygen in the medium (page 711), Attree and Fowke (1993) matured white spruce embryos within a large chamber supported on a flat absorbent bed above the surface of a circulated liquid culture medium. Using this method it was possible to vary the osmotic potential of the medium while the air space could be controlled to provide an optimum gaseous environment. The alternative might have been to have suspended the embryos in a bioreactor in which the PEG solution was highly oxygenated, but this was found to lead to excessive foaming.

A bioreactor in which shoot hedges could be maintained on a circulated liquid medium was described on page 799. Several similar systems have been devised in which cultured material is supported on an inert substrate and fed with liquid medium. In the 'Agro–Clonics' system, the flow of liquid and gases was controlled through electronically–controlled pumps and valves (Farrell, 1987). Hale *et al.* (1992) have described culturing shoot clusters of *Begonia* and *Citrullus*, and leaf discs of tobacco, on Sigma membrane rafts, irrigated with static non–replenished, or continuously circulated medium. Fresh weight gains were better on liquid medium than on agar, especially when the liquid medium was circulated continuously through microbial filters. Watermelon shoots growing on liquid medium in these conditions still became hyperhydric.

Pâques (1991) describes growing shoots of an apple rootstock experimentally in large rigid or flexible containers. Explants were inserted on polyurethane wetted with liquid medium, and in later versions of the apparatus, a controlled atmosphere was introduced under slight positive pressure to assist in maintaining axenic conditions. Another computer controlled apparatus for introducing and removing liquid medium into large containers was devised by Simonton *et al.* (1991) and used for the culture of *Spathiphyllum* shoot cultures with a shallow layer of medium continuously present. A modification of the apparatus allowed the intermittent immersion of explants (Krueger *et al.*, 1991, see below).

Reactors giving intermittent immersion

Plant organs often grow well in shaken liquid medium; in vessels where liquid medium is pumped into a vessel to immerse, or partly immerse, the tissues, and then removed; and in vessels which are rolled, or rocked from end to end, so that the cultured material is wetted intermittently. A feature of these systems is that, compared to paddle stirred and airlift bioreactors, plant material is subjected to less shear stress and gaseous transfer is improved.

There is now an increasing body of results to show that shoot cultures can be grown with improved rates of growth and shoot proliferation when they are periodically immersed in a liquid medium. For example when *Amelanchier* × *grandiflora* shoots, planted into a supporting screen in 7 litre vessels, were immersed in liquid medium containing 4.4 µM BAP for 5 minutes in every 60 minutes, they showed stress during the first 21 days, but in a second 21 day period grew much more rapidly and produced many more axillary shoots than explants grown on agar in baby food jars. The interval between immersions was shown to be important; continuous contact with a liquid medium, or more frequent immersion of the shoots led to hyperhydricity (page 658).

The first apparatus to immerse plant tissues periodically, was devised by Steward *et al.* (1952) and called an 'auxophyton'. It consisted of several T–shaped tubes, each with two closed ends and a side neck in the centre through which inoculum was introduced. The tubes were rotated end over end. Because of their limited size, such 'tumble–tubes' tended to be replaced by nipple flasks (Part 1, page 7) of up to 1 litre capacity, which could contain a much larger number of explants (Steward and Shantz, 1956).

Apparatus for large–scale treatments. Tumble–tubes and nipple flasks have mainly been used for callus cultures. Harris and Mason (1983) devised two machines which could be used for micropropagation. They were designed to tilt, or rock, a large number of cheaply purchased vessels ranging in capacity from 50 to 910 ml to an angle of 30–40 degrees on each side of the vertical every 30 seconds. Only a small amount of liquid medium was placed in each vessel (*e.g.* 5 ml in a 50 ml Erlenmeyer flask, 50 ml in a 910 ml wide mouthed Mason home canning jar placed on its side). Using this system, the rate of growth and axillary shoot proliferation of 5 plants was much greater than when they were cultured continuously on an agar solidified medium. Small shoot tips could not be placed directly into liquid medium because they "appeared to drown": for the first 14–28 days of culture the explants were therefore grown on agar medium.

In an automated bioreactor designed by Tisserat and Vandercook (1985), liquid medium was pumped into a large container over a period of about 40 seconds, submerging tissues or organs, and then allowed to drain away over a period of 1–10 minutes. The immersion cycle was repeated several times a day, 12 times apparently being optimal for most species. The interval over which drainage took place did not affect results. Tissue growth or axillary shoot production was frequently greater in the bioreactor than in cultures grown on an identical agar medium.

A rotating drum bioreactor is a scaled up version of the auxophyton of Steward *et al.* A large drum or flask, only partly filled with medium and usually fitted with impeller blades, is rolled over and over at a slow speed. In *Cephaelis*, a larger number of adventitious shoots was obtained if internode segments were cultured in a 10 litre rotated drum fermentor equipped with a 'cell rotator' (Hario Co., Japan), rather than in an airlift reactor. The small number of shoots in the airlift apparatus was thought to be due to hydrodynamic stress (Yoshimatsu and Shimomura, 1991).

A bioreactor for producing microtubers. A patented bioreactor for producing potato microtubers which uses intermittent submergence is described in a following section (page 813).

The nutrient mist bioreactor

Aeroponic culture was mentioned on page 804. An aeroponic method more closely related to the reality of micropropagation was devised by Weathers and Giles (1987; Giles and Weathers, 1992) and provides an alternative method whereby cultures can be periodically moistened with medium. Tissues were placed aseptically onto a porous support such as filter paper, rockwool, or polyurethane foam, and wetted with the fine droplets of a nutrient mist. Spray droplets were generated ultrasonically by an electronic transducer immersed in a reservoir of medium outside the culture chamber, and the mist was introduced above the plants and distributed throughout the chamber by a stream of filtered air (although any desired gas mixture could be circulated). In another version of the same principle, the medium reservoir and mist generator were located within the culture vessel (Karata *et al.*, 1991). In both systems excess solution drained back to the reservoir.

Aeroponic culture in a bioreactor (at one time called a 'Mistifier') (Fox, 1980; Weathers *et al.*, 1988), has been reported to result in rapid shoot proliferation and good shoot extension of several plants. These attributes were better in *Musa, Cordyline*, and *Nephrolepis* when **MS** medium (containing 2% sucrose 1 mg/l BAP and 0.1 mg/l NAA) was sprayed, than when shoots were cultured on an agar medium (Weathers *et al.*, 1988). Other plants to give satisfactory growth have been *Brassica, Daucus, Ficus, Lycopersicon* (Weathers and Giles, 1988) and *Solanum* (Karata *et al.*, 1991).

The apparent ability to culture shoots without hyperhydricity, the ease with which the medium can be varied, and the apparent suitability of the apparatus for use in photoautotrophic conditions, makes aeroponic culture of interest for the scale up of micropropagation. Disadvantages for routine micropropagation could lie in the complexity of the apparatus. The difficulty of maintaining cultured material in an aseptic condition might be overcome by using a sugar–free medium in autotrophic conditions.

Contamination in bioreactors

One of the reasons why micropropagation has continued to be carried out for so long in relatively small containers, is that, with reasonable precautions, contamination can be contained and prevented from spreading. Cross contamination in bioreactors presents much greater problems, and it becomes necessary to take special precautions to ensure that the cultured material does not contain latent infections, or that contaminants are not introduced during operation.

Commercial propagation using bioreactors

As will be apparent from the preceding pages, the technology to permit large scale plant propagation using liquid media is still at an experimental stage and is not yet sufficiently reliable. Each of the pieces of apparatus so far devised has its disadvantages. Thus although there is

a great deal of interest in propagation using bioreactors, commercial applications have been slow to develop.

The large–scale production of bulbs

The production of bulbs in liquid media has been mentioned on page 806 and is discussed in Chapter 17. Work on lily bulbs has been most prominent and lilies can be propagated from bulb-scales by these techniques on a large scale.

Takahashi *et al.* (1992) recorded cultures grown in bubble fermentors, and in a rotated tank of up to 2000 litres capacity, stir driven with a paddle impeller. In both kinds of container, the speed of agitation had to be carefully controlled because, when it became excessive, the number of bulblets decreased, probably because the sites of bud initiation were damaged. To obtain the production of 2–2.5 bulblets per bulb scale it was necessary to maintain 40 p.p.m. dissolved oxygen. Using a medium containing ½**MS** macronutrients and 2% sucrose (initial water potential *ca.* –268 kPa or –2.6 atm), bulblets had a high water content and tended to become necrotic. The water potential was therefore lowered by adding sorbitol 12.5 or 40 g/l sorbitol to give an observed initial water potential of –4 or –7.5 atm (–405 or –760 kPa). This resulted in final water potentials of, respectively, –2.1 and –5.3 atm. under which conditions the water content of the bulblets was reduced, but their subsequent growth unimpaired. Bulblet formation and the size of the bulblets produced was increased, if during continuous culture over a six month period, the medium was replaced each time its concentration had been reduced by 50%.

The production of potato tubers

The large scale production of potato microtubers has been practised for several years and, as it can now be carried out in bioreactors, the cost of propagating virus–free stock should fall as commercial production increases.

Microtubers of potato can be produced in an airlift bioreactor (see page 1124 and Table 136), although it seems to be necessary to control the degree to which shoots are submerged at different cultural stages.

An alternative method for the large scale production of small tubers was described by McCown and Joyce (1991). It consists of a translucent cylinder about 60 cm long by 7.5 cm (diameter) into which liquid medium is inserted to occupy less than 10% of the volume. The cylinder is then slowly rotated on its horizontal axis. Potato shoots and microtubers were produced in this apparatus by appropriate changes of medium without any direct manual manipulations. Previously–produced microtubers were loaded into the vessel and gave rise to shoots, the apices of which were encouraged to become necrotic by culture on a medium low in calcium (see pages 653 and 654). Change to a medium which included adequate calcium induced the formation of lateral shoots, upon which miniature tubers were induced to form by a change in the cultural environment.

The 'Vitriomatic System'

The most ambitious attempt at large–scale micropropagation so far described in the literature is the 'Vitriomatic System' of Plant Biotech Industries in Israel (Levin, 1988; 1989). This consisted of a 10–50 litre bioreactor (for growth and/or morphogenesis), coupled to a bioprocessor (to separate and size propagules and distribute them to culture vessels). The bioprocessor was designed to work with both organogenic and embryogenic cultures (Levin *et al.*, 1988). To ensure that cultures did not become contaminated, the apparatus was contained in a clean room and operatives wore fully protective gowns and face masks.

Plants handled were those capable of direct morphogenesis, such as *Begonia, Saintpaulia*; potatoes and *Lilium* (capable of producing storage organs *in vitro*); ferns (capable of regenerating from macerated tissue); and several plants which were probably multiplied *via* somatic embryogenesis. Where propagation was based on shoot organogenesis, clusters of meristems were multiplied in a liquid medium, and then broken up by the processor into suitably sized pieces. These were dispensed into plastic matrices (Waters *et al.*, 1987) and placed into large culture boxes where plantlets developed (Levin *et al.*, 1988; Levin and Vasil, 1989). Hyperhydricity of leafy material was said to have been controlled in the bioreactors using a proprietary procedure, but some species were nevertheless susceptible (Aitken–Christie, 1991).

This kind of apparatus would appear to be suitable for producing plants from calloids and meristematic nodules (including those formed in the presence of growth retardants), in species where culture of these tissues is possible in liquid medium.

The Vitriomatic system was said to be capable of producing plantlets at a much lower cost than from micropropagation systems using small vessels and manual separation. Plantlets were transferred to soil by an automated transplanter (see below).

The large scale production of somatic embryos

So far only relatively few plants have been propagated commercially from somatic embryos; they include poinsettia, oil palm and date palm. The potential for multiplying other crops, particularly forest trees, by this means is very large, providing technical problems can be solved.

One of the problems preventing the use of somatic embryos is that they are seldom of uniform size or stage of development. Methods for maturing embryos and sorting them to obtain uniform batches are therefore important.

Somatic embryos might be planted into the soil directly or encapsulated (Chapter 14); or could be germinated, and the seedlings planted in plugs for later field delivery. Machines for field planting are available (see below) making plug–grown plants suitable for establishing high value crops.

Machines for field planting

Machines have been developed to assist the transplanting of seedlings into soil, or moving seedlings which have been planted in plugs into larger pots (Kutz *et al.*, 1987). Detection and handling seems to be easier to arrange with plugs than with individual seedlings. A machine for transplanting plugs was described by Ting and Giacomelli (1988). Aitken–Christie (1991) described a series of machines developed in Australia to commercial application, by which lettuce seeds were planted into small containers of soil, and the seedlings, graded for size, transplanted to larger containers. Devices such as this could be used for transplanting plants propagated by tissue culture. By raising plantlets at Stage III in separate cells of a plastic matrix, Plant Biotech Industries Ltd. succeeded in using a microprocessor–controlled transplanting machine to transfer the plantlets to nursery trays containing a soil mixture (Levin *et al.*, 1988; Levin and Vasil, 1989). Machines are commonly used for transplanting seedlings or plantlets into soil in the field. Seedlings can be bare rooted (as in the case of rice), and sometimes have been pre–grown in flats, cellular trays, or plugs (Brewer, 1991) as is usually the case with seedling trees.

PATENTS

The nature of patents

A patent is a grant entitling its owner to the exclusive right to make, use, or sell an invention during a limited period of time. Generally speaking, a patentable invention must comprise the whole or part of a machine, product or process which is capable of industrial application. Intellectual ideas and creations, such as scientific hypotheses, mathematical techniques and computer programs are not patentable unless they are an essential part of an apparatus or technique. Patents belong to their inventors but because, in most cases, inventors are employees bound by contracts of employment, ownership is usually assigned to an employer.

Before a patent is granted, it is necessary to convince examiners that the invention is unique and has not already been described, or covered by a previous patent application. Patents can also be revoked if it can be shown that their substance had been disclosed prior to filing. It is therefore essential not to disclose information in any form about inventions of commercial significance until a patent application has been made. Scientists in academic institutions often make the mistake of writing a paper about a discovery, only to realise at a later date that this has prejudiced a possible patent claim.

In the case of improvements to those methods of plant tissue culture which are already in widespread use, it may be difficult to prove that a discovery is not obvious in view of previous disclosures in the literature. Is it a unique discovery to show that methods which have already proved to be successful, can be extended to a further species (see for example Kawamura and Yamazaki, 1987; page 823) ? Is it possible to patent a medium for use on sunflowers which specifies commonly used vitamins, the preferred mixture of which was previously used by Gamborg in 1966 for *Glycine, Reseda* and *Solanum* (see Paterson, 1985; page 819) ?

Patents relating to plant tissue culture

During the last few years there have begun to be many published patents in the field of plant biotechnology and plant tissue culture. Those on plant tissue culture, as it relates to micropropagation, cover a number of areas which may be conveniently categorised in the following way:

- Methods of tissue culture and micropropagation. These may be either:
  - techniques which are generally applicable, or
  - ones related to specific crop plants.
- Patents on apparatus and equipment.
- Patents on equipment and techniques to enable scale–up and cost reduction in commercial micropropagation.

The subjects of some recent patents in these areas are summarised in Table 136. Look up their author/s in the bibliography to find patent numbers.

Patents on the industrial production of plant cells and the production and isolation of secondary plant products are outside the scope of the present book. A few patents on methods applicable to plant breeding and genetic engineering have come to light during searches for micropropagation patents. Although the list is not complete, they have been included to indicate the patenting activity in this area. The patents include:

- the use of tissue culture methods (and somaclonal variation resulting therefrom) as methods for plant improvement;
- methods for the genetic manipulation of plants;
- plants which have been altered through gene transfer.

Patent applications

A patent application is often filed first in the inventor's home country and, depending on the importance attached to the discovery and the regions of the world where protection is thought to be necessary, may then be filed separately in other individual countries or on an international basis. The date of first filing establishes a priority date for comparison with other claims, and for possible patents in other countries.

International filings, which are made by making an application through the European Patent Convention (EPC) or Patents Cooperation Treaty (PCT), can also be made directly. When an EPC patent application is made it is possible to designate in which of the 17 Western European countries contracted to the scheme, the patent should become effective. If a European patent is finally granted, patent rights will automatically be obtained in these countries. The process of making a PCT application is similar: following a single application in one language, the applicant may designate in which of the 53 participating countries the patent is desired, but each designated country then processes the application (although translations of the original application may be required at this stage).

Payments are required for the filing and examination of patent applications, and when patents are granted, for their maintenance. Thus, even though a patent has been granted, it may be allowed to lapse by non–payment of renewal fees once the first enthusiasm of the inventor, or his assignee, has waned and it is realised that little commercial return is likely to result by maintaining the claim. Patents also lapse at the end of their registered life, the length of which varies from country to country (currently 20 years from the date of filing in Europe).

In the case of inventions considered to be important, the original patent eventually becomes just the first of a family of patents with the same claim or claims. Thus although each invention in Table 136 is referenced to only one major patent application or patent, there will frequently be other applications or granted patents of the same nature. The European Patent No. 141373 (Redenbaugh, 1991b) granted to Plant Genetics, Inc. is one of 11 patents on the same subject applied for, or granted, in 14 countries. To discover the nature of other filings and the full history of this or other patents, it would be necessary to conduct a patent search. Searches are now possible using internationally–available databases.

The legal aspects of plant tissue culture patents were reviewed by Bagwill (1981).

Protecting processes

Patents are best suited to inventions which are likely to lead to the development of products, or processes leading directly to a distinct commercial product. They are not entirely satisfactory for the protection of techniques for improving routine tissue culture processes (such as a series of media and growth regulants for improving embryogenesis), unless it is believed that the new method will become the only economic way to propagate a plant, or the only economic method of obtaining a plant product which will be required on a large scale. Patents are published documents and therefore advertise the areas in which an organisation is working and the advances which have been made. Thus before applying for, or deciding to maintain, a patent application which covers a method of plant propagation, the assignees might ask themselves questions such as:

- Does the new technique give our organisation a competitive advantage?

    – What is the best way to use the advantage? Should it be kept as a trade secret or advertised in the form of a patent?

- Is the invention likely to lead to a unique product or technique which can be marketed on a large scale?

If a patent seems to be appropriate, a decision on whether or not to file might be preceded by questions such as:

- Is the technique likely to lead to a major advance in the way plants or specified plants are propagated, so that it will be uneconomic for others to micropropagate the plant unless they are able to use the method described in the patent?

- If no product will result from the invention, is it going to be obvious if laboratories or individuals use the patented technique without permission?

- Are we going to be able to discover where possible infringements of the patent have taken place and shall we have the means to legally enforce our claims?

Decisions on whether or not to patent a process can also be governed by a person's view of the future of biotechnology. For example, the value of patenting a method for obtaining somatic embryogenesis in sunflowers might be questioned if one believes that in the foreseeable future this technique will only be used by laboratories to produce a few plants for experimental purposes. If however one envisages that most sunflower crops throughout the world will soon be initiated from encapsulated somatic embryos, and that the use of true seeds will be a thing of the past, obtaining patents on methods for producing somatic embryos of this plant becomes imperative. An over–optimistic view of the pace of biotechnological change is probably inevitable from those working exclusively in the field, and managers faced with the decision to patent, or not to patent, an apparent discovery, will generally decide that it is better to do so, just in case the enthusiastic advice they are receiving from research staff should prove to be correct.

Almost invariably in plant tissue culture there is more than one way of solving a problem. This is well illustrated in Table 136 by the different *in vitro* methods which have been claimed for producing tubers from potatoes. Thus

a) it can be very difficult to judge how a new technique will measure up to alternatives, and

b) even where the use of a new method can be effectively monitored, the chances of obtaining a patent which will limit the activity of competitors are often diminished.

To be effective, a new process must produce an advantage of sufficient magnitude to persuade others that it is not economic to use alternative techniques.

The timing of patenting. As patents have only a limited life it is ideal not to file a claim on a new invention until it has been fully developed. This is seldom done for fear that a rival concern will make the same, or a similar discovery, and invalidate the research investment which has been made. Immediate filing gives little difficulty when a satisfactory product can be developed very shortly after the initial invention. Unfortunately biological processes are extraordinarily fickle so that it may take many years to develop a technique to the point of sale. During this period, competitors have been made aware of your organisation's research activity (and so may be led in the same direction), and the period of protection afforded by the patent is being dissipated.

Enforcing patents on minor discoveries. The processes covered by many patents on plant tissue culture are likely to be used on a relatively small scale and, as there are now many laboratories throughout the world using tissue culture methods, it would be very difficult and costly to discover those engaged in an illegal application to enable enforcement action. Payne (1988) agreed with these observations and maintained that processes are probably best protected by being kept as trade secrets. His publication gives guidelines on which kind of protection should be sought and should be referred to for a review of the application of trade secret law in biotechnology.

Processes which may lead to major products. Processes which enable the production of an identifiable agricultural or horticultural product, required on a large scale, may be exceptions to the above comments. Table 136 shows that there have been many recent patents on the encapsulation of plant parts, particularly somatic embryos, to enable them to be stored and planted in an analogous fashion to true seeds (see Chapter 14, page 717). The methods involved provide good examples of processes which might lead to a major technological advance and it is easy to understand why patents have been filed on this technology. It is unfortunate for the inventors and their assignees that published results suggest that results with encapsulated somatic embryos have not so far been sufficiently consistent or reliable to permit widespread development.

Product patents

Patents relating to specific pieces of apparatus could be of greater commercial benefit than many process patents and more capable of control.

The benefit from selling a chemical product exclusively for use in plant tissue culture is likely to be small com-pared, say, to the profit resulting from the sale of a plant fungicide or herbicide. A novel chemical with cytokinin action, would for example, be required by tissue culture laboratories in only very small total quantities. As there are few other uses for compounds of this kind, even if a new product were to be much more effective than existing ones, the cost of its development is unlikely to be worthwhile to a chemical company. A possible exception is a non–toxic product with a highly unique effect, such as the gelling agent 'Gelrite'. An effective product arising from the patent of Boxus and Pâques (1986), which claimed the use of hydrolysed agar to prevent vitrescence, might have a fairly large market.

Several patents are concerned with new containers for plant tissue culture and especially relate to the use of gas permeable materials for constructing or sealing vessels. Recent interest in growing cultures and rooting shoots on porous supports is also reflected in numerous applications for patents on suitable materials. Apart from the inventions described in Table 136, Aitken–Christie (1991) listed a capillary support system (Komatsu Ltd. — Japanese patent); a viscous slurry or granule support covered with a cellulose filter (Humboldt University — German patent); and floating water supports for Liliaceae culture (Mitsubishi Petrochemical Co. — Japanese patent).

Patent applications on apparatus and equipment must show that they incorporate a real invention. Can one defend the novelty of a "box for tissue culture covered with a removable translucent semi–permeable membrane", when such equipment has been described previously and is already in everyday use?

Large–scale automated propagation

It will be seen from the table that a comparatively large number of patents covers techniques and apparatus suitable for large scale micropropagation. The importance of reducing the cost of micropropagation mentioned on pages 794 *et seq.*, has resulted in several patents on apparatus and methods for detecting, and then mechanically cutting and transplanting, cultured material. Such equipment would mainly be used in conjunction with conventional shoot and node culture. By contrast, there are as yet comparatively few claims on new techniques and apparatus for large–scale micropropagation, although methods for somatic embryogenesis feature prominently.

There have been attempts to market complete systems for micropropagation by shoot culture (*e.g.* Fari *et al.*, 1987), but one doubts that many clients would be persuaded to invest in a prescribed collection of apparatus, when a laboratory can readily be equipped with the wide selection of alternative equipment already on the market.

Table 136. Some recent patents in micropropagation and related fields of biotechnology.

Brief description of content	Patent assigned to:	Inventor/s (see the Bibliography)
Tissue culture and propagation methods for specific crops		
Methods for cereals		
A method for regenerating cereal plants from tissue cultures. Tissue is cultured on a callus induction medium containing specified auxins or auxin mixtures and then transferred to a series of 1–4 differentiation media, selected from 5 different kinds, each containing different mixtures of regulants.	Sungene Technologies Corp. (U.S.A.)	Cheng (1986)
Regenerating plants from barley microspores using media containing sucrose, glucose, an oligosaccharide or a polysaccharide.	Shell Oil Co., Sittingbourne (U.K.)	Hunter (1989)
Protoplast isolation from cell cultures of Gramineae (sub-family Poaideae — *Avena, Triticum, Secale, Hordeum*), the regeneration of callus and entire fertile plants. Optionally the protoplasts may be used for the incorporation of exogenous DNA and the regeneration of transgenic plants.	Ciba Geigy AG (Germany)	Horn *et al.* (1989)
Methods for *Cucumis*		
A method for isolating protoplasts of *Cucumis* and culturing them to produce somatic embryos and plantlets. The use of a specific enzyme solution is claimed for isolation, followed by (a) culture to produce cell colonies; (b) culture with 2,4-D and BAP to produce mini-calli and somatic embryos; (c) regeneration of plantlets in a PGR-free medium. Optionally callus of embryoids may be stored in a frozen condition.	Plant Cell Res. Inst. (U.S.A.)	Trulson and Shaheen (1988a)
A method for regenerating *Cucumis* spp. plants from somatic embryos. Explants are cultured on media containing BAP and 2,4-D, or NAA, BAP and 2,4-D to produce somatic embryos. These are optionally cultured to promote further development or maturation, and/or cultured to regenerate plants.	Plant Cell Res. Inst. (U.S.A.)	Trulson and Shaheen (1988b)
Methods for *Glycine*		
A four stage process for the regeneration of soybean: (1) Culture of an explant on MS salts, vitamins and sucrose plus 2,4-D, and optionally IAA and ABA; (2) transfer of embryogenic callus to a similar medium plus specific alternative regulants to effect embryo maturation; (3) subculturing callus and somatic embryos to a similar medium with different regulants to effect shoot formation; (4) subculturing callus plus shoots to a final medium for root formation.	Sungene Technologies Corp. (U.S.A.)	Hemphill and Eikenberry (1987)
A method for inducing somatic embryogenesis in *Glycine* using cotyledon tissue from immature embryos. The tissue is cultured on a medium containing an auxin and less than 2% sucrose; whole plants are regenerated on an appropriate medium.	Lubrizol Genetics, Inc.; Univ. Kentucky Res. Foundation, Inc. (U.S.A.)	Collins *et al.* (1988)
A method and media for the regeneration of *Glycine* species with somaclonal variation.	Lubrizol Genetics, Inc. (U.S.A.)	Barwale and Widholm (1990)

Source: World Patent Index, Derwent Information Ltd.   Copyright acknowledged

Brief description of content	Patent assigned to:	Inventor/s (see the Bibliography)
Embryogenesis of *Glycine* species from cotyledonary tissue, using media with phenoxy-acid auxins, dicamba or picloram, and methods for the recovery of whole plants from somatic embryos. These include maturation and germination in MS or B5 media with IBA, ABA, GA$_3$ and activated charcoal.	United Agriseeds, Inc. (U.S.A.)	Ranch and Bucheim (1991)
[See also Tomes (1991) below]		
Methods for *Helianthus*		
A culture medium especially for sunflower, which contains mineral salts, vitamins, plant growth regulators, sucrose and a hardening agent. The vitamins comprise up to and including 500 (100) mg/l inositol, 40 (0.1) mg/l thiamine HCl, 20 (0.5) mg/l nicotinic acid and 40 (0.5) mg/l pyridoxine HCl (preferred concentrations are given in brackets). The composition also optionally included 2 mg/l glycine.	Stauffer Chemical Co. (U.S.A.)	Paterson (1985)
Media for the suspension culture of sunflowers and a method for screening the oil content of varieties through the characteristics of suspension cultures.	Stauffer Chem. Co. (U.S.A.)	Everett (1986)
Regeneration of sunflowers by somatic embryogenesis. Cells or tissue are cultured in a medium containing 2.2–4.4 μM cytokinin (but no auxin) to obtain embryogenic calli and somatic embryos. Embryos are germinated on a medium containing 0.44–4.4 μM cytokinin and optionally placed on a further medium to promote root growth.	Rhone-Poulenc Agrochemie, France	Freyssinet and Freyssinet (1991a,b)
A three stage process for obtaining plant regeneration from sunflowers: (1) Explants cultured on a medium containing amino acids, ABA, and BAP to cause callus formation; (2) Callus subcultured to a medium lacking amino acids but containing IAA and kinetin to ensure shoot formation; (3) shoots rooted on a medium containing auxin.	Sungene Technologies Corp. (U.S.A.)	Cooley and Wilcox (1989a)
A four stage process for regenerating sunflowers by embryogenesis or organogenesis: (1) Explants are placed on a medium consisting of MS salts, vitamins amino acids and sucrose (preferably. 7–14%, esp. 12%) and 2,4-D and ABA; (2) callus is obtained on a similar medium to (1) with 4–8% (esp. 6%) sucrose and BAP, with or without ABA; (3) callus is moved to similar liquid medium (no amino acids) with 2–4% (esp. 3%) sucrose and IAA and kinetin to affect shoot formation; (4) shoot are rooted in medium with 2–3% (esp. 2%) sucrose and IAA.	Sungene Technologies Corp. (U.S.A.)	Cooley and Wilcox (1984, 1989b)
A process for regenerating sunflower plants through embryogenesis. Embryogenic callus is obtained by culturing explants on a medium containing mineral salts, vitamins, amino acids and 2,4-D, with or without ABA. Callus is subcultured to a similar medium lacking amino acids and containing IAA, with or without kinetin. Embryos are germinated on a third medium without amino acids or regulants.	Sungene Technologies Corp. (U.S.A.)	Cooley and Wilcox (1989c)
Methods and media for the regeneration of sunflower plants from cotyledon explants and protoplasts.	Lubrizol Genetics Inc. (U.S.A.)	Power and Firoozabady (1991)
A variety of sunflower selected for the capacity of hypocotyl explants to regenerate plants with high frequency.	Pioneer Hi-Bred International, Inc. (U.S.A.)	Bidney *et al.* (1992)

Source: World Patent Index, Derwent Information Ltd.   Copyright acknowledged

Methods for potato and other tuberous plants

Brief description of content	Patent assigned to:	Inventor/s (see the Bibliography)
The production of potato propagation material free from virus and viroids. The method comprises isolating cells of potato shoot apex tissue, multiplying the cells, rooting the resulting shoots, or inducing tuber formation, and transplanting plants or minitubers to produce plants.	Novotrade RT; Meriklon Kutatsi (Hungary)	Foglein et al. (1988a)
A method for increasing potato tubers. Tuber formation is induced in vitro on rooted plants which are then planted into solid media in glasshouses. Tubers are formed while the plants are sprayed periodically with anti–gibberellin chemicals (AGC) which limit shoot growth. Harvested tubers are replanted with further limitation of haulm growth by AGC.	Novotrade RT; Foglein F.; Roautlader Co. (Hungary)	Foglein et al. (1988b)
A method for inducing a high rate of in vitro tuber formation in potato in which shoot necrosis is induced. Treated shoots transferred to an alternative medium become branched and are suitable to be placed in conditions encouraging tuberisation.	Wisconsin Alumni Research Foundation (U.S.A.)	Joyce and McCown (1989)
A method for the large-scale propagation of plants forming tubers, rhizomes or corms, such as potato, taro, konjak, Scopolia japonica and Chinese yam. In vitro plants are almost submerged in liquid medium, the quantity of which is slowly reduced causing the production of storage organs.	Kyowa Hakko Kogyo Co. Ltd., Ibaraki, Japan	Takayama and Akita (1988, 1991)
Microcuttings (especially those of potato) are grown autotrophically in an organised array in high light with CO_2 enrichment on a substrate where nutrient and water retention vary in different localities. The array of plant material is cut in a single operation with a special apparatus which is included in the claims.	Microprop Ireland Ltd.; Synthetic Substrate Holdings (Eire)	Long and Perrin (1993)
Tubers are formed much more rapidly on potato stolons if they are first cultured on macronutrients specified in the patent (characterised by high NO_3^- and low NH_4^+), with supplementary CO_2, in light of high PPF; kept in low light for 8–12 days; and then returned to high PPF.	Commissariat Energie Atomique (France)	Chagvardieff and Toussaint (1993)

See also Allard et al. (1991), page 830

Methods for Zea

Brief description of content	Patent assigned to:	Inventor/s (see the Bibliography)
Tissue culture and plant regeneration of corn inbred 'B73' and its clones. The formation of embryogenic callus and embryogenic cell suspensions are claimed as new in these genotypes, together with the plants, mutants and variants regenerated thereby.	Stauffer Chemical Co. (U.S.A.)	Lower (1985)
A process for regenerating corn plants whereby (a) chloramben or dicamba are added to a medium to induce callus formation and enable callus maintenance; (b) these regulants, or a mixture of either one with 2,4-D, is used in a medium to induce shoot and root formation. Plantlets are optionally subcultured to another medium for development.	Sungene Technologies Corp. (U.S.A.)	Close (1986)
Regenerating plants from callus of Zea diploperennis and interspecific hybrids, selection of somaclonal variants and gene transfer in these plants for crop improvement.	DNA Plant Technology Corp. (U.S.A.)	Sondahl et al. (1988)

Source: World Patent Index, Derwent Information Ltd.   Copyright acknowledged

Brief description of content	Patent assigned to:	Inventor/s (see the Bibliography)
Nutrients or minerals are advantageously delivered to plant tissue cultures at or near optimum levels over prolonged periods from controlled release sources. Macro- or micro- nutrients are surrounded by a water permeable wall for this purpose, especially one composed of a heat cured alkyd resin–cyclopentadiene copolymer.	Grace-Sierra Horticulture (U.S.A.)	Sluis et al. (1990)
The use of a culture filtrate from a photosynthetic prokaryotic micro-organism such as Cyanobacteria or photosynthetic bacteria to improve growth, embryogenesis, the regeneration of whole plants and/or the formation of secondary products.	Matsunaga T.; Pentel Co. Ltd. (Japan)	Hishinuma et al. (1990)
The stimulation of embryogenesis or the the growth and division of plant cells by adding arabinogalactan proteins to the culture medium.	Sandoz Ltd., Sandoz AG	Kreuger et al. (1991)
The addition of a calcium ionophore (e.g. AZ1187), cyclic AMP and/or a polyamine (e.g. spermidine or putrescine) to a medium promotes the formation of adventitious embryos and bulbs. Use in the families Papaveraceae, Solanaceae (except Torenia), Umbelliferae, Rosaceae, Liliaceae (except Lilium), Compositae, Geraniaceae, Cucurbitaceae and Gramineae is claimed.	Mitsui Petrochemical Industries (Japan)	Anon (1992)
Methods of culture		
The propagation of plants from explants (preferably taken from young seedlings) placed on an agar medium for 3–5 weeks and then transferred to a liquid medium (both media containing a growth regulator). When shoots are obtained, the cultures are subcultured in liquid medium. The method is specifically applied to Digitalis, Dioscorea, Chrysanthemum, Pyrethrum, Catharanthus, Pinus, Papaver, Yucca, and Guayale and other latex containing plants.	Minnesota University (U.S.A.)	Staba and Lui (1981)
The growth and differentiation of plant cells, callus, or tissue is stimulated by the passage of an electric current, preferably in the presence of an auxin capable of undergoing polar transport.	National Research and Development Corp. (U.K.)	Goldsworthy and Rathore (1985a)
The preparation of suspension cultures by exposing live plant tissue to mechanical shearing for a time insufficient to cause loss of viability.	Albright and Wilson Ltd. (U.K.)	Mavituna et al. (1986)
The in vitro culture of plant cells, seeds and the like, on objects floating on the top of a liquid nutrient medium. The floating bodies are typically those of a polymer, especially polypropylene.	Agrogen-Stiftung (Switzerland); Knopf U.C.	Knopf (1986)
The mass propagation of woody plants by culturing shoot tips (1) in a rotated liquid medium to form shoot primordia; (2) followed by culture on a stationary liquid medium to regenerate shoots. Both steps are conducted under illumination, viz. step (1) 2000–20 000 lux, and step (2) 1000–4000 lux. Also claimed is a method for producing protoplasts from shoot primordia. Although the primary claim refers to woody plants (examples given), the technique is also said to be applicable to herbaceous plants e.g. Petunia, tobacco and wheat.	Oji Paper Co. (Japan)	Doi et al. (1991b)
A process for culturing plant cells in a liquid medium without agitation or fixation.	Nestec S. A., Tours, France	Petiard and Yvernel (1991)

Source: World Patent Index, Derwent Information Ltd.   Copyright acknowledged

Brief description of content	Patent assigned to:	Inventor/s (see the Bibliography)
Two-phased media		
Use of a two-phase medium for shoot cultures in which shoot cuttings are planted on a solidified medium, a liquid medium (optionally containing growth regulants) then being added over the solid medium to submerge or partly submerge the plant material.	Gyogynoveny Kutato Intezet; Rozmaring Mezogazda; Novotrade RT. (Hungary)	Molnar et al. (1986, 1989)
Macerated tissues		
The propagation of plants from macerated tissue fragments. The technique is said to be applicable to Boston ferns and also to plants such as potatoes, Crocus, Philodendron, raspberry and grape.	—	Lindemann (1984)
Somatic embryogenesis		
The regeneration of plants from morphologically competent cell suspensions maintained by serial subculture. Somatic embryos, from which complete plants can be obtained, are formed when cell aggregates are transferred to an appropriate medium.	Zoecon Corp. (U.S.A.)	Christianson et al. (1986)
Improving somatic embryogenesis by adding maltose to the medium as a carbohydrate source, additionally together with a source of the ammonium ion.	Plant Genetics, Inc. (U.S.A.)	Stuart et al. (1986)
Somatic embryogenesis is enhanced by culturing plant tissues on a medium containing ammonium ions and at least one amino acid selected from proline, alanine, arginine, glutamine, asparagine, serine, ornithine, and glutamic acid and their amides, alkyl esters and dipeptidyl derivatives. These amino acids (excepting alanine, glutamine and serine) and their derivatives, may alternatively be added to a medium without ammonium ions.	Plant Genetics, Inc.; Battelle Development Corp. (U.S.A.)	Stuart (1987)
Embryogenesis in the families Liliaceae, Araceae, Dioscoreaceae and Gramineae is enhanced by growing plant material in a medium containing 0.1–30 mg/l ancymidol. Pieces of the dwarfed plants so obtained (in the case of Gramineae, the extreme base of the stem) are then cultured in a medium containing auxin to produce somatic embryos.	Kyowa Hakko Kogyo Co. Ltd. (Japan)	Arima et al. (1989)
A method for inducing somatic embryogenesis by including at least one synthetic auxin with a specified formula (structural alternatives given) in the medium.	Plant Genetics, Inc. (U.S.A.)	Stuart et al. (1990)
A method for producing mature somatic embryos, the novel claim of which seems to be the inclusion of a maturation stage in which the embryos are moved to a medium containing ABA.	Plant Genetics, Inc. (U.S.A.); Kirin Beer Co. Ltd. (Japan)	Fujii et al. (1990)
Preventing hyperhydricity		
Addition of hydrolysed agar to a medium used for micropropagation prevents hyperhydricity, particularly in woody plants. The hydrolysate is prepared by exposing agar to an acid, preferably at pH3–4 and 100–120°C for 30–60 minutes.	Station des Cultures Fruitières et Maraichères (Belgium); Personal Production Co.	Boxus and Pâques (1990)
Acclimatization and hardening		
A method for planting micropropagated shoots directly into the field without a prior acclimatization procedure. Shoots are pretreated on a medium with more sugar but less nitrogen than at the multiplication stage, and then exposed to a root-inducing compound. They are planted in the field under translucent moisture barriers.	Plant Research Laboratories (U.S.A.)	Driver (1987)

Source: World Patent Index, Derwent Information Ltd.   Copyright acknowledged

Inventor/s (see the Bibliography)	Patent assigned to:	Brief description of content
Roberts (1988)	Imperial Chemical Industries PLC (U.K.)	Enhancing the survival of plants during acclimatization by incorporating into the *in vitro* medium 0.001–10 mg/l of an inhibitor of the gibberellin pathway.
Kreitinger *et al.* (1991)	Weyerhaeuser Co. (U.S.A.)	The *in vitro* hardening of plants, especially plantlets produced from somatic embryos, by planting them in plugs. The plants are initially grown with a carbon source which is withdrawn during a hardening stage, when light and gases are made available sufficient to support autotrophic growth.
Foeglein (1993)	Foeglein F.; Verschoor F.A.; Foeglein Kerteszeti BT A & F.	The *in vitro* hardening of tissue cultured plants grown individually under sterile conditions in a 'fertile soil', the osmotic pressure of which has been increased by the addition of sugars or salts. Treated plants can be stored at 5°C for 30–50 days. [see also Tanimoto *et al.* (1989) below]

Protoplast isolation

Inventor/s (see the Bibliography)	Patent assigned to:	Brief description of content
Doi *et al.* (1991a)	Oji Paper Co. (Japan)	Protoplasts derived from shoot apices by enzymatic treatment are cultured and plants regenerated (using seemingly well-known procedures). The method is said to have an advantage in the propagation of woody plants.
Dam *et al.* (1994)	Carlsberg Forskningscenter (Denmark)	Plant regeneration from protoplasts, cells or tissues is assisted by co-cultivation with pollen microspores or anthers, an extract thereof, or a medium preconditioned by their prior presence.

Methods for encapsulating plant material

Inventor/s (see the Bibliography)	Patent assigned to:	Brief description of content
Redenbaugh (1986)	Plant Genetics, Inc. (U.S.A.)	The preparation of an analogue to natural seed by encapsulating meristematic plant tissue in a gel which permits development.
Redenbaugh and Reyes (1985, 1987)	Plant Genetics, Inc. (U.S.A.)	Surrounding plant material, such as seeds and somatic embryos, with a capsule containing at least one material and preferably an encapsulating material (sodium alginate and several other named alternatives) together with an outer membrane (several named polymers and long chain molecules).
Redenbaugh and Slade (1987, 1988)	Plant Genetics, Inc. (U.S.A.)	A process for creating analogues of seeds by encapsulating totipotent meristematic tissue (TMT). TMT is obtained from seeds with the seed coat removed, or from somatic embryos, and is encapsulated in a hydrated gel capsule, for example, composed of sodium alginate optionally complexed with a calcium salt, or Terrasorb, a gelatinised starch-hydrolysed polyacrylonitrile graft co-polymer.
Gray and Conger (1989)	University of Florida (U.S.A.)	Synthetic seeds which can be stored and easily handled are prepared by drying somatic embryos in an atmosphere or osmotic environment providing a relative humidity of 30–85%. Reducing the moisture content of embryos thereby to 4–15% stops their growth.
Redenbaugh (1991b)	Plant Genetics, Inc. (U.S.A.)	Encapsulating meristematic tissue of plants in a hydrogel containing at least one adjuvant capable of enhancing growth and development.

Source: World Patent Index, Derwent Information Ltd.   Copyright acknowledged

Inventor/s (see the Bibliography)	Patent assigned to:	Brief description of content
Redenbaugh M.K. et al. (1987); Nelson et al. (1988)	Plant Genetics, Inc. (U.S.A.)	Not strictly to do with plant tissue culture, but related. Seeds can be hydrated and pregerminated before planting by enclosing them in a capsule containing free water in conditions which permit germination. The addition of an osmotic regulator to the capsule prevents radical emergence.
Redenbaugh (1988)	Plant Genetics, Inc. (U.S.A.)	Not strictly to do with plant tissue culture, but related. It comprises a method of encapsulating seeds in a water saturated matrix and a method of delivering capsules to the environment.
Bower et al. (1992)	Weyerhaeuser Co.	The encapsulation of somatic embryos in a plant gel containing an oxygen-carrying compound and apparatus for so doing.
Bewley et al. (1993)	University of Guelph (U.S.A.)	A process for inducing desiccation tolerance in somatic embryos to enable production of artificial seeds. Embryos as early as the torpedo stage are cultured with abscisic acid for sufficient duration and at a sufficient concentration to effect physiological changes. The embryos are then dried.
Masuda and Sakamoto (1993)	Kirin Beer Co. Ltd. (Japan)	A method for encapsulating plant material in alginate beads with a hard outer coat.

Apparatus and equipment for plant tissue culture

Supports for plant material

Inventor/s (see the Bibliography)	Patent assigned to:	Brief description of content
Oishi (1987)	Oishi T.; Nippon Steel and Chemical Co. (Japan)	Supports for plant material are comprised of vertically oriented SiO_2/Al_2O_3 ceramic fibres.
Hodds et al. (1988)	Baumgartner Papiers (Switzerland)	A sterile culture medium comprising a plug of water absorbent fibrous material and a retaining sleeve or chemical coating open at one end or both ends. (Patent from the manufacturer of Sorbarods)
Perrin (1993)	Synthetic Substrates Holdings (U.K.)	Rigid polyurethane foam is formed into suitable shapes for receiving plants and is used as a substrate for rooting cuttings and raising seedlings.
Graham and Szmidt (1994)	University of Strathclyde (U.K.)	A porous substrate for plant propagation comprised especially of plastic bonded perlite or vermiculite.
Renn and Snow (1994)	FMC Corp. (U.S.A.)	A porous matrix produced from glucomannan and at least one other gel-forming polysaccharide, used as a support for tissue cultures and for rooting micropropagated shoots.

Containers and closures

Inventor/s (see the Bibliography)	Patent assigned to:	Brief description of content
Waters et al. (1987)	Plant Biotech Industries (Israel)	A system for evenly distributing plant propagules on a growth matrix containing an array of growing cells, and moving plantlets so obtained to second-stage supports in which the cells are more widely spaced. The system is especially suitable for mechanised transplanting.

Source: World Patent Index, Derwent Information Ltd.   Copyright acknowledged

Brief description of content	Patent assigned to:	Inventor/s (see the Bibliography)
A culture vessel containing a flat fine screen above the base which keeps a tissue culture in optimal contact with a (liquid) medium.	Plant Biotech Industries; Milouda Ltd. (Israel)	Levin (1988)
Plant tissue cultures are provided with a flowing nutrient medium as a film, or via drip feed tubes. The process allows the medium to be changed readily	.Robarts A. W. (Great Britain)	Firn et al. (1989)
A system for growing lows the medium to be changed readily	.Robarts A. W. (Great Britain)	Firn et al. (1989)
A system for growing living organic matter within an enclosure formed by a gas-permeable, liquid-impermeable membrane.	Agristar, Inc. (U.S.A.)	Kertz (1989a,b)
Chambers suitable for plant culture are formed by heat sealing a membrane, especially a double layer of polyethylene film.	Agristar, Inc (U.S.A.).	Kertz (1990a)
An enclosure made of a gas-permeable, liquid impermeable membrane which can be deliberately ruptured without damaging the integrity of the whole enclosure. For plant tissue culture, the compartment would contain a medium.	Agristar, Inc (U.S.A.).	Kertz (1990b)
A gas permeable translucent membrane used to seal a container, or to make a container, suitable for the culture of plant or animal material. The preferred material is Chevron high density polyethylene 9650.	Agristar, Inc (U.S.A.).	Kertz (1990c)
An apparatus to be used in conjunction with the plant chambers described in Kertz (1990a), whereby chambers can be loaded with plant material and sealed. Alternatively chambers can be opened and the plant material cut and re-inserted into fresh chambers which are then sealed.	Agristar, Inc (U.S.A.).	Kertz (1990d)
A tissue culture flask with optical properties on the inner surface, closed by a flexible transparent film which may be peeled off to allow access to the culture flask.	Costar Corporation	Lyman and Mathus (1990)
A conically shaped container of semi-permeable and translucent material is used to house shoots to be rooted in vitro. Shoots are placed in a spongy artificial substrate at the bottom of the container. The substrate is soaked with a liquid rooting medium.	Permx BV. (The Netherlands)	Van Oeveren (1990)
A process of culturing cell masses in a succession of oxygen–permeable compartments.	Baxter International, Inc. (U.S.A.)	Thiarol et al. (1991)

Dispensing media

Brief description of content	Patent assigned to:	Inventor/s (see the Bibliography)
The automated preparation of media from basic ingredients and solidifying agents and the aseptic dispensing of selected formulations into vessels.	Kontaka Alkatr. Sze.; Feherjetechn. Tudoma; Fari, M.	Fari (1988)

Equipment and methods for large scale micropropagation

Brief description of content	Patent assigned to:	Inventor/s (see the Bibliography)
Automated or semi-automated propagation by culturing a large number of densely packed meristematic areas which are automatically separated and thinned and transported in bulk to an apparatus where the tissue is washed free from phytotoxic debris and propagules of uniform size are selected. The propagules are automatically transported and distributed on the surface of a medium.	Plant Biotech Industries Ltd. (Israel)	Levin (1988)

Source: World Patent Index, Derwent Information Ltd. Copyright acknowledged

Brief description of content	Patent assigned to:	Inventor/s (see the Bibliography)
Fermentors and large scale culture vessels		
A method for regenerating, propagating, rooting and acclimatizing plant material *in vitro* in a single culture tank. Cultures are initiated heterotrophically, but for regeneration and acclimatization are growth autotrophically.	Mitsui Petrochemical Industries Co. Ltd.	Tanimoto *et al.* (1989)
Cells or plant tissues are cultured in a vessel which is rotated about its own axis or eccentrically. The axis may be horizontal or inclined at less that 20 degrees. The vessel does not contain paddles and is filled with plant material and medium. Plant material may be anchored, supported on carrier particles, or not anchored.	Japan Synthetic Rubber Co. Ltd.	Tosaki *et al.* (1989)
A fermentor for the culture of shear-sensitive cells containing an Archimedian screw auger with provisions to reduce turbulence.	Canadian Patents & Development Ltd.	Armstrong *et al.* (1990)
An air lift fermentor which contains a mechanism for agitating suspension cultures with appropriate inlet and outlet ports.	Celltech Ltd.	Thompson and Wood (1990)
Cutting, handling and placing plant material		
A method for culturing many cell or callus cultures in wells on a plate, using a porous wick to transfer liquid medium from a container beneath.	Agracetus Madison Corporation (U.S.A.)	Yang and Paau (1986)
A method for cutting plant tissue for micropropagation. The cutter rotates around the node of a plant making one cut below and two cuts above it. The cut piece is retained in a recess of the cutter, expelled by a pushing member and placed flat on a propagation medium, then rotated to stand upright.	Brown F.R.; Twyford Plant Laboratories	Brown F.R. (1988)
Inocula for commercial scale plant tissue culture are provided by cutting slices with a reciprocating or multiple bladed knife.	Mitsui Petrochemical Industries Co. Ltd. (Japan)	Hirata *et al.* (1989)
Particles in a suspension capable of growing into plants (propagules) are separated by size using a fluidic switch. Separated propagules are cultured on a cellulosic material on which growing sites are so ordered as to permit eventual mechanical separation of the plants obtained.	Albright and Wilson Ltd. (U.K.)	Mavituna *et al.* (1989)
Cutting plant material with a laser beam using either continuous power or a pulsed beam. A shield gas (preferably nitrogen or CO_2) is used around the plant to be cut to prevent charring from excess heat.	Enso-Gutzeit OY; Kemira OY (Finland)	Jokinen *et al.* (1990)
An apparatus for selecting suitable propagules for subculture and transferring them from a liquid medium in a predetermined quantity and at a predetermined rate to one or more cultivation boxes. The cultivation box has gas and medium supply systems.	Komatsu Seisakusho (Japan)	Sei (1990)
An automated propagation system in which plant material in a culture flask is cut into plugs. Extraneous medium or plant material is removed and plugs are then ejected using fluid pressure into media in additional containers.	Hartmans Plants, Inc. (U.S.A.)	Tur-Kaspar *et al.* (1990)

Source: World Patent Index, Derwent Information Ltd.   Copyright acknowledged

Brief description of content	Patent assigned to:	Inventor/s (see the Bibliography)
This patent does not refer to tissue culture but is relevant to planting propagated material in the greenhouse. It describes an apparatus for transplanting seedlings and small plants into larger pots or containers.	Williames Hi-Tech International Pty. Ltd. (Australia)	Williames (1990)
A method and apparatus to cut the top from a tissue culture vessel with a laser beam, which then cuts the plant material inside.	British Technology Group PLC; National Research and Dev. Corp. (U.K.)	Brown and Billington (1991)
A method specially suited to the micropropagation of potatoes, whereby shoots grown on a gelled medium are cut into pieces having at least one tip or node, and the pieces transferred in bulk by air flow or gravity to fresh medium for subculture. Propagules (microtubers ?) are finally harvested by combine with a comb to separate them from the gelled medium.	Allard J.; British Technology Group Ltd. (U.K.)	Allard et al. (1991)
A tubular cutting device which cuts and removes a portion of a micropropagated shoot and transfers it to a nutrient medium.	British Technology Group Ltd.; National Research and Dev. Corp. (U.K.)	Billington and Grundson (1991)
A robotic cutting, handling and planting tool designed specifically for use in micropropagation.	British Technology Group PLC.; National Research and Dev. Corp (U.K.)	Billington and Grundson (1992)
A holder for gripping and manipulating a plantlet during micropropagation procedures has a pair of cantilevered rollers which are moved by motors and also pneumatically.	British Technology Group Ltd.; National Research and Dev. Corp. (U.K.)	Billington and Brown (1991)
An apparatus which cuts shoots close to their bases, divides them into smaller pieces, and plants the pieces for subculturing.	Commonwealth Industrial Gases Ltd. (Australia)	Hanseler (1992)
An apparatus including a tank for cell or organ culture and a cutting device within the tank. The plant material is moved against the cutter or a movable cutter is urged against the plant material.	Mitsui Petrochemical Industries Ltd., Kuga, Japan	Kawarabayashi et al. (1991a); Hirata et al. (1992)
Nodes are cut from micro plants by placing them within an inverted tray which is rotated, impinging the plants against a rotary cutter. Nodes fall into a second tray containing culture medium which is automatically conveyed away to be wrapped in film for re-culture.	Microprop Ireland Ltd. (Eire); Perrin A.P.; Synthetic Substrates Holdings Ltd.	Cassells et al. (1993)
Plant location methods and equipment (used in conjunction with some cutting and handling devices)		
A method whereby voids between shoots of a plant are located by processing the image generated by a video camera. The positions are used to define suitable cutting lines from the voids through associated callus.	British Technology Group Ltd.; National Research and Dev. Corp (U.K.)	Davis et al. (1992)
A method for determining the features of plant material which facilitates cutting by non-manual means. A camera-generated image of the material is processed by microcomputer which determines the tone assigned to each pixel. By storing co-ordinates of the pixels in a database, selected features of the plant can be identified and stored for determining the locations of cuts.	Commonwealth Industrial Gases Ltd. (Australia)	Schonstein and Johnson (1986)

Source: World Patent Index, Derwent Information Ltd.   Copyright acknowledged

Brief description of content	Patent assigned to:	Inventor/s (see the Bibliography)
A method for identifying the stem of a plant from a generated image. To be used in a method of harvesting.	British Technology Group PLC; National Research and Dev. Corp. (U.K.)	McFarlane (1992)
Greenhouse control equipment (The following citations came indirectly from a search related to micropropagation, and so are likely to be only a small sample of the patents filed in this area)		
An apparatus consisting of two temperature sensitive elements, one exposed to mist or spray, the other adapted to sense the wet bulb temperature of the environment. A device responsive to the temperature difference between the elements controls mist or spay applications.	Lynch K.J.E.; Lynch G.M.	Lynch (1982)
A system whereby vapour pressure deficit above crops can be calculated to initiate a suitable water supply.	OCS, Inc. (U.S.A.)	Oglevee and Oglevee (1989)
Apparatus for monitoring the vapour pressure deficit and light intensity over crops in a greenhouse and ensuring therefrom that an appropriate supply of water is provided.	OCS, Inc. (U.S.A.)	Oglevee and Oglevee (1994)
Plant culture and propagation in mist		
A technique for plant propagation in which a finely atomised aqueous composition is sprayed intermittently onto a portion of plants in closed vessels.	Schorr S.M.; Genesis Technology, Inc; P.O. Holdings S.A. (U.S.A. and Australia)	Schorr and Stoner (1985)
A method and apparatus for culturing plants in a nutrient mist which can be emitted through a nozzle using a pressurised gas, the gas being required for cell metabolism.	Bio Rational Technologies, Inc. (U.S.A.)	Giles and Weathers (1992)
The use of tissue culture in plant breeding (only a small sample of the patents in this area)		
A process for obtaining salt-tolerant plants by culturing disorganised plant cells exhibiting genetic variability, in salt solutions of a concentration normally sufficient to be injurious. Plants with genes for resistance may be regenerated from the surviving cells or tissue.	Crop Development Center, Univ. of Saskatchewan	McHughen (1987)
A method for the regeneration of *Zea diploperennis* from callus after several subcultures by omission of the auxin 2,4-D: the use of somaclonal variants of hybrids between *Euchlaena mexicana* (teosinte) and *Zea mays* in breeding: a protocol for gene transfer.	DNA Plant Technology Corporation	Sondahl and Evans (1987)
A method for producing somaclonal variants of tomato by culturing tissues with high cytokinin concentrations.	Campbell Soup Company (U.S.A.)	Evans and Sharp (1988)
A method for producing herbicide-resistant plant tissues, plants and seeds, especially by obtaining and manipulating altered acetohydroxyacid synthase enzymes, and the genes which encode them.	Molecular Genetics, Inc. (U.S.A.)	Anderson and Hibberd (1988)
Use of a promotor region from crown gall tumours to drive the expression of foreign structural genes in plants: construction of a selectable marker and vectors for gene transmission.	Lubrizol Genetics, Inc. (U.S.A.)	Gelvin (1988)
Characterization of a gene 'Fix D' which can activate the nitrogen fixing genes of *Rhizobium* and its combination with structural genes to regulate the expression of rhizobial symbiosis.	Lubrizol Genetics, Inc. (U.S.A.)	Puhler *et al.* (1988)

Source: World Patent Index, Derwent Information Ltd.   Copyright acknowledged

Brief description of content	Patent assigned to:	Inventor/s (see the Bibliography)
The transformation of shoot cultures, especially those of poplar, with foreign DNA using an *Agrobacterium* system, and the regeneration of transformed plants therefrom.	—	Fillatti and Comai (1988)
Regenerating somaclonal variants from plant tissue cultures by maintaining the cultures in the presence of unusually high concentrations of plant growth regulators.	DNA Plant Technology Corporation	Evans *et al.* (1988a,b)
Methods for producing haploid tomato plants by anther culture and fertile diploids by doubling the chromosome number.	Campbell Soup Company (U.S.A.)	Evans and Morrison (1988)
The transformation of plants by insertion of a DNA fragment combined with an inducible plant promoter derived from root nodule genes, plasmids or a transformed *Agrobacterium* rhizogene strain.	A/S De Danske Sakkerfabrikker	Marcker *et al.* (1990)
An *in vitro* method for screening and selecting *Glycine max* plants resistant to brown stem rot, by culturing callus in the presence of a culture filtrate of the causal agent, *Phialophora gregata*.	Lubrizol Genetics, Inc., Board of Trustees of the Univ. of Illinois	Guan *et al.* (1990)
The use of cloning or an expression vector carrying a gene which encodes a 5–enolpyruvyl–shikimate–3–phosphate synthase polypeptide. When the gene is expressed in a plant cell, the polypeptide, or an enzyme active portion thereof, is transferred from the cytoplasm into chloroplasts, imparting a considerable degree of glyphosate resistance to cells and the plants regenerated from them.	Monsanto Company (U.S.A.)	Shah *et al.* (1990) Kishore and Shah (1990)
Plants which have been transformed to contain genes expressing the coat proteins for Potato Viruses X and Y. The transgenic plants are resistant to the viruses. Resistance conveyed to the potato cv. 'Russet Burbank' is given as an example.	Monsanto Company (U.S.A.)	Tumer (1990)
The use of anther culture in a breeding programme to obtain homozygous plants with or without a self-incompatibility determinant. Lines established from these plants are crossed giving seed heterozygous for the self-incompatibility factor. This is used in the production of commercial F_1 hybrid seed.	Kingroup, Inc. (U.S.A.), Chatham, Canada	Scott-Pearse (1991)

Source: World Patent Index, Derwent Information Ltd.   Copyright acknowledged

17

Micropropagation in Practice

Since the first edition of this book was published, research into propagating plants by tissue culture has progressed steadily and methods have been published which are applicable to plants of many different genera. The literature provides details of techniques by which the propagation of a large number species might be based, and there are examples of commercial micropropagation in most of the classes of plants instanced in this chapter. However, many of the plants listed in the tables are not currently multiplied by micropropagation laboratories and sold in large numbers. This is often because it is not commercially profitable, and sometimes because markets for micropropagated plants have not been developed.

Other plants whose large–scale production by tissue culture is not economic, may be micropropagated on a much smaller scale for specific purposes (*e.g.* to establish disease–free stock which can be used for conventional propagation, to build up stock plants of new varieties, or to maintain specific lines for plant breeding programmes). Certain plants have been studied for just their scientific interest, while botanic gardens have become increasingly involved in the micropropgation of wild species which have become endangered.

AIMS OF THIS CHAPTER

Tabulated references

In this chapter we have presented lists of plants whose multiplication, by one *in vitro* method or another, has been reported in the scientific literature. The published accounts of plant tissue culture and micropropagation are voluminous and appear worldwide in numerous journals and books, many of which we have not been able to consult on account of insufficient time or inaccessibility. Consequently, the lists presented in this book are to a certain extent incomplete. However they do indicate the wide range of research on *in vitro* propagation, and the diligent will soon be able to follow up other work on any plant of interest by obtaining the original papers we have listed and by studying the bibliographies therein.

It is important to recognise that many published papers only indicate that certain plants have the potential to be propagated by tissue culture. The methods set forth may not be sufficiently reliable, or may not result in a sufficiently rapid rate of plantlet production, to be useful for practical purposes. Alternatively, plants of the species may not command a sufficiently high price to make commercial micropropagation worthwhile. Literature references provided in the tables of this chapter can therefore often only be taken as a guide to the particular plant species. It has already been emphasised many times in this text that genotype has a large effect on the success of micropropagation. This inevitably means that, even though there is a published method for micropropagation of a given species, it may prove to be difficult or impossible to multiply all varieties of it *in vitro*. It is also highly likely that the published method will need to be slightly modified if the cultivar or species to be propagated is not the same as in the original work.

Many listed papers describe methods for shoot regeneration from callus cultures, which are often inappropriate for commercial micropropagation. These have nevertheless been included because of their value as models for genetic manipulation experiments. In other instances the methods given in papers are not sufficiently complete in description or achievement to provide a possible method of micropropagation where genetic homogeneity is required. A simple ranking system has therefore been appended to help in the selection of appropriate techniques. The symbol 'YY' has been placed in Column 6 of the tables where a method has seemed to us to be particularly successful.

Using the list in the 'COST 1987' survey of European Tissue Culture Laboratories for 1993, plants which are currently micropropagated by European commercial tissue culture laboratories have been marked or listed in the tables: an asterisk (*) denotes that species or cultivar are known to have been propagated; the symbol ✤ has been used where a plant or plants of that *genus* are known to have been multiplied. Some of the plants multiplied in European laboratories are not mentioned in our tables of publications. This may be because:

— Our literature survey is not sufficiently extensive;

> The literature on plant tissue culture is now very large, and to make a comprehensive survey of all publications across the world has been beyond our capabilities.

— Suitable techniques have been discovered by commercial laboratories but not published.

> Tissue culture laboratories do their own research and develop techniques to propagate plants which are often kept as commercial secrets.

Organisation of the tables

Rather than present the results of published work on micropropagation as one long table, plants have been grouped according to their perceived uses in the following way:

Herbaceous ornamentals

> Herbaceous plants grown as garden flowers, foliage plants and pot plants
>
> Bulbs
>
> Cacti
>
> Ferns
>
> Orchids

Woody ornamentals

> Woody shrubs and trees grown as landscape plants and garden ornamentals

Forest trees

> Broad-leafed forest trees
>
> Gymnospermous forest trees

Fruit and nut crops

> (Herbaceous, shrub and tree crops grown for fruit production. Includes rootstocks).

Field crops

> Temperate broad-leafed crops
>
> Cereals
>
> Grasses

Root and tuber crops

Legumes

Subtropical and tropical field crops

Vegetables

> (includes tomatoes and peppers)

Spices and Condiments

Medicinal plants

> (Includes some plants grown for valuable secondary products)

Conservation of wild species

This classification is necessarily somewhat arbitrary, and readers should refer to the indices at the end of the book to locate information on species which seem to be missing or misplaced. The indices should also be used to obtain information on aspects of the micropropagation of species which are not summarised in this chapter, but discussed elsewhere in the book.

Many botanical names have been changed in recent years. Copying the latin names by which plants were described in the original papers, resulted in plants frequently being listed under two or more names. To correct the situation we have used the botanical names given in the latest editions of the Royal Horticultural Society *Index of Garden Plants* and in *The Plant Book* by D.J. Mabberley. We hope that the pseudonyms provided will assist those used to previous nomenclature and will clarify any confusion.

Methods of micropropagation

Accompanying the list of plants in each of the above sections, we have summarised the principal methods by which the important or typical species are multiplied. These are largely prepared from published work but can be adapted to provide more cost effective methods of commercial micropropagation. For example, it will often be possible to add a supplement to Stage II semi-solid media to avoid having to transfer cultures to fresh containers for elongation and rooting. The way that these techniques have been used in *Cordyline* propagation are described on page 705.

Although we have described the techniques used to propagate many economically important plants, it is impossible to mention all the available information in a few paragraphs, and for a critical analysis of methods applicable to any one kind of plant, we strongly recommend that the referenced scientific papers should be consulted. Similarly it has not been possible to describe methods for every plant in the accompanying lists.

Note that, in the main, the accounts provided describe only those techniques which at present provide a practical means of micropropagation. These are usually shoot culture methods, but sometimes include other *modi operandi*, such as embryogenesis or regeneration from adventitious shoots. To review all the different types of tissue culture which have resulted in plant production is beyond the scope of these books.

Describing protocols

Because of the large number of variables affecting the success of micropropagation, those seeking to propagate a plant naturally tend to use a method which has been found to be successful by another researcher. They may make slight changes to the previous protocol and find that these are equally successful, or give even better results. However it is very seldom that a publication discusses the advantages or disadvantages of one protocol over another, so in assessing the various ways in which plants of a particular kind might be propagated, one is presented with a spectrum of techniques, in particular a range of alternative media and alternative combinations of growth regulants.

In these circumstances there are two strategies which can be adopted in trying to work out an efficient protocol:

- Search for prominent themes and follow their implications; and/or,
- Try the simplest of the techniques or media which have been used in the past, and then explore whether more complex alternatives give better results.

The large number of unexplained alternative techniques for propagating any one plant species or genus presents difficulties to the reviewer as much, or more, than to the experimenter. In trying to describe the most effective protocol, how annoying it is to discover that, in each paper one reads on propagating a particular species or genus, there are slight unexplained alternatives in the choice of medium! How even more annoying when the alternatives are between, for example, the concentration of micronutrients, the level of chelated iron, or the relative concentration of organic constituents! Surely such minor changes were not justified? Was it really beneficial to alter the quantity of thiamine in **MS** medium from 0.1 to 0.4 mg/l? Why did they do it? There is no explanation in the paper. Was it just a whim, or did they carry out prior experimentation to show that the higher concentration gave better results? Thus it is that one cannot make firm recommendations, but only present the most likely alternatives and hope that the descriptions on the following pages are of some value.

Media tables. In the sections which follow there are tables which list media used for particular species or genera. We wished these to be comparative, but also allow the reader to be able to prepare a medium of choice. Each table therefore compares the concentrations of macronutrient ions, but lists other ingredients in mass values. Because it is difficult to calculate the weights of compounds necessary for the preparation of macronutrient solutions, appropriate recipes for them have been listed in an Appendix. The ingredients from which the macronutrients of well known media can be prepared, are given in Table 48 (pages 393 *et seq.* of Part 1).

HERBACEOUS ORNAMENTALS

The multiplication of ornamental plants for the horticultural industry is still by far the largest practical application for plant tissue culture and provides the major occupation for commercial micropropagation laboratories. Ornamentals which are micropropagated commercially are sold eventually (but not necessarily by the original producer) as pot plants, plants intended for cut flower production, as bulbs and corms, or as plants for parks, gardens and landscaping. In the tables which follow, reports on the micropropagation of ornamentals have been divided into those on herbaceous and woody species. Descriptions of the multiplication of ferns, bulbs, cacti and orchids have been dealt with separately.

The cost factor

As explained in the previous chapter, ramets produced by tissue culture are still expensive, so until robotics or other less labour intensive methods become a reality, it is still only possible to find markets for plants which have a high retail value, or which have a high intrinsic value to growers or breeders (*e.g.* virus–free stock, foundation stock of a new variety, lines of plants required for breeding programmes). However, satisfactory techniques are available for the multiplication of many ornamental species of interest to the horticultural trade which are difficult or slow to multiply by other methods of 'macropropagation'.

Published accounts of ornamentals which can be propagated *in vitro* are very numerous, but methods described are often inadequate and/or uneconomic for commercial practice. There are, for example, research reports describing the *in vitro* vegetative propagation of annual ornamentals such as *Antirrhinum, Nicotiana* and *Petunia*, but few laboratories will consider the vegetative propagation of plants of this nature which can be cheaply and easily raised from seed.

Techniques

Most herbaceous ornamental species are propagated by shoot culture, although plants in the families Gesneriaceae and Begoniaceae are most frequently multiplied from buds regenerated directly on explants. Many bulbous plants are also increased from adventitious buds and bulbils on scale-leaf explants. Indirect shoot formation in callus cultures is now seldom used as a method for routine micropropagation of ornamental plants, except for *Anthurium*.

Techniques for the multiplication of some of the species of importance in commercial micropropagation are discussed in the paragraphs that follow.

Review articles. Review articles on the micropropagation of ornamentals were written by Holdgate (1977), Hughes (1981) and Harney (1982). The book edited by Ammirato *et al.* (1990) contains reviews of the techniques used for many herbaceous ornamentals.

METHODS FOR SPECIFIC PLANTS

Alstroemeriaceae
Alstroemeria (Peruvian Lily)

Alstroemeria is popular with florists and is also grown as a garden ornamental. New hybrids are regularly produced but differ in the ease with which they can be micropropagated according to the vigour, internode length and degree of branching of their rhizomes. These morphological factors combine to determine the rate at which rhizomes can be propagated and can be used in breeding programmes for the selection of cultivars suitable for *in vitro* multiplication (Buitendijk *et al.*, 1992).

Node culture

Alstroemeria plants form a fleshy rhizome from which new shoots arise from lateral buds. Cultures are most easily initiated from rhizome tips, but Hussey *et al.* (1980) found that they could be started from dormant axillary rhizome initials at the base of shoots, or from inflorescence explants. Cultures can also be initiated from rhizome segments consisting of one or more internodes from which roots have been removed and shoots cut away above the first node.

The sterilisation of explants from rhizomes grown underground can present a problem. Pederson and Brandt (1992) used 3 separate immersions in 1% sodium hypochlorite, the first for 10 minutes, the second for 5 minutes and the third for 1 minute. Before each treatment, scale leaves were trimmed.

Medium. Most experiments have shown **MS** or **LS** medium with 30–40 g/l sucrose to be suitable for the isolation and multiplication of *Alstroemeria*. The inclusion of 100 mg/l casein hydrolysate during culture initiation helps to reveal contaminated cultures. Elliott *et al.* (1993)

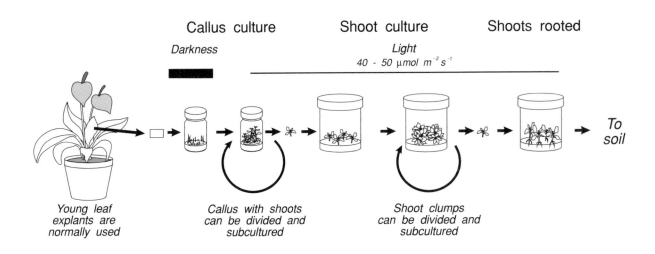

Fig. 150. The most commonly used method for the micropropagation of *Anthurium*.
[This is essentially the method of Leffring and Soede (1978a,b) — see text].

showed that rhizome multiplication depended on phosphate supply. An adequate increase in rhizome and shoot fresh weight did not occur until the concentration of PO_4^{3-} was 1.25 mM (as in **MS** medium) or 2.5 mM. The selection of vitamins has varied. Pierik *et al.* (1988b) used only 0.4 mg/l thiamine (no inositol), others have employed the vitamins of **LS** or **MS** media, or those of **Venverloo (1973)**.

Propagation. The chosen explants of *Alstroemeria* produce rhizomes *in vitro*, the lateral buds of which give rise to shoots. At each subculture, rhizomes are divided into segments of one or two nodes. If no cytokinin is added to the medium, roots are also formed from shoot bases.

Rhizome tips and shoot apices exert strong apical dominance which prevents the growth of dormant rhizome buds. To increase the rate of propagation, 1–5 mg/l BAP is usually added to the medium to promote the formation of branched rhizomes (Hussey *et al.*, 1980; Pierik *et al.*, 1988b; Gabryszewska and Hempel, 1985). Rhizome branching is also enhanced by removing both rhizome apices and aerial shoots from rhizome segments at each subculture (Bond and Alderson, 1993b). Some workers have added a small amount of auxin (*e.g.* 0.01 mg/l NAA) but this is probably unnecessary.

Rooting. Rooting is inhibited by BAP, but divisions of the rhizome-bearing shoots can be rooted on a medium containing 0.5–1 mg/l NAA (Pierik *et al.*, 1988b). However, others have preferred to use IBA: Hussey *et al.*,

(1980) promoted rooting with 0.03 mg/l of this auxin and Gabryszewska and Hempel (1985) found that the growth of upright shoots and roots was satisfactory on a medium containing 2 mg/l IBA. Rooting has generally been obtained on the same medium as that used for shoot proliferation. Pierik *et al.* (1988b) added 50 g/l sucrose to **MS** medium.

Conditions. Rhizome cultures have usually been maintained at 21°C and Pierik *et al.* (1988b) found that 8 h days under an irradiance of 7 µmol m^{-2} s^{-1} was adequate for rhizome growth. Bond and Alderson (1992a) reached contrary conclusions and showed that rhizomes multiplied most rapidly when incubated at 15°C in an 8 h day where the PPFD was 23.3 µmol m^{-2} s^{-1}.

Araceae
Anthurium spp.

Of the many species in this genus, *A. andraeanum* and *A. scherzerianum* are most widely known. They are grown in the tropics and sub–tropics as outdoor ornamentals. In temperate climes, *A. andraeanum* is cultivated by nurserymen for cut flower production, and the smaller *A. scherzerianum* as a flowering pot plant. Some other species, such as *A. crystallinum*, *A. macrolobum*, *A. pandulifolium*, *A. veitchii* and *A. warocqueanum*, are grown for their attractive foliage.

The flowers of *Anthurium* are arranged upon a cylindrical spadix at the base of which is a bract (spathe) which is usually brightly coloured. As anthuriums are outbreeding, and batches of plants raised from seed display marked variability, there has been an opportunity to clone varieties with desirable characteristics using tissue culture. Large numbers of anthurium plants are cloned by micropropagation in the Netherlands (Van der Meijs, 1980; Pierik, 1991a).

Shoot culture

A method for shoot culture of *Anthurium* was described by Kunisaki (1980). Vegetative buds were cultured first of all in a liquid medium containing **MS** salts, 0.4 mg/l thiamine HCl, 0.5 mg/l each of nicotinic acid and pyridoxine HCl, 15% coconut milk and 2% sucrose. Shoots were multiplied on the same agar–solidified medium (without coconut milk) and 0.2 mg/l BAP. Multiple shoots were produced from 2–node stem sections. Shoots formed in shoot cultures have been found to arise both from axillary buds and adventitiously (Geier, 1990).

Shoot culture has the disadvantage that only a small number of buds can be excised from one stock plant, explants are very likely to be contaminated, and the stock plant is virtually destroyed during dissection.

Adventitious shoots from callus

Despite the possibility of using shoot culture, *Anthurium* is frequently micropropagated by procedures which rely, at least in part, on the production of adventitious shoots from callus cultures. This genus is thus one of the few in which indirect shoot regeneration is employed.

Pierik and co-workers (1974a,b) first developed a method of propagating *Anthurium* from callus cultures. In early experiments callus was initiated from seed embryos. In later work (Pierik *et al.*, 1975d; 1979b; Pierik and Steegmans, 1975e; 1976a), segments of the leaves of mature plants were used as explants. Callus capable of producing adventitious shoots can be obtained from a variety of tissues, including spadix, spathe, peduncle, and the petioles and laminae of young leaves. Spadix explants usually require to be transferred to fresh medium several times before they start to produce callus. They also have a strong floral determination and are liable to regenerate putative ovules, stigmas and styles during several transfers (Geier and Reuther, 1981; Geier, 1982a).

Sections cut from young leaves are now most commonly used in *Anthurium* micropropagation. In most genotypes these explants provide callus capable of producing adventitious shoots when incubated in the dark at 25°C on a suitable medium. Etiolated adventitious shoots arise spontaneously from the primary callus which can be subdivided and subcultured again in the dark to obtain more shoots. If the callus is transferred to the light (40–50 μmol m^{-2} s^{-1}), shoots of normal appearance are produced. Callus can also be subdivided at this stage for further shoot proliferation. On a standard medium, callus is either not produced from non–responsive genotypes, or callus is formed but does not give rise to adventitious shoots.

Although shoots have resulted from indirect shoot formation, variability in populations of micropropagated anthuriums is said not to be high. Variation increases if non–regenerative callus is subcultured before shoot regeneration, or if shoot–forming callus is divided and subcultured many times to obtain shoot multiplication. To ensure that plant uniformity remained within acceptable limits, Leffring *et al.* (1976a) and Leffring and Soede (1978a,b) suggested that the adventitious shoots produced by callus cultures should be subcultured to a medium which allowed the development of axillary shoots. This combination of indirect adventitious shoot regeneration followed by shoot culture, appears to be the method of micropropagation which has been most widely used in commercial practice. It is illustrated in Fig. 150.

Media. Geier (1986, 1987, 1990) found that callus initiation and multiplication of shoot–forming callus, in both *A. andraeanum* and *A. scherzerianum*, was satisfactory on the medium of **Bourgin and Nitsch (1967) H** in which ammonium nitrate was reduced to 200 mg/l (2.5 mM). The medium was augmented with 20 g/l sucrose. This reduction in the NH$_4^+$ ion concentration to 2.5 mM (from 9.0 mM in **Bourgin and Nitsch (1967) H** medium) resulted in callus and adventitious shoots being produced in a wider range of genotypes, and in more shoots being regenerated (Geier, 1986).

Other research workers (Pierik, 1975a; Pierik and Steegmans, 1976a; Fersing and Lutz, 1977; Leffring and Soede, 1979a,b) have used ½**MS** salts, normal **MS** vitamins, and 20–40 g/l glucose for callus cultures. Sometimes the concentrations of magnesium sulphate and calcium chloride have been kept at the same level as in full strength **MS** (Kuehnle and Sugii, 1991).

Growth regulators. Growth regulants added to these media to induce callus formation followed by shoot regeneration have been:

0.1 mg/l 2,4–D and 1 mg/l BAP	Geier (1986)
0.08 mg/l 2,4–D and 3 mg/l 2–iP	Leffring and Soede (1979a,b)

Shoot proliferation. Axillary and adventitious shoot proliferation from shoots separated from callus cultures can be carried out in **Bourgin and Nitsch (1967)** with 20 g/l sucrose (Geier, 1990) or a medium containing ½**MS** salts (with only 200 mg/l NH$_4$NO$_3$), **MS** vitamins and 40 g/l glucose (Leffring and Soede, 1979a,b; Geier, 1990). This stage of propagation is identical to the shoot culture technique for which Kunisaki (1980) used **MS** medium (see above). It may be carried out in a liquid, or on a semi–solid medium.

Although shoot proliferation is induced by 0.2–0.5 mg/l BAP, the subsequent capacity of shoots to form roots decreases if subculturing is continued. It may therefore be preferable to employ up to 3 mg/l kinetin to induce shoot multiplication (Leffring and Soede, 1979a,b).

Rooting

Shoot and plantlet survival has generally been low when *ex vitro* rooting of *Anthurium* shoots has been attempted. Shoots are therefore generally rooted *in vitro* on a dilute medium without regulants, or one containing a low concentration of auxin.

Other Araceae

The attractive sagittate (arrow–shaped), hastate (spear–shaped) or peltate (petiole joined at a point towards the centre of the lamina) leaves of many genera of the Araceae, their 'flowers', and the ease with which plants can be grown, has led to their popularity as ornamentals. Apart from *Anthurium* described above, plants in this family commonly sold as pot plants include:

Grown for flowers and foliage	*Zantedeschia*
	Spathiphyllum
Grown for foliage	*Caladium* (leaves often multi-coloured)
	Dieffenbachia (foliage often variegated)
	Scindapsus (foliage often variegated)
	Monstera (climbers)
	Philodendron (climbers)
	Syngonium (climbers)

One suspects that several of these genera could be multiplied using the method developed for *Anthurium*, but shoot culture is preferred where a satisfactory rate of multiplication is possible, and must be used where chimeral leaf markings are to be retained.

Araceae
Spathiphyllum

Fonnesbech and Fonnesbech (1979) found that to avoid systemic infections, cultures were best initiated from lateral buds. By transferring stem segments thereafter onto **LS** medium with 30 g/l sucrose and 0.2–2 mg/l PBA

or kinetin, approximately 4 axillary or adventitious shoots could be obtained per subculture.

Spathiphyllum has been widely propagated by micropropagation laboratories but the market for vegetatively produced plants has collapsed recently due to the development of new varieties which can be grown from seeds.

Araceae
Syngonium

The technique developed for *Syngonium podophyllum* by Miller and Murashige (1976) was also employed by Makino and Makino (1978). Lateral buds were isolated into slowly rotated liquid **Miller and Murashige (1976) IV** medium (30 g/l sucrose) containing 1 mg/l IAA and 3 mg/l 2–iP and incubated at 27°C in a 16 h day (1000 lux). When transferred to a stationary liquid medium of the same composition, but supplemented with 20 mg/l 2–iP (plus 3 mg/l IAA —Makino and Makino), clumps of shoots were formed which could be subcultured by division. Alternatively, individual shoots were moved to **LS** medium with 3 mg/l IAA, to be rooted. Illumination was increased at Stage II to 3000 lux, and at Stage III to 10 000 lux.

Araceae
Caladium (Angel's Wings)

Shoot culture. The desirable variegation and colour patterns in the leaves of certain *Caladium* varieties appear to be due to their chimeral nature. Such plants can be multiplied by shoot culture, although many shoots may arise adventitiously. The method used by Cooper and Cohen (1983) was similar to that used by Cohen (1982) for *Zantedeschia* (*q.v.*). Explants of *C. × hortulanum* were established, on agar–solidified **LS** medium (30 g/l sucrose) with 1 mg/l BAP. Growth was initially slow but shoots were formed, together with suppressed bud tissue at the shoot bases. If shoots were cut off and the shoot bases subcultured, the multiplication rate gradually increased during progressive transfers. Shoots elongated and formed roots when the BAP concentration was reduced to 0.1 mg/l.

Callus culture. Culturing sections of young leaves on semi–solid modified **MS** medium with 1 mg/l 2,4–D and 1 mg/l kinetin caused callus to be produced which could be multiplied on a liquid medium, or induced to regenerate shoots on a medium supplemented with 1 mg/l NAA and 1 mg/l BAP. Plants were obtained which had leaf patterns unlike that of the stock plant (Sahavacharin, 1982). Hartman (1974) propagated *Caladium*

found *Aechmea* lateral bud explants were liable to browning and so kept them in a solution of citric and ascorbic acids before inoculation.

Bromeliaceae
Aechmea, Ananas, (and *Cryptanthus*)

MS medium is suitable for *Aechmea, Ananas*, and *Cryptanthus*. Shoot proliferation may be faster if, at Stage II, liquid medium is used and the phosphate level is increased (Jones and Murashige, 1974; Mathews *et al.* 1976). Pineapple (*Ananas comosus*) is commonly multiplied using **MS** medium (see page 1020).

Jones and Murashige (1974) placed explants of *Aechmea* on **MS** medium containing 100 mg/l citric acid (to prevent browning). Growth regulants at Stage I were 1.75 mg/l IBA and 1.75 mg/l NAA. Shoot multiplication occurred when explants were moved to **Jones and Murashige (1974) B** medium (Jones and Murashige, 1974). An alternative medium used by Hosoki and Asahira (1980b) at this stage was **MS** salts with the micronutrients and organics of **Ringe and Nitsch (1968)**. Shoot proliferation was promoted by 2 mg/l IAA, 40 mg/l adenine sulphate and 2 m/l IAA (Jones and Murashige, 1974), or 1 mg/l NAA and 1 mg/l BAP (Hosoki and Asahira, 1980b).

During Stage II multiplication, shoots can arise from leaves (Hosoki and Asahira, 1980b; Zimmer and Pieper, 1975) and so in many cultures shoots probably have both an adventitious and an axillary origin. Callus-like growth or basal callus has also been reported in Bromeliaceae culture (Mekers, 1977; Mathews *et al.* 1976; Zimmer and Pieper, 1976).

Micropropagation of *Aechmea fasciata* has been found to give rise to a higher than expected frequency of variability in regenerated plants (Jones and Murashige, 1974; Zimmer and Pieper, 1976). The variation, which increases with progressive subcultures, is not, according to Jones and Murashige (1974) due to changes in ploidy. They recommend no more than three subcultures of this species to keep a high percentage of uniform ramets. As Bromeliads with chimeral leaf variations are highly likely to lose their characteristic leaf patterns (Chapter 3), micropropagation is only recommended where it is possible to ensure that shoots arise from axillary buds. Abnormal plants sometimes result from the micropropagation of *Ananas comosus*.

Bromeliaceae
Guzmania, Tillandsia, and *Vriesea*

These genera, all in the tribe Tillandsioideae, behave rather differently in culture to other Bromeliaceae. Although some plants have been multiplied in full strength **MS** (Hosoki and Asahira, 1980b), Mekers (1977) and Mekers and Van Onsem (1983) found that at this concentration the medium was less suitable for these genera and that they grew better on more dilute preparations such as **Knudson (1946) C**, or **MS** salts at half to one quarter of the normal strength. **Knudson (1946) C** medium has an ionic concentration which is approximately one third that of **MS**, but it is proportionately high in phosphate. Agar–solidified media are better than liquid formulations (Mekers, 1977).

Stage I cultures of *Vriesea* were grown by Mekers and Van Onsem (1983) on $\frac{1}{3}$**MS** salts plus **Mekers (1977) A** vitamins, 4 mg/l glycine, 30 g/l sucrose and 0.5 mg/l NAA.

> **Mekers (1977) A** vitamins contain (mg/l) 100 *myo*–inositol, 5 thiamine–HCl, 5 nicotinic acid, and 0.5 pyridoxine–HCl.

Stage II cultures were grown on a similar low salts medium as that used at Stage I, but containing 0.1–0.5 mg/l NAA and 0.5–1 BAP (or 1–5 mg/l 2i–P), actual concentrations varying with cultivar. All cultures survived when the Stage II medium was solidified with agar. Some died on liquid medium but the survivors showed more axillary shoot proliferation. As growth improved when leaves elongated above the liquid, it is probable that addition of a liquid upper phase to an agar–based medium after a period of preliminary growth would give good results.

Optimum concentrations of growth regulators at Stage II for other Tillandsioideae had previously been found by Mekers (1977) to be:

Tillandsia polystachya	0.5 mg/l NAA, 1 mg/l BAP, 40 mg/l adenine
Vriesea heliconioides	1.0 mg/l IAA, 0.5 mg/l BAP, 40 mg/l adenine
Vriesea splendens	1.0 mg/l NAA, 0.1 mg/l BAP, 40 mg/l adenine
Vriesea 'Myers Favoriet'	1.0 mg/l NAA, 0.5 mg/l BAP, 40 mg/l adenine

The production of axillary shoots induced at Stage II must be arrested before plants are transferred to the soil. Shoots

Table 139. Media and growth regulators used for meristem culture of carnation.

Medium	Sugar (g/l)	Growth regulators (mg/l)	Support	Reference
½**Knop (1965)** + ½**Berthelot (1934) Dilution** + 1 mg/l thiamine	40 glu	1 NAA, 8 adenine	Filter paper wicks	Baker and Phillips (1962)
Knop (1965) + ½**Berthelot (1934) Dilution** + 1 mg/l thiamine	40 glu	1 NAA	Filter paper wicks	Stone (1963)
½**MS** salts + 1 mg/l thiamine	20 suc	0.1 NAA, 0.1 GA$_3$	Static liquid ‡	Pennazio (1975)
MS	30 suc	1 kin †	Filter paper wicks	Gukasyan *et al.* (1977)
LS	30 suc	0.3 IAA, 1 kin	0.6% agar	Shabde and Murashige (1977)

†   Shoots needed to be rooted afterwards on agar–solidified **White (1954)** (plus FeEDTA) supplemented with 1 mg/l NAA;

‡   Without paper supports.

separated from Stage II cultures are therefore moved to a semi–solid medium. Supplemented with auxin, **Knudson (1946) C** or a medium containing ⅓ – ½**MS** salts is suitable. Mekers and Van Onsem (1983) used 0.5 mg/l NAA plus 1 mg/l IBA for *Vriesea*, Mercer and Kerbauy (1992), 0.1 mg/l NAA. Mekers (1977) found that NAA was toxic to *Tillandsia* at this stage, but that IAA was suitable. More than one subculture may be necessary to restore apical dominance and for roots to be induced.

Caryophyllaceae
Dianthus spp. and hybrids
(Carnation and Pink)

Because of their attractive flowers, many species of *Dianthus* are grown as garden ornamentals. Improved forms and interspecific hybrids of *Dianthus caryophyllus* are cultivated as border and perpetual flowering carnations, and because these plants are widely grown as glasshouse crops for cut flower production, their tissue culture has been most studied.

Uses for tissue culture

Carnations (like chrysanthemums) are readily propagated from cuttings produced from stock plants in greenhouses by specialised growers. The price of cuttings is well below the cost of producing shoots or plantlets through micro-propagation (page 788) so that, at present, tissue culture is only used to provide virus–free stock.

Meristem tip culture

To obtain plants which are likely to be virus–free, mer-istem cultures are usually initiated with shoot tips bearing two small leaf initials 0.25–1 mm in length.

These explants may be cultured in a variety of ways. Media and growth regulators which have been used by various workers are shown in Table 139. Roots are formed voluntarily on the base of shoots unless cytokinin has been included in the medium, when a separate rooting stage may be required. However shoot growth and axil-lary branching are promoted by cytokinin. Pennazio (1975) found that kinetin inhibited simultaneous rooting, but that adenine did not do so providing its concentration was less than 10 mg/l.

Using conventional means of propagation, it can take several years to multiply virus free plants to obtain a sufficient number of stock plants for cutting production. During this time precautions must be taken to ensure against reinfestation of the pathogen–free material. There is thus an opportunity to provide the plantlets required as stock plants by multiplying plants obtained by meristem culture (once they have been virus tested).

Shoot and node culture

Cultures have in the past often been initiated from shoot tips and multiplication achieved by the production of lateral (or adventitious shoots), but carnation can also be propagated, like *Dendranthema*, by the culture of nodes which give rise to shoots that are again divided (Dereud-dre *et al.*, 1987; 1988).

Media. The salts of **MS** medium have been used in virtually all the reported descriptions of shoot and node culture in *Dianthus*. Petru and Landa (1974) and Hempel (1979) used a medium containing only 50 mg/l *myo*–inositol and this concentration (in conjunction with the rest of **MS** vitamins at normal strength) was found experi-mentally by Davis *et al.* (1977) to support the best shoot

Table 140. Growth regulators used to obtain direct shoot formation from carnation explants cultured on **MS** medium.

Explant	Auxin (mg/l)	Cytokinin (mg/l)	Reference
Sections of nodes	0.1 IAA	1 BAP	Roest and Bokelmann (1981)
Petal bases	1 NAA	1 BAP	Leshem (1986)
Young petals	2 NAA	0.5 BAP	Vainstein et al. (1992)
	0.93 NAA †	2.25 BAP	Nakano et al. (1994)
	0.93 NAA †	1.1–2.2 TDZ	
	0.93 NAA †	1.2–2.5 2Cl–4PU	
Petal sections	3 NAA	1 BAP	Simard et al. (1992)
Leaves ex i.v. plants	0.3 NAA	0.3 BAP	Van Altvorst et al. (1992)

† These were alternative treatments

growth. Other modifications which resulted in improved growth were:

- Using 50 g/l sucrose, 40 g/l glucose, or 20 g/l each of both sugars;

- Adding 0.74 mg/l (5 µM) cinnamic acid and 3 g/l casein hydrolysate to the medium.

Davis et al. found that the shoots had a higher fresh weight when grown with **MS** micronutrients than with those of **Heller (1953; 1955)**, but Dencso (1987) found it advantageous to reduce the concentration of **MS** micronutrients to $\frac{1}{10}$ because there was then less hyperhydricity.

Growth regulators. Because of the susceptibility of Dianthus to hyperhydricity, kinetin is more frequently added to the medium for Dianthus than BAP. Examples of commonly used combinations of auxin and cytokinin are:

NAA mg/l	Kinetin mg/l	References
0.1	0.5	Earle and Langhans (1975) Dencso (1987)
0.2	2.2	Davis et al. (1977)
0.02	2.0	Jelaska and Šutina (1977)
0.09	2.9	Dabski et al. (1979)
0.5	0.5	Ziv et al. (1983)

Hempel (1979) was able to obtain a high number of shoots when cultures were first grown on modified **MS** medium containing 1.35 mg/l BAP and then afterwards moved to 0.9 mg/l kinetin. However the shoots produced were not of a normal appearance.

Hyperhydricity. Hyperhydricity is commonly encountered during tissue culture of Caryophyllaceae and can make micropropagation difficult. The susceptibility of Dianthus to hyperhydricity has led to the genus often being used in research into this subject. Methods whereby the symptoms can be reduced have been mentioned in Chapter 13.

Carnation shoots should have a glaucous appearance in vitro and are showing symptoms of vitrescence if they become translucent. Shoot culture of carnation frequently results in a high proportion of translucent plants, most of which do not survive transfer to soil. Rapid shoot proliferation occurs if multiple shoots, produced during carnation shoot culture, are transferred to an agitated liquid medium (Earle and Langhans, 1975), but shoots grown on a liquid medium are very liable to have a water–soaked appearance. Cultivar 'Pallas' did not form multiple shoots on an agar–solidified medium, but did so in a liquid medium, but then all the shoots were glassy (Dencso, 1987).

Ziv and Ariel (1992) found that hyperhydricity could be reduced in Dianthus cultures by altering the concentrations of NH_4^+ and NO_3^- in **MS** medium to respectively, 6 mM and 40 mM, but possibly the best preventative measure is to keep cultures in vessels covered with porous filters which allow free gaseous exchange. Shoot and internode length are less under these conditions but this drawback can be avoided if water is added to the vessels at regular intervals to compensate for evaporation (Majada et al., 1992).

Direct shoot formation.

Adventitious shoots can be induced to form on a variety of Dianthus explants (Table 148). Successful growth regulator treatments in some experiments where **MS** medium was used, are shown in Table 140. Carnation plants regenerated from petal and anther explants are liable to flower prematurely when acclimatized and grown in greenhouse or growth room (Villalobos, 1981; Kakehi, 1979; Nakano *et al.*, 1994).

Organised callus

Shoot apices of carnation mutilated with a razor blade appeared to produce an organised callus on a modified **White (1954)** medium supplemented with 2 mg/l NAA. This produced a mass of adventitious shoots when transferred to a medium with half the concentration of auxin (Hackett and Anderson, 1967).

Compositae (Asteraceae)

Dendranthema × *grandiflorum* (= *Chrysanthemum* × *morifolium*)

(Chrysanthemum)

The very many varieties of *Dendranthema* × *grandiflorum* which are grown for cut flower production and as garden plants, are readily propagated from cuttings by conventional techniques. Large scale micropropagation is not economic and is only practised to raise and maintain stocks of virus–free plants for use as stock plants.

Meristem, shoot and node culture

Meristems of *Dendranthema*, usually taken from heat–treated plants, are cultured to obtain virus free plants. Some authors have described the culture of meristems on **MS** medium, but as shoot tips are very likely to give rise to callus when grown in this way, it may be better to use a dilute medium (*e.g.* one comprising, together with vitamins, **Knop (1865)** macronutrients and **Berthelot (1934)** micronutrients — Hollings, 1965). Single shoots and plantlets were obtained from small meristems by Earle and Langhans (1974a) on **LS** medium providing they only added a low concentration of NAA and no cytokinin. Shoots were very likely to have callus at their bases. Protocols for indexing chrysanthemum plants for the presence of virus are given by Horst (1990).

Shoot cultures producing multiple shoots have been initiated from shoot tips cultured on **MS** medium (30 g/l sucrose) containing 0.2 mg/l NAA, 2 mg/l kinetin and 0.2 mg/l GA_3 (Sangwan *et al.*, 1987), but probably the simplest and most reliable way to multiply chrysanthemums is to use node culture. Stems cut into nodal segments cultured on **MS** medium without regulants, or supplemented with 0.01 mg/l NAA and 0.1 mg/l BAP, produce single shoots which, when incubated at 23°C in 16 h light (50–60 μmol m^{-2} s^{-1}) can be divided into nodal segments and subcultured every 6 weeks (Roberts and Smith, 1990).

Table 141. Treatments resulting in callus initiation and shoot regeneration in *Dendranthema* × *grandiflorum*. The medium used is shown in square brackets: the sucrose concentration in round brackets.

	Explant	Medium and growth regulators used Growth regulators in mg/l	Results obtained	Reference
1.	Shoot apices	[†] (2) 0.2 NAA + 2 kinetin + 1 GA₃	Multiple shoots on same medium	Sangwan and Harada (1977)
1.	Shoot apices	[†] (2) 1 2,4-D	Callus formation	Sangwan and Harada (1977)
2.	Callus	[†] (2) 1 NAA + 0.5 kinetin	Adventitious shoots	
1.	Shoot apices	[MS ‡] (3) 1 IAA + 1 BAP	Organised callus with adv. shoots	Ahmed and Andrea (1987)
2.	Organised callus	[MS ‡] (3) 0.025–0.05 IAA + 0.05–0.1 BAP	Callus proliferated	
1.	Leaf and Stem	[MS] (3) + 2 2,4–D	Callus formation	Bhattacharya *et al.* (1990)
2.	Callus	[MS] (3) 0.1 IAA + 0.2 BAP	Adventitious shoots	
3.	Shoots	[MS] (3) 0.1 IAA + 0.2 BAP (liquid), Shoots multiplied rapidly		
1.	Stem sections	[MS ¶] (2) 2 NAA + 0.8 kinetin	Callus formation	Hill (1968)
2.	Callus	[MS ¶ ††] (2) 1 kinetin ‡	Shoot regeneration	

†   The medium of **Nitsch and Nitsch (1965) S** — see Part 1, page 386

‡   But with the micronutrients of **Heller (1953, 1955)**, see Part 1, page 403

¶   But with slightly altered micronutrients, and approximately ⅕ the normal concentration of nicotinic acid and pyridoxine HCl.

†† Medium supplemented with peptone at this stage

Fig. 151. Chrysanthemum microcuttings rooted into plugs.

Direct shoot formation

Adventitious shoots have been induced to develop on a variety of *Dendranthema* explants, including the tubular or ligulate corollas ('petals', ray florets) of mature flowers, and other explants listed in Table 148. Cultures have almost always been incubated on **MS** medium, but there has been variation in the growth regulators which authors have found to give the best results. For example:

Explant	Growth regulators	References
Stem and leaf	1 mg/l NAA and 0.5 mg/l BAP	Lu *et al.* (1990)
Stem and leaf from *in vitro* cultures	0.9 mg/l NAA and 1.1 mg/l BAP	Kaul *et al.* (1990)
Stem	0.2 mg/l NAA + 2 mg/l kinetin	Chaney *et al.* (1985)

The optimum combination of growth regulators to obtain direct shoot formation from inflorescence pedicels was found by Roest and Bokelmann (1975) to vary with genotype. The presence of 0.01 mg/l IAA together with 1 mg/l BAP was best for cv. 'Super Yellow', but better results were obtained with 'Bravo' when the IAA concentration was increased to 1 mg/l. Sections cut from the top of young 8 cm stems produced more shoots per explant than sections cut from lower down the stem (Lu *et al.*, 1990).

Direct embryogenesis

Using the medium of **Heinz and Mee (1969)** supplemented with 1 mg/l 2,4–D and 0.2 mg/l BAP, May and Trigiano (1991) obtained the direct formation of somatic embryos on leaf midrib sections excised from stock plants in 12 out of 23 chrysanthemum cultivars.

Embryogenesis did not occur in darkness and was reduced when explants were continuously cultured in a 16 h photoperiod (25 μmol m^{-2} s^{-1}). Most embryos were formed following 28 days dark incubation, followed by 10 days in the light and a further 10 days of darkness, and when 120 g/l sucrose was added to the medium.

Regeneration from callus cultures

Highly regenerative callus can be obtained from many different *Dendranthema* explants (Table 148). A variety of media has been used successfully for this purpose, although in most published experiments **MS** macronutrients have been employed. The fact that micronutrients and vitamins have varied suggests that the exact composition of these components is not important. Growth regulators used to induce callus and adventitious shoot formation are shown in Table 141.

An organised callus seems to be produced frequently from shoot apex explants (Earle and Langhans, 1984c; Ahmed and Andrea, 1987). Callus of this kind has the capacity to produce plantlets after repeated subcultures and is also very likely to be capable of producing genetically–uniform plants (Part 1, page 54). Ahmed and Andrea (1987) noted that, compared to apices from normal plants, those excised from heat–treated plants survived better, and produced callus which grew and multiplied more rapidly.

Many chrysanthemum varieties are chimeras, the characteristics of which are liable to be lost during micropropagation, especially if this relies on direct shoot formation or indirectly formed adventitious shoots (Bush *et al.*, 1974; 1976). *Dendranthema* plants regenerated from callus cultures have, in any case, been found to display much somaclonal variation (Miyazaki *et al.*, 1976; Miyazaki and Tashiro, 1978a). Meristem culture of the variety 'Blanche Poitevine Supreme' on **MS** medium resulted in plants with phenotypes which were strikingly different from the parent plant (Votruba and Kodytek, 1988).

Rooting

Dendranthema shoots are readily rooted *extra vitrum (Fig. 151), but where in vitro* root formation is required, it can be obtained by culturing shoots on ½**MS**, **MS** or **White (1954)** (10–30 g/l sucrose) without regulants (Kaul *et al.*, 1990), or with the medium supplemented with 0.1 mg/l IAA (Roest and Bokelmann, 1975; Sangwan *et al.*, 1987), or 0.01–0.1 mg/l NAA (Roberts and Smith, 1990; Smith E.F. *et al.*, 1991). Nodes cultured on medium devoid of growth regulators produce shoots which are self–rooting.

Compositae (Asteraceae)
Gerbera jamesonii

In vitro methods have proved to be highly successful for the multiplication of *Gerbera*, and currently, plants of this genus are probably micropropagated in larger numbers than any other (Pierik, 1991a,b). Plantlets are mainly sold to nurserymen for cut flower production. As the genus is heterozygous and varieties do not come true from seed, before the advent of micropropagation techniques, clones could only be increased slowly by crown divisions.

Shoot culture

The standard methodology for shoot culture was devised by Murashige *et al.* (1974). Their medium is listed in Table 47 (Part 1, page 386).

> These authors initiated cultures from shoot tips and grew them, during shoot multiplication at Stage II, with 45 g/l sucrose, 0.5 mg/l IAA and 10 mg/l kinetin added to an agar solidified medium. Cultures were maintained at 27°C with 12–16 h of 1000 lux illumination per day and subcultured at intervals of 4–8 weeks. Using MS salts instead of those used by Murashige et al. has no effect on propagation rate during one subculture (Wozniak et al., 1982), but reducing the concentration of micronutrients to ¹⁄₁₀ the normal level, has an immediate depressing effect on the number of axillary shoots produced (Dencso, 1987).

Soczek and Hempel (1988) studied the effect of the organic components of the medium of **Murashige *et al.* (1974).** For the 3 cultivars they studied, thiamine, *myo*–inositol, pyridoxine, adenine sulphate and L–tyrosine appeared to produce no benefit. However, nicotinic acid (10 mg/l) was essential and, in at least one cultivar, its omission caused a significant drop in the rate of multiplication. A similar result was obtained during one subculture by Wozniak *et al.* (1982).

Although the rate of shoot multiplication is high when 0.5–1.25 mg/l BAP is added to **Murashige *et al.* (1974) medium** (Blakesley and Lenton, 1987; Hempel *et al.*, 1985), shoots may become hyperhydric in the presence of this cytokinin (Hempel *et al.*, 1985; Dencso, 1987; Meyer and Van Staden, 1988; Kataeva *et al.*, 1991). The usual practice is to add kinetin to the medium, the most effective concentration of which varies with the cultivar to be propagated. Pierik *et al.* (1982) and Hempel *et al.* (1985) found that 5–10 mg/l kinetin resulted in shoots of high quality. Wozniak *et al.* (1982) discovered that an initial kinetin level of 10 mg/l became toxic after many subcultures, and 3–5 mg/l (depending on the cultivar) gave a faster rate of shoot multiplication and better shoot quality.

Although an agar–solidified medium is often described for gerbera, Stage II cultures proliferate satisfactorily on a static liquid medium.

Rooting

Separated shoots produced by the propagation method of Murashige *et al.* were found to root poorly if moved directly from the multiplication medium to soil, even if first dipped into auxin solutions. Shoots were also very liable to damping off. Much better results were obtained if shoots were subcultured for 10 days on the same medium as that used for multiplication, but containing no cytokinin and 10 mg/l IAA. Increasing the light level to at least 3000 lux was also beneficial. Treated in this way, almost all the shoots rooted when moved *ex vitro*. Separated shoots were found to root much more readily than shoot clusters. Root initiation and later plant survival was said to be improved by adding 2.6 mg/l ABA to the root induction medium (Wozniak *et al.*, 1982).

To root *Gerbera* shoots *in vitro*, Pierik *et al.* (1975a) used a medium containing **MS** macronutrients, 45 g/l sucrose and either 10 mg/l IAA or 10 mg/l IBA.

Direct and indirect shoot initiation

Direct and/or indirect shoot formation can be achieved by using suitable *Gerbera* explants:

Explants	Medium used	Reference
Young capitula	½MS macros + Heller (1953) micros	Pierik *et al.* (1975a)
	Based on MS	Laliberté *et al.* (1985)
Leaves from shoot cultures	High phosphate, but other ions slightly less concentrated than in MS salts	Reynoird *et al.* (1993)
	LS	Jerzy and Lubomski (1992)

The media above were supplemented with:

Regulants (mg/l)	Reference
10 BAP + 0.1 IAA	Pierik *et al.* (1975a)
1–2 BAP + 0.1 IAA + 80 AdS	Laliberté *et al.* (1985)
2.2 BAP + 0.44 NAA + 20 AdS ± 0.022–0.22 TDZ	Reynoird *et al.* (1993)
3 BAP + 0.5 IAA	Jerzy and Lubomski (1992)

Conti *et al.* (1991) tested new genotypes for their ability to respond to the micropropagation method of Laliberté *et al.* (1985), but only five out of 30 were considered to give a satisfactory response.

When capitula are used as explants, florets are removed before sterilisation and each capitulum divided into 4 segments bearing a 2 cm portion of the scape. Explants are best kept in the dark for 4 weeks before being transferred to continuous light (Pierik *et al.*, 1973, 1975a). An incubation temperature of 25°C has been found to be satisfactory.

The propagation of *Gerbera* is slower when shoots are derived directly from capitulum explants than when they are produced from shoot cultures, but losses during culture initiation are smaller. Pierik *et al.* (1975a, 1979a) therefore suggested that micropropagation could be conveniently started using capitula and the shoots obtained therefrom subsequently progressed to shoot culture.

Geraniaceae

Pelargonium spp.　(Pelargonium or Geranium)

Many varieties and species of *Pelargonium* are cultivated as garden ornamentals and pot plants. Those which are most popular, and hence of chief importance to the horticultural industry, are:

- *P.* × *hortorum* (zonal pelargoniums, used for bedding displays),

    P. × *hortorum* has resulted from interspecific hybridisation, with *P. zonale*. The leaves are rounded and have a conspicuous central zone which is maroon or bronze in colour. Flowers are single (with five petals), semi–double or double.

Some authors describe propagating *P. zonale* varieties, when it is highly probable that they have been dealing with plants of *P.* × *hortorum*. This is confusing, as the genuine *P. zonale* species is still in cultivation.

- *P.* × *domesticum* (Regal pelargoniums)

    Regal pelargoniums have deeply serrated leaves and broadly trumpet shaped flowers. Plants are grown for display out–of–doors but, as flowers are liable to weather damage, they are also favoured as specimen pot plants. Plants of this group are hybrids of *P. grandiflorum* with other species, and are sometimes described as *P. grandiflorum* hybrids or varieties. As the true *P. grandiflorum* is still cultivated, it can be difficult to ascertain which kind of plant has been cultured.

- *P. peltatum* (Ivy–leafed pelargoniums)

    Leaves are broadly similar in shape to those of common ivy. Stems are long and trailing, making plants very suitable for hanging baskets. Flowers are similar to those of *P.* × *hortorum*.

Several true *Pelargonium* species are also grown in gardens, mainly for their foliage, which is often attractively scented. *P. graveolens, P. capitatum,* and *P. crispum* are some of these.

Many kinds of pelargonium can be raised from seed, but vegetative propagation is still used extensively by horticulturist for named cultivars and plants which are readily obtained from cuttings. As with carnations and chrysanthemums, the use of micropropagation for mass propagation of *Pelargonium* species and cultivars is generally uneconomic. Tissue culture is mainly used to free plants from pathogens and to build up stocks of pathogen–free mother plants.

Meristem culture. Amongst the several diseases to which pelargoniums are susceptible, viruses and bacterial blight disease and bacterial stem rot (both caused by *Xanthomonas campestris* pv. *pelargonii*) are difficult to control during conventional propagation, but can be eliminated using meristem culture. The methods used by Cassells *et al.* (1980) and Reuther (1988) to obtain plants free from *X. pelargonii* are illustrated in Part 1 (pages 135 and 139). Heat therapy of mother plants at 38°C (day) and 35°C (night) is adequate for reducing tobacco ringspot infection in geranium meristems (Horst *et al.*, 1976).

There seem to be two ways of culturing meristem tips of *Pelargonium*.

- In the first method, using a low strength medium and minimal concentrations of growth regulators, meristems develop conventionally into single shoots which can be rooted. This technique was used by Pillai and Hildebrandt (1968), Horst *et al.*

(1976) and Beauchesne *et al.* (1977), two of whose media are given in Table 142. Once shoots had two well developed leaves, Beauchesne *et al.* transferred them to the same medium as that listed in the table, but without peptone and yeast extract and with only 10 g/l glucose.

Pelargonium meristems are very liable to callus in culture. Beauchesne *et al.* found that this was less likely with meristems of *P. × hortorum* than with those of *P. peltatum*, providing low concentrations of growth regulators were used: 0.01–0.25 mg/l IAA, 0.1–0.5 mg/l 2–iP, and 2 mg/l adenine were recommended.

— In the second method of meristem culture, the explants have been cultured in such a way that some axillary and many *adventitious* shoots arise. In some reports, shoots have been derived from callus tissue. Adventitious shoots can also arise from an organised calloid tissue of the kind noted, for example, in *Dendranthema* (page 849). That such shoots did not have a normal adventitious origin was demonstrated by Cassells *et al.* (1980) who found that a chimera of *P. × hortorum* could be regenerated with its cell layers preserved. Variability in leaf characteristics was found in plants obtained from meristem culture of some non–variegated *P. × hortorum* varieties, and in *P. peltatum*, where shoots were regenerated mainly from unorganised callus, the plants eventually produced were highly variable (Reuther, 1983; 1988c).

Media used by Debergh and Maene (1977) and Cassells *et al.* (1980), which led to adventitious shoot formation from meristem tips, are given in Table 143. It will be seen that the concentration of NO_3^- and NH_4^+ is much higher than in the media listed in Table 142. On the medium of Cassells *et al.*, meristems 'proliferated' and could be subdivided and subcultured onto fresh medium. If left undivided, cultures gave rise to shoots which were excised and rooted *in vitro*. Debergh and Maene (1977) found that several axillary shoots (and later adventitious shoots) were obtained if the apices of individual buds developing on proliferating meristems were subcultured to fresh medium containing 0.5 mg/l IAA and 10 mg/l kinetin.

Blackening. Blackening of explants can be prevented by preliminary culture on basal medium without growth regulators (and especially by avoiding the early administration of cytokinin) (Debergh and Maene, *loc. cit.*), by moving explants to a fresh position on the medium if a surrounding halo of pigment is observed (Cassells *et al. loc. cit.*), and by transferring them to fresh medium after one week (Harney, *loc. cit.*).

Table 142. Media and growth regulators used for *Pelargonium* meristem culture, to obtain single shoots.

Components		Horst *et al.* (1976)	Beauchesne *et al.* (1977)
Macronutrients (meq/l)	NO_3^-	29.5	24.0
	PO_4^{3-}	2.8	12.0
	SO_4^{2-}	2.3	4.0
	Cl^-	4.5	0.5
	K^+	15.0	10.5
	Ca^{2+}	4.5	8.0
	Na^+	—	—
	Mg^{2+}	2.3	4.0
	NH_4^+	15.5	10.0
Microelements		Unique mixture	**MS**
	NaFeEDTA (mM)	0.04	0.1
Vitamins (mg/l)	Inositol	100	100
	Thiamine (HCl)	0.075	1.0
	Nicotinic caid	0.375	1.0
	Pyridoxin (HCl)	0.375	1.0
	Ca pantothenate	—	1.0
	Biotin	—	0.01
Amino acids (mg/l)	Glycine	1.5	—
	Cysteine	2	—
	Glutamine	—	100
	Peptone of casein	—	250
	Yeast extract	—	250
Sugars (g/l)		30 Suc	30 Glu
Growth regulators (mg/l)	IAA	—	0.25
	NAA	1	—
	Kinetin	0.04	10
	2–iP	—	0.1
	GA_3	—	1
	Coconut milk	10%	—

Tables listing media in Chapter 17 give the comparative concentrations of macronutrient ions. Weights of salts from which each formulation can be prepared are given in the Appendix.

Node culture

Node culture provides a very simple method of multiplying pelargoniums. Defoliated shoots with 6–8 internodes from *in vitro* cultures, cut into single node segments, will produce an axillary shoot from the lateral bud if cultured

Callus which gave rise to adventitious shoots was obtained by Raman (1977) by culturing flower peduncle sections on a medium containing **MS** salts, and by Peck and Cumming (1984b) using flower corolla explants. These were cultured on a medium based on **Jones and Murashige (1974) B** salts which included the growth regulators adenine (125 mg/l), NAA (1 mg/l) and BAP (5 mg/l).

Gesneriaceae
Episcia

Episcia is another genus of the Gesneriaceae whose species are cultivated as pot plants. Like *Saintpaulia* it can be readily propagated from leaf sections, although several reports suggest that leaf sections readily form callus.

Callus which gave rise to shoots was produced on **MS** containing 0.2 mg/l IAA and 0.2 mg/l kinetin (Johnson, 1978b) or 0.1 mg/l NAA and 0.5 mg/l BAP (Bilkey and McCown, 1979). The latter is the same medium and growth regulators as induced regenerative callus from *Saintpaulia* petioles (Bilkey *et al.*, 1978). The callus formed on each explant did not produce shoots until it had increased in size to weigh *ca.* 3 g. Shoots produced roots when subcultured onto a medium with 0.1 mg/l NAA and 0.01 mg/l BAP (Bilkey and McCown, 1979) or 0.1–1 mg/l NAA (Johnson, 1978b).

Chin (1979, 1980) initiated callus from sections of the leaves of the variegated variety of *E. cupreata* 'Pink Brocade'. Green shoots were produced from callus formed on green leaf sections, but albino ones on the callus which developed on parts of the leaves which did not contain chlorophyll, proving that 'Pink Brocade' is a chimera. Occasionally shoots with both green and white leaf markings were produced from the callus derived from green tissues, suggesting that this tissue still contained some albino cells.

Gesneriaceae
Kohleria

Geier (1982b) obtained adventitious shoots on internode segments of *Kohleria* hybrids using a medium also used for *Saintpaulia* [(**Bourgin and Nitsch (1967) H** containing 0.5 mg/l IAA and 1 mg/l kinetin].

Gesneriaceae
× Achimenantha

Adventitious shoots were formed on the edges and on the veins of ×*Achimenantha* leaf sections incubated on **MS** medium supplemented with 5 mg/l IAA. The shoots could be multiplied by transfer to medium containing 0.1 mg/l IAA and 10 mg/l kinetin, or rooted with 1 mg/l IAA (Griffis *et al.*, 1982). Roh and Wocial (1989) employed flower buds or scales excised from rhizomes as explants. The former were the best source of adventitious shoots, but the latter appeared to give rise to the strongest shoots. **Heinz and Mee (1969)** medium with modified macronutrients was used on this occasion.

Table 148. Published reports on the tissue culture of ORNAMENTAL HERBACEOUS PLANTS.

Species name	Type of Culture	Source of explant	Results		References
Acanthaceae					
Ruellia humilis	Embryo	Isolated embryos	Germination	Y	Baskin & Baskin (1971)
Agavaceae					
❖ *Agave sp.*	Callus	Cut seed fragments	Shoot regeneration: rooted plants	–	Groenewald *et al.* (1977)
Agave spp.	Callus	Stem sections	Shoot formation & multiplication. Shoots rooted	–	Madrigal-Lugo *et al.* (1990)
Agave spp.	Shoot	Lateral buds	Shoot multiplication. Shoots rooted	YY	Madrigal-Lugo *et al.* (1990)
Sansevieria cylindrica (Mother-in-law's tongue)	Callus	Leaf	Adventitious shoots	–	Hunault (1976)
Sansevieria trifasciata	Callus	Leaf sections	Meristemoid induction & shoot development. Rooted	–	Blazich & Novitzky (1984)
Aizoaceae					
Mesembryanthemum crystallinum	Direct/Callus	Hypocotyledonary node, leaf	Adv. shoots. Shoots rooted *in vitro*	Y	Meiners *et al.* (1991)
Mesembryanthemum floribunda	Callus	Root, stem, leaf	Indirect embryogenesis. Plants regenerated & flowered	–	Mehra & Mehra (1972)
Alstroemeriaceae					
❖ *Alstroemeria* 'Parigo Pink' (Peruvian lily)	Node	Rhizome tips *ex vitro* cultures	Multiple shoots & rhizome initials. Studied P effect	Y	Elliott *et al.* (1993)
Alstroemeria cv. 'Zebra'	Node	Rhizome segments	Rhizome proliferation, then shoot elongation & rooting	YY	Gabryszewska & Hempel (1985)
Alstroemeria	Node	Rhizome tips	Rhizomes formed. Nodal sections subcultured. Shoots. rooted	YY	Hussey *et al.* (1979)
Alstroemeria 'Toledo' and other hybrids	Node	Rhizome segments	Rhizomes multiplied and later rooted	YY	Pierik *et al.* (1988)
Alstroemeria hybrid	Shoot	Disinfected rhizome tips	Uninfected shoots	Y	Pedersen & Brandt (1992)
Alstroemeria hybrids 'Valiant', 'Parade', 'Eleanor'	Node	Nodal sections of rhizomes	Lateral rhizomes & multiple aerial shoots. Some rooting	YY	Bond & Alderson (1993a,b)
Alstroemeria hybrids	Embryo rescue	Embryos, 7d after pollin.	Seedling growth	–	Winski & Bridgen (1988)
Amaranthaceae					
Amaranthus spp.	Callus	Hypocotyls of aseptic sdlgs.	Plant regeneration (route unknown)	–	Locy & Fisher (1985)
Amaranthus caudatus L. 'Pan' (Love-lies-bleeding)	Shoot	Shoot tips	Shoots flowered *in vitro*	Y	Tisserat and Galleta (1988).
Amaranthus gangeticus L.	Shoot	Shoot tips	Shoots flowered *in vitro*	Y	Tisserat and Galleta (1988).
Amaranthus hypochondriacus L. (Prince's feathers)	Direct	Leaf discs	Embryoids from surface & veins	–	Flores *et al.* (1981)
Amaranthus hypochondriacus	Direct	Hypocotyl segments	Adventitious shoots	–	Flores *et al.* (1981)
Amaranthus hypochondriacus	Shoot	Shoot tips	Shoots flowered *in vitro*	Y	Tisserat and Galleta (1988).
Celosia cristata (Cockscomb)	Shoot	Shoot tips	Basal callus & fasciated shoots	–	Driss-Ecole (1981)
Ptilotus sp.	Shoot	Shoots	Shoots rooted	–	Whish *et al.* (1992)
Amaryllidaceae					
Cooperia pedunculata Herb. = *Zephyranthes drummondii*	Ovule	Ovules	Seedling growth	Y	Sachar & Kapoor (1958)
Apocynaceae					
Amsonia tabernaemontana	Shoot (L/S)	Shoot tips	Shoot multiplication. Rooted plants	YY	Molnar (1987)
Catharanthus roseus (L.) G. Don	Callus	Stem or fruit pod	Adventitious shoots	–	Ramawat *et al.* (1978)
Catharanthus roseus (Madagascan periwinkle)	Callus/Direct	Infected *in vitro* plantlets	Transformed plants recovered via hairy root cults.	–	Brillanceau *et al.* (1989)

	Species name	Type of Culture	Source of explant	Results		References
	Catharanthus roseus	Pollen germination	Pollen	Germination stimulated by spermidine. MGBG inhibited	—	Prakash et al. (1988)
	Catharanthus roseus	Shoot	Infected shoot tips	Regeneration of infected shoots	—	Bertaccini et al. (1992)
	Catharanthus roseus var. 'Little Delicata'	Shoot?	Seedling shoot segments	Multiple shoots	Y	Endo et al. (1987)
	Catharanthus roseus	Shoot	In vitro shoots ex nodal cuttings	Lateral shoots. Rooted plants (in 2-phased medium)	Y	Molnar (1987)
	Vinca minor (Lesser periwinkle)	Node	Single node	Axillary shoot proliferation. 100% rooting	YY	Stapfer & Heuser (1985)

Araceae

Amorphophallus — See Root and Tuber Crops Table

	Species name	Type of Culture	Source of explant	Results		References
*	Anthurium andraeanum Lind. (Flamingo flower)	Callus	Leaf tissue	Adventitious shoots with roots	—	Fersing & Lutz (1977)
	Anthurium andraeanum [various cvs.]	Callus	Petiole & leaf tissue	Callus initiation	—	Kuehnle & Sugii (1991)
	Anthurium andraeanum	Callus	Various young tissues	Indirect adventitious shoots. Shoots rooted	—	Pierik et al. (1974a,b)
	Anthurium andraeanum	Callus	Young leaf tissue	Adv. shoots (callus subcultured). Plants	Y	Pierik et al. (1979b)
	Anthurium andraeanum	Shoot	2-node stem sects. of i. v. shoots	Multiple shoots	YY	Kunisaki (1980)
	Anthurium andraeanum	Shoot	Vegetative buds	Shoot growth	Y	Kunisaki (1980)
*	Anthurium scherzerianum Schott.	Callus	Leaf tissue	Adventitious shoot regeneration. Rooted plantlets	—	Fersing & Lutz (1977)
	Anthurium scherzerianum	Callus	Sections of young leaves	Callus subcult. 2 yr. in dark. Adv. shoots. Plants	—	Geier (1986)
	Anthurium scherzerianum	Callus	Young leaf tissues	Adventitious shoots. Shoots rooted	—	Pierik & Steegmans (1976a)
	Anthurium scherzerianum	Direct	Seeds	Multiple adventitious/axillary shoots	Y	Zimmer & Bahnemann (1982)
	Anthurium scherzerianum	Direct/Callus	Inflorescence fragments	Neoform. floral parts, shoots, embryogen. Plants	Y	Geier (1982a)
	Anthurium scherzerianum	Shoot	Shoots from callus cultures	Ax. & adv. shoots (rooted poorly)	Y	Geier (1986)
	Anthurium scherzerianum Genotypes AS-1, R-1	Callus/Shoot	Spadix & leaf segments	Adventitious shoots (multiplied). Rooted plants	Y	Geier (1987)
	Anthurium spp.	Callus/Shoot	Various	Shoot formation & multiplication. Shoots rooted	—	Geier (1990)
	Anthurium spp. [various]	Shoot	Axillary buds	Shoot formation & multiplication. Shoots rooted	YY	Geier (1990)
❖	Caladium bicolor (Angel's wings)	Callus	Young leaves	Adventitious buds; shoots. Rooted plantlets	—	Sahavacharin (1982)
	Caladium × hortulanum	Callus	Shoot tips	Adventitious shoots. Plantlets (were virus-free)	—	Hartman (1974)
❖	Caladium × hortulanum	Shoot	Dormant buds, 1–2 mm, ex rhizome	Multiple shoots, elongated & rooted	YY	Cooper & Cohen (1983)
❖	Dieffenbachia spp.	Shoot	Axillary buds	Axillary shoot prolif. Plants	YY	Litz & Conover (1977)
❖	Monstera deliciosa (Swiss Cheese Plant)	Shoot	Seedling shoot tips	Axillary shoot proliferation. Shoots rooted	YY	Fonnesbech & Fonnesbech (1980)
❖	Philodendron erubescens K. Koch & Aug. 'Royal King'	Shoot	Shoot tips, lateral buds	Investigated shoot elongation & rooting	YY	Maene & Debergh (1985)
*	Scindapsus aureus	Shoot	Lateral buds	Shoot multiplication. Shoots rooted	YY	Miller & Murashige (1976)
	Spathiphyllum wallisii Regel.	Shoot	Shoot tips	Investigated shoot elongation & rooting	YY	Maene & Debergh (1985)
*	Spathiphyllum × clevelandii (Peace lily)	Shoot/Direct	Buds, stem (& infloresc.) pieces	Shoot growth, adv. shoots. Shoots mult. & rooted	Y	Fonnesbech & Fonnesbech (1979)
	Syngonium podophyllum (Goosefoot plant)	Shoot	Shoot tips	Shoot multiplication. Shoots rooted	YY	Makino & Makino (1978)
	Syngonium podophyllum	Shoot	Lateral buds	Shoot multiplication. Shoots rooted	YY	Miller & Murashige (1976)
	Zantedeschia hybrids (Calla lily)	Shoot	Rhizome buds	Multiple axillary shoots. Rooted plants	YY	Cohen (1982)

Asclepiadaceae

	Species name	Type of Culture	Source of explant	Results		References
	Hoya carnosa	Callus	Interveinal leaf sections	Somatic embryogenesis	—	Maraffa et al. (1981)

Asteraceae See Compositae

Balsaminaceae

	Species name	Type of Culture	Source of explant	Results		References
❖	Impatiens [abortive hybrids]	Ovule	Ovules	Plantlets	—	Arisumi (1980)
❖	Impatiens [interspecific hybrids]	Ovule/embryo	Ovules excised from fruits	Germination of hybrids from 38 of 36 crosses	Y	Arisumi (1985)
	Impatiens platypetala Lindl.	Ovule	Immature ovules	Ovule germination & seedling growth	Y	Han & Stephens (1992)
	Impatiens platypetala & spp.	Shoot	Shoot tips (2-4 mm)	Shoot proliferation. Shoots (3-10 mm) rooted in vitro	YY	Stephens et al. (1985)
	Impatiens spp. [50 cvs.]	Meristem	Apical meristems	Virus-free plantlet regeneration	Y	Gera & Dehan (1992)

Begoniaceae

	Species name	Type of Culture	Source of explant	Results		References
❖	Begonia [many different spp.]	Direct	Leaf segments	Adv. shoots on non-sterile media. Plants	YY	Bowes & Curtis (1991)
❖	Begonia [many different spp.]	Shoot	Apical & axill. buds	Shoot prolif. on non-sterile media. Plants	YY	Bowes & Curtis (1991)
	Begonia × cheimantha (Christmas begonia)	Direct	Petiole segments (5 mm)	Adventitious shoots, rooted	Y	Fonnesbech (1974 a,b,c)
*	Begonia × cheimantha (Christmas begonia)	Callus	Petiole sections	Adv. shoots ex primary callus	—	Ramachandra & Khatamian (1989)
	Begonia erythrophylla J. Neumann 'Beefsteak'	Direct	Stem sections	Vegetative shoot buds & roots	Y	Berghoef & Bruinsma (1979 c)
	Begonia franconis	Direct	Flower pedicels	Flower buds & some vegetative buds	Y	Berghoef & Bruinsma (1979 c)
	Begonia franconis	Direct	Leaf segments	Adv. shoots (tested for systemic bacterium)	—	Hakkaart & Versluijs (1983a)
*	Begonia × hiemalis Fotsch. (Elatior begonia)	Direct	Sections of flower peduncle	Adventitious shoots. Rooted plants	Y	Appelgren (1984)
	Begonia × hiemalis [several vars.]	Direct	Leaf, stem, petiole, inflor.	Adv. shoots. Shoots rooted	Y	Bigot (1981 a,b)
	Begonia × hiemalis	Direct	Various	Direct shoot formation. Shoots rooted	Y	Bigot (1982)
	Begonia × hiemalis	Direct	Leaf-petiole discs (5 mm)	Direct adventitious shoots. Rooted plants	Y	Mikkelsen & Sink (1978b)
	Begonia × hiemalis	Direct	Leaf segments from in vitro shoots	Adventitious shoots with basal roots. Plants	Y	Reuther & Bhandari (1981)
	Begonia × hiemalis	Direct	Leaf sections	Adventitious shoots. Rooted	Y	Roest (1977)
	Begonia × hiemalis	Direct	1 cm petiole segments	Adv. shoots, elongated in liquid shake culture	YY	Simmonds & Werry (1987)
	Begonia × hiemalis 'Schwabenland Pink'	Direct	Petiole segments (5 mm)	Shoot initiation. Shoots all rooted	Y	Simmonds (1984)
	Begonia × hiemalis	Direct	Sections of young leaves; petioles	Shoot differentiation. Rooted plantlets	Y	Takayama & Misawa (1981 ; 1982b)
	Begonia × hiemalis	Direct	Leaf, petiole & inflorescence segments	Bud development & multiplication. Plantlets rooted	YY	Takayama (1990)
	Begonia × hiemalis	Direct	Petiole pieces (4 mm)	Shoot and root buds. Plantlet formation	Y	Welander (1979)
	Begonia × hiemalis	Meristem	Shoot tips	Virus-free plantlets	Y	Reuther & Bhandari (1981)
	Begonia × hiemalis	Meristem	Tips of in vitro shoots	Shoots, rooted. Most plants virus-free	Y	Hakkaart & Versluijs (1983a)
	Begonia × hiemalis [several cvs.]	Direct	Petiole segments (8—10 mm)	Shoot buds	Y	Thakur (1975)
	Begonia picta	Callus	Axenic leaves	Adventitious shoots. Rooted	—	Cassells & Morrish (1985)
	Begonia rex	Direct	Petiole of 9 cm leaf	Bud induction	Y	Cassells & Morrish (1985)
	Begonia rex	Direct	Leaf vein epidermis	Adventitious shoot buds	Y	Chlyah & Tran Thanh Van (1975)
	Begonia rex	Direct	Leaf discs	Adventitious shoots & roots	Y	Schott & Schraudolf (1967)
	Begonia rex cv. 'Peacock'	Direct/Shoot	In vitro cultured shoot clusters	Shoot growth	Y	Hale et al. (1992)
*	Begonia semperflorens	Direct	Leaf or petiole	Plantlets via adventive buds or embryoids	Y	Sehgal (1975)
	Begonia semperflorens	Direct	Seedling leaves	Adventitious shoot buds	Y	Thakur (1973)
	Begonia spp.	Direct	Floral stalk sections	Vegetative and floral buds	Y	Ringe & Nitsch (1968)

	Species name	Type of Culture	Source of explant	Results		References
	Begonia spp.	Direct	Leaf discs & petioles	Adventitious vegetative buds	Y	Ringe & Nitsch (1968)
*	Begonia × tuberhybrida [2 cvs.]	Callus	Petioles from shoot cultures	Adv. shoots: regen. callus subcultured indefinitely	—	Viseur & Lievens (1987)
	Begonia × tuberhybrida [2 cvs.]	Direct	Petioles from shoot cultures	Adventitious shoots	Y	Viseur & Lievens (1987)
	Begonia × tuberhybrida [2 cvs.]	Shoot	Shoot tips	Single shoots	—	Viseur & Lievens (1987)
Bromeliaceae						
*	Aechmea fasciata (Urn plant)	Shoot	Shoot tips	Shoot proliferation. Shoots rooted, plantlets	YY	Jones & Murashige (1974)
	Aechmea fasciata	Shoot/Direct	Lateral buds	Axillary and adventitious shoots. Rooted	YY	Hosoki & Asahira (1980b)
	Aechmea fasciata & other spp.	Shoot/Direct	Axill.buds of lat. shoots	Adventitious & axillary shoots; some callus	Y	Zimmer & Pieper (1975 ; 1976)
	Ananas erectifolius	Shoot/Callus	Shoot tips	Axillary shoots & embryogenesis (PLB formation)	Y	Mapes (1973)
	Guzmania sp.	Callus	Shoot tips	Protocorm-like bodies. Embryogenesis. Plants	—	Mapes (1973)
	Guzmania spp.	Direct	Lateral buds	Adventitious bud formation. Shoots rooted in vitro	Y	Hosoki & Asahira (1980b)
	Portea petropolipana	Callus	Shoot tips	PLB formation. Planlet growth	—	Mapes (1973)
	Quesnelia quesneliana	Direct	Lateral buds	Adventitious buds & shoots. Shoots rooted	Y	Hosoki & Asahira (1980b)
	Nidularium fulgens Lem.	Shoot	Shoot tips	Axillary shoot proliferation. Rooted plants	YY	Pierik & Steegmans (1984)
❖	Tillandsia [several cvs.]	Shoot	Immature embryos	Shoots multiplied, elongated & rooted	YY	Labus-Schneider & Abel (1991)
	Tillandsia polystachya	Shoot	Shoot tips ex in vitro seedlings	Shoot proliferation & growth. Shoots rooted	YY	Mekers (1977)
❖	Vriesia [several cvs.]	Shoot	Axillary shoot tips	Multiple shoots. Rooted plants	YY	Mekers & Van Onsem (1983)
	Vriesea fosteriana L.B.Smith	Direct	In vitro seedlings or their leaves	Multiple advent. shoots. 100% rooting	YY	Mercer & Kerbauy (1992)
	Vriesea heliconioides Hook. ex Walp.	Shoot	Shoot tips ex in vitro seedlings	Shoot proliferation. Shoots rooted	YY	Mekers (1977)
	Vriesea 'Myers Favoriet'	Shoot	Shoot tips ex in vitro seedlings	Shoot proliferation. Shoots rooted	YY	Mekers (1977)
	Vriesea poelmannii	Direct	Lateral buds, & young leaves ex resulting cultures	Adventitious buds. Shoots rooted	Y	Hosoki & Asahira (1980b)
	Vriesea splendens Lem. (Flaming sword)	Shoot	Shoot tips ex in vitro seedlings	Shoot proliferation. Shoots rooted	YY	Mekers (1977)
Campanulaceae						
*	Campanula isophylla Moretti. [various genotypes]	Shoot & node	Shoot tips or nodes	Mulatiple shoots. Rooted	YY	Brandt (1992)
Cannaceae						
❖	Canna indica	Direct	Rhizome segments	Direct bud & shoot initiation	Y	Kromer (1979)
Caryophyllaceae						
*	Dianthus barbatus (Sweet William)	Meristem	Meristem tips	Single rooted shoots	Y	Hollings (1965)
*	Dianthus caryophyllus L. [various cvs.] (Carnation)	Callus	Petal, calyx sections & nodes	Multiple adv. shoots. Rooted	—	Frey & Janick (1991)
	Dianthus caryophyllus	Callus	Mutilated shoot apices	Callus with green areas. Adv. shoots & roots	—	Hackett & Anderson (1967)
	Dianthus caryophyllus	Callus	Vitrified axillary buds	Shoots from callus at base. Some normal plantlets	—	Leshem (1986)
	Dianthus caryophyllus	Callus	Seedling hypocotyl	Adventitious shoots, rooted	—	Petru & Landa (1974)
	Dianthus caryophyllus	Direct	Vitrified petal base	Some normal adventitious shoots. Rooted plantlets	—	Leshem (1986)
	Dianthus caryophyllus [several cvs]	Direct	Innermost petals from buds	Adventitious shoots	Y	Nakano et al. (1994)
	Dianthus caryophyllus cvs. 'Ronald' & 'Niky'	Direct	Irradiated petal sections	Shoots. Regenerant somaclonal variation assessed	Y	Simard et al. (1992)
	Dianthus caryophyllus cv. 'White Sim'	Direct	Petals ex young buds	Multiple shoot formation followed by rooting	YY	Vainstein et al. (1992)
	Dianthus caryophyllus.	Direct	Leaves ex in vitro-grown plants	Shoot formation followed by rooting	YY	Van Altvorst et al. (1992)

Species name	Type of Culture	Source of explant	Results		References
Dianthus caryophyllus	Embryogenic callus	Internode tissue	Plant regeneration	—	Frey *et al.* (1992)
Dianthus caryophyllus	Embryogenic callus	Internode tissue	Plant regeneration	—	Frey *et al.* (1992)
Dianthus caryophyllus	Meristem	Meristem tips	Shoot growth & plantlet formation	Y	Hackett & Anderson (1967)
Dianthus caryophyllus	Meristem	Meristem tips	Single shoots, rooted in culture	Y	Hollings (1965)
Dianthus caryophyllus cv. 'Nelken'	Meristem	Meristems	Shoot prolif. & multi. Rooted ex vitro	Y	Majada *et al.* (1992)
Dianthus caryophyllus	Meristem	Meristem tips	Rooted plantlets	Y	Pennazio (1975)
Dianthus caryophyllus	Meristem	Shoot apical meristem	Single rooted plantlets	Y	Shabde & Murashige (1977)
Dianthus caryophyllus	Meristem	Meristem tips	Plantlet growth. Virus-free plants.	Y	Stone (1963)
Dianthus caryophyllus cv. 'Ceris royall'	Meristem	Apical buds	Shoot growth	—	Ziv & Ariel (1992)
Dianthus caryophyllus	Meristem/Shoot	Meristem tips	Shoot growth, multiplication. Rooted plantlets	YY	Denaso (1987)
Dianthus caryophyllus	Meristem/Shoot	Meristem tips	Axillary shoots (deformed)	—	Hempel (1979)
Dianthus caryophyllus	Meristem/Shoot	Merisem tips (0.2—0.5 mm)	Multiple shoots. Rooted plants	YY	Jelaska & Sutina (1977)
Dianthus caryophyllus	Shoot	Shoot tips	Single shoots: rooted plantlets	—	Baker & Phillips (1962)
Dianthus caryophyllus cv. 'Scania 3C'	Shoot	In vitro shoot tips	Axillary shoots. Rooted plants	Y	Dabski *et al.* (1979)
Dianthus caryophyllus	Shoot	Shoot tips (1 mm)	100% survival. Multiple shoots. Rooted plantlets	YY	Davis *et al.* (1977)
Dianthus caryophyllus	Shoot	Shoot tips	Multiple shoot formation. Rooted plantlets	YY	Earle & Langhans (1975)
Dianthus caryophyllus	Shoot	Shoot tips	Shoot growth. Shoots rooted	—	Gukasyan *et al.* (1977)
Dianthus caryophyllus	Shoot	Lateral shoot tips	Shoot growth: axillary shoots	Y	Kozak & Hempel (1979)
Dianthus caryophyllus	Shoot	Vitrified shoot tips	Some normal shoots obtained. Rooted plantlets	—	Leshem (1986)
Dianthus caryophyllus	Shoot	Shoot tips	Axillary shoot proliferation	Y	Schnapp & Preece (1986)
Dianthus caryophyllus	Shoot	Shoot tips	Shoot proliferation	Y	Takayama & Misawa (1982 c)
Dianthus caryophyllus	Shoot	Shoot tip	Shoot proliferation	Y	Ziv *et al.* (1983)
Dianthus caryophyllus cv. 'Scania 3C'	Shoot/Direct	Shoot apices ex leaf axils	Multiple axillary & adv. shoots	—	Weryszko & Hempel (1979)
Dianthus caryophyllus	Shoot/Direct/Callus	Nodal stem segments	Multiple axillary & adv. shoots. Rooted	Y	Roest & Bokelmann (1981)
Dianthus caryophyllus	Shoot/Orgd.callus	Shoot tips	Shoots (inc. adv. from small basal callus). Rooted	Y	Petru & Landa (1974)
Dianthus caryophyllus [3 vars.]	Single node	Single node cuttings	Shoot growth	YY	Dereuddre *et al.* (1987)
Dianthus caryophyllus var. 'Eolo'	Single node	Single node cuttings	Shoot growth	YY	Dereuddre *et al.* (1988)
Dianthus caryophyllus. cv. 'Oscar'	Suspension	Meristematic apices	Shoot formation followed by rooting	—	Ruffoni *et al.* (1992)
Dianthus zeyheri Sond. subsp. *natalensis* Hooper	Shoot	Shoot tips	Multiple shoots. Hyperhydricity	—	Crouch & Van Staden (1993)
* *Gypsophila paniculata* L.	Callus	Leaf discs	Adventitious shoots	—	Kusey & Hammer (1977)&
Gypsophila paniculata	Node	Single nodes	Non-vitrescent shoots propagated	YY	Dillen & Buysens (1989)
Gypsophila paniculata	Shoot	Shoot tips	Axillary shoot proliferation. Rooted *in vitro*	yy	Kusey *et al.* (1978 ; 1980)
Silene hybrid L.	Node	Single node segments	Shoot formation followed by rooting	Y	Ault (1992)
Silene schafta	Embryo	Ovules & placenta	Embryos formed & seedlings	Y	Zenkteler (1967)
Cephalotaceae					
Cephalotus follicularis Albany (Pitcher plant)	Direct	Leaves	Adventitious shoots. Rooted plants	Y	Woodward *et al.* (1991)
Cephalotus follicularis	Shoot	Shoot tips	Rapid shoot proliferation	YY	Adams *et al.* (1979a)

	Species name	Type of Culture	Source of explant	Results		References
	Asparagus setaceus	Shoot	Tips of lateral shoots	Axillary shoot growth	Y	Fonnesbech (1975)
	Blandfordia grandiflora R.Br. (Christmas bells)	Shoot	Shoot tips (0.5 cm)	Multiple shoot formation. Shoots rooted	YY	Johnson & Burchett (1991)
	Blandfordia grandiflora	Shoot	Shoots (2 cm)	Shoot multiplication & elongation. Shoots rooted	Y	Johnson (1992)
❖	Gasteria croucheri (Hook.) Bak.	Callus	Leaf pieces	Long-term prod. of adv. shoots. Plants	Y	Bayley & Van Staden (1987)
	Gasteria carinata var. verrucosa	Callus	Leaf sections	Callus growth & embryogenesis. Plantlets	—	Beyl & Sharma (1983)
❖	Haworthia [10 species]	Callus	Flower gynoecium & inflor. segs.	Adventitious shoots from inflorescence segments.	—	Kaul & Sabharwal (1972 ; 1975)
	Haworthia arachnoidea (L.) Duval.	Direct/Indirect	Perianth of young buds	Shoot & flower formation directly and via callus	—	Konishi et al. (1982)
	Haworthia cymbiformis (Haw) Duval.	Direct/Callus	Perianth of young buds	Shoot & flower formation directly and via callus	—	Konishi et al. (1982)
	Haworthia fasciata (Willd.) Haw.	Callus	Basal sections of lower leaves	Embryogenesis. Plantlets obtained	—	Beyl & Sharma (1983)
	Haworthia planifolia Haw.	Callus	Leaf sections	Adventitious shoots and well developed roots	Y	Wessels et al. (1976)
	Haworthia turgida Haw. pallidifolia G.G. Smith'	Direct/Callus	Isolated ovaries before anthesis	Adv. shoots and roots. Plants in soil	Y	Majumdar (1970)
	Heloniopsis orientalis (Thunb.) Tan.	Callus	Stem internode, leaves	Adventitious buds. Rooted plants	—	Kato (1975 a,b)
	Heloniopsis orientalis	Direct	Mature leaf, no midrib	Adventitious buds	Y	Kato & Kawahara (1972) &
	Heloniopsis orientalis	Node	Stem node	Complete plants	Y	Kato (1975 a,b)
	Hemerocallis [several cvs.] (Daylily)	Callus	FLower buds (0.5—1 mm)	Adv. shoots. Rooted plants	—	Heuser & Harkar (1976)
	Hemerocallis cvs. 'Eenie Weenie', 'Scarlet Tanager'	Callus, Suspension	Shoot tips	Shoots regenerated, rooted	—	Griesbach (1988)
	Hemerocallis [5 cvs.]	Callus/Suspension	Distal/proximal half flower bud	Structures with shoots and roots. Plants	Y	Krikorian & Kann (1979 ; 1981)
	Hemerocallis cv. 'Stella d'ora'	Shoot	Shoot tips	Shoot proliferation	Y	Leifert et al. (1989b)
	Hemerocallis cvs. 'Autumn Blaze', 'Fire Cap'	Suspension	Callus (source not given)	Cell cluster, embryogenesis. Plants	—	Krikorian et al. (1981)
	Hemerocallis cv. 'Autumn Blaze' [diploid]	Suspension/Callus	Floral buds	Plants with parental morphology & chromosomes	Y	Krikorian et al. (1981 ; 1982a)
	Hemerocallis hybrid 'Clipper Cherry'	Callus	Petals & sepals ex imm. flowers	Adv. shoots with roots. Plants	—	Apps & Heuser (1975)
	Hemerocallis hybrid	Callus	Petal parts	Adventitious shoots, rooted to give plants	—	Heuser & Apps (1976)
*	Hemerocallis lilio-asphodelus L. = H. flava L.	Callus	Young leaf callus, colchicine ttd.	Tetraploid or octaploid plantlets regenerated	—	Chen & Goeden-Kallemeyn (1979)
	Hemerocallis lilio-asphodelus	Callus	Adv. roots on petal callus	Adv. shoots. Plants	—	Chen & Holden (1972)
	Hemerocallis tetraploids	Callus	Flower scape sections	Adventitious shoots, rooted	—	Meyer (1976b)
❖	Hosta cv. 'Blue wedgewood'	Node	Single nodes	Multiple shoots, rooted. Studied antibiotic effects	—	Leifert et al. (1992)
	Hosta decorata L.H. Bail.	Direct/Shoot	Shoot tips ex axillary buds	Adventitious and axillary shoot proliferation	YY	Papachatzi et al. (1981)
	Hosta decorata	Shoot	Shoot tips	Shoot multiplication	Y	Hammer (1976)
	Hosta plantaginea (Lam.) Asch.	Callus	Immature inflorescence	Numerous adventitious shoots. Rooted plants	—	Papachatzi et al. (1980)
	Hosta plantaginea	Direct	Leaf & leaf frags. of i. v. leaves	Adventitious shoots. Rooted plants	Y	Papachatzi et al. (1980)
	Hosta sieboldiana (Hook.) Engl. & Prantl.	Direct	Florets of inflorescence	Shoots & rooted plantlets	Y	Meyer (1980)
	Hosta tsushimensis Fujita	Direct/Shoot	Immature flower buds	Adv. shoots, multiplied by shoot culture. Rooted i.v.	YY	Banko & Smith (1985)
❖	Ophiopogon japonicus (Thunb.) Ker-Gawl. (Lily-turf)	Embryogenic callus	Meristem tips	Embryo development. Plantlets	—	Strandberg (1993)
Lythraceae						
	Cuphea wrightii	Shoot	Adventitious shoots from callus	Shoot proliferation. Shoots rooted as planlets	Y	Janick & Whipkey (1986)
	Lythrum salicaria L. (Purple loosestrife)	Shoot	Shoot tips	Shoot multiplication	Y	Heuser (1982)
	Lythrum virgatum L.	Shoot	Shoot tips (5-10 mm)	Axillary shoot proliferation..hoot rooted ex vitro	YY	Heuser (1983)

Species name	Type of Culture	Source of explant	Results		References
Malvaceae					
Abelmoschus manihot (L.) Medik. (Aibika)	Embryo	Immature embryos	Some seedling growth	—	Patil (1966)
Alcea rosea L. = Althaea rosea (L.) Cav. (Hollyhock)	Callus	Hypocotyls or cotyledons	Indirect embryogenesis	—	Lawrence et al. (1982)
Alcea rosea	Callus	Cotyledons, hypocotyls	Embryogenesis. Embryoids	—	Reynolds et al. (1981a)
Hibiscus acetosella Welw. ex Hiern.	Callus	Seedling stems or hypocotyls	Embryogenesis. Growth of some embryos	—	Reynolds et al. (1980 ; 1981a)
Hibiscus acetosella	Direct	Cotyledon or primary leaf	Shoot and/or plantlet regeneration	Y	Blackmon et al. (1981 a)
Hibiscus acetosella	Direct/Callus	Half cotyledons	Shoot regeneration from 40% explants	—	Blackmon & Reynolds (1982)
Hibiscus acetosella	Direct/Callus	Seedling cotyledons & leaves	Direct adv. shoots. Embryogenic callus, embryos, plants	—	Reynolds & Blackmon (1983)
Marantaceae					
❖ Maranta leuconeura E. Morr. (Prayer plant)	Shoot	Lateral buds (2-5mm)	Shoot proliferation. Shoot rooted	YY	Dunston & Sutter (1984)
Nelumbonaceae					
Nelumbo lutea Willd. Pers. (American lotus)	Embryo	Embryos from imm. receptacles	Rhizome growth. Plants	Y	Kane et al. (1988a)
Nymphaceae					
❖ Nymphaea Hybrid 'James Brydon' (Water lily)	Shoot	Rhizome tips	Multiple shoots. Rooted plants		Lakshmanan (1994)
Paeoniaceae					
* Paeonia lactiflora (Peony)	Embryo	Immature embryos from seeds	Germination. Seedlings; plants	Y	Zilis & Meyer (1976)
Paeonia lactiflora cv. 'Sarah Bernhardt'	Shoot	Single node segs. ex sprouted rhizome buds	Shoot formation & multiplication, then rooting	Y	Albers & Kunneman (1992)
Paeonia lactiflora 'Takinoyosooi' & 'S. Bernhardt'	Shoot	Rhizome apex & lateral buds	Multiple axillary shoots. Rooted	YY	Hosoki et al. (1989)
Papaveraceae					
Eschscholzia californica Cham. (Californian poppy)	Callus	Placental tissue	Embryogenesis. Embryoid proliferation	—	Kavathekar & Ganapathy (1973)
Eschscholzia californica	Ovule	Placenta plus ovules	Ovules fertilised. Seedlings which formed adv. embryos	—	Kanta & Maheshwari (1963)
Meconopsis simplicifolia (D.Don) Walp.	Callus	Seedling sections	Multiple shoots. Rooted		Sulaiman & Babu (1993)
Meconopsis simplicifolia (Himalayan blue poppy)	Callus/Suspension	Hypocotyl & leaf segments	Embryogen. Plantlets		Sulaiman et al. (1991)
Papaver orientale (Oriental poppy)	Callus	Aseptic seedlings	Embryogenesis	—	Schuchmann & Wellman (1983)
Peperomiaceae					
❖ Peperomia caperata Yunck. (Emerald ripple pepper)	Callus	Petiole sections	Adv. shoots ex primary callus	—	Ramachandra & Khatamian (1989)
Peperomia fraseri C.DC = P. resediflora Lind. & A.	Direct	Leaf segments	Adv. shoots on non-sterile media. Plants	YY	Bowes (1990)
Peperomia pseudorufescens	Direct	Leaf discs	Shoot induction & proliferation. Shoots rooted	YY	Henny (1978)
Peperomia serpens (Sw.) Loud. = P. scandens	Direct	Leaf & petiole segments	Direct shoot bud formation	Y	Klimaszewska (1979)
Peperomia serpens	Direct	Leaf pieces	Direct rooted shoots	YY	Kukulczanka et al. (1977)
Plumbaginaceae					
❖ Limonium sp. = Statice sp.	Shoot	Axillary buds	Shoot proliferation. Shoots rooted	YY	Harazy et al. (1985)
Podophyllaceae					
❖ Podophyllum pleianthum Hance	Callus	Leaf laminae & petioles	Multiple adv. shoots. Rooted	—	Fujii et al. (1986)
Polemoniaceae					
Phlox paniculata L. (Summer perennial phlox)	Direct	Internode stem	Direct shoot proliferation. Shoots rooted	YY	Schnabelrauch & Sink (1979)
Phlox paniculata	Meristem	Shoot tips (1mm)	Shoot & root growth	Y	Olesen & Fonnesbech (1975)
Phlox subulata varieties (Ground phlox)	Shoot	Shoot tips	Multiple axillary shoots. Shoots rooted	YY	Schnabelrauch & Sink (1979)

galum thyrsoides) produces adventitious shoots *in vitro* on almost any organ, without the use of growth regulators (Hussey, 1975b): adventitious shoots or bulblets may also be formed directly on leaf, flower bud, scape and ovary explants of *Hyacinthus*.

The multiplication stage

In most genera of bulbous plants, the main shoot shows strong apical dominance. This means that, even when a cytokinin is added to the medium, newly formed shoots or bulblets may not proliferate freely *in vitro* from axillary shoots. When axillary or adventitious shoots on explants give rise to bulblets, these can often be divided and used as explants to produce yet more bulblets. This is essentially the method by which *Lilium* is propagated.

When shoots are produced from explants, multiplication can often be enhanced by treatments which destroy the main shoot apex and allow new axillary and adventitious shoots to develop. Newly–formed axillary or adventitious shoots or bulblets are therefore sometimes cut into halves or quarters. This technique is effective, for example, in some varieties of *Narcissus* (Hussey and Hilton, 1980a; Hussey, 1982), *Freesia* (Hussey (1976c), *Hippeastrum* (Hussey and Hargreaves, 1974) and *Allium* (Hussey and Falavigna, 1980) (see figure on page 1186).

The apical dominance of shoots may also be weakened if cultures are incubated in shaken liquid medium. Bergoñón *et al.* (1992) obtained more shoot proliferation when shoot clusters of *Narcissus papyraceus* were cultured on agitated liquid medium than when they were grown on agar–solidified medium.

Preventing the onset of dormancy in cultures

In some genera, the development of bulblets at the base of shoots occurs *in vitro* by a 'natural' onset of dormancy. After several weeks of culture, shoots and plantlets of the Iridaceae, tend to become dormant and form bulbs or corms, thus preventing continued shoot multiplication. Such dormancy can be prevented in *Freesia* by splitting crowns down the middle (see above).

Another effective way to promote sustained growth of the cultures of tunicate species, is to cut down developing adventitious shoots to a height of only 1–2 mm above the basal plate. The plate then grows laterally providing more tissue from which shoots can be initiated (Hussey and Hilton, 1980a). The technique is effective, for instance, on *Narcissus, Allium, Tulipa* and *Nerine*.

Shoot dormancy of *Narcissus* can be overcome by a long period of cold treatment (6–8 weeks at 5°C — Hussey and Hilton, 1980a), or by the application of gibberellic acid (Seabrook, 1990). Increasing the concentration of the cytokinin BAP in the medium is also sometimes effective, but this treatment may be followed by an increased rate of branching, decreased rooting and abnormal physiology. Normal rooted plantlets can be obtained if the concentration of BAP is eventually lowered (Hussey, 1976c).

Cultural environment

Table 149 gives examples of the temperatures and lighting conditions found to be suitable for the micropropagation of some bulb–forming plants. Procedures relying on shoot growth and shoot multiplication need to be conducted in the light, but bulblet formation is often best when explants are incubated in the dark. Shoot and bulblet regeneration in species which are adapted to cool climates (*Narcissus, Tulipa*) is often best at 19–25°C, while it is possible to use higher temperatures for species which originate from warmer climates (*Hymenocallis, Lilium*). Choice of the correct temperature can therefore greatly influence the success of micropropagation. Shoot regeneration from bulb scale explants of *Iris × hollandica* was little different at 15° or 20°C, but was poor at 25°C (Van der Linde *et al.*, 1988). A high proportion of *Nerine bowdenii* twin scale explants formed bulblets at 17–22°C, but incubation at higher temperatures was less successful (Jacobs *et al.*, 1992).

Media and growth regulators

Media based on **MS** salts have been widely used for the multiplication of plants producing bulbs or corms, although some authors have added additional phosphate. More dilute media (*e.g.* $^1/_2$**MS**) have been used on occasions and are often employed for rooting adventitious shoots of those plants which do not readily produce a storage organ.

Although it is not always necessary to add a cytokinin to the medium to obtain adventitious shoot or bulblet formation from bulb scale explants (page 890), an auxin (usually 0.1–4 mg/l NAA) is commonly combined with a cytokinin (often 1–16 mg/l BAP) to induce axillary shoots or bulblets. The presence of a cytokinin, such as BAP, is necessary to promote axillary shoot proliferation in plants such as *Gladiolus, Freesia* and *Iris* (Hussey and Hilton, 1975; Hussey, 1977a,b).

Table 149. Examples of the conditions in which cultures of bulb–forming plants are incubated.

Plant	Stage	Explant	Lighting level — Irradiance μmol m⁻² s⁻¹	Lighting level — Illuminance lux	Photoperiod hours	Temperature °C	Results	References
Hymenocallis littoralis	I	Bulb scales	Darkness		—	28	Bulblet initiation	Backhaus *et al.* (1992)
	II		(12.5)	1000	16	28	Shoot proliferation	
Iris × hollandica	I,II	Bulb scales	Darkness (better than 30 μmol m⁻² s⁻¹)		—	20	Adv. shoots, then bulblet formation	Van der Linde et al. (1988)
Lilium auratum	II	Bulb scale pieces	0–23 μmol m⁻² s⁻¹ showed little difference		24	20 (opt.)–25	Differentiation and growth of bulblets	Takayama and Misawa (1979)
Lilium speciosum	II	Bulb scale pieces	24	—	16	21	Adv. shoots and bulblets	Van Aartrijk and Blom-Barnhoorn (1979)
Lilium speciosum	II	Bulb scale pieces	30	—	16	20	Bulblet formation	Gerrits *et al.* (1992)
Lilium longiflorum	II	Bulb scale pieces	Darkness		—	25 or 30	Bulblet formation	Stimart and Ascher (1981a,b)
Muscari botryoides	I,II	Bulb epidermal layers	(19)	1500	24	22–24	Bulblet formation	Kromer and Kukulczanka (1992)
Narcissus cvs.	II	Sections of scale + basal plate	65–79	—	16	20	Adv. shoot formation; shoot multiplication	Squires and Langton (1990) Chow *et al.* (1992a)
Narcissus papyraceus	II	Axillary shoots	100	—	16	25/22 (d/n)	Shoot multiplication in liquid medium	Bergoñón *et al.* (1992)
Nerine bowdenii	I,II	Twin scale segments	20	—	16	22	Bulblet formation	Jacobs *et al.* (1992)
Tulipa gesneriana	I,II	Stem discs	Darkness		—	19–20	Adventitious buds	Le Nard and Chanteloube (1992)
	II	Adventitious buds from stem discs (above)	Darkness		—	5	Bulblet induction	
	II		Darkness		—	20	Bulblet formation	

The effect of ethylene. Thorpe and co-workers (Thorpe *et al.* 1981; Huxter *et al.* 1981) concluded that ethylene inhibited adventitious shoot formation of tobacco, during the first 5 days of the initiation period, but thereafter it speeded up primordium formation. In bulbs, the effect of ethylene appears to depend on genotype. A slight, but insignificant, increase in the number of shoots produced on sections of the immature floral stems of tulips was obtained by Taeb and Alderson (1987, 1990) when the concentration of ethylene was raised within vessels. Similarly, adding 1–10 µM ACC or 0.1–100 µM ethephon to the medium had no promotive effect, and ethephon treatments resulted in shorter shoots and at the highest levels inhibited shoot growth (Alderson and Taeb, 1990; Taeb and Alderson, 1990).

However, the number of adventitious buds formed on bulb scale explants of lily *was* increased if ethylene was applied in the gas phase above the cultures during the first 3–7 days of culture (Van Aartrijk *et al.*, 1985) and in tulip 0.1–10 mg/l ACC enhanced the formation of bulbs on pre–formed shoots (Alderson and Taeb, 1990; Taeb and Alderson, 1990).

Bulb formation

As mentioned previously, at some stage it is usually desirable to obtain fully formed bulblets from cultures for planting *ex vitro*. Bulblet formation is usually associated with the onset of natural dormancy (*i.e.* entry of the tissues into a state where meristems are temporarily incapable of growth). This condition seems to be partly regulated by endogenous abscisic acid because, in *Lilium* fluridone, a compound which inhibits ABA biosynthesis, prevents dormancy (Gerrits *et al.*, 1992), but other factors are also involved.

In cultures of some genera of the Liliaceae and Amaryllidaceae, shoots tend to senesce after several subcultures and naturally form a dormant bulblet at the base. Bulblets which are produced naturally *in vitro* are easily managed, but where culture results in shoots, it is usual to try to induce bulblets to form at the shoot bases before transfer is attempted. In liquid shake culture, bulb scale explants of *Narcissus papyraceus* produce shoots (see below). If transferred to the external environment as separations from liquid shake culture, only 68% of these shoots survived, whereas if bulblets were first induced to form at the base of the shoots, all survived when transferred to soil (Bergoñón *et al.*, 1992).

In other genera, for example *Tulipa*, bulblet formation is not induced unless explants or shoots (buds) are cold-treated (see below) or exposed to light of high photon fluence which has a high proportion of its energy in the far red wavelengths (see below). Cold treatment can also enhance bulblet formation of *Hyacinthus* (Liliaceae).

The dormancy which newly derived bulblets display is unavoidable. Although it can be advantageous, because it ensures that the bulblets do not sprout *in vitro*, bulblets may need to be treated before they are planted to ensure that they resume active growth.

Effect of cold on bulb formation

In plants such as tulip and narcissus, bulblet initiation is promoted by placing shoots or explants into a cold environment, but bulblet growth only takes place when the cultures are moved to a higher temperature. Thus leaf explants of *Hyacinthus orientalis* required to be kept at 4°C for a minimum of 8 weeks, after which bulblets were formed during culture at 23°C (Bach *et al.*, 1992b). Discs cut from the stems of *Tulipa gesneriana* produced adventitious buds in the dark at 19–20°C. These were transferred to a sugar enriched medium without growth regulators and kept at 5°C for bulb initiation: bulblets were then produced when cultures were returned to 20°C (Le Nard and Chanteloube, 1992). Unfortunately in this experiment, bud formation was not synchronous, so that the cold treatment was necessarily applied to buds in different stages of formation. This resulted in bulblets of assorted sizes and stages of development, which consequently had varying capacities for survival when planted *extra vitrum*.

In *Iris × hollandica*, Van der Linde *et al.* (1988) obtained an inconsistent improvement in bulblet formation from cold treatment (5°C for 4 weeks). It was only effective on shoots produced on single outer scale explants (not on those excised from double inner scales). Promotion was greatest when the treatment was applied at late stages of culture. In this plant, Mielke and Anderson (1989) found that bulblet formation could be promoted by incubating axillary shoots for 25 weeks in darkness at 22°C.

Water potential of the medium

Bulblet formation is usually enhanced by the presence of relatively high concentrations of sucrose. This seems sometimes to be due to the nutritional effect of sucrose and, in other instances, to be partly due to the medium having a low water potential. In the latter cases, suitable media have a high concentration of sucrose, or include an inert osmoticum such as sorbitol, mannitol or PEG together with sucrose.

Although a decreased water potential has been shown to be involved in the bulbing of lilies (see page 890), there is some contrary evidence, because increasing the concentration of **MS** salts has no effect (De Klerk *et al.*,

1990). Raising the sucrose content of **MS** medium from 3% to 6% improved bulb formation on cultured *Tulipa* shoots but, in a medium containing 3% sucrose and 3% mannitol, explants and shoots were killed (Taeb and Alderson, 1990b). In this plant it appeared that dormancy was associated with a high endogenous level of sucrose in adventitious shoots.

Paclobutrazol. Explants taken from the leaves of *in vitro* cultures of *Hyacinthus orientalis* cultured at 23°C with 8 mg/l paclobutrazol, formed bulblets, whereas those from cultures grown at this temperature without the retardant produced only shoots bearing a single leaf. To obtain bulblets without paclobutrazol it was necessary to keep the shoot cultures from which explants were sourced, at 4°C for from 4 to 20 weeks. The maximum number of bulbs per explant occurred after 16 weeks treatment (Bach *et al.*, 1992a). Applied to *in vitro* cultured bulblets of *Lilium*, paclobutrazol reduced the level of dormancy (Gerrits *et al.*, 1992).

Cold storage. Bulblets of *Allium* can be stored for up to 1 year in the dark at 4°C (Keller, 1991). The viability of bulblets during this treatment was enhanced by adding 0.1% ethephon to the culture medium for two weeks before storage commenced.

Overcoming bulblet dormancy

Ideally, bulblets produced during micropropagation should not be induced to pass into a state of deep dormancy or it will be difficult to induce them to commence active growth *extra vitrum*. The nature and extent of dormancy is usually determined by the manner in which cultures have been treated. In *Lilium longiflorum* and *L. speciosum*, Stimart and Ascher (1981a,b), Paffen *et al.* (1990), and Aguettaz *et al.* (1990) have found that dormancy depends on the temperature at which bulblets are formed. In the first of these reports, bulblets produced in cultures incubated at 30°C were generally less dormant when they were removed from culture and planted in vermiculite than bulblets formed at 25°C (which required to be chilled for two weeks to produce leaves as rapidly). The manner in which cultural temperature influences dormancy could, however, be genetically determined, because in two varieties the reverse situation occurred.

Bulblets of *L. speciosum* formed at 15°C showed little dormancy but only a small proportion of those produced at higher *in vitro* temperatures sprouted if planted in soil without prior cold treatment (De Klerk *et al.*, 1990).

The degree of dormancy of *L. auratum* bulblets can be modified by the concentration of sucrose added to the medium (Part 1, page 211), and the sprouting of cold–treated bulblets is influenced by the concentration of auxin which was present in the medium in which they were formed (Van Aartrijk and Blom–Barnhoorn (1979).

Cold treatments to reverse dormancy

In nearly all cases, the dormancy of a high proportion of the bulblets produced by *in vitro* culture can be reversed, causing growth to be recommenced, if they are kept in the cold before being planted in soil. Examples of the duration of treatments which have been found to be effective before bulblets are planted out, are given in Table 12 (Part 1, page 210). Higgins and Stimart (1990) found that as the period during which *Lilium longiflorum* bulblets were stored at 4°C was increased from 1 to 6 weeks, the number of days required before first leaf emergence decreased, but the number of days to anthesis, the average number of leaves and the average number of flower buds on each stem, increased. However, the length of the cold treatment which is necessary may vary according to the size of bulblets, small ones requiring a shorter treatment than large ones (Paek, 1982).

Methodology. To economise on space, bulblets are usually harvested before cold treatment and placed into a refrigerator in a moist environment (*e.g.* within plastic bags containing moist sterile vermiculite). Zhola *et al.* (1992) placed bulblets of *Lilium* onto a rooting medium containing 0.5 mg/l IAA and then gave the cultures a 6–8 week cold treatment (2–4°C) at the end of the rooting phase, just before transplanting. *Tulipa* bulblets were dried and stored in darkness at 20°C after removal from culture. They were then planted and given a cold treatment of 9–11 weeks to break their dormancy: larger bulbs emerged and grew more satisfactorily than smaller ones (Hulscher *et al.*, 1992).

Gibberellins

Dormancy of *Lilium* bulblets can be partly reversed by adding 1 mg/l gibberellic acid (Aguettaz *et al.*, 1990) or GA$_{4+7}$ (Gerrits *et al.*, 1992) to the medium. Gibberellic acid can also accelerate the growth of bulbs after a cold treatment (Tymoszuk *et al.*, 1979), but is no substitute for low temperature storage.

CALLUS CULTURES OF BULBOUS PLANTS

Callus cultures can be initiated from bulb scales and other vegetative tissues of bulb- and corm-producing species, but selection of the correct initial explant is important and propagation from callus cultures has generally been avoided because of the well-known tendency of callus to differentiate genetically-aberrant plants.

TECHNIQUES FOR SOME BULBOUS SPECIES

Amaryllidaceae
Narcissus (Daffodil, Narcissus)

Many varieties of *Narcissus* are cultivated as ornamentals and are described as daffodils, narcissus or jonquils. Microporpagation is useful for rapidly building up stocks of new varieties, but is unlikely to be economic for routine propagation (see below).

Propagation from twin–scale explants

Treatment of bulbs. Explant material is usually removed from bulbs which have been kept in the cold. Because this improves the responsiveness of explants when shoot-derived explants are required, bulbs are kept at room temperature for 2–3 weeks after cold treatment to allow shoots to begin elongation.

Explant preparation. To obtain twin–scale explants, the dry outer scales, the remains of roots, and the upper two–thirds of a bulb are removed. The remainder of the bulb is surface sterilised, divided into segments and split into twin scale pieces each attached to a thin segment of the adjoining basal plate. The outer scales of bulbs produce the most adventitious shoots, but as they are usually highly contaminated, some researchers have used only the inner ones, restricting the number of shoots obtained during the initial induction phase. Hol and Van der Linde (1990) discovered that the proportion of cultures which was contaminated by *Fusarium* fungus could be greatly reduced by treating bulbs in hot water at 54°C for 1–3 hours, before twin scale explants were dissected and treated with bleach solution (1% NaOCl for 30 minutes).

Depending on the size of bulbs, it may be possible to obtain 50–60 twin scale explants per bulb: each is finally trimmed to *ca.* 5 mm (wide) × 10mm.

Shoot proliferation. Adventitious bulblets are formed in the dark on **MS** medium without regulants, but it is usual to culture explants on a medium containing NAA (1 mg/l) and BAP (*e.g.* 2 mg/l) [although Hussey (1982) thought that a cytokinin was unnecessary]. Squires and Langton (1992) transferred shoots for further growth to **MS** medium with 1 mg/l IBA instead of NAA. Leaves were then removed from the bulblet formed at the base of each shoot, and the bulblets split longitudinally and subcultured to obtain shoot clumps, shoots and further bulblets. These could be divided in the same fashion with subcultures at 4–6 week intervals.

In some experiments, proliferation and bulblet formation has declined after 2–3 subcultures, but on **MS** medium containing 0.1 mg/l NAA and 1 mg/l BAP, Chow *et al.* (1992a) found that further shoot proliferation (page 881) could be encouraged, once large sized shoots had been harvested, by trimming back leaves remaining on shoot clumps to 20 mm. By using a more severe trimming routine at each alternate subculture, in which all green tissues were removed and shoot clumps cut down to the basal plate at each subculture, it was found that the production of new shoots could be increased consistently.

Large shoots are finally transferred to a medium containing 5–10 g/l activated charcoal, but lacking growth regulators, on which after several transfers, shoots produce bulblets (Steinitz and Yahel, 1982).

Using liquid culture. The apical shoot of *Narcissus papyraceus* was strongly dominant, but by subculturing shoot clusters on agitated liquid **MS** medium containing 6% sucrose (without regulants) at 25/22°C (16h in 100 μmol m^{-2} s^{-1}), 10–12 shoots were produced per explant and clusters could be divided every 2 weeks (Bergoñón *et al.*, 1992).

Using scape sections and leaf bases

Adventitious shoots are formed on scape sections and the bases of immature leaves dissected from cold treated bulbs. To obtain explants from the latter, the dry outer leaves and the white fleshy scale leaves are carefully removed when shoots are projecting approximately 5 cm above the top of the bulb. A shoot with immature foliage leaves then remains in a protective sheath. This structure with a small portion of the basal plate is washed and sterilised, and the sheath aseptically removed. Explants are obtained by excising the floral shoot and cutting the scape into 3 mm segments. The yellow or green top of the immature foliage leaves is removed, and the bases cut into 2mm × 10 mm (long) segments.

Seabrook (Seabrook *et al.*, 1976; Seabrook, 1990) recommended that such explants be placed on a semi–solid medium of **Ziv *et al.* (1970)** with 160 mg/l adenine sulphate, 1 mg/l BAP and 1 mg/l NAA. Adventitious shoots and bulblets are only regenerated from scape sections if explants are inverted before being placed onto the medium. Leaf bases are placed in an upright position.

Transfer and acclimatization

Seabrook *et al.* (1976) cultured bulblets on ½**MS** (30 g/l sucrose) with 0.1 mg/l NAA at 18°C in an illuminance of 3000 lux during a 16 h day so that they produced leaves and roots before transfer. Plantlets rooted in this way could be successfully transferred to the field, providing they had developed from bulblets which weighed at least 250 mg (Steinitz and Yahel, 1982). A less troublesome procedure is to obtain bulblets without leaves which can be planted directly into greenhouse or field.

Bulblet formation

To suspend active proliferation and obtain bulblets, shoots are excised and transferred to **MS** medium lacking regulants, or containing a low concentration of auxin (*e.g.* 0.1 mg/l NAA). After several transfers, an increasing number of large shoots is obtained which, if left on **MS** medium for up to 3 months, senesce leaving dormant bulbils (Squires and Langton, 1990). In *Narcissus papyraceus*, shoots needed to be subcultured from liquid onto a semi–solid **MS** medium containing 3% sucrose to form roots and an enlarged bulblet. The presence of 90 g/l sucrose (when the total osmolality of the medium would be *ca.*395 mOs/kg before sugar hydrolysis), rather than 30 g/l sucrose, greatly stimulated bulb formation in a medium without BAP (which was found to inhibit bulb formation) (Chow *et al.*, 1992b).

Seabrook and Cumming (1983) and Seabrook (1990) also found that a medium with a relatively high osmotic concentration favoured bulb formation. They recommended one containing 8.0 mM K^+ and 5.5 mM (16.5 meq/l) PO_4^{3-}, supplemented with 16g/l glucose, 8 g/l mannitol, and 1 g/l activated charcoal. The total osmolality of the solutes in this preparation would be *ca.* 186 mOs/kg. The presence of adequate K^+ and an above average concentration of PO_4^{3-} was also thought to promote bulbing.

The small bulblets obtained from micropropagation are usually dormant. To try to overcome dormancy, bulblets still in their culture vessels are often stored in the dark at 5°C for 8–12 weeks and, after washing and treatment with fungicide, are planted out in the greenhouse or field (Squires and Langton, 1990). Losses are often experienced at this stage: some bulblets may not resume growth and others fail to develop into plants.

Callus cultures

Plant regeneration from callus of *Narcissus* is comparatively easy and may be accomplished *via* indirect shoot formation (*e.g.* in *Hyacinthus*, Hussey, 1978b). Cummings *et al.* (1976) obtained numerous adventitious shoots from callus-like growths from leaf base, scape and ovary explants of *Narcissus*: proliferating shoot apices were induced on the medium of **Ziv *et al*. (1970)**, containing 1mg/l NAA and 10 mg/l BAP.

The cost of plantlets

Squires and Langton (1990) calculated that, using the micropropagation technique outlined above, 2.6 minutes of operator time (*i.e.* for both cultural operations and media preparation) were required to produce one new

bulblet of *Narcissus*. If the cost per hour of transfer work were to be 6.825 currency units (see page 779), the cost of producing one bulblet would be:

$$\frac{6.825}{60} \times 2.6 = 0.296 \text{ currency units}$$

This demonstrates that the techniques currently available for the micropropagation of *Narcissus* are not economic for the large scale multiplication of bulbs intended for general planting. The time to produce each bulblet would need to be reduced by 50–100 fold.

Amaryllidaceae

Nerine

Nerine is micropropagated far less widely than *Lilium* but nevertheless, is multiplied by tissue culture laboratories more frequently than many other bulbs, for example, in 1990, *ca.* 0.5×10^6 *Nerine* bulblets were produced through tissue culture in the Netherlands. The frost hardy *Nerine bowdenii* is the most widely known species in the temperate climates of the Northern hemisphere.

To propagate *Nerine bowdenii*, *N. sarniensis* and *Nerine* hybrids using bulb scale explants, Pierik and Ippel (1977) removed the roots and just the lower (outer) part of the basal plate, the dry outer tunica and the top one third of each bulb (3.8–4.5 cm diameter). The bulbs were then cut into quarters and the old brown flower stem, which was then revealed within the bulb, was removed. The quarters were rinsed in 70% ethanol for a few seconds and in 2% NaOCl for 25 minutes, before rinsing, and were then cut to obtain rectangular and uniformly–sized double scale explants connected by some of the basal plate. These were 1.5–2.5 cm long by 1.0–1.5 cm wide (the size depending on the genotype of the material). It is best to insert explants with their distal end in the medium and the basal plate upwards (Jacobs *et al.*, 1992). Pierik and Ippel (*loc. cit.*) cultured explants on semi–solid **LS** medium (but with only $\frac{3}{4}$ the normal concentration of micronutrients), while Jacobs *et al.* (1992) employed standard **MS** medium; in both cases 30 g/l sucrose was added. The earlier authors found that 0.1 mg/l IBA promoted bulb formation but Jacobs *et al.* added only 1 mg/l BAP to the medium, because in their experiments auxin did not improve bulb yield.

Bulblets are produced on double scale explants cultured at 17–25°C (temperatures in the middle of these range are apparently optimal) and in light of 20–65 $\mu mol\ m^{-2}\ s^{-1}$ PPFD. Bulblets arise from axillary buds as well as from adventitious initials which develop on the basal plate region of the explants (Grootarts *et al.*, 1981).

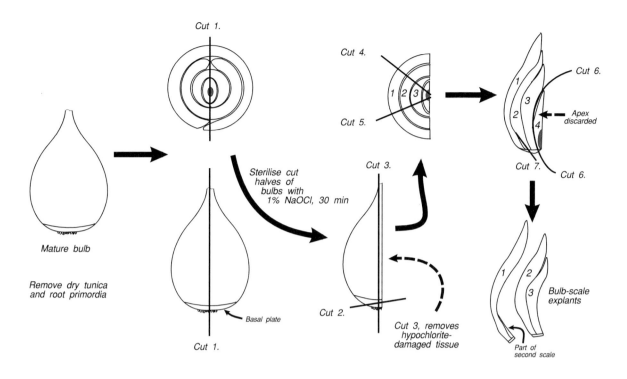

Fig. 153. Stages in the preparation of bulb-scale explants of *Iris* × *hollandica* [After Van der Linde *et al.*, 1988].

Before planting bulblets in soil, Pierik and Ippels subcultured them to a medium without regulants on which, during dark incubation over a six week period, they formed roots and leaves, and bulblet growth continued.

Callus cultures of *Nerine*

Bulblets appear in the callus of *Nerine* during shoot regeneration (Jacobs *et al.*, 1992 — Table 152). Plantlets have also been obtained from somatic embryos of *Nerine* 'Mansellii' which developed in flower pedicel callus initiated on **MS** medium supplemented with 2.25 mg/l BAP and 2.2 mg/l 2,4–D (afterwards subcultured into liquid medium with 0.05 mg/l NAA, 2.25 mg/l BAP or 2.0 mg/l 2–iP). Embryos germinated on a medium without regulants, and plantlets formed bulblets with roots, on a medium containing 6% sucrose and a low concentration of NAA (Lilien–Kipnis *et al.*, 1992b).

Other Amaryllidaceae

Methods suitable for the propagation of *Narcissus* and *Nerine* can be applied to other plants of the Amaryllidaceae. Some species in which successful *in vitro* multiplication has been achieved are listed in Table 152.

Iridaceae
Bulbous *Iris*

The many cultivated species, varieties and hybrids within the genus *Iris* are usually divided into four botanical sections. Plants of three sections produce rhizomes; those in the fourth, to which the following paragraphs refer, have a bulbous rootstock to which are attached thick storage roots. Reports on the micropropagation of bulbous irises usually relate to the hybrids resulting from the crosses between *Iris xiphium* and *Iris tingitana* or *Iris latifolia*. These are often called 'Dutch Irises' and grouped under the name *Iris* × *hollandica*.

Iris × *hollandica*

Iris × *hollandica* bulbs grown in soil may each produce up to 5 daughter bulbs per year so that, relying on natural vegetative increase, it could take about 10 years to build up a commercial stock of a new cultivar (Hussey 1976a). Fortunately there are several ways in which these bulbs can be propagated *in vitro*.

Bulb scale explants. As with other bulbous species, plants can be multiplied by the culture of bulb scale explants. The method by which Van der Linde *et al.*

(1988) sectioned bulbs to obtain suitable single– or double–scale explants is shown in Fig. 153. In this plant, large longitudinal sections of bulb scales have been found to produce more adventitious shoots per unit area than small pieces. To produce adventitious shoots, the explants prepared by Van der Linde *et al.* were cultured at 20°C in the dark on semi-solid ½MS salts supplemented with **LS** vitamins and 30 g/l sucrose. Bulblets could then be induced to form at the base of some of the shoots if cultures were kept in the cold for a period and then returned to 20°C. Using this technique, 50 bulblets could be obtained from one mother bulb in 6 months.

Flower stem explants. Hussey (1976a) used 1 mm sections of the flower stalk from sprouted bulbs as explants. Adventitious shoots which rooted spontaneously were produced on **Heinz and Mee (1969)** medium containing 0.02–2 mg/l NAA. Plants became dormant after 6–10 weeks in culture and formed a small resting bulb. However if BAP (0.03–0.12 mg/l) was added to the medium, dormancy was prevented and lateral branching was promoted.

Shoot culture. An alternative method of propagating *Iris × hollandica* is that used by Mielke and Anderson (1989) and Anderson *et al.* (1990). Shoot apices (0.5–0.8 mm) dissected from sprouting mother bulbs grew into shoots and proliferated axillary shoots on a semi–solid **LS** medium containing 3% sucrose and supplemented with 170 mg/l NaH$_2$PO$_4$.2H$_2$O, 80 mg/l adenine sulphate dihydrate, 1.5 mg/l IAA and 1.5 mg/l BAP. To induce bulb formation, shoots were first moved to an intermediate medium (**LS** with 6% sucrose plus 0.5 NAA and 0.05 μM kinetin) for three weeks and then transferred to unsupplemented **LS** medium with 6–8% sucrose. Shoots were kept in the dark on this medium at 5°C for 4 weeks, then at 30°C for 5–8 weeks and were then returned to 5°C before being planted in soil. When bulblets matured, their outer scales began to turn brown, just as they do in the field. Cold treatment was not essential to promote bulblet formation but synchronized the breaking of dormancy.

Liliaceae
Hyacinthus orientalis   (Hyacinth)

Hyacinths are readily propagated *in vitro* and a variety of explants has been used for the purpose. Adventitious bulblets arise directly from:

- Bulb scales;
- Inflorescence stem sections;
- Foliage leaf sections.

Bulblets, and shoots which produce basal bulblets, can also be obtained from:

- Existing axillary buds dissected from the interior of mature bulbs.

Bulb scale explants. Fleshy bulb scales are obtained from mature bulbs which have been cold stored to remove their dormancy. Bulblets are only produced on the lower part (that proximal to the basal plate) and so the top third of the bulb can be removed. The remainder is then quartered vertically, revealing scales attached to the basal plate. They are detached (and depending on the expected contamination) treated first with fungicide and then with hypochlorite solution. Explants measuring approximately 1 cm in length (from top to bottom of the scale) and 0.5 cm in width are cut from each scale and placed horizontally but in an inverted position (that part of the scale which was originally towards the outside of the bulb, downwards) on a semisolid medium, 4–5 in a 125 ml vessel. **MS** or **LS** medium is most commonly used. Bulblets will probably regenerate without growth regulators, but better results are likely if the medium is supplemented with 1 mg/l IBA or IAA. Bulblets can also be regenerated from basal plate tissue.

On explants incubated at 20–25°C in low light, bulblets form in 8–9 weeks. These can be further multiplied by division into further scale segments, or more easily if each bulblet is re–cultured after two shallow cross–shaped vertical cuts are made into the basal plate, or if each bulblet is cut vertically into halves. Such treatments destroy apical dominance and encourage new bulblets to be produced.

If adventitious shoots are produced, they can be subcultured once they have reached a basal diameter of *ca.* 6 mm, by trimming their tops and cutting them in half. This process can be repeated at intervals of 8–12 weeks. Eventually the vigour of shoots declines and dormant bulblets are produced so that further subculturing becomes impossible. Bulblets usually require a chilling treatment to break their dormancy before they are planted *extra vitrum*.

Other explants from within the bulb. When the scales have been removed from a bulb, the inflorescence stem bearing immature leaves is revealed. After surface sterilisation, these leaflets can also be used as explants for adventitious shoot regeneration. Sections of approximately 1 cm^2 are suggested. The remaining inflorescence stem is a further source of explants. It should be cut vertically into sections of *ca.* 5 mm height. Both kinds of explant are cultured in the same way as bulb scale explants.

Inflorescence stem and foliage leaf sections. Inflorescence stem (scape) sections have the advantage that they are more likely to provide uncontaminated cultures than bulb scales, because they are excised after the inflorescence has emerged from the bulb. Furthermore, their excision does not destroy the bulb.

Bulbs are grown in pots under clean conditions in the greenhouse or growth room until just before the flowers are expected to open. The entire inflorescence stem is then cut off and the non–regenerative part below the florets discarded. The hollow at the base is then sealed, and the stem complete with florets, surface sterilised. The pedicels of each floret and sections of the scape can be used as explants. Scape sections are usually prepared by cutting the whole inflorescence stem longitudinally into two, and then excising 5 mm vertical sections, each with a node where a floret was inserted. Adventitious shoots are regenerated from these explants, in the same conditions that are suitable for bulb scales.

Liliaceae
Lilium (Lilies)

Although some species and interspecific hybrids of *Lilium* are propagated from seeds, most cultivars grown and sold commercially are multiplied vegetatively.

Conventional propagation methods. *Lilium* plants are very capable of natural vegetative propagation without the aid of tissue culture. Bulblets are often formed underground at the base of stems from axillary buds in the axils of leaves, and in many species also on the aerial parts of stems in leaf axils. The scales of bulbs also produce adventitious bulblets very freely when separated. Detached bulb scales are usually kept in a sterile medium such as peat or vermiculite until they have produced bulblets, but in some circumstances can even be planted directly into the soil to give rise to new plants.

The number and rate of growth of bulblets produced from bulb scales may be increased by a cold pre-treatment of mother bulbs, the optimum length and extent of which varies between cultivars. For some, 1 month at 10°C may be adequate; others may require 2–3 months at 0°C.

Embryo rescue

Embryo culture techniques have been used to rescue the hybrid embryos formed as a result of wide crosses within the genus. Such embryos would otherwise have failed to grow because the endosperm within the seed did not develop in a normal way. Culture on a medium lacking nitrate or ammonium ions, but reinforced with a mixture of amino acids, assists initial embryo growth. Embryo germination can then be promoted by transfer to a dilute mineral salts medium (Stimart and Ascher, 1974).

Fig. 154. Shoots developing from a *Lilium* explant bulb scale.

Meristem culture

Vegetatively propagated lilies are liable to become infected with virus diseases. A proportion of the plants obtained by culturing 0.2–0.5 mm meristems on semi–solid **LS** medium containing 20–40 g/l sucrose and 0.1 mg/l NAA is likely to be virus–free, but the absence of infection needs to be carefully checked by using appropriate ELISA, serological and electron microscopy tests (Chapter 5). Adding virazole to the culture medium may increase the proportion of plantlets lacking some viruses (Simpkins *et al*, 1981; Cohen *et al*., 1985).

Compared to infected plants, virus-free lilies are altogether more vigorous, and produce larger bulbs yielding plants with more flower buds and leaves, and leaves of a larger size.

Micropropagation

There is a very large literature on the micropropagation of *Lilium* which can only be briefly summarised in these

Table 150. Examples of *Lilium* explants, apart from bulb scales, from which shoot and bulblet regeneration has been obtained.

Explant	Species	Reference
Flower bud segments	*Lilium* cvs.	Zhola *et al.* (1992)
Leaf segments	*L. rubellum*	Niimi and Onozawa (1979) Niimi (1984)
Shoot tips	*L. speciosum*	Takayama and Misawa (1979)
Stem and peduncle sections	*L. rubellum*	Niimi and Watanabe (1982) Niimi (1984)
	L. speciosum	Takayama and Misawa (1979)
Stem sub-epidermal tissue	*Lilium* 'Enchantment'	Bigot (1974)
Petal sections	*L. rubellum*	Niimi (1984)
	L. speciosum	Takayama and Misawa (1979)
Embryo cotyledons	*Lilium* 'Pink Trumpet'	Zimmerman and Ascher (1982)

pages. *Lilium* is as yet the only bulbous genus which is micropropagated on any appreciable scale. Van der Linde (1992), quotes data of Pierik to show that *ca.* 23×10^6 *Lilium* plants were produced by Dutch micropropagation laboratories alone in 1990.

Bulb scale explants. Bulb scale sections are the most commonly used explant. The outer ones on a bulb are often heavily contaminated and are probably best discarded, but the central and inner scales (which are the most regenerative) can usually be surface sterilised to an acceptable level by using 1% NaOCl for 25–30 minutes. As with many other bulbous species, regeneration is often best from explants taken from mother bulbs which have been stored in the cold.

The basal parts of bulb scales produce more adventitious buds than the apical portion. Furthermore, because wounding stimulates the formation of new buds, more bulblets are produced per unit area of scale if small explants are used, rather than large ones. It therefore pays to cut each scale leaf, or scale leaf base, into 4–8 pieces. During excision and cutting, the polarity of each scale leaf should be noted carefully because explants should be placed abaxial side down on the medium. Subcultures can be initiated from any of the scale leaves of bulblets formed during the previous passage.

Cultured bulb scale explants give rise to adventitious shoots which, depending on the method of culture, take the form of shoots with basal scales, loosely grouped bulb scales, or bulblets. Stimart and Ascher (1978a) found that bulblets of *Lilium longiflorum* were produced more rapidly from bulb scale explants and also grew at a faster pace when cultures were maintained at 30°C rather than 25°C. However the average fresh weight and number of scales of bulblets regenerated is greater at 25°C than at 30°C (Higgins and Stimart, 1990). Culture temperature

also affects dormancy and the rate of growth and development of plants derived from the bulblets in the field.

Other explants. It is possible to regenerate lilies from explants other than bulb scales. Examples of alternative explants from which plantlets have been obtained are shown in Table 150

The capacity of leaves of *L. rubellum* leaf sections to give rise to adventitious bulblets disappeared at about the time plants came into flower (Niimi and Onozawa, 1979).

Media for propagation

Although many workers have used **MS** medium, **LS** medium is perfectly adequate and Van Aartrijk and Blom–Barnhoorn (1980) showed that there was little benefit from adding the three extra vitamins in **MS** medium. For some *Lilium* species there may, however, be an advantage in increasing the concentration of **MS** salts by 1.5–2-fold. Takayama and Misawa (1979) found the best concentration for *Lilium auratum* was twice that in the normal **MS** medium. As in other bulbous species, some researchers have preferred to use a medium in which **MS** salts are reinforced with additional phosphate [*e.g.* **Murashige et al. (1972b)** medium, used by Dabrowski *et al.*, 1992].

Sucrose concentration. Although satisfactory bud and bulblet formation may occur in **LS** medium containing 30–100 g/l sucrose, 30–40 g/l is usually preferred, as dormancy is enhanced by high concentrations.

In liquid culture, bulblets of *Lilium longiflorum* had a high water content and some became necrotic unless the final water potential of the medium was reduced to between –203 to –507 kPa. This was achieved by adding sorbitol to $\frac{1}{2}$**MS** medium to give an initial total water potential of –405 to –760 kPa (Takahashi *et al.*, 1992: see page 813). If the final water potential of the medium (*i.e.* at the end of a passage on nutrients and sugars) was reduced to less than –507 kPa by adding extra amounts of sorbitol, dormancy was increased and leaf emergence from bulblets was poor when they were removed from culture.

Growth regulators

Some highly regenerative varieties of *Lilium* produce adventitious bulblets freely *in vitro* without the need to add any growth regulants to the medium. In others there is an advantage from including an auxin. NAA is usually chosen, the optimum concentration varying between species and cultivars, and according to the degree of cold to

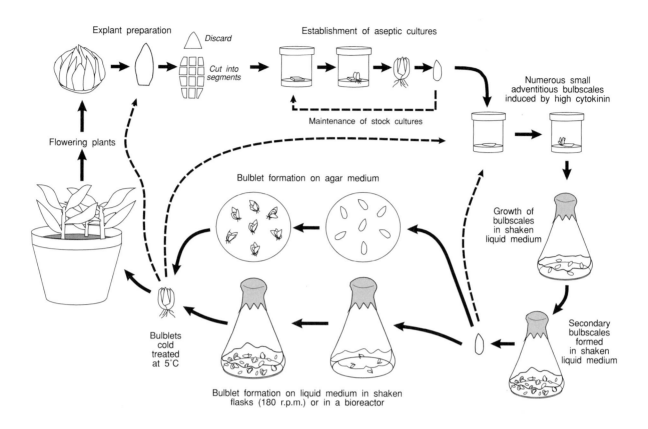

Fig. 155. Stages in the mass propagation of *Lilium auratum*.   [Diagram based on the results of Takayama and Misawa (1982a,c; 1983a,b)].

which mother bulbs have been exposed. In many reports, no increase in bulblet formation has been apparent from the further addition of a cytokinin, while in others, such an addendum has been found beneficial. For example, Dabrowski *et al.* (1992) obtained the highest rate of bulblets formation from scale explants of *Lilium* 'Sonnentiger' if the medium was supplemented with 0.1 mg/l NAA and 3 mg/l kinetin or 0.3 mg/l 2–iP.

Using liquid media

Adventitious shoots, leaflets and bulblets are also produced on bulb scales of *Lilium* in liquid medium, without damaging hyperhydricity being apparent. This makes it possible to conduct the multiplication of lilies, by growing cultures in large flasks of liquid medium.

The procedures used by Takayama and Misawa (1982a,c; 1983a,b) for the mass-propagation of lilies, are illustrated in Fig. 155. Bulb scales were inoculated onto **MS** medium with 0.1 mg/l NAA and 10 mg/l kinetin (which in this case was found to be advantageous). Adventitious leafy scales were formed which were transferred to liquid **MS** with 0.1 mg/l NAA and a high sucrose level (90 g/l)

shaken at 180 rpm. The scales proliferated further and grew to a size where, on either liquid or solid **MS** medium (without cytokinin), they produced bulblets.

This procedure has since been revised by Takahashi *et al.* (1992) who were able to culture scales in a 2000 litre fermentors (see page 813) to obtain up to 790 bulblets with a diameter greater than 5 mm, per litre of medium.

In *Lilium japonicum*, Maesato *et al.* (1991) found that the highest number of bulblets arose in cultures incubated on **MS** medium without growth regulators; the addition of 2 mg/l NAA to the medium caused the production of a smaller number of bulblets, but those formed had roots and leaves, and could be established more quickly in soil than bulblets without leaves.

Callus culture

Lilium plants give rise to highly regenerative callus which has been said to maintain genetic stability over long periods (Hussey, 1977a) (page 81, Part 1). Sheridan (1968) initiated callus of *L. longiflorum* from sections cut from the top of stems (from which young leaves had been removed) on **LS** medium containing 2 mg/l IAA. Shoots were produced when the callus was subcultured to a shaken liquid or agar–solidified medium without regulants. By contrast, Priyadarshi and Sen (1992) induced callus to form on sections of young bulb scales of the same species by culture on **MS** medium supplemented with 1 mg/l 2,4–D and 0.25 mg/l BAP, in the dark. The callus was multiplied on the same medium containing 1mg/l NAA and 0.25 mg/l BAP and gave rise to plantlets when transferred to the light and BAP was omitted from the medium.

Liliaceae

Tulipa   (Tulip)

In view of their economic importance, tulips have proved to be annoyingly more difficult to propagate through tissue culture than some other bulbous species. Shoots and bulblets can be initiated from bulb scale explants of *Tulipa* both directly and *via* callus (Rivière and Müller, 1976; Nishiuchi, 1979), but regeneration is slow and unpredictable.

Shoot culture

Hussey and Hilton (1980b) dissected 3–5 mm axillary buds from sprouted bulbs and cultured them on **MS** medium containing 0.12 mg/l NAA and 4 mg/l BAP. Cutting back developing shoots allowed further proliferation of both adventitious and axillary shoots. A similar technique was used by Hulschier *et al.* (1992) who obtained single shoots on a medium containing 0.1 mg/l NAA and 0.5 mg/l BAP, maintained at 15°C in a 16 h day (600 lux). If cut longitudinally and subcultured on the same medium, an average of 1.5 shoots was obtained from 80% of the explants.

Adventitious shoots

Adventitious shoots can be reliably produced from 1 mm thick sections of immature floral stems dissected from dry bulbs (Alderson *et al.*, 1983; Taeb and Alderson, 1987; Hulscher *et al.*, 1992) but, once bulbs have begun active growth, there is an almost total loss of regenerative ability from this type of explant (Wright and Alderson, 1980; Wright *et al*, 1982; Alderson *et al*, 1983).

On **MS** medium with 6% sucrose and 1 mg/l NAA and 1 mg/l BAP, adventitious shoots arise directly from the epidermis of the floral stem. Alderson and Taeb (1990) found that most shoots were produced from explants taken from bulbs which had been stored for only a few months. These had floral stems with a high water content.

Bulblet formation

Cold treatments. Tulip shoots produced *in vitro* do not normally produce bulbs unless established cultures are placed in a temperature of 4–5°C for 2–4 months. An alternative method is to place newly–initiated cultures into the cold for a two week period. This results in direct bulblet formation at 20°C in about 13 weeks (Baker and Wilkins, 1988). Bulbs also formed on *Tulipa* shoots when they were transferred to a medium with 70 g/l sucrose and kept in the dark at 4°C for 10 weeks and then cultured at 23°C for 12 weeks (Hulscher *et al.*, 1992).

Taeb and Alderson (1990b) found that the proportion of shoots which produced bulbs was increased if the subculturing interval was lengthened from 8, to 12 or 16 weeks, and if after 16 weeks, shoots were moved from medium (**MS**) containing 3% sucrose to one with 6% sucrose. By then keeping the cultures at 4°C for 12 weeks before final incubation at 20 or 25°C for 20 weeks, an average of 21.7 shoots were obtained per explant. However, even after this lengthy procedure, only 20.7% of the shoots produced bulblets.

Alternatives to cold. It may be possible to dispense with a cold treatment, because Taeb and Alderson (1990a) have shown that bulb formation could be stimulated on shoots of *Tulipa* 'Merry Widow' by culturing shoots in long days where the light had high irradiance and a low red to far–red ratio. The promotion of bulb formation in onion by light having a defined ratio of red to far red energy has been the basis of patents (Chapter 16).

Having obtained shoots from floral stem sections, Wright *et al.* (1982) and Alderson *et al* (1983) induced the formation of well–developed bulblets without cold treatment by soaking the shoots for 15 h in 1 mg/l GA_3, and afterwards maintaining them for 8–10 weeks in aseptic conditions. However this seems to be a less reliable technique and, in more recent research, keeping shoots in the cold seems to be preferred.

Adding 1–100 μM ACC (a natural ethylene precursor) to the medium used for subculturing increased the proportion of shoots producing bulblets (Taeb and Alderson, 1990c).

PROPAGATION OF CORM-PRODUCING SPECIES

Instead of producing storage organs composed of swollen leaf bases (bulbs), some monocotyledons store food reserves in swollen stem bases (corms) which encompass 3–4 nodes and attendant axillary buds.

Iridaceae
Gladiolus

Gladiolus is a genus within the Iridaceae in which corms are formed at the base of the stem. These carry a number of axillary buds.

Meristem culture

Meristem culture is effective for eliminating virus diseases from *Gladiolus*, especially if combined with the prior heat treatment of corms or plants. A suitable medium for explant initiation is ½MS medium containing 0.2–0.5 mg/l BAP. The plantlets obtained can be rooted on the same medium (see below), or can be multiplied using shoot culture techniques.

Shoot cultures

Shoot cultures of *Gladiolus* can be initiated from terminal and axillary buds excised from *Gladiolus* corms. Multiplication has been achieved in two ways:

- Shoots can be grown from the excised meristems, and induced to proliferate upon subculture. Shoots can be rooted and transplanted into soil, or can be induced to produce cormlets *in vitro*.

- Buds can be induced to proliferate without the formation of leaves. If individual buds are separated they can then be grown into plantlets which produce cormlets.

Shoot proliferation. The first of these techniques was investigated by Hussey and Wyvill (1972), Hussey and Hilton (1976) and Hussey (1976c; 1977a,b). Axillary shoots were induced to proliferate and develop into independent detachable plantlets on ½LS medium containing 20 g/l sucrose and 0.12–2.0 mg/l BAP, according to cultivar. If the tops of shoots were removed once shoots had grown to 5–6 cm and the remaining 8 mm of the shoot bases was subcultured, axillary shoots were produced which, after about 6 weeks of culture, could be subdivided and trimmed for further multiplication. Shoots left undisturbed produced small corms which could be planted in compost.

Lilien–Kipnis and Kochba (1987) and Lilien–Kipnis *et al.* (1992a) used **MS** medium for shoot proliferation, added less BAP (0.07–0.7 mg/l) but included 0.002–0.02 mg/l NAA. Kinetin (2 mg/l) can be used in place of BAP. Shoots were then subjected to a definite rooting stage. **MS** medium containing 60 g/l sucrose, 0.02–1.9 mg/l NAA and 0.5–5 g/l activated charcoal is suitable for this purpose. The plantlets produced were then planted into the greenhouse where they produced cormlets. Dormant corms could also be obtained by keeping shoots on the rooting medium for 3–4 months.

Effect of anti–gibberellins. After being established (Stage I) on ½MS salts (with full vitamins and organics) plus 0.05 mg/l NAA and 2.25 mg/l BAP, Ziv (1989) transferred shoot buds of *Gladiolus* 'Eurovision' directly to an agitated liquid version of the Stage I medium supplemented with daminozide (2.5 mg/l), ancymidol (2 mg/l), uniconazole (1 mg/l) or paclobutrazol (1mg/l). The explants proliferated into massive bud aggregates, or protocorms (with paclobutrazol), under these conditions.

Subcultured onto a Stage II semi–solid medium (of the same composition as that used at Stage I) plus 'polymer mixture K' (which increases the viscosity of the medium but does not affect matric potential) and 0.026 mg/l ABA, the buds or protocorms produced at Stage II formed shoots which produced up to 9 cormlets with short thick leaves per explant. The cormlets were not dormant and grew into plantlets in the greenhouse.

The growth inhibiting effects of paclobutrazol and uniconazole carried over to Stage II where they inhibited leaf elongation.

An alternative and effective technique used by Steinitz *et al.* (1991), was to transfer shoots from which the leaves and roots had been trimmed, to a shaken liquid medium containing 60 g/l sucrose and 10 mg/l paclobutrazol. In these conditions corm formation occurred at the base of shoots in the light or the dark.

Adventitious shoot formation

An alternative method of propagating *Gladiolus* is to induce the formation of adventitious shoots from corm sections. De Bruyn and Ferreira (1992) cultured explants on **MS** medium for this purpose, finding that shoot formation was best in *G. daleni* with the addition of 0.5 mg/l BAP, and in *G. tristis* with 1–2 mg/l BAP. Shoots of *G. daleni* produced corms *in vitro*, but few were obtained from *G. tristis*. Both shoots and corm production were optimal when 60–90 g/l sucrose was added to the medium and cultures were incubated at 15°C (compared to 20 or 24°C).

Shoots can be rooted in medium containing auxin and activated charcoal and then planted out, but they establish best at *ca*. 17°C. Plants kept in the shade at 27–28°C during the day and at 19–21°C in the night survived less well (Lilien-Kipnis and Kochba, 1987). Corms and cormels are produced as the plants grow to maturity.

If left in the culture jar, *Gladiolus* shoots eventually senesce and form a resting corm, but De Bruyn and Ferreira (1992) found that corm formation was enhanced by adding 60–90 g/l sucrose to **MS** medium and when cultures were kept at 15°C. Mannitol could not be substituted for all or part of the sucrose and so corm formation seemed to be unrelated to the water potential of the medium (cf. page 883).

In some corm-producing plants, adventitious shoots (or regenerative callus, see below) can be induced to form from sections of immature stalk (scape) tissue taken from just beneath the inflorescence. Tissue from this region usually remains regenerative until flower emergence.

Callus cultures

Callus capable of regenerating adventitious shoots has been obtained from several explants, especially 3–4 mm sections of young inflorescence stems, cut before the inflorescence begins to emerge (Ziv *et al.*, 1970; Ziv and Halevy, 1972). The sections are incubated at 25°C in the light, distal side downwards on semi–solid **MS** medium containing additional phosphate (*e.g.* **Murashige *et al.* (1972b)** medium with 30 g/l sucrose — Ziv and Lilien–Kipnis, 1990). This is supplemented with 0.7 mM adenine sulphate, 5–10 mg/l NAA and 0.5 mg/l kinetin to induce callus formation. Explants showing proliferation, or callus, are subcultured to the same medium containing 0.5 mg/l kinetin, or 0.25–1 mg/l BAP, for adventitious root, shoot and cormlet formation. Shoots can be rooted as described above; cormlets formed *in vitro* can be planted in soil or used to start new cultures (Hussey, 1978b).

Iridaceae
Crocus sativus   (Crocus)

Corm fragments of this plant could be induced to produce small cormels if they were cultured for two months on a medium consisting of **B5** salts and **MS** organics which contained 1 mg/l 2,4-D and 0.1 mg/l kinetin. When transferred to the same medium with 2 mg/l 2,4-D, the cormels proliferated in a similar fashion to orchid protocorms (Homes *et al.*, 1987).

Iridaceae
Freesia

Freesia plants produce a corm from which several small daughter corms usually arise at the base towards the end of the current year's growth. New plants can be initiated from these small cormlets, or can be raised from seeds.

Shoot culture

Hussey (1977a) propagated *Freesia* hybrids from axillary bud explants in a similar fashion to *Gladiolus*, adding 0.5–2.0 mg/l BAP to $\frac{1}{2}$**LS** medium to encourage the growth of axillary shoots which were then subcultured. Corms could be produced *in vitro* by keeping shoot cultures at 15°C for ten weeks and then moving them to a medium containing 10 mg/l of either NAA or 2,4–D, at 23°C.

Direct shoot regeneration

Shoot tissue explants. The procedure used by Hussey (1977a) was to culture 1 mm thick sections of soft stems with 0.12 mg/l NAA for 12 h in liquid culture. When the explants were then transferred to a medium containing 0.5–1.0 mg/l BAP, adventitious shoots were formed which gave rise to axillary shoots.

An alternative method of propagation, more suited to large scale multiplication, was reported by Doi *et al.* (1992). Cormlets from stock plants, after a treatment to overcome their dormancy, were sterilised and cultured in the dark on the medium of **Ringe and Nitsch (1968)** (modified to contain **MS** salts and FeEDTA), containing 5 mg/l BAP, until they produced shoots about 3 cm long. When sections of these shoots, 5 mm in length, were incubated in the dark on a shaken liquid medium of the same composition but with 1 mg/l NAA and 1 mg/l BAP, shoot primordia were formed. The primordia proliferated during several subcultures in the dark on a liquid medium containing **MS** salts (but only $\frac{1}{10}$ the normal concentration of ammonium nitrate) and 1 mg/l BAP, and could be induced to form shoots when moved to the same medium solidified with agar in light of high fluence (102 μmol m^{-2} s^{-1} during a 16 h day, 26°/20°C day/night).

There were then alternative methods of obtaining corms:

In the first, shoots were rooted in regulant–free medium in an atmosphere enriched with 0.1% carbon dioxide, potted out and acclimatized. Plants needed to be maintained above 18°C for several weeks and then exposed to chilling to induce flower bud

Fig. 157. Multiple shoots formed during micropropagation of *Mammillaria hernandezii.*

Fig. 158. Rooted shoots of *Mammillaria* ready for transfer to pots.

Table 154. Examples of growth regulator treatments which have been effective in inducing callus formation in Cactaceae.

Plant	Explant	Growth regulators	References
Mammillaria elongata	Tubercles	6 mg/l 2,4–D + 1–2 mg/l kin or 2–iP	Johnson and Emino (1979)
	Stem slices, perianth and ovary wall	5 mg/l 2,4–D + 2 mg/l kinetin + 20% CM	Mehra and Cheema (1980a)
Mammillaria spp.	Seedling tissue	2,4–D + 1 mg/l GA$_3$	Damiano *et al.* (1986)
Mammillaria woodsii	Pith tissue	2 mg/l IAA + 2 mg/l kinetin	Kolar *et al.* (1976)
Coryphantha macromeris	Seedling shoots	10 mg/l BAP + 0.005 mg/l 2,4–D	Smith R. H. *et al.* (1991)

it may be necessary to remove the apex of shoots to promote axillary bud proliferation.

Johnson *et al.* (1976) found that the Christmas cactus (*Schlumbergera bridgesii*) and the Easter cactus (*S. gaertneri*) could be propagated rapidly on rotated liquid **LS** medium containing 10 mg/l kinetin. An average of nine shoots per explant were produced in 8 weeks. Liquid medium may not be suitable for other genera as hyperhydricity has sometimes been a problem (Leonhardt and Kandeler, 1987).

Shoot growth, as opposed to shoot multiplication, may require a medium with less cytokinin and a slightly higher level of auxin. Depending on species, shoots may be rooted *in vitro* on a medium lacking regulants, or one containing a low concentration of auxin alone (*e.g.* 1 mg/l NAA, or 0.001–0.1 IBA). Root formation is sometimes better on ½**MS** salts than on full strength **MS**. Rooting *ex vitro* is equally possible.

Indirect morphogenesis

It appears to be relatively easy to regenerate shoots from callus of the Cactaceae.

Media containing **MS** salts have almost always been used to obtain callus. Some examples of treatments which have been successful are given in Table 154. Adventitious shoots have been formed when such callus is moved to a medium lacking regulants, or to one containing a high level of cytokinin and little auxin (*e.g.* 10 mg/l 2–iP + 1 mg/l IBA — Johnson and Emino, 1979).

The callus produced from seedling explants of *Mediocactus* cultured with 2.7–5.4 µM NAA, gave rise to somatic embryos, which later germinated on a medium without growth regulants (Infante, 1992).

Table 155. Published reports on the tissue culture of CACTI and SUCCULENT PLANTS.

Species name	Type of Culture	Source of explant	Results		References
Cactaceae					
Akersia sp. [chlorophyll-deficient cactus]	Shoot	3 mm shoots or one areole	Shoot proliferation & elongation	YY	Lassocinski (1985)
Astrophytum myriostigma Lem.	Shoot	Areoles plus adjacent meristems	Callus then axillary bud growth. Shoots rooted	Y	Vyskot & Jara (1984)
Cephalocereus senilis (Harv.) Schum.	Shoot	Cladode sections	Axillary shoots. Rooted plants	YY	Corona & Yanez (1984)
Coryphantha macromeris (Engelm.) Lem.	Callus	Shoot explants from seedlings	Adventitious shoots. Shoots rooted	—	Smith *et al.* (1991)
Echinocereus pectinatus (Scheidw.) Engelm.	Callus	Seedling shoot pieces	Shoot regeneration. Shoots rooted.	—	Ault & Blackmon (1985)
Echinocereus pectinatus	Shoot	Seedling shoot pieces	Axillary shoot proliferation. Shoots rooted.	YY	Ault & Blackmon (1985)
Echinopsis spachiana (Lem.) Fried. & G.Rowl. = *Trichocereus spachianus*	Shoot	Areoles + adjacent meristems	Axillary buds & callus formation. Shoots rooted	Y	Vyskot & Jara (1984)
Epiphyllum chrysocardium Alex.	Shoot	Stem cuttings	Axillary shoot formation. Shoots rooted.	Y	Gaiser *et al.* (1981)
Epiphyllum chrysocardium	Shoot	Stem cuttings	Growth of axillary buds. Shoots rooted	Y	Lazarte *et al.* (1982)
Escobaria [2 species]	Shoot	Shoot tips	Axillary shoot proliferation. Shoots rooted	YY	Clayton *et al.* (1990)
Ferocactus cylindraceus (Engelm.) Orcutt. = *F. acanthodes* (Lemaire) Br. & Rose	Shoot	Shoot apex of axenic seedlings	Axillary shoots from aureoles. Rooted plants	YY	Ault & Blackmon (1987)
Ferocactus emoryi (Engelm.) Orcutt. = *Ferocactus covillei* Britt. & Rose	Shoot	Seedling shoot pieces	Axillary shoot proliferation. Direct rooting	YY	Ault & Blackmon (1985)
Ferocactus wislizenii (Engelm.) Britt & Rose	Shoot	Seedling shoot pieces	Axillary shoot proliferation. Direct rooting	YY	Ault & Blackmon (1985)
Gymnocalycium mihanovichii (Fric and Gürke) Britt. & Rose. 'Hibotan' [chloroph.-deficient]	Shoot	3 mm shoots or one areole	Shoot proliferation & elongation	YY	Lassocinski (1985)
Hatiora gaertneri (Reg.) Barthlott. = *Schlumbergera gaertneri*	Shoot	Shoot tips	9 rootable shoots/explants	YY	Johnson *et al.* (1976)
Leuchtenbergia principis Hook.	Shoot	Tops of aseptic seedlings	Multiple shoots	Y	Starling (1985)
Lobivia sp. [chloroph.-deficient]	Shoot	3 mm cacti or one areole	Shoot proliferation & elongation	YY	Lassocinski (1985)
Mammillaria [21 spp.]	Callus	Seedling	Shoot formation. Shoots rooted	—	Damiano *et al.* (1986)
Mammillaria carmenae Castañeda.	Shoot	Mammillae plus adjacent meristems	Axillary bud growth (some callus). Shoots rooted	Y	Vyskot & Jara (1984)
Mammillaria elongata DC.	Callus	Stem of flowering shoot	Rooted plantlets	—	Mehra & Cheema (1980a)
Mammillaria elongata	Direct	Tubercles	Shoot initiation. Shoots rooted	Y	Johnson & Emino (1979)
Mammillaria prolifera (Mill.) Haw.	Shoot	Mammillae plus adjacent meristems	Axillary bud growth (some callus). Shoots rooted	—	Vyskot & Jara (1984)
Mammillaria san-angelensis Sanchez-Mejorada	Shoot	Apex, or lat. sects. *i.v.* plantlets	Multiple axillary shoots	YY	Martinez-Vazquez & Rubluo (1989)
Mammillaria woodsii Craig	Callus	Pith ex stem segments	Adventitious shoots, then multiple shoots. Rooted	—	Kolar *et al.* (1976)
Mammillaria wrightii Engelm. & Bigelow	Shoot	Shoot tips	Axillary shoot proliferation. Shoots rooted	YY	Clayton *et al.* (1990)
Selenicereus setaceus (DC.) Werderm = *Mediocactus coccineus* Britt. & Rose (Yellow pitaya)	Shoot	Seedling epicotyls	Multiple shoots. Shoots rooted	YY	Infante (1992)
Selenicereus setaceus	Cactus	Seedling cotyledons & roots	Somatic embryogenesis. Embryos germinated	—	Infante (1992)
Opuntia amyclaea	Shoot	Cladode sections with lateral buds	Axillary shoot proliferation. Rooted plants	YY	Escoba *et al.* (1986)
Pediocactus [5 species]	Shoot	Shoot tips	Axillary shoot proliferation. Shoots rooted	YY	Clayton *et al.* (1990)

Species name	Type of Culture	Source of explant	Results		References
Pediocactus [2 species]	Shoot	Young mamills	Axillary shoot growth. Hyperhydricity	Y	Leonhardt & Kandeler (1987)
Schlumbergera × *buckleyi* (T. Moore) Tjaden. = *S. bridgesii*	Shoot	Shoot tips	9 rootable shoots/explant	YY	Johnson *et al.* (1976)
Sclerocactus [2 species]	Shoot	Shoot tips	Axillary shoot proliferation. Shoots rooted	YY	Clayton *et al.* (1990)
Sclerocactus papyracantha (Engelm.) N.P. Tayl. = *Toumeya papyracantha* (Engelm.) Britt. & Rose	Shoot	Shoot tips	Axillary shoot proliferation. Shoots rooted	YY	Clayton et al. (1990)

When Fernández *et al.* (1991) fragmented fronds of aseptically–grown *Asplenium nidus–avis*, the tissue pieces became completely brown during incubation, but within two months produced new green cellular clusters from which sporophytes were formed.

Green globular bodies

Higuchi *et al.* (1987) discovered a new way of micropropagating ferns. Runner tips of *Nephrolepis cordifolia* cultured on ¼MS medium with 0.5 mg/l BAP, formed green globular bodies, presumed to be aggregates of shoot primordia, or the fern equivalent of somatic embryos (see page 809). The bodies proliferated when subcultured on the same medium, but produced plantlets when transferred to a regulant–free medium. Higuchi and Amaki (1989; Amaki and Higuchi, 1991) have since found that green globular bodies can be produced from several genera of ferns by culturing rhizome sections on media containing BAP. The optimum concentration of cytokinin and the concentration of the medium varied with genus:

Genus of fern	**MS** dilution	BAP (mg/l)
Adiantum	½	1.0
Asplenium	¹/₁	0.5
Nephrolepis	¼	0.5
Pteris	½	0.5
Rumohra	¹/₁	1.0

Regeneration of plants from *Adiantum* and *Rumohra* required the presence of 0.5–1 mg/l NAA. The rate of growth and proliferation of green globular bodies varied considerably between species. In *Adiantum raddianum* and *Asplenium nidus* it was too low for commercial micropropagation.

Direct shoot regeneration

We have mentioned above that direct shoot formation often occurs in shoot cultures of ferns. Adventitious shoots have also been induced to form on sporophyte tissue such as sections of rhizome or frond (Table 157).

Young sporophyte tissue from *in vitro* cultures is likely to be a suitable source of explants.

Hirsch (1975) found that young leaves from cultures of *Microgramma vacciniifolia* produced both aposporous gametophytes and directly regenerated sporophytes on a medium (Table 156) without sucrose. When 20–40 g/l sucrose was added to the medium, the proportion of sporophytes to gametophytes was considerably increased.

Callus from sporophytic tissues

Callus can be initiated from both gametophytic and sporophytic tissues of ferns. Breznovits and Mohay (1987) found that gametophyte tissue of many different ferns often developed callus if it was moved from **Moore (1903)** medium, to **MS** medium containing 0.5% sucrose, 2 mg/l IAA and 0.5 mg/l BAP. Adventitious haploid sporophytes arose apogamously from the callus.

White (1954) medium, supplemented with 2% sucrose, 300 mg/l casein hydrolysate, 10% coconut milk and 2 mg/l 2,4-D was more suitable than **MS** for growth of callus initiated from *Pteris vittata* rhizomes. When subcultured onto media without auxin, the callus gave rise to sporophytes when 40 g/l sucrose was present, and gametophytes after prolonged culture on medium with no carbohydrate or casein hydrolysate (Kshirsaga and Mehta, 1978). Similar results have been obtained in other fern species (Bristow, 1962; Hirsch, 1975).

Rooting

Sporophytes grown, for example, from fragmented tissues on media without growth regulators, form roots spontaneously and can be transferred to soil for acclimatization without further treatment. The shoots obtained from 'shoot' culture on media containing high phosphate and a cytokinin can probably be rooted directly *ex vitro* in cool shaded conditions. However, some workers have preferred *in vitro* rooting on ½MS medium (no added phosphate) without growth regulators. Paek *et al.* (1984) kept cultures of *Nephrolepis exaltata* in the dark for root induction and initiation.

Table 157. Published reports on the tissue culture of FERNS and CLUB MOSSES.

Species name	Type of Culture	Source of explant	Results		References
FELICINAE (Ferns)					
Adiantaceae					
Adiantum capillus-veneris L.	Direct	Coiled-up young leaves	Adventitious shoots. Rooted plants	Y	Pais & Casal (1987)
Adiantum cuneatum	Shoot/Direct	Rhizome tips	Adventitious & axill. shoot prolif.	YY	Murashige (1974)
Adiantum pedatum L.	Prothallus	Prothalli	Apogamous sporophytes formed	—	Whittier & Steeves (1960)
Adiantum pedatum	Shoot	Shoot apex	Shoot growth: one plant per explant	Y	Wetmore (1954)
Adiantum raddianum C. Pred. 'Fritz Luthri'	Calloid	Rhizome segments	Slow-growing globular bodies. Plantlets	Y	Amaki & Higuchi (1991)
Adiantum tenerum Sw.	Homogen. tissue	Prothalli from spores	Prothallus *ex vitro*. Sexual sporophytes	YY	Knauss (1976)
Aspidiaceae					
Dryopteris filixmas (L.) Schott.	Callus	Gametophy. ex germinated spores	Haploid apogamous sporophytes.	—	Breznovits & Mohay (1987)
Matteuccia struthiopteris (L.) Todaro	Shoot	Lateral buds of rhizomes	Shoot proliferation. Rooted	YY	Dykeman & Cumming (1985)
Matteuccia struthiopteris	Shoot	Shoot apices	Shoot multiplication. Shoots rooted. Plants	YY	Hicks & Von Aderkas (1986)
Matteuccia struthiopterus	Shoot	Rhizome pieces + meristems	Aposporous gametophytes	—	Von Aderkas (1986)
Phanerophlebia falcatum	Callus/Direct	Sporophyte tiss. (ex germ. spores)	Adventitious shoots, elongated and rooted	—	De Garcia & Furelli (1987)
Rumohra (Arachniodes) adiantiformis 'Florida'	Calloid	Rhizome segments	Green globular bodies. Plantlets	YY	Amaki & Higuchi (1991)
Aspleniaceae					
* *Asplenium nidus* L.	Calloid	Rhizome segments	Slow-growing globular bodies. Plantlets	Y	Amaki & Higuchi (1991)
Asplenium nidus	Calloid	Rhizome segments	Green globular bodies, proliferated. Plants	YY	Higuchi & Amaki (1989)
Asplenium nidus	Direct	Rhizome segments	Green globular bodies	YY	Higuchi & Amaki (1989)
Asplenium nidus-avis L.	Direct	Sections of frond	Sporophyte & gametophyte formation. Sporophytic plants	Y	Fernandez *et al.* (1991)
Blechnaceae					
Blechnum brasiliense Desv. [& cv. 'Crispum']	Homogen. tissue	Prothalli from spores	Prothallus. Sexual sporophytes	YY	Janssens & Sepelie (1989)
* *Blechnum gibbum* (Labill.) Mett. [variant]	Homogen. tissue	Prothalli from spore germination	Prothallus. Apogamous sporophytes	YY	Janssens & Sepelie (1989)
Blechnum punctulatum Sw.	Homogen. tissue	Prothalli from spores	Prothallus. Sexual sporohytes	YY	Janssens & Sepelie (1989)
Cyatheaceae					
Cyathea dregei Kunze	Germination	Spores	Gametophyte tissue. Macerated for *ex vitro* sporophytes	Y	Finnie & Van Staden (1987)
Cyathea gigentia	Shoot	Leaflet primordia, apical meristem	Fronds developed. Rooted plantlets	Y	Padhya (1987)
Davalliaceae					
❖ *Davallia fejeensis* Hook.	Direct/Callus	Macerated shoot tips	Multiple shoots from plated tissue	Y	Cooke (1979)
Dennstaedtiaceae					
Pteridium aquilinum (L.) Kuhn` (Bracken)	Germination	Spores	Gametophytes grown & immobilised in polyurethaane foam	—	Douglas & Sheffield (1990)
Gleicheniaceae					
Dicranopteris linearis	Sun Fern	Green sporangia	Prothalli & sporophytes	Y	Henson (1979)

Species name	Type of Culture	Source of explant	Results		References
Marsileaceae					
Marsilea quadrifolia	Direct	Sporophyte shoot segments	Sporophytes with rhizomes	Y	Breznovits & Mohay (1987)
Pilularia globulifera L.	Direct	Sporophyte shoot segments	Sporophytes with rhizomes	Y	Breznovits & Mohay (1987)
Oleandraceae					
Nephrolepis cordifolia (L.) Presl.	Calloid	Rhizome segments	Green globular bodies. Plantlets	YY	Amaki & Higuchi (1991)
Nephrolepis cordifolia	Calloid	Runner tips	Green globular bodies, proliferated. Plants	YY	Higuchi et al. (1987)
Nephrolepis cordifolia	Callus	Leaves, roots, runners	Gametophyte regeneration, or roots + a few sporophytes	—	Sulklyan & Mehra (1977)
Nephrolepis cordifolia	Callus	Leaves, roots, runners	Gametophyte regeneration, or roots + a few sporophytes	—	Sulklyan & Mehra (1977)
* Nephrolepis exaltata (L.) Schott.	Direct	Sporophyte shoot segments	Sporophytes with rhizomes	Y	Breznovits & Mohay (1987)
Nephrolepis exaltata	Direct	Stolon segments (1—2 cm)	Numerous adventitious shoots	Y	Padhya (1987)
Nephrolepis exaltata	Shoot	Runner tips	Multiple shoots. Plants	Y	Soede (1981)
Nephrolepis exaltata 'Bostoniensis'	Direct	Runner tips	Adventitious shoot formation	Y	Loescher & Albrecht (1978)
Nephrolepis exaltata 'Bostoniensis'	Shoot	Runner tips	Shoot proliferation. Plants	YY	Borgan & Naess (1987)
Nephrolepis exaltata 'Bostoniensis'	Shoot	Runner tips	Multiple shoots. Rooted	YY	Paek et al. (1984)
Nephrolepis exaltata 'Bostoniensis'	Shoot/Callus	Runner-tips	Culture storage studied	—	Hvoslef-Eide (1992)
Nephrolepis exaltata 'Bostoniensis'	Shoot	Runner tips	Multiple shoot formation	Y	Leffring & Soede (1982)
Nephrolepis exaltata 'Bostoniensis'	Shoot	Runner tips	Multiple shoot formation	Y	Leffring & Soede (1982)
Nephrolepis exaltata 'Scottii'	Shoot	Runner tips	Multiple shoots. Rooted	YY	Paek et al. (1984)
Nephrolepis falcata (Cav.) C. Chr.	Shoot	Runner tips (2cm)	Shoot proliferation. Shoots rooted	YY	Beck & Caponetti (1983)
Nephrolepis falcata	Shoot	Runner tips (2cm)	Shoot proliferation. Shoots rooted	YY	Beck & Caponetti (1983)
Nephrolepis spp.	Shoot	Rhizome tips	Shoot proliferation. Shoots rooted	YY	Petersen (1979)
Nephrolepis spp.	Shoot	Rhizome tips	Shoot proliferation. Shoots rooted	YY	Petersen (1979)
Nephrolepis spp.	Shoot & Direct	Stolon tips	Axillary & adventitious shoots	Y	Henson (1979)
Nephrolepis spp.	Shoot & Direct	Stolon tips	Axillary & adventitious shoots	Y	Henson (1979)
Ophioglossaceae					
Botrychium dissectum Spreng. ssp. obliquum	Prothallus	Gametophytes	Prothalli with sex organs	—	Whittier (1972 : 1976)
Botrychium dissectum ssp. obliquum	Sporophytic growth	Leaves of sporophyte	Gametophytes by apospory	—	Whittier (1978)
Osmundaceae					
Osmunda cinnamonea L.	Prothallus	Prothalli	Apogamous sporophytes	—	Whittier & Steeves (1960)
Osmunda regalis L.	Callus	Gametophy. ex germinated spores	Haploid apogamous sporophytes.	—	Breznovits & Mohay (1987)
Osmunda regalis	Direct	Gametophy. ex germinated spores	Apogamous sporophyte formation	Y	Breznovits & Mohay (1987)
Todea barbara (L.) T.Moore (King fern)	Embryo ex prothalli	Embryo/Shoot	Embryo growth. Young sporophytes	—	DeMaggio & Wetmore (1961)
Polypodiaceae					
Drymoglossum piloselloides (L.) Presl.	Direct	Strips from young fronds	Aposporous gametophytes	—	Kwa et al. (1988)
Microgramma vacciniifolia (Langsd. and Fisch.) Copel.	Callus	Young leaves	Sporophytic and gametophytic regenerants	—	Hirsch (1975)
Microgramma vacciniifolia	Direct	Juv. leaves ex plants ex rhiz. callus	Gametophytes & sporophytes - mainly latter if sugar in medium	Y	Hirsch (1975)

	Species name	Type of Culture	Source of explant	Results		References
❖	*Platycerium bifurcatum* (Cav.) C.Chr.	Direct	Young leaves ex *in vitro* plants	Adventitious shoots, rooted	Y	Camloh & Gogala (1991)
	Platycerium coronarium (Stag's horn fern)	Green sporangia	Spore germination	Prothalli & sporophytes	—	Henson (1979)
	Platycerium stemaria (Beauv.) Desv.	Direct/Callus	Shoot tips macerated	Multiple shoots from plated tissue	—	Cooke (1979)
	Platycerium stemaria & spp.	Shoot	Shoot tips	Adventitious & axillary shoots	Y	Hennen & Sheehan (1978)
Pteridaceae						
	Pteris cretica L. 'Albolineata'	Callus	Gametophytes ex germinated spores	Haploid apogamous sporophytes.	—	Breznovits & Mohay (1987)
	Pteris cretica 'Albolineata'	Direct	Gametophytes ex germinated spores	Apogamous sporophyte formation	Y	Breznovits & Mohay (1987)
	Pteris ensiformis Burm. f. 'Victoriae'	Calloid	Rhizome segments	Rapidly-growing globular bodies. Plantlets	YY	Amaki & Higuchi (1991)
	Pteris henryii	Callus	Gametophytes ex germinated spores	Haploid apogamous sporophytes. Plants	—	Breznovits & Mohay (1987)
	Pteris vittata L.	Callus	Rhizome pieces	Sporophytic plantlets or regeneration of gametophytes	—	Kshirsagar & Mehta (1978)
	Pteris vittata	Callus	Rhizome segments	Many adventitious shoots (diploid). Rooted	—	Padhya (1987)
	Pteris vittata	Shoot	Rhizome segments with apex	Multiple shoots. Rooted plantlets	Y	Padhya (1987)
Schizaeaceae						
	Anemia phyllitides (L.) Swartz	Germination	Spores	Gametophytes grown and immobilized in polyurethane foam	—	Douglas & Sheffield (1990)
	Lygodium japonicum	Protoplast	Leaves from *in vitro* sporophytes	Gametophytes regenerated	—	Maeda *et al.* (1990)
Sinopteridaceae						
	Cheilanthes alabamensis (Buckl.) Kunze	Prothallus	Spores	Gametophytes, then apogamous sporophytes	—	Whittier (1965)
	Cheilanthes tomentosa Link.	Prothallus	Spores	Gametophytes, then apogamous sporophytes	—	Whittier (1965)
	Notholaena Sun-tuff	Fern	Mature sori on leaflets	Plantlet formation	YY	Dethier Rogers & Banister (1992)
	Notholaena 'Sun-tuff'	Fern	Mature sori on leaflets	Plantlet formation	YY	Dethier Rogers & Banister (1992)
*	*Pellaea rotundifolia* (Forst.f.) Hook.	Homogen. tissue	Prothalli from spores	Prothallus. Sexual sporophytes	YY	Janssens & Sepelie (1989)
Thelypteridaceae						
	Ampelopteris prolifera (Retz.) Copel.	Callus	Germinating spores and leaves	Apogamous sporophytes	—	Mehra & Sulklyan (1969)
	Cyclosorus contiguous	Callus	Gametophytes ex germin. spores	Haploid apogamous sporophytes. Plants	—	Breznovits & Mohay (1987)
	Cyclosorus dentatus	Suspension	Callus ex sporophyte root apices	Gametophytes & sex organs. Sporophytes	—	Mehra & Palta (1971)
LYCOPODINAE (Club mosses)						
Lycopodiaceae						
	Lycopodium cernuum L.	Shoot	Shoot apices	Shoot growth and formation of strobuli (cones)	YY	Wetmore (1954)
	Lycopodium spp.	Spore germination	Spores	Growth of gametophytes	—	Freeberg & Wetmore (1957)
Selaginellaceae						
	Selaginella willdenovii (Desv.) ex Poir) Bak. (Peacock Fern)	Shoot	Shoot apices	Shoot growth	Y	Wetmore (1954)

The following plant species are also being micropropagated in European laboratories:
Actinopteris radiata; Goniophlebium subauriculatus; Microsorium pteropus; Nephrolepis; Platycerium willinckii.

THE PROPAGATION OF ORCHIDS

Many genera of the Orchidaceae produce flowers of outstanding beauty and are consequently highly valued as ornamental plants. Orchids are herbaceous perennials and can be raised from seed or propagated vegetatively.

Despite the variation naturally abundant in orchids, growers and hobbyists are continually trying to create new forms through carefully controlled hybridisation. Many bi– and pluri–generic hybrids have been produced in the pursuit of this quest.

Conventional methods of propagation

Propagation from seeds. Historically, raising orchid plants from seeds has not been easy. Seeds are very small (see later) and normally require to be sown in soil infected with a symbiotic mycorrhizal fungus (Part 1, page 131) before they will germinate. One method of obtaining germination has therefore been to sow seed onto soil which has been mixed with soil gathered from around a growing plant. Much more reliable germination and early seedling growth can be obtained by *in vitro* seed culture.

Vegetative propagation. Plants of orchid hybrids raised from seed are genetically heterogeneous. It is therefore necessary to use vegetative multiplication to perpetuate selected varieties but, using conventional techniques, the potential for so doing is limited and only a small number of plants can be produced in a given time.

Orchids fall into two categories according to their manner of vegetative growth:

- **Monopodial orchids** (*e.g. Arachnanthe, Vanda*) in which the shoot apex continues vegetative growth over several years, producing a shoot with many leaves and lateral buds, some of which give rise to inflorescences;

- **Sympodial orchids** (*e.g. Cattleya* and *Cymbidium*) in which growth continues by a succession of branches. The axis of each branch has only a limited potential for growth and forms a pseudobulb bearing several leaves, which stops growing at the end of a season (inflorescences being produced on a lateral axis), or when a terminal inflorescence is produced.

The methods suitable for vegetative propagation, and the kind of explants which can be obtained to initiate tissue cultures, vary between the two types.

Apart from *in vitro* culture, monopodial orchids such as *Arachnis* and *Vanda* can be propagated from tip cuttings, and orchids of some other genera (*e.g. Phaius* and *Phalaenopsis*) may be increased by flower stalk cuttings. Orchids of all kinds can be divided, but the frequency with which this is possible is generally low: *Cattleya* plants, for instance, can usually only be split once in every three years. Some orchids (*e.g.* those in the genera *Dendrobium* and *Epidendrum*) produce offsets in their leaf axils (called *keikis*) which often root while still attached to the plant, and require only to be snapped off and replanted.

GERMINATING ORCHID SEEDS *IN VITRO*

Germination and seedling growth of orchids can be promoted *in vitro* in two ways:

- By sowing seeds in the presence of a symbiotic mycorrhizal fungus which has been specially isolated and cultured on a synthetic medium;

- By sowing seeds on a plant culture medium which, in the absence of a symbiotic fungus, provides the nutrients required for early seedling development.

The most appropriate method varies from one genus to another.

Using mycorrhizal infection

The ease with which most orchids of commercial interest can be germinated asymbiotically led to a decline in the use of symbiotic germination, and interest has only been aroused in recent years when difficulty has been experienced in germinating some wild terrestrial orchids, endangered by modern lifestyles.

When the presence of a symbiotic fungus is used to assist the germination of orchid seeds *in vitro*, an appropriate fungus is isolated from orchid roots. Sections of washed roots are examined under a dissecting microscope for the presence of coils of fungal hyphae. These are dissected away from orchid tissue and inoculated onto a fungal isolation medium. Three media which have been used for this purpose are shown in Table 158. Fungi growing on the medium which appear to be mycorrhizal are subcultured until they are free from contaminants. Clements *et al.* (1986) and Mitchell (1989) describe pouring plates in which there are areas without medium. When an isolate from the initial medium is transferred in agar to such

Table 158. Three media used for the isolation of orchid symbiotic fungi.

Components	Burgeff (1936) MN + N	Clements and Ellyard (1979)	Clements et al. (1986) §
Macronutrients (meq/l)			
NO_3^-	—	3.53	4.23
PO_4^{3-}	20.60	4.41	4.41
SO_4^{2-}	10.00	0.81	0.81
Cl^-	3.51	1.34	1.34
K^+	8.59	2.81	2.81
Ca^{2+}	1.80	—	4.23
Na^+	1.71	3.53	—
Mg^{2+}	2.43	0.81	0.81
NH_4^+	7.57	—	—
Microelements (mg/l)			
$FeSO_4.7H_2O$	10 (0.036 mM Fe)	—	—
Organic additions (g/l)			
Yeast extract	—	0.1	0.1
Potato starch	3	—	—
Sucrose	—	5	5
Streptomycin sulphate	—	0.05	—
Agar	15	8	10
pH	?	4–5	?

Recipes for the preparation of the macronutrients in this, and other tables in Chapter17 will be found in the Appendix.

Table 159. Three media used for the germination of orchid seeds in the presence of symbiotic fungi.

Components	Burgeff (1936) Sb	Clements and Ellyard (1979)	Clements et al. (1986)
Macronutrients (meq/l)			
NO_3^-	—	—	1.69
PO_4^{3-}	22.04	—	4.41
SO_4^{2-}	2.43	—	0.81
Cl^-	3.51	—	1.34
K^+	7.35	—	2.81
Ca^{2+}	1.80	—	1.69
Na^+	1.71	—	—
Mg^{2+}	2.43	—	0.81
NH_4^+	—	—	—
Microelements (mg/l)			
$FeSO_4.7H_2O$	10 (0.036 mM Fe)	—	—
Organic additions (g/l)			
Yeast extract	—	0.1‡	0.1
Na nucleinate	0.5	—	—
Potato starch	5	—	—
Powdered rolled oats	—	2.5 (3.5‡)	3.5
Sucrose	—	—	2
Agar	12	6	10
pH	?	5.2–5.5	?

‡ Not in original description, but included by Clements (1989).

voids (3–5 mm away from the fresh medium), fungal hyphae grow from the agar blocks and bridge the gap. Contaminating bacteria are thus left behind in the agar inocula, which are later removed. It is important to make a number of fungal isolates initially, because it is very likely that some will not prove to be effective symbionts.

To initiate symbiotic cultures, sterilised mature seeds of the orchid are placed onto an appropriate semi–solid medium (Table 159) just before, or at the same time as, the medium is inoculated with an appropriate fungus. The medium for symbiotic sowings should not be reinforced with complex additives. The addition of banana pulp, or fruit juice, for example, may cause orchid seeds or protocorms to be overgrown by the fungus (Clements, 1989).

The effectiveness of different fungal isolates can be tested by inoculating each one onto medium carrying samples of the same seed. Those which do not promote germination can be discarded and the remainder subcultured for use on other occasions. Clements et al. (1986) found that

only 25% of fungi isolated from European terrestrial orchids were effective symbionts.

Fungal isolates can be used for more than one kind of orchid, but are unlikely to be effective universal symbionts. Clements and Ellyard (1979) found that a fungus isolated from the orchid *Pterostylis vittata* would promote the germination of several species in this genus, but that other species germinated better in the presence of a fungus obtained from *P. hamata*.

Vessels containing seed are incubated in light or darkness until protocorms appear. Cultures must thereafter be kept in the light to encourage shoot and root growth. Because the fungus is still assisting seedling nutrition, young plants may need to be spaced out so that they have sufficient fungal exposure, the fungus needing to explore a larger volume of medium to obtain the nutrients which the plantlets require.

Mycorrhizal infection appears to provide sugars necessary for embryo germination, and later to increase the availability of organic nitrogen compounds, vitamins and growth substances to young orchid plants. Ueda and Torikata (1974) discovered marked cytokinin activity in extracts made from rhizomes of *Cymbidium* carrying a symbiotic infection. This was considerably diminished in asymbiotic rhizomes. Extracts of mycorrhizae cultured on sterile media apart from an orchid plant, showed no cytokinin activity.

Germination on nutrient media

Nutrient media

Knudson (1922) found that seeds of orchids can often be germinated in sterile culture, in the absence of fungi, providing adequate nutrients are supplied. Knudson (1922; 1925; 1943; 1946) was the one of the first to describe suitable media and **Knudson (1946) C** medium is still widely used to germinate seeds of tropical orchids. Many other compositions have since been suggested in the literature. That of **Vacin and Went (1949)**, for example, has proved to be of general value.

> The composition of these two media is given in Table 47, page 382 *et seq.*, Part 1.

Micronutrients. Both **Vacin and Went (1949)** and **Knudson (1946) C** provide only Mn^{2+} and Fe^{2+} but, as it is likely that seedling growth will be improved if other minor elements are present in the medium, it is advisable to replace the micronutrients in the original compositions by those of $\frac{1}{2}$**MS** or **MS**. It is also recommended that the ferric tartrate or ferric sulphate listed in the recipes for early orchid media should be replaced with 0.05–0.1 mM iron chelated with EDTA.

Vitamins. Vitamins have often not been added to media for germinating tropical orchids, but several workers have found that seedling growth can be improved when undefined supplements, such as banana homogenate (Mowe, 1973; Ernst, 1974, 1975) and coconut milk (McIntyre *et al.*, 1974; Mathews and Rao, 1980), which could contribute vitamins, are added to the medium. In some instances thiamine (Mead and Bulard, 1979) and nicotinic acid (particularly) (Mathews and Rao, 1980) have been found to stimulate seedling growth (Arditti, 1984).

Growth regulators

There are some reports that a low concentration of auxin or cytokinin has stimulated germination and seedling growth, but these substances do not appear to be required by most cultures. Adding activated charcoal (*e.g.* 1 g/l) to the medium into which seedlings are transplanted, can enhance growth, especially in species which are liable to release phenolic substances (Van Waes, 1987).

Seeds of terrestrial orchids

Because terrestrial native orchids are under threat in many parts of the world, research has been devoted to their conservation in recent years. Many of these species, especially those from temperate latitudes, do not germinate well on media used for tropical orchids, but have been germinated in the presence of a symbiotic fungus, or aseptically by using more complex media, using either mature seeds or ovules gathered from green pods.

Some examples of media used for asymbiotic germination of terrestrial orchids are given in Table 160. The media of **Muir and Mitchell (1989)** and **Harvais (1982)** respectively allowed successful germination of *Cypripedium calceolus* and *C. reginae*, and that of **Arditti et al. (1985)** of *Cypripedium, Calypso bulbosa, Piperia elegans* var. *elata*, and *Platanthera saccata*.

A wide range of different orchids has been raised with **Norstog (1973) Barley II** medium (originally formulated to promote the growth of immature cereal embryos) (Henrich *et al.*, 1981) and with **Van Waes and Debergh (1986)** medium (Van Waes and Debergh, 1986; Van Waes, 1987), two media which do not contain inorganic nitrogen. This is possibly because the seeds of terrestrial orchids are sensitive to high salt concentrations. Van Waes and Debergh (1986) found that although the omission of inorganic nitrogen resulted in the best overall germination, and was essential for *Epipactis helleborine*, other orchids would germinate in the presence of either organic or inorganic nitrogen.

Although not essential for germination, NO_3^- and NH_4^+ are required to obtain the optimum rate of growth of cultures once seedlings have developed. Media in Table 160, apart from **Van Waes and Debergh (1986)**, have been used during both germination and seedling growth. It is recommended that micronutrients should always be provided, with iron in a chelated form.

Stages in seedling development

Seeds of orchids are very small and contain little more than a naked embryo (which may consist of only 30 or so cells) within a mericarp. Upon germination the embryo enlarges to form a swollen corm–like structure, known as a protocorm (pages 55–56, Part 1). Protocorms formed *in vivo* become green and their growth relies partly on the supply of carbohydrates by a symbiotic fungus, and partly on photosynthesis. During *in vitro* germination, where sugars are provided by the medium, protocorm growth can take place in the dark.

Table 160. Five media which have been used for the non-symbiotic germination of terrestrial orchids.

Components	Norstog (1973) Barley II †	Harvais (1982) ‡	Arditti et al. (1985) *	Van Waes & Debergh (1986) ††	Muir & Mitchell (1989) §
Macronutrients (meq/l)					
NO_3^-	—	22.85	5.71	—	4.38
PO_4^{3-}	20.06	4.41	2.65	6.61	2.20
SO_4^{2-}	6	1.62	2.11	0.81	0.81
Cl^-	20.12	1.34	—	—	0.67
K^+	16.74	4.79	0.88	2.2	2.39
Ca^{2+}	10.06	3.39	2.96	—	3.39
Na^+	—	—	—	—	—
Mg^{2+}	6.0	1.62	2.11	0.81	0.81
NH_4^+	—	17.49	2.75	—	—
Microelements (mg/l)					
$MnSO_4.4H_2O$	3.96	2.03	—	25.0	5.89
$MnCl_2.2H_2O$	—	—	—	—	3.62
$ZnSO_4.7H_2O$	0.5	0.5	—	10.0	1.72
H_3BO_3	0.5	0.5	—	—	1.24
KI	—	0.1	—	—	—
$CoCl_2.6H_2O$	0.025	20.4	—	0.25	—
$CuSO_4.5H_2O$	0.025	0.5	—	0.025	0.05
$Na_2MoO_4.2H_2O$	0.025	0.02	—	0.25	0.059
Ferric citrate $5H_2O$	10	—	—	—	12.5
$FeSO_4.7H_2O$	—	—	5.53	—	5.56
Ammonium ferric citrate	—	25	—	—	—
NaFeEDTA	—	—	—	36.71	—
$Na_2EDTA.H_2O$	—	—	—	—	7.46
Vitamins (mg/l)					
Inositol	50	—	0.1	991.0	100
Thiamine HCl	0.25	5.0	1.0	0.5	—
Nicotinic acid	—	10.0	—	5.0	2.5
Pyridoxine HCl	0.25	—	1.0	0.5	—
Ca pantothenate	0.25	5.0	—	—	—
Folic acid	—	—	1.0	0.5	—
Biotin	—	—	1.0	0.05	0.005
Amino acids (mg/l)					
Alanine	50	—	—	—	—
Arginine	10	—	—	—	—
Cysteine	20	—	—	—	—
Glutamine	400	—	—	102.3	—
Glycine	—	—	—	2.0	—
Leucine	10	—	—	—	—
Methionine	10	—	—	—	—
Phenylalanine	10	—	—	—	—
Tyrosine	10	—	—	—	—
Peptone	—	—	—	—	2.5
Casein hydrolysate	—	—	—	500.0	—
Other additives					
Malic acid (g/l)	1.0	—	—	—	—
Ammonium citrate (mg/l)	19	—	—	—	—
Yeast extract (mg/l)	—	—	—	—	50
Potato extract ¶ (ml/l)	—	50	—	—	100
Sucrose (g/l)	10	—	—	20	16
Glucose (g/l)	—	20	10	—	—
Growth regulators					
NAA (mg/l)	—	0.1	—	—	—
Wuchstoff 66f ** (ml)	—	—	0.1	—	—
Kinetin (mg/l)	—	1.0	—	—	—
BAP ¶¶ (mg/l)	—	—	—	0.2	—
Coconut milk (ml/l)	—	—	50	—	—

NOTES TO TABLE $$$

¶ Potato extract prepared here by boiling 200 g peeled potato in one litre water, straining the liquid and making up to 1 litre.

** Thought to be an auxin solution.

¶¶ Inclusion beneficial for some genera, not others.

Recipes for the preparation of the macronutrients in this, and other tables in Chapter 17 will be found in the Appendix.

Typically a seed gives rise to a single protocorm which in turn develops into a seedling, but protocorms may divide. Division can be promoted by appropriate *in vitro* treatments and then more than one plantlet may be derived from a single seed. If young leaves or roots of seedlings are sectioned and placed on an appropriate medium, they too can be induced to give rise to multiple protocorms (Griesbach, 1986). Under the influence of high auxin treatments, seedling protocorms can also be induced to produce callus tissue from which adventitious shoots can be differentiated and grown into plantlets (Rao, 1977). Seedling protocorms and young seedlings are thus alternative explants for the vegetative propagation of orchids (Fig. 162).

During the normal process of germination, protocorms of some orchids become covered with fine rhizoids. Protocorms later give rise to roots and shoot buds. Stages in the development of seedlings of two orchid species are shown in Fig. 161.

Sowing seeds

The large numbers of orchid seedlings which can be reliably obtained with aseptic techniques has led dedicated growers to use only these methods for seed germination of tropical orchids. Seedlings grow slowly and flowering plants are usually only obtained after several years.

Sterilising seed. The very small seeds of orchids are sterilised as shown on page 118 of Part 1, or are placed into tubes of hypochlorite solution (containing wetter), either directly or after being first wrapped in a filter paper. Bleach solution is usually left in contact with seeds for a few minutes, but where contamination has been severe, the period of exposure has been considerably increased (page 122).

When seeds have been directly immersed, the sterilant solution is conveniently removed by filtration. One way to do this is to place a porous filter paper into a Buchner funnel and cover it with hypochlorite solution for a minute or so. The sterilant solution containing the seeds is then also introduced, and the combined solution withdrawn under vacuum. The funnel is then re-

Table 161. Some examples of orchid culture in liquid media.

Plant	Results	References
Aranda, Aranthera	Protocorm proliferation	Cheah & Sagawa (1978), Lim-Ho (1982)
Cattleya	Protocorm formation & growth	Morel (1974) Scully (1967), Lim-Ho (1982)
Cymbidium	Callus & protocorm initiation	Reinert and Mohr (1967)
	Protocorm proliferation	Wimber (1963)
Dendrobium	Protocorm initiation	Morel (1974), Lim-Ho (1982),
Oncidium	Protocorm formation & proliferation	Lim-Ho (1982)
Phalaenopsis	Protocorm formation & proliferation	Griesbach (1983) Von Schmude (1985)
Laeliocattleya	Callus protocorm formation	Churchill *et al.* (1971
Portea petropolipana	Callus and protocorm formation	Mapes (1973)
Thunia alba	Protocorm formation	Singh and Prakash (1984)
Vanda hybrid	Protocorm proliferation	Kunisaki *et al.* (1972)
Vanda spp	Protocorm formation only	Morel (1974)

Cultural conditions. Explant survival and protocorm formation can occur in darkness or light. For culture of tropical orchids, light of low energy irradiance and a fairly high incubation temperature (*e.g.* 22–28°C), is usually adopted.

Subcultures

When subdivided and subcultured, individual protocorms often produce adventitious protocorms. Morel (1964) found that if protocorms 2–3 mm in length were cut into 3–4 slices, new protocorms would form on the segments. It is now common to cut protocorms into several pieces during subcultures. If *Cymbidium* protocorms were cut into two and crushed, there was a 6–7 fold increase in the number of secondary protocorms compared to whole organ culture (Bivins and Hackett, 1969). Protocorms are usually subcultured onto exactly the same medium as that used at Stage I.

Plantlet formation

Plantlet formation generally occurs when intact protocorms are subcultured to an agar solidified medium. For some varieties, it can be beneficial at this stage to use **White (1954)** or **MS** medium instead of **Knudson (1946) C** or **Vacin and Went (1949)**. Sucrose is usually added to the medium at least to the stage where a leaf has formed. Thus although *Vanda* produces protocorms most freely when there is no sucrose in the medium (page 924), the production of plantlets in this genus has been found to be optimal

when media contained 10–20 g/l sucrose (Kunisaki *et al.*, 1972).

Sucrose can be omitted once plantlets have formed and growth will continue supported by photosynthesis, provided cultures are kept in high irradiance light (Arditti and Ernst, 1984). For root formation on *Cymbidium* protocorms, Albouy *et al.* (1988) used medium containing 20 g/l sucrose, but the concentration was reduced to 5 g/l thereafter during plantlet growth. Transfer to a medium lacking sugar is essential in some genera to promote greening and plantlet differentiation (*e.g.* in *Phalaenopsis* — Intuwong and Sagawa, 1974; in Sarcanthine orchids — Sagawa and Kunisaki, 1982).

The addition of activated charcoal to the medium may assist protocorm proliferation and plantlet development (Van Waes, 1987; Albouy *et al.*, 1988).

Using explants other than shoot apices

Explants other than shoot tips can be used to commence orchid cultures which will produce protocorms. In fact, it is probable that any part of an orchid plant which contains meristematic tissues can be used as initial explant material (Goh, 1982).

Leaf explants

Several workers have found protocorms to be formed directly on young leaves, or indirectly on the callus initiated from them. Cultures can sometimes be started

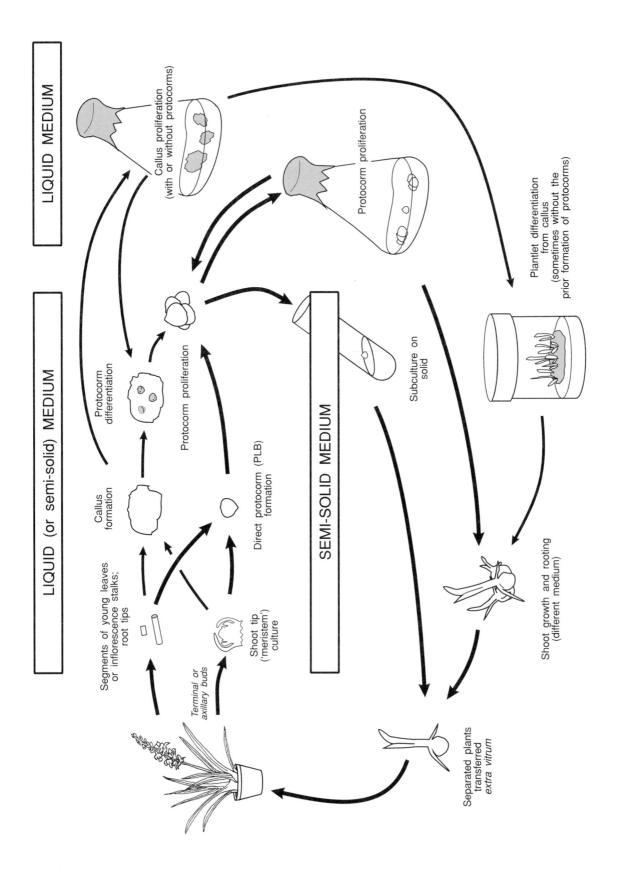

Fig. 162. The methods by which orchids are generally micropropagated. Propagation from directly-formed protocorms is to be preferred.

from sections of the young leaves of mature plants, for example in:

×*Laeliocattleya*	Churchill *et al.* (1971)
×*Ascocenda*	Fu (1979)
×*Renantanda*	Goh and Tan (1979)

The young leaves of seedlings (or even whole seedlings — Pierik and Steegmans, 1972) are usually highly regenerative (Champagnat *et al.*, 1970; Tanaka *et al.*, 1975), but this source of explant material is of little use to those wishing to propagate a defined variety. Of greater use in clonal propagation are the leaves and stems of young plantlets produced by *in vitro* culture. These too provide highly regenerative explants (Tanaka and Sakanishi, 1977; Vij *et al.*, 1984).

The production of callus. Although leaf tissue may sometimes be induced to give rise to callus directly, in many of the published experiments which describe its use as explant material, a morphogenic callus has been obtained. This may then give rise to adventitious shoots or may produce protocorms, from which plantlets may be differentiated.

Callus was produced when 2 mm (or smaller) tips of leaves from year–old seedlings of *Epidendrum* were cultured in shaken liquid **MS** medium supplemented with 1 mg/l 2,4–D and 0.5 mg/l BAP. Adventitious shoots were formed on the callus when it was transferred to agar–solidified **MS**. These developed into rooted plantlets on a medium similar to **Knudson (1922, 1943) B** or on **Knudson (1946) C** (Churchill *et al.*, 1970, 1973).

Explants from young leaves of *Renantanda* 'Ammani' produced callus when cultured on **Vacin and Went (1949)** supplemented with coconut milk. This began to differentiate protocorms in the same medium, but did so more rapidly when transferred to medium without coconut milk (Goh, 1990).

In ×*Laeliocattleya*, choice of medium determined whether callus was formed, or protocorms were produced directly from explants. For example, callus was obtained on shaken liquid **Knudson (1946) C** medium (20 g/l sucrose) (especially if 2–chlorophenoxyacetic acid was included in the primary culture medium) and this produced protocorms on a solidified version of the same medium. However, protocorms were produced directly on explants in shaken liquid **Ball *et al.* (1971) M** medium, which has no NH_4^+ ions.

The latter medium contains 525 mg/l KNO_3; 250 mg/l $MgSO_4.7H_2O$; 250 mg/l KH_2PO_4 and 200 mg/l $Ca_3(PO_4)_2$; 7.5 mg/l $MnSO_4.4H_2O$; 250 mg/l $FeSO_4.7H_2O$; 10 g/l sucrose and 500 ml/l coconut milk.

Protocorms can also be produced from cell suspensions and the callus derived from them. Rosettes of protocorms (separated for multiplication purposes) were produced from *Cymbidium* callus when suspension cultured cells were inoculated onto a solid medium containing coconut milk, but not auxin (Steward and Mapes, 1971a).

Although morphogenic callus has mainly been obtained from leaf tissues, it is possible to obtain indirect regeneration from explants of other kinds. In *Paphiopedilum*, protocorms were occasionally formed on the callus which developed on young inflorescences and leaf tips, but plantlets were only obtained infrequently (Stewart and Button, 1975). Intuwong and Sagawa (1973) did however obtain callus which produced protocorms by culturing young (1.5 cm or less) inflorescences of ×*Ascofinetia*.

Adventitious shoots. Occasionally, shoots may be formed directly from explants, and not *via* the direct formation of protocorms. Leaves of *Renanthera imschootiana*, inserted base down in agar–solidified **Mitra *et al.* (1976) medium** (containing 20 g/l peptone and 20 g/l sucrose), supplemented with 1 mg/l NAA and 10 mg/l BAP, gave rise to adventitious shoots directly, the leaves of which could be subcultured with the same result (Seeni and Latha, 1992).

Root explants

Attempts to culture the tips, or sections, of roots or rhizomes have yielded a low rate of success. Structures of this kind taken from plants growing *in vivo* will normally have fungal associations. However, it should be possible to derive suitable explants from roots produced on plantlets grown aseptically *in vitro*. Beechey (1970) suggested that aerial roots might be used as explants, but pointed out that difficulties could arise because of their special anatomical structure. Using *Epidendrum* plantlets regenerated *in vitro*, Stewart and Button (1978) failed to establish cultures from root sections (4–8 mm long) which had a velamen (a layer of tissue possessed by aerial roots, responsible for water absorption), but were able to obtain a single plantlet from one of several green root tip (1–4 mm) cultures.

Seedling root tips (but not those from mature plants) of a *Phalaenopsis amabilis* hybrid, produced callus and then protocorm–like–bodies on solid **MS** medium, and these gave rise to plantlets when transferred to a nutrient solution (Tanaka *et al.,* 1976). However neither these authors, using a similar method, nor Goh (1970) could establish cultures from *Vanda* root tips.

Other methods of micropropagation

Orchids can be propagated *in vitro* without the initiation and proliferation of protocorms using shoot, node culture, or rhizome culture.

However, it can be difficult to obtain uncontaminated explants for cultures of this kind. *Paphiopedilum* plants, for instance, have very short stems and Stewart and Button (1975) found it particularly difficult to obtain bacteria–free cultures. In these circumstances, shoot tip explants from the shoot apex or from lateral buds have the disadvantage that the mother plant may need to be sacrificed to obtain them with no guarantee that cultures may not become irreversibly contaminated.

Shoots from nodal cuttings

If it is difficult to obtain shoot tip explants to initiate cultures of proliferating protocorms, it may be possible to initiate *in vitro* shoot cultures from nodal cuttings. The leaves of axenic shoots from these cultures may then provide suitable explants for protocorm production.

The use of nodal cuttings taken from flower stalks to initiate shoot cultures has proved successful in, for example, *Dendrobium* (Singh and Sahawa, 1972; Nuraini and Mohd. Shaib, 1992); *Oncidium* (Nuraini and Mohd. Shaib, 1992); *Phalaenopsis* (Arditti *et al.* 1977; Reisinger *et al.* 1976; Tanaka and Sakanishi, 1978) and *Vanda* (Sagawa and Sehgal, 1967). Procedures have been very similar in the different genera and have been well documented in the literature for the benefit of growers (*e.g.* Scully, 1965; Sagawa and Sehgal, 1967; Intuwong *et al.* 1972). Some workers have found it necessary to break the dormancy of buds by removing apical dominance with an anti–auxin, higher concentrations being required with increasing distance from the apex (Mosich *et al.* 1974; Reisinger *et al.* 1976).

Nodes cut from scapes usually give rise to shoots from the lateral buds which are present. Sometimes protocorms also arise directly on the explants. These can be transferred to an appropriate medium and multiplied in the conventional way. Nuraini and Mohd. Shaib (1992) found that in *Dendrobium, Oncidium* and *Phalaenopsis,* the proportion of explants which gave rise to shoots was greatest if dissection was carried out when scapes had reached the fully–formed flower stage (before any of the flower buds had opened).

A method of increasing the number of regenerants from nodal buds has been to wound the explant. Tse *et al.* (1971) and Hackett *et al.* (1972) induced continued adventitious bud proliferation from callus which arose after removing two thirds of the original bud. **MS** or **Knudson (1946) C** medium, supplemented with auxin (2 mg/l NAA), proved to be the best substrates. Stewart and Button (1976) also noted that many plantlets could be regenerated from damaged buds, whereas single plants arose from entire buds in single node cultures.

Lateral buds from *Phalaenopsis* flower stalks produced reproductive structures when cultured at 20–25°C but vegetative shoots at 28°C (Tanaka and Sakanishi, 1978).

The growth of rhizomes

Rhizome sections from *Spathoglottis plicata* seedlings on **MS** medium with two auxins (NAA and 2,4–D), a cytokinin (kinetin) and coconut milk, callused and could be induced into rhizogenesis but no other type of morphogenesis (Bapat and Narayanaswamy, 1977). More recently, segments of seed-derived rhizomes of *Cymbidium kanran* (Shimasaki and Uemoto, 1990) and *C. forrestii* (Paek and Yeung, 1991) have been induced to grow and proliferate on **MS** medium (20–30 mg/l sucrose) containing 1–2 mg/l NAA which, without cytokinin, suppressed shoot formation. The production of shoots from rhizomes was enhanced by adding 2 mg/l NAA, 5 mg/l BAP and 50 g/l sucrose to the medium (Paek and Yeung, 1991) and/or by reducing the concentration of KNO_3 and NH_4NO_3 in the medium to 950 and 412.5 mg/l respectively (Shimasaki and Uemoto, 1991).

Interestingly, apical flower buds of *Cymbidium goeringii* were found to give rise directly to rhizomes when cultured on **MS** medium (20 g/l sucrose) supplemented with 0.1 mg/l NAA and 10 mg/l NAA. The rhizomes branched profusely when transferred to a medium with only 1 mg/l NAA: shoots could be induced to form on rhizomes when they were moved to **MS** containing 1–10 mg/l NAA and 0.1 mg/l BAP (Shimasaki and Uemoto, 1991).

Variable plants

Orchid plants differing from the original stock plants occasionally result from the *in vitro* vegetative propagation of orchids (Part 1, page 85). Protocorms have been said to arise from the epidermis of shoot apex explants (Champagnat and Morel, 1972), and if this is the case, then it is easy to see that floral characteristics of chimeral plants could be lost during propagation. Somaclonal variation may also arise where callus formation precedes protocorm formation. Vajrabhaya (1977) also thought that the markings of some orchid flowers could be attributed to virus infections. Elimination of the virus during *in vitro* culture would result in plants with floral characteristics which are not the same as those of the stock plant.

Reviews

Reviews of the micropropagation of orchids will be found in Morel (1974), Arditti (1977), Holdgate (1977), Rao (1977), Goh (1982 & 1990), Sagawa (1990); and in the book of Arditti and Ernst (1993).

Table 162. Published reports on the tissue culture of ORCHIDS.

Orchidaceae

Species name	Type of Culture	Source of explant	Results, References		References
×*Aeridachnis* hybrids	Direct/Callus	Apical or axillary meristem	Protocorm proliferation. Rooted plantlets	YY	Lim-Ho (1982)
Aerides odorata Lour.	Direct	Immature embryos	Protocorm formation, plantlets obtained	Y	Valmayor and Sagawa (1967)
Aerides sp.	Embryo/seed	Green pods	Seedling growth	Y	Sagawa and Valmayor (1966)
Anacamptis pyramidalis (L.) Rich. (Pyrimidal orchid)	Seed germination	Seeds	Protocorms: aseptic seed germination	Y	Van Waes and Debergh (1986)
Anacamptis pyramidalis	Seed germination	Ripe seeds	Germination, protocorms, seedling growth	Y	Van Waes (1987)
Aplectrum hyemale	Seed germination	Seeds	Germination (protocorms), shoots	Y	Henrich *et al.* (1981)
Arachnis hybrid	Direct	Apical or axillary meristem	Protocorms formed and multiplied. Rooted plantlets	YY	Lim-Ho (1982)
×*Arachnostylis* hybrids	Direct	Apical or axillary meristem	Protocorms formed and multiplied. Rooted plantlets	YY	Lim-Ho (1982)
×*Aranda* hybrid	Direct/Callus	Shoot tips and lateral buds	Protocorm formation and proliferation. Rooted plants	YY	Cheah and Sagawa (1978)
×*Aranda* hybrids	Direct/Callus	Meristem or leaf	Protocorms initiated and multiplied. Rooted plants	YY	Lim-Ho (1982)
×*Aranda* hybrids	Direct/Callus	Shoot apex & axillary buds	Protocorm formation and proliferation. Rooted plants	YY	Sagawa and Kunisaki (1982)
×*Aranthera* hybrid	Direct/Callus	Shoot tips and lateral buds	Formation and proliferation of PLBs : plantlets	YY	Cheah and Sagawa (1978)
×*Aranthera* hybrids	Direct/Callus	Shoot apex; axillary buds	PLB initiation and proliferation. Plantlets	YY	Sagawa and Kunisaki (1982)
Arundina graminifolia (D.D. ● Hochr.= *A. bambusifolia*	Direct	Shoot tips (6–8 mm)	Protocorm formation. Shoot buds at base of explant	Y	Mitra (1971)
Arundina graminifolia	Direct	Stem disc (1–2 mm)	Shoot bud initiation	Y	Mitra (1971)
Arundina graminifolia	Meristem	Shoot tips (2 mm)	Single plantlets	Y	Mitra (1971)
Arundina graminifolia	Seed germination	Seed	Germination, plantlets	Y	Mitra (1971)
×*Ascofinetia* 'Cherry Blossom'	Callus	Young inflorescence (1.5 cm)	Protocorms formed and multiplied. Plants	YY	Intuwong and Sagawa (1973)
×*Ascofinetia* hybrids	Direct/Callus	Inflorescence segments	Protocorms formed and proliferated. Greening. Plants	YY	Sagawa and Kunisaki (1982)
Bletilla sp.	Seed germination	Seeds	Germination. Seedlings	Y	Strauss and Reisinger (1976)
Brassavola cucullata (L.) R.Br.	Germination	Seeds	Protocorm formation, then seedling growth	Y	Brown *et al.* (1982)
Brassavola cucullata	Seed germination	Imm. embryos from green pods	Protocorms then seedling growth	Y	Valmayor and Sagawa (1967)
Brassavola nodosa (L.) Lindl.	Embryo/Germin.	Imm. embryos from green fruits	Protocorm formation, then seedling growth	Y	Valmayor and Sagawa (1967)
Brassavola nodosa	Germination	Seeds	Protocorm formation, then seedling growth	Y	Brown *et al.* (1982)
Brassia caudata (L.) Lindl.	Germination	Seeds	Protocorm formation, then seedling growth	Y	Yates and Curtis (1949)
×*Brassocattleya*	Callus	Various shoot explants	Protocorms. Plantlet formation	Y	Kukulczanka (1980)
×*Brassocattleya* hybrid	Embryo/seed	Undifferentiated embryos	Germination and growth	Y	Bahme (1949)
Broughtonia sanguinea (Sw.) R.Br.	Embryo/seed	Immature embryos	Seedling growth	Y	Valmayor and Sagawa (1967)
×*Burkillara* hybrid	Direct	Apical meristem	Protocorm init. and multiplication. Rooted plantlets	—	Lim-Ho (1982)
Caladenia sp.	Seed germination	Seeds	Protocorms, plantlets	Y	McIntyre *et al.* (1974)
❖ *Calanthe*	Seed germination	Seeds	Seedlings	Y	Yates and Curtis (1949)
Calanthe discolor Lindl.	Seed germination	Mature seeds	Germination improved by sonication (4 min)	Y	Miyoshi and Mii (1988)
Calochilus robertsonii	Seed germination	Seeds	Plantlets	Y	McIntyre *et al.* (1974)

Species name	Type of Culture	Source of explant	Results, References		References
Calopogon tuberosum BSP = C. pulchellum (Salis.) R. Br.	Seed germination	Seed	Germination	—	Curtis (1936)
Calopogon tuberosum	Seed germination	Seed	Germination and seedling growth	Y	Stoutamire (1964)
Calopogon ttuberosum	Seed germination	Seeds	Germination and shoot initials	—	Henrich et al. (1981)
Calypso bulbosa (L.) Oakes	Embry/Seed	Immature seeds	Protocorms and seedling growth	Y	Arditti et al. (1985)
Catasetum hybrid	Direct	Seedling root tips (1.5 mm)	Protocorm proliferation. Plants	YY	Kerbauy (1984a)
Catasetum fimbriatum (Morr.) Lindl.	Direct	Seedling root-tip segments	PLB formation	Y	Colli and Kerbauy (1993)
Cattleya aurantiaca (Batem. ex Lindl.) P.N. Don.	Direct/Callus	Seedlings	Protocorm formation and proliferation. Plantlets	Y	Pierik and Steegmans (1972)
Cattleya aurantiaca	Seed germination	Seeds	Protocorm formation: seedling growth	Y	Brown et al. (1982)
Cattleya aurantiaca	Seed germination	Seeds	Protocorm formation: seedling growth	Y	Pierik and Steegmans (1972)
Cattleya aurantiaca	Seed germination	Seed	Seedling growth	Y	Strauss and Reisinger (1976)
Cattleya aurantiaca	Seedling growth	Seeds	Protocorms and seedling growth	Y	Thurston et al. (1979)
Cattleya bowringiana O'Brien [& spp.]	Embryo/seed	Immature embryos	Seedlings obtained	Y	Valmayor and Sagawa (1967)
Cattleya elongata Barb. Rodr.	Seed germination	Seeds	Protocorm formation and seedling growth	Y	Brown et al. (1982)
Cattleya hybrid	Embryo/Seed	Undifferentiated embryos	Seedling germination and growth	Y	Bahme (1949)
Cattleya hybrid	Seed germination	Seeds	Aseptic seedling germination	Y	Knudson (1922)
Cattleya hybrid	Seed germination	Seeds	Protocorms: seedling growth	Y	La Garde (1929)
❖ Cattleya hybrids	Shoot	Lower node meristem	Growth initiation	Y	Ichihashi and Kako (1973)
Cattleya labiata Lindl.	Callus	Callus tissue	Protocorm formation and plantlets	—	Stoltz (1979b)
Cattleya labiata	Seed germination	Seeds	Seedling germination and growth	Y	Raghavan (1964)
Cattleya labiata	Seed germination	Seed	Germination (protocorms) and seedling growth	Y	Yates and Curtis (1949)
Cattleya mossiae Hook.	Seed germination	Seeds	Germination	Y	Knudson (1946)
Cattleya sp.	Callus	Meristem	Protocorm regeneration. Plantlets rooted	Y	Lindemann et al. (1970)
Cattleya sp.	Callus	Lateral bud meristems	Protocorm formation and growth. Plantlets	Y	Reinert and Mohr (1967)
Cattleya spp.	Callus	Small shoot apices	Callus; protocorms (divided). Rooted plantlets	Y	Scully (1967)
Cattleya sp.	Direct	Shoot apices	Protocorm formation and proliferation	Y	Morel (1965b)
Cattleya spp.	Direct	Bud shoot tips	Protocorms on leaf bases, multiplied. Rooted plants	Y	Morel (1974)
Cattleya spp.	Embryo/Seed	Seeds (both ripe & unripe)	Seed germination	Y	Spoerl (1948)
Cattleya sp.	Seed germination	Seeds	Protocorms and seedlings	Y	Champagnat et al. (1970)
Cattleya spp.	Seed germination	Seed	Protocorm formation and seedling germination	Y	Dalla Rosa and Laneri (1977)
Cattleya sp. [& hybrids]	Seed germination	Seed	Germination and seedling growth	Y	Knudson (1951)
Cattleya sp.	Seed germination	Seeds	Seedling growth	Y	Mariat (1952)
Cattleya sp.	Seed germination	Seeds	Seedling germination and growth	Y	Raghavan and Torrey (1964b)
Cattleya spp.	Shoot	Shoot apex or dormant bud	Shoot elongation and axill. branching. Rooted plants	Y	Huang (1984)
Cattleya sp.	Direct	Young leaves of seedlings	Protocorm formation	Y	Champagnat et al. (1970)
Cattleya trianae Lind. & Rchb. f.	Seed germination	Seeds	Protocorms; seedling growth	Y	Noggle and Wynd (1943)
Cattleya trianae	Seed germination	Seeds	Protocorms; seedling growth	Y	Wynd (1933a)
Cattleya trianae	Seed germination	Seeds	Germination and seedling growth	Y	Wynd (1933 b,c)

the medium in addition to 2–iP, finding that it assisted axillary bud break and sustained shoot growth at Stage II. This practice has been copied by several other investigators.

High rates of shoot multiplication can sometimes be achieved using up to 15 or 17 mg/l 2–iP (Anderson, 1975; Economou *et al.* 1981, 1982; Hannapel *et al.* 1981). This cytokinin has sometimes been mixed with 1–4 mg/l IAA, although clear benefits from the inclusion of an auxin have not always been apparent, and its presence may lead to callus formation (see below). The optimum level of growth regulators differs between varieties and, particularly between species (Norton and Norton, 1985). For one selected hybrid, 5 mg/l 2–iP plus 1 mg/l IAA was optimal (Strode *et al.*, 1979). The best quality shoots of some deciduous azaleas was obtained by using 2 mg/l 2–iP (Briggs *et al.*, 1988b).

Shoot proliferation. Shoot proliferation is usually from axillary buds but, especially if high concentrations of 2–iP have been used, a granular callus–like tissue can be formed at the base of explants and shoot clumps, from which adventitious shoots can arise (Kyte and Briggs, 1979). Adventitious shoots can also be formed directly from stem and leaf tissues. Their occurrence is more frequent in cultures of some genotypes.

McCown and Lloyd (1983) found that, amongst 7 genotypes, adventitious shoots arose in cultures of *R.* × 'Boule de Neige' and *R.* × 'PJM'. They recommended that as adventitious shoots may be aberrant, it is advisable to harvest only axillary shoots. Adventitious shoots were recognised by their late emergence and small leaf size.

The formation of adventitious shoots can be minimised by:

– Using the minimum concentration of 2–iP necessary to promote axillary shoot formation;

– Using 2–iP as the only growth regulator, and omitting auxin;

– Re–initiating cultures from shoots rather than by dividing the basal shoot mass;

Shoots should be decapitated and placed horizontally on the medium.

By placing 4 six–node stem sections into 100–150 ml bottles containing 30 ml medium, McCown and Lloyd (1983) were able to harvest 20–80 shoots from each vessel in 8–16 weeks.

Storage. Stage II cultures with large shoots could be stored for 12 months at 4°C in the light (14 h; 30 µmol m^{-2} s^{-1}) while still retaining their capacity for multiplication (Baubault *et al.*, 1991).

Other types of cultures

Direct shoot formation. A granular, green and apparently semi-organised, 'callus' similar to that sometimes formed at the base of shoot clumps in shoot cultures (Kyte and Briggs, 1979) was obtained by Meyer (1982) on the pedicels and base of the ovary of *Rhododendron catawbiense* florets. The tissue produced a large number of shoots in culture which could be further proliferated.

A similar technique was used by Dai *et al.* (1987) with *R. prinophyllum*. Dormant flower buds were sterilised and the florets excised from them. These were placed horizontally on **Anderson (1978, 1980)** medium (30 g/l sucrose) containing 1–4 mg/l IAA and 5–15 mg/l 2–iP. After two weeks incubation the petals separated naturally and could be excised and discarded, leaving the ovary wall in contact with the medium. Both Meyer and Dai *et al.* found that it was necessary at this stage to incubate explants for 2–4 weeks in the dark.

After the cultures had been placed in a 16 h photoperiod, shoots arose directly from the ovary wall, from the surface cells of the flower pedicels and indirectly from ovary wall callus. Shoot regeneration continued and shoots proliferated when explants were transferred to the medium of **Economou and Read (1984)** supplemented with 1 mg/l IAA and 5 mg/l 2–iP.

Direct adventitious shoot formation also occurs when segments of leaves excised from *in vitro* shoot cultures are incubated on a suitable *Rhododendron* medium. Imel and Preece (1988) found that leaves first incubated for two weeks with 10.1 mg/l 2–iP and 2 mg/l IBA, formed adventitious shoots on medium supplemented with 0.2–2 mg/l thidiazuron. In the experiments of Iapichino *et al.* (1992) shoot formation occurred in the presence of 1 mg/l IBA and 15 mg/l 2–iP. These regulants were added to **Anderson (1978, 1980)** medium (30 g/l sucrose) supplemented with 100 mg/l *myo*–inositol, 174 mg/l adenine sulphate dihydrate.

Indirect shoot formation. As will be seen from Table 174, callus can be initiated from shoot tips and floral parts of *Rhododendron* by incubating explants in the presence of both an auxin and a cytokinin (Table 163). Shoots can be regenerated on the same medium if IAA is used as an auxin at Stage I, but if the induction medium contains 2,4-D, transfer to a second medium with revised growth regulators will be necessary.

Rooting

Rhododendron shoots can be rooted *in vitro*, but rooting is now commonly carried out after shoots have been transferred to the external environment.

In vitro **rooting.** Rooting can be induced by placing shoots into a basal medium supplemented with activated charcoal (Meyer, 1981), or into medium containing IAA or IBA [sometimes also supplemented with activated charcoal (Dabin and Bouharmont, 1983; Dai *et al.*, 1987)]. Baubault *et al.* (1991) used **MS** medium (15 g/l sucrose) supplemented with 2 mg/l IAA, but a more dilute medium could undoubtedly be used with success. Pierik and Steegmans (1975c) studied root formation on stem explants cultured on ½**Knop (1965)** macronutrients (20 g/l glucose) plus ½**Heller (1953; 1955)** micronutrients (but 0.07 mM NaFeEDTA) containing 20 mg/l IAA. Speed of rooting was greatly increased when a strip of bark was removed from the explants.

Economou and Read (1986a) obtained the highest percentage of rooted shoots of deciduous azaleas when Stage II recultures were grown in a 16 h photoperiod providing a PPFD of 10 μmol m^{-2} s^{-1}. Shoot length and the quality of rooted microcuttings was less if cultures had been kept under 75 μmol m^{-2} s^{-1}.

Ex vitro **rooting.** Shoots are often transferred directly from the multiplication medium to the external environment for rooting, but pretreatment with auxin will usually improve root formation, especially if shoots have been cultured with high concentrations of cytokinin. Douglas (1984) kept shoots for 10 days in a salts–only medium containing 5–15 mg/l IBA, before planting them out and Meyer (1982) cultured adventitious shoots on a medium containing 4 mg/l IAA and 1 g/l activated charcoal. Some shoots began to root in this medium, and the rest rooted readily when planted *extra vitrum*. Adventitious shoots formed in the presence of 8.1 mg/l 2–iP, required to be cultured for 1–2 months on medium without growth regulators and with 2 g/l activated charcoal before they were suitable for rooting *extra vitrum* (Pogany and Lineberger, 1990).

Composts used for rooting and establishment have included:

Components of mixture	Proportions	Reference
Peat, perlite and vermiculite	1 : 1 : 1	Barnes (1985)
Peat, perlite	2 : 1	Economou *et al.* (1981)
Peat, perlite	1 : 1	Economou & Read (1984)
Sphagnum peat, coarse sand	1 : 2	Ettinger & Preece (1985)
Peat-based compost, granulated pine bark	1 : 1	Marks (1991a)

Other Ericaceae

Other woody ericaceous plants can be propagated using media and growth regulator treatments similar to those described for *Rhododendron*. *Kalmia latifolia* is difficult to propagate by conventional means, and since micropropagation became possible, there has been a rapid increase in the numbers of plants of this magnificent shrub which have been sold. McCulloch (1988) found that shoot multiplication occurred on **Lloyd and McCown (1981) WPM** medium containing 0.4 mg/l 2–iP (no auxin). If 2 mg/l 2–iP was used, cultures often became cytokinin habituated and then shoot quality and the rooting ability of shoots declined. Shoot cultures could be stored in the dark at *ca.* 3°C for 1–2 years.

Euphorbiaceae

Many species of *Euphorbia* are grown as garden ornamentals in both temperate and tropical climates on account of their attractive foliage or habit or growth. Flowers are usually small and insignificant, but associated terminal bracts are brilliantly coloured.

Euphorbiaceae
Euphorbia pulcherrima   (Poinsettia)

E. pulcherrima is a woody shrub, native of the subtropics, but has become a popular pot plant in colder climates where large numbers are sold during the Christmas season.

Micropropagation

E. pulcherrima can be propagated through somatic embryogenesis. Several papers by Preil and co–workers (1983, 1988, 1991) describe how the process may be scaled–up and carried out in bioreactors. In the method described by Preil (1991) and Preil and Beck (1991), shoot tips were cultured on agar–solidified **MS** medium supplemented with 2 mg/l IAA and 0.2 mg/l BAP (**composition 1**). After 2–3 weeks, explants which had produced compact primary callus were transferred to liquid **MS** medium containing 0.2 mg/l PCPA and 0.2 mg/l BAP (**composition 2**) in an Erlenmeyer flask on a rotary shaker. The cell aggregates so obtained were filtered off and placed with the filter paper on an agar–solidified medium (**comp. 2**) and gave rise to a friable embryogenic callus which was used to maintain stock suspension cultures in an 18 h photoperiod [subcultured at 10–14 day intervals by addition of fresh medium (⅔) to the filtrate (⅓) obtained by passing the culture through 500 μM stainless steel mesh].

To induce the formation of somatic embryos, stock suspensions at the stationary phase were used to inoculate Erlenmyer flasks or a 2 litre bioreactor vessel (using **comp. 2**) at a cell density less than 10^5 cells per ml. The drop in cell density seemed to serve as an essential trigger to embryo formation.

Embryos grew to the globular or heart stage in suspension. They were filtered off and placed (with the paper) in Petri dishes of **MS** medium containing only 0.05 mg/l BAP (**comp. 3**). Normal–looking embryos were picked from the dishes and subcultured in dishes (**comp. 3**) in which they germinated and reached a stage when they could be moved to soil.

Although the DNA content of cells in callus cultures and suspensions was seen to vary greatly, less than 2% of the plants obtained were found to show abnormalities. However, the commercially desirable branching habit of certain cultivars was lost, possibly due to the elimination of a virus–like factor (Dole and Wilkins, 1988).

Euphorbiaceae
Euphorbia fulgens   (Scarlet plume)

Shoot cultures of *E. fulgens* can be established, and shoots multiplied, on **MS** medium containing 1.1–2 mg/l zeatin (Zhang *et al.*, 1986, 1987). The maximum rate of shoot proliferation has been found to occur when 45 g/l sucrose is added to the medium (Zhang and Stolz, 1989a). Zhang and Stolz (1989b) rooted cuttings *ex vitro* in a wet tent (page 727).

The micropropagation of some other species of *Euphorbia* is mentioned in the section describing the propagation of wild species.

Labiatae
Lavandula   (Lavender)

Callus capable of forming somatic embryos was obtained by Quazi (1980) by culturing nodes of *L. angustifolia* and *L. latifolia* on the medium of **Kartha** *et al.* (**1984a**), supplemented with 1 mg/l NAA and 4 mg/l BAP. Somatic embryos were differentiated when the callus was subcultured to medium containing 2 mg/l 2,4–D and 4 mg/l BAP.

Single or multiple shoots were produced when explants of the same kind were placed on filter paper supports irrigated with liquid **Kartha** *et al.* (**1984a**) medium, this time containing 5 mg/l IAA, 0.5 mg/l BAP and 5 mg/l GA$_3$.

Magnoliaceae
Magnolia   (Magnolia)

Shoots in cultures of *Magnolia* × *soulangiana* were multiplied by Maene and Debergh (1985) on the medium commonly used in Debergh's laboratory:

> **MS** macronutrients and FeEDTA, supplemented with 120 mg/l NaH$_2$PO$_4$.H$_2$O; the micronutrients of **Bourgin and Nitsch (1967) H**; and the micronutrients of **LS** medium.

Einset (1987) used **LS** medium for this species, supplemented with 6.1 mg/l (30 µM) 2–iP. The cytokinin only induced multiple shoot formation after cultures had stabilised.

Moraceae
Ficus

Several species of *Ficus*, which are tropical epiphytes or trees, have become popular house plants in temperate climates. Plants have handsome evergreen foliage and can tolerate light of low irradiance.

Shoot culture

Medium. Shoot cultures of *Ficus* can be established and propagated on **MS** or **LS** medium, but better rates of shoot multiplication are obtained if the medium is supplemented with 120–170 mg/l NaH$_2$PO$_4$.H$_2$O (Makino *et al.*, 1977; Maene and Debergh, 1983). Other slight modifications to composition have been made by various workers, but not with obvious advantage.

Growth regulators. Growth regulators used in Stage II cultures have included:

0.3 mg/l IAA, 30 mg/l 2–iP, 80 mg/l AdS dihydrate	Makino *et al.* (1977)
1 mg/l IAA, 2.5›5 mg/l BAP, 80 mg/l AdS dihydrate	Maene and Debergh (1983)
2 mg/l BAP	Kristiansen (1992)

Elongation. Some authors have found it necessary to elongate shoots before rooting by reducing the cytokinin concentration in the medium (*e.g.* by using 0.05 mg/l BAP plus 1 mg/l IAA — Maene and Debergh, 1983; 0.05 mg/l BAP, 2–iP and kinetin plus 1.4 mg/l GA$_3$ — Jona and Gribaudo, 1987).

Rooting. Microcuttings of *Ficus* can be rooted *in vitro* in **MS** or **LS** medium without NaH$_2$PO$_4$.H$_2$O or growth regulators (no adenine sulphate either). Media with lower ionic concentrations, for example ½**MS** (Wainwright and Scrace, 1989), or a medium based on **Knop** macronutrients (Jona and Gribaudo, 1987, 1988b) are equally suitable. It may be advantageous to add 0.1–0.3% activated charcoal (Makino *et al.*, 1977; Kristiansen, 1992).

Alternatively shoots can be rooted *extra vitrum* after having been dipped into an IBA solution. Maene and Debergh (1983) placed untreated shoots in stonewool blocks which were saturated with an aqueous IBA solution (2 mg/l, washed out after 6 days).

Oleaceae
Forsythia, Ligustrum, Syringa

Several woody shrubs in the family Oleaceae are popular garden ornamentals. Methods for micropropagation have been studied in only a few species, possibly because many are readily propagated from conventional cuttings.

Shoot and node cultures

Shrubs in the Oleaceae have been propagated by both shoot and node culture (Part 1, pages 51 and 52).

Media. Media containing **MS** salts have been found to be satisfactory for shoot and node culture of *Forsythia, Ligustrum*, and *Syringa*. Preparations have usually been supplemented with 100 mg/l *myo*–inositol and higher concentrations of the remaining vitamins than are normally present in **MS**, but whether such changes are necessary has not been demonstrated. Sucrose has been customarily added to cultures at a concentration of 20–30 g/l, but Pierik *et al.* (1988c) discovered that 35 g/l promoted a greater rate of shoot growth in node cultures, and hence a faster rate of propagation.

In *Syringa vulgaris* cultures, leaf curling was prevented by increasing **MS** macronutrients to 1.5 times their normal concentration, and the occurrence of leaf yellowing eliminated by adding 0.14 mM NaFeEDTA (instead of 0.1 mM) (Pierik *et al.*, 1988c).

It seems probable that **Rugini (1984) OM** medium used for the culture of olive (page 1035), would be suitable for other Oleaceae

Shoot culture. Growth regulators used to obtain shoot proliferation in two genera are shown in Table 164.

Node culture. Einset and Alexander (1985) found that ornamental Oleaceae tended to produce monopodial (unbranched) axes even in the presence of high concentrations of cytokinin, and were therefore more easily propagated by culture and reculture of single node explants. This conclusion was shared by Pierik *et al.* (1988c), for although axillary branching could be induced in *Syringa* by adding 5–10 mg/l 2–iP to the medium, shoots were compact, and difficult to separate. They also suffered from strong leaf curl. By contrast, shoot growth could be promoted by using only 0.4–1 mg/l 2–iP (depending on genotype). An alternative is to use 0.5 mg/l thidiazuron (Einset and Alexander, 1985). Rejuvenation may be necessary to obtain rapid stem elongation (and later, good rooting). In the experiments of Pierik *et al.* this did not occur in some genotypes until many subcultures had been made.

Conditions. Although single node cultures may be grown in a PPFD of *ca.* 50 μmol m^{-2} s^{-1} (Einset and Alexander, 1985; Welander N.T., 1987), shoot elongation is better if photon fluence is reduced to *ca.* 20 μmol m^{-2} s^{-1} (16 h daily) (Pierik *et al.*, 1988c). Growth of *Syringa* shoots is more normal if cultures are incubated at 21°C rather than at higher temperatures (Welander N.T., 1987; Pierik *et al.*, 1988c).

Rooting

Shoots of *Syringa* can be rooted in rockwool plugs or vermiculite after having been dipped in auxin solution or auxin–containing talc (Hildebrandt and Harney, 1983; Pierik *et al.*, 1988c).

Onagraceae
Fuchsia

The genus *Fuchsia* contains approximately 100 species of trees and shrubs, but only a few are cultivated, most of the favoured ornamentals being hybrids which have arisen from crosses mainly between *F. fulgens* and *F. magellanica*. Fuchsias can be readily and rapidly propa-

Table 164. Growth regulators used for shoot culture of two ornamental Oleaceae.

Species	Culture initiation (mg/)l	Shoot proliferation (mg/l)	References
Syringa vulgaris	0.25 IAA, 0.1 BAP	0.1 NAA, 7.5 BAP	Hildebrandt and Harney (1983)
Forsythia × *intermedia*	—	0.01 IBA, 0.01 TDZ, 0.2 BAP	McClelland and Smith (1990)

gated from softwood cuttings so that micropropagation is expected to be of little interest to growers, except for the rapid initial multiplication of a new cultivar.

Shoot culture

It is probable that *Fuchsia × hybrida* can be cultured successfully on a wide range of media, **B5** and **MS** both having been used with success. Stevenson and Harris (1980) established shoot tips of cv. 'Swingtime' on agar slants of **B5** medium (without regulants, 30 g/l sucrose) during two weeks. A purple exudate often came from the cut ends of explants 4–12 h after culture initiation. Its occurrence was less if the concentration of the medium was lowered to $\frac{1}{4}$ its normal concentration, or if 100 mg/l PVP was added to the medium, but the pigment did not affect growth, so that PVP was not always used.

Stage II cultures were started by moving explants to liquid medium, containing 3 mg/l BAP, in flasks which were tilted to 35° from the vertical every 30 seconds causing tissues to be alternately submerged and exposed. Shoot numbers increased 50–fold every 4 weeks. Shoots elongated and rooted on **B5** medium without growth regulators and could be planted *extra vitrum* after 3 weeks.

Kevers *et al.* (1983) found that shoot cultures of 18 cultivars of *F. × hybrida* provided axillary shoots on **MS** medium supplemented with 0.1 mg/l NAA and 1 mg/l BAP. In this experiment, liquid medium (static or agitated) was less effective than that solidified with Difco agar.

Storage. Cultures of cv. 'Swingtime' stored at 4°C for four months continued proliferation when returned to liquid medium containing cytokinin (Harris and Stevenson, *loc. cit.*).

Proteaceae

The 75 genera of Proteaceae are evergreen shrubs or trees, natives mainly of the tropics and subtropics, especially in southern Africa and Australia. Those which are cultivated as garden ornamentals and pot plants tend to prefer neutral or acid soils. Few species are frost hardy.

Explants

Shoot tip explants of *Proteaceae* can be difficult to culture because of their hairy surface. Sterilisation is difficult and the matted wooly surface causes explants to be covered in a layer of liquid. Shoot cultures are therefore commonly initiated from stem sections bearing one or more nodes. Heavy contamination of the stem segments of a dwarf clone of *Leucospermum cordifolium* necessi-

tated the addition of 150 mg/l rifampicin to the medium (Tal *et al.*, 1992b).

Ben–Jaacov and Jacobs (1986) used sections of semi–hardened stems carrying lateral buds, but Rugge *et al.* (1990) found that more shoots grew from *Leucospermum* explants prepared from non–lignified tissue than from those taken from semi–lignified material: there was no bud growth from lignified stems. Bud break was also increased by subjecting non–lignified explants to 5°C for one week before culture, and by leaving one leaf (with its distal portion removed) on stem sections carrying 3–5 nodes. It was thought that retention of the leaf provided a much greater contact with the medium. Buds distal to the leaf sprouted in greater numbers than those nearest to it.

Watad *et al.* (1992b) partly etiolated shoots of *Protea obtusifolia* by enclosing them in brown paper bags before excising 2–4 node stem sections. The treatment lessened browning of the cultured tissues and caused axillary buds to be more likely to sprout. Shoot growth was also assisted if some leaves were retained on the explants. A different approach to shoot elongation was used on *Telopea* plants by Offord *et al.* (1992): the leaves of greenhouse–grown plants were sprayed with 60 µM GA_{4+7}.

Proteaceae
Leucospermum

Shoot cultures of *Leucospermum* have been cultured on **Anderson (1978; 1980)** medium (Ben–Jaacov and Jacobs (1986) or $\frac{1}{2}$**MS** (Tal *et al.*, 1992a), containing 1–2 mg/l BAP. The further addition of 1 mg/l GA_3 increased the rate of shoot multiplication and growth (Tal *et al.*, 1992b).

Kunisaki (1989) obtained round green proliferating bodies when axillary buds of a *Leucospermum* hybrid were cultured for two months on liquid $\frac{1}{2}$**MS** medium (apparently without inositol and glycine) containing 20 g/l sucrose and 0.2 mg/l BAP. Vessels were incubated at 27°C and kept in continuous light (25 µmol m^{-2} s^{-1}) on a roller drum. The proliferations grew into shoots on filter paper bridges wetted with the same medium, and once shoots had appeared they could be transferred to an agar solidified medium (0.05 mg/l BAP) for elongation.

Proteaceae
Telopea speciosissima   (Waratah)

Single node explants of this shrub were isolated by Seelye (1985) on **LS** agar medium (30 g/l sucrose) supplemented with 0.05 mg/l IBA, 0.3 mg/l BAP and 0.1 mg/l GA_3 and by Offord *et al.*, 1990, 1992) on **MS** (with twice the normal concentration of chelated iron, but no growth regulators). Once bud break had occurred Seelye moved explants to ½**MS** salts supplemented with **LS** vitamins with the same growth regulators as were used at Stage I, except that the concentration of GA$_3$ was increased to 2 mg/l. The presence of gibberellic acid was said to prevent the formation of fasciated shoots (page 742). Offord *et al.* (1992) obtained shoot proliferation by moving explants to medium supplemented with only 0.3 mg/l BAP (shoots had many abnormalities if higher concentrations were used) and also found that the simultaneous addition of up to 0.9 mg/l GA$_3$ improved shoot elongation.

Proteaceae

Grevillea

Six species and cultivars of *Grevillea* were propagated by Watad *et al.* (1992a) on ½**MS** medium (30 g/l sucrose) supplemented with 1 mg/l BAP. By contrast, Bunn and Dixon (1992a) used **WPM** medium for *G. scapigera*. Cultures were initiated on filter paper bridges wetted with medium containing 20.5 g/l sucrose, 20 μM zeatin riboside and 0.7 mg/l GA$_3$ and were kept in the dark for one week before being moved to 16 h light of 40 μmol m^{-2} s^{-1} PPFD. After a further 3 weeks, explants could be moved

to agar solidified **WPM** containing 1.1 mg/l kinetin and 0.1 mg/l BAP for shoot proliferation.

Rooting

Shoots of Proteaceae have been rooted *in vitro* and *ex vitro* and appear to require treatment with auxin for these purposes. Shoots to be rooted *in vitro* can be pre–dipped into an auxin solution before culture (Table 165), or auxin can be incorporated into the medium (Table 166).

It has been found that to form roots and become acclimatized, some Proteaceae (for example some *Grevillea* and *Leucospermum* species), require to be kept in light of high fluence, and certainly in *Grevillea*, placing shoots in darkness inhibits root formation (Williams *et al.*, 1985). *Leucospermum cordifolium* rooted well *in vitro* (Table 166) under a PPFD of 210 μmol m^{-2} s^{-1}, but less well in light of smaller fluence (Tal *et al.*, 1992a,c).

Acclimatization. *In vitro*–rooted plantlets of *Leucospermum* were weaned in a ventilated 'dry' fog under an illumination of *ca.* 21 000 lux and were found to establish more rapidly than plants rooted *extra vitrum* (Tal *et al.*, 1992b,c). Plantlets of *Grevillea* 'Roundo', which had been rooted *in vitro*, also survived better in a fogging environment (but less well under mist) (Tal *et al.*, 1992c). The survival of plants of both these genera was much reduced *extra vitrum* when in an illumination of 7000 lux, rather than 14 000 lux (Tal *et al.*, 1992b).

Table 165. Procedures for rooting Proteaceae when shoots were given an acute treatment with auxin followed by culture in a growth regulator–free medium.

Plant	Dipping treatment	Shoot subsequently cultured on		References
		Medium	Sucrose (g/l)	
Telopea speciosissima	0.5–1.0 g/l IBA solution (few seconds)	½**LS**	30	Seelye (1985)
Leucospermum hybrid	50–100 mg/l IBA (4 days)	½**MS** + 0.25 %AC	20	Kunisaki (1989)

Table 166. Media and growth regulators used for rooting Proteaceae when auxin was incorporated into the medium.

Plant	Shoots cultured on			References
	Medium	Auxin/s (mg/)l	Sucrose (g/)l	
Leucospermum cordifolium	½**MS** (agar)	1–3 IBA	50	Tal *et al.* (1992a,c)
Grevillea 'Roundo'	½**MS** (agar)	1 NAA	30	Watad *et al.* (1992a)
Grevillea rosmarinifolia	**MS** (paper bridges)	0.1 NAA	30	Ben–Jaacov and Dax (1981)

Shoots of *Telopea speciosissima* rooted well *in vitro* when placed in crushed quartz sand, irrigated with $\frac{1}{2}$MS medium containing 10 mg/l IBA, but none of the rooted plants could be acclimatized (Offord *et al.*, 1990, 1992). Was this because the light provided was of insufficient flux density?

***Ex vitro* rooting.** Although, as mentioned above, some workers have found shoots rooted *in vitro* could be established most easily in the external environment, microcuttings have been satisfactorily rooted outside the culture vessel. *Grevillea* shoots dipped in commercial rooting powder could be rooted *extra vitrum* (Bunn and Dixon, 1992a), and a higher proportion of *Stirlingia latifolia* shoots were rooted *ex vitro* than *in vitro* (Bunn and Dixon, 1992c).

Seelye (1985) discovered that *Telopea speciosissima* shoots were best grown for two weeks outside the culture vessel before they were dipped into a 500–1000 mg/l IBA solution for a few seconds (Seelye (1985). Plantlet survival was reduced if shoots were dipped before this time. However, shoots of *Telopea speciosissima* could be successfully rooted and established *ex vitro* if they were dipped into a 3 mg/g IBA powder and then placed in a 1 : 2 peat : perlite mix in fog until rooted and growth had commenced. Survival was poor under mist or in a humidity tent (Offord *et al.*, 1990, 1992).

Rosaceae
Rosa   (Rose)

Most of the numerous cultivated varieties of rose have resulted from interspecific hybridisation and are known as *Rosa × hybrida*. Even though the beauty and charm of wild species roses cause many to be cultivated in gardens, hybrids have the most popular appeal and therefore present the largest opportunity for mass vegetative propagation. Methods for propagating roses *in vitro* are now sufficiently reliable for commercial application, but must compete with well–tried methods of budding or grafting onto rootstocks, or the rooting of cuttings. In the hands of experts these techniques are efficient, reliable and cheap and can even be partly mechanised (Van der Pol and Breukelaar, 1982).

Traditional propagation relies on a large supply of budwood and, as this takes several years to build up, micropropagation will always be useful to enable plants of new varieties of hybrid rose to be increased in number rapidly, thus reducing the time required for introduction to the market.

Rose cultivars growing on their own roots, have been found to compare favourably with budded and grafted plants both when first planted in the field and after a four year period (Martin *et al.*, 1981), and presumably have comparable long term vigour and longevity. Compared to the total sales of rose plants, the number of micropropagated units produced in Europe in 1988 was not large (Pierik, 1991a).

Dwarf varieties of rose make attractive pot plants. For this purpose they are usually propagated from softwood cuttings. However, micropropagated plants eventually have an improved appearance and floral characteristics (earlier flowering, shorter shoots with more, longer laterals — Chapter 15, page 749). Growers therefore have to balance the much higher cost of the micropropagated plantlets against the possible increased value of their product in the long term (Dubois *et al.*, 1988).

Shoot culture

Micropropagation of both *Rosa × hybrida* and species roses (Rosten and McCown, 1981) is accomplished through shoot culture which is relatively easy to carry out. Explants have included the tips of growing shoots, lateral buds or lateral buds borne on short segments of stems. The age of the shoots from which such nodal explants are excised and the position of nodes on the shoot can influence how successfully cultures can be initiated (Part 1, page 260).

Media. MS medium gives good growth and shoot proliferation at Stages I and II (Davies, 1980), but some workers have modified the vitamin content, often without good cause. Hasegawa (1979, 1980) advocated an increase in the thiamine HCl level of **MS** to 0.5 ıng/l and several other workers have followed this recommendation. Although it is possible to obtain shoot multiplication on **Lloyd and McCown (1981) WPM** medium (Rosten and McCown, 1981; Wilkowske, 1981), it is less favoured than **MS**.

Agar–solidified media have frequently been used for rose shoot cultures, but Chu *et al.* (1993) found that shoot growth was more rapid on a stationary liquid medium. Explants were floated on the surface of the medium without support.

Plant growth regulators. A cytokinin is essential to induce axillary shoot proliferation and a low concentration of auxin is occasionally also provided. Some specific examples of the growth regulators added to the medium by different authors, are shown in Table 167. The same media and growth regulators have usually been employed for both Stages I and II of shoot cultures, but Rosten and McCown (1981) first established shoot tips on a medium containing only 0.9 mg/l BAP, before increasing the concentration for some varieties at Stage II.

Several workers have added gibberellic acid to the medium. The presence of 0.1 mg/l (together with 1 mg/l BAP) was found by Valles and Boxus (1987a,b) to pre-

Table 167. Examples of media and growth regulators employed for shoot cultures of *Rosa*.

Plant	Medium	Sucrose (g/l)	Growth regulators (mg/l)	Reference
Rosa × hybrida	MS	40	0.004 NAA, 2 BAP, 0.1 GA$_3$	Davies (1980) Horn *et al.* (1988b)
	MS‡ + B5 vits	30	0.1 NAA, 1.0 BAP, 0.1 GA$_3$	Douglas *et al.* (1989)
	MS	30	1.5 BAP	Sallanon and Maziere (1992)
	MS	10–40§	1.8 BAP	Langford and Wainwright (1988)
Rosa chinensis	MS (but 0.5 mg/l thiamine HCl)	30	0.1 NAA, 1 BAP	Rogers and Smith (1992)
	MS	30	0.01 NAA, 0.1 BAP	Chu *et al.* (1993)
Rosa (Dwarf cultivars)	MS (modified).	30?	0.1–0.5 IBA, 0.1–2 BAP	Dubois and De Vries (1988)
	MS	30	0.5–1.0† BAP	Badzian *et al.* (1991)

§   Studied the effect of sucrose concentration, see text;

‡   But Fe as 40 mg/l FeDTPA (Sequestrene 330);

†   Depending on cultivar.

Table 168. Media and growth regulators used to root rose shoots *in vitro*.

Medium	Sugar (g/l)	Growth regulators (mg/)l	References
MS	40 sucrose	None	Davies (1980)
MS	30 sucrose	0.5 IBA	Dohare *et al.* (1991)
MS	40 glucose	0.4 IBA, 0.5 IAA (+ 0.2 g/l act. charcoal)	Ghashghaie *et al.* (1992)
½MS + MS organics	30 sucrose	0.1 NAA + 0.05 IAA (or IBA)	Khosh-Khui and Sink (1982b)
½MS + LS vitamins	30 sucrose	0.5 IBA	Donnelly and Skelton (1989)
¼MS salts	30 sucrose	0.1 IAA	Douglas *et al.* (1989)
½MS salts + MS vits?	30 sucrose	None, but 1 g/l activated charcoal	Badzian *et al.* (1991)
¼MS salts + Staba vits.	30 sucrose	None	Skirvin and Chu (1979a)
¼MS salts + LS vits.	30 sucrose	None or 0.1 NAA	Podwyszynska and Hempel (1988)
¼MS salts + B5 vits.	30 sucrose	0.1 IAA	Douglas *et al.* (1989)
WPM	20 sucrose	0.2 IBA	Alderson *et al.* (1988)

vent apical necrosis in cv. 'White Dream', while 1 mg/l GA$_3$ plus 5 mg/l BAP was necessary for shoot proliferation of cv. 'Goldy'. The rate of shoot proliferation was also greater in two other cultivars when 0.1 or 0.3 mg/l GA$_3$ was added to 5 mg/l BAP.

Sucrose concentration. Davies (1980) recommended the addition of 40 g/l sucrose to **MS** medium. Others have used 30 g/l. Langford and Wainwright (1987, 1988) showed that, even though they were not photoautotro-

phic, shoots were capable of significantly more photosynthesis in the presence of 20 g/l, rather than 40 g/l sucrose. However, hyperhydricity was rare with 40 g/l but increased as the sucrose concentration was decreased.

Browning. Freshly excised rose tissues are liable to turn brown and exude phenolic substances into the medium, but measures discussed in Chapter 13 provide an effective control. Transfer of newly excised explants to fresh medium every 3–5 days until exudation is no longer a

Table 169. Treatments which led to adventitious shoot formation from callus of rose.

Callus initiation			Shoot regeneration		References
Medium	Status	PGRs	Medium	PGRs	
		(mg/l)		(mg/l)	
MS medium	0.25% Gelrite	1.9 NAA	**MS** (but no NH$_4$NO$_3$)	0.17 IAA + 2.25 BAP	Ishioka and Tanimoto (1990)
½**MS** salts + **MS** vits.† (liquid, shaken)	Agar	0.01 NAA + 0.22 BAP	Callus mass subcultured on same medium. Adventitious shoots began to form after 5 months		Burger *et al.* (1990)

† Also included 0.2 mg/l biotin; 1 mg/l riboflavin; 1 mg/l ascorbic acid; 1 mg/l choline chloride; 1 mg/l cysteine.

problem (Skirvin *et al.*, 1990), and the addition of 50 mg/l ascorbic acid and 150 mg/l PVP to the medium (Rogers and Smith, 1992) have been effective. An alternative has been to rinse explants in a PVP solution before they are placed on the culture medium (Mederos and Rodríguez Enríques, 1987). To prevent the occurrence of browning in subcultures, Pittet and Moncousin (1981) kept newly inoculated vessels in complete darkness for 2 days.

Cultural conditions. Cultures have usually been incubated in a 16 h day (PPFD 20–80 µmol m^{-2} s^{-1}) at a constant temperature of 21–25°C, or in 23–26°C (day) and 19–22°C (night).

Subcultures. Subcultures can be initiated with basal shoot clumps or from nodal cuttings of shoots. In both cases the number of axillary shoots produced may be increased if the tips of shoots are removed during the progress of the culture (Bressan *et al.*, 1982). As this means opening vessels and manipulating explants on an extra occasion, it has seldom been thought to be worthwhile. A marked increase in the number of axillary shoots produced by cultures on **MS** medium supplemented by 0.3 mg/l IAA and 3 mg/l BAP, was obtained by Voyiatzi and Voyiatzis (1988) by adding 100 mg/l methyl laurate to the medium (Part 1, page 469).

The presence of a low level of ethylene in culture vessels has been shown by Kevers *et al.* (1992) to enhance the rate of shoot proliferation in *R.* × *hybrida* cultures. It is therefore important to select the correct size of vessel and closure for cultures. Vessels which were tightly sealed, or which had lids closed with film, contained up to 700 p.p.m. ethylene after 20 days and in these, shoot multiplication was inhibited. The highest rate of proliferation in this experiment occurred in 600 ml vessels containing 100 ml medium, which were covered with only a transparent film. Adding inhibitors of ethylene biosynthesis (0.01–0.1 mM CoCl$_2$ or 2.5–50 mg/l AVG) also increased the rate of shoot multiplication.

Rooting

In published accounts of rose propagation, shoots separated from Stage II cultures have generally been rooted *in vitro* on agar media of low ionic concentration, either with, or without, the presence of auxin (Table 168). Valles and Boxus (1987a) rooted many varieties of *R.* × *hybrida* on a low salt medium containing 3 mg/l IBA. Maximum rooting of 3 other cultivars occurred when the medium contained 1 mg/l IBA and 1 mg/l BAP, and root induction and development did not take place in cv. 'White Dream' unless BAP was present. Alderson *et al.* (1988) experimented with rooting rose shoots in 2 cm long Sorbarods. In aseptic conditions rooting occurred when the rods were soaked with **WPM** medium containing 20 g/l sucrose and 0.2 mg/l IBA. Root formation was also possible in non–aseptic conditions providing sucrose was omitted from the medium and fungicide added (see page 703).

Rose shoots harvested from Stage II cultures have been found to root poorly if planted directly into compost, but satisfactory rooting can occur if shoots are first pretreated with auxin to induce root formation. Pittet and Moncousin (1982) placed shoots in a solution of 1 mg/l NAA for one hour (the further presence of vitamin D$_2$ was said to be beneficial). Longer treatments were favoured by Avramis *et al.* (1982b), who cultured harvested shoots for 5 days in shaken liquid **MS** salts (60 g/l sucrose) containing 0.5 mg/l NAA, and by Douglas *et al.* (1989), who precultured shoots for 2 weeks in liquid medium containing 0.1 mg/l IAA. In each case treated shoots rooted well when they were afterwards planted *ex vitro* in a potting substrate.

Other methods of propagation

Callus capable of regenerating adventitious shoots can be obtained by culturing stem internodes, nodes, or immature embryos (Table 174): media and growth regulators

Table 170. Media and growth regulators which resulted in somatic embryogenesis in *Rosa*.

Medium	Sucrose (g/l)	PGRs (mg/)l	Medium	PGRs (mg/l)	References
Callus initiation			**Indirect embryogenesis**		
½MS	30	1 NAA + 0.5–2 2,4–D + 0.5 BAP	½MS + 200–800 mg/l proline†	0.01 NAA + 0.5 BAP + 0.1 GA₃	Rout *et al.* (1991)
Embryogenic callus initiation			**Plantlet growth**		
½MS ‡	20	0.05 NAA (or 0.1 NOA) + 0.1 kin	½MS	1 IAA + 2 BAP	De Wit *et al.* (1990)

†   Proline essential for the induction of embryogenesis (Part 1, page 289);

‡   Dark incubation for 2 weeks then 16 h day (1500 lux).

were as shown in Table 169. Callus capable of regenerating somatic embryos has also been obtained by culturing immature leaf and stem segments (Rout *et al.*, 1991), or leaves from *in vitro* shoot cultures (De Wit *et al.*, 1990). In both cases ½MS medium was used (Table 170).

Other Rosaceae

Many woody genera of Rosaceae, apart from roses, are cultivated for their value as ornamentals in gardens and landscape plantings. These plants are relatively easy to propagate *in vitro* using shoot culture on **LS** or **MS** medium (30–40 g/l sucrose).

Culture of some plants in genera of the tribe Maloideae (*e.g. Amelanchier, Chaenomeles, Crataegus, Photinia*) may benefit from the addition of sorbitol to the medium (pages 323 and 1040). In some papers the investigators have combined **MS** salts with other vitamins and/or amino acids, but the advantage of making such alterations is seldom explained. On just a few occasions **Lloyd and McCown (1986) WPM** medium has been used (*e.g.* for *Potentilla* — Remphry *et al.*, 1993). Brand and Cullina (1992) obtained roughly equivalent rates of shoot multiplication from two species of *Aronia* on **WPM** or **MS** medium.

Shoot multiplication of many woody Rosaceae can be induced by including BAP in the medium as the only growth regulator. Norton and Boe (1982) added from 0.5 to 2.5 mg/l according to genus.

Rosaceae
Spiraea

Examples of the growth regulators selected for *Spiraea* shoot cultures are shown in Table 171. The effect of red light in reinforcing the action of cytokinin (Part 1, page 222) was demonstrated by Herrington and McPherson (1993). *S. nipponica* shoot cultures were subcultured in light of low fluence (16 h daily) for four weeks. During this period the light was either

a) white (15–23 µmol m^{-2} s^{-1}), or
b) predominantly in the red/far red wavelengths (8.7–15.9 µmol m^{-2} s^{-1}).

Table 171. Examples of growth regulators used for *Spiraea* shoot cultures.

Species	Growth regulators (mg/l)	References
Spiraea japonica	1.1 BAP	Lane (1979c)
	0.5 BAP	Norton and Boe (1982) Norton and Norton (1986a,b; 1988b,c)
Spiraea nipponica	0.25–0.5 BAP†	Herrington and McPherson (1993)
Spiraea × vanhouttei	1.1 BAP ‡	Yang and Read (1993)
	1.1 BAP + 0.18–0.88 IAA ‡	
	0.1–0.17 TDZ ‡	

†   0.25 mg/l sufficient in combination with red/far red light treatment (see text).

‡   Alternative treatments.

Cultures of both kinds were moved to high fluence white light (47–62 µmol m^{-2} s^{-1}) for one week before shoots were harvested. BAP had the maximum effect in treatment b), which resulted in the highest rates of shoot proliferation.

Rosaceae
Amelanchier   (Service berry)

Several species of *Amelanchier* are cultivated as ornamentals. They are hardy deciduous shrubs which bear profuse white blossom in spring and have foliage which is brightly coloured in autumn. Fruits of the service berry can be eaten when overripe.

Shoot cultures of *Amelanchier* can be grown on **LS** or **MS** medium. Krueger *et al.* (1991) found $\frac{1}{2}$**LS** (30 g/l sucrose) was sufficient: some other authors have modified **MS** medium, for example by adding the vitamins of **B5** medium (Caswell *et al.*, 1986), or of **Ziv *et al.* (1970)**†.

> †100 mg/l *myo*–inositol, 0.5 mg/l thiamine HCl, 5 mg/l nicotinic acid and 1 mg/l pyridoxine HCl.

Shoot proliferation has been induced by the following growth regulators:

A. alnifolia	2.5 BAP + 0.1 NAA	Caswell *et al.* (1986)
A. grandiflora	1 BAP	Kreuger *et al.* (1991)
A. laevis	2.5BAP + 0.1 NAA	Behrouz and Lineberger (1981a)
	0.56 BAP	Hajela *et al.* (1993)
A. spicata	0.2 BAP + 0.01 TDZ + 0.01 IBA	McClelland and Smith (1990)

Rosaceae
Malus and Prunus

In temperate climates the attractive flowers and/or fruits of species and cultivars of *Malus* and *Prunus* have led to their popularity as ornamental shrubs or trees.

Methods for their micropropagation are not widely different to those employed for fruiting apples and *Prunus*. Please see the section on fruit and nut crops.

In vitro rooting of Rosaceae

The low salt media and low auxin concentrations suitable for rooting roses (Table 168) are also suitable for the *in vitro* rooting of other Rosaceae. Examples of treatments which have been successful are shown in Table 172.

Norton and Boe (1982) found that lower concentrations of IBA were required to induce root formation in Rosaceae if cultures were incubated for one week in total darkness, before being placed in light (16 h photoperiod). Shoots of some genera only formed roots if first kept in the dark, but *Chaenomeles japonica* requires to be kept continuously in light.

Shoots can also be rooted in plugs. Wainwright and Scrace (1989) rooted *Potentilla fruticosa* shoots in Sorbarods, using a similar technique to that employed for rose (page 949). Shoots were briefly dipped into a 0.2 mg/l IBA solution and inserted into plugs wetted with $\frac{1}{2}$**MS** medium containing 20–40 g/l sucrose.

Theaceae
Camellia

The genus *Camellia* comprises a large number of species, all of which are evergreen trees or shrubs. Several species are prized for their beautiful flowers and there are many named cultivars (over 2000 of *C. japonica*) and hybrids. The genus includes *C. sinensis* (Tea), mentioned on page 1170.

Shoot culture

Media. Interestingly, in *Camellia* the necessary medium to give satisfactory shoot proliferation, is influenced by the juvenility status of explants. Although in cultures initiated from explants of 4–5 month–old seedlings, cultures can be initiated and shoot proliferation obtained on a medium containing **MS** salts (Medium **1**, Table 173) (Samartin *et al.*, 1984; Samartin, 1989; Vieitez *et al.*,

Table 172. Successful treatments for *in vitro* rooting of plants in the Rosaceae.

Plant	Medium	Auxin (mg/l)	References
Photinia fraseri	$\frac{1}{2}$**WPM**	0.004 NAA	Leifert *et al.* (1992)
Aronia (2 spp.)	$\frac{1}{2}$**MS**	1.0 IBA	Brand and Cullina (1992)
Spiraea	$\frac{1}{2}$**MS**	0.02 NAA	Lane (1979c)
Prunus cistena	$\frac{1}{2}$**MS**	0.2 NAA	Lane (1979c)

Table 173. Media used for the shoot culture of *Camellia*.

Components	Samartin (1989) mod. MS	1/2MS	Beretta and Eccher (1987)	Vieitez et al. (1985a) H+SO$_4$	Vieitez et al. (1984) H+SO$_4$ (2N)	Vieitez et al. (1989a) H+SO$_4$	Lloyd & McCown (1981) WPM	Samartin (1992) mod. B5
	①	②	③	④	⑤	⑥	⑦	⑧
Macronutrients (meq/l)								
NO$_3^-$	39.4	19.7	24.36	7.05	14.11‡	8.81	9.7	24.72
PO$_4^{3-}$	3.74	1.87	5.95	2.71	2.71	3.39	3.74	3.26
SO$_4^{2-}$	3.0	1.5	0.61	4.02	6.03	4.53	14.36	4.05
Cl$^-$	5.98	2.99	1.02	11.08	11.08	13.85	1.3	2.04
K$^+$	20.04	10.02	13.85	10.06	10.06	12.58	12.6	24.72
Ca^{2+}	5.98	2.99	1.02	1.02	1.02	1.28	6.01	2.04
Na$^+$	0	0	0	7.96	15.02	9.95	0	1.08
Mg^{2+}	3.0	1.5	0.61	2.02	2.02	2.53	3.0	2.02
NH$_4^+$	20.61	10.30	12.49	2.0	4.0‡	2.0	4.99	2.02
Microelements (mg/l)								
MnSO$_4$.4H$_2$O	22.3	11.15	13.4	22.3	22.3	22.3	29.43	13.2
ZnSO$_4$.7H$_2$O	8.6	4.3	6.3	8.6	8.6	8.6	8.6	2.0
H$_3$BO$_3$	6.2	3.1	3.7	6.2	8.6	6.2	6.2	3.0
KI	0.83	0.42	0.49	0.83	0.83	0.83	—	0.75
CoCl$_2$.6H$_2$O	0.025	0.013	0.015	0.025	0.025	0.025	—	0.025
CuSO$_4$.5H$_2$O	0.025	0.013	0.015	0.025	0.025	0.025	0.25	0.025
Na$_2$MoO$_4$.2H$_2$O	0.25	0.13	0.15	0.25	0.25	0.25	0.25	0.25
NaFeEDTA	0.1 mM	0.05 mM	0.2 mM	0.1 mM	0.1 mM	0.1 mM	0.1 mM	0.1 mM
Vitamins (mg/l)								
Inositol	100	50	100	100	100	100	100	100
Thiamine HCl	1.0	0.05	1.0	1.0	1.0	1.0	1.0	10.0
Nicotinic acid	1.0	0.25	1.0	0.1	0.1	1.0	0.5	1.0
Pyridoxine HCl	1.0	0.25	1.0	1.0	1.0	—	0.5	1.0
Ca pantothenate	1.0	5.0	1.0	—	—	0.5	—	—
Folic acid	—	—	—	—	—	0.01	0.5	—
Biotin	0.01	—	0.01	0.1	—	—	0.05	0.005
p–aminobenzoic acid	—	—	—	—	—	1.0	—	—
Riboflavin	—	—	—	—	—	0.1	—	—
Ascorbic acid	2.0	—	—	2.0	2.0	—	—	—
Amino acids (mg/l)								
Glycine	2	1	—	—	—	—	2.0	—
Sugars (g/l)								
Sucrose (g/l)	30	30	—	30	30	30	30	30
Glucose (g/l)	—	—	30	—	—	—	—	—
Growth regulators (mg/l)								
IAA	—	—	0.2	—	—	—	—	—
NAA	—	—	—	0.1	0.1	—	—	0.1
IBA	—	—	—	—	—	0.01	0.01	—
Kinetin	1.0	1.0	—	—	—	—	—	—
BAP	1.0	2.5†	2.3	1.0	1.0	1.0	1.0	0.5
Adenine	—	—	20	—	—	—	—	—
GA$_3$	—	5.0†	0.7	—	—	—	—	—

† These levels for shoot proliferation. Only 0.1–0.5 mg/l BAP (no GA$_3$) for establishment; see text for reference to usage.

‡ This mixture of ions arrived at by doubling the concentration of sodium nitrate and ammonium sulphate in **Vieitez et al. (1985a) H+SO$_4$** medium. The resulting formulation has very high concentrations of Na$^+$ and Cl$^-$ ions. A better medium would result from reducing the concentration of both and raising the concentration of Ca^{2+}.

The weights of salts necessary to prepare the macronutrients listsed here, and in otherTables of Chapter 17, are given in the Appendix.

No. of shoots

Shoot length (mm)

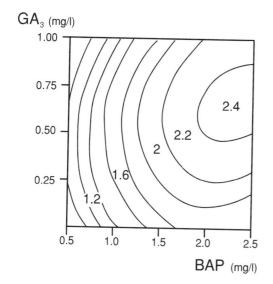

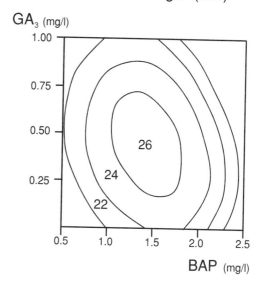

Fig. 163. Contour diagrams depicting the effect of BAP and GA₃ on the number and length of shoots in *Camellia* shoot cultures. [from data of Beretta and Eccher, 1987].

1991), in cultures started with mature plants, shoot proliferation is best on less concentrated media such as:

½MS	2*	Carlisi and Torres (1985a,b; 1986)
Beretta and Eccher (1987)	3	Beretta and Eccher (1987)
Vieitez *et al.* (1985a) H + SO₄	4	Samartin (1989)
Vieitez *et al.* (1989a) H + SO₄	6	Vieitez *et al.* (1989a)

or media containing **WPM** salts (Medium **7**; Vieitez *et al.*, 1989b; San–Jose *et al.*, 1991) or **B5** salts (Medium **8**; Samartin, 1992).

* Medium number in Table 173.

Of these media, **5** to **8** seem to be particularly appropriate, suggesting that a low concentration of ammonium is important. Although suitable for culture initiation, the concentration of nitrogen in Medium **4** is too low for effective shoot growth of *C. japonica* and shoots cultured for long periods become chlorotic, grow slowly and have small leaves. Doubling the inorganic nitrogen concentration corrected these symptoms (**Medium 5**; Samartin, 1989).

In cultures initiated from adult explants on **MS** medium there is progressive leaf browning and bud necrosis (Samartin, 1989), but it is possible that, as shoots became more juvenile through repeated subculturing, it might be possible to increase the concentration of ammonium ions in the medium without these ill effects.

Shoot proliferation and growth can be improved if, rather than transferring Stage II cultures, further liquid medium is added after 4 weeks (Vieitez *et al.*. 1989a).

Growth regulators. Growth regulators used with the media discussed above to encourage shoot proliferation, are also listed in Table 173. The interaction observed in cultures of *C. saluensis* × *C. japonica* between BAP and GA₃ is shown in Fig. 163.

Conditions. Cultures are usually incubated in a temperature of 25°C (day)/18–20°C (night) in light of *ca.* 30 µmol m⁻² s⁻¹ flux density. Samartin (1989) found that shoot proliferation was the same in a 12 h or in a 16 h day.

Rooting

***Ex vitro* rooting.** *Camellia* shoots can be rooted *ex vitro* if they are pre–treated with auxin. Mohan Jain (1991) placed shoots of *C. sinensis* (tea), in a 50 mg/l IBA solution for 2 hours, while Samartin (1992) placed shoots of *C. sasanqua* in a more concentrated (1g/l IBA ethanol/water) solution for 20 minutes. Such treatments are usually followed by a dip into a fungicidal solution before the cuttings are planted in a suitable substrate. Samartin (1992) used a 1 : 1 mixture of fine sand and peat.

***In vitro* rooting.** Shoots of *Camellia* have been rooted *in vitro* after being dipped into an auxin solution (1 g/l IBA for 15–20 minutes) and then cultured on a low salts medium (without regulants) containing 60 g/l sucrose or 30 g/l glucose (San–Jose *et al.*, 1991). The rate of root formation and the proportion of shoots which form roots is considerably increased if cultures are kept in the dark for 9–18 days (Vieitez *et al.*, 1989a) before being placed in light (12 h daily, 30 μmol m^{-2} s^{-1} PPFD) (Samartin, 1992; Vieitez *et al.*, 1989a).

Organogenesis

Direct embryogenesis. Direct embryogenesis can be induced on cotyledon segments (Kato, 1989; Plata and Vieitez, 1990) and especially on the axis, of immature zygotic embryos (Plata and Vieitez, 1990; Vieitez and Barciela, 1990) cultured on **MS** medium without growth regulators or with the inclusion of 0.5–1 mg/l IBA (Plata and Vieitez, 1990). Whether the further addition of 1–4 mg/l BAP (Kato, 1989) is advantageous is uncertain (Vieitez and Barciela, 1990). Secondary and tertiary embryogenesis occurs when somatic embryos are subcultured to medium containing 1 mg/l GA$_3$ (Kato, 1989) or 0.5–1 mg/l IBA (Plata and Vieitez, 1990). Embryos have been germinated on medium supplemented with 1 mg/l GA$_3$ and 1 mg/l IAA (*C. reticulata* — Plata and Vieitez, 1990) or 0.1–1 mg/l IBA and 0.1–1 mg/l BAP (*C. japonica* — Vieitez and Barciela, 1990).

Indirect embryogenesis. Callus of *C. reticulata* initiated from the cotyledons of immature embryos on **MS** medium supplemented with IBA or NAA, produced somatic embryos when subcultured onto medium containing 0.5 mg/l IBA and 1 mg/l BAP (Plata and Vieitez, 1990).

Table 174. Published reports on the tissue culture of WOODY ORNAMENTAL PLANTS.

	Species name	Type of Culture	Source of explant	Results		References
Acanthaceae						
*	*Actinidia arguta* (Sieb. & Zucc.) Planch.	Shoot	Shoot tips	Multiple shoots	Y	Einsett (1987)
	Actinidia kolomikta (Rupr. & Maxim.) Maxim.	Shoot	Shoot tips	Multiple shoots	Y	Einsett (1987)
	Aphelandra squarrosa Nees. (Zebra plant)	Shoot	Axillary & apical buds (1–2 mm)	Multiple shoots. Rooted *in vitro*. Plants	YY	Bohnke *et al.* (1983)
	Crossandra infundibuliformis (L.) Nees.	Shoot	Axillary & apical buds (1–2 mm)	Multiple shoots. Rooted *in vitro*. Plants	YY	Bohnke *et al.* (1983)
Agavaceae						
❖	*Cordyline stricta* (Sims) Endl.	Callus	Stem	Adventitious shoots	—	Debergh (1975; 1976)
	Cordyline stricta	Single node	Stem nodes	Shoots from buds, some roots	Y	Debergh (1975; 1976)
	Cordyline terminalis (L.) Kunth = *C. fruticosa*	Callus	Shoot tips (3 mm)	Adventitious shoots	—	Mee (1978)
	Cordyline terminalis (Hawaiian ti plant)	Shoot	*In vitro* axillary buds (2–4 mm)	Shoot proliferation. Shoots elongated & rooted	YY	Evaldsson & Welander (1985)
	Cordyline terminalis	Shoot	Stem pieces (5 mm)	Multiple axillary shoots. Rooted plantlets	YY	Kunisaki (1975)
	Cordyline terminalis	Shoot	Shoot tips	Multiple shoots. Rooted *in vivo*	YY	Maene & Debergh (1983)
	Cordyline terminalis cv. 'Merrouw Debergh'	Shoot	Shoot tips	Investigated shoot elongation & rooting	YY	Maene & Debergh (1985)
	Cordyline terminalis cv. 'Merrouw Debergh'	Shoot	*In vitro* shoot clusters	Shoots multiplied, elongated & rooted. Plants	YY	Maene & Debergh (1987)
	Cordyline terminalis	Shoot	Shoot tips	Shoot proliferation. Rooted plantlets	YY	Miller & Murashige (1976)
	Cordyline terminalis 'Atom'	Shoot/Callus	Axillary buds	Culture storage studied	—	Hvoslef-Eide (1992)
❖	*Dracaena fragrans* (L.) Ker-Gaw.	Callus	Young stem segs.	Shoot regen. & multiplication. Rooted	—	Vinterhalter (1989)
	Dracaena fragrans	Direct	Shoot cultures	Rooted. Formation of lateral roots studied	—	Vinterhalter & Vinterhalter (1992)
	Dracaena marginata 'Tricolor'	Callus	Stem pieces (0.5 cm)	Multiple shoots produced, and then rooted.	—	Chua *et al.* (1981)
	Dracaena surculosa (Gold-dust dracaena) = *D. godseffiana*	Shoot	Shoot tips	Shoot initiation and multiplication. Shoots rooted.	YY	Miller & Murashige (1976)
	Nolina recurvata (Lem.) Hemsl. = *Beaucarnea recurvata*	Shoot	Shoot apices	Multiple shoot production followed by rooting	YY	Samyn (1993)
❖	*Yucca* spp.	Shoot	Axillary buds	Axillary shoot proliferation. Plants	YY	Litz & Conover (1977)
	Yucca elephantipes Reg.	Shoot	Shoot tips	Axillary shoots. Rooted plantlets moved to soil	YY	Pierik & Steegmans (1983)
	Yucca schidigera Roezl. ex Ortgies.	Callus	Hypocotyl sections	Light-mediated root formation	—	MacCarthy & Staba (1985)
Aquifoliaceae						
*	*Ilex aquifolium* L. (Holly)	Embryo	Heart-shaped embryos ex mat. seed	Germination. Seedling growth	Y	Hu (1975)
	Ilex aquifolium	Embryo	Zygotic heart stage embryos	Studied effect of light on embryo growth & developt.	—	Ferreira & Hu (1989)
	Ilex aquifolium	Embryo	Zygotic embryos	Germination & growth. Adv. embryos on cotyledons	—	Hu & Sussex (1972)
	Ilex aquifolium	Embryo	Zygotic embryos	Seedlings & adventitious embryoids	—	Hu *et al.* (1978)
	Ilex aquifolium	Shoot	Apical & axillary buds	Axillary shoots, elongated & rooted	YY	Morte *et al.* (1991)
	Ilex cassine L.	Embryo	Heart-shaped embryos ex mat. seed	Germination. Seedling growth	Y	Hu (1975)
	Ilex cornuta Lindl. & Paxt. 'Hitchcock'	Embryo	Heart-shaped embryos ex mat. seed	Germination. Seedling growth	Y	Hu (1975)
	Ilex crenata Thumb 'Convexa' & Yellow berried form	Embryo	Heart-shaped embryos ex mat. seed	Germination. Seedling growth	Y	Hu (1975)

Species name	Type of Culture	Source of explant	Results		References
Ilex glabra (L.) A.Gray	Embryo	Heart-shaped embryos ex mat. seed	Germination. Seedling growth	Y	Hu (1975)
Ilex longipes Chapm. ex Trel.	Embryo	Heart-shaped embryos ex mat. seed	Germination. Seedling growth	Y	Hu (1975)
Ilex opaca Ait. cv. 'Forage' (American holly)	Embryo	Zygotic heart stage embryos	Studied effect of light on embryo growth & develpt.	—	Ferreira & Hu (1989)
Ilex opaca 'Forage' & other cvs.	Embryo	Heart-shaped embryos ex mat. seed	Germination. Seedling growth	Y	Hu (1975)
Ilex pedunculosa Miq.	Embryo	Heart-shaped embryos ex mat. seed	Germination. Seedling growth	Y	Hu (1975)
Ilex pernyi Franch 'Recurva'	Embryo	Heart-shaped embryos ex mat. seed	Germination. Seedling growth	Y	Hu (1975)
Ilex serrata Thunb.	Embryo	Heart-shaped embryos ex mat. seed	Germination. Seedling growth	Y	Hu (1975)
Ilex verticillata (L.) A.Gray	Embryo	Heart-shaped embryos ex mat. seed	Germination. Seedling growth	Y	Hu (1975)
Araliaceae					
Hedera canariensis L. (Algerian ivy)	Node	Single node stem cuttings	Shoots developed	Y	Al-Juboory *et al.* (1991a)
* *Hedera helix* L. (English ivy)	Direct/Callus	Debladed petioles	Root initiation	—	Geneve *et al.* (1990)
Hedera helix	Callus	Mature stem	Embryogenesis. Juvenile plantlets obtained	—	Banks (1979)
Hedera helix	Callus	Juvenile reversion stem	Juvenile shoots regenerated. Elongated and rooted	—	Banks (1979)
Hedera helix	Direct rooting	Juvenile apex	Rooting in high light	—	Hackett (1970)
Hedera helix	Direct rooting	Adult apex	Rooting in low light	—	Hackett (1970)
Hedera helix	Direct/Indirect	Embryos, cotyledons or hypocotyls	Adventitious shoots (juvenile) & roots. Rooted plants	—	Banks *et al.* (1979)
✦ *Schefflera pueckleri* (K.Koch.) Frodin. = *Tupidanthus calyptratus*	Shoot	Shoot tips	Axillary shoot proliferation. Multiplied & rooted	YY	Matsuyama & Murashige (1977)
Asclepiadaceae					
Araujia sericofera Brot. (Cruel plant)	Direct/Callus	Immature seeds	Somatic embryos. Plantlets	—	Torné *et al.* (1992)
Araujia sericofera	Direct	Transverse leaf slices	Adventitious shoots; rooted plantlets	Y	Tideman & Hawker (1982)
Araujia sericofera	Shoot	Stem node	Axillary shoot proliferation. Shoots rooted	YY	Tideman & Hawker (1982)
Asclepias curassavica L. (Bloodflower)	Callus	Segments of twining stems	Embryogenesis. No plantlets obtained	—	Prabhudesai & N'yanaswmy (1974)
Asclepias erosa	Callus	Shoot tips (5 mm) or nodes	Multiple shoots from callus. Shoots rooted	—	Lee & Thomas (1985b)
Berberidaceae					
Berberis thunbergii DC (Barberry)	Shoot	Axil. buds & later, tipless shoots	Shoot multiplication. Rooted plants	YY	Karhu & Hakala (1991)
Berberis thunbergii atropurpurea nana (Crimson pygmy)	Shoot	Two-node explants	Axillary shoots. Slow and poor rooting	Y	Uno & Preece (1987)
Mahonia aquifolium cvs. 'Appollo' & 'Undulata'	Shoot	Axillary buds ex *in vitro* plantlets	Shoot multiplication. Rooted ex vitro	Y	Daguin *et al.* (1992)
Mahonia repens G. Don.	Shoot	Shoot tips & lateral buds	Axillary shoots. Rooted plants	YY	Garton & Moses (1986)
Bignoniaceae					
Chilopsis linearis (Cav.) Sweet. (Desert willow)	Direct	Cotyledons from seedlings	Adventitious shoots	—	Still *et al.* (1985)
Chilopsis linearis	Shoot	Adult & sdlg. shoot tips & *i.v.* adv. shoots	Multiple shoots (basal callus on shoot clumps). Plants	YY	Still *et al.* (1985)
Caprifoliaceae					
Lonicera [5 spp.] (Honeysuckle)	Shoot	Irradiated shoots ex *i.v.* plants	Shoot proliferation, rooted	Y	Cambecedes *et al.* (1992)
* *Lonicera fragrantissima* Lindl. & Paxt.	Suspension	Stem & leaf callus	Not specified. Used for protoplast culture	—	Georges *et al.* (1992)
Lonicera periclymenum L. cv. 'Serotina Honeysuckle'	Single node	Nodal explants	SHoot growth, multiplied from nodes. Rooted plants	YY	Boonmour *et al.* (1988)
Lonicera spp.	Callus	Stem, leaf & root segments	Shoot regeneration	—	Georges *et al.* (1992)
✦ *Viburnum × burkwoodii* Burk. & Skipw.	Embryo	Immature embryos from seeds	Germination. Seedlings: plants	Y	Zilis & Meyer (1976)

	Species name	Type of Culture	Source of explant	Results	References	
	Viburnum lantana L. (Wayfaring tree)	Embryo	Immature embryos from seeds	Germination. Seedlings; plants	Zilis & Meyer (1976, 1978)	Y
	Viburnum lentago L. (Sheep-berry)	Embryo	Immature embryos	Germination. Plants in soil	Zilis & Meyer (1978)	Y
	Viburnum lentago	Callus/Direct	Sdlg. shoot tips, hypocotyls	Adventitious shoots	Zilis & Meyer (1978)	—
	Viburnum lentago	Direct	Zygotic embryos	Adv. shoots from hypocotyl	Zilis & Meyer (1978)	—
	Viburnum lentago	Embryo	Immature embryos from seeds	Germination. Seedlings; plants	Zilis & Meyer (1976)	Y
	Viburnum rhytidophyllum Hemsl.	Embryo	Immature embryos	Germination. Plants in soil	Zilis & Meyer (1978)	Y
	Viburnum sieboldii Miq.	Embryo	Immature embryos	Germination. Plants in soil	Zilis & Meyer (1978)	Y
	Weigela cv. 'Bristol Ruby'	Direct	Shoot internodes ex i.v. plants	Shoot formation & multiplication. Shoots rooted	Duron (1992)	Y
◆	*Weigela florida* (Bunge.) A.DC.	Shoot	Axillary buds near apex	4 shoots/explant. Shoots rooted	Calvert & Stephens (1986)	YY
	Chenopodiaceae					
	Rhagodia spirescens F.v.M.	Direct rooting	Axillary or adventitious shoots	Studied rooting. All shoots rooted.	Williams *et al.* (1985)	—
	Compositae					
	Phaenocoma prolifera (L.) D. Don.	Node/Direct	Shoot segments	Shoot formation, proliferation then rooting		Y
	Cornaceae					
	Cornus florida L. 'Cherokee Princess' & unknown cv.	Callus	Zygotic embryos, 12-15 weeks postanthesis	Embryogenesis. Few plants recovered	Trigiano *et al.* (1989)	—
	Ephedraceae					
	Ephedra foliata	Callus	Female gametophyte	Shoot bud and/or root formation	Bhatnagar & Singh (1984)	—
	Ephedra foliata	Callus	Female gametophyte ex seeds.	Multiple root and shoot formation. Plantlet growth.	Konar & Singh (1979)	—
	Ephedra fragilis Desf.	Node	Nodal sections	Shoot proliferation. Shoots rooted	O'Dowd & Richardson (1993)	Y
	Ephedra gerardiana Wallich.	Callus	Not given	Embryogenesis, & shoot formation	Ramawat & Arya (1976)	—
	Ericaceae					
	Arctostaphylos × media Greene.	Shoot	Shoot tips (15 mm)	Shoot proliferation (up to 12 shoots/explant)	Norton & Norton (1985)	YY
◆	*Arctostaphylos uva-ursi* (L.) A.Gray (Bearberry)	Shoot	Shoot tips (15 mm)	Shoot proliferation (up to 16 shoots/explant)	Norton & Norton (1985)	YY
	Arctostaphylos uva-ursi	Shoot		Shoot proliferation. Rooting in v. & ex v. similar	Norton & Norton (1988)	—
*	*Erica carnea* L. (Winter heath)	Shoot	Shoot tips (15 mm)	Max. of 10 shoots/explant	Norton & Norton (1985)	YY
	Gaultheria hispidula (L.) Muhlenb. ex Bigelow.	Shoot	Shoot tips (15 mm)	Maximum of 4 shoots/explant	Norton & Norton (1985)	YY
◆	*Kalmia angustifolia* L. (Sheep laurel)	Shoot	Shoot tips (15 mm)	Maximum of 3 shoots per explant	Norton & Norton (1985)	Y
	Kalmia latifolia L. (Mountain laurel)	Shoot	Stem tips	Axillary shoots, multiplied	Lloyd & McCown (1981)	Y
	Kalmia latifolia	Shoot	Shoot segments	Multiple shoots. Rooted plants	McCulloch (1988)	YY
◆	*Pieris floribunda* Benth. & Hook.	Meristem/Shoot	Meristem tips	Culture established. Shoot multiplication (no details)	Uosukainen (1987)	Y
◆	*Rhododendron* cvs. 'White Lights', 'Access', '800113' (Deciduous azaleas)	Callus	Stem internode pieces (2–3 mm)	Adv. shoots. Shoots rooted ex vitro	Economou *et al.* (1988)	—
	Rhododendron sp. [several cvs.] (Deciduous azaleas)	Shoot	Shoot tips	Shoot proliferation. Rooted plants	Briggs *et al.* (1988b)	Y
	Rhododendron sp. 800374 (Deciduous azalea)	Shoot	Shoot tips	Multiple shoots. Rooted studied effects of light	Economou & Read (1986a)	—
	Rhododendron spp. (Hybrid azaleas)	Shoot	Shoot tips	Axillary shoot multiplication. Shoots rooted	Ma & Wang (1977)	YY
	Rhododendron sp. 3 cvs. (Deciduous azaleas)	Shoot/Direct	Shoot cultures	Investigated effect of cytokinin TDZ	Briggs *et al.* (1988a)	—
	Rhododendron spp. (Deciduous azaleas)	Shoot	Shoot tips	Axillary shoot proliferation. Shoots rooted	Economou & Read (1984, 1986b)	YY

Species name	Type of Culture	Source of explant	Results		References
Rhododendron spp. [& hybrids] (Native azaleas)	Shoot	Shoot tips	Shoot multiplication	Y	Hannapel *et al.* (1981)
Rhododendron catawbiense Michx.	Callus	Flower pedicel	Shoot regeneration & growth. Shoots rooted	–	Meyer (1982)
Rhododendron degronianum ssp. *yakushimanum* Carr. cvs. 'Dopey,' 'Happy' & 'Sneezy'	Shoot/Node	Apical tips & 3 or 4 bud nodal segs.	Shoot proliferation. Shoots rooted	YY	Marks (1991a, b)
Rhododendron forestii Diels.	Shoots	Shoot tips (15 mm)	Maximum of 2.5 shoots/explant	Y	Norton & Norton (1985)
Rhododendron keiskei Miq.	Shoot	Shoot tips (15 mm)	Maximum of 2 shoots/explant	Y	Norton & Norton (1985)
Rhododendron minus var. *chapmanii = R. chapmanii*	Shoot	Decapitated shoot tips (5 nodes)	Shoot multiplication. Rooted plants	YY	Barnes (1985)
Rhododendron prinophyllum (Small) Millais	Direct/Callus	Florets (petals later excised to leave ovaries)	Adv. shoots, multiplied and rooted	YY	Dai *et al.* (1987)
Rhododendron racemosum Franch.	Shoot	Shoot tips (15 mm)	Maximum of 3 shoots/explant	Y	Norton & Norton (1985)
Rhododendron simsii Planch.	Shoot	Shoot tips or shoot segments	Elongated shoots rooted. Axill. shts. post rooting	Y	Dabin & Bonharmont (1983)
Rhododendron simsii [vars.]	Shoot	Shoot tips (0.5 mm)	3-5 axillary shoots/explant. Shoots rooted	YY	Preil & Engelhardt (1977)
Rhododendron sp.	Direct	Wounded stem sections	Rooting, especially when inverted	Y	Pierik & Steegmans (1975 c)
Rhododendron spp. [70 clones]	Meristem/Shoot	Meristem tips	Culture established. Shoot multiplication (no details)	Y	Uosukainen (1987)
Rhododendron spp.	Shoot	Seedling shoot tips	Axillary shoot proliferation. Shoots rooted	Y	Anderson (1975, 1978a,b)
Rhododendron spp.	Shoot	Stem cuttings (5 cm)	Axillary shoots. Shoots rooted	YY	Kyte & Briggs (1979)
Rhododendron spp.	Shoot & Direct	Stem tips	Axillary & adventitious shoot proliferation. Rooted	YY	McCown & Lloyd (1983)
Rhododendron williamsianum Rehd. & Wils.	Shoot	Shoot tips (15 mm)	Maximum of 2 shoots/explant	Y	Norton & Norton (1985)
Rhododendron (Exbury hybrids)	Shoot & Direct	Shoot tips (10-15 mm)	Adventitious & axillary shoot proliferation. 90% rooting	YY	Fordham *et al.* (1982)
Rhododendron × 'Gibraltar', × 'Old Gold' (Exbury hybrids)	Callus	Shoot sections from shoot tip cultures	Subcultured, then shoot regeneration	–	Harbage & Stimart (1987)
Rhododendron × Catawba [3 cvs.]	Callus	Florets	Adv. shoots	–	Kavanagh *et al.* (1986)
Rhododendron [several spp. & varieties]	Callus	Flower plus pedicel	Adv. shoots. Juvenile plants obtained	–	Meyer (1984)
Rhododendron [White-flowered cvs.]	Direct	Leaf segs. ex shoot cults.	Multiple shoots. Rooted	Y	Iapichino *et al.* (1992)
Rhododendron × P.J.M. cvs.	Direct	Leaves from shoot cultures	Adventitious shoots	Y	Imel & Preece (1988)
Rhododendron × PJM cvs.	Shoot	Shoot tips (5 cm)	Shoot proliferation. 80% rooting	YY	Ettinger & Preece (1985)
Rhododendron × 'Purple Splendour'	Shoot	Shoot tips	Shoot proliferation. Rooting *in vitro*	Y	Baubault *et al.* (1991)
Rhododendron [Selection '704-692-1450']	Shoot	Shoot tips (1 × 2 mm)	Multiple shoots	Y	Strode *et al.* (1979)
Rhododendron cvs.	Shoot	Shoot tip	Shoot proliferation. Shoots pretreated & rooted	YY	Douglas (1984)
Rhododendron hybrid [*R. laetum* × *aurigeranum*]	Callus	Various somatic tissues	Shoot regeneration	–	Iapichino *et al.* (1991)
Rhododendron hybrids	Shoot	Shoot tips (15 mm)	Optimal shoot formation	Y	Norton & Norton (1985)
Rhododendron × 'Boule de Neige'	Shoot	Shoot tips	Axillary shoot proliferation	Y	Smith & McCown (1983)
Rhododendron × *limbatum* 'Pres. Roosevelt' [Chimera]	Direct	Florets ex buds	Shoot proliferation. No variegated shoots	–	Pogany & Lineberger (1990)
Rhododendron × *limbatum* 'Pres. Roosevelt' [Chimera]	Shoot	Vegetative buds & shoot tips	Shoot proliferation. Some variegated	–	Pogany & Lineberger (1990)
Rhododendron × 'Rose Elf'	Shoot	Shoot tips	Shoot proliferation. Shoots rooted	YY	Anderson (1984a)

Euphorbiaceae

Species name	Type of Culture	Source of explant	Results		References
Acalypha wilkesiana Muell.Arg. (Copper leaf)	Shoot	Stem node segments	Shoot proliferation: rooted	YY	Stoltz (1979a)
❖ *Codiaeum bonplandianum* Baill.	Callus	Endosperm with intact embryo	Embryogenesis. Non-viable embryoids	–	Bhojwani (1966)
Codiaeum bonplandianum	Embryo	Zygotic embryos	Seedlings in 3 weeks	Y	Bhojwani (1966)

	Species name	Type of Culture	Source of explant	Results		References
	Codiaeum variegatum (L.) Bl.	Callus	Isolated zygotic embryos	Both adventious roots & shoots initiated	—	Chikkannaiah & Gayatri (1974)
	Codiaeum variegatum	Callus	Isolated zygotic embryos	Embryogenic callus. Some adventitious roots too	—	Chikkannaiah et al. (1976)
❖	Euphorbia fulgens Karw. ex Klotzsc.	Node	Single node of apical shoot	Shoot proliferation. Direct rooting of 100% of shoots	YY	Zhang et al. (1986)
	Euphorbia fulgens (Scarlet plume)	Shoot	Single nodes ex apical shoots	Shoot proliferation	—	Zhang & Stoltz (1989a)
	Euphorbia fulgens	Shoot	Nodal sections & shoot tips ex apical shoots	Shoot proliferation. Rooted plants	YY	Zhang et al. (1987)
*	Euphorbia pulcherrima Willd. ex Klotzsch.	Direct	Seedling hypocotyl	Plants via direct adventitious shoots	YY	Nataraja et al. (1973)
	Euphorbia pulcherrima 'A. Hegg,' (Poinsettia)	Suspension	Tissues of chimeral plant	Two types of plant regenerated	—	Preil & Engelhardt (1982)
	Euphorbia pulcherrima cv. 'Preduza'	Suspension	Callus ex shoot tips & stem segs.	Adv. shoots & embryoids. Plants regenerated	—	Preil et al. (1983)
	Euphorbia pulcherrima 'Angelika'	Suspension	Callus ex shoot tip & young stem segments	Embryogenesis in a bioreactor. Embryos and plantlets	Y	Preil et al. (1988)
	Jatropha integerrima Jacq. = J. panduraefolia	Callus	Endosperm	Adventitious shoots & roots	—	Srivastava & Johri (1974)
	Jatropha integerrima	Embryo	Zygotic embryos with endosperm	Seedling growth	—	Srivastava & Johri (1974)
Gesneriaceae						
	Nematanthus hybrid	Shoot	Shoot tips of floral branches	Shoot proliferation. Shoots rooted in vitro. Plants	YY	Lê (1988)
	×Smithicodiana 'Cerulean Mink'	Direct	Leaf sections	Shoot initiation and multiplication. Shoots rooted	YY	Griffis et al. (1982)
Goodeniaceae						
	Dampiera diversifolia De Vriese	Shoot	Mature plant shoot tips	Multiple shoots, elongated. 92% rooting. Plants	YY	Williams et al. (1984; 1985)
Grossulariaceae						
❖	Ribes inebrians Lindl. (Wax currant)	Shoot	Shoot tips	Shoot proliferation & elongation. Rooted as cuttings	YY	Wochok & Sluis (1980a)
Haemodoraceae						
❖	Anigozanthos flavidus DC (Kangaroo paw)	Shoot	Shoot tips and lateral buds	Shoot proliferation. Shoots rooted	YY	Ellyard (1978 a,b)
	Anigozanthos manglesii D.Don.	Shoot	Shoot tips and lateral buds	Multiple shoots. Rooted	YY	Ellyard (1978 a,b)
	Anigozanthos pulcherrimus Hook.	Shoot	Apical shoots and axillary buds	Multiple axillary shoots. Rooted	YY	McComb & Newton (1981)
	Macropidia fuliginosa	Shoot	Shoot tips and lateral buds	Multiple shoots. Rooted plantlets	YY	Ellyard (1978 a,b)
	Macropidia fuliginosa	Shoot	Apical and (dormant or sprouted) lateral buds	Shoot proliferation. Shoots rooted in vitro	YY	McComb & Newton (1981)
Hamamelidaceae						
	Hamamelis × intermedia Rehd.	Shoot	Terminal & lateral buds	Studied the prevention of browning	—	Christiansen & Fonnesbech (1975)
Hydrangeaceae						
❖	Hydrangea sp.	Meristem/Shoot	Meristem tips	Culture established. Shoot multiplication (no details)	Y	Uosukainen (1987)
	Hydrangea macrophylla (Thunb.) Ser. (Florists' hydrangea)	Shoot	Shoot tips 10-15 mm	Shoot multiplication. Shoots rooted in vitro	YY	Jones J.B. (1979)
	Hydrangea macrophylla (Florists' hydrangea)	Shoot	Shoot tips	Shoot proliferation. Shoots rooted extra vitrum	YY	Bailey et al. (1985; 1986)
	Hydrangea macrophylla	Shoot	Shoot tips (0.1-0.5 cm)	Shoot proliferation. Shoots (2-3 cm) rooted in vitro	YY	Stoltz (1984)
Hypericaceae						
❖	Hypericum canariense L.	Shoot	Shoot apex & axillary buds	Plants propagated & rooted	Y	Mederos Molina (1991)
Labiatae						
*	Lavandula angustifolia Mill. = L. officinalis Chaix × L. latifolia Villars	Callus	Stem material	Adv. shoots from 2-yr. old cultures	—	Webb et al. (1984)

Species name	Type of Culture	Source of explant	Results		References
Lavandula angustifolia (English lavender)	Callus	Stem material	Adv. shoots from 2-yr. old cultures	–	Webb et al. (1984)
Lavandula angustifolia cv. 'Rosea'	Shoot	Nodes with 1–2 cm shoot tip	Axill. shoot multiplication. Rooted plants	YY	Oliphant (1988)
Lvandula angustifolia	Shoot	Veg. stem nodes, flower spikes	Multiple shoots. Rooted plants	YY	Panizza et al. (1988)
Lavandula angustifolia	Callus	Nodes, shoot tips, calyx	Adventitious shoots. Rooted plantlets	–	Panizza et al. (1988)
Lavandula angustifolia × L. latifolia	Callus	Sh. tip, stem node, fl. bud, calyx	Adv. shoots. Shoots rooted.	–	Panizza & Tognoni (1988)
Lavandula angustifolia × L. latifolia	Shoot	Node stem segments	Axill. shoot proliferation. Rooted plants	YY	Panizza & Tognoni (1988)
Lavandula angustifolia & L. latifolia	Shoot/Callus	Shoot buds	Axillary shoots, plants; or embryogenesis ex callus	YY	Quazi (1980)
Lavandula angustifolia	Callus	Lateral buds	Embryogenesis. Plantlets	–	Quazi (1980)
Lavandula angustifolia	Shoot/Callus	Lateral buds	Single or multiple axillary shoots obtained and rooted	–	Quazi (1980)
Lavandula angustifolia	Callus	Lateral buds	Embryogenesis. Somatic embryos and plantlets	–	Quazi (1980)
Lavandula latifolia Medik.	Callus	Seedling cotyl., hypocotyl, root	Adventitious shoots. Rooted plants	–	Calvo & Segura (1988)
❖ Lavandula latifolia Medicus (Lavender)	Callus	Leaves ex in vitro seedlings	Shoots regenerated. 95% rooting	–	Calvo & Segura (1989)
Lavandula latifolia	Callus	Cotyledons ex 30 day-old seedlings	Shoot formation & elongation. Shoots rooted	–	Jordan et al. (1990)
Lavandula latifolia	Direct	Hypocotyl explants	Adventitious shoots, elongated & rooted	–	Calvo & Segura (1989)
Lavandula latifolia	Shoot/Callus	Lateral buds	Single or multiple axillary shoots. Rooted	Y	Quazi (1980)
Prostanthera eurybioides F.v.M.	Direct rooting	Axillary or adventitious shoots	Studied rooting. 70% shoots rooted	–	Williams et al. (1985)
Prostanthera rotundifolia R. Br.	Shoot	Shoot tips ex mature plants	Shoot proliferation & elongation. 92% shoots rooted	YY	Williams et al. (1984, 1985)
Prostanthera striatiflora R.Br.	Direct rooting	Axillary or adventitious shoots	Studied rooting. All shoots rooted.	–	Williams et al. (1985)

Leguminosae

Species name	Type of Culture	Source of explant	Results		References
Acacia 'mimosa' vars. 'Tournaire', 'Gaulois'	Shoot	Seedlings and buds from mature plants	Shoot proliferation, rooted in vitro	YY	Ruffoni et al. (1991)
Acacia baileyana F.U.M.	Shoot	Seedlings and buds from mature plants	Shoot proliferation, rooted in vitro	YY	Ruffoni et al. (1991)
Acacia dealbata Link.	Shoot	Aseptic seedlings without roots	Shoot proliferation, rooted in vitro	YY	Ruffoni et al. (1991)
Acacia howitti F. Muell.	Shoot	Seedlings and buds from mature plants	Shoot proliferation, rooted in vitro	YY	Ruffoni et al. (1991)
Acacia longifolia var. 'Floribunda' (Acacia rootstock)	Shoot	Seedlings and buds from mature plants	Shoot proliferation, rooted in vitro	YY	Ruffoni et al. (1991)
Acacia melanoxylon R.Br.	Shoot	Axillary and apical buds	Shoot proliferation, rooted in vitro	YY	Ruffoni et al. (1991)
Acacia uncinata Lodd.	Shoot	Aseptic seedlings without roots	Shoot proliferation, rooted in vitro	YY	Ruffoni et al. (1991)
Retama monosperma (L.) Boiss. = Genista monosperma	Shoot	Shoot tips	Shoot multiplication	Y	Curir et al. (1986)

Liliaceae

Species name	Type of Culture	Source of explant	Results		References
Danae racemosa (L.) Moench. = Ruscus racemosus	Shoot/Direct	Seedlings or rhizome buds	Growth of rhizome with shoots. Subdiv. or shoots rooted	Y	Curir et al. (1988)
Dracaena deremensis Engl.	Callus	Stem	Adventitious shoot formation	–	Debergh (1975; 1976)
Dracaena deremensis	Single node	Stem nodes	Shoots from buds, some rooted	Y	Debergh (1975; 1976)
Dracaena fragrans (L.) Ker-Gaw.	Direct	Internode	Shoot and root formation. Plant regeneration	YY	Hunault (1976)
Lapageria rosea Ruiz & Pav. (Ornamental liane)	Shoot	Terminal & axillary buds	Devised 3 methods of getting rooted plants	YY	McKinless et al. (1988)
Lapageria rosea	Shoot/Callus	Terminal & axillary buds	Adv. shoots ex callus. Rooted plantlets	–	Jordan et al. (1983)
Ruscus hypophyllum L.	Callus	Young stem internode (4-6 mm)	Shoot buds. 90% rooting of 2-4 shoot clusters	–	Jha & Sen (1985)
Ruscus hypophyllum	Direct	Precultured young inflorescence	Vegetative & floral buds	Y	Ziv (1983)
Ruscus hypophyllum	Shoot & Direct	Precultured rhizome & shoot buds	Axillary & adventitious buds	Y	Ziv (1983)

	Species name	Type of Culture	Source of explant	Results		References
Lythraceae						
	Cuphea wrightii	Callus	Shoot tips or leaves	Adventitious shoots	—	Janick & Whipkey (1986)
	Lagerstroemia indica L. (Crepe myrtle)	Callus	Cotyledon or hypocotyl	Adventitious shoots. Planlets	—	Blackmon et al. (1981a)
	Lagerstroemia indica	Callus	Cotyledon & hypocotyl	Small no. of adv. shoots from primary callus	—	Blackmon et al. (1981b)
	Lagerstroemia indica	Shoot	2-node stem sections	7-8 (2 cm-long) shoots per explant (90-95% rooted).	YY	Zhang & Davies (1986)
	Lagerstroemia speciosa (L.) Pers. = L. flos-reginae	Shoot	Nodal segments with 2 axillary buds	Multiple shoot formation. Shoots rooted in vitro	YY	Paily & D'Souza (1986)
Magnoliaceae						
	Magnolia hybrids [& sp.]	Callus	Axillary buds	Callus growth. Studied best media	—	Biedermann (1987)
	Magnolia [3 species]	Callus	Immature seeds, bisected longitudinally	Somatic embryos produced & germinated	—	Merkle & Wiecko (1990)
	Magnolia grandiflora L.	Embryo	Mature embryos	Germination	—	Le Page-Degivry (1970)
	Magnolia maccarophylla Michx. (Big leaf Magnolia)	Embryogenic callus	Immature seed halves	Plantlet regeneration	—	Merkle & Watson-Pauley (1993)
*	Magnolia × soulangeana Soul. Bod.	Embryo	Mature embryos	Germination	—	Le Page-Degivry (1970)
	Magnolia × soulangeana	Shoot	Shoot tips	Investigated shoot elongation & rooting	YY	Maene & Debergh (1985)
	Magnolia × soulangiana	Shoot	Shoot tips	Slow shoot growth	—	Einset (1986)
Malvaceae						
	Abutilon indicum (L.) Sweet.	Callus	Sections of young leaves	Adv. shoots	—	Shanthamma & Sudarshana (1986)
Moraceae						
	Broussonetia kazinoki Sieb.	Direct	Hypocotyl	Adventitious shoots (& roots)	Y	Ohyama & Oka (1980)
	Ficus benjamina L. [8 clones]	Shoot	Shoot tips	Shoot proliferation. Shoots rooted	YY	Kristiansen (1992)
	Ficus benjamina	Shoot	Shoot tips	Multiple shoots. Rooted in vivo	YY	Maene & Debergh (1983)
	Ficus benjamina	Shoot	Shoot tips	Establishment of subcultures. Direct rooting	Y	Makino et al. (1977)
*	Ficus elastica Roxb. ex Hornem. 'Decora'	Shoot	Shoot tips	Establishment of subcultures. Rooted	Y	Makino et al. (1977)
	Ficus lyrata Warb. (Fiddle-back fig)	Callus	Leaf	Adventitious shoot formation. Direct rooting	—	Debergh & De Wael (1977)
	Ficus lyrata	Callus	Sections of young leaves with midrib	Adv. shoots from primary callus	—	Jona & Gribaudo (1988)
	Ficus lyrata	Direct	Sections of young leaves with main vein	Adventitious shoots. Elongated shoots rooted. Plants	YY	Jona & Gribaudo (1987, 1988)
	Ficus lyrata	Shoot	Shoot tips	Shoot proliferation. Shoots rooted	YY	Wainwright & Scrace (1989)
	Ficus lyrata = F. pandurata	Shoot	Shoot tips	Establishment of subcultures. Direct rooting	Y	Makino et al. (1977)
Musaceae						
❖	Musa ornata Roxb. (Ornamental banana)	Embryogenic callus	Zygotic embryos	Plants from somatic embryos	—	Cronauer-Mitra & Krikorian (1988)
Myoporaceae						
	Eremophila lanii F. Muell	Direct rooting	Adventitious or axillary shoots	Studied methods of rooting. 62% shoots rooted	Y	Williams et al. (1985)
	Myoporum parvifolium R. Br.	Direct	Adventitious or axillary shoots	85% shoots rooted	Y	Williams et al. (1985)
Myrtaceae						
	Chamelaucium uncicatum Schauer (Geraldton wax)	Shoot	Nodal explants	Shoot multiplication. Rooted plants	YY	Page & Visser (1989)
❖	Eugenia smithii Poir. (Lilly-Pilly)	Shoot	Nodes and apical tips	Shoot formation & multiplication, followed by rooting	YY	Toussaint et al. (1992)
	Leptospermum brachyandrum (F. Muell.) (Druce Tea tree)	Shoot	Mature nodal pieces	Multiple axillary shoots. Rooted	—	Shipton & Jackes (1986)

	Species name	Type of Culture	Source of explant	Results		References
	Leptospermum polygalifolium Salisb. = *L. flavescens* (Common Tea tree)	Shoot	Mature nodal pieces	Multiple avillary shoots. Rooted	—	Shipton & Jackes (1986)
	Leptospermum petersonii F.M. Bail. (Tropical Tea tree)	Shoot	Mature nodal pieces	Multiple axillary shoots. Rooted	—	Shipton & Jackes (1986)
	Myrtus communis L. (Myrtle)	Shoot	Shoot tips (5-10 mm)	8 shoots/culture. 75% rooting	YY	Khosh-Khui *et al.* (1984)
	Myrtus communis	Shoot	Shoot tip	5-10 shoots in 10-15 weeks	Y	Uhring (1983)
	Verticordia grandis J.L. Drumm. ex Meissn.	Shoot	Shoot tips	Shoot multiplication. Rooted plants	YY	De Fossard & De Fossard (1988)
Nandinaceae						
	Nandina domestica Thunb. (Sacred bamboo)	Shoot	Lateral buds	Shoot proliferation	Y	Gould & Murashige (1985)
	Nandina domestica	Shoot	Terminal or lateral buds	Multiple shoots. 61% rooting	YY	Smith R.H. (1983)
Nyctaginaceae						
*	*Bougainvillea glabra* Choisy in DC	Shoot	Shoot apices	Shoot proliferation. Shoots rooted	YY	Chaturvedi *et al.* (1978)
	Bougainvillea glabra	Shoot	Shoot tips	Shoot multiplication. Rooted plants	YY	Sharma A.K. *et al.* (1981)
Oleaceae						
	Forsythia × intermidia Zab. 'Sunrise'	Shoot	2—3 node explants ex *i.v.* cultures	Shoot proliferation. Shoots rooted	YY	McClelland & Smith (1990)
	Forsythia mandshurica	Single node	Seedling shoot tips & nodes	Shoots (cut up for subculture). Rooted plants	YY	Einset & Alexander (1985)
	Forsythia ovata Nak. (Korean forsythia)	Meristem/Shoot	Meristem tips	Culture established. Shoot multiplication (no details)	Y	Uosukainen (1987)
	Forsythia ovata	Single node	Sht. tips & nodes (g'house plants)	Shoots (cut up for subculture). Rooted plants	YY	Einset & Alexander (1985)
*	*Jasminum officinale* L.	Callus	Nodal stem sections	Entire plants regenerated	—	Khoder *et al.* (1979)
	Ligustrum obtusifolium Rehd.	Single node	Seedling shoot tips & nodes	Shoots (cut up for subculture). Rooted plants	YY	Einset & Alexander (1985)
	Syringa reticulata (Bl.) Hara	Single node	Shoot tips & nodes (g'house plants)	Shoots (cut up for subculture). Rooted plants	YY	Einset & Alexander (1985)
*	*Syringa vulgaris* cv. "Vesper" (Common lilac)	Shoot	Shoot tips (5-10 mm)	Shoot multiplication. 80% rooting	YY	Hildebrandt & Harney (1983)
	Syringa vulgaris L. [3 rootstocks & 5 cvs.]	Single node	Shoot tips	Shoot growth. Single nodes recultured or shoots rooted	YY	Pierik *et al.* (1988)
	Syringa × chinensis Willd. cv. 'Saugeana Rouen'	Single node	Nodal segments from *i.v.* shoots	Shoots with several nodes. Rooted	Y	Welander N.T. (1987)
	Syringa × diversifolia Rehd.	Single node	Shoot tips & nodes (g'house plants)	Shoots (cut up for subculture). Rooted plants	YY	Einset & Alexander (1985)
	Syringa × hyacinthiflora (Lemoine) Rehd. cv. 'Excel'	Shoot	Shoot tips	Multiple shoots	Y	Einsett (1987)
	Syringa × hyacinthiflora cv. 'Excel'	Single node	Sht. tips & nodes (g'house plants)	Shoots (cut up for subculture). Rooted plants	YY	Einset & Alexander (1985)
Onagraceae						
❖	*Fuchsia × hybrida* Hort. ex Vilm. 'Keystone' & 'Rose of Castille'	Callus	Single nodes	Plant regeneration	—	Chow *et al.* (1990)
	Fuchsia × hybrida 'Swingtime', 'Rose Van d'Bergh'	Callus	Ovary slices	Embryogenesis	—	Dabin & Beguin (1987)
	Fuchsia × hybrida	Shoot	Shoot tips	Shoot proliferation	YY	Harris & Mason (1983)
	Fuchsia × hybrida [18 cvs.]	Shoot	Shoot tips & nodes	Axillary shoots. Rooted & moved to soil	YY	Kevers *et al.* (1983)
	Fuchsia × hybrida	Shoot	Shoot tips	Shoots multiplied, elongated and rooted	YY	Stevenson & Harris (1980)
Paeoniaceae						
❖	*Paeonia suffruticosa* Andr. (Moutan paeony)	Direct	Shoots ex *in vitro* cultures	Root formation & development	—	Bouza *et al.* (1992)
❖	*Paeonia suffruticosa* var. 'Papaveracea'	Node	Nodal segments (1—2 cm)	Multiple shoot proliferation. Shoots rooted	YY	Harris & Mantell (1991)

Species name	Type of Culture	Source of explant	Results		References
Passifloraceae					
❖ Passiflora × alato-caerulea	Direct	Stem internode (10-12 mm) or leaf disc (5 mm)	Multiple adventitious shoots. Shoots rooted	YY	Muralidhar & Mehta (1982)
Passiflora × alato-caerulea	Direct	Leaf discs	Direct shoot initiation. Shoots rooted	Y	Muralidhar & Mehta (1986a)
Passiflora × alato-caerulea	Node	Pre-chilled axillary buds	59-62 shoots/bud. Shoots rooted	YY	Muralidhar & Mehta (1982)
Passiflora × alato-caerulea	Shoot	Shoot apices (2-3 mm)	3-4 shoots/apex. Shoots rooted	YY	Muralidhar & Mehta (1982)
Passiflora caerulea L.	Callus	Leaf discs (1 mm)	Shoot initials	—	Scorza & Janick (1979)
Passiflora caerulea	Direct	Entire plant	Buds on roots	—	Montaldi (1972)
Passiflora foetida L.	Callus	Leaf discs (1 mm)	Rhizogenesis only	—	Scorza & Janick (1979)
Passiflora mollissima (HBK) L.H. Bail.	Callus	Axillary buds	Shoots via basal callus. Shoots rooted	—	Robles (1978)
Passiflora suberosa L.	Callus	Leaf discs (1 mm)	Shoots and flowers	—	Scorza & Janick (1979)
Philadelphiaceae					
* Philadelphus lewisii Pursh.	Meristem/Shoot	Meristem tips	Culture established. Shoot multiplication (no details)	Y	Uosukainen (1987)
Plumbaginaceae					
Plumbago indica L.	Direct	Internode sections	Flower formation	—	Nitsch & Nitsch (1965)
Plumbago indica	Direct	Stem sections	Root &/or shoot formation	Y	Nitsch & Nitsch (1967a)
Plumbago indica	Direct	Stem sections	Flower & vegetative buds	Y	Nitsch & Nitsch (1967b)
Plumbago indica	Direct	Internode segments	Adventitious flower buds	—	Nitsch et al. (1967)
Plumbago indica	Direct	Stem sections	Vegetative shoots in long days, flowers in short days	—	Nitsch (1965)
Plumbago indica	Direct	Stem segments	Adventitious shoot or flower buds	Y	Nitsch (1968)
Plumbago rosea L.	Callus	Seedling stem segments	Adventitious shoots. Rooted plants	—	Kumar & Bhavanandan (1988)
Proteaceae					
Grevillea curviloba MacGillivray = G. biternata	Direct rooting	Adventitious or axillary shoots	70% shoots rooted	—	Williams et al. (1985)
Grevillea rosmarinifolia A.Cunn.	Node/Shoot	Shoot nodal segments	Shoot multiplication. Rooted plants	YY	Ben-Jaacov & Dax (1981)
Grevillea scapigera A.S.George	Direct	Leaves minus petioles	Shoot formation	Y	Bunn & Dixon (1992)
Grevillea scapigera	Shoot	Shoot tips and axillary nodes	Shoot formation	YY	Bunn & Dixon (1992)
Grevillea sscapigera	Direct	Leaves minus petioles	Shoot formation	Y	Bunn & Dixon (1992)
Grevillea spp. [various]	Node	2-node shoot segments	Shoot formation & proliferation. Shoots rooted	YY	Watad et al. (1992a)
Leucospermum cv. 'Red Sunset'	Node	Multinodal (3-5) segs.	Studied factors affecting bud break	Y	Rugge et al. (1990)
Leucospermum hybrid 'Hawaii Gold'	Shoot	Axillary buds	Shoot 'propagules' on liquid media. Rooted plants	YY	Kunisaki (1989)
Leucospermum cordifolium (Knight) Fourc.	Shoot	2-node shoot segments	Shoot formation & multiplication. Shoots rooted	YY	Tal et al. (1992b)
Leucospermum cordifolium	Direct rooting	Nodal segment ex in vitro plant	Roots formed	—	Tal et al. (1992a)
Leucospermum cordifolium × L. lineare 'Red Sunset'	Shoot	Sections of semi-hard stems	Buds sprouted	—	Ben-Jaacov & Jacobs (1986)
Protea cynaroides L. (King protea)	Shoot	Lignotuber sprouts	Buds sprouted	—	Ben-Jaacov & Jacobs (1986)
Protea obtusifolia Meissn.	Shoot	Etiolated 2—4 node terminal shoot segs.	Axillary buds sprouted	Y	Watad et al. (1992b)
Serruria florida Knight.	Shoot	Semi-hard stem sects. below apex	Shoot proliferation	Y	Ben-Jaacov & Jacobs (1986)
Stirlingia latifolia (R.Br.) Steudel (Blueboy)	Shoot	Shoot tips	Shoot formation. Rooted plants	YY	Bunn & Dixon (1992c)

Species name	Type of Culture	Source of explant	Results		References
Telopea speciosissima (Sm.) R.Br. (Waratah)	Direct	Microshoots ex node culture	Various rooting systems studied	Y	Offord & Campbell (1992)
Telopea speciosissima	Node	Single nodes	Shoot proliferation & elongation	Y	Offord *et al.* (1992)
Telopea speciosissima	Shoot	Single axillary nodes ex terminal growth	Shoot multiplication. Shoots rooted directly. Plants	YY	Offord *et al.* (1990)
Telopea speciosissima	Shoot	Single nodes ex g'house plants	Multiple shoots in subcultures. Rooted plants	YY	Seelye (1985)
Ranunculaceae					
❖ *Clematis* cv. 'Montana rubens'	Node	Single nodes	Multiple shoots, rooted. Studied antibiotic effects	–	Leifert *et al.* (1992)
Clematis sp.	Shoot	Vegetative & reprod. stem apices	Multiple shoots	Y	Kratz & Langhans (1978)
Rosaceae					
❖ *Amelanchier alnifolia* Nutt. (Smoky Saskatoon)	Shoot	Shoot tips	Shoot proliferation. Tested cold hardiness	Y	Caswell *et al.* (1986)
Amelanchier alnifolia	Shoot	Shoot tips	Shoot multiplication	YY	Harris & Mason (1983)
Amelanchier alnifolia Nutt. [4 cvs.]	Shoot	Shoot tips	Multiple shoots. Rooted ex vitro. Dormancy broken	YY	Pruski *et al.* (1990)
Amelanchier laevis Wieg.	Shoot	Shoot tips (1.5 cm)	Multiple axillary shoots	YY	Behrouz & Lineberger (1981 a,b)
Amelanchier laevis L. (Juneberry)	Shoot	Shoot tips	Multiple shoot formation then rooting	YY	Hajela *et al.* (1993)
Amelanchier spicata (Lam.) K. Koch (Low shadblow)	Shoot	2–3 node explants from *i.v.* cults.	Shoot proliferation. Shoots rooted	YY	McClelland & Smith (1990)
Amelanchier × grandiflora Rehd. 'Princess Diana' (Serviceberry)	Shoot	Stage II shoot cultures	Shoot proliferation in programmable apparatus	Y	Krueger *et al.* (1991)
Amelanchier × grandiflora cv. 'Princess Diana'.	Shoot/Direct	*In vitro* shoots	Shoot formation & growth	–	Robacker & Simonton (1992)
❖ *Aronia arbutifolia* (L.) Pers. 'Brilliantissima' (Red chokeberry)	Shoot	Shoot tips	Shoot formation, then rooting	Y	Brand & Cullina (1992)
Aronia melanocarpa (Michx.) Ell. (Black chokeberry)	Shoot	Shoot tips	Shoot formation, then rooting	Y	Brand & Cullina (1992)
Chaenomeles japonica (Thunb.) Spach.	Shoot	Shoot tips	Axillary shoot proliferation. Rooted plants	YY	Norton & Boe (1982)
Chaenomeles japonica	Shoot	Shoot tips (15 mm)	Continued shoot proliferation over 9 cycles	YY	Norton & Norton (1986b)
❖ *Cotoneaster dammeri* Schneid.	Shoot	Shoot tips	Axillary shoot proliferation. Rooted plants	YY	Norton & Boe (1982)
Cowania mexicana + Fallugia paradoxa	Micrografting	Seedling rootstock/*i.v.* shoot tip	Few plants survived after 20 weeks	–	Kyle & Righetti (1986; 1988)
Cowania mexicana + Purshia glandosa	Micrografting	Seedling rootstock/*i.v.* shoot tips	Plants. Actinorrhizal nodules	Y	Kyle & Righetti (1988)
Cowania mexicana (Torr.) Jeps. var. 'Stansburiana'	Shoot	Shoot tips	Shoot proliferation	YY	Kyle & Righetti (1988)
❖ *Crataegus* cv. 'Toba'	Shoot	Shoot tips	Axillary shoot proliferation. Rooted plants	YY	Norton & Boe (1982)
Crataegus brachyacantha Sarg. & Engelm.	Shoot	Shoot tips	Shoot proliferation. Rooted plants	YY	Norton & Boe (1982)
Crataegus brachyacantha	Shoot	Shoot tips (15 mm)	Shoot proliferation (rate down after 5th subcult.)	YY	Norton & Norton (1986b)
Fallugia paradoxa + Purshia glandosa	Micrografting	Seedling rootstock/*i.v.* shoot tip	Small no. plants with normal growth after 60 wks.	Y	Kyle & Righetti (1988)
Fallugia paradoxa + Cowania mexicana	Micrografting	Seedling rootstock/*i.v.* shoot tips	No plants survived after 20 weeks	–	Kyle & Righetti (1988)
Fallugia paradoxa (D.Don) Endl.	Shoot	Shoot tips	Shoot proliferation	–	Kyle & Righetti (1988)
❖ *Malus* 'Almey'. (Crabapple)	Shoot	Shoot tips	Shoot multiplication	YY	Turner & Singha (1988)
Malus 'Almey'. 'Eleyi' & 'Hopa'	Shoot	Shoot tips (2 cm)	Shoot proliferation. Shoots rooted	YY	Singha (1981; 1982b)
Malus 'Almey'. & 'Hopa'	Shoot	Shoot tips	Shoot proliferation	Y	Singha (1982b; 1984)
Malus 'Almey'.	Shoot	Shoot tips	High rate of shoot proliferation	YY	Singha *et al.* (1987)
Malus 'Dainty'. & 'Golden Hornet'	Shoot	Shoot tips	Axillary shoot proliferation. Shoots rooted *in vitro*	YY	Norton & Boe (1982)
Malus prunifolia Borkh. 'xanthocarpa' (Asiatic crab.)	Shoot	Shoot tips	Multiple shoots. Rooted plants	Y	Aldwinckle & Gustafson (1981)

	Species name	Type of Culture	Source of explant	Results		References
	Malus sp. (Weeping crab apple)	Embryo	Mature seed embryos	Seedling growth, even if cotyledons removed	—	Nickell (1951)
	Malus sylvestris	Meristems	Axillary bud meristem	Shoot growth. Shooted rooted in vitro	Y	Walkey (1972)
	Malus × zumi var. calocarpa	Shoot	Shoot tips (2 cm)	Shoot proliferation. Shoots rooted	YY	Singha (1981; 1982b)
	Malus × purpurea 'Eleyi'	Shoot	Shoot tips (2 cm)	Shoot proliferation. Shoots rooted	YY	Singha (1981; 1982b)
	Malus × perpetu 'Evereste'	Shoot	Shoot tips (1 cm)	Shoot proliferation. 100% rooting	YY	Duron (1984)
	Malus × sublobata 'Novole'	Callus/Direct	Leaf tissue	Adventitious shoots	—	Dufour (1990)
*	Photinia × fraseri cv. 'Red Robin' Dress.	Node	Single nodes	Multiple shoots, rooted. Studied antibiotic effects	—	Leifert et al. (1992)
❖	Potentilla fruticosa. L. (Shrubby cinquefoil)	Shoot	Shoot tips	Shoot proliferation. Shoots rooted	YY	Wainwright & Scrace (1989)
	Potentilla fruticosa	Shoot	Shoot tips	Shoot proliferation. Shoots rooted	YY	Norton & Boe (1982)
	Potentilla fruticosa [2 var.]	Shoot	Shoot tips (15 mm)	Shoot proliferation (rate fell after 5 – 8 subcultures)	YY	Norton & Norton (1986b)
	Potentilla fruticosa 'Snowbird' & 'Pink Whisper'	Shoot	Shoot tips	Shoot multiplication. Degree of branching studied	Y	Remphrey et al. (1993)
	Prunus cvs. 'Pandora' & 'Accolade'	Shoot	Shoot tips	Shootlet differentiation. Shoot elongation & rooting	YY	Boxus (1975)
*	Prunus cerasifera Ehrh. (Myrobalan cherry plum)	Shoot	Shoot tips	Shoot proliferation. Shoots rooted	YY	Garland & Stoltz (1981)
	Prunus cerasifera	Shoot	Shoot tips	Shoot multiplication. Shoots rooted	YY	Hammerschlag (1982b)
	Prunus cerasifera Myrobalan seedling Mr. S. 2/5	Shoot	Shoot apices	Multiple shoots, elongated and rooted	Y	Loreti et al. (1983)
	Prunus cerasifera [various seedling selections]	Shoot	Shoot tips from forced shoots	Shoot multiplication & elongation. Rooted plants	Y	Morini et al. (1991)
	Prunus cerasifera Mr. S. 2/5	Shoot	Shoot tips ex in vitro culture	Shoots multiplied & rooted. Photoperiod studied	YY	Morini et al. (1991)
	Prunus cerasifera Mr. S. 2/5	Shoot	Shoot tips ex shoot cultures	Shoot multiplication. Studied light & sucrose effects	Y	Morini et al. (1992)
	Prunus cerasifera	Shoot	Shoot tips	Axillary shoot proliferation. Shoots rooted	YY	Norton & Boe (1982)
	Prunus cerasifera	Shoot	Apical shoot tip (20 mm)	Axillary shoot proliferation	Y	Norton & Norton (1986a)
	Prunus cerasifera 'Thundercloud'	Shoot	Shoot tips (15 mm)	Shoot proliferation (at a relatively low rate)	YY	Norton & Norton (1986b)
	Prunus cerasifera	Shoot	Shoot tips	Shoot multiplication. In vitro rooting	Y	Norton & Norton (1988a)
	Prunus × cistena (Hansen) Koehne.	Shoot	Shoot tips	Shoot multiplication. Shoots rooted	YY	Lane (1979 c)
*	Prunus mahaleb L.	Callus	Leaf discs	Adventitious roots	—	Hedtrich (1977)
	Prunus mahaleb 'Dwarf Mahaleb' (Dwarf rootstock)	Shoot	Shoot tips	Shoot multiplication. Rooted plants	YY	Ranjit et al. (1988a)
	Prunus nipponica Matsum.	Shoot	Shoot tips	Shootlet differentiation. Shoot elongation & rooting	YY	Boxus (1975)
	Prunus pseudocerasus Lindl.	Callus	Stem internode	Root induction	—	Feucht & Dausend (1976)
	Prunus tenella Batsch. (Dwarf Russian almond)	Shoot	Shoot tips ex plants in pots	Multiple shoots. Rooted plants	YY	Alderson et al. (1987)
	Prunus tomentosa Thunb. (Downy cherry)	Shoot	Shoot tips	Shoot proliferation. Shoots rooted	YY	Norton & Boe (1982)
	Prunus tomentosa	Shoot	Shoot tips (15 mm)	Shoot proliferation (rate fell after 5th subcult.)	YY	Norton & Norton (1986b)
	For other Prunus sp. — see Fruit & Nuts table.					
	Purshia glandulosa Curran	Shoot	Shoot tips	Shoot proliferation	—	Kyle & Righetti (1988)
	Purshia glandulosa + Fallugia paradoxa	Micrografting	Seedling rootstock/i.v. shoot tip	Few plants survived after 20 weeks	Y	Kyle & Righetti (1988)
	Purshia glandulosa + Purshia tridentata	Micrografting	Seedling rootstock/i.v. shoot tip	High percentage plant survival	Y	Kyle & Righetti (1988)
	Purshia glandulosa + Cowania mexicana	Micrografting	Seedling rootstock/i.v. shoot tips	Plants. Actinorrhizal nodules	Y	Kyle & Righetti (1988)
	Purshia tridentata + Fallugia paradoxa	Micrografting	Seedling rootstock/i.v. shoot tip	Few plants survived after 20 weeks	Y	Kyle & Righetti (1988)
	Purshia tridentata + Purshia glandosa	Micrografting	Seedling rootstock/i.v. shoot tip	36% plant survival	Y	Kyle & Righetti (1988)
	Purshia tridentata + Cowania mexicana	Micrografting	Seedling rootstock/i.v. shoot tips	Plants. Actinorrhizal nodules	Y	Kyle & Righetti (1988)

Species name	Type of Culture	Source of explant	Results		References
Purshia tridentata (Pursh) DC	Shoot	Shoot tips	Shoot proliferation	—	Kyle & Righetti (1988)
Pyracantha coccinea Roem.	Shoot	Shoot tips	Shoot proliferation. Shoots rooted	YY	Norton & Boe (1982)
Pyrus amygdaliformis Vill.	Callus	Leaves of in vitro shoots	Adv. shoots on primary callus. Multiplied	—	Dolcet-Sanjuan et al. (1991)
Pyrus amygdaliformis	Shoot	Shoot tips	Prolif. optimised with high light & high cytokinin	YY	Dolcet-Sanjuan et al. (1991)
Pyrus betulifolia Bunge.	Shoot	Shoot tips	Shoot multiplication. Rooted plants	YY	Dolcet-Sanjuan et al. (1991)
* Rosa chinensis Jacq. 'Minima' [4 cvs] = R. indica (Miniature)	Direct/Callus	Shoots ex in vitro cultures	Root formation studied	—	Rogers & Smith (1992)
Rosa chinensis 'Minima'	Shoot	Shoots ex in vitro node cult.	Shoot multiplication	Y	Chu et al. (1993)
Rosa chinensis 'Minima' cv. 'Tipper'	Shoot	Microshoots ex in vitro cultures	Shoot proliferation. Shoots rooted	Y	Smith et al. (1992)
Rosa chinensis	Node	Nodal stem (2-3 cm)	Axillary shoots. Rapid shoot proliferation	Y	Rosten & McCown (1981)
Rosa chinensis	Shoot	Nodal cuttings, or shoot apices	Multiple shoots, rooted plants	YY	Avramis et al. (1982 a,b)
Rosa damascena Mill.	Callus	Stem internode sections	Multiple buds. Rooted plantlets	—	Ishioka & Tanimoto (1990)
Rosa damascena	Shoot	Shoot tip or lateral buds	Axillary shoot proliferation. Shoots rooted	YY	Khosh-Khui & Sink (1982a,b)
Rosa damascena	Callus	Immature embryos	Shoots regenerated & rooted	—	Burger et al. (1990)
Rosa hybrida L. 'Bridal Pink' [& other cvs.]	Callus	Immature leaf & stem segments	Somatic embryogen. Low rate of germination	—	Rout et al. (1991)
Rosa hybrida cv. 'Landora'	Callus	1 cm node cuttings	Adventitious shoots	—	Valles & Boxus (1987b)
Rosa hybrida [3 cvs.]	Direct	Shoots (4-6 mm)	Adventitious root growth	Y	Hyndman et al. (1982 a,b)
Rosa hybrida [3 cvs.]	Direct	Shoot cultures	Investigated alternative methods of rooting	Y	Alderson et al. (1988)
Rosa hybrida cvs. 'Domingo', 'Vickey Brown'	Embryogenic callus	Leaves from in vitro shoot cultures	Somatic embryos and shoots. Rooted plantlets	—	De Wit et al. (1990)
Rosa hybrida 'Queen Elizabeth' (Floribunda rose)	Meristem	Virus-infected meristems	Shoots regen. (virus-free). Rooted	YY	Douglas et al. (1989)
Rosa hybrida	Node	Single node segs.	Plantlet regeneration	Y	Arnold et al. (1992)
Rosa hybrida	Not given	Not given	Shoot multiplication. Rooted under various RH	—	Ghashghaie et al. (1992)
Rosa hybrida cv. 'Madame G. Delbard'	Shoot	Lateral buds	Shoot proliferation. Studied conditions form i.v. rooting	Y	Badzian et al. (1991)
Rosa hybrida [7 cvs. miniature]	Shoot	Shoot tips	Multiple shoots, rooted. Plants better than controls	Y	Dubois & Devries (1988)
Rosa hybrida [36 miniature cvs.	Shoot	Shoot tip or lateral buds	Axillary shoot proliferation. Rooted plants	YY	Dubois et al. (1988)
Rosa hybrida [many dwarf cvs.]	Shoot	Stem segments with 1 dormant bud	Axillary shoot proliferation. Rooted plants	Y	Langford & Wainwright (1987, 1988)
Rosa hybrida 'Iceberg', 'Peace'	Shoot	Shoot tips	Shoot multiplication	YY	Bressan et al. (1982)
Rosa hybrida	Shoot	Shoot tips and lateral buds	Axillary shoot proliferation. Shoots rooted in vitro	YY	Dohare et al. (1991)
Rosa hybrida cv. 'Super Star'	Shoot	Axillary buds from actively growing shoots	5-fold mult. rate. Rooted plants	YY	Hasegawa (1979, 1980)
Rosa hybrida	Shoot	Shoot tips or lateral buds	Shoot proliferation. Shoots rooted	YY	Khosh-Khui & Sink (1982 a,b)
Rosa hybrida	Shoot	Shoot tip or lateral buds	Axillary shoot proliferation. Shoots rooted	Y	Mederos & Rodriguez. Enriquez (1987)
Rosa hybrida cv. 'Golden Times'	Shoot	1 cm nodes of various ages	Shoot growth/proliferation (dep. on age & bud position)	Y	Podwyszynska & Hempel (1988)
Rosa hybrida [5 cvs.]	Shoot	Shoot tips (10—15 mm)	Shoot multiplication. Shoots rooted in vitro	Y	Kevers (1992)
Rosa hybrida 'Madame G. Delbard'	Shoot	Shoot cultures	Shoot multiplication. Role of C2H4 studied	Y	Sallanon & Maziere (1992)
Rosa hybrida 'Madame G. Delbard'	Shoot	In vitro shoot clump	Shoot growth & multiplication. Assessed humidity effects	Y	Sallanon et al. (1993)
Rosa hybrida 'Madame G. Delbard'	Shoot	Not given	Studied i.v. & greenhouse leaf stomata structure	—	Skirvin & Chu (1979a)
Rosa hybrida	Shoot	Shoot tips	Axillary shoot proliferation. Shoots rooted	YY	Valles & Boxus (1987a)
Rosa hybrida [12 cvs.]	Shoot	1 cm stem cuttings with 1 bud	Axillary shoots, rooted in vitro	YY	

Species name	Type of Culture	Source of explant	Results		References
Rosa hybrida cv. 'Dr. Verhage'	Shoot	SHoot explants from *i.v.* cultures	Compared manual tipping & PGRs for shoot formation	Y	Voyiatzi & Voyiatzis (1988)
Rosa hybrida	Shoot	Shoot tips	Axillary shoot proliferation. 70-100% rooting	YY	Davies (1980)
Rosa hybrida 'Queen Elizabeth'	Shoot	Shoot tips (1—2 mm)	Axillary shoot proliferation. Shoots rooted	YY	Donnelly & Skelton (1989)
Rosa hybrida [many varieties]	Shoot (meristem)	Shoots or meristems	Shoot proliferation (general method described)	YY	Martin *et al.* (1981)
Rosa hybrida 'Sunburst Red', 'Toy Clown' & 'Fiona'	Shoot/Node	Shoot tips and nodes	Multiple shoots. Rooted	YY	Douglas *et al.* (1989)
Rosa hybrida [14 cvs.]	Shoot/Node	Stem nodes (2—3 cm length)	Multiple shoots. Rooted	YY	Horn *et al.* (1988)
Rosa laevigata Michx.	Direct	Leaves ex *i.v.* cultures	Adv. shoots. Rooted	Y	Lloyd *et al.* (1988)
Rosa multiflora L. cv. 'Montse'	Shoot	Shoots ex *in vitro* cultures	Leaf anatomy studied	—	Capellades *et al.* (1990)
Rosa multiflora cv. 'Montse'	Shoot	Etiolated shoots	Studied effect of sucrose on starch content & photosyn.	—	Capellades *et al.* (1991)
Rosa multiflora	Shoot	Shoot tips	Shoot growth, roots	Y	Elliott (1970)
Rosa nitida Willd.	Node	Nodal stem (2-3 cm)	Axillary shoot proliferation	Y	Rosten & McCown (1981)
Rosa persica × *R. xanthina*	Callus	Internode segments	Adventitious shoots. Rooted	—	Lloyd *et al.* (1988)
Rosa persica × *R. xanthina*	Direct	Leaves ex *i.v.* cultures & roots	Adv. shoots. Rooted	Y	Lloyd *et al.* (1988)
Rosa sp. 'Petite Folie' (Miniature rose)	Callus	10 mm stem sections	Callus growth	—	Aril & Khatamian (1988)
Rosa [several spp. & hybrid]	Shoot	Terminal buds	Shoot multiplication	YY	Lloyd *et al.* (1988)
Rosa wichuraiana Crep.	Direct	Leaves ex *i.v.* cultures	Adv. shoots. Rooted	Y	Lloyd *et al.* (1988)
Spiraea 'Froebelii'	Shoot	Shoot tips	Shoot multiplication. *In vitro* rooting	Y	Norton & Norton (1988d)
Spiraea sp.	Shoot	Shoot tips	Shoot proliferation		Norton (1988)
Spiraea [no species given]	Shoot/direct	Shoot tips?	Axillary & adv. shoots. Rapid shoot proliferation	Y	Norton & Norton (1988c)
* *Spiraea japonica* 'Bumalda' L. = *S. bumalda*	Shoot	Shoot tips	Axillary shoot proliferation. Shoots rooted	YY	Lane (1979 c)
Spiraea japonica	Shoot	Shoot tips	Axillary shoot proliferation. Shoots rooted	YY	Norton & Boe (1982)
Spiraea japonica	Shoot	Apical shoot tip (20 mm)	Axillary shoot proliferation	Y	Norton & Norton (1986a)
Spiraea nipponica Maxim.	Shoot	Shoot tips ex *in vitro* cultures	Shoot multiplication. Various light regimes used	Y	Herrington & McPherson (1993)
Spiraea nipponica	Shoot tip	Shoots	Shoot proliferation	YY	Norton & Norton (1988b)
* *Spiraea* × *vanhouttei* (C.Briot) Zab.	Shoot	Forced shoots or shoots ex in vitro cult.	Shoot proliferation	Y	Yang & Read (1993)

Rubiaceae

Species name	Type of Culture	Source of explant	Results		References
Alberta magna E.H. Mey	Shoot	Shoot tip (6 mm long) from seedling	Shoot proliferation. Rooted plants	YY	Ben-Jaacov *et al.* (1991)
Bouvardia ternifolia (Cav.) Schldl.	Callus	Root or leaf tissue	Shoot regeration. Shoots rooted	—	Fernandez & De Jimenez (1982)
Bouvardia ternifolia	Protoplast	Suspension (ex root or leaf callus)	Microcalli. Shoot regeneration. Rooted plantlets	—	Fernandez & De Jimenez (1982)
* *Gardenia augusta* (L.) Merrill. = *G. jasminoides*	Shoot	Shoot apices & nodal segs. ex *i.v.* shoots	Shoot proliferation	Y	Berrios & Economou (1991)
Gardenia augusta	Shoot	Shoot tips (10-15 mm)	Shoot proliferation. Rooted plants	YY	Economou & Spanoudaki (1985)
Gardenia augusta	Shoot	Shoot tips ex 2 yr-old plant (1–1.5 cm)	Propagated using basal shoot mass. Rooted plants	YY	Economou & Spanoudaki (1986)
Mitragyna parvifolia (Roxb.) Korth.	Shoot	Shoot tips (40 yr.-old tree)	Multiple shoots. Rooted	YY	Roy *et al.* (1988)

Rutaceae

Species name	Type of Culture	Source of explant	Results		References
Correa decumbens F.v.M.	Direct rooting	Axillary or adventitious shoots	Studied conditions for rooting. 95% shoots rooted	—	Williams *et al.* (1985)
Eriostemon australasius Pers.	Shoot	Apical & axillary buds	Shoot multiplication. Shoots elongated & rooted	YY	Plummer & De Fossard (1982)

Species name	Type of Culture	Source of explant	Results		References
Scrophulariaceae					
Angelonia salicariefolia Humb. & Bonpl.	Single node	Nodal explants	Shoots which were rooted later	YY	Datta & Datta (1984)
Leucophyllum candidum 'Silver Cloud' (xerophyte)	Single node?	Nodes 1—3 cm	Shoot growth	Y	Closs & Peffley (1988)
Penstemon serrulatus Menz.	Shoot/Node	Seedling shoot tips & nodal sections	Multiple shoots. Rooted	YY	Wysokinska (1993)
Solanaceae					
Datura stramonium L. (Thorn apple)	Embryo	Immature zygotic embryos	Seedling growth	Y	Sanders & Burkholder (1948)
Datura stramonium	Embryo	Young embryos or proembryos	Viable seedlings, or shoots which were rooted	Y	Van Overbeek *et al.* (1941)
Datura stramonium	Embryo	Embryos (0.15–0.2 mm)	Embryo growth; viable seedlings	Y	Van Overbeek *et al.* (1942)
Datura stramonium	Embryo/Direct	Seed embryos	Embryo growth: adventive embryos	Y	Sanders (1950)
Datura stramonium	Root	Root tips	Isolated root culture	—	Bonner (1940b)
Lycium barbarum L. (Duke of Argyll's tea tree)	Direct/Callus	Leaves of *in vitro* plants	Adv. shoots. Rooted plants	—	Ratushnyak *et al.* (1990)
❖ *Nicotiana glauca* Graham.	Direct	Stem sections	Adventitious shoots. Shoots rooted	YY	Smith & Murashige (1970)
Nicotiana glauca	Direct	Isolated root cultures	Adventitious shoots	Y	Zelcer *et al.* (1983)
Nicotiana glauca	Meristem	Apical domes ex *in vitro* plants	Single rooted shoots	Y	Smith & Murashige (1970)
Nicotiana glauca × *N. langsdorffii*	Callus	Stem pith	Shoots & roots	—	Cheng & Smith (1973)
Styraceae					
Halesia tetraptera Ellis. = *H. carolina* (Snowdrop tree)	Shoot	Shoot tips	Axillary shoot proliferation. Rooting *extra vitrum*	YY	Brand *et al.* (1985; 1986)
Halesia tetraptera	Shoot	Shoot tips	Shoot proliferation	Y	Brand (1993)
Theaceae					
Camellia saluenensis × *C. japonica* cv. 'Debbie'	Callus	Internodal stem segments	Shoot formation & proliferation	—	Tosca *et al.* (1992)
* *Camellia japonica* L.	Direct	Cotyledon segments	Somatic embryo, plants	—	Kato (1989)
Camellia japonica	Direct & Callus	Immature zygotic embryo tissue	Direct & indirect embryogen. Plantlets	—	Vieitez & Barciela (1990)
Camellia japonica 'Alba Plena'	Direct embryogen.	*In vitro* plantlets regen. ex juv. tiss.	Plantlets regen. from germinated embryos	Y	Vieitez *et al.* (1991)
Camellia japonica var. 'Purple Dawn'	Shoot	Mature shoot tip or node	Shoot multiplication when *i.v.* nodes subcultured	Y	Carlisi & Torres (1986)
Camellia japonica	Shoot	Shoot tips ex 5 month-old plants	Shoot proliferation. 90% shoots rooted	YY	Samartin *et al.* (1984; 1986)
Camellia japonica [seedlings] & 'Alba Plena'	Shoot	Shoot tips and/or nodal segments	Shoot multiplication. Shoots rooted in dark	YY	Samartin (1989)
Camellia japonica 'Alba Plena' (50yr.-old tree)	Shoot	Apex & node segs. of *i.v.* shoots	Multiple shoots. Rooted	YY	Vieitez *et al.* (1989)
Camellia japonica 'Alba Plena'	Shoot	Axillary buds ex seedling	Shoot multiplication, shoots rooted	YY	Vieitez *et al.* (1991)
Camellia japonica 'Alba Plena'	Shoot & Node	Shoot tips or nodes	Ax. shoot proliferation. Rooting studied	YY	Vieitez *et al.* (1989)
Camellia reticulata Lindl. cv. 'Mouchang'	Callus	Cotyl. sects. & embryonic axis ex seeds	Indirect somatic embryogenesis	—	Plata & Vieitez (1990)
Camellia reticulata cv. 'Captain Rawes'	Callus	Leaf sections ex *in vitro* culture	Shoot formation & multiplication. Rooted poorly.	—	San-Jose & Vieitez (1992)
Camellia reticulata cv. 'Mouchang'	Direct	Cotyl. sects. & embryonic axis ex seeds	Primary & secondary embryo formation. Germination	Y	Plata & Vieitez (1990)
Camellia reticulata cv. 'Captain Rawes'	Shoot	*In vitro* shoot tips or nodes	Shoots multiplied and rooted	YY	San-Jose & Vieitez (1992)
Camellia reticulata cv. 'Captain Rawes'	Shoots & nodes	Shoot tips & nodal sections	Shoot proliferation, shoots rooted	YY	San-Jose *et al.* (1991)
Camellia saluenensis × *C. japonica* cv. 'Debbie'	Shoot	*In vitro* shoots	Shoot proliferation (studied opt. PGRs)	Y	Beretta & Eccher (1987)

Table 177. Media and growth regulators used at Stage I of *Eucalyptus* shoot cultures.

Species	Medium ‡	Growth regulators mg/l	Reference
E. marginata	**MS†**	0.47 NAA + 0.56 BAP	McComb and Bennett (1982)
E. macarthurii *E. smithii* *E. saligna* *E. macarthii* × *E. grandis*	**MS**	0.1 BAP	Le Roux and Van Staden (1991)
E. grandis	5	1 NAA + 1 BAP	Lakshmi Sita and Shobha Rani (1985)
E. grandis	**MS**	0.05 NAA + 0.5 BAP	Warrag et al.(1989)
E. tereticornis	**MS**	0.2 IAA + 1 NAA + 1.0 BAP	Rao (1988)
E. tereticornis	4	0.1 NAA + 0.5 BAP	Das and Mitra (1990)
E. sideroxylon	3	0.09–0.19 NAA + 0.45–0.9 BAP	Burger (1987)
M. citriodora	**MS**	0.2 kin + 0.5 BAP	Gupta and Mascarenhas (1987)
E. camaldulensis *E. globulus* *E. terreticornis* *E. torelliana*	1	0.2 kin + 0.3 BAP	Gupta and Mascarenhas (1987)

† But omitted glycine.

‡ Numbers refer to the media listed in Table 176.

Media. Although more complex media have been used (de Fossard *et al.* 1978; de Fossard, 1981), cultures can be satisfactorily initiated and shoot proliferation induced on media containing **MS** or ½**MS** salts. In the examples of successful formulations given in Table 176, only that of **Das and Mitra (1990)** has a ratio of inorganic ions which differs from **MS**. In other experiments, just the organic components of **MS** medium have been varied. McComb and Bennett (1982) found that they could omit glycine from **MS** medium.

Culture initiation. Explants are liable to release phenolic substances when first inoculated onto a medium. Several workers have found that the presence of soluble PVP (0.5–1 g/l M.W. 40 000–360 000) solves this problem. Newly initiated cultures are also often kept in the dark for 5 days before being placed in the light.

Examples of the media and growth regulators which have been employed for culture initiation are given in Table 177. Media are usually solidified with agar at this stage. Cultures have been incubated at 25–28°C (sometimes with a night temperature of 20–25°C) in a 16 h photoperiod (20–30 μmol m^{-2} s^{-1}).

Shoot multiplication and elongation. Satisfactory shoot growth usually takes place during shoot multiplication and only in some reports has a separate elongation stage been necessary (Table 178). Media are often gelled

with agar, but growth of *E. grandis* cultures was better, and there was no hyperhydricity, if 2 g/l Gelrite was added to the medium instead (Le Roux and Van Staden, 1991). The formation and growth of axillary shoots in some *Eucalyptus* species is rapid on a shaken liquid medium (Gupta and Mascarenhas, 1987).

Compared to cultures initiated from seedling material, those started from mature explants often have a low initial rate of shoot multiplication, and some may not start to multiply until they have been subcultured for 6–10 months (McComb and Bennett, 1982).

Rooting

Shoots can be rooted *in vitro* by culture on an agar– or Gelrite–gelled medium which has a low concentration of macronutrients, such as ¼–½MS (½MS is Medium **2** in Table 176), **WPM**, **White(1954)**, or **Knop (1965)**. Media are supplemented with 20 g/l sucrose and an auxin, typically 0.5–5 mg/l IBA.

Root formation is increased if shoots are pre–incubated in the dark for 3–10 days, before being placed in the light (Rao, 1988; Das and Mitra, 1990). Some workers have obtained improved rooting by placing shoots into liquid medium containing auxin, and keeping them in the dark for 3–4 days during root induction. Shoots are then incubated in the light on a semi–solid medium without auxin, often on one containing 2.5 g/l activated charcoal. Strong plantlets with well developed roots may be obtained if shoots are finally transferred to a liquid medium without charcoal for 2–3 weeks before acclimatization (Mascarenhas *et al.*, 1982; Gupta *et al.*, 1983; Rao, 1988). Le Roux and Van Staden (1991) kept shoots in light of a low photon fluence (5 μmol m^{-2} s^{-1}) during root formation.

Roots are produced on only a few of the shoots obtained from early subcultures of mature plant material. The proportion rooted rises however, sometimes quite sharply, after several subcultures. Shoots from cultures initiated from 20 year–old trees did not root at all until the fourth subculture (when 35–40% rooted) but at the fifth and subsequent passages 45–50% rooted (Gupta *et al.* 1981). Sometimes cultures may have to be continued for 10–15 months before satisfactory rooting occurs (McComb and Bennett, 1982).

Salicaceae

Populus spp.   (Poplar, Cottonwood)

Trees in the genus *Populus* are probably the fastest growing native trees of the Northern hemisphere. Some species are used in shelter belts and other species (and interspecific hybrids) are grown for timber, and for the manufacture of paper pulp and matches. Most poplars

Table 178. Media and growth regulators used for shoot proliferation and shoot elongation in *Eucalyptus*. Where an elongation stage is not indicated, sufficient shoot elongation occurred on the Stage II medium.

Species	Stage	Medium §	Growth regulators (mg/l)	Reference
E. marginata	II	MS†	0.47 NAA + 0.56 BAP	McComb and Bennett (1982)
E. macarthurii *E. smithii* *E. saligna* *E. macarthii* × *E. grandis*	II	5	0.01 NAA + 0.2 BAP	Le Roux and Van Staden (1991)
E. grandis	II	5	1 NAA + 1 BAP	Lakshmi Sita and Shobha Rani (1985)
	IIIa (elong.)	5	1 GA$_3$	
E. grandis	II	MS	0.6 BAP	Warrag *et al.*(1989)
	IIIa (elong.)	MS	2.5 IAA + 1 zeatin	
E. tereticornis	II	MS	0.02 NAA + 0.1–2 BAP	Rao (1988)
E. tereticornis	II	4	0.1 NAA + 0.5 BAP	Das and Mitra (1990)
	IIIa (elong)	4‡	0.01 NAA + 0.1 BAP + 1 GA$_3$	
E. sideroxylon	II	3	0.09–0.19 NAA + 0.45–0.9 BAP	Burger (1987)
M. citriodora	II	MS	0.2 kin + 0.5 BAP	Gupta and Mascarenhas (1987)
E. camaldulensis *E. globulus* *E. terreticornis* *E. torelliana*	II	1	0.2 kin + 0.5 BAP	Gupta and Mascarenhas (1987)
	IIIa (elong.)	1 (liquid)	0.05 kin + 0.1 BAP	

    †   But omitted glycine.

    ‡   The addition of 2 g/l activated charcoal was beneficial

    §   Numbers refer to the media listed in Table 176.

can be propagated by grafting, or from stem or root cuttings, but some may be produced more rapidly and cheaply using micropropagation.

Shoot culture

Cultures have been initiated with shoot tips and lateral buds from both leafed and dormant shoots. Sections of stem bearing a node have often been used. Newly elongated shoots from which the leaves and terminal shoots have been removed can also be used as explants. Adventitious shoots, which are readily produced on poplar explants directly (see below) or indirectly from callus, can also be used to initiate shoot cultures (Thompson and Gordon, 1977; Coleman and Ernst, 1990).

Media. A surprisingly wide range of media has been used for the shoot culture of *Populus* (Table 179). Welander *et al.* (1989a) compared several media and found that medium **4** was best for culture initiation of *Populus* × *wilsocarpa*, but that shoot multiplication and elongation were best carried out on **WPM** medium. Chun *et al.* (1986) initiated cultures on a medium described by

Gresshoff and Doy (1972a,b), but transferred sections of axillary shoots to **MS** for shoot proliferation. In most other cases the same medium has been used at Stage I and Stage II. Species in which shoot proliferation has been obtained using the other media[‡] listed in Table 179, have been:

P. alba × *P. grandidentata*	1[‡]	Chun *et al.* (1986)
P. alba × *P. grandidentata*	6	Son and Hall (1990a,b)
P. ciliata	1	Mehra and Cheema (1980b)
P. deltoides	7	Coleman and Ernst (1990)
P. flevo *P. nigra* *P. yunnanensis*	2	Whitehead and Giles (1976
P. tremula	3	Nadel *et al.* (1992)
P. trichocarpa	6	Nadel *et al.* (1992)
P. tremuloides	5	Garton and Moses (1986)
P. tristis × *P. balsamifera*	8	Thompson and Gordon (1977)
P. × *wilsocarpa*	5	Welander *et al.* (1989a)

Stage II cultures have nearly always been conducted on media gelled with agar, or with Gelrite (McCown and

Table 179. Media which have been used for the culture of *Populus*. (see text).•
Ingredients from which macronutrients can be prepared are given in the Appendix.

Components	MS	Whitehead & Giles (1977)	½MS	Welander *et al.* (1989)	Lloyd & McCown (1981) WPM	Nadel *et al.* (1992) †	Driver and Kuniyuki (1984) DKW ‡	Thompson and Gordon (1977)	Coleman & Ernst (1989) WNA
	①	②	③	④	⑤	⑥	⑦	⑧	⑨
Macronutrients (meq/l)									
NO_3^-	39.4	39.4	19.7	27.99	9.7	13.30	34.3	39.4	37.55
PO_4^{3-}	3.74	3.74	1.87	8.81	3.74	3.30	5.71	7.44	3.75
SO_4^{2-}	3.0	3.0	1.5	8.5	14.36	0.14	23.91	3.0	14.36
Cl^-	5.98	5.98	2.99	2.25	1.3	0.44	2.00	5.98	1.3
K^+	20.04	20.04	10.02	30.93	12.6	6.48	19.81	20.04	12.6
Ca^{2+}	5.98	5.98	2.99	2.25	6.01	8.12	18.60	5.98	18.24
Na^+	—	—	—	—	—	—	—	1.23	—
Mg^{2+}	3.0	3.0	1.5	1.5	3.0	0.14	6.00	3.0	3.0
NH_4^+	20.61	20.61	10.30	7.0	4.99	6.25	17.70	20.61	20.61
Microelements mg/l									
$MnSO_4.4H_2O$	22.3	22.3	11.2	22.3	29.4	6.6	44.2	22.3	29.4
$ZnSO_4.7H_2O$	8.6	8.6	4.3	8.6	8.6	1.5	—	8.6	8.6
$Zn(NO_3)_2.6H_2O$	—	—	—	—	—	—	17.0	—	—
H_3BO_3	6.2	6.2	3.1	6.2	6.2	1.5	4.8	6.2	6.2
KI	0.83	0.83	0.42	0.83	—	0.4	0.83	0.83	—
$CuSO_4.5H_2O$	0.025	0.025	0.012	0.025	0.25	0.13	0.25	0.025	0.25
$Na_2MoO_4.2H_2O$	0.25	0.25	0.12	0.25	0.25	0.13	0.39	0.25	0.25
$CoCl_2.6H_2O$	0.025	0.025	0.012	0.025	—	0.13	—	0.025	—
$NiSO_4.6H_2O$	—	—	—	—	—	—	0.005	—	—
NaFeEDTA (mM)	0.1	0.15	0.05	0.1	0.1	0.05	0.12	0.1	0.1
Vitamins (mg/l)									
myo–Inositol	100	100	50	100	100	50	10	100	100
Thiamine HCl	0.1	0.1	0.05	1.0	1.0	5.0	2.0	0.4	1.0
Nicotinic acid	0.5	0.5	0.25	0.5	0.5	0.5	1.0	—	0.5
Pyridoxine HCl	0.5	0.1	0.25	0.5	0.5	0.5	—	—	0.5
Biotin	—	—	—	—	—	1.0	—	—	—
Amino acids (mg/l)									
Glycine	2.0	—	1.0	2.0	2.0	—	2.0	—	2.0
Lysine	—	100.0	—	—	—	—	—	—	—
Casein hydrolysate	—	—	—	—	—	—	—	—	500
Other additives (g/l)									
MES buffer	—	—	—	—	—	0.5	—	—	—
Adenine sulphate (.2H₂O)	—	0.02	—	—	—	—	—	0.08	—
Sucrose (g/l)	30	20	?	20	30	?	30	20	30

† The authors state that they used ½ **Gresshoff and Doy (1974)** medium, but that paper describes two media, which are modifications of **Gresshoff and Doy (1972a,b) DBM1** and **DBM2**. We think that the second of these was used as the basis of the present medium, because a comment is made about the absence (low concentration?) of chloride ions. Medium **6** also contained 3 mM Ca gluconate.

‡ See the notes on this medium given at the foot of Table 201, page 1030.

Table 180. Growth regulators added to media during the initiation and multiplication stages of *Populus* shoot cultures.

References	Growth regulators at	
	Stage I (mg/l)	Stage II (mg/l)
Garton and Moses 1986	0.3 BAP	0.3 BAP
Coleman and Ernst (1990)	0.25 zeatin†	0.25 zeatin
Chun and Hall (1986) Chun *et al.* (1986)	0.2 BAP	0.2 BAP
Mehra and Cheema (1980b)	0.2 BAP + 0.02 IBA	0.2 BAP + 0.02 IBA
Thompson and Gordon (1977)	0.3 BAP + 0.01 IAA‡	0.3 BAP + 0.01 IAA‡
Whitehead and Giles (1976)	0.2 BAP‡	0.1 BAP + 0.02 NAA‡
Welander *et al.* (1989a)	0.5 BAP	0.1 BAP + 0.001 NAA

† Optimum concentration depended on the genotype of *P. deltoides*

‡ Plus adenine sulphate (see Table 179).

McCown, 1987; Coleman and Ernst, 1990). The rate of growth and shoot proliferation of a *Populus* hybrid was greater when cultures were grown on liquid **WPM** medium, although shoots soon began to show symptoms of hyperhydricity, especially if the medium was agitated (Chun *et al.*, 1986).

The presence of 3 mM calcium gluconate and MES buffer in Medium **6**, helped to prevent the leaf yellowing and shoot tip necrosis which otherwise occurred (Nadel *et al.*, 1992).

Growth regulators. Shoot proliferation has often been obtained by supplementing the medium with only a cytokinin growth regulator, although a low concentration of auxin has been added by some workers to assist shoot elongation. Some examples of the regulants used at Stages I and II are shown in Table 180.

Shoot elongation is usually unnecessary where shoots have been cultured with a low concentration of cytokinin, but Welander *et al.* (1989a) placed shoots onto **WPM** medium with 1 mg/l GA$_3$ for 3–4 weeks before they were rooted *extra vitrum*.

Rooting

As with many other genera of dicotyledonous trees, shoots of *Populus* can be rooted *extra vitrum*, without auxin treatment, if inserted into an open 'compost' and

Table 181. Media and growth regulators used for *in vitro* rooting of *Populus* shoots.
Numbered media are those referred to in Table 179.

Species	Medium	Regulants (mg/l)	References
P. tristis × *P. balsamifera*	1	0.01 IBA	Thompson and Gordon (1977)
P. flevo *P. nigra* *P. yunnanensis*	2	0.01 BAP + 0.01 NAA	Whitehead and Giles (1977)
P. deltoides	9	1 IBA	Coleman and Ernst (1989)
P. euramericana	½WS‡	0.2 NAA	Chalupa (1974)

‡ ½**Wolter and Skoog (1966)** salts (prepared from the macronutrients shown in the Appendix, plus 6.65 mg/l MnSO$_4$.4H$_2$O, 2.85 mg/l ZnSO$_4$.7H$_2$O, 1.6 mg/l H$_3$BO$_3$, 0.8 mg/l KI, 1 mM NaFeEDTA) and only 2 g/l sucrose.

Species name	Type of Culture	Source of explant	Results		References
Quercus robur	Shoot	Juvenile & rejuvenated (epicormic) shoot tips	Multiple shoots, rooted	Y	Vermeer *et al.* (1991)
Quercus robur	Shoot	Embryonic axes	Multiple shoots ex cotyledonary node. Shoots rooted	YY	Vieitez *et al.* (1985)
Quercus robur	Shoot	Sdlg. or presoaked adult shoot tips	Axillary shoot prolif. 60% adult source shoots rooted	YY	Vieitez *et al.* (1985)
Quercus rubra L. (Red oak)	Callus	Male catkins	Callus degenerated after 5 months. No embryoids	—	Gingas (1991)
Quercus rubra	Callus	Seedling internode	Somatic embryogenesis	—	Seckinger *et al.* (1979)
Quercus rubra	Shoot	Juvenile (& rejuvenated) shoots	Shoot growth during at least 6 subcults.	—	Rancillac *et al.* (1991)
Quercus shumardii Buckl. (Shumard oak)	Node	Node ex etiolated plant	Shoot proliferation. Shoots rooted	YY	Bennett & Davies (1984 b)
Quercus shumardii	Shoot	Seedling node	Axillary shoot proliferation. 73% rooting	YY	Bennett & Davies (1986)
Quercus shumardii	Shoot	Single node stem sections	Multiple shoots. Rooted plants	YY	Bennett (1987)
Quercus suber L. (Cork oak)	Node & shoot	Apical/nodal segs. ex seedlgs or adult trees	Shoot multiplication & rooting	YY	Mancanera & Pardos (1990)
Quercus suber	Shoot/Direct	Embryonic axis without cotyledons	Many axillary & adv. buds. Rooted plants	Y	Bellarosa (1988)
Quercus suber	Shoot	Embryonic axes from seeds	Shoots multiplied & subcultured. Rooted plants	YY	Deidda *et al.* (1988)
Quercus suber	Shoot	Axill. buds of young plant	Elongation of axillary shoots	Y	Pardos (1981)
Quercus virginiana Mill. (Live oak)	Shoot	Single node stem sections	Multiple shoots. Rooted plants	YY	Bennett (1987)

Hamamelidaceae

Species name	Type of Culture	Source of explant	Results		References
❖ *Liquidambar styraciflua* L., vars. 'Moraine', 'Variegata'	Direct	Mature-phase petioles, leaves	Adv. shoots. Rooted plants	Y	Brand & Lineberger (1988)
Liquidambar styraciflua (American sweet gum)	Callus/Suspension	Hypocoyl sections	Adv. shoots and embryogenesis. Plantlets from embryos	—	Sommer & Brown (1980)
Liquidambar styraciflua 'Variegata'	Direct	Leaf sections	Multiple shoots, rooted	Y	Brand & Lineberger (1991)
Liquidambar styraciflua	Direct rooting	*In vitro* shoots	Shoots rooted better on paper rafts than on agar	—	Lee *et al.* (1986)
Liquidambar styraciflua	Direct/Shoot	Seedling hypocotyls	Adv. shoots multiplied by shoot culture and rooted *i.v.*	Y	Sommer (1983)
Liquidambar styraciflua	Shoot	Lat. bud ex seedlings & mature plants	Multiple shoots. Rooted plants	YY	Sutter & Barker (1984)
Liquidambar styraciflua	Shoot	Shoot tips (1–1.5 cm) ex mat. trees	Shoot multiplication. Shoots rooted *in vitro*	YY	Sutter & Barker (1985)

Hippocastanaceae

Species name	Type of Culture	Source of explant	Results		References
* *Aesculus hippocastanum* L. (Horse chestnut)	Callus	Cotyledon fragments ex ripe seeds	Embryogenesis. Embryo germination after long cold trmt.	—	Profumo *et al.* (1991)
Aesculus hippocastanum	Direct/Callus	Somatic zygotic embryos	Adventive embryos. Poor regen. to plantlets	—	Kiss *et al.* (1992)
Aesculus hippocastanum	Embryogenic callus	Immature embryos	Somatic embryos. Germinated. Plants	—	Radojevic (1988)
Aesculus hippocastanum	Meristem/Shoot	Adult/juv. shoots & dormant buds	Shoot rosettes. Multiple shoots, rooted	YY	Radojevic *et al.* (1987)

Juglandaceae — See Fruit and Nuts Table.

Leguminosae

Species name	Type of Culture	Source of explant	Results		References
Acacia albida	Direct/Shoot tip	Cotyledon with stem piece	Shoot formation & proliferation. Rooted	Y	Duhoux & Davies (1985)
Acacia auriculiformis Cunn. ex Benth. (Black wattle)	Shoot	Axillary buds ex *in vitro* seedlings	Multiple shoots	Y	Mittal *et al.* (1989)
Acacia koa A.Gray	Callus	Seedling shoot tip	Shoots regenerated & rooted	—	Skolmen & Mapes (1976 ; 1978)
Acacia melanoxylon R.Br. (Blackwood Acacia)	Embryo	Embryos from seeds	Germination, seedlings. Plants	Y	Jones (1986)
Albizia amara Boivin. (Indian walnut)	Direct	Sdlg., root, hypocotyl, & cotyledon	Adventitious shoots, rooted	Y	Tomar & Gupta (1986)
Albizia amara	Direct	Seedling hypocotyls	Shoot formation. Plants	YY	Tomar & Gupta (1988b)
Albizia falcataria (L.) Fosb.	Direct/Callus	Cotyledon segs. ex *in vitro* seedlings	Multiple shoots. Rooted	Y	Kumar Sinha & Mallick (1993)

Species name	Type of Culture	Source of explant	Results		References
Albizia lebbeck (L.) Benth.	Callus	Stem or petiole sects. ex mat. trees	Multiple shoots. Shoots rooted	—	Gharyal & Maheshwari (1990)
Albizia lebbeck	Callus	Seedling, hypocot., cotyl., root, rachis, leaf	Adv. shoots or embryogenesis. Rooted plants	—	Varghese & Kaur (1991)
Albizia lebbeck	Callus/Direct	Roots, cotyledons, leaflets	Direct & indirect shoots. Shoots rooted	—	Gharyal & Maheshwari (1983)
Albizia lebbeck	Direct embryogen.	Seedling hypocotyl	Embryoids gave shoots only. Shoots rooted	—	Gharyal & Maheshwari (1981)
Albizia lebbeck	Meristem	Meristem tip	Successful plant production	Y	Gharyal & Maheshwari (1983)
Albizia lebbek	Direct/Callus	Sdlg., hypocotyl, root & cotyledon	Adventitious shoots. Rooted plantlets	—	Upadhyaya & Chandra (1983)
Albizia lucida	Direct	Sdlg., root, hypocotyl & cotyledon	Adventitious shoots, rooted	Y	Tomar & Gupta (1986)
Albizia lucida	Direct	Seedling hypocotyls	Shoot formation. Plants	YY	Tomar & Gupta (1988b)
Albizia odoratissima	Shoot	Shoot tips	Multiple shoots. Rooted	YY	Phukan & Mitra (1982)
Albizia procera (Roxb.) Benth.	Shoot	Shoot tips of mature tree	Multiple shoots. Rooted	YY	Roy & Datta (1985)
Albizia richardiana King	Direct	Sdlg., root, hypocotyl & cotyledon	Adventitious shoots, rooted	Y	Tomar & Gupta (1986)
Albizia richardiana	Direct	Seedling hypocotyls	Shoot formation. Plants	YY	Tomar & Gupta (1988b)
Albizia richardiana	Direct/Callus	Seedling hypocotyls	Adventitious shoot formation. Rooted	—	Tomar & Gupta (1988a)
Albizia richardiana	Morphogenic callus	Seedling hypocotyls	Somatic embryos & adventitious shoots. Plants	—	Tomar & Gupta (1988a)
Bauhinia purpurea L.	Callus	Stem cuttings	Shoots &/or roots. Shoots rooted	—	Kumar (1992)
Bauhinia variegata L. (Orchid tree)	Node	Nodes ex mature trees	Shoot proliferation. Shoots rooted	YY	Mathur & Mukunthakumar (1992)
Caesalpinia pulcherrima (L.) SW. (Flamboyant tree)	Node	Nodes	Multiple shoots. Rooted	YY	Rahman *et al.* (1993)
Cassia fistula L. (Pudding–pipe tree)	Callus	Cotyledon segments	Indirect adventitious shoots	—	Lee & Rao (1980)
Cassia fistula	Callus	Stem or petiole sections ex mature trees	Multiple shoots. Shoots rooted	—	Gharyal & Maheshwari (1990)
Cercis canadensis L. (Redbud)	Direct	Zygotic embryos 96–110d post anthesis	Somatic embryos. One plant obtained	—	Trigiano *et al.* (1988)
Cercis canadensis	Direct embryogen.	Immature zygotic embryos	Embryos & adventitious roots. Embryos germinated	Y	Geneve & Kester (1990)
Cercis canadensis	Shoot	Single node	Shoot multiplication	Y	Bennett & Davies (1985)
Cercis canadensis var 'mexicana'	Shoot	Shoot tips	Multiple shoots. Rooted plants	YY	Bennett (1987)
Cercis canadensis var. alba	Shoot	2–node sections, spring flush mature plants	Multiplication. Rooted plants	Y	Yusnita *et al.* (1990a)
Crotalaria burhia	Callus/Direct	Stem pieces	Adventitious shoots	—	Raj Bhansali *et al.* (1978)
Crotalaria juncea L.	Callus	Seedling stem & leaf pieces	Adventitious shoots: embryogenesis from leaf callus	—	Ramawat *et al.* (1977)
Dalbergia latifolia Roxb. (East India rosewood)	Callus	Shoots from 5 year-old trees	Adventitious shoots. Rooted. Plants	—	Lakshmi Sita *et al.* (1986)
Dalbergia latifolia	Callus	Shoot tips/segments ex 50 yr–old trees	Shoots regenerated. Rooted	—	Ravishankar Rai & J. Chandra (1988)
Dalbergia latifolia	Callus	Shoot & leaf segments	Adventitious shoots, rooted plants	—	Sankara Rao *et al.* (1985)
Dalbergia latifolia	Callus	Shoots from 6 year-old plants	Adventitious buds, shoots. Rooted	—	Sankara Rao (1986)
Dalbergia latifolia	Direct	Shoot & root segs. (5 yr–old tree)	Adventitious shoots, rooted as plantlets	Y	Mascarenhas *et al.* (1982a)
Dalbergia sissoo Roxb. ex DC. (Indian teakwood)	Callus	Nodal tissue	Adventitious shoots which were rooted	—	Datta *et al.* (1983)
Dalbergia sissoo	Callus	Callus ex base of sht. cult. clumps	Adventitious shoots. Rooted plants	—	Mukhopadhyay & Bhojwani (1986)
Dalbergia sissoo	Direct/Callus	Seedling root pieces (1 cm)	Adventitious shoots. Rooted as plantlets	—	Mukhopadhyay & Mohan Ram (1981)
Dalbergia sissoo	Direct/Callus	Seedling hypocotyl sections (1 cm)	Adventitious shoots (& on isolated callus). Rooted	Y	Sharma & Chandra (1988)
Dalbergia sissoo	Node	Single nodes ex young 12–yr–old shoots	Single shoots divided up, rooted *in vitro*	Y	Mukhopadhyay & Bhojwani (1986)

	Species name	Type of Culture	Source of explant	Results		References
	Gymnocladus dioicus (L.) K.Koch (Kentucky coffee tree)	Shoot	Sdlg. & mature 3-node stem sects.	Multiple shoots. Only sdlg. shoots elongated & rooted	Y	Geneve et al. (1990)
	Gymnocladus dioicus	Shoot	Axillary buds & shoot tips	Nodular tissue; shoots formed and later rooted	Y	Smith & Obeidy (1991)
	Leucaena leucocephala (Lam.) De Wit	Shoot	Single node ex shoot of mature tree	Shoot proliferation. Shoots rooted in vitro	YY	Goyal et al. (1985)
	Parkinsonia aculeata L. (Jerusalem thorn)	Node	Nodes ex mature trees	Shoot proliferation. Shoots rooted	YY	Mathur & Mukunthakumar (1992)
	Prosopis alba Griseb. Clone B2V50	Shoot	Axillary buds	Shoot mult. depended on N source. Shoot tip necrosis	—	Green et al. (1990)
	Prosopis juliflora (Sw.) D.C. Clones 8001, 8004	Single node	Deleafed single nodes	Shoot growth. Some basal callus	—	Wainwright & England (1987)
	Prosopis tamarugo Phil.	Callus & shoot	Various explants ex in vitro seedlings	Multiple axillary &/or adventitious shoots. Rooted	Y	Nandwani & Ramawat (1992)
*	Robinia pseudoacacia L. (Black locust)	Direct	Immature leaf & cotyl. sections	Shoot formation followed by rooting	Y	Arrillaga & Merkle (1993)
	Robinia pseudoacacia	Shoot	Shoot segments	Multiple shoots. Shoots rooted	YY	Chalupa (1981 a, 1983)
	Senna siamea (Lam.) Irwin & Barn. = Cassia siamea	Callus	Stem or petiole sections ex mature trees	Multiple shoots. Shoots rooted	—	Gharyal & Maheshwari (1990)
	Sesbania aculeata (Poir.) (Prickly sesban)	Direct	Seedling hypocotyl sections	Multiple shoots. Direct rooting	YY	Bansal & Pandey (1993)
	Sesbania bispinosa (Jacq.) W.Wight	Direct	Seedling hypocotyls & cotyledons	Adventitious shoots. Rooted plants	Y	Kapoor & Gupta (1986)
	Sesbania grandiflora (L.) Poir.	Direct	Seedling hypocotyls & cotyledons	Adventitious shoots. Rooted plants	Y	Khattar & Mohan Ram (1983)
	Sesbania sesban	Direct	Hypocotyl segments	Direct shoot regeneration	Y	Khattar & Mohan Ram (1982)
	Sophora secundiflora (Ort.) Lag ex DC. (Texas Mountain Laurel)	Shoot	Shoot tips & single node sections	Multiple shoots. Rooted (20%) plants	Y	Froberg (1986)

Loranthaceae

	Species name	Type of Culture	Source of explant	Results		References
	Nuytsia floribunda (Labill.) R.Br. ex G.Don.	Callus	Seed embryos	Embryoids, roots, & shoots	—	Nag & Johri (1969 ; 1976)

Magnoliaceae

	Species name	Type of Culture	Source of explant	Results		References
	Liriodendron chinense × L. tulipifera	Embryogenic callus	Zygotic embryos & endosperm	Somatic embryos. Plantlets	—	Merkle et al. (1993)
	Liriodendron tulipifera L. (Tulip tree)	Callus	Not given	Embryogenesis. Embryoid growth	—	Wetzstein et al. (1986)
	Liriodendron tulipifera	Callus/suspension	Immature embryos	Embryogenesis. Plants transferred to soil	—	Merkles & Sommerh (1986)

Meliaceae

	Species name	Type of Culture	Source of explant	Results		References
	Azadirachta indica A. Juss.	Callus	Decapitated seedlings	Adventitious shoots. Plant regeneration rarely	—	Rangaswamy & Promila (1972)
	Azadirachta indica	Embryo/Callus	Adult embryos	Seedlings or callus & then adventitious shoots	Y	Rangaswamy & Promila (1972)

Moraceae

	Species name	Type of Culture	Source of explant	Results		References
	Maclura pomifera (Raf.) Schneid (Osage orange)	Shoot	Shoot tips & nodal sections	Shoot prolif. Some callus. Plants	Y	King & Morehart (1988).

Myrtaceae

	Species name	Type of Culture	Source of explant	Results		References
	Eucalyptus bridgesiana R.Bak. (Apple box)	Node & Callus	Node of 5-year-old tree	Axillary shoot formation. Semi-differentiated callus	Y	Durand-Cresswell & Nitsch (1977)
	Eucalyptus camaldulensis Dehnh. (River red gum)	Calloid	Shoot tips	Tissue subcultured. Plant regeneration	YY	Boxus et al. (1991)
	Eucalyptus camaldulensis	Node	Nodes	Shoot development. Direct rooting	Y	Gonçalves (1975)
	Eucalyptus camaldulensis	Shoot	Node of mature tree	Shoot formation, proliferation, & elongation. Rooted	Y	Gupta et al. (1983)
	Eucalyptus camaldulensis	Shoot	Nodal sects. ex seedlings or coppices	Multiple shoots. Rooted plants	YY	Hartney (1982 ; 1983)
	Eucalyptus citriodora Hook. (Lemon-scented gum)	Callus	Cotyledon	Shoot regeneration. Direct rooting	—	Lakshmi–Sita (1979)
	Eucalyptus citriodora	Direct embryogen.	Decoated mature seeds	Plantlets regenerated from germinated embryos	Y	Muralidharan et al. (1989)
	Eucalyptus citriodora	Shoot	Shoot apices	Multiple shoots	Y	Grewal et al. (1980)
	Eucalyptus citriodora	Shoot	Vegetative buds of 20-yr-old trees	Axillary bud proliferation. Direct rooting	YY	Gupta et al. (1981)

Species name	Type of Culture	Source of explant	Results		References
Eucalyptus citriodora	Shoot	Seedling apex	Shoot proliferation. Direct rooting	YY	Gupta et al. (1981)
Eucalyptus citriodora	Shoot	Shoot tips (5mm)	Shoot multiplication	Y	Lakshmi–Sita & Vaid'than (1979)
Eucalyptus citriodora	Shoot	Terminal buds (10–20 yr old tree)	Shoot proliferation & elongation. Direct rooting	YY	Mascarenhas et al. (1982 a,b)
Eucalyptus curtisii	Shoot	Nodal sects. ex seedlings or coppices	Multiple shoots. Rooted plants	YY	Hartney (1982 : 1983)
Eucalyptus dalrympleana Maid. (Mountain gum)	Direct	Node of 5–yr.–old, leaf of adult tree	Direct rooting	Y	Durand–Cresswell & Nitsch (1977)
Eucalyptus ficifolia F. Muell. (Red–flowering gum)	Shoot	eedling node	Multiple bud formation. Direct rooting	YY	De Fossard (1978 : 1981)
Eucalyptus ficifolia	Shoot	Adult or seedling node	Multiple bud formation. Direct rooting	YY	Barker et al. (1977)
Eucalyptus ficifolia	Shoot	Seedling & adult nodes	Multiple shoots. Rooted plants	YY	De Fossard & Bourne (1976)
Eucalyptus ficifolia	Shoot	I.v. shoots from adult trees	Shoot multiplication. Shoots rooted	YY	De Fossard et al. (1978)
Eucalyptus ficifolia	Shoot	Nodal sects. ex seedlings or coppices	Multiple shoots. Rooted plants	YY	Hartney (1983)
Eucalyptus ficifolia	Shoot & Callus	In vitro seedling node	Multiple buds & shoot growth. Direct rooting	Y	De Fossard et al. (1977)
Eucalyptus ficifolia	Shoot & Callus	Adult node	Multiple buds; shoot growth. Shoots root but degenerate	—	De Fossard et al. (1977)
Eucalyptus globulus subsp. bicostata Kirkpat.	Shoot	Nodal sects. ex seedlings or coppices	Multiple shoots. Shoots rooted poorly	Y	Hartney (1982 : 1983)
Eucalyptus globulus (Tasmanian blue gum)	Shoot	Terminal buds (10–20 yr old tree)	Axillary shoot proliferation & elongation. Rooted	YY	Mascarenhas et al. (1982a)
Eucalyptus grandis Hill ex Maid. (Rose gum)	Direct	Node of 4–yr–old tree, & crown leaf of 5–yr–old tree	Direct rooting	Y	Durand–Cresswell & Nitsch (1977)
Eucalyptus grandis	Node	Coppice or seedling node	Good shoot growth. Direct rooting	Y	De Fossard et al. (1977)
Eucalyptus grandis	Node	Nodes	Shoot development. Direct rooting	Y	Gonçalves (1975)
Eucalyptus grandis	Node & Callus	Nodes above node 14, from pretreated nodal stem	Plantlet formation; roots derived via callus	—	Cresswell & Nitsch (1975)
Eucalyptus grandis [3 genetic lines]	Nodular callus	Hypocotyls of young seedlings	Multiple shoots over 3 yrs. Rooted plants	Y	Warrag et al. (1991)
Eucalyptus grandis	Shoot	Nodes	Shoot development. Direct rooting	Y	Gonçalves (1975)
Eucalyptus grandis	Shoot	Nodal sects. ex seedlings or coppices	Multiple shoots. Rooted plants	YY	Hartney (1982 : 1983)
Eucalyptus grandis	Shoot	Nodal segments from 5 yr–old trees	Multiple shoots. Rooted plants	YY	Lakshmi Sita & Shobha Rani (1985)
Eucalyptus grandis	Shoot	Seedlings without roots	Shoot clumps subcultured. Rooted plants	YY	Lubrano (1991)
Eucalyptus grandis	Shoot	Young shoots	Axillary shoot proliferation & elongation. Rooted	YY	Sankara & Venkateswara (1985)
Eucalyptus grandis	Shoot	Nodes ex 5–year–old trees	Multiple shoots. Rooted	YY	Warrag et al. (1989)
Eucalyptus grandis	Shoot & Callus	Nodes above node 14, from pretreated nodal stem	Plantlet formation; roots derived via callus	—	Cresswell & Nitsch (1975)
Eucalyptus gunnii Hook. [4 clones] (Cider gum)	Shoot	Not given	Shoot multiplication	—	Damiano et al. (1987)
Eucalyptus gunnii	Shoot	Nodes from sterile seedlings	Shoots multiplied, elongated in dark. Rooted plants	YY	Lubrano (1988)
Eucalyptus macarthurii Deane & Maid.	Direct	Crown leaf of 5–year–old tree	Root formation	Y	Durand–Cresswell & Nitsch (1977)
Eucalyptus macarthurii	Shoot	Nodal explants ex seedlings & clonal hedges	Shoot proliferation. Rooted shoots to field	YY	Le Roux & Van Staden (1991)
Eucalyptus macarthurii × E. grandis	Shoot	Nodal explants ex seedlings & clonal hedges	Shoot proliferation. Rooted shoots to field	YY	Le Roux & Van Staden (1991)
Eucalyptus marginata Donn. ex Sm.	Callus	Stamens from mature tree	Shoot & plantlet formation from filament–derived callus	—	McComb & Bennett (1982)
Eucalyptus marginata	Shoot	Shoot tips of mature tree	Shoot multiplication. Direct rooting	YY	McComb & Bennett (1982)
Eucalyptus nitens (Deane & Maid.) Maid.	Node & Callus	Node of 5–year–old tree	Axillary shoots. Semi–differentiated callus	—	Durand–Cresswell & Nit' (1977)
Eucalyptus nova–anglica	Direct	Shoot tips & nodal stem	Adventitious bud proliferation; shoot growth. Rooted	YY	Mehra–Palta (1982)

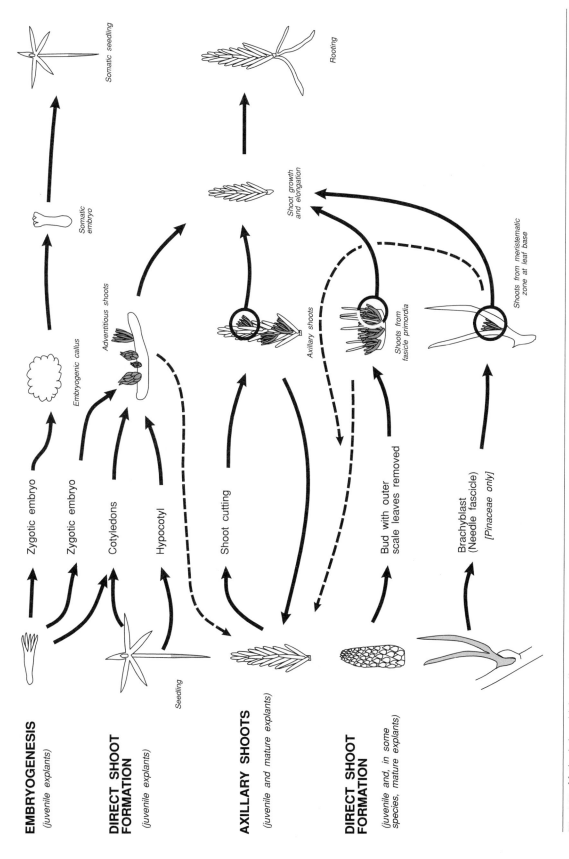

EMBRYOGENESIS
(juvenile explants)

DIRECT SHOOT FORMATION
(juvenile explants)

AXILLARY SHOOTS
(juvenile and mature explants)

DIRECT SHOOT FORMATION
(juvenile and, in some species, mature explants)

Zygotic embryo

Zygotic embryo

Cotyledons

Hypocotyl

Shoot cutting

Bud with outer scale leaves removed

Brachyblast (Needle fascicle)
[Pinaceae only]

Seedling

Somatic seedling

Somatic embryo

Embryogenic callus

Adventitious shoots

Rooting

Shoot growth and elongation

Axillary shoots

Shoots from fascicle primordia

Shoots from meristematic zone at leaf base

Fig.165. Methods by which conifers may be propagated.

Direct shoot formation

Embryo and seedling explants

Shoots can be induced to form directly on the zygotic embryos of conifers and on the organs of young seedlings, especially cotyledons, hypocotyls and shoot apices. When zygotic embryos are used as explants, buds generally arise directly from cotyledons and hypocotyls. In most experiments, expanded seedling cotyledons have yielded more adventitious shoots than whole embryos, hypocotyls, or other seedling tissues, and have consequently become the most widely used explant (Tables 185 and 193). The regenerative capacity of cotyledons has been found to be dependent on their age. Cotyledons from one–day–old *Pinus radiata* seedlings were in the best physiological condition for shoot production (Aitken-Christie *et al.*, 1982), while those from Douglas fir had an optimum age of 2–4 weeks (Wochok and Abo El-Nil, 1977a,b). On the other hand, Cheng (1977) found no influence of age (2 weeks or 2 months old) on the number of shoots produced by the cotyledons of Douglas fir seedlings.

The number of shoots formed by embryo or seedling explants can be greatly influenced by pre–treatment procedures. *Pinus* seeds are often advantageously cold stratified (Smeltzer *et al.*, 1977; Reilly and Washer, 1977) or treated with H_2O_2 to break their dormancy before embryos are excised and cultured (Mehra-Palta *et al.* 1977; Mott and Amerson, 1981). Compared to results from stratified or non–treated seed, a greater proportion of cotyledons of *Pinus taeda* and *P. monticola* produced buds (and there was a greater number of buds per plant) if the embryos from which they were derived had been pre-treated with H_2O_2 for 5–7 days before cotyledon excision (Mott *et al.* 1977a; Mott and Amerson, 1981). *Pinus contorta* embryos produced more buds if they were first cultured in the dark and then moved to high illuminance. There was no such requirement by *Picea sitchensis* embryos (Webb and Street, 1977).

Alternative explants.

Female strobili. Discs cut from immature female strobili of mature *Larix decidua* and *Pinus mugo* trees (near to the junction of the strobilus with the stalk), produced adventitious shoots when incubated on a medium containing BAP (Bonga 1981, 1982c, 1984). However, the frequency of success was low. Buds of *Pseudotsuga menziesii* already determined to become female cones did not revert to vegetative growth *in vitro* (Gupta and Durzan, 1987a).

Brachyblasts. The leaves or needles of Pinaceae are borne on short shoots of limited growth, which are vari-ously described as spurs, needle fascicles, or *brachyblasts*. At the apex of a brachyblast, a dome–shaped meristematic cell cluster replaces a typical apical bud. Culture of brachyblasts, (particularly those newly formed on juvenile plants, or those formed *in vitro*, having needles only 10–15 mm long) on a medium containing cytokinin, can cause one or more buds to be produced. These are usually classed as adventitious shoots although, as they arise from a pre-existing meristematic area, have sometimes been classified as axillary. Procedures for the induction, formation and elongation of brachyblast shoots are very similar to those described above for shoots derived from embryo explants. In some species it has been possible to root brachyblasts before the meristem is released from dormancy. Subsequent shoot elongation results in a rooted plantlet.

Leaf primordia. Adventitious shoots can be induced to form on young leaves excised from buds just as they break into fresh growth from dormancy. In *Picea abies*, it was important to excise leaves with the basal cushion of meristematic tissue below the abscission zone, because many shoots were produced from this region. Most shoots were formed on leaves 3–5 mm in length and their number decreased as leaves aged and grew larger (Jansson and Bornman, 1980, 1981).

Shoot explants. Adventitious shoots can be initiated on excised shoot primordia and on shoot apices (see below).

Media and growth regulators

The composition of media which have been commonly used for conifers is given in Table 184. The macronutrients of several of these formulations are based on the macronutrients of **Gamborg (1966)** and **Schenk and Hildebrandt (1972)**. The ionic concentration of most media in the table is less than that of **MS** medium and none of them contains a high concentration of ammonium ions. Shoots have been regenerated using **MS** medium, but this is more often used with the salts at half their normal concentration [*e.g.* as in **Cheng (1977, 1978)** medium] or with the omission of ammonium nitrate. Embryos of *Pinus elliottii* died on **MS**, but produced a high number of adventitious shoots when ammonium nitrate was left out of the medium **Pérez–Bermúdez and Sommer (1987)**.

Table 185 shows that adventitious shoots have been directly initiated by incubating embryo and seedling explants on a wide variety of media. No consistent pattern emerges for the nutritional requirements of different genera, making it difficult to recommend one medium in preference to another. Nevertheless, bud formation and shoot growth has sometimes been demonstrated to be better on specific formulations. Perhaps **Lloyd and McCown (1981) WPM** has been under used?

Ellis *et al.* (1991) found that buds could be regenerated on *Picea glauca* explants placed on either $\frac{1}{2}$**SH** or **WPM** medium. Although higher concentrations of cytokinin were required on **WPM**, the buds produced were visually more uniform, less hyperhydric, and elongated faster than on $\frac{1}{2}$**SH**. In addition more shoots survived after 6 months of culture when grown on **WPM** medium. Adventitious shoot formation of *Calocedrus decurrens* was also better on **WPM** (medium **13**) than on **MS** (medium **1**), **Gresshoff and Doy (1972)** (medium **4**), or **Bornman (1983) MCM** (medium **15**) (**Jelaska, 1987**).

Adventitious shoots occurred with greater frequency on seedlings of *Chamaecyparis obtusa* when they were incubated on **Campbell and Durzan (1975)** medium (**8**) than on **MS** or several other media (Ishii, 1986). **Campbell and Durzan (1975)** medium was also most effective for shoot elongation. Shoot production from *Pinus strobus* embryos was better on **Aitken–Christie (1984) LP** medium (**16**) than on **MS** (**1**) or media **6** and **11** (Chesick *et al.*, 1991).

Cotyledons of *Pinus taeda* and *P. virginiana* produced adventitious shoots on medium **18**, which has little inorganic nitrogen but contains 10 mM glutamine and 0.57 mM arginine. The addition of these amino acids separately to medium **8**, decreased the number of seedling explants of *Chamaecyparis obtusa* forming buds, but when 1.37 mM glutamine was combined with 1.51 mM asparagine, a larger proportion of explants responded (Ishii, 1986).

Growth regulators. Several cultural steps are usually necessary to obtain fully formed adventitious shoots (Table 185), so that plantlets produced by this means are costly.

Typically, adventitious shoots are induced to form when explants are placed horizontally on a medium containing a cytokinin (usually BAP) (Reilly and Washer, 1977; Von Arnold, 1982), but buds are not differentiated from sub–epidermal meristemoids until the growth regulator is removed. The number of shoots ultimately produced by an explant can depend on the time that explants are exposed to the induction medium, although, even within one species, the optimum can vary with genotype (Go *et al.*, 1993).

A low concentration of an auxin is sometimes also incorporated beneficially into the induction medium (Minocha, 1978; Brown and Sommer, 1977b), but high auxin levels promote the formation of unorganised callus (Von Arnold and Eriksson, 1978). Instead of inducing shoot formation by exposure to a low concentration of cytokinin over several days, treatment with a single short pulse (an acute dose) of cytokinin (*e.g.* exposure to 0.25 mM BAP solution for 30 minutes — Bonga, 1984) is also effective. There is then no need to incorporate cytokinin into the medium.

Following shoot induction, explants are transferred to a medium lacking cytokinin for shoot formation. The small buds which are produced may elongate on the Stage II medium, but this is unusual. Generally, after one or more transfers, explants or excised shoots, need to be moved to a third medium (also without cytokinin) on which they are elongated until they are of a sufficient size for rooting. Growth is generally slow and explants bearing shoots, or separated shoots, frequently require to be transferred to fresh medium several times (Horgan, 1987). When elongating individual shoots of *Pinus elliottii*, Lesney *et al.* (1988) made a fresh cut at the base of the stem at each transfer.

Shoot elongation often does not take place unless activated charcoal is added to either the Stage II medium, or the Stage III elongation medium. Whether the effect of charcoal is due to adsorption of the inhibitory substances in agar, or to the removal of free cytokinin remaining in the explant (Mehra–Palta *et al.*, 1978; Amerson *et al.*, 1988), is unclear. The poor light transmission through stacked vessels filled with a charcoal–containing medium, and the lack of elongation and slow decline of the cultures in its absence, led Nairn to experiment with media containing Gelrite instead of agar. Directly formed shoots of *Pinus radiata* were found to elongate without charcoal as the concentration of agar in the medium was decreased. Although growth was improved on medium solidified with only 2g/l Gelrite, shoots became hyperhydric after 4 transfers. A blend of 1.94 g/l Gelrite and 0.24 g/l agar was therefore used routinely. Any shoots which became hyperhydric on this mixture were briefly transferred to medium containing 1.8 g/l Gelrite and 0.8 g/l agar where the symptoms were corrected.

Table 184. Some of the media used for the culture of coniferous trees.

Components	MS	Cheng (1977, 1978)	Litvay et al. (1981) LM	Gresshoff and Doy (1972) Medium 1	Sommer et al. (1975) GD	Reilly and Washer (1977) GD	Horgan and Aitken (1981) GD mod.	Campbell and Durzan (1975)	Schenk and Hildebrandt (1972)
	1	**2**	**3**	**4**	**5**	**6**	**7**	**8**	**9**
Macronutrients (meq/l)									
NO_3^-	39.4	19.7	39.4	9.89	9.89	9.89	9.89	21.65	24.72
PO_4^{3-}	3.74	1.87	7.49	2.59	2.59	2.59	2.59	3.74	7.82
SO_4^{2-}	3.0	1.5	15.01	5.05	5.05	5.05	5.05	3.0	3.24
Cl^-	5.99	2.99	0.29	6.06	6.06	6.06	6.06	0.87	2.72
K^+	20.04	10.02	21.29	13.91	13.91	13.91	13.91	5.48	24.72
Ca^{2+}	5.99	2.99	0.29	2.04	2.04	2.04	2.04	8.29	2.72
Na^+	—	—	—	1.07	1.07	1.07	1.07	—	—
Mg^{2+}	3.0	1.5	15.01	2.02	2.02	2.02	2.02	3.0	3.24
NH_4^+	20.61	10.3	20.61	3.02	3.02	3.02	3.02	10.0	2.6
Microelements (mg/l)									
$MnSO_4.4H_2O$	22.3	11.15	27.7	13.2	13.2	13.2	20.0	22.3	13.2
$ZnSO_4.7H_2O$	8.6	5.25	43.0	3.0	3.0	3.0	1.0	8.6	1.0
H_3BO_3	6.2	3.1	31.0	3.0	3.0	3.0	5.0	6.2	5.0
KI	0.83	0.4	4.15	0.75	0.75	0.75	1.0	0.83	1.0
$CuSO_4.5H_2O$	0.025	0.013	0.5	0.25	0.25	0.25	0.2	0.025	0.2
$Na_2MoO_4.2H_2O$	0.25	0.15	1.25	0.25	0.25	0.25	0.2	0.25	0.1
$CoCl_2.6H_2O$	0.025	0.013	0.13	0.25	0.25	— *	0.2	0.025	0.1
NaFeEDTA (mM)	0.1	0.022	0.1	0.1	0.1	0.1	0.054	0.1	0.054
Vitamins (mg/l)									
Inositol	100.0	250.0	100.0	100.0	10.0	10.0	10.0	100.0	1000.0
Thiamine HCl	0.1	2.5	0.1	10.0	1.0	1.0	1.0	0.4	5.0
Nicotinic acid	0.5	—	0.5	1.0	0.1	0.1	0.1	—	5.0
Pyridoxine HCl	0.5	—	0.1	1.0	0.1	0.1	0.1	—	0.5
Pantothenic acid	—	—	—	—	—	—	—	—	—
Biotin	—	—	—	—	—	—	—	—	—
Folic acid	—	—	—	—	—	—	—	—	—
Amino acids and amides (mg/l)									
Glycine	2.0	—	—	4.0	—	—	—	—	—
L–alanine	—	—	—	—	—	—	—	—	—
L–arginine	—	—	—	—	—	—	—	—	—
L–asparagine	—	—	—	—	—	—	—	—	—
L–cysteine HCl	—	—	—	—	—	—	—	—	—
L–glutamine	—	—	—	—	—	—	—	—	—
L–phenylalanine	—	—	—	—	—	—	—	—	—
L–tyrosine	—	—	—	—	—	—	—	—	—
Urea	—	—	—	—	—	—	—	—	—
Special sugars (g/l)									
(See notes)	None	None	None	None	None	None	None	None	None

Table 184, continued.

Components	Horgan and Aitken (1981) SH mod.	Reilly and Washer (1977) SH	Von Arnold & Eriksson (1981) LPm	Lloyd and McCown (1981) WPM	David *et al.* (1982a)	Bornman (1983) MCM	Aitken–Christie (1984) LP	Gupta and Durzan (1985) DCR	Amerson *et al.* (1988) BLG
	10	**11**	**12**	13	**14**	**15**	**16**	**17**	18
Macronutrients (meq/l)									
NO_3^-	24.72	24.72	33.78	9.7	24.0	24.0	32.96	13.07	1.0
PO_4^{3-}	7.82	7.82	7.49	3.75	3.0	6.0	5.95	3.75	3.75
SO_4^{2-}	3.24	3.24	3.0	14.36	2.0	8.0	2.92	3.0	3.0
Cl^-	2.72	2.72	2.44	1.3	1.0	2.0	–	1.16	15.99
K^+	24.72	24.72	21.29	12.6	15.0	24.0	19.79	4.61	12.25
Ca^{2+}	2.72	2.72	2.44	6.01	5.0	4.0	10.16	5.86	5.99
Na^+	—	—	—	—	—	—	—	—	—
Mg^{2+}	3.24	3.24	3.0	3.0	2.0	2.0	2.92	3.0	3.0
NH_4^+	2.6	2.6	14.99	4.99	6.0	6.0	5.00	5.0	—
Microelements (mg/l)									
$MnSO_4.4H_2O$	20.0	13.2	2.2	29.43	11.15	0.22	20.0	29.43	22.3
$ZnSO_4.7H_2O$	1.0	1.0	‡	8.6	4.3	2.9	8.6	8.6	8.6
H_3BO_3	5.0	5.0	0.63	6.2	3.1	1.6	6.2	6.2	6.2
KI	1.0	1.0	0.75	—	0.42	0.25	0.08	0.83	0.83
$CuSO_4.5H_2O$	0.2	0.2	0.0025	0.25	0.012	0.025	0.25	0.25	0.025
$Na_2MoO_4.2H_2O$	0.2	0.1	0.025	0.25	0.125	0.24	0.25	0.25	0.25
$CoCl_2.6H_2O$	0.2	0.1	0.0025	— *	0.012	0.024	0.025	0.025	0.025
NaFeEDTA (mM)	0.054	0.054	0.05	0.1	0.05	0.1	0.11	0.1	0.1
Vitamins (mg/l)									
Inositol	1000.0	100.0	100.0	100.0	100.0	90.0	1000.0	200.0	100.0
Thiamine HCl	5.0	5.0	5.0	1.0	0.37	1.7	0.4	1.0	0.1
Nicotinic acid	5.0	5.0	2.0	0.5	—	0.6	—	0.5	0.5
Pyridoxine HCl	0.5	0.5	1.0	0.5	—	0.5	—	0.5	0.1
Ca pantothenate	—	—	—	—	—	1.2	—	—	—
Biotin	—	—	—	—	—	0.125	—	—	—
Folic acid	—	—	—	—	—	1.1	—	—	—
Amino acids and amides (mg/l)									
Glycine	—	—	2.0	2.0	—	1.9	—	2.0	—
L–alanine	—	—	0.05	—	—	—	—	—	—
L–arginine	—	—	0.01	—	—	—	—	—	—
L–asparagine	—	—	—	—	—	—	—	—	100.0
L–cysteine HCl	—	—	0.02	—	—	—	—	—	—
L–glutamine	—	—	0.4	—	—	—	—	—	1462
L–phenylalanine	—	—	0.01	—	—	—	—	—	—
L–tyrosine	—	—	0.01	—	—	—	—	—	—
Urea	—	—	—	—	—	150.0	—	—	—
Special sugars (g/l)									
(See notes)	None	None	†	None	None	None	None	None	None

Table 185. Illustrating the stages, media and growth regulators used for the direct regeneration of shoots from coniferous tree explants.　　Text marks refer to notes at the end of the table.
The media in Table 184 are indicated within square brackets, sucrose concentrations (%) within round brackets ;　AC= activated charcoal.

Conifer species	Explant	Shoot induction (growth regs. in mg/l)	Shoot formation	Shoot elongation	References
Calocedrus decurrens	Zygotic embryos or cotyledonary nodes from 14 day old seedlings	[13] (3) + 1.6 BAP	[13] (3) + 0.01 NAA	[13 or ½ × 12§] (2) + 0.01 NAA	Jelaska (1987) Jelaska and Libby (1988)
Chamaecyparis nootkatensis	Mature zygotic embryos	[9] (3) + 0.35 BAP	[9] (3) None		Kurz *et al.* (1989)
Chamaecyparis obtusa	Seedlings, 1 week old	[8] (3) + 2.25 BAP + 0.005 NAA	[8] (3) + 0.005 NAA		Ishii (1986)
Larix decidua	Immature female strobili	[8 or ½ × 3¶¶] + 10 BAP	[½ × 3 ¶¶] None. Shoots failed to elongate		Bonga (1984)
	Resting buds from mature trees	56.3 BAP 30 min then [½ × 12] (?) + 1.1 BAP + 1.1 kinetin	[½ × 12] (1) None	[12] (2) None	Bonga and Pond (1991)
Larix decidua *Larix × eurolepis* *Larix leptolepis*	Shoot primordia from buds of 30 year–old tree	[½ × 3] (3)+ 0.1 TDZ (3–7 days) or 2 BAP (3 weeks)	[½ × 3] (3) None (monthly subcultures)		
Larix laricina	Shoot primordia from buds of 30-year old tree	[½ × 3¶¶] (3) + 2 BAP + 0.1 IBA (3 weeks)	[½ × 3¶¶] (3) + 0.1 IBA (monthly subcultures)		
Picea abies	Zygotic embryos	[½ × 9] (1) + 1.1 BAP	[½ × 9] (1) None		Von Arnold and Eriksson (1987)　Von Arnold (1987)
Picea abies	Zygotic embryos	56.3 BAP 30 min then [½ × 12] (?) None 10 days	[½ × 12] (1) None	[12] (2) None	Von Arnold and Hakman (1988b)
Picea glauca	Seedling hypocotyls	[8] (3) + 2.25 BAP	[8] (3) None		Campbell and Durzan (1975)
Picea glauca	Zygotic embryos and seedling hypocotyls	[13] (3) + 2.2 BAP (or 11–22 zeatin + 0.01 TDZ)	[13] (3) None		Ellis *et al.* (1991)
Picea ormorika	Seedling shoots and cotyledons	[12‡] (3.1) + 1 BAP	[12‡] (3.1) None		Budimir and Vujicic (1992)
Pinus brutia	Zygotic embryos or cotyledons	[10§§] (3) + 3 BAP	[10] (3) None		Abdullah *et al.* (1981)
Pinus canariensis	Newly germinated zygotic embryos	[15] (3) + 2.2 BAP	[½ × 14] (3?) None	[½ × 14] (3?) None + 0.05% AC	Martínez Pulido *et al.* (1991; 1992)
Pinus caribea	Embryos	[2] (3) + 2 BAP (1 week)	[2] (2) None		Halos and Go (1993) Go *et al.* (1993)
Pinus contorta	Seedling cotyledons and hypocotyls	[½ × 12] (3.4) + 2.25 BAP (21 days)	[½ × 12] None (7 days)	[¼ × 12] None (60 days) then [⅛ × 12] None (90 days)	Patel and Thorpe (1984)
Pinus duragensis *Pinus greggi*	Mature zygotic embryos	[9 ††] (3) + 3 BAP	[9] (2) 4 BAP ‡‡	[9] None	López–Peralta *et al.* (1991)
Pinus echinata	Cotyledons from germinated seeds	[7] + 10 BAP (4–6 weeks)	As above	As above	
Pinus virginiana	Cotyledons from embryos	[5] (3) + 10 BAP + 0.01 NAA (6 weeks)	[5] None (3–4 week transfers)	[½ × 5] None (6-8 weeks then individual shoots to same)	Lesney *et al.* (1988)
Pinus elliotii					

concentration is increased (e.g. to 0.5 mg/l), the proportion of shoots forming roots diminishes and the rate of root growth is decreased (Abdullah et al., 1989).

As with other plants, auxin can be applied in various ways. Rancillac et al. (1982) suggested that conifer shoots could be treated in one of three ways:

- Treated with a high concentration (10–100 μM) for a short interval (up to 24 h);

- placed in a moderate concentration (1–5 μM) for 15–20 days;

- incubated with a low concentration (0.1–0.01 μM) permanently in contact with the shoots.

In many species it is necessary to transfer shoots to a regulant–free medium after incubation with auxin for approximately 15 days (i.e. to use the second strategy), otherwise roots do not grow. After a preliminary exposure to auxin (sometimes in the dark), shoots are moved to a medium with the same composition (or to one with a greater ionic concentration than the first) to encourage root growth (Mehra–Palta et al., 1978; Rancillac et al., 1982; Franco and Swartz, 1985; Gupta and Durzan, 1987c; Saravitz et al., 1991; Halos and Go, 1993). Examples of such treatments are shown in Table 187, but auxin concentrations which necessitate a transfer to auxin–free medium in one species, permit root induction and root growth in another. The range of auxin concentrations specified for the third option above is therefore too low for some conifers.

Martínez–Pulido et al. (1991) obtained a considerable improvement in the rooting of Pinus canariensis shoots, by incubating them (after a 4h pulse with 203 mg/l IBA) in a sterile mixture of peat and vermiculite, instead of on medium solidified with 0.5% Gelrite. The peat/vermiculite was wetted with medium **15** ($^1/_4$ strength) containing 1% sucrose. The same nutrients were in the gelled medium.

Rooting extra vitrum

Conifer shoots can be rooted under non–sterile conditions and often a higher proportion of shoots can be rooted in this manner than in vitro (Kurz et al., 1989). Mudge (1986) and Swartz et al. (1988) were unable to root Pinus mugo and Pinus strobus shoots in vitro, but 25–28% rooted outside the culture vessel. Some examples of successful ex vitro rooting are shown in Table 188.

Plagiotropy of tissue cultured plants

Plagiotropic growth is sometimes observed on shoots of mature conifers while they are in the culture vessel. In these circumstances it has been shown that the response

Table 189. The proportion of Pinus brutia plants which had a plagiotropic, orthotropic or intermediate habit when derived from adventitious or axillary shoots of seedling origin [results of Abdullah et al. (1989)].

Source	Stature of seedlings		
	Straight %	Upright but bushy at base %	Bushy or plagiotropic %
Adventitious shoots	16	31	50
Axillary shoots	70	30	0

is induced by light, because if shoots are kept in darkness they grow upright, but revert to a plagiotropic stance when returned to light (Bigot and Engelmann, 1987).

Plagiotropy is presumably caused by the determination of cells at the apex to produce or distribute growth substances in a polarized fashion and it is sometimes suggested that it is associated with the mature phase of conifer growth (McKeand, 1985). Another hypothesis is that it is related to a poor root system. Unlike seedlings which have many fine lateral roots, tissue cultured plantlets have thick unbranched roots and in Pinus taeda have been shown to be relatively inefficient at nitrogen and phosphorus uptake (McKeand and Allen, 1985). These theories do not explain how some plants in a group resulting from micropropagation, can be orthotropic, others plagiotropic and the remainder have an intermediate habit. Remarkably, Abdullah et al. (1989) found that plants obtained from adventitious shoots formed on embryonic tissues of Pinus brutia were much more likely to be plagiotropic than plants which arose from axillary shoots on seedling meristems (Table 189).

EMBRYOGENESIS

Because the large–scale cloning of forest trees using tissue culture techniques is only likely to be economic when plantlets can be produced as cheaply as seedlings, much research has been given to the study of somatic embryogenesis in conifers, both the production of somatic embryos and their conversion into plants.

Induction of embryogenesis

Plantlets have been obtained from the somatic embryos of several conifers. Embryogenic callus has only been initiated from juvenile tissues. Most success is obtained using as explants, unfertilised female gametophytes and immature or mature zygotic embryos, although the shoot

Table 190. Examples of media used for the initiation and proliferation of embryogenic tissue and embryo maturation in conifers.

Components	Von Arnold & Eriksson (1981) LPm	Von Arnold and Hakman (1988b) ††	Lainé and David (1990)	Nørgaard and Krogstrup (1990) §	Litvay et al. (1981) LM	Verhagen and Wann (1989) ½BLG (Initiation)	Verhagen and Wann (1989) HM (Maturation)	Krogstrup (1986) BMI-S	Finer et al. (1989) §§
	①	②	③	④	⑤	⑥	⑦	⑧	⑨
Macronutrients (meq/l)									
NO_3^-	33.78	24.39	24.39	19.7	39.4	0.5	33.78	26.5	13.07
PO_4^{3-}	7.49	3.75	3.75	1.87	7.49	1.88	7.50	1.87	3.75
SO_4^{2-}	3.0	1.5	1.5	1.5	15.01	1.3	3.0	1.5	3.0
Cl^-	2.44	1.22	1.22	2.99	0.29	7.99	2.45	2.99	1.16
K^+	21.29	10.65	10.65	10.02	21.29	6.12	21.29	23.72	4.61
Ca^{2+}	2.44	1.22	1.22	2.99	0.29	3.0	2.45	2.99	5.86
Na^+	—	—	—	—	—	—	—	—	—
Mg^{2+}	3.0	1.5	1.5	1.5	15.01	1.3	3.0	1.5	3.0
NH_4^+	14.99	14.99	14.99	10.3	20.61	—	14.99	3.4	5.0
Microelements (mg/l)									
$MnSO_4.4H_2O$	2.2	1.1	22.3	11.15	27.72	11.15	2.6	11.15	29.43
$ZnSO_4.7H_2O$	‡	1.44	8.6	4.3	43.0	4.3	2.87	4.3	8.6
H_3BO_3	0.63	0.32	6.2	3.1	31.0	3.1	0.63	3.1	6.2
KI	0.75	0.42	0.83	0.21	4.15	0.42	0.75	0.41	0.83
$CuSO_4.5H_2O$	0.0025	0.0013	0.025	0.013	0.5	0.013	0.0025	0.013	0.25
$Na_2MoO_4.2H_2O$	0.025	0.013	0.25	0.13	1.25	0.13	0.025	0.13	0.25
$CoCl_2.6H_2O$	0.0025	0.0013	0.025	0.013	0.13	0.013	0.0025	0.013	0.025
NaFeEDTA (mM)	0.05	0.025	0.05	0.05	0.1	0.05	0.05	0.05	0.1
Vitamins (mg/l)									
myo–Inositol	100.0	50.0	100.0	100.0	100.0	50.0	100.0	991.0	200.0
Thiamine HCl	5.0	2.5	1.0	1.0	0.1	0.05	5.0	1.0	1.0
Nicotinic acid	2.0	1.0	10.0	0.5	0.5	0.25	2.0	0.5	0.5
Pyridoxine HCl	1.0	0.5	10.0	0.5	0.1	0.05	1.0	0.5	0.5
Ca pantothenate	—	—	1.0	—	—	—	—	—	—
Biotin	—	—	0.01	—	—	—	—	—	—
Amino acids (mg/l)									
Glycine	2.0	1.0	—	2.0	—	—	—	2.0	2.0
L–alanine	0.05	0.025	—	—	—	—	—	—	—
L–arginine	0.01	0.005	—	—	—	—	—	—	—
L–asparagine	—	—	—	—	—	50.0	—	—	—
L–cysteine HCl	0.02	0.01	—	—	—	—	—	—	—
L–glutamine	0.4	0.2	200.0	(500)*	—	750.0	—	—	50.0
L–phenylalanine	0.01	0.005	—	—	—	—	—	—	—
L–tyrosine	0.01	0.005	—	—	—	—	—	—	—
Casein hydrolysate	—	—	—	(500)*	—	—	—	—	500.0
Special sugars (g/l)									
	†	††	—	—	—	—	†	—	—

† As originally formulated, **LPm** medium contains 34.2 g/l sucrose, 0.18 g/l glucose, 0.15 g/l xylose and 0.15 g/l arabinose. These sugars also used in **HM** medium.   ‡ The medium originally contained 10 µM ZnEDTA. This can be replaced by 2.87 mg/l $ZnSO_4.7H_2O$.

§ This medium is ½**MS** with altered vitamins.   * Enhanced callus proliferation.when included.

†† The medium is ½**LPm** medium but retains 15 mM NH_4NO_3. It has ½ the special sugars in **LPm** medium.   When used by Von Arnold and Hakman (1988a,b) and Mo et al. (1989), the medium also contained 10.3 g/l sucrose.

§§ This is **Gupta and Durzan (1985) DCR** medium (Medium **17** in Table184), with added amino acids.

apices and cotyledons of seedlings have also been employed (Attree *et al.*, 1990a; Budimir and Vujicic, 1992).

Explants

Female gametophytes and zygotic embryos. The stage of female cone development at which embryogenic explants can be obtained varies between genera. When the best response is obtained from megagametophyte explants (as for example in some species of *Larix*) or from immature precotyledonary zygotic embryos (in *Pinus*), the interval during which explants can be gathered from female cones can be very limited. The time available can sometimes be extended for a short while if cones are refrigerated, but the proportion of explants giving rise to embryogenic tissue diminishes after several weeks of cold storage.

The use as explants of megagametophytes in which the archegonia are not yet fertilised, can result in the production of haploid embryogenic callus and the formation of haploid somatic embryos (Von Aderkas *et al.* 1987, 1990; Von Aderkas and Bonga, 1988) (*i.e.* gynogenesis — page 36). When later–stage megagametophytes have been used as explants, embryogenic tissue has been found to arise exclusively from the immature embryo (Schuller *et al.*, 1988; Klimaszewska, 1989). Such megagametophytes have been halved to reveal the young embryo, or cultured intact, when embryogenic callus has proliferated and extruded through the micropyle (Finer *et al.*, 1989). The presence of more than one fertilised embryo within a megagametophyte makes it possible to obtain embryogenic tissue of mixed genotype (Becwar *et al.*, 1991). The continued attachment of a zygotic embryo to the female gametophyte has been shown to enhance, or be essential for the formation of embryogenesis callus (Gupta and Durzan, 1986a; Klimaszewska, 1989).

In some genera it is possible to induce embryogenesis from mature embryos in which the cotyledons have formed. Mature embryos are probably the most suitable explant in *Picea,* and in some species embryos excised from seeds stored for several years have given rise to embryogenic tissue (Tautorus *et al.*, 1990; Tremblay, 1990).

Seedling explants. The dissection of female gametophytes or zygotic embryos from cones or seeds is laborious and the discovery that embryogenesis can be induced on cotyledons and stem tissue of germinated seedlings, of at least some species (Krogstrup, 1986; Attree *et al.*, 1990a) is a great step forward.

Embryo formation. Explants cultured on an appropriate combination of nutrients and growth regulators either give rise directly to embryogenic tissue or produce a callus tissue from which somatic embryos are differenti-

ated later, often on a medium without growth regulators. In the former case, the tissue is frequently composed of proliferating early–stage embryos with attached suspensors.

When immature zygotic embryos are isolated before culture, embryogenic tissue may arise directly from the suspensor or from cells at the embryo apex. Immature zygotic embryos may also be stimulated to undergo cleavage polyembryogenesis of a similar kind to that which occurs during zygotic embryo formation (Part 1, page 32). A tissue mass is formed as the process becomes recurrent. From more mature embryos, embryogenic tissue has been observed to arise from the hypocotyl region, from the cotyledons and from the radicle.

Embryogenic tissue of conifers is recognisable by its white mucilaginous appearance, which usually contrasts with green non–embryogenic tissue. Conifer embryos have long suspensors and when somatic embryos are directly initiated and proliferate *in vitro*, a tissue, which is often called an embryonal suspensor mass, is initiated.

It is likely that, as has been found in *Picea abies* (Mo *et al.*, 1989), new embryogenic cultures of gymnosperms can be obtained by using somatic embryos as explants.

Media and growth regulators

Media, very similar to those used for direct shoot formation and 'shoot' culture of conifers, are used for the induction of embryogenic tissue. **MS**, $^{1}/_{2}$**MS**, and **Gupta and Durzan (1985) DCR** (medium **17** in Table 184) media have been employed in several experiments together with the further examples listed in Table 190. Of these, **Von Arnold and Eriksson (1981) LP** medium (medium **1** in Table 190) has been employed most frequently, usually at full strength, but sometimes at half its normal concentration. However, in some experiments the amino acids have been omitted and, in others, the special sugars. **Litvay *et al.* (1981) LM** (medium **5**) has also often been used at half strength.

Thus in most reports of the induction of embryogenesis, explants have been cultured on media in which there are lower concentrations of macronutrient ions than in **MS**, and in particular less NH_4^+, this often being totally or partially provided by reduced nitrogen in the form of amino acids. Adding 500 mg/l (3.4 mM) L–glutamine to Medium **3** (Table 190) improved the rate at which embryogenic callus tissue of *Abies nordmanniana* proliferated (Nørgaard and Krogstrup, 1990).

Media are gelled, sometimes with agar, but now more frequently with 3–4 g/l Gelrite.

Table 191. Examples of the media and growth regulators used to initiate embryogenic callus in some conifer species.

Conifer species	Explant	Medium	Sucrose (%)	Growth regulators (mg/l)	References
Abies alba	Megagametophytes with immature embryos	[SH **]	3	1 BAP	Schuller *et al.* (1988)
Abies nordmanniana	Immature embryos	4	3	2.2 BAP (or 0.02 TDZ)	Norgaard and Krogstrup (1990)
Larix decidua	Gametophyte	MS, 5 or ½ × 5‡	2	2 BAP or 2 2–iP or 2 kin	Nagmani and Bonga (1985)
Larix × eurolepis	Half megagametophyte with attached immature embryo	17✤, 3◆ or MSG♥	2	2 2,4–D + 0.5 BAP	Klimaszewska (1989)
Picea abies	Cold–stored immature embryos	1	3.42	2 2,4-D + 1.13 BAP	Hakman and Von Arnold (1985)
Picea abies	Mature embryos	1	1	2.2 2,4–D + 1.1 BAP	Von Arnold and Hakman (1986)
Picea abies	Mature and immature embryos	2	1.03	1.9 NAA (or 1.1–4.4 2,4–D) + 1.1 BAP (darkness)	Von Arnold and Hakman (1988a,b)
Picea abies	Mature embryos	1 §§	1	2.2 2,4–D + 1.1 BAP	Jain et al. (1988)
Picea abies	Mature embryos	2	1.03	2 2,4–D + 1 BAP	Mo *et al.* (1989)
Picea abies	Mature embryos	6	2	2 NAA + 1 BAP	Verhagen and Wann (1989)
Picea abies	Mature embryos	1, or ½ × 1	(1)	2 2,4–D + 1.1 BAP	Kvaalen and Von Arnold (1991)
Picea glauca	Mature embryos	5 ¶¶	1	2 2,4–D + 1.1 BAP	Tremblay (1990)
Picea glauca *Picea mariana*	Seedling apices and cotyledons	1*	3.1	1 BAP + 2 2,4-D	Attree *et al.* (1990a)
Picea glauca	Immature embryos	1	3.4	2 2,4–D + 1.13 BAP	Roberts *et al.* (1989)
Picea ormorika	*In vitro* seedlings.	1†	3.1	5.07 BAP then PGR–free medium. Prolif of e'gen tissue with 2 2,4–D + 1 BAP	Budimir and Vujicic (1992)
Picea mariana	Immature embryos	1	1	2 2,4–D + 1 BAP	Tautorus *et al.* (1990)
	Mature embryos	½ × 5 ††	2	2 2,4–D + 1 BAP	^
Pinus caribaea	Megagametophyte	3	3	2.2 2,4–D + 1.1 BAP	Lainé and David (1990)
Pinus elliottii	Immature embryos	WPM	3	4.4 2,4–D + 0.5 BAP + 0.5 kinetin	Jain et al. (1989)
Pinus strobus	Immature gametophyte	9	3	2 2,4–D + 1 BAP	Finer *et al.* (1989)
Pseudotsuga menziesii	Gametophyte	4 ¶	1.5 ?	11 2,4–D + 4.3 kin + 4.5 BAP	Gupta *et al.* (1988)

* Omitted the special sugars. †　Amino acids omitted.

‡ Each medium supplemented with 500 mg/l glutamine and 1000 mg/l casein hydrolysate.

§ Left out the amino acids and used **LPm** sugars at full strength. ¶　But with 1000 mg/l inositol, 450 mg/l glutamine and 500 mg/l casein hydrolysate.

✤ Medium **17** of Table 184 plus 50 mg/l glutamine and 500 mg/l casein hydrolysate

◆ Medium **3** of Table 184 plus 500 mg/l glutamine and 1000 mg/l casein hydrolysate

♥ This medium is given in Becwar *et al.* . (1987).

†† But with ½ macro– and micro–nutrients, 0.1 mM NaFeEDTA, and 438.5 mg/l (3 mM) glutamine and 1 g/l casein hydrolysate.

‡‡ With the addition of 250 mg/l glutamine §§　But with ZnEDTA, amino acids, and sugars (apert from sucrose) omitted.

¶¶ But with the concentrations of macro– and micro–nutrients halved, with 500 mg/l glutamine and 1 g/l casein hydrolysate added. and with Fe as 28 mg/l DTPA (Sequestrene 330Fe). **　But with 50 mg/l *myo*–inositol.

Examples of the media and growth regulators used to initiate embryogenic callus in particular conifer species are shown in Table 191. Embryogenic tissue has sometimes been induced by the presence of just a cytokinin, but in most experiments an auxin has also been added to the medium.

Proliferation of embryogenic tissue

Embryogenic tissue usually proliferates when subcultured to the same medium as that used for induction. This may be semi–solid, or an agitated liquid if suspensions are required. Suspensions have been cultured in shaken flasks and small bioreactors.

Embryo maturation

Growth regulators

As mentioned on page 710 *et seq.*, proliferation of conifer somatic embryos is arrested and embryo maturation promoted, by subculturing embryogenic tissue and developing embryos on a medium supplemented with a low concentration of ABA (*e.g.* 0.5–38 µM, 0.13–10 mg/l, depending on genotype and the period during which embryos are exposed to the regulant) for one or more subcultures. Adding a low concentration of auxin to the medium in addition to the ABA is also sometimes found to be promotive (Boulay *et al.*, 1988; Roberts *et al.*, 1989), but cytokinins are omitted. The proportion of embryos which mature can depend on the period of exposure to ABA. In two *Picea* species, Attree *et al.* (1990b) found that the presence of 16 µM ABA for 28 days gave the best results.

At this stage of the maturation process, cultures are usually maintained in the dark.

Media

The same medium as was used for the induction and proliferation of embryogenic tissue is often used at the maturation stage, although when **Von Arnold and Eriksson (1981) LPm** has been used at Stage I, it has sometimes been used at ½ strength at the maturation stage. However, if embryogenic tissue has been induced to form, and has been subcultured, on a medium containing a low concentration of nitrate ions, it may be necessary to transfer it to another medium. Verhagen and Wann (1989) found that Medium **6** in Table 190 promoted the formation of embryogenic tissue of *Picea abies* and prevented the exclusive proliferation of non–embryogenic tissue. But although embryogenic tissue could be subcultured on the same medium, no embryo development occurred unless it was transferred to Medium **7**.

The addition of 50 mM (7.3 g/l) glutamine to **Gupta and Durzan (1986) DCR** medium (Medium **17** in Table 184) was essential for embryo development of *Pinus strobus*. Without it embryogenic callus continued to proliferate (Finer *et al.*, 1989). **DCR** medium supplemented with 450 mg/l glutamine and 500 mg/l casein hydrolysate was also used for embryo maturation of *Pseudotsuga menziesii* (Gupta *et al.*, 1988).

Media are often supplemented with 20 g/l sucrose. Lelu *et al.* (1994b) found that 20 g/l sucrose was better than 10 g/l for *Larix* × *leptoeuropaea*, but 60 g/l was necessary for *Pinus strobus* (Finer *et al.*, 1989).

Gas exchange seems to be important for embryo maturation, because embryos do not develop in suspensions, but only when tissue is transferred to a semi–solid medium, or onto polyurethane foam irrigated with liquid medium (Pâques *et al.*, 1992). Transfers are facilitated if embryogenic tissue or embryos are supported on a filter paper, or nylon mesh, placed on top of the medium (Attree *et al.*, 1990a; Budimir *et al.*, 1992).

Cultural procedures

To remove previously used growth regulators and so help to arrest proliferation, embryogenic tissue is often washed, or moved to a medium without growth regulators, before being subcultured to a further medium containing ABA. Embryogenic callus of *Picea abies* was subcultured to a PGR–free medium containing 10 g/l activated charcoal for one week before transfer to **HM** medium (number 7 in Table 190) containing 1 µM each of ABA and IBA (Verhagen and Wann, 1989).

The protocol followed by Atree *et al.* (1989, 1990a) for *Picea glauca* and *P. mariana* was to wash suspension cultured embryos and suspend them for a short interval in distilled water before placing them on filter paper supports on the surface of agar–solidified ½ **LPm** medium (medium **1** in Table 190 with 20 g/l sucrose) containing 3 mg/l ABA. After 28 days of dark incubation, the embryos were moved to the same medium (20 g/l sucrose), this time with no growth regulators. Embryos with small cotyledons could be separated from callus after a further 7–14 days and these were cultured independently on the same medium in low light (37 µmol m^{-2} s^{-1}) where they germinated and became ready for transfer.

Germination

The proportion of somatic embryos which germinates into plantlets is often low because roots elongate erratically and slowly. There can also be a considerable variation in the capacity of somatic embryos from different sources to develop into plants (Becwar *et al.*, 1986). Germination is improved if embryos are desiccated at high humidity (Chapter 14, page 711) before being placed on a low salts medium. Plantlets are finally moved to sterile compost and gradually acclimatized.

Somatic embryos of conifers have also been the subject of encapsulation studies (Attree and Fowke, 1993 and page 717).

Table 192. Published reports on the tissue culture of CONIFER TREES.

	Species name	Type of Culture	Source of explant	Results		References
Araucariaceae						
*	*Araucaria cunninghamii* D.Don. (Hoop pine)	Shoot	Seedling stem segments	Shoots from bud traces. Some shoots rooted	Y	Haines & De Fossard (1977)
Cupressaceae						
	Calocedrus decurrens (Torr.) Florin. (Incense cedar)	Direct	Zygotic embryos or cotyl. nodes ex 144-old sdlgs.	Adventitious shoots. Rooted	Y	Jelaska & Libby (1988)
	Calocedrus decurrens	Direct	Cotyledons ex embryos /seedlings	Adventitious shoots, elongated and rooted	Y	Jelaska (1987)
	Calocedrus decurrens	Shoot	Adventitious shoots formed *in vitro*	Axillary shoots. Rooted plants	YY	Jelaska & Libby (1988)
	Calocedrus decurrens	Shoot	Shoot tip ex 5 year-old tree	Multiple shoots. Rooted plantlets	YY	Jelaska (1987)
	Calocedrus decurrens	Shoot	Seedling hypocotyl + cotyl. node	Axillary shoots, elongated and rooted	YY	Jelaska (1987)
	Chamaecyparis nootkatensis (D.Don.) Spach.	Direct/Callus	Mature embryos	Multiple shoots. Rooted	Y	Kurz et al. (1989)
	Chamaecyparis nootkatensis	Shoot	Seedling shoot tips	Axillary branching	—	Kurz (1986)
	Chamaecyparis obtusa Endle. (Hinoki cypress)	Direct	One week-old *in vitro* seedlings	Adv. shoots on cotyledons & hypocotyl. Rooted plants	Y	Ishii (1986)
	Cupressus arizonica Green (Arizona cypress)	Direct	Stem (<6 m-old) sections	Adventitious shoots. Plants regenerated	Y	Cheng (1978b)
	Cupressus lusitanica Mill. (Mexican cypress)	Direct	Cotyledonary node + apex + 5 mm hycotyl of sdlg.	Adventitious shoots; rooted plantlets	Y	Franco & Swartz (1985)
	Cupressus sempervirens L. (Italian cypress)	Direct	Cotyledons & hypocotyls	Adventitious shoots	Y	Vestri et al. (1991)
	Cupressus sempervirens [3 cvs.]	Shoot	Sht. tips from top of 15-yr old tree	Shoot multiplication	—	Capuana et al. (1991)
	Platycladus orientalis (L.f.) Franco = *Biota orientalis*	Direct	Seedling hypocotyl (1 cm)	Adventitious shoots. Rooted	Y	Thomas & Tranvan (1982)
*	*Tetraclinis articulata* (Vahl) Mast. (Cartagena cypress)	Shoot	Shoot tips ex 1 year old seedlings	Shoot multiplication, rooted	YY	Monte et al. (1992)
	Thuja plicata D.Don (Western red cedar)	Direct	Cotyledons	Shoots from meristemoids. Shoots rooted	YY	Coleman & Thorpe (1977)
	Thuja plicata	Shoot & direct	Mature lateral shoot tips	Multiple adventitious & axillary buds. Shoots rooted	YY	Coleman & Thorpe (1977)
Ginkgoaceae						
*	*Ginkgo biloba* L. (Maidenhair tree)	Callus	Embryos from mature seeds	Embryogenesis. Embryos grew to cotyledonary stage	—	Yates (1986)
	Ginkgo biloba	Embryo	Seed embryos	Seedling growth	—	Ball (1956 a,b; 1959)
	Ginkgo biloba	Suspension	Embryo-derived callus	Studied effects of media compositions	—	Carrier et al. (1990)
Pinaceae						
❖	*Abies alba* Mill. (European silver fir)	Callus	Female gametophyte sections ex immature seeds	Somatic embryogenesis. Few embryos developed cotyledons	—	Schuller et al. (1989)
	Abies nordmanniana Spach. (Caucasian fir)	Embryogenic callus	Imm. pre-cotyl. zyg. embryos	Somatic embryos, but no plants	—	Norgaard & Krogstrup (1990)
	Larix decidua Mill. (European larch)	Callus	Inverted seedling hypocotyl segs.	Adventitious buds. Shoots	—	Karnosky & Diner (1986)
	Larix decidua	Callus	Gametophyte	Embryogenesis. Plantlets	—	Nagmani & Bonga (1985)
	Larix decidua	Direct	Discs cut from female strobili	Adv. shoots. Callus from shoots also regenerated shoots	—	Bonga (1984)
	Larix decidua	Direct	Young seedlings	Adventitious shoots (7.3/seedling). Rooted	—	Denoso (1991)
	Larix decidua	Shoot/Direct	*In vitro* shoots, needles	Axillary & adventitious shoots. Rooted	—	Karnosky & Diner (1986)
	Larix occidentalis Nutt. (Western larch)	Shoot	Buds, stems & terminal meristems	Multiple shoots, elongated	YY	Chesick et al. (1990)
	Larix spp.	Direct/Callus	Primordial shoots ex buds	Multiple advent. buds, elongating to shoots	—	Bonga & Pond (1991)
*	*Larix × eurolepis* 'Henry'	Callus	Buds ex cuttings (12 year-old tree)	Adventitious shoots produced for up to 1 year	—	Laliberté & Lalonde (1986)

shoots rooted and more shoots were produced per shoot (Marin *et al.*, 1993).

Subcultures. *Malus* subcultures are usually carried out at 4–5 week intervals. New cultures can, of course be initiated with shoot tips, but a greater rate of shoot proliferation can be obtained by using nodal sections of stem or by dividing and subculturing the basal mass after shoots have been removed (Hutchinson, 1984b; 1985b). There is a fairly high risk of obtaining adventitious shoots if the basal shoot mass is subcultured persistently. Nodes of 'Northern Spy' inserted vertically in the medium produced more shoots than those which were placed horizontally (Hutchinson, 1982; 1985b), but Gološin and Radojevic (1987) found the reverse to be true with 'M.26' and 'M.27' and thought this was due to improved BAP uptake.

The average number of shoots produced per explant per month increases during the first few subcultures and by subculture 5 may range from 2 to 6 or more, depending on cultivar.

In vitro rooting

As it has been difficult to obtain a high proportion of rooted and established plantlets from many *Malus* genotypes, a great deal of the research on the micropropagation of this genus has been concentrated on rooting and its physiology. Shoots separated from Stage II cultures have often been reported to have been rooted *in vitro*, but can also be directly rooted in a non–sterile medium.

Media. LS or MS medium has been employed for *in vitro* rooting, but a less concentrated salt solution [*e.g.* as provided by ½LS medium (better results than full strength medium, Hutchinson 1985b) or ½MS salts plus full MS vitamins] containing 30 g/l sucrose is commonly recognised to be most suitable. Sriskandarajah *et al.* (1990a) found that 3 apple cultivars rooted well if they were placed on a medium containing MS medium from which NH_4NO_3 had been omitted. The low concentration of NH_4^+ in **Quoirin and Lepoivre (1977)** medium possibly accounts for its successful use as a rooting medium by some workers (Welander, 1982; Alvarez *et al.* 1989 Van der Krieken *et al.* 1991), even though the total ionic concentration is high.

Hutchinson (1984b) discovered an interaction between the salt strength of the medium and the concentration of IBA required for rooting: more cuttings rooted on ½MS medium with 1 μM IBA (the best overall treatment) than on full strength MS, but using 5 μM IBA the reverse was the case.

Growth regulators. IBA is generally recognised to be the most effective auxin for root induction in *Malus*. NAA and NOA are liable to induce the formation of basal callus, which inhibits root formation (Hutchinson 1985b, Sriskandarajah *et al.* 1990a). The most effective concentration of IBA varies with genotype, for example 2.4 mg/l was best for 'M.9' rootstock, but 0.8 mg/l induced roots most effectively on 'M.26' (Alvarez *et al.*, 1989). In 'M.9' and 'Jork', root induction did not take place until shoots had been cultured for 5 days in the presence of 2 mg/l IBA (Van der Krieken *et al.*, 1991) .

The promotion of rooting by synthetic auxins is often synergised by phenolic compounds, and phloroglucinol is again frequently promotive (Part 1, page 430). Even if phloroglucinol does not stimulate shoot proliferation, its use at Stage II can increase the percentage of root initiation and root number when shoots are transferred to rooting medium (James and Thurbon, 1981a,b).

Acute auxin treatments. In most reported experiments, chronic auxin treatments (*i.e.* where auxin is added to the medium so that shoots are continuously exposed, page 676) have been used to induce *in vitro* rooting, but acute treatments can also be successful. Shoots of rootstock 'M.9' produced callus when continually exposed to NAA placed in the medium, but a high proportion formed roots if they were dipped for 2 minutes in a 300 mg/l (1.61 mM) NAA solution and were then cultured on an auxin–free medium (Lane and McDougald, 1982).

The longer explants are in contact with auxin, the smaller the concentration which is required. Kataeva and Butenko (1987) rooted microcuttings of two apple cultivars by dipping them in a 100 mg/l IBA solution for 3–8 hours before placing them on an auxin–free medium. An alternative technique has been to culture shoots on MS medium containing 3 mg/l IBA for 4 days, followed by transfer to a medium with ½ strength salts and no growth regulators, for root formation (James and Thurbon, 1979; Webster and Jones, 1989a,b; 1991).

Substrate. Many reports of *in vitro* rooting describe the use of agar solidified medium, but root growth may be better in rotated liquid (Sriskandarajah and Mullins, 1981; 1982). Even so, plants are usually fragile, translucent and difficult to establish. Thus it is better to root shoots in a porous substrate such as course sand, irrigated with medium, in which there is also good root growth and from which plantlets can be transferred with little disturbance (Hutchinson, 1982a; 1985b).

Activated charcoal has sometimes been added to the rooting medium together with auxin (Cheema and Sharma, 1983), or in the absence of auxin after shoots have been given an auxin pre–treatment (Snir and Erez, 1980), but its addition has not always improved rooting (Liu *et al.*, 1981).

Juvenility. As in other woody plants established from mature tissues, shoots of *Malus* produced from initial

Table 207. Examples of treatments which have resulted in the direct formation of shoots on sections of leaves excised from shoots of *in vitro* cultures of *Malus*

Medium	Sucrose (g/l)	Growth Regulators (mg/l)	References
Chu *et al.* (1975) N6	30	5 BAP + 0.2–2 NAA	Fasolo *et al.* (1988a,b)
Chu *et al.* (1975) N6 macros + **MS** micros & vitamins	30	5 BAP + 0.2 NAA	Welander (1988b)
LS	20	1 BAP + 1 NAA	Predieri and Malavisi (1989)
		2.2 TDZ + 0.2–1 NAA	
½**MS** + 'Staba' vitamins † (but 1.3 mM glycine and 0.28 mM ascorbic acid	30	0.5 NAA + 0.9 TDZ	Korban *et al.* (1992)
MS	30	0.5 NAA + 2.0 BAP + 1 mM putrescine ‡	James *et al.* (1988)

† See Part 1, page 414.

‡ Putrescine (.2HCl) only increased regeneration frequency when the adaxial surface of explants was in contact with the medium.

subcultures may not root well. The capacity to root will usually improve as subculturing is continued. At first only 8% of shoots produced from *Malus* 'Jonathan' shoot cultures formed roots, but after 9 subcultures the proportion which rooted rose to 95% (Mullins *et al.*, 1986). By contrast, 'Golden Delicious' shoots produced during the first 18 months of shoot culture rooted well on **LS** plus 1 mg/l IBA, but then became difficult to root by any method (Patena *et al.*, 1988).

Etiolation. A dark treatment either before or after auxin treatment (see Table 105, page 689) enhances root formation in many *Malus* genotypes. One commonly used method of etiolation has been to place cultures in the dark for up to 2 weeks, and then allow shoots to re–green for up to two weeks before rooting is attempted.

Shoots are weakened by etiolation and Webster and Jones (1989) found that even though the rooting of etiolated shoots was improved, their survival during establishment was reduced: in this case, the treatment had no advantage.

Establishment. Methods for weaning and establishment are no different to those used for other plants. Kunneman and Albers (1992) found that it was important to select the correct compost for transplanting. Survival was best in a mixture containing 35 parts peat and 65 parts perlite and decreased as the proportion of peat was increased.

Direct rooting

Many of the reports on *in vitro* rooting do not describe the proportion of plantlets which were weaned and established *extra vitrum*. In some other cases the proportions of shoots rooted and established have been low. These factors, together with the elaborate procedures in some *in vitro* rooting protocols, would make it desirable that

direct rooting should be used where plant costs are critical.

There are relatively few accounts of direct rooting, but it is possible. Various methods of auxin pre–treatment have been evaluated. Having incubated shoots of 'M.26', 'McIntosh' and 'Matsa' for 3–7 days in the dark on liquid **MS** medium (15 g/l sucrose) containing 0.3 mg/l IBA, Welander (1982) and Zimmerman and Fordham (1985) obtained good rooting when shoots were then transferred to non–sterile conditions. Shoots of 'M.9' rootstock dipped in a powder containing auxin and fungicide and then planted in sand, rooted in humid conditions as well as *in vitro*–rooted shoots and a greater proportion became established after weaning (Webster and Jones, 1989; 1991).

Other results have not been so encouraging. Kunneman and Albers (1992) found that the survival of shoots rooted *in vitro* was greater than that of cuttings planted *extra vitrum* without roots. Similarly, even though roots of *Malus* produced *in vitro* died during acclimatization through lack of secondary thickening (page 672), shoots continued to grow while new adventitious roots were being formed. This meant that, at the end of the acclimatization phase, plants were significantly taller and had a greater leaf area than comparable shoots which had been rooted directly (McClelland *et al.*, 1990).

Embryogenesis

Embryogenesis. Direct somatic embryogenesis has been induced on the nucellus tissue of *Malus* ovules cultured in darkness on **MS** medium without growth regulators (Eichholtz *et al.*, 1979; James *et al.*, 1984b) and also on the leaves of seedlings when the medium of **Kartha *et al.* (1974a)** was supplemented with 3 mg/l NAA and 10 mg/l BAP (Liu *et al.*, 1983b). Embryo–like structures have also been obtained on leaf segments of shoots cultured *in vitro* (Welander, 1988b) and shoot tip explants (James *et al.*, 1984a), by culturing these explants on medium containing 5 mg/l BAP and 0.2 mg/l NAA. Plants were obtained from some adventitious embryos, not through embryo germination but when shoots were formed from secondary embryos or through the growth of axillary buds (James *et al.*, 1984b).

Indirect embryogenesis from callus formed on apple seedling tissues was reported by Mehra and Sachdeva (1984).

Direct shoot formation

As will be seen from Table 216, direct adventitious shoot formation has been induced on several different types of explant, and especially on sections of leaves excised from shoots which have been cultured *in vitro*. Table 207 shows examples of the treatments which have been employed on leaf explants. Maximum shoot number occurs if sections of young expanding leaves are incubated with their adaxial surface in contact with the medium (Welander, 1988) and if cultures are incubated in darkness or in red light (Welander, 1988; Predieri and Malavasi, 1989). More shoot initials are formed per unit leaf area if leaves are cut into strips, rather than being used for the excision of leaf discs (James *et al.*, 1988).

Fasolo *et al.* (1988b) and Welander (1988) found that shoots were produced more consistently if explants were cultured on the medium, or at least the macronutrients of **Chu** *et al.* **(1975) N6**, instead of **MS** medium.

Rosaceae
Prunus   (Plum, Cherry, Almond, Peach, Apricot)

There are over 400 species of evergreen and deciduous shrubs or trees in the genus *Prunus*. Several of these species are grown as valuable fruit crops (all producing drupes as fruits), a few as timber trees, and many others as ornamentals, mainly on account of their attractive flowers. Emphasis will be given in the following paragraphs to fruit and nut–producing species of the genus, but methods used to propagate ornamental *Prunus* trees (Table 174) are obviously relevant.

The place for micropropagation. Mature trees of *Prunus* cannot be propagated from cuttings, and in some species (*e.g.* almond) even cuttings taken from seedlings are difficult to root (Rugini and Verma, 1983). Most cultivars are therefore grafted onto known rootstocks and, as in *Malus*, the value of planting self–rooted trees is not obvious. Growers have therefore not opted to plant large numbers of micropropagated trees, although there has been an opportunity to propagate rootstocks, particularly those which are used for peach. In 1988, 10 million peach rootstocks and 0.6 million plum, cherry and apricot rootstocks were produced by Italian commercial micropropagation laboratories (Pierik, 1991a).

There is little published work on the micropropagation of ornamental *Prunus* species, and it is surprising that these forms, which include the Sata–zakura group of Japanese flowering cherries, are not multiplied *in vitro* more widely, for here one would expect that the rate of vegetative propagation by traditional techniques would be low and the method by which the trees are rooted, less important.

Shoot culture

Prunus species are almost exclusively micropropagated by shoot culture, techniques being very similar to those used for *Malus* and, as in that genus, explants can be derived from a variety of sources:

- actively–growing terminal buds of mature trees (Miller *et al.*, 1982; Rugini and Verma, 1983);

- dormant shoot buds (Quoirin *et al.*, 1974, 1975; Tabachnik and Kester, 1977; Hammerschlag, 1982a; Ochatt and Caso, 1982);

- apices of forced shoots (Hammerschlag, 1981a, 1982a);

- dormant flower buds, which often contain vegetative primordia, besides a flower initial (Lane, 1982).

As explained in Chapter 8 (page 255) shoots bearing dormant buds usually need to be stored in the cold for several weeks before bud–derived explants will grow actively *in vitro*.

Media. In the great majority of published experiments on *Prunus* shoot culture, **MS** or **LS** medium, or a medium comprising **MS** salts with modified organic constituents, was used at both Stage I and Stage II. In a few reports, less explant mortality occurred during establishment if a medium without ammonium ions was used at Stage I. Snir (1982a,b) and Rugini and Verma (1982, 1983) used **Tabachnik and Kester (1977)** medium to establish shoot tips of sweet and sour cherries. **Tabachnik and Kester (1977)** medium which contains the micronutrients and organic compounds of **MS**, but the following macronutrients (meq/l):

NO_3^-	PO_4^{3-}	SO_4^{2-}	Cl^-	K^+	Ca^{2+}	Na^+	Mg^{2+}	NH_4^+
11.63	4.4	6.8	—	3.44	9.65	—	6.8	—

was originally devised for shoot proliferation of almond and almond × peach clones. Rugini and co–workers found it not to be suitable for almond (*P. dulcis = P.*

Table 208. Media, apart from **MS**, which have been used for the shoot culture of *Prunus*.. The composition of each medium is given in Table 209.

Prunus species	Medium number in Table 209	Nature	References
P. persica hybrid	①	½MS + extra phosphate	Reeves *et al.* (1983)
P. persica	②	Unique	Jona and Vigliocco (1985, 1987)
P. armeniaca	③	**Lloyd and McCown (1981) WPM**	Snir (1984)
Prunus 'P.S.B2' (Peach rootstock)	③	**Lloyd and McCown (1981) WPM**, but MS organics and 10 mg/l ascorbic acid	Morini and Conceti (1985)
P. armeniaca	④	Unique	Marino *et al.* (1991) Marino(1991)
P. avium	⑤	MS but ½ NH_4NO_3	Righetti *et al.* (1988)
P. avium *P. mahaleb*	⑥	Unique	Ranjit *et al.* (1988a)
Prunus avium 'Mazzard F12/1' (Cherry rootstock)	⑦	Unique	Tchernets *et al.* (1987)
Prunus 'Colt' (Cherry rootstock)	⑧	Unique	

amygdalus) at Stage II (Rugini and Verma, 1983) and preferred to use **MS** medium, although this may need to be supplemented with 45 g/l fructose, instead of sucrose, to prevent hyperhydricity (page 1047) (Rugini *et al.*, 1987).

Hammerschlag (1982b) advocated placing explants onto a liquid medium (vessels on a roller drum turned at 7 r.p.m.) for 7 days before placing them on an agar medium. This was said to reveal contaminated cultures through medium turbidity, and in the absence of contamination to increase the subsequent rate of shoot proliferation.

Shoot culture media have usually been supplemented with 20–30 g/l sucrose, but Tchernets *et al.* (1987) found that shoot proliferation could be increased in *P. avium* 'Mazzard F12/1' and *Prunus* 'Colt' by adding, respectively, 41 and 45 g/l. Exceptionally, Marino *et al.* (1991) have reported that in cultures of *P. armeniaca*, shoot multiplication was greater when 21.3 g/l (116.8 mM) sorbitol was added to the medium (Tables 208 and 209) instead of 20 g/l (58.4 mM) sucrose (*c.f.* the situation in *Malus*, page 1039).

Alternative media. Several alternative media, some of which are listed in Tables 208 and 209, have been used

at Stage II of *Prunus* cultures, instead of media containing **MS** salts. In papers describing these alternatives there is usually no comparison with the results which would have been obtained had **MS** medium been used, but where **MS** medium was deliberately modified (Ranjit *et al.*, 1988a; Reeves *et al.*, 1983; Marino *et al.*, 1991; Marino, 1991; Tchernets *et al.* 1987), one presumes that shoot growth and shoot number *were* improved by so doing. Several workers have described employing **Lloyd and McCown (1981) WPM** medium, either unmodified (Snir, 1984), with modified organics (Tables 208 and 209), or with no chloride ions† and 0.16 mM NaFeEDTA (Pevalek–Kozlina and Jelaska, 1987).

It is noticeable that several of the alternative media contain less NH_4^+ than **MS** medium. Working with cherry rootstocks, Tchernets *et al.* (1987) found that, compared to the rate of shoot multiplication on **MS** medium, 'Mazzard F12/1' proliferated more rapidly when there was less NO_3^- than in MS (Medium **7** in Table 209), but that 'Colt' produced more shoots when both NO_3^- and NH_4^+ were increased in concentration (Medium **8**).

---

†   The recipe for preparing these macronutrients was not disclosed.

Table 209. The composition of media (apart from **MS**) described in Table 208 which have been used for the shoot culture of *Prunus*.

Components	Medium (see Table 208)							
	①	②‡	③	④	⑤	⑥	⑦	⑧
Macronutrients (meq/l)								
NO_3^-	19.7	33.0	9.7	29.1	29.1	19.7	27.5	46.3
PO_4^{3-}	5.57	12.00	3.74	11.25	3.75	3.75	3.75	3.75
SO_4^{2-}	1.5	3.0	14.36	3.0	3.0	3.0	3.0	3.0
Cl^-	2.99	—	1.3	5.99	5.99	2.99	5.99	5.99
K^+	10.02	22.0	12.6	22.54	20.0	10.65	8.17	20.04
Ca^{2+}	2.99	10.0	6.01	5.99	5.99	2.99	5.99	5.99
Na^+	1.23	—	—	—	—	—	—	—
Mg^{2+}	1.5	3.0	3.0	3.00	3.0	3.0	3.0	3.0
NH_4^+	10.31	5.0	4.99	10.3	10.31	10.31	20.61	27.48
Microelements (mg/l)								
$MnSO_4.4H_2O$	11.2	45.55	29.4	22.3	22.3	22.3	22.3	22.3
$ZnSO_4.7H_2O$	4.3	8.63	8.6	8.6	8.6	8.6	8.6	8.6
H_3BO_3	3.1	6.18	6.2	6.2	6.2	6.2	6.2	6.2
KI	0.42	0.083	—	0.083	0.83	0.42	0.83	0.83
$CuSO_4.5H_2O$	0.012	0.025	0.025	0.025	0.025	0.025	0.025	0.025
$Na_2MoO_4.2H_2O$	0.13	0.24	0.25	0.25	0.25	0.25	0.25	0.25
$CoCl_2.6H_2O$	0.012	0.024	—	0.025	0.025	0.012	0.025	0.025
NaFeEDTA (mM)	0.1	0.2	0.1	0.15	0.1	0.1	0.054	0.054
Vitamins (mg/l)								
myo–Inositol	100	100	100	150	100	100	100	100
Thiamine HCl	1.0	1.0	1.0	1.5	0.1	0.1	0.4	0.4
Nicotinic acid	—	0.062	0.5	0.5	0.5	0.5	—	—
Nicotinamide	2.0	—	—	—	—	—	—	—
Pyridoxine HCl	2.0	—	0.5	0.5	0.5	0.5	—	—
Ca pantothenate	1.0	0.48	—	1.0	—	—	—	—
Folic acid	0.5	0.009	—	—	—	—	—	—
Biotin	1.0	0.098	—	0.01	—	—	—	—
Choline chloride	1.0	—	—	—	—	—	—	—
p–aminobenzoic acid	0.5	1.37	—	—	—	—	—	—
Riboflavin	0.5	—	—	—	—	—	—	—
Ascorbic acid	50.0	—	—	—	—	—	—	—
Vit. B_{12}	0.0015	—	—	—	—	—	—	—
Amino acids (mg/l)								
Glycine	2.0	—	2.0	2.0	2.0	2.0	—	—
Sugars (g/l)								
Sucrose	30	20	30	—	30	30	45	41
Sorbitol	—	—	—	21.3	—	—	—	—

‡ Compositions given in the 1985 and 1987 papers differ slightly. That of the 1987 paper given here.

Recipes for the preparation of the macronutrients in this table will be found in the Appendix.

Table 210. Growth regulators added to the medium at Stage II to induce axillary shoot proliferation in *Prunus*.

Plant	Cytokinin (mg/l)	Auxin (mg/l)	GA3 (mg/l)	References
P. armeniaca	2 2–iP	—	—	Snir (1984)
P. armeniaca	0.5–1 BAP	—	—	Marino (1991) Marino et al. (1991)
P. avium (7 sweet cherry cvs.) †	1 BAP	1 IBA	0.5	Snir (1982b)
	1 BAP	0.1 IBA	0.5	
	2 BAP	0.1 IBA	0.5	
P. avium	1.0 BAP	—	—	Righetti *et al.* (1988)
P. avium 'Mazzard 12/1' (rootstock)	2.3 BAP	—	—	Tchernets *et al.* (1987)
P. avium × *P. pseudocerasus* 'Colt' (rootstock)	2 BAP	0.7 IBA	4.5	
P. avium × *P. mahaleb* 'MXM 2' †	0.2 BAP	0.01 IBA	—	Zilkah *et al.* (1992)
'MXM 46'	6 BAP	0.01 IBA	—	
'MXM 60'	0.5 BAP	0.01 IBA	0.2	
P. dulcis	0.7 BAP	0.01 NAA	—	Rugini and Verma (1982)
P. cerasifera rootstock	1.0 BAP	0.01 IBA	—	Hammerschlag (1982b)
P. cerasifera 'Mr. S. 2/5' rootstock	0.6 BAP	0.06 IBA	0.17–24	Morini *et al.* (1991a; 1992)
P. cerasifera (seedling selections)	0.4 BAP	0.08 IBA	0.15	Morini *et al.* (1991b)
P. cerasus	0.7 BAP	0.1 IBA	0.1	Marin and Gella (1987b)
P. cerasus	1.0 BAP	1.0 IBA	0.1	Snir (1983)
P. domestica 'Stanley'	1.1 BAP	—	—	Pietropaolo and Reisch (1984)
P. domestica 'Stanley', 'President'	0.8 BAP	0.01 IBA	0.03	Jona and Vigliocco (1987)
P. insitia *P. persica* × *P. amygdalus*	0.7 BAP	—	0.3	Loreti *et al.* (1988)
P. persica × *P. amygdalus*	0.6–1.0 BAP	0.1 IBA	—	Martinelli (1985)
P. persica	1.0 BAP	0.01–0.1 IBA	—	Hammerschlag (1980, 1981b)
P. persica	1.1 BAP	0.25 IBA	0.01	Jona and Vigliocco (1985
P. persica 'Nemaguard' rootstock	2 BAP	0.1 NAA	—	Miller *et al.* (1982)
P. persica hybrid	1.0 BAP, 80 AdS	0.01 IBA	—	Reeves *et al.* (1983)
Prunus 'P.S. B2' (peach rootstock)	1.2 BAP	—	—	Morini and Concetti (1985)
Prunus 'Hally Jolivette' (ornamental cherry)	1.0 BAP	0.1 NAA	—	Lineberger (1982, 1983)

† Optimum concentrations of regulants varied with cv.

Growth regulators for shoot culture

Examples of growth regulators used to induce axillary shoot proliferation in Stage II *Prunus* cultures are shown in Table 210. In almost all reports, BAP has been used as the chosen cytokinin and has been combined with a low concentration of auxin, usually IBA. The addition of a low concentration of gibberellic acid is sometimes advantageous. Two examples in the table demonstrate how the optimum concentration of growth regulators varies even between closely related genotypes.

Snir (1984) used 2–iP to produce multiple shoots from *P. armeniaca* cultures, but others have obtained only single shoots when BAP has been replaced with 2–iP or kinetin (Martinelli, 1985). Mante *et al* (1989) obtained good shoot proliferation in peach, plum and cherry cultures by adding 1.1–2.75 mg/l thidiazuron and 0.56 mg/l IBA to a slightly modified **MS** medium.

Establishment. That it can be important to use a different medium at Stage I has been mentioned above. Explants can often be established on media containing the

quat, are of only local interest. Besides fruit, some members of the genus are used for the extraction of essential oils.

Fruit–bearing *Citrus* are all small trees and are grown as clones which are normally propagated by budding or grafting scions onto known rootstocks. Although there are some monoembryonic *Citrus* clones forming only one zygotic embryo per seed, many other kinds are polyembryonic. Polyembryonic varieties possess a genetic factor which, either upon fertilisation or upon the initial growth of a fertilised zygotic embryo, causes the nucellus surrounding the ovule to generate one or more somatic embryos. In these circumstances a seed frequently produces more than one seedling. One may be of hybrid origin, the other/s of somatic origin and identical to the parent. Further development of the zygotic embryo is sometimes suppressed and then all seedlings obtained from a polyembryonic maternal parent are apogamous. This can create problems in *Citrus* breeding.

Citrus seedlings, including those of nucellar origin, show persistent juvenile traits (such as thorniness) and trees need to grow for several years before they assume an adult flowering and fruiting habit. Unlike seedlings, adult buds or shoots grafted onto rootstocks do not lose their capacity to flower.

Micropropagation could possibly be used in *Citrus* to provide selected varieties on their own roots or to produce rootstocks. Uniform rootstock clones are at present obtained from nucellar seedlings of varieties giving a high proportion of polyembryonic seeds. Kitto and Young (1981) give three reasons why micropropagation from non–nucellar vegetative tissue could be beneficial:

- several years are required before sufficient seed can be produced from a newly–introduced rootstock;

- some desirable rootstock clones may not produce nucellar seedlings, or may be seedless (or only produce few seeds);

- scion cultivars might (it was hoped) fruit more precociously on rootstocks derived from vegatively–propagated shoots than on those produced from seedlings.

Media for micropropagation

Citrus tissue cultures have been most frequently established on **MS** medium or on the medium of **Murashige and Tucker (1969)** (Part 1, page 386) (**MT** medium). When used to induce embryogenic or organogenic callus, these media are often supplemented with casein hydrolysate (*e.g.* 1 g/l), malt extract (*e.g.* 0.5–1 g/l) or coconut milk, and 30–50 g/l sucrose. Murashige and Tucker (1969)

found that adding 100 ml/l orange juice to their medium improved callus growth, and this has been confirmed by others. Adding it to **MS** medium (with twice the normal concentration of vitamins) allowed organogenic callus of several *Citrus* species to be maintained for up to 2 years, whereas otherwise it could not be retained for more than 3 subcultures (Duran–Vila *et al.*, 1989).

Media of lower ionic concentration have usually been employed for *in vitro* rooting.

Embryogenesis

Explanted nucellus tissue of both naturally monoembryonic and polyembryonic *Citrus* varieties can continue to give rise directly to adventitious embryos in aseptic culture (Rangan *et al.*, 1968; Esan, 1973). Embryos are formed preferentially from the nucellus tissue in the micropylar– (as opposed to the chalazal–) half of both fertilised and unfertilised ovules. Table 87 in Chapter 12 gives examples of media and growth regulators which have been found to be effective.

Somatic embryos are also formed directly on cultured embryos and ovules (of both zygotic and nucellar origin) which are dissected from seeds (Ranga Swamy, 1959, 1961; Sabharwal, 1963). Moore (1985) used **MT** medium (50 g/l sucrose) supplemented with 0.5–1 g/l malt extract for embryo induction for this purpose.

In many *Citrus* species and cultivars, embryogenic callus can be induced from nucellus tissue on **MS** or **MT** medium, supplemented with 500 mg/l malt extract (see pages 613 and 630) and 50 g/l sucrose, without the addition of growth regulators. It is often subcultured on a medium containing IAA (0.1–1 mg/l) and kinetin (1 mg/l), but after several subcultures becomes auxin– and cytokinin–habituated, and maintains a low level of embryoid development when subcultured at 4–5 week intervals. The frequency of embryoid formation in the next subculture is increased by aging the callus during a 14 week passage, or by omitting sucrose during a single passage (Kochba and Button, 1974).

Embryo–forming callus can also be obtained from ovules, zygotic embryo explants, and juice vesicles excised from immature fruits (Nito and Iwamasa, 1990), but induction here may require the presence of auxin and/or cytokinin. Callus initiated from other explants is most likely to give rise to adventitious shoots.

Nucellar callus is not composed of normal parenchymatous tissue, but solely of numerous self–replicating proembryoids (Button *et al.*, 1974), embryos (which develop into plants), and pseudobulbils (Button and Botha, 1975). Embryo formation in such tissue is inhibited by auxins (IAA, NAA), cytokinins (kinetin, BAP, 2–iP) and GA_3, except at low concentrations, but can recommence once the growth regulators are removed (Kochba *et al.,* 1972, 1974; Kobayashi *et al.,* 1985). Gibberellic acid on its own, or combined with adenine sulphate (Kochba *et al.,* 1972, 1974) does, however, stimulate root formation from small embryoids, and from larger ones with partially–formed root zones. Stimulants of embryogenesis include inhibitors of auxin synthesis (Kochba and Spiegel–Roy, 1977), low levels (0.01–1.0 mg/l) of ethephon, ABA (0.5 mg/l), chlormequat (Kochba *et al.,* 1978a) and the sugars galactose, lactose and maltose (Kochba *et al.,* 1978b, 1982; Button, 1978).

Maturation and germination. Embryos have been induced to enlarge by subculture to **MT** medium (50 g/l sucrose) supplemented with 1–1.5 g/l malt extract (Moore, 1985; Grosser *et al.,* 1988). Enlarged embryos are then moved to the same medium (with or without malt extract) (20–25 g/l sucrose) containing 1–10 mg/l GA_3 (Spiegel–Roy and Vardi, 1984), or 1 mg/l GA_3 and 15 mg/l coumarin (Grosser *et al.,* 1988). Spiegel–Roy and Vardi (1984) then moved cotyledonary embryos to test tubes containing **MT** medium (50 g/l sucrose), 1 mg/l GA_3 and 40 mg/l adenine sulphate dihydrate. To improve the root system a further move to filter paper bridges wetted with **MS** salts and 20 g/l sucrose, was advocated. Grosser *et al.,* (1988) placed developed embryos without roots onto **MT** medium supplemented with 5 mg/l BAP and this induced the multiplication of shoots which were afterwards rooted.

Adventitious shoot formation

Direct adventitious shoot formation has been observed on various explants derived from seedlings and on parts excised from plants grown *in vitro,* such as internodes, leaves, epicotyls and roots (Table 216).

The same kinds of explants may give rise to callus from which shoots can be regenerated. **MS** and **MT** media have again been most commonly used, sometimes containing an organic supplement (usually malt extract). Callus is initiated on media supplemented with auxin and cytokinin (*e.g.* 10 mg/l NAA + 0.25 mg/l BAP — Duran–Vila *et al.,* 1989), and shoots are regenerated on medium containing a high proportion of cytokinin to auxin (*e.g.* 1.5 mg/l BAP + 0.5 mg/l IAA — Islam *et al.,* 1993).

Grosser and Chandler (1986) found that adventitious shoot formation on seedling stem sections was promoted when **MT** medium was supplemented with 90–150 μM (13–22 mg/l) coumarin.

Shoot culture

Shoot cultures can be initiated from shoot tips, from fragmented shoot tips (Barlass and Skene, 1982b), or from nodal segments. **MS** medium has been most commonly employed, sometimes with additional vitamins. Preferred growth regulators have varied in different experiments and need to be adjusted according to genotype (Duran–Vila *et al.,* 1989; Marin and Duran–Vila (1991). Some examples of treatments which have resulted in shoot proliferation are:

Species	Growth regulators (mg/l)	References
C. sinensis × Poncirus C. limon C. sinensis	2.25 BAP	Barlass and Skene (1982b)
C. sinensis × Poncirus	1 BAP + 40 AdS + 0.5 IBA	Starrantino and Caruso (1988b)
Poncirus trifoliata	0.5 BAP + 40 AdS + 0.25 IBA	Starrantino and Caruso (1988b)
C. sinensis C. aurantifolia	1 BAP	Duran–Vila et al. (1989) Marin and Duran–Vila (1991)
C. medica	0.1 BAP	Duran–Vila et al. (1989)

In some reports, explants have been taken from seedlings. Altman and Goren (1971, 1974, 1978) observed shoot growth on **MT** medium from buds of 40 year–old trees taken after the spring flush, but shoot multiplication did not occur. However, in subsequent experiments, axillary shoots have been obtained from cultures initiated from field–grown plants and these have been rooted (Barlass and Skene, 1982b; Bouzid, 1986; Sim *et al.,* 1989; Starrantino and Caruso, 1987).

Rooting

Roots can be induced to form *in vitro* on media containing low salt concentrations, such as **White (1954)** (Barlass and Skene, 1982b), but often shoots have been rooted on **MS** or **MT**: $\frac{1}{2}$**MS** is probably more suitable. Media have been supplemented with either NAA or IBA (1–2 mg/l). Transfer to a medium without growth regulators can promote root growth. Kitto and Young (1981) obtained incomplete rooting but found that approximately half of the shoots which had not formed roots did produce them during the establishment stage, suggesting that rooting *extra vitrum* is possible, after *in vitro* root induction.

The proportion of shoots which form roots has tended to be low in *Citrus* and many workers have reported that a large proportion of rooted plantlets perished during acclimatisation. Islam *et al.* (1993) found that for successful establishment, rooted shoots needed to be kept at 30°C in continuous light for 7–10 days until the roots became brown. Possibly this treatment encourages the roots to develop secondary thickening (page 672).

Species name	Type of Culture	Source of explant	Results		References
Mangifera indica	Embryogenic callus	Nucellus ex immature fruit	Embryo maturation, & limited germination	—	Litz (1984b)
Mangifera indica 'Parris' & 'James Saigon'	Suspension	Immature half-ovule cultures	Embryogenesis. Somatic embryos matured & germinated	—	De Wald *et al.* (1989)
❖ *Pistacia atlantica* Desf.	Shoot	Seedling apical & axillary buds	Multiple shoots. Rooted plants	Y	Barghchi (1986b)
Pistacia atlantica	Shoot	Shoot tips ex seedlings & 4-year-old plants	Shoot multiplication. Shoots rooted *in vivo*	Y	Martinelli (1988)
Pistacia integerrima (Pistacio rootstock)	Shoot	Shoot tips ex seedlings & 4-year-old plants	Shoot multiplication. Shoots rooted *in vivo*	Y	Martinelli (1988)
Pistacia khinjuk Stocks. (Bombay mastic)	Shoot	Seedling apical & axillary buds	Multiple shoots. Rooted plants	Y	Barghchi (1986b)
Pistacia mutica Fisch. & C.A.Mey	Shoot	Seedling apical & axillary buds	Multiple shoots. Rooted plants	Y	Barghchi (1986b)
Pistacia palaestina Boiss.	Shoot	Seedling apical & lateral buds	Multiple shoots. Rooted plants	Y	Barghchi (1986b)
Pistacia terebinthus L. cv. 'Tsikoudia' [Pistacio rootstock]	Shoot	Shoot tips	Shoot proliferation. Rooted plants	YY	Pontikis (1984)
Pistacia vera L. (Pistachio nut)	Callus	Shoot tips & nodal buds	Adventitious shoots in 10% of cultures	—	Barghchi & Alderson (1983)
Pistacia vera	Direct	Seedling epicotyls	Adventitious shoots. Rooted plants	Y	Yucel *et al.* (1991)
Pistacia vera [several cvs.]	Micrografting	Shoot apices	Mature scion tips grafted onto seedlings. Shoots	Y	Barghchi (1986a)
Pistacia vera [& two cvs.]	Shoot	Shoot tips & nodal buds	Multiple shoots. Rooted shoots to soil	YY	Barghchi & Alderson (1983)
Pistacia vera	Shoot	Shoot tips ex *in vitro* seedlings	Axillary shoots. Shoots rooted	YY	Barghchi & Alderson (1983)
Pistacia vera	Shoot	Tip of 2-year-old bush (5-8 mm)	Shoot proliferation. 50% rooting	YY	Barghchi & Alderson (1985)
Pistacia vera [several cvs.]	Shoot	Meristem tips	Multiple shoots but vitrescence occurred	—	Barghchi (1986a)
Pistacia vera	Shoot	Seedling apical & axillary buds	Multiple shoots.	Y	Barghchi (1986b)
Pistacia vera [3 cvs].	Shoot	Shoot tips ex young grafted plants	Shoot multiplication. Shoots rooted *in vivo*	Y	Martinelli (1988)

Annonaceae

Annona muricata L. (Prickly custard apple)	Direct	Seedling hypocotyl sections	Multiple advent. shoots. Rooted	YY	Bejoy & Hariharan (1992)
Annona squamosa L. (Sweet Sop)	Callus	Mature endosperm tissue	Shoot differentiation. Triploid plants	—	Nair *et al.* (1986)
Annona squamosa	Direct	Seedling leaf base with petiole	Shoots (and some callus). Shoots rooted. Plants	Y	Nair *et al.* (1984)
Annona squamosa × *A. cherimola*	Shoot	Nodes with axillary buds	Rooted plantlets moved to field	YY	Nair *et al.* (1984)

Averrhoaceae – See Oxalidaceae

Bromeliaceae

* *Ananas comosus* (L.) Merr. (= *A. sativa*) (Pineapple) cv. 'Queen'	Callus	Crown apical domes	Protocorm-like bodies. Adventitious shoots. Rooted	—	Fitchet (1990 c)
Ananas comosus	Callus	Shoot tips	Embryogenesis ('protocorm-like bodies'). Plantlets	—	Mapes (1973)
Ananas comosus	Callus	*In vitro* shoots	Adv. shoots, multiplied by shoot culture. Plants	—	Mathews & Rangan (1981)
Ananas comosus	Callus	*In vitro* leaves	Adventitious shoots	—	Rangan & Mathews (1980)
Ananas comosus	Callus	Callus at base of shoot cultures	Adventitious shoots. Plants, some variants	—	Rangan & Mathews (1980)
Ananas comosus hybrid	Callus	Seeds	Shoots from embryo callus. Rooted	—	Srinivasa Rao *et al.* (1981)
Ananas comosus cv. 'Smooth Cayenne'	Callus	Various	Shoot regeneration. Some variable plants	—	Wakasa (1979)
Ananas comosus .	(Callus) Shoot	Lateral buds	Multiple shoots. Rooted *in vitro*	YY	Drew (1980)
Ananas comosus	Callus/Shoot	Terminal & axillary buds	Adventitious & axillary shoots. Uniform plants	YY	DeWald *et al.* (1988)
Ananas comosus	Direct/Callus	*In vitro* shoots or half shoots	Adventitious shoots. Rooted with difficulty	—	Mathews *et al.* (1976)

Species name	Type of Culture	Source of explant	Results		References
Ananas comosus cv. 'Smooth Cayenne'	Shoot	Crown axillary leaf bud	Plantlet (fragments then subcultured)	Y	Pannetier & Lanaud (1976)
Ananas comosus	Shoot	Terminal or axill. buds from crown	Up to 8 axillary shoots per explant	Y	Mathews et al. (1976)
Ananas comosus	Shoot	Stem fragments	Axillary shoots. Poor rooting	—	Aghion & Beauchesne (1960)
Ananas comosus cvs. 'Queen', 'Smooth Cayenne'	Shoot	Lateral buds from crown	Shoot multiplication. Rooted *in vitro*	YY	Fitchet (1990a)
Ananas comosus cv. 'Kew'	Shoot	Shoot tips	Bud proliferation. Shoots rooted	YY	Hirimburegama & Wijesinghe (1992)
Ananas comosus	Shoot	Shoot tips	One plant per shoot tip	Y	Lakshmi-Sita et al. (1974)
Ananas comosus	Shoot	Dormant lateral bud from crown	Multiple axillary shoots. Shoots rooted	YY	Mathews & Rangan (1979)
Ananas comosus cv. 'Smooth Cayenne'	Shoot	Crown axillary leaf bud	Axillary shoot proliferation	YY	Pannetier & Lanaud (1976)
Ananas comosus	Shoot	Lateral buds	Multiple axillary shoots. Plants	YY	Rangan & Mathews (1980)
Ananas comosus	Shoot	Crown buds	Single shoots & multiple axillary shoots. Plants	YY	Zepeda & Sagawa (1981)

Cactaceae

Species name	Type of Culture	Source of explant	Results		References
Selenicereus setaceus (DC.) Werdderm. = *Mediocactus coccineus*	Shoot	Seedling epicotyls	Multiple shoots. Rooted	YY	Infante (1992)

Caricaceae

Species name	Type of Culture	Source of explant	Results		References
Carica × *heilbornii*	Single node/Shoot	Node segments	Single shoots, then shoot multiplication. Rooted	YY	Cohen & Cooper (1982)
Carica papaya L. (Pawpaw or Papaya)	Callus	Cotyledon midrib or lamina	Callus growth, roots, shoots	—	Litz et al. (1983)
Carica papaya	Callus	Stem segments ex *in vitro* plantlets	Adventitious shoots. Not rooted	—	Rajeevan & Pandey (1983)
Carica papaya	Callus	Seedling	Embryogenesis. Enzyme activity of embryoids assessed	—	Yamamoto & Tabata (1989)
Carica papaya	Direct	Shoots ex *in vitro* cultures	Rooting. Improved with riboflavin	Y	Drew et al. (1991)
Carica papaya	Direct	Immature zygotic embryos	Somatic embryo formation. Plants	—	Fitch & Manshardt (1990)
Carica papaya [4 cvs.]	Embryogenic callus	Hypocot. sections ex *in vitro* sdlgs.	Embryo maturation & germ. Plantlets	—	Fitch (1993)
Carica papaya 'Hybrid 14'	Node	Single node segments ex apically dominant plants	Shoot formation, then rooting	YY	Drew (1992)
Carica papaya cv. 'Sunrise Solo'	Shoot	Side shoots/apex field-grown trees	Shoot multiplication. Rooted. Poor plant survival	YY	De Winnaar (1988)
Carica papaya	Shoot	Shoot tips ex *in vitro* culture	Shoot proliferation, shoots rooted *ex vitro*	YY	Kataoka & Inoue (1992)
Carica papaya	Shoot	Shoot apices	Axillary buds. Shoot proliferation. Rooted plants	YY	Litz & Conover (1978a)
Carica papaya	Shoot	Shoot tips ex male, female & bisexual plants	Shoot proliferation	YY	Litz & Conover (1981c)
Carica papaya	Shoot	Tips of callus-regenerated shoots	Lateral shoot proliferation	Y	Litz et al. (1983)
Carica papaya	Shoot	Entire plantlets, or with apices or shoots removed	Multiple shoots, rooted	YY	Miller & Drew (1990)
Carica papaya	Shoot	Lateral buds or seedling shoot tips	Shoot multiplication. Rooted plants	YY	Rajeevan & Pandey (1983)
Carica papaya	Shoot	Lateral buds (5 mm)	Shoot multiplication. Rooted. Stunted plantlets	Y	Rajeevan & Pandey (1986)
Carica papaya [Dioecious line]	Shoot	Axillary buds	Shoot multiplication, elongation & rooting	YY	Reuveni et al. (1990)
Carica papaya [4 cvs.]	Shoot	Shoot apices	Axillary shoots. Tested for disease resistance	Y	Sharma & Skidmore (1988)
Carica papaya	Shoot	Axill. buds ex 3 yr-old field plants	Shoot multiplication. Rooted plants	Y	Shlesinger et al. (1987)
Carica papaya	Shoot	Small axillary shoot buds	Shoot proliferation	YY	Drew (1988)
Carica papaya var. 'Honey Dew'	Shoot/Callus	Shoot buds ex saplings & fruit-bearing plants	Shoot formation. Multiplied & rooted	Y	Mondal et al. (1990)
Carica papaya	Shoot/Node	Axillary buds	Shoot proliferation. Rooting of shoots studied	YY	Drew & Miller (1989)

	Species name	Type of Culture	Source of explant	Results		References
	Carica papaya × C. cauliflora	Callus/Suspension	Fertilized ovules	Embryogenesis. Plant regeneration	—	Litz & Conover (1981 a,b; 1982; 1983)
	Carica papaya × C. cauliflora	Embryo	95 day hybrid embryos	Embryo germination (also adv. shoots). Plants	Y	Rojkind et al. (1982)
	Carica papaya × C. cauliflora	Callus	Ovules 65-days post-pollination	Embryogenesis. Plants regenerated	—	Moore & Litz (1984)
*	Carica pentagona (Heilb.) Badillo (Babaco)	Callus	23–140 day-old ovules, dissected lengthwise	Somatic embryogenesis. Plantlets regenerated	—	Vega de Rojas & Kitto (1991)
	Carica pubescens Lenné & K.Koch = C. candamarcensis (Mountain papaya)	Callus	Immature pericarp	Somatic embryogenesis. Plantlets	—	Jordan et al. (1983)
	Carica pubescens	Suspension	Hypocotyl callus	Embryogenesis in susps. or callus	—	Jordan (1987)
	Carica stipulata	Suspension	Friable callus ex peduncle	Embryogenesis	—	Litz & Conover (1980 a)

Clusiaceae

	Species name	Type of Culture	Source of explant	Results		References
	Garcinia mangostana L. (Mangosteen)	Direct	Segments of seed	Multiple shoots, 20% rooted plants	Y	Normah et al. (1992)
	Garcinia mangostana	Direct	Half seeds or slices	Single or multiple shoots dep. on medium	Y	Teo (1992)

Corylaceae

	Species name	Type of Culture	Source of explant	Results		References
*	Corylus avellana L. cv. 'Casina' (Filbert, hazelnut)	Callus	Seedling cotyledon sections	Adventitious root formation	—	Gonzalez et al. (1991)
	Corylus avellana	Callus	Isolated seed embryos	Embryogenesis & embryoid germination. Adv. shoots	—	Radojevic et al. (1975)
	Corylus avellana	Direct	Seedling cotyledonary nodes	Proembryogenic cells. Embryoids. Plants	—	Pérez et al. (1983)
	Corylus avellana	Direct	Shoot & cotyledon node segs. ex 20 d-old seedlings	Adventitious shoots. Rooted plants	Y	Pérez et al. (1985)
	Corylus avellana	Direct	Cotyledonary node of 20-d-old seedling	Embryogenesis. Embryo proliferation & germination	Y	Pérez et al. (1986)
	Corylus avellana	Direct	Embryos from mature seeds	Multiple adventitious shoots. Rooted plants	Y	Pérez et al. (1987)
	Corylus avellana cv. 'Tonda Gentille delle Langhe'	Node & shoot	Single nodes & apical buds	Multiple shoots. 100% rooted	YY	Diaz-Sala et al. (1990)
	Corylus avellana	Shoot	Shoot tips ex sdlgs & g'house trees	Axillary shoot multiplication. Rooted plantlets	YY	Anderson (1984)
	Corylus avellana [3 cvs]	Shoot	Shoot tips	Some shoot proliferation. Rooted plantlets	Y	Kai et al. (1984)
	Corylus avellana cv. 'Gironell'	Shoot	Juvenile & adult explants	Adult cultures rejuvenated after 8th transfer.	—	Melé & Messeguer (1986)
	Corylus avellana cv. 'Gironell'	Shoot	Seedling/adult nodal sections	Multiple shoots (most from juvenile material)	Y	Messeguer & Melé (1987)
	Corylus avellana	Shoot	Single nodes ex adult material	Single shoots. Rooted plants	—	Pérez et al. (1987)
	Corylus avellana [3 vars.]	Shoot	Nodal segments 2 yr-old tree	Shoot proliferation. Rooted plants	Y	Rodriguez et al. (1988)

Cucurbitaceae — See the Vegetable Table also

	Species name	Type of Culture	Source of explant	Results		References
	Citrullus lanatus (Thunb.) Matsum. & Nak. = C. vulgaris (Watermelon)	Callus	Sdlg. cotyl. or hypocotyl segments	Shoot regeneration. Shoots rooted	—	Srivastava et al. (1989)
	Citrullus lanatus	Direct	Cotyledons from 5-d-old seedlings	Adventitious shoots, rooted	Y	Dong & Jia (1991)
	Citrullus lanatus	Direct	Half-cotyledon	Shoot regeneration from 4% explants	—	Blackmon & Reynolds (1982)
	Citrullus lanatus cv. 'Charlee'	Direct/Shoot	In vitro cultured shoot clusters	Shoot growth	Y	Hale et al. (1992)
	Citrullus lanatus	Shoot	Seedling shoot tips (1–3 mm)	Multiple shoots. Rooted plantlets	YY	Barnes (1979)
	Citrullus lanatus Diploid & tetraploid genotypes	Shoot	Seedling shoot tips	Shoot proliferation, rooted	YY	Compton et al. (1993)
	Citrullus lanatus cv. 'Charlee'	Shoot	Meristems ex in vitro cultures	Prolif. & elongation in liquid & solid media	Y	Desamero et al. (1993)
❖	Cucumis melo L. (Melon)	Callus	Hypocotyl segments	Embryogenesis	—	Blackmon et al. (1981b)
	Cucumis melo cv. 'Topmark'	Callus	Cotyledons	Shoot formation, followed by rooting	—	Chee (1991)

Species name	Type of Culture	Source of explant	Results		References
Cucumis melo cvs. 'Hales Best', 'Iroquois', 'Perlita'	Callus	Cotyledons	Adventitious shoots	—	Mackay & Ng (1988)
Cucumis melo	Callus	Cotyledons of axenic seedlings	Adventitious shoots, grown and rooted as plantlets	—	Moreno *et al.* (1985)
Cucumis melo [15 cvs.]	Callus	Cotyledon segments	Adventitious shoot buds & shoots (depended on genotype)	—	Orts *et al.* (1987)
Cucumis melo	Callus	Seedling leaf & petiole segments	Shoots, some rooted	—	Punja *et al.* (1990)
Cucumis melo	Callus	Cotyl. or embryo axis from seeds	Adventitious shoots & roots	—	Rao *et al.* (1982)
Cucumis melo cv. 'Hale's Best', 'Jumbo'	Callus and direct	Seedling cotyledon segs.	Multiple buds. Developed into shoots & rooted	—	Niede *et al.* (1989)
Cucumis melo	Direct	Cotyledon or primary leaf	Shoot and/or plantlet regeneration	—	Blackmon *et al.* (1981a)
Cucumis melo [4 cvs.]	Direct	Cotyledon and primary leaf	Adventitious shoots on veins & cut edges	Y	Blackmon *et al.* (1981b)
Cucumis melo cvs. 'Hales Best', 'Iroquois', 'Perlita'	Direct	Cotyledons	Shoot formation	Y	Mackay & Ng (1988)
Cucumis melo [2 cvs.]	Direct	Seedling cotyledons	Embryogenesis. Embryoids. A few plants	—	Trulson & Shahin (1986)
Cucumis melo	Direct/Callus	Half leaf or half cotyledon	Shoot regeneration	—	Blackmon & Reynolds (1982)
Cucumis melo cv. 'Pusa Sharbati'	Direct/Callus	Young seedling leaves	Direct & indirect adventitious shoots. Plants	Y	Kathal *et al.* (1988)
Cucumis melo [18 cvs.]	Direct/Callus	Seed sections	Somatic embryogenesis	—	Oridate *et al.* (1992)
Cucumis melo	Embryo	Seed embryos	Embryos germinated to give plants	Y	Norton (1981)
Cucumis melo (Saccharinus Xinjiang muskmelon)	Protoplast	Cotyledons of i.v. seedlings	Protocalli. Plants regenerated	—	Li *et al.* (1990)
Cucumis melo	Shoot	Shoot tips of axenic seedlings	Shoot multiplication	Y	Moreno *et al.* (1984)
Cucumis melo cv. 'Noy Yizre'e'	Shoot	Apical buds ex seedlings	Growth of shoots, rooted. Vitrescence with BAP	—	Leshem *et al.* (1988a)
Ebenaceae					
Diospyros kaki L. cv. 'Jiro' (Japanese persimmon)	Callus	Leaf primordia	Callus maintained for 4 yrs. Bud formation	—	Tamura *et al* (1992)
Diospyros kaki 'Jiro'	Callus	Primordial & young leaves & intermode sections	Adventitious bud formation	—	Tao & Sugiura (1992)
Diospyros kaki 'Jiro'	Callus	Leaf primordia	Adventitious shoots. Plants	—	Tao *et al.* (1991)
Diospyros kaki	Callus	Young embryo hypocotyl	Whole plant regeneration	—	Yokoyama & Takeuchi (1976)
Diospyros kaki 'Jiro'	Protoplast	Callus	Protoplast isolation. Cell colonies	—	Tao *et al.* (1991)
Diospyros kaki cv. 'Hiratanenashi'	Shoot	2 mm apex of dorm. bud (mat. trees)	Shoot rosettes. Shoots elongated & rooted	YY	Sugiura *et al.* (1986)
Diospyros kaki	Shoot/single node	Shoot tips or single nodes	Shoot growth, some axillary shoots. Poor rooting	Y	Cooper & Cohen (1985)
Elaeagnaceae					
Elaeagnus angustifolia L. [several clones] (Russian olive)	Shoot	Seedling apical buds	Adventitious & axillary shoots. Rooted	YY	Bertrand & Lalonde (1985)
Elaeagnus angustifolia	Shoot	Shoot tips 1–1.5 cm ex flushed growth	Multiple shoots. Rooted plants	YY	Economou & Spanoudaki (1988)
Ericaceae					
Vaccinium cv. 'Nortblue' (Half-high blueberry)	Shoot	Shoot tips	Shoots proliferated & rooted. Studied field performance	Y	Read *et al.* (1989)
Vaccinium interspecific hybrids	Shoot/direct/callus	Shoot tips (1–2 mm)	Axillary & adventitious shoots. Rooting extra vitrum	YY	Zimmerman & Broome (1980)
Vaccinium angustifolium Ait. (Low-bush blueberry)	Direct/Callus	Cotyledons & hypocotyl sections	Adventitious shoots. Shoot elongation	Y	Nickerson (1978)
Vaccinium angustifolium	Node	Single node	Shoot proliferation & development. 67% rooting	YY	Frett & Smagula (1983)
Vaccinium angustifolium	Shoot	Single nodes from shoot apex	Growth of 2 explants. Shoot multiplication	YY	Brissette *et al.* (1990)
Vaccinium ashei Reade (Rabbit-eye blueberry)	Shoot	Juvenile shoot tips (5 mm)	5-15 shoots 4 cm long in 4 months. 100% rooting	YY	Lyrene (1980)

Species name	Type of Culture	Source of explant	Results		References
Musa acuminata cvs. 'Dwarf Cavendish' 'Valery'	Callus	Leaf base explants	Early stage somatic embryos? No shoots formed	—	Jarret *et al.* (1985)
Musa acuminata = Musa cavendishii	Callus	Young leaves and stems	Adventitious shoots. Rooted plants	—	Drew (1986)
Musa acuminata	Callus	Meristem tips	Adventitious shoot formation	—	Ma et al. (1978)
Musa acuminata	Direct	Inflorescence segments	Adventitious bud formation	Y	Ma et al. (1978)
Musa acuminata	Meristem	Lateral bud apices	Shoot growth. Virus-free plants	Y	Berg & Bustamante (1974)
Musa acuminata cv. 'Williams'	Meristem	Lateral bud apices	Shoot growth. Virus-free plants	Y	Bower & Fraser (1982)
Musa acuminata cv. Cavendish AAA	Meristem	Meristem tips	Viability prolonged by use of ribose	Y	Ko *et al.* (1991)
Musa acuminata AAA cv. 'Highgate'	Organised callus	Shoot tips (2 mm) with 2–3 leaf primordia	Plantlets regenerated	Y	Cronauer-Mitra & Krikorian (1987)
Musa acuminata [2 AAA clones]	Shoot	Inflor. tips at green fruit stage	Lateral buds, multiplied. Rooted plants	YY	Drew (1986)
Musa acuminata cv. 'Williams' (AAA group)	Shoot	Sections of sucker	Various decontamination methods compared	—	Hamill *et al.* (1993)
*Musa acuminata*AAA 'Grande Naire'	Shoot	Shoot apex halved longitudinally	Shoot proliferation. Rooted in vitro	YY	Oglesby & Griffis (1986)
Musa acuminata AAA cv. 'Mons Mari'	Shoot	BBTV infected vegetative shoot/floral apices	Shoots. Assessed BBTV infection of regenerants	—	Drew *et al.* (1989)
Musa acuminata cvs. 'Mas' & 'Berangan'	Shoot	Shoot apices ex young suckers	Shoot formation & proliferation. Shoots rooted	YY	Aziz *et al.* (1992)
Musa acuminata 'Dwarf Cavendish'	Shoot	Tip (0.2–0.5 mm) of male flower	Shoot growth & multiplication. Virus-free plants	YY	Cronauer & Krikorian (1985 a.b)
Musa acuminata	Shoot	Rhizome shoot tips	Multiple shoots. Shoots rooted	YY	Doré Swamy *et al.* (1983)
Musa acuminata	Shoot	Shoot tips	Shoot proliferation. Shoots rooted	YY	Novák *et al.* (1986)
Musa acuminata AAA 'Dwarf Cavendish'	Shoot	Shoot tips ex small suckers	Shoot proliferation. Rooted plants	Y	Rodriguez & Lorenzo Martin (1987)
Musa acuminata AAA 'Dwarf Cavendish'	Shoot	*In vitro* shoots	Shoot proliferation	—	Rodriguez Enriquez *et al.* (1987)
Musa acuminata & hybrid	Shoot	Shoot tips cut longitudinally	6–12 shoots per apex plus roots	Y	Gupta (1986a)
Musa balbisiana	Embryo	Zygotic embryos	Seedling growth	Y	Cox *et al.* (1960)
Musa balbisiana	Seed germination	Embryos ex water-soaked seeds	Germination optimized	Y	Afele & De Langhe (1991)
Musa × paradisiaca L. AAB cv. 'Bluggoe'	Callus	Meristematic layers ex shoot cult.	Embryogenesis. Bi-polar embryoids	—	Banerjee *et al.* (1987)
Musa × paradisiaca cvs. 'Mysore', 'Apple'	Callus	Leaf base explants	Early stage somatic embryos? No shoots formed	—	Jarret *et al.* (1985a)
Musa × paradisiaca AAB [3 cvs.]	Direct	Terminal flower buds (normally determinate)	Vegetative shoot clusters in bract axils. Rooted plants	YY	Cronauer-Mitra & Krikorian (1988)
Musa × paradisiaca [triploid ABB]	Direct	Pieces of in vitro shoot cultures	Proembryonic cell clumps. Green somatic embryos	—	Cronauer & Krikorian (1983)
Musa × paradisiaca = *M. sapientum*	Direct	Decapitated shoot apex	Adventitious buds. Shoots rooted	YY	Hwang *et al.* (1984)
Musa × paradisiaca	Shoot	Pretreated & halved shoot tip	Axillary bud proliferation. Shoots rooted	YY	Jarret *et al.* (1985a)
Musa.× paradisiaca cv. 'Agbagba' AAB	Shoot/meristem	Shoot tips ex buds or suckers	Advent. nodules with many meristems. Variable plants	Y	Vuylsteke *et al.* (1988)
Musa × paradisiaca [triploid ABB]	Shoot	Sucker shoot tips	Shoot multiplication	YY	Cronauer & Krikorian (1983)
Myrtaceae					
Acca sellowiana O.Berg = *Feijoa sellowiana*	Callus/Shoot	Stem callus ex immature leaves	Adv. shoots. Shoot multiplication. Rooted plants	—	Bhojwani *et al.* (1987)
Acca sellowiana	Shoot	Single nodes ex 2–3 y-old plants	Shoots established. Limited multiplication	—	Bhojwani *et al.* (1987)
Acca sellowiana	Shoot	Shoots ex aseptic seedlings	Shoot multiplication. Rooted plants	YY	Bhojwani *et al.* (1987)
❖ *Myricaria cauliflora* (DC.) O.Berg. (Jaboticaba)	Callus	Adv. embryos on *i.v.* ovule cultures	Somatic embryogenesis. Germination of embryoids	—	Litz (1984a)
Psidium guajava L. cv. 'Chittidar' (Guava)	Shoot	Nodes from new growth flush	Axillary shoots. Nodes subcultured. Rooted plants	YY	Amin & Jaiswal (1988)

Species name	Type of Culture	Source of explant	Results		References
❖ Syzygium cumini (L.) Skeels. (Jambolan)	Shoot & node	Shoot tips & nodes ex seedlings	Multiple shoots (nodal explants better). Rooted	YY	Yadav et al. (1990)
Oleaceae					
❖ Olea europaea L. cvs 'Tanche,' 'Picual' (Olive)	Callus	Cotyledon fragments	Adventitious shoots. Rooted plants	—	Canas & Benbadis (1988)
Olea europaea [3 cvs.]	Direct	Petioles ex in vitro shoots	Shoot regen. Shoots rooted	Y	Mencuccini & Rugini (1993)
Olea europaea	Direct/Callus	75 day-old embryos	Embryogenesis. Plants regenerated	—	Rugini (1988)
Olea europaea	Node	Single node cuttings	Shoot proliferation & elongation. Shoots rooted	YY	Rugini & Fontanazza (1981)
Olea europaea cv. 'Mora'	Shoot	Apical flush buds	Shoot proliferation (studied control of vitrescence)	Y	Rugini et al. (1987)
Olea europaea var. sylvestris (Miller) Lehr. (Wild olive)	Callus	Cotyledon segments & radicles ex zygotic embryos	Rhizogenesis &/or somatic embryogenesis	—	Orinos & Mitrakos (1991)
Olea europaea cv. 'Moraiola'	Direct/Callus	Petioles from i.v. plants	One adventitious shoot per explant	—	Mencuccini et al. (1991)
Olea europaea cv 'Picual'	Shoot	Single node cutting with leaf ex i.v. seedling	Single shoots	—	Garcia-Berenguer & D-Gonzalez (1990)
Olea europaea sativa 'Kalamon'	Node	Single nodes	Shoot proliferation. Shoots rooted	YY	Rama & Pontikis (1990)
Oxalidaceae					
Averrhoa carambola L. 'Sub-acidic' form (Star fruit)	Callus	Sdlg. hypocot. & cotyl. segments	Multiple shoot formation. Shoots rooted.	—	Amin & Razzaque (1993)
Averrhoa carambola	Callus	Seedling leaf pieces	Adventitious shoots	—	Litz & Conover (1980b)
Averrhoa carambola cv. 'B1O'	Callus	Basal portion of seedling stem	Shoot formation & multiplication. Shoots rooted	—	Rashid et al. (1992)
Averrhoa corambola cv. 'B1O'	Direct	Root segments ex in vitro seedlings	Shoot formation & multiplication. Shoots rooted	YY	Rashid et al. (1992)
Passifloraceae					
* Passiflora edulis Sims. (Passion fruit)	Callus	Axillary buds	Shoots via basal callus. Shoots rooted	—	Robles (1978)
Passiflora edulis × P. edulis f. flavicarpa cv. 'E23'	Node/Shoot	Adult nodes & axillary buds	Shoot growth	—	Drew (1991)
Passiflora spp. [8 spp. & 1 hybrid]	Shoot/Direct/Callus	Seedling shoot tips	Shoot growth, multiplication & rooting	Y	Drew (1991)
Punicaceae					
Punica granatum L. [two clones] (Pomegranate)	Callus	Pieces of mature leaves	Adventitious shoots, elongated and rooted	—	Omura et al. (1987)
Punica granatum	Node	Mature stem node segments	Multiple shoot formation & elongation. Shoots rooted	YY	Mascarenhas et al. (1982b)
Punica granatum nana (Dwarf pomegranate)	Node	Single nodes	Shoot formation	Y	Zhang & Stolte (1991)
Punica granatum nana	Shoot	Single nodes	Shoot proliferation	Y	Zhang & Stoltz (1991)
Rosaceae					
* Cydonia oblonga Mill. 'East Malling Quince A'	Callus	Leaves of in vitro shoots	Adv. shoots on primary callus. Multiplied	—	Dolcet-Sanjuan et al. (1991)
Cydonia oblonga	Shoot	Terminal or axillary buds	Single shoot; proliferation on subculture. Plantlets	YY	Al Maarri et al. (1986)
Cydonia oblonga	Shoot	Shoot tips (2–3 cm)	Shoots multiplied & rooted. Fe-chlorosis studied	Y	Dolcet-San Juan et al. (1990)
Cydonia oblonga	Shoot	Shoot tips	Shoot multiplication. Rooted plants	YY	Dolcet-Sanjuan et al. (1991)
Cydonia oblonga 'A' rootstock	Shoot	Shoot tips	Shoot proliferation	Y	Gulsen & Dumanoglu (1991)
Cydonia oblonga	Shoot	Shoot tips	Prolif. Studied effect of media, agar & Ca levels	Y	Singh et al. (1990)
Cydonia oblonga cv. 'MA'	Shoot	Shoot tips	Shoot multiplication. Rooted	YY	Vinterhalter & Neskovic (1992)
Fragaria [several different spp.] (Strawberry)	Germination	Seeds	In vitro seed germination	—	Straathof & Goldy (1987)
Fragaria cv. 'Fern'	Meristem	Runner meristem tips	Single or proliferated plants (PGR dependant)	Y	Mohamed et al. (1991)
* Fragaria × ananassa cv. 'Nyono'	Callus	Anthers	Shoot formation. Shoots rooted	—	Amimoto (1992)

Species name	Type of Culture	Source of explant	Results		References
Fragaria × ananassa cv. 'Aiberry'	Callus	Ovary	Shoot formation. Shoots rooted	—	Amimoto (1992)
Fragaria × ananassa cv. 'Hoko-wase'	Callus	Runner-tip meristems	Multiple shoot formation. Shoots rooted	—	Yoshihara & Hanyu (1992)
Fragaria × ananassa Duch. [9 varieties]	Callus	Leaf or petiole ex *in vitro* cultures	Plants regenerated. Marked somaclonal variation	—	Jones *et al.* (1988)
Fragaria × ananassa	Callus	Cotyledons ex mature achenes	Multiple shoots. Plantlets	—	Miller & Chandler (1990)
Fragaria × ananassa cv. 'Redcoat'	Callus	Immature leaves	Adventitious shoots, rooted	—	Nehra & Stushnoff (1988)
Fragaria × ananassa [7 cultivars]	Callus	Young leaf discs	Adv. shoot formation	—	Nehra *et al.* (1988)
Fragaria × ananassa cv. 'Redcoat'	Callus	Leaf sections	Plant regeneration. Somaclonal variation studied	—	Nehra *et al.* (1992)
Fragaria × ananassa [several cvs.]	Callus	Petals, ovaries	Adv. shoots (regen. cv. specific). Rooted plants	—	Predieri *et al.* (1989)
Fragaria × ananassa [several cvs.]	Callus	Stipules ex *in vitro* shoot culture	Shoot formation & multiplication. Shoots rooted.	—	Rugini & Orlando (1992)
Fragaria × ananassa 'Redcoat'	Direct	Leaf discs ex young leaves	Multiple adventitious shoots	Y	Nehra *et al.* (1988, 1989)
Fragaria × ananassa 'Hiku' & 'Jonsok'	Direct	Leaf disks	Multiple shoot formation	Y	Sorvari *et al.* (1993)
Fragaria × ananassa	Embryo	Immature embryos	Plantlet regeneration from embryogenic tissue	Y	Wang D. *et al.* (1984)
Fragaria × ananassa	Meristem	Meristem tips	Plantlets, virus-free	—	Adams (1972)
Fragaria × ananassa	Meristem	Meristem	Multiple virus-free shoots formed. Rooted	YY	Boxus (1974 a,b) &
Fragaria × ananassa	Meristem	Meristem tip	Juvenile plantlet	Y	Damiano (1980)
Fragaria × ananassa	Meristem	Meristem tip	Rooted plantlets	Y	McGrew (1980)
Fragaria × ananassa	Meristem	Meristem tip	Virus-free plantlet growth	Y	Mullin & Schlegel (1976)
Fragaria × ananassa [6 genotypes]	Meristem/Shoot	Runner apical meristems	Shoot proliferation	Y	Simpson & Bell (1989)
Fragaria × ananassa	Meristem/Shoot	Young runner meristem	Axillary shoot proliferation. Direct rooting	YY	Boxus *et al.* (1984)
Fragaria × ananassa [several cvs.]	Meristem/Shoot	Meristem tips	Multiple shoots. Rooted plants	YY	Zimmerman (1981)
Fragaria × ananassa	Meristem	Shoot tip or lateral buds	Virus-free plantlet growth	Y	Van Hoof (1974)
Fragaria × ananassa	Meristem	Meristem tips	Virus-free shoot growth & rooting	Y	Vine (1968)
Fragaria × ananassa	Node	Single nodes ex *in vitro* plant	Multiple shoot formation & growth	Y	Lee & de Fossard (1975; 1977)
Fragaria × ananassa	Shoot	Small shoot tips	Multiple shoot formation. Rooted	YY	Anderson *et al.* (1982)
Fragaria × ananassa [several cvs.]	Shoot	Shoot tips	Multiple shoots. Rooted	Y	Atkinson *et al.* (1986)
Fragaria × ananassa [4 cultivars]	Shoot	Meristem tips	Studied effect cytokinin on regen. plants in field	YY	Beech *et al.* (1988)
Fragaria × ananassa	Shoot	Shoot tips	Shoot multiplication	Y	Cossio & Menin (1982)
Fragaria × ananassa	Shoot	*In vitro* shoot (virus-indexed)	Multiple shoots. Shoots rooted	YY	Damiano (1980)
Fragaria × ananassa cv. 'Cambridge Favourite'	Shoot	Vegetative buds from stolons	Multiple shoots. Rooted plants	YY	Hunter *et al.* (1983)
Fragaria × ananassa cv. 'Asaka'	Shoot	Plantlets ex *in vitro* cultures	Studied photoauto & photomixotrophic growth	—	Kozai *et al.* (1991)
Fragaria × ananassa [2 cvs.]	Shoot	Shoot tips	Induced runner formation *in vitro*	YY	Zatyko *et al.* (1989)
Fragaria × ananassa	Shoot/Direct	Seeds germinated *in vitro*	Multiple shoots. Rooted plants	Y	Izsak & Izhar (1983)
Fragaria grandiflora, F. vesca	Meristem	Meristem tips	Virus-free shoot formation	Y	Mullin *et al.* (1974)
Fragaria sp. cv. 'Gorella'	Direct/Callus	Not specified	Shoot proliferation. Shoots rooted	Y	Jemmali *et al.* (1992)
Fragaria vesca L. (Wild strawberry)	Callus	Sects. of young leaves or petioles	Differentiations, induced by cell wall hydrolysates	—	Bois (1992)
Fragaria vesca	Meristem	Meristems	Virus free plants	—	Belkengren & Miller (1962)
Fragaria vesca	Meristem	Meristem tips	Plantlets, virus-free	Y	Miller & Belkengren (1963)

Species name	Type of Culture	Source of explant	Results		References
Fragaria vesca cv. 'Albo-Marginata' [chimeral strawberry]	Shoot	*In vitro* shoots	Shoot proliferation. Chimeral separation	Y	Marcotrigiano *et al.* (1987)
Fragaria vesca cv. 'Albo-Marginata'	Shoot	Runner tips	Single rooted plantlets	Y	Marcotrigiano *et al.* (1987)
Fragaria vesca	Shoot	Infected & healthy stolon tips	Regeneration of plantlets	Y	Spiegel & Martin (1992)
Malus P60 [rootstock]	Direct	*In vitro* shoots	Rooting. Assessed effect of arginine	Y	Orlikowska (1992)
Malus [several genotypes]	Direct/Callus	Leaf segments ex *in vitro* cultures	Shoot regeneration	Y	Korban *et al.* (1992)
Malus M26, M.27, MM.106 [rootstocks]	Meristem/Shoot	Meristems ex adult material	Shoot growth & multiplication. Rooted plants	YY	Golosin & Radojevic (1987)
Malus M.25 [rootstock]	Shoot	*In vitro* shoots ex shoot cultures	Multiple shoots. Rooted plants	Y	Cheema & Sharma (1983)
Malus P2 & M9 [rootstocks]	Shoot	Cold-treated *in vitro* shoots	Shoot proliferation	Y	Orlikowska (1992)
Malus M.26 [rootstock]	Shoot	Shoot tips	Shoot proliferation. Rooted plantlets	Y	Rosati *et al.* (1988)
Malus M.9 [rootstock]	Shoot	Not stated	Shoot proliferation	Y	Seingre (1991b)
Malus M9 [rootstock]	Shoot	Shoot tips	Shoot proliferation. Shoots rooted	YY	Webster & Jones (1989)
Malus B9, Ottawa 3, P2, P22 [rootstocks]	Shoot	Shoot tips (0.5 cm)	Multiple shoot formation. Shoots rooted	YY	Webster & Jones (1991)
Malus baccata × M. pumila	Shoot	*In vitro* shoots (1.5 cm)	Optimised shoot proliferation	Y	Singha (1982 a,c)
Malus hybrids [4 columnar selections]	Shoot	Shoot tips (0.5–1 cm)	Multiple shoot formation. Rooted	YY	Marin *et al.* (1993)
Malus M.26 [rootstock]	Callus	Leaf discs ex in vitro cultures	Adventitious shoots. Multiplied & rooted	—	James *et al.* (1984)
Malus M.25 [rootstock]	Callus	Rooted in vitro shoots	Adventitious shoots from callus on roots. Shoots rooted	—	Jones *et al.* (1984)
Malus M.25, M.27 [rootstocks]	Callus	Internode segs. of in vitro shoots	Adventitious shoots. Multiplied & rooted	—	James *et al.* (1984)
Malus M.4 [rootstock]	Callus	Meristem & leaf primordia	Shoot formation. Shoots rooted	—	Ochatt & Caso (1983)
Malus M.7 [rootstock]	Direct	Shoot tips	Shoots rooted	Y	Jones & Hatfield (1976)
Malus M.26 [rootstocks]	Direct	Axillary shoot tips	Embryoid-like structures on leaves. Some shoots	—	James et al. (1984)
Malus M26 [rootstock]	Direct	I.v. shoots ex juv.& mature sources	Studied effect of auxin on root formation	—	Welander & Snygg (1987)
Malus A2 [rootstock]	Direct	I.v. shoots ex juv.& mature sources	Studied effect of auxin on root formation	—	Welander & Snygg (1987)
Malus M26 [rootstock]	Direct/Callus	Leaves ex in vitro cultures	Multiple adventitious shoots	Y	Predieri & Malavasi (1989)
Malus M.26 [rootstock]	Direct/Callus	Leaf segments ex in vitro shoots	Adv. shoots, embryo-like structures. Rooted plants	Y	Welander (1988)
Malus [4 rootstocks]	Direct/Embryogen.	Nucellus tissue	Somatic embryos	–	James *et al.* (1984b)
Malus M9, M26 [rootstocks]	Shoot	Shoot cultures	Shoot multiplication. Rooted shoots	YY	Alvarez *et al.* (1989)
Malus M.26 [rootstock]	Shoot	Shoots	Shoot proliferation. Used to study water transport	Y	Shackel et al. (1990)
Malus M.26 [rootstock]	Shoot	Shoot apices	Axillary shoots. Rooted	YY	Welander (1988)
Malus M.9 [rootstock]	Shoot	Shoot tips	Multiple shoots. Shoots rooted	YY	James & Thurbon (1979)
Malus M.4 [rootstock]	Shoot	Shoot tips	Shoot proliferation	Y	Dunstan *et al.* (1985)
Malus M.27 [rootstock]	Shoot	Shoot tips	Shoot proliferation	Y	Flegmann & Wainwright (1981)
Malus M.9, M.26 [rootstocks]	Shoot	Shoot tips	Shoot multiplication. Shoots rooted	YY	James & Thurbon (1981 a,b)
Malus M.26 [rootstock]	Shoot	Pretreated shoot tips	Shoot proliferation. Shoots rooted	YY	Jones *et al.* (1977)
Malus M.7, M.26 [rootstocks]	Shoot	Shoot tips	Single unbranched shoots	—	Jones (1967)
Malus M.7, M.26 [rootstocks]	Shoot	Shoot tips (1–2 cm)	Shoot proliferation. Shoots rooted	YY	Jones (1976)
Malus [7 rootstocks]	Shoot	Shoot tips collected in spring	Multiple shoots. Rooted (except M.26)	YY	Liu *et al.* (1981)
Malus M.27 [rootstock]	Shoot	Shoot tips	Multiple shoots. Rooted plants, not acclimatized	Y	Loreti *et al.* (1981)

Species name	Type of Culture	Source of explant	Results		References
Malus M.26, M.27, MM104 [rootstocks]	Shoot	Shoot tips ex sprouted buds	Multiple shoots. Shoots rooted	Y	Nemeth (1981)
Malus M.26 [rootstock]	Shoot	Shoots from in vitro cultures	Multiple shoots. Rooted shoots acclimatized	YY	Simmonds (1983)
Malus M.9 & Ottawa-3 [rootstocks]	Shoot	Shoot tips	Multiple shoots. Shoots rooted	Y	Strahlheim & Cailloux (1981)
Malus M9 & cv. 'Jork'	Shoot	Not given	Shoot prolif. Studied effect of IBA on rooting	Y	Van der Krieken et al. (1991)
Malus M.7 [rootstock]	Shoot	Shoot tips	Shoot multiplication. Shoots rooted	YY	Werner & Boe (1980)
Malus sp. 'Delicious' & 'Antanovka' seedlings	Shoot	Dormant buds	Shoot growth after cold treatment	—	Borkowska & Habdas (1982)
Malus × domestica Borkh. [several cvs.]	Callus	Wounded leaves ex i.v. shoot cults.	Multiple adventitious shoots	—	Fasolo et al. (1989)
Malus × domestica 'Golden Delicious'	Shoots & Direct	Shoots ex in vitro cults.	Studied shoot prolif. & rooting	Y	Baraldi et al. (1991)
Malus × domestica	Callus	Seedling leaf	Shoot formation & elongation. Shoots rooted	—	Liu et al. (1983a)
Malus × domestica	Callus	Seed, cotyledon, or leaf	Rhizogenesis	—	Mehra & Sachdeva (1979)
Malus × domestica	Callus	Stem, cotyl., embryo, or shoot tip	Shoot regeneration	—	Mehra & Sachdeva (1979)
Malus × domestica	Callus	Various	Indirect embryogenesis. Embryoids germinated	—	Mehra & Sachdeva (1984)
Malus × domestica Borch [several cvs.]	Callus/Direct	Leaf tissue	Adventitious shoots	—	Dufour (1990)
Malus × domestica cv. 'Golden Delicious'	Direct	Internode segments from i.v. shts	Shoot regeneration. Shoots rooted	—	Belaizi et al. (1991)
Malus × domestica Borkh. cv.' McIntosh'	Direct	Leaves from in vitro cultures	Adventitious shoots	Y	Elobeidy & Korban (1988)
Malus × domestica [several cvs].	Direct	Leaves from in vitro cultures	Adventitious shoots	Y	Fasolo et al. (1988)
Malus × domestica cv. 'Jonathan'	Direct	Cotyledons ex seed embryos	Adv. shoots	—	Joung et al. (1987)
Malus × domestica	Direct	Cotyledons from embryo	Adventitious shoots proximally	—	Kouider et al. (1984a)
Malus × domestica	Direct	Embryos 6.5–14 wk post anthesis	Multiple shoots	Y	Kouider et al. (1985)
Malus × domestica	Direct	Cotyledons from young embryos	Multiple shoots	Y	Kouider et al. (1985)
Malus × domestica	Direct	Seedling leaf & cotyledon	Adventitious shoots, & some adventitoius roots	Y	Liu et al. (1983a)
Malus × domestica 'McIntosh'	Direct	Shoots ex in vitro cultures	*Ex vitro* and *in vitro* rooting compared	Y	McClelland et al. (1990)
Malus × domestica	Direct	Embryos ex cold-treated seeds	Adventitious buds on petiole of cotyledon. Rooted	Y	Rubos & Pryke (1984)
Malus × domestica 'Gala, 'Royal Gala,' 'Jonagold'	Direct	Microcuttings ex in vitro cults.	Adv. rooting. Macronutrients effects studied	Y	Sriskandarajah et al. (1990)
Malus × domestica Borkh. cvs. 'Delicious, ' 'Wine sap'	Direct/Callus	Embryo axis sections	Adventitious shoots	—	Korban & Skirvin (1985)
Malus × domestica [4 cvs.]	Direct/Callus	Leaf discs/strips ex shoot cultures	Multiple adventitious shoots. Rooted	Y	James et al. (1988)
Malus × domestica cv. 'Antonovka'	Direct/Callus	Cotyls. & embryonic axes ex seeds	Adventitious shoots (rooted poorly)	—	Sinska (1988)
Malus × domestica [various cvs.]	Direct/Callus	Leaf halves ex in vitro cultures	Multiple adventitious shoots	Y	Sriskandarajah et al. (1990)
Malus × domestica 'Gala'	Direct/Callus	Leaves ex pretreated i.v. cultures	Multiple shoots regenerated	Y	Swartz et al. (1990)
Malus × domestica [several cvs.]	Direct/Callus	Leaf segments ex in vitro shoots	Adv. shoots, embryo-like structures. Rooted plants.	Y	Welander (1988)
Malus × domestica 'Golden Delicious'	Direct embryogen.	Micropyl. leaf of nucellus	Embryogenesis, embryos. Adventive embryos on cotyledons	—	Eichholtz et al. (1979)
Malus × domestica 'Golden Delicious'	Direct embryogen.	Nucellus tissue	Somatic embryos	—	James et al. (1984b)
Malus × domestica	Direct embryogen.	Seedling leaf (1 × 1 cm)	Plantlets from germinated embryoids.	Y	Liu et al. (1983b)
Malus × domestica [several cvs.]	Direct?	Leaves from in vitro shoots	Adventitious shoots	—	Fasolo et al. (1988)
Malus × domestica	Embryo	Seed embryo or embryo axis	Growth of single shoot	—	Kouider et al. (1984a)
Malus × domestica	Embryo	Mat. embryos 14 wk post anthesis	One shoot & one root per embryo	—	Kouider et al. (1985)
Malus × domestica cv. 'Yuzhnoe'	Meristem	Shoot meristems	Hyperhydricity & necrosis studied. Shoots hard to root	—	Kataeva et al. (1991)
Malus × domestica	Meristem	Meristem tips	Shoot proliferation. Shoots rooted	YY	Lane (1978)

Species name	Type of Culture	Source of explant	Results		References
Malus × domestica	Meristem	Meristem tips (1 mm)	Shoot proliferation, following abnormal growth. Rooted	Y	Pua et al. (1983)
Malus × domestica	Meristem	Axillary bud meristems	Shoot proliferation. Shoots rooted	YY	Sriskandarajah & Mullins (1981)
Malus × domestica cv. 'Jonathan'	Meristem/Shoot	Meristem tips	Multiple shoots. Rooted plants	Y	Huth (1978)
Malus × domestica	Micrografting	Apices of 'M9' and 'R. du Canada'	Apices grafted onto seedlings	—	Alskief & Villemur (1978)
Malus × domestica	Micrografting	Field & in vitro shoot tips	Apices grafted onto decapitated seedling rootstocks	—	Huang & Millikin (1980)
Malus × domestica Various cvs.	Node/Shoot	Axillary bud cultures	Proliferating cultures maintained	Y	Sriskandarajah et al. (1990)
Malus × domestica	Shoot	Shoot tips	Multiple shoots. Rooted after dark treatment	YY	Anderson (1982)
Malus × domestica cv. 'Golden Delicious'	Shoot	Shoot tips	Shoot proliferation	Y	Brand (1993)
Malus × domestica cv. MM106	Shoot	Shoot tips	Shoot proliferation. Tested cold hardiness	Y	Caswell et al. (1986)
Malus × domestica Ottawa-3	Shoot	Shoot tips	Multiple shoots. Shoots rooted	Y	Chong & Pua (1985)
Malus × domestica	Shoot	Buds plus 1-2 cm of attached stem	Shoot growth	—	Dutcher & Powell (1972)
Malus × domestica	Shoot	Shoot tips	Shoot growth. Shoots not rooted	—	Elliott (1972)
Malus × domestica [3 cvs.]	Shoot	In vitro shoots (1 cm long)	Multiple shoots. Rooted (Compared media)	—	Fiorino & Leva (1983)
Malus × domestica cv. 'Northern Spy'	Shoot	Shoot tips	Shoot proliferation. Shoot rooted in vitro	YY	Hutchinson (1984b)
Malus × domestica cv. 'Northern Spy'	Shoot	Shoot tips	Multiple shoots. Rooted plants	YY	Hutchinson (1985)
Malus × domestica cv. 'Wellspur'	Shoot	Shoot tips	Multiple shoots. Rooted plantlets	Y	Jacoboni & Standardi (1982)
Malus × domestica [5 cultivars]	Shoot	Shoot tips	Shoot proliferation. Shoots rooted in vitro	YY	Jones et al. (1979)
Malus × domestica cvs. 'Redspur' & 'Goldspur'	Shoot	Shoot tips	Multiple shoots. Rooted plants	YY	Jones et al. (1985)
Malus × domestica cv. 'Jonathan'	Shoot	Shoot tips	Shoot multiplication	Y	Joung et al. (1987)
Malus × domestica [2 cultivars]	Shoot	Shoot tips (adult trees)	Shoot proliferation. Shoots rooted in vitro	Y	Kataeva & Butenko (1987)
Malus × domestica	Shoot	Cryopreserved shoot tips	Shoot multiplication	—	Katano et al. (1983)
Malus × domestica	Shoot	Shoot tips	Multiple shoot proliferation. Shoots rooted	YY	Lane & McDougald (1982)
Malus × domestica	Shoot	Shoot tips	Multiple shoot proliferation	Y	Lane et al. (1982)
Malus × domestica	Shoot	Shoot tips	Multiple shoots. Rooted	YY	Lane (1982)
Malus × domestica [seedlings of 5 cvs.]	Shoot	Aseptic shoot tips	Multiple shoots. Rooted shoots	Y	Liu et al. (1981)
Malus × domestica [16 cvs.]	Shoot	Actively growing shoot tips ex adult trees	Cultures established. Contam. minimized with 8-HQS	Y	Mattanovich et al. (1991)
Malus × domestica cv. 'McIntosh'	Shoot	2–3 node explants from i.v. cult.	Shoot proliferation. Shoots rooted	YY	McClelland & Smith (1990)
Malus × domestica cvs. 'Jonathan,' 'Richared'	Shoot	Nodal segments	Multiple shoots. Rooted plants	YY	Mullins et al. (1986)
Malus × domestica cv. 'Fuji'	Shoot	Cryopreserved shoot tips	Regrowth of shoots. Rooted	—	Niino et al. (1992)
Malus × domestica cv. 'Golden Delicious'	Shoot	Shoot tips	Shoot proliferation. Rooted plants	Y	Patena et al. (1988)
Malus × domestica	Shoot	Apical shoot tips (2-3 cm)	Axillary shoot proliferation. 100% rooting	YY	Snir & Erez (1980)
Malus × domestica [3 cvs.]	Shoot	Isolated buds from adult trees	Multiple shoots. Rooted plants	YY	Sriskandarajah & Mullins (1982)
Malus × domestica cvs. 'Jonathan,' 'Delicious'	Shoot	Nodal segments	Multiple shoots, rooted (after several subcults.)	YY	Sriskandarajah et al. (1982)
Malus × domestica	Shoot	Commercial culture	Shoots differentiated & rooted	Y	Travers et al. (1985)
Malus × domestica cv. 'Gala'	Shoot	Shoot tips	8 shoots/explant. Shoots elongated & rooted	YY	Van Nieuwkirk et al. (1986)
Malus × domestica cv. 'Akero'	Shoot	Shoot tips	Shoot proliferation. Shoots rooted	YY	Welander (1985b)
Malus × domestica [several cvs.]	Shoot	Shoot apices	Axillary shoots. rooted	YY	Welander (1988)

Species name	Type of Culture	Source of explant	Results		References
Malus × domestica [5 cvs.]	Shoot	*In vitro* shoot tips	Studied tipping, photoperiod, explant posit. on prolif.	YY	Yae *et al.* (1987)
Malus × domestica [several scion cvs.]	Shoot	Shoot tips	Multiple shoots. Rooted plants transferred to soil	YY	Zimmerman & Fordham (1985)
Malus × domestica	Shoot	Dormant buds	Growth of short shoots. Shoots proliferated & rooted	YY	Zimmerman (1984a)
Malus × domestica	Shoot	Shoot tips (1–2 cm)	Growth of terminal & lateral buds. Shoots rooted	YY	Zimmerman (1984a)
Malus × domestica [various cvs.]	Shoot	Shoot tips	Shoot proliferation. Up to 100% rooting	YY	Zimmerman (1984 b)
Prunus [3 species & hybrid]	Callus	Rooted *in vitro* plantlets	Nodules on roots proliferated. Plants regenerated	—	Druart (1980)
Prunus sp. 'P.S. B2' (Peach rootstock)	Shoot	Shoot tips (10–12 mm)	Multiple shoots, elongated & rooted. Plants	YY	Morini & Concetti (1985)
Prunus 'Colt' & 'Mazzard F12/1' [Cherry rootstocks]	Shoot	Not given	Shoot proliferation (media optimized)	Y	Tchernets *et al.* (1987)
Prunus americana Marsh. (American plum)	Embryo	Young embryos	Development & germination	Y	Tukey (1938)
Prunus armeniaca L. cv. 'Royal' (Apricot)	Callus	Immature embryos	Shoot regeneration	—	Pieterse (1989)
Prunus armeniaca cv. 'Royal	Direct	Immature embryos	Advent. buds. Some developed into shoots & rooted	Y	Pieterse (1989)
Prunus armeniaca	Embryo	Young embryos	Development & germination	Y	Tukey (1938)
Prunus armeniaca [various cvs.]	Germination	Pollen	Studied effects of temp. on germination	—	Egea *et al.* (1992)
Prunus armeniaca cv. 'Canino'	Micrografting	Shoot tips ex *in vitro* shoots	Grafts onto seedling rootstocks	—	Deogratias *et al.* (1991)
Prunus armeniaca	Node	Nodal stem	70% shoot development. 70–90% rooting	YY	Snir (1984)
Prunus armeniaca	Shoot	Shoots from *in vitro* cultures	Shoot proliferation. Tested different media	—	Marino *et al.* (1991)
Prunus armeniaca	Shoot	Shoot tips	Shoot proliferation	Y	Marino (1991)
Prunus armeniaca	Shoot	Shoot tips	Axillary shoot proliferation. Shoots rooted	YY	Skirvin *et al.* (1980)
Prunus avium L. cv. 'Stella' (Wild & Sweet cherry)	Callus	Intermodal segments	Studied effect of juvenility	—	Oliveira & Browning (1993)
Prunus avium [several genotypes]	Callus	Basal callus ex shoot cultures	Shoot regeneration	—	Pevalek-Kozlina & Jelaska (1987)
Prunus avium L.	Direct/Callus	Distal 50 mm of roots of microprop. plantlets	Adventitious shoots, rooted plantlets	Y	Pedrotti & Cornu (1991)
Prunus avium	Direct embryogen.	Immature zygotic embryos	Low frequency embryo formation	—	De March *et al.* (1993)
Prunus avium	Embryo	Seed embryos	Viable seedlings	Y	Tukey (1933)
Prunus avium [irradiated F12/1 clones]	Shoot	Shoot tips	Shoot multiplication. Rooted plants	Y	Ancora *et al.* (1982)
Prunus avium [many varieties]	Shoot	Adult meristems	Shoot multiplication. Plants	YY	Cornu & Chaix (1981)
Prunus avium [rootstock F12/1]	Shoot	Shoot tips	Shoot proliferation.Shoots rooted	YY	Jones & Hopgood (1979)
Prunus avium [rootstock & scion cvs.]	Shoot	Shoot tips	Multiple shoots	Y	Paul & Feucht (1985)
Prunus avium [several genotypes]	Shoot	Apical & axillary buds	Shoot proliferation. Rooted *in vitro*. Plants	YY	Pevalek-Kozlina & Jelaska (1987)
Prunus avium L. cv. '46-1'	Shoot	Shoot tips	Shoot multiplication. Rooted plants	YY	Ranjit *et al.* (1988 a.b)
Prunus avium	Shoot	*In vitro* shoots	Shoot multiplication	—	Righetti *et al.* (1988)
Prunus avium [selected seedlings]	Shoot	Shoot tips	Shoot proliferation. Rooted plants	Y	Sauer (1983)
Prunus avium [several cvs.]	Shoot	Shoot tip (1 mm)	Shoot proliferation. 80% rooting	YY	Snir (1982 a.b)
Prunus avium × P. mahaleb	Meristem	Bud tips	Shoot formation & multiplication, then rooting	YY	Zilkah *et al.* (1992)
Prunus avium × P. pseudocerasus 'Colt' (Cherry rootstock)	Callus	Root segments	Adventitious shoots. Shoots rooted	—	Jones *et al.* (1984)
Prunus avium × P. pseudocerasus 'Colt'	Protoplast	Cell suspensions	Protoplasts electroporated. Callus colonies. Plants regenerated	—	Ochatt *et al.* (1988)
Prunus avium × P. pseudocerasus 'Colt'	Shoot	Shoots ex *in vitro* cultures	Shoot proliferation	Y	Wilkins & Dodds (1983)
Prunus avium × P. pseudocerasus 'Colt'	Shoot	Shoot tips	Shoot multiplication. Rooted plants	YY	Ranjit *et al.* (1988a)

17. MICROPROPAGATION IN PRACTICE

	Species name	Type of Culture	Source of explant	Results		References
*	*Prunus cerasus* L. cv. 'Montmorency' (Sour cherry)	Direct	Cold-stored mature cotyledons	Multiple shoots produced	Y	Mante *et al.* (1989)
	Prunus cerasus	Embryo	Young embryos	Development & germination	Y	Tukey (1938)
	Prunus cerasus	Protoplast	Leaves of *i.v.* shoot cultures	Callus. Adv. roots gave shoots (mainly directly)	–	Ochatt & Power (1988)
	Prunus cerasus Clones CAB 41B, CAB 5H	Shoot	Imm. tips of actively growing shts.	Multiplication & rooting	Y	Borkowska & Szczerba (1990)
	Prunus cerasus cv. 'Schattenmorelle'	Shoot	Shoot tips	Multiple shoots. Rooted plantlets	Y	Cossio *et al.* (1981)
	Prunus cerasus cv. 'Vladimir'	Shoot	Shoot tips	Multiple shoots. Rooted plants	YY	Cossio (1981a)
	Prunus cerasus [4 cvs.]	Shoot	Shoot tips	Shoots multiplied, elongated & rooted	Y	Marin & Gella (1987)
	Prunus cerasus cv. 'Masto de Montanana'	Shoot	Not given	Shoot multiplication after 200 days storage at -3°C	–	Marino *et al.* (1985)
	Prunus cerasus var. CAB 11E	Shoot	Shoot tips	Shoot multiplication. Rooted planlets	Y	Paul & Feucht (1985)
	Prunus cerasus [rootstock & scion cvs.]	Shoot	Shoot tips	Shoot proliferation. Rooted plantlets	Y	Ponchia & Roselli (1980)
	Prunus cerasus [2 clones]	Shoot	Shoot tips	Axillary shoot proliferation. Shoots rooted	YY	Skirvin *et al.* (1980)
	Prunus cerasus	Shoot	Shoot tips	Shoot proliferation. Shoots rooted	YY	Skirvin *et al.* (1981b)
	Prunus cerasus	Shoot	Shoot tips (1 mm)	Axillary shoot proliferation. Shoots rooted	YY	Snir (1983)
	Prunus cerasus	Shoot	Shoot tips (1 mm)	Multiple shoots. Rooted	Y	Mante *et al.* (1989)
*	*Prunus × domestica* L. cvs. 'Stonley' & B 70173 (European plum)	Direct	Cold-stored mature cotyledons	Shoot regeneration	–	Bassi & Cossio (1991)
	Prunus × domestica [2 cvs.]	Direct/Callus	Leaves from elongated *in vitro* shoots	Rooted. Studied different light wavelengths	Y	Rossi *et al.* (1993)
*	*Prunus × domestica* ssp. *insititia* (L.) Schneid. = *P. insititia* [rootstock GF655/2]	Direct	*In vitro* shoots	Shoot proliferation. Shoots rooted	YY	Jones & Hopgood (1979)
	Prunus × domestica ssp. *insititia* 'Pixy'	Shoot	Shoot tips	Shoot proliferation & rooting	Y	Loreti *et al.* (1988)
	Prunus × domestica ssp. *insititia* GF 655/2	Shoot	Shoot tips from suckers	Shoot proliferation. Some vitrescence	–	Ambrozic Turk *et al.* (1991)
	Prunus × domestica 'bistrica'	Shoot	Shoot apices	Multiple shoots. Rooted plantlets	Y	Baleriola-Lucas & Mullins (1984)
	Prunus × domestica cvs. 'd'Agen', 'd'Ente 707'	Shoot	Buds ex cuttings stored at 0-4°C	Multiple shoots elongated and rooted	Y	Jona & Vigliocco (1987)
	Prunus × domestica [2 cvs.]	Shoot	Shoot tips	Shoot proliferation. Studied BAP metabolism	YY	Mariano (1988)
	Prunus × domestica cvs. 'Obilnaga', 'Santa Rosa'	Shoot	Shoot tips	Multiplication after 200 days storage at -3°C.	–	Marino *et al.* (1985)
	Prunus × domestica var. D 1869 (Peach rootstock)	Shoot	Shoot tips (5-15 mm)	Shoot multiplication. Shoots rooted	YY	Pietropaolo & Reisch (1984)
	Prunus × domestica cv. 'Stanley'	Shoot	Shoot tips	Axillary shoot proliferation. Shoots rooted	YY	Skirvin *et al.* (1980)
	Prunus × domestica	Shoot	Shoot tips	Shoot proliferation. Shoots rooted	YY	Seirlis *et al.* (1979)
	Prunus × domestica, P. mariana	Callus	Juvenile shoot sections	Adventitious shoots	–	Antonelli (1991)
	Prunus dulcis (Mill.) D.A.Webb = *P. amygdalus* (Almond)	Embryogenic callus	Immature embryos 9 mm long	Early stage embryos	–	Hisajima (1982a)
	Prunus dulcis cv. 'Tuono'	Shoot	Seed	Multiple shoots. Shoots rooted	YY	Hisajima (1982b)
	Prunus dulcis	Shoot	Zygotic embryo	Multiple shoot formation & multiplication	Y	Rugini & Verma (1982; 1983)
	Prunus dulcis	Shoot	Shoot tip ex 6-year-old tree	Shoot proliferation & elongation. Shoots rooted	YY	Rugini *et al.* (1987)
	Prunus dulcis	Shoot	Apical flush buds	Shoot proliferation (studied control of vitrescence)	Y	Tabachnik & Kester (1977)
	Prunus dulcis cv. 'Tuono'	Shoot	Shoot tip ex dormant bud	Axillary shoot proliferation. Shoots rooted via callus	Y	Mehra & Mehra (1974)
	Prunus dulcis & hybrids	Callus	Embryo or cotyledon	Shoot formation. Shoots rooted	–	Skirm (1942)
	Prunus dulcis	Embryo	Immature embryos	Over 70% embryos germinated	Y	
	Prunus hybrids					

CEREALS AND GRASSES

Uses for micropropagation

Most cereals and forage grasses are propagated efficiently and cheaply from seeds, so that vegetative multiplication is not required except for specialist purposes such as the production of clones of individual plants for evaluation and use as seed parents in breeding programmes. Vegetative propagation of annual cereals by traditional means has been either difficult or impossible, and although perennial grasses can be increased by division or from cuttings or tillers, using these techniques to obtain a large number of plants from a single selection can take a long while.

Callus cultures

Callus cultures of cereals and grasses can only be initiated from tissues that are young and meristematic. Explants are derived from root tips, nodes, shoot primordia, seeds and seed embryos (see review by Yamada, 1977), from young leaf tissue, or from immature inflorescences [*e.g.* the male inflorescence (tassel) of maize].

Only young newly initiated leaves or the basal parts of actively–growing leaves are capable of proliferating and giving rise to callus, and as leaves age, their tissues rapidly lose this capability (Wernicke and Brettell, 1980; Zamora and Scott, 1983). The leaves of graminaceous plants grow from basal meristems and so perhaps only actively dividing leaf cells may be competent to go on growing and dividing *in vitro*.

Where seed embryos have been employed, it has usually been the tissue of the scutellum which has proliferated *in vitro* (La Rue, 1952; Narayanaswamy, 1959; Green and Phillips, 1975; Springer *et al.*, 1979), although callus derived from the selective proliferation of mesocotyl tissue has been reported (Rangan, 1976; Granatek and Cockerline, 1979; Torné *et al.*, 1980). The quantity of callus produced can depend on the orientation of the embryo on the medium. The best position for callus induction seems to vary between one kind of cereal and another. In barley, rye and older oat embryos, the greatest callus growth has occurred with the scutellum in contact with the medium (Cummings *et al.*, 1976; Dunwell and Cornish, 1980; Dale and Deambrogio, 1979). Green and Phillips (1975) obtained the best response from maize embryos which were placed with their scutella facing upwards, away from the medium. Dunwell and Cornish (1980) showed that the positional effect was not due to gravity.

CEREALS

Cereal crops are the most important sources of human food, through the direct or indirect consumption of grain. Indirect feeding to farm animals (sometimes also accompanied by the consumption of stems and foliage), result in items in human diet such as dairy products, meat, eggs and alcoholic drinks. In order of global economic importance the chief kinds of cereal are wheat, rice and maize. The other cereals (barley, oats, rye, sorghum and millets) have specialised use, but although they can be significant in local diets and economies, are not generally grown on such a large scale as the other three.

Adventitious shoot formation

Until relatively recently, callus (or pseudocallus) cultures of cereals and grasses have not been found to have the same morphogenic capacity as those derived from broad–leafed plants. Reports of somatic embryo formation were very rare and even indirect shoot regeneration was not commonly or readily obtained. Cultures producing shoots generally gave rise to only small numbers of plantlets, and their morphogenic ability soon disappeared, especially if the density of meristematic primordia was too greatly reduced upon subculturing. King *et al.* (1978) conjectured that shoots regenerated from most cereal cultures may not have arisen adventitiously, but may have been derived from shoot primordia which were pre–formed in the original explant and were stimulated to grow and divide under *in vitro* conditions. Nevertheless, shoots were shown to be formed *de novo* in cereal callus cultures (Rangan, 1974; Dunstan *et al.*, 1978; Nakano and Maeda, 1979; Shimada and Yamada, 1979; Springer *et al.*, 1979) and calluses composed of a mass of proliferating primordia have originated from leaf tissue in which pre–formed meristems were improbable (Wernicke and Brettell, 1980).

However, it is now thought that embryogenesis is the principle method of regeneration in the Gramineae, and that what have appeared to be adventitious shoots in callus cultures of cereals and grasses have, on most occasions, arisen from somatic proembryos. The green leafy structures from which shoots have sometimes been observed to originate, were probably the enlarged scutella of somatic embryos which germinated precociously and gave rise to multiple shoot apices (Vasil 1982, 1983, 1985; Vasil and Vasil, 1982b). Shoots which arise in this

Table 221. Media most commonly used for the initiation of embryogenic callus in cereals.

Components	MS	Green (1982) §	Carman et al. (1988a)	Armstrong and Green (1985) ‡
	①	②	③	④
Macronutrients (meq/l)				
NO_3^-	39.4	39.4	78.8	27.99
PO_4^{3-}	3.74	3.74	7.5	8.81
SO_4^{2-}	3.0	3.0	6.0	8.5
Cl^-	5.98	5.98	11.98	2.25
K^+	20.04	20.04	40.08	30.93
Ca^{2+}	5.98	5.98	11.98	2.25
Na^+	—	—	—	—
Mg^{2+}	3.0	3.0	6.0	1.5
NH_4^+	20.61	20.61	41.22	7.0
Microelements (mg/l)				
$MnSO_4.4H_2O$	22.3	22.3	44.6	4.4
$ZnSO_4.7H_2O$	8.6	8.6	17.2	1.5
H_3BO_3	6.2	6.2	12.4	1.6
KI	0.83	0.83	1.66	0.8
$CuSO_4.5H_2O$	0.025	0.025	0.05	—
$Na_2MoO_4.2H_2O$	0.25	0.25	0.5	—
$CoCl_2.6H_2O$	0.025	0.025	0.05	—
NaFeEDTA (mM)	0.1	0.1	0.2	0.1
Vitamins (mg/l)				
myo–Inositol	100.0	—	100.0	—
Thiamine HCl	0.1	0.5	0.1	1.0
Nicotinic acid	0.5	—	0.5	0.5
Pyridoxine HCl	0.5	—	0.5	0.5
Amino acids (mg/l)				
Glycine	2.0	—	—	2.0
L–asparagine	—	150.0	—	—
L–proline	—	—	—	2878.0†

† This is equivalent to 25 mM proline. Other workers have added lower concentrations of this amino acid, *e.g.* 20 mM (Kamo *et al.*, 1985; McCain *et al.*, 1988), 6 mM with 100 mg/l casamino acids (Fransz *et al.*, 1989).

‡ This is the medium of **Chu *et al.* (1975) N6** with the addition of 25 mM proline.

§ This medium, which is given in Sears and Deckard (1982), is attributed in the paper to C.E.Green.

way are the equivalent of tillers and need to be rooted to obtain plantlets.

Green areas (spots) have often been noted in cereal callus prior to morphogenesis. Heyser and Nabors (1982a) suggested that their distribution might be explained by the separation of adjacent green areas through the more rapid proliferation of dedifferentiated cells. Green cells may stimulate meristem (or somatic embryo) formation by the production of localised gradients of plant growth substances.

Embryogenesis

Explants

Embryogenic callus of cereals is most commonly initiated from immature zygotic embryos (when the callus usually arises from the scutellum, but sometimes from the epiblast), from young leaf tissue, from immature inflorescences and very rarely from root explants. Detaching wheat spikes from the plant for a short period before explants are excised has been found to increase the frequency of embryogenesis (Carman and Campbell, 1988).

It was originally customary, firstly to obtain callus growth and only then to seek to induce morphogenesis. It has since been appreciated that embryogenic callus usually arises directly from the explant, but as more than one type of callus can be initiated, it is necessary to be able to recognise the type which will possess embryogenic capacity. The appropriate kind must then be separated and subcultured. Embryogenesis is sometimes only recognised as having taken place when plantlets are produced with both shoots and roots, but somatic embryos often do not form shoots while exogenous auxin is available.

Callus types. Authors have frequently recorded the appearance of two or more recognisably–different kinds of callus from their explants. Embryogenic callus may differ in appearance in different species. For example Haydu and Vasil (1981) obtained from *Pennisetum* leaf segments:

- a white compact embryogenic callus;

- a pale grey and/or yellowish brown soft, friable non–embryogenic callus;

- a yellowish–brown soft callus producing a gelatinous substance on its surface.

From embryonic explants of *Avena sativa*, Heyser and Nabors (1982a) obtained embryogenic callus which was white to opaque and convoluted; and non–embryogenic callus which was yellow to translucent and rough in appearance.

In some species different kinds of embryogenic callus have been obtained and, because they have a fairly consistent appearance, they have been given names. In maize, two kinds of embryogenic callus have been found to arise from the scutellum of immature embryos. The first type which is compact, irregularly shaped, nodular, and white or yellow in colour, has been termed 'Type I', while a highly friable type, first described by Green (1982), which superficially appears to be undifferentiated, but which is found to contain somatic embryos when examined microscopically, has been called 'Type II' (Armstrong and Green, 1985)*. Similarly, Redway et al. (1990) noted that, apart from a watery non–embryogenic callus, two kinds of embryogenic callus were formed from immature embryos of wheat:

- TYPE A, an off–white, compact and nodular callus; and

- TYPE B, a white and compact callus.

After 4–7 subcultures these two kinds gave rise to what were termed:

- TYPE C, an aged a compact and nodular callus; and

- TYPE D, an aged and friable embryogenic callus.

However, embryogenic callus can differ in appearance between species and even from one cultivar to another, and so may not always be so visually distinct as in the instances quoted above.

Media used for cereals

Callus and embryogenic callus of cereals have been initiated on a variety of media, but those incorporating the salts of **MS**, $2 \times$ **MS**, or **Chu** *et al.* **(1975) N6** have been used in the majority of experiments (Table 221). For example, embryogenic callus can be obtained by culturing immature wheat embryos on $\frac{1}{2}$**MS**, **MS**, or **MS** with double the normal concentration of salts (as in Medium **3** in Table 221), but most callus is usually obtained using the last two of these alternatives. Simply doubling the concentration of **MS** macronutrients is also effective (He *et al.*, 1988).

Casein hydrolysate (*e.g.* 100–200 mg/l), casamino acids (*e.g.* 500 mg/l) and/or glutamine (*e.g.* 500 mg/l) are also often added to **MS** medium to promote the initiation of embryogenic callus (*e.g.* in *Eleusine coracana*, Wazizuka and Yamaguchi, 1987; and in wheat, Ozias–Akins and Vasil, 1983a,b).

Chu *et al.* **(1975) N6** medium (or another medium which includes a relatively low concentration of inorganic NH_4^+ ions — Rapela, 1985) to which L–proline has been added, appears to give the highest frequency of embryogenic callus and somatic embryo formation in *Zea mays* (Armstrong and Green, 1985; Songstad *et al.*, 1988). Embryogenesis can also be induced by culturing maize explants on **MS**, but the addition of proline to this medium, which has a much higher level of NH_4^+ than **N6** (Table 49, page 398), does not improve embryogenesis of maize in the same fashion (Armstrong and Green, 1985). However, in other cereals, supplementing **MS** medium with proline may give some benefit. For instance, the presence of up to 12 mM proline in **MS** medium increased the frequency of embryogenic callus formation in rice (Chowdhry *et al.*, 1993).

Embryogenic callus cultures of maize have also been obtained on **MS** medium supplemented with 15 mM L–asparagine (Table 221, medium **2**) (Green and Phillips, 1975; Green 1977; Santos *et al.*, 1984; Torné *et al.*, 1984), but others have found that, unlike proline supplements, additions of asparagine to **Chu** *et al.* **(1975) N6** medium inhibit plant formation from embryogenic callus (Kamo *et al.*, 1985).

Vitamins. Although mixtures of inorganic ions, nitrate, ammonium and amino acids have been discovered which are effective in promoting embryo formation and growth, the requirement of the Gramineae for vitamins during embryogenesis is far less clear. Embryogenic cultures of many cereals have been obtained by culturing explants on **Linsmaier and Skoog (1965)** medium, which compared to **MS**, contains only 100 mg/l and 0.4 mg/l thiamine HCl (Nishi *et al.*, 1973; Heyser *et al.*, 1983; Vences *et al.*, 1986; Mohmand and Nabors, 1990, 1991; Mohmand, 1991). It is possibly significant that **LS** medium contains more thiamine than **MS**, for when using **MS** medium for cereals or grasses, some other investigators have found it beneficial to increase the concentration of this vitamin above 0.1 mg/l (Table 222).

Effective protocols

Growth regulators required for callus initiation have been discussed in Chapter 12 and combinations which are effective in inducing adventitious shoot and somatic embryo formation have been presented in tables on pages 608 and 631.

Typical protocols for obtaining somatic embryos from cereals are given in Table 222. Embryogenesis is induced

---

* Note that callus termed Type I or Type II in other species may have different characteristics

Table 222. Examples of protocols which, in cereals, have been effective in initiating embryogenic callus and obtaining somatic embryos. Media showed in square brackets are as indicated in Table 221; sucrose concentrations are shown in rounded brackets.

Plant	Explant	Callus initiation (growth regulators in mg/l)	Somatic embryo formation (growth regulators in mg/l)	Embryo growth (growth regulators in mg/l)	References
Hordeum vulgare	Immature zygotic embryos	[1] (3) + 2 2,4–D (dark)		Calli with embryos to [1] None	Ruíz *et al.* (1991)
Hordeum vulgare	Sections of young leaves	[1] (3) + 2 2,4–D (16h 12 μmol m^{-2} s^{-1})		Calli with embryos to [1] None	Ruíz *et al.* (1991)
Hordeum vulgare	Shoot tips	[1 §] (3) 1.8 IAA + 3.3 2,4–D + 0.3 2–iP	[1 §] (3) None	[1 §] (3) None	Weigel and Hughes (1984)
Oryza sativa	Dehusked seeds	[1 ‡] (2) + 2.2 2,4–D (after 30 days to same medium)	[1] + 10% CM + 0.5 IAA + 5 kin (subcultured on same after 30 d)		Chowdhry *et al.* (1993)
Oryza sativa	Dehusked seeds	[1 *] (4) + 0.2–1 2,4–D + 0.1–0.5 kin ‡‡ (dark, 4 weeks)	[LS] + 0.4 IAA + 0–5 BAP ‡‡ (8 weeks)		Oard and Rutger (1988)
Oryza sativa	Dehusked seeds	[1] + 1 2,4–D + 0.3 kin (dark)	[††] + 10% CM + 1 IAA + 3 kin		Vajrabhaya *et al.* (1989)
Pennisetum americanum	Immature inflorescences	[1] 5 2,4–D + 1 kin (12.1 μmol m^{-2} s^1). Embryogenic callus subcultured on [1] + 0.5 2,4–D + 1 NAA + 0.5 BAP	[1] + 0.1 IAA + 1 BAP		Pius *et al.* (1993)
Triticum aestivum	Immature zygotic embryos	[1 ¶] (3) + 2 2,4–D	[1] (3) + 1 IAA + 1 zeatin	[1] None	Vasil *et al.* (1990)
Secale cereale	Young inflor. or Imm.embryos	[1 ¶¶] + 1–2 2,4–D	[1 ¶¶] None	[1 ¶¶] + 2 zeatin + 8 thiourea	Krumbiegel–Schroerem *et al.* (1984)
Sorghum bicolor	Immature inflorescence segments	[1 §§] (2) + 2.5 2,4–D + 0.05 kinetin (dark) (subcultured on [1] (3.0) + 2.5 2,4–D + 0.1 kinetin (dark)	[1 §§] (2) + 0.2 kinetin (14 h 150–200 μmol m^{-2} s^{-1})		Cai and Butler (1990)
Triticum aestivum	Immature zygotic embryos	[2] (2) + 1 2,4–D Subcultured on same medium with 0.5 2,4–D at 21 day intervals	[2] + 0.1 2,4–D (21 days). Shoot growth, roots inhibited)		Sears and Deckard (1982)
Zea mays	Immature zygotic embryos	[4 †] (2) (dark) + 0.5 2,4–D transferred to [4†] (3) + 1–2 2,4–D	[4] (6) None	[4] (2) None	McCain *et al.* (1988)
	Immature zygotic embryos	[1] (3) (dark) + 0.5 2,4–D transferred to [1] (3) + 1–2 2,4–D	[1] (6) None	[1] (3) None	

† But only 20 mM proline and including 200 mg/l casein hydrolysate.   ‡ Plus 12 mM proline or 0.24 mM L–tryptophan.

§ **MS** salts with 500 mg/l inositol and 5 mg/l thiamine.   ¶ Supplemented with 100 mg/l casein hydrolysate and 500 mg/l glutamine.

* But with **LS** vitamins and 100 mg/l L–tryptophan   †† **White (1954)** medium but with 200 mg/l $(NH_4)_2SO_4$.

‡‡ The best combination of auxin and cytokinin varied with cultivar.   §§ With the addition of 150 mg/l L–asparagine.

¶¶ But with 0.5 mg/l thiamine HCl.

on a Stage I medium containing auxin, 2,4–D being most commonly used, but picloram and dicamba are also very effective in some species.

Immature zygotic embryo explants may germinate prematurely instead of producing callus. Such precocious germination can sometimes be prevented by adding ABA to the medium. Carman *et al.* (1988b) found that 0.1–0.5 mg/l was effective in the wheat variety 'PCYT20'.

Somatic embryos sometimes become apparent on the Stage I medium, but more usually they develop at the next stage at which the auxin concentration has been reduced. The addition of cytokinin may also be advantageous at Stage I, II or III and development of young embryos into plantlets is often improved in its presence. A large num-

ber of robust plantlets of *Pennisetum americanum* developed when 1 mg/l of 2–iP or zeatin was present in the medium (Vasil and Vasil, 1981b).

The addition of 100–200 μM silver nitrate or 250 μM norbornadiene to the callus initiation medium can increase the the number of plants regenerated from embryogenic cultures of maize (Songstad *et al.*, 1988). The time at which these inhibitors are introduced can be critical. The best time to introduce silver nitrate was found by Duncan and Widholm (1988) to be 21 days after culture initiation, especially if the regeneration medium contained BAP.

Osmolality. Embryogenic callus is usually initiated with 20–30 g/l sucrose in the medium, but up to 60 g/l has been

Table 223. Media used for embryo rescue in *Hordeum.*

Components	Gamborg *et al.* (1968) B5 ①	Norstog (1973) Barley II ②	Jensen (1977) C–17 ③
Macronutrients (meq/l)			
NO_3^-	24.72	—	5.46
PO_4^{3-}	3.26	20.06	5.48
SO_4^{2-}	4.05	6.0	2.63
Cl^-	2.04	20.12	5.41
K^+	24.72	16.74	6.08
Ca^{2+}	2.04	10.06	3.4
Na^+	1.08	—	0.72
Mg^{2+}	2.02	6.0	2.63
NH_4^+	2.02	—	2.49
Microelements (mg/l)			
$MnSO_4.4H_2O$	13.2	3.96	0.5
$ZnSO_4.7H_2O$	2.0	0.5	0.25
H_3BO_3	3.0	0.5	5.0
KI	0.75	–	0.1
$CuSO_4.5H_2O$	0.025	0.025	0.012
$Na_2MoO_4.2H_2O$	0.25	0.025	0.012
$CoCl_2.6H_2O$	0.025	0.025	0.012
NaFeEDTA (mM)	0.1†	0.03‡	0.06§
Vitamins (mg/l)			
myo–Inositol	100.0	50.0	50.0
Thiamine HCl	10.0	0.25	0.25
Nicotinic acid	1.0	—	—
Pyridoxine HCl	1.0	0.25	0.25
Ca pantothenate	—	0.25	0.25
Ascorbic acid	—	—	0.5
Amino acids (mg/l)			
Glycine	—	—	0.75
L–alanine	—	50.0	30.0
L–arginine	—	10.0	20.0
L–Aspartic acid	—	—	30.0
L–cysteine	—	20.0	—
L–glutamine	—	400.0	—
L–glutamic acid	—	—	150.0
L–leucine	—	10.0	10.0
L–lycine	—	—	10.0
L–phenylalanine	—	10.0	10.0
L–proline	—	—	50.0
L–serine	—	—	25.0
L–threonine	—	—	10.0
L–tyrosine	—	10.0	—

found to be more effective in some species. Galiba and Erdei (1986) showed that in wheat, one of the functions of sucrose is to regulate the water potential of the medium: if only 10 g/l sucrose was added to **MS** medium, shoot formation was increased by the further addition of mannitol. After initiating callus of *Zea mays* on Medium **4** with 20 mM proline, Kamo *et al.* (1985) found that more plants were obtained per embryo if the Stage II medium was supplemented with 60 g/l sucrose. Similarly in wheat, after initiating embryogenic callus on Medium **2** with 20 g/l sucrose (and 7 g/l agar — observed osmolarity 161 mOs/kg, see Part 1, page 331), the onset of regeneration and the extent of shoot formation were increased if the Stage II medium contained 50 g/l sucrose (observed osmolality 251 mOs/kg), 20 g/l sucrose plus 30 g/l mannitol (observed osmolality 330 mOs/kg), or 20 g/l sucrose and 50 g/l PEG (MW 8000) (observed osmolality 193 mOs/kg) (Brown *et al.*, 1989).

Suspension cultures

Suspension cultures in which cells retain a capacity to produce somatic embryos, can be initiated from the embryogenic callus of many cereal and grass species. Just occasionally difficulty has been reported in setting up such cultures; for example, Wernicke *et al.* (1982) found that an embryogenic callus of *Sorghum* was extremely sensitive to wetting and, in a liquid culture medium, it became necrotic and died.

However, cytological and karyological changes tend to accumulate rapidly in suspensions, and these lead to a loss of morphogenic capacity or the regeneration of plants which are albinos or which possess other genetic variations. Thus in experiments of Van der Valk *et al.* (1988), the plants obtained from seed or immature inflorescence callus of *Poa pratensis* were green, but all those obtained from suspension cultures were albino. Similarly all the plants produced from suspension cultures of *Bromus inermis* were without chlorophyll (Gamborg *et al.*, 1970).

Nevertheless, suspension cultures which resulted in apparently normal plants have been obtained in several species, *e.g.*:

Notes to Table 223

† **B5** medium was originally formulated with 0.05 mM Fe chelated with Sequestrene 330 (DTPA). It is now more commonly used with 0.1 mM NaFeEDTA.

‡ The original formulation contained 10 mg/l ferric citrate (0.03 mM Fe). This could reasonably be substituted with 0.03 mM NaFeEDTA.

§ 0.06 mM Fe was supplied originally by 3 mg/l ferric citrate and 17.5 mg/l NaFeEDTA.

Panicum maximum	Lu and Vasil (1981b)
Pennisetum americanum	Vasil and Vasil (1981b)
Bothriochloa ischaemum	Johnson and Worthington (1987)
Zea mays	Kamo and Hodges (1986)
Triticum aestivum	Redway *et al.* (1990)

Of the four kinds of callus noted to arise from wheat embryos (see page 1095), only types **C** and **D** could form stable suspensions. Types **A** and **B** failed to dissociate in a liquid medium (Redway *et al.*, 1990).

Plant regeneration from cereal cultures often declines after several months and callus which had been morphogenic may then produce roots and no shoots. However, Wang and Nguyen (1990) found that it was possible to obtain suspensions of *Triticum aestivum* which maintained the capacity to regenerate shoots for several years. Their procedure was to transfer callus newly derived from immature zygotic embryos, into liquid **MS** supplemented with 1 mg/l 2,4–D. Free–floating cells were removed and roots induced to form by reducing the concentration of auxin. This could be done by transfer to fresh medium containing 0.25 mg/l 2,4–D, or by retaining the culture on the original medium for approximately 3 months. The suspension was sieved at this stage and only rootless cell clumps, thought to be competent to regenerate shoots, were retained. These were grown on **MS** with 0.25 mg/l 2,4–D. Several subcultures were made, replacing $\frac{2}{3}$ of the suspension with fresh medium, until active cell division commenced, at which time subculture intervals were reduced to every 10–14 days. Shoots could be regenerated at any time from such new suspensions by plating cells, and cell aggregates, onto **MS** containing 0.1–0.25 2,4–D. The shoot–producing callus so obtained was moved to **MS** with 0.1 mg/l 2,4–D for shoot growth, and shoots rooted on $\frac{1}{2}$**MS** without growth regulators.

Embryo rescue

Immature zygotic embryos of cereals can be successfully grown *in vitro* to produce seedlings, if they are excised and transferred aseptically to sterile media shortly after pollination. The technique has been employed for several years to rescue the haploid embryos which result from crossing *Hordeum bulbosum* with *Hordeum vulgare* and *Triticum aestivum*. Embryos are cultured, without growth regulators, on media such as **Gamborg *et al.* (1968) B5**, **Jensen (1977) C–17**, and **Norstog (1973) Barley II** (Table 223).

Shoot cultures

Shoot culture of cereals is seldom used, but is discussed on page 1108, along with shoot culture of grasses and bamboos.

Species name	Type of Culture	Source of explant	Results		References
Triticum × Secale hybrids	Embryo	Immature embryos	Seedling growth	Y	Táira & Larter (1978)
* Zea mays L. [several lines] (Maize)	Embryogenic callus	Immature embryos	Studied % variant plants ex Type-I, Type-II callus	—	Armstrong & Phillips (1988)
Zea mays [3 inbred lines]	Callus	Immature embryos	Embryogenesis. High rate of plant regeneration	—	Duncan & Widholm (1988)
Zea mays [Inbred line FR27 rhm]	Callus	Dicamba-treated kernels	Increased induction frequency of regenerated callus	—	Duncan et al. (1989)
Zea mays	Callus	Immature embryos	Shoot buds & small leaves. Plantlet growth	—	Green & Phillips (1975)
Zea mays	Callus	Embryos	Plant regeneration	—	Green (1977)
Zea mays	Callus	Macerated embryo	Bud formation. No plants	—	Gresshoff & Doy (1973)
Zea mays	Callus	Mesocotyl segments	Roots, few aerial. Followed by shoots, rooting directly	—	Harms et al. (1976)
Zea mays	Callus	Shoot apex	Adventitious shoot formation	—	Jayos-Rios (1985)
Zea mays	Callus	Suspensions ex embryo callus	Embryogenesis. Plants with abnormalities	—	Kamo & Hodges (1986)
Zea mays	Callus	Zygotic embryos	Embryogenesis. Plant regeneration	—	Kamo & Hodges (1986)
Zea mays [Inbred line B73]	Callus	Immature embryos	Organogenic then embryogenic callus. Plants	—	Lowe et al. (1985)
Zea mays [2 inbred lines]	Callus	Immature embryos	Studied effect of mutagens on growth & regeneration	—	Moustafa et al. (1989)
Zea mays	Callus	Seed embryo of one line	Rooted plantlets	—	Novak et al. (1979)
Zea mays	Callus	Immature embryos (1–1.5 mm)	Plantlet regeneration	—	Rapela (1985)
Zea mays [several genotypes]	Callus	Immature tassels	Embryogenic callus. Plant regeneration	—	Rhodes et al. (1986)
Zea mays [Monosomics & aneuploids]	Callus	Immature tassels	Plants regenerated, many with altered karyotypes	—	Rhodes et al. (1986)
Zea mays	Callus	Seedling node meristem	Shoot formation. Plants not transferred to soil	—	Santos et al. (1984)
Zea mays [2 cvs.]	Callus	Nucellar meristems, young seeds	Shoot regeneration. Variable chromosome number	—	Sladky & Havel (1976)
Zea mays	Callus	Mesocotyl	Shoot regeneration. Shoots rooted	—	Torné et al. (1980)
Zea mays	Callus	Immature embryos	Shoots & plantlets. Plantlet growth	—	Torné et al. (1984)
Zea mays	Callus	Unfertilized ovaries	Embryogenesis. Plantlets from germinated embryoids	—	Truong–Andre & Demarly (1984)
Zea mays cvs. H99, W77–R3019	Callus, azide–treat.	Immature zygotic embryos	Selected amino–acid over–producing plants	Y	Miao et al. (1988)
Zea mays Inbred line 57	Direct embryogen.	Seedling leaf segments	Studied explant embryogenic competence	Y	Dole elová et al. (1992)
Zea mays Inbred line A 188	Direct/Callus	Imm. embryos (1–2 mm long)	Embryogenesis. Plantlets	—	Kamo et al. (1985)
Zea mays	Embryo	Seed embryos	Seedling growth	Y	Andronescu (1919)
Zea mays	Embryo	Seed embryos	Embryo germination & plants	Y	McDaniel (1977)
Zea mays Inbred A 188	Embryogenic callus	Immature embryos	Embryogenesis. Embryoid germination. Plants	—	Armstrong & Green (1985)
Zea mays [elite inbred lines]	Embryogenic callus	Immature zygotic embryos	Embryogenesis in most genotypes	—	Chalmers & Thompson (1986)
Zea mays line A188	Embryogenic callus	Immature embryos	Isozyme analysis carried out	—	Fransz et al. (1989)
Zea mays	Embryogenic callus	Immature embryos	Embryo growth. Plantlets from germinated embryos	—	Green (1982)
Zea mays	Embryogenic callus	Immature seed embryos	Plantlets from germinated embryoids	—	Lu C. et al. (1982)
Zea mays [one inbred, two hybrids]	Embryogenic callus	Immature embryos	Somatic embryo formation. Plants	—	McCain et al. (1988)
Zea mays	Embryogenic callus	Immature embryos (1–1.5 mm)	Plantlets from germinated embryoids	—	Rapela (1985)
Zea mays cvs. Pa 91, H99	Embryogenic callus	Immature embryos	Increased plant regeneration using ethylene antagonists	—	Songstad et al. (1988)
Zea mays Inbred B73	Embryogenic callus	Imm. embryos 8–10d. post anthesis	Callus X–rayed. Mutant plants regenerated	—	Wang et al. (1988)
Zea mays [elite inbred lines]	Embryonic callus	Immature zygotic embryos	Plant regeneration from most genotypes	—	Wilkinson & Thompson (1986)

Species name	Type of Culture	Source of explant	Results		References
Zea mays Inbred A 188	Fertilisation	Ear segments (10–14 ovaries)	Fertilisation with single pollen grains	—	Hauptli & Williams (1988)
Zea mays	Fertilisation/Embr.	Excised ovaries with cob secments	*In vitro* fertilization. Embryo growth, plantlets	—	Havel & Novak (1981)
Zea mays	Fertilisation/Ovary	Mature ovary	46% ovules fertilized. Some normal kernel development	—	Gengenbach (1977)
Zea mays [2 cvs.]	Fertilization	Ovary plus section of cob	Kernel growth. Some germination *in situ*	—	Sladky & Havel (1976)
Zea mays [various inbred lines & hybrids]	Meristem	Shoot apices	Plantlets recovered, 1 per explant	Y	Bommineni *et al.* (1989)
Zea mays	Node	Seedling stems with 5–6 nodes	One shoot from each axillary bud. Shoots rooted	Y	King & Shimamoto (1984)
Zea mays cv. A188	Protoplast	Callus ex immature embryos (18–20 day post-pollination)	Embryo–like structures	—	Chang (1983)
Zea mays	Root	Root tips	Isolated root culture	—	Robbins & Maneval (1923)
Zea mays	Root	Root tips	Isolated root culture	—	Robbins (1922a,b)

GRASSES AND BAMBOOS

Embryogenesis and adventitious shoot formation

Like cereals, grasses have mainly been propagated through embryogenesis, but callus cultures are often obtained which appear to give rise to shoots adventitiously. However, as root growth is frequently inhibited by auxin in embryogenic cultures, it has been suggested that what may appear to be adventitious shoots may sometimes (if not invariably in the Gramineae) have arisen from pro–embryos which have developed abnormally (page 1093).

Any explant which contains meristematic tissue is a potential source of callus: in grasses, as in cereals, this includes seeds (caryopses), zygotic embryos (especially immature ones), apical meristems, immature inflorescences, immature leaves, stem nodes, and sometimes roots. Plants cannot be regenerated from all callus cultures and embryogenic or organogenic tissue is more likely to be obtained from some explants than others. Immature zygotic embryos and young leaf tissue appear to be the best explants: the production of somatic embryos from roots is rare.

Media

MS medium, or the salts of MS with slightly modified vitamins have been used in the great majority of published experiments. **Chu et al. (1978)** N6 (medium 4 in Table 221, but without the addition of proline), or the macronutrients of this medium with slight amendments to the nature of the other ingredients, has been used in some experiments. Complete N6 medium was, for example, best for *Cynodon dactylon* (Ahn et al., 1985), and although MS gave an equally high frequency of embryogenic callus, more typical embryos were produced in a shorter time from callus initiated on N6 medium (Wang and Vasil, 1982).

In a few instances B5 or, more especially, **Schenk and Hildebrandt (1972)** media have been employed. SH medium was more effective than MS medium for callus initiation from imbibed seeds of *Bromus inermis*, although MS was preferable for callus maintenance (Molnar and Grainger, 1982). SH medium contains only a low concentration of NH_4^+ ions, so that in cultures maintained on it, cell proliferation may be restricted unless organic nitrogen is also provided. Embryogenic callus of *Dactylis glomerata* containing root primordia, gave rise to slow growing callus with superficial embryos on SH containing 30 μM dicamba but, when 1.5 g/l casein hydrolysate was present in the medium (Gray et al., 1984), a callus

was obtained composed mainly of developing embryos in a matrix of undifferentiated cells.

Gelling agents. Media have usually been gelled with agar, but Gelrite has been used in some recent experiments. The proportion of *Poa pratensis* calli which produced shoots was twice as high when MS medium (0.4 mg/l thiamine HCl) was gelled with 3 g/l Gelrite rather than 8 g/l agar (Van Ark et al., 1991).

Protocols

Methods for adventitious shoot formation and somatic embryogenesis, are very similar to those used for cereals, but dicamba and picloram have possibly been used more frequently for callus induction.

Some examples of protocols which have led to the formation of adventitious shoots, or somatic embryos are given in Table 225. The shoots obtained by McDonnell and Conger (1984) from *Poa pratensis* callus, formed roots on SH medium with half the normal concentration of salts (and no growth regulators). The table shows that, in grasses, embryos are differentiated when callus is moved from the induction medium to one containing a reduced concentration of auxin, or no auxin at all.

Cytokinins have sometimes been added, together with auxin, to callus induction and embryo differentiation media, but abscisic acid has seldom been found to be necessary. However, Van Ark et al. (1991) found that the percentage of *Poa pratensis* calli which gave rise to embryos of embryo–like structures was increased if 0.1 μM ABA was added to both the differentiation and regeneration media, or 1.0 μM to just the differentiation medium. The stage at which ABA is added may be important. Adding 0.1–1 μM ABA (together with 2,4–D) to the medium used for callus initiation from *Dendrocalamus strictus* seeds reduced the number of somatic embryos produced.

Albinos

The occurrence of albinos which lack chlorophyll, amongst the plants regenerated from cultures of Gramineae, was mentioned in Part 1 (pages 63 and 75–76). A high proportion of albinos is often obtained amongst plantlets of this family derived through anther culture but, in cereals, they tend to occur at lower frequency when embryogenic callus is obtained from somatic explants. For example, only a small number of albino plants resulted from *Hordeum spontaneum* and *Hordeum bulbosum* cultures (Breiman, 1985).

Table 225. Examples of protocols which have led to the formation of adventitious shoots or somatic embryos of grasses.

Species	Explant	Callus induction/growth (growth regulators in mg/l)	Somatic embryo formation (differentiation) (growth regulators in mg/l)	Plantlet regeneration (growth regulators in mg/l)	References
Bromus inermis	Imbibed seeds	[**SH**] (3) + 9.5 2,4–D + 2 pCPA + 0.1 kin Maintained on [**MS**] (3) + 0.5–2 2,4–D	[**MS**] None		Molnar and Grainger (1982)
Eymus canadensis	Immature embryos or inflor. segments	[**MS**] + 2 2,4–D (Dark 4 weeks). Subcultures on [**MS**] + 2 2,4–D (110 µmol m^{-2} m^{-1})	[**MS**] + None or 0.3 GA$_3$		Park and Walton (1989)
Festuca rubra	Mature caryopses	[**MS**] + 4.4 2,4–D (dark 26°C) (subcultured every 8 weeks)	[½ × **MS**] None (22°C, 12h 74 µmol m^{-2} s^{-1})		Torello *et al.* (1985)
Lolium multiflorum	Bases of tillers	[**MS**] (3) + 10 2,4–D (liqid ag., 13 days, 22°C, 30 µmol m^{-2} s^{-1}). Subculture on [**MS**] (3) + 2 2,4–D (13 days)	[**MS¶**] agar (3) + 2 2,4–D + 0.2 BAP	[**MS ¶**] agar (3) None Embryos to [**MS¶**] agar (3) + 0.2 kinetin	Jackson and Dale (1989)
Poa pratensis	Mature embryos	[**SH†**] (2) + 4.4 dicamba or 14.5 picloram (dark 15°C). Maintained on [**SH†**] (2) + 4.4 dicamba or 14.5 picloram (dark 4°C 7 days)	[**SH†**] (2) + 0.22 dicamba or 0.72 picloram	[**SH‡**] (2) None	McDonnell and Conger (1984)
Poa pratensis	Seeds	[**MS§**] (3) + 2 mg/l 2,4–D (6 weeks, dark 25°C)	[**MS§**] (3) + 2 mg/l 2,4–D (3 weeks, dark 25°C)	[**MS§**] (3) + 0.2 mg/l 2,4–D + 0.26 ABA (3 weeks, dark 25°C)	Van Ark *et al.* (1991)

† **SH** salts with 1 g/l inositol and 5 mg/l thiamine HCl.   ‡ With the salts in the medium reduced to ½ their normal concentration

§ With the concentration of thiamine increased to 0.4 mg/l   ¶ Plus 100 mg/l casein hydrolysate.

However a fairly high number of albinos is obtained when plantlets are regenerated from somatic embryos and adventitious shoots of some grasses, although the proportion of abnormal plantlets obtained varies greatly between genotypes. In *Lolium multiflorum*, only 1.8% of all the plantlets produced from somatic embryos were albino in genotype '24/4' but, from cultures of genotype '17/9', the average proportion of albino shoots regenerated from several different treatments was 18%. In the latter variety, the incidence of albino plants increased with incubation temperature. At 25°C (the temperature at which most plantlets were obtained), 21% of plants were chlorophyll deficient (Jackson and Dale, 1988).

Embryogenic or organogenic callus which becomes green, or which develops green spots, is more likely to produce green plants than callus lacking chlorophyll. In *Echinochloa oryzicola*, Takahashi *et al.* (1984) obtained green plants from callus with green spots, and albino plants from callus lacking any green colour. Such a clear distinction was not apparent in *Puccinellia limosa* cultures where, although almost all the plants produced from non–green callus were albino, 13–25% of the plants from green callus were also without chlorophyll.

Shoot and node cultures

C.W. Smith (1965, 1968) showed that the apices of wheat embryos could be grown to produce several shoots apiece. The feasibility of propagating maize plants by shoot tip culture was investigated by Raman *et al.* (1980). They found that only the lowermost buds of maize seedlings could be used. Lateral buds removed from positions higher up the stem, yielded plants with a terminal inflorescence containing both staminate and pistillate flowers. Buds normally giving rise to ears, grew to produce short plants with a totally female terminal inflorescence. Difficulty was experienced in rooting the shoots that were obtained. Shoot culture would be useful to plant breeders if it produced clonal replicas of selected mature plants of maize.

Meristem or shoot culture of some grasses is possible, and can be used as a means of keeping stock plants of a new cultivar virus–free, for propagating clones for research purposes (Dale, 1975b), or for the rapid increase of new varieties that are subsequently to be multiplied from seed. The rate of propagation *in vitro* can be considerably in excess of that possible by conventional means. Dalton and Dale (1981) were able to produce 40 tillers per month

	Species name	Type of Culture	Source of explant	Results		References
	Pennisetum purpureum	Embryogenic callus	Young leaf pieces	Plantlet regeneration	—	Chandler & Vasil (1984)
	Pennisetum purpureum	Embryogenic callus	Immature leaves	Embryogenesis. Some somatic embryos and plants	—	Haydu & Vasil (1981)
	Phragmites australis (Cav.) Trin. ex Steud. (Carrizo)	Callus	Mature seeds	Embryogenesis (continued in long-term culture). Plants	—	Straub et al. (1988)
*	Poa pratensis L. (Kentucky blue grass)	Callus	Mature embryos	Shoot regeneration. Shoots rooted	—	McDonnell & Conger (1984)
	Poa pratensis cv. 'Geronimo'	Callus	Seeds	Shoots and somatic embryos	—	Van Ark et al. (1991)
	Poa pratensis [many cvs.]	Callus	Seeds or immature inflorescences	High frequency green plant regeneration	—	Van der Valk et al. (1988)
	Poa pratensis cvs. 'Fylking,' 'Adelphi'	Single node	Seeds or nodes ex greenhouse plants	Plants with shoots & roots. Transferred to soil	YY	Pieper & Smith (1988)
	Poa pratensis cvs. 'Geronimo', 'Kimono'	Suspension	Callus or mature embryos	Albino plantlets only	—	Van der Valk et al. (1988)
	Poa supina	Callus	Seed embryo	Viable plantlets	—	Montenegro et al. (1980)
	Puccinellia distans (L.) Parl. Wild type	Embryogenic callus	Dehusked seeds	Green & albino plantlets regen.	—	Binh et al. (1989)
	Puccinellia limosa (Schur.) Holmbg. (Soft marsh grass)	Embryogenic callus	Seeds	Plantlets regenerated	—	Heszky et al. (1989)
	Sorghastrum nutans (L.) Nash (Indian grass)	Callus	Very young inflorescence	Plantlet regeneration	—	Chen et al. (1979)
	Stipa viridula Trin. (Green needlegrass)	Callus	Young inflorescence	Shoots regenerated (some albino); plants	—	Lo et al. (1980)
	Uniola paniculata L. (Seaside oats)	Callus	Caryopses	Shoot regeneration. Rooted. Plants	—	Hovanesian & Torres (1986)
❖	Zea diploperennis Teosinte	Callus	Shoot apex, inflorescences, immature embryos	Plant regeneration after several passages	—	Prioli et al. (1985)
	Zea diploperennis	Callus	Immature embryos & leaf tissues	Embryogenesis. Plant regeneration	—	Swedlund & Locy (1988)
	Zoysia japonica Steud. (Japanese lawngrass)	Callus	Mature caryopses	Embryogenesis. Plantlets regenerated	—	Asano (1989)

ROOT AND TUBER CROPS

Araceae

Colocasia, Amorphophallus, Xanthosoma   (Tuber–producing aroids)

Certain members of the Araceae produce edible corms which are widely used as vegetables in the South Pacific, South America and the West Indies. *Colocasia, Amorphophallus* and *Xanthosoma* are most widely cultivated and edible corms are obtained from numerous varieties within each genus. The leaves and petioles of *Colocasia esculenta* are also eaten as a vegetable.

Plants are very liable to be infected with virus diseases, in particular Dasheen Mosaic virus, but virus–free plants can be obtained from cultured shoot tips. These explants generally give cultures producing axillary shoots (Jackson *et al.*, 1977b). Another approach has been to micropropagate plants derived from seedlings which can be expected to be virus–free (Jackson *et al.*, 1977a).

Araceae

Colocasia esculenta   (Taro)

Shoot cultures. Shoot cultures of taro, subcultured at 3–monthly intervals, were described by Bessembinder *et al.* (1993). They were initiated on the following medium, supplemented with 1 mg/l IBA and 5 mg/l BAP:

> ½**MS** salts (plus an extra 1 g/l KNO₃) with 30 g/l sucrose, 100 mg *myo*–inositol, 10 mg/l thiamine, 100 mg/l casein hydrolysate and 50 mg/l L–cysteine HCl.

Excessive callusing occurred unless the concentration of regulants was gradually reduced to 0.1 mg/l IBA and 1 mg/l BAP.

Such cultures could be stored in a viable condition for over 8 years in the dark at 9°C if transferred to fresh medium every 2–3 years.

Callus cultures. A morphogenic callus has been found to be readily obtained from buds dissected from petiole bases (Yam *et al.*, 1990 a,b,c), or from shoot tips (Hartman, 1974). Abo El–Nil and Zettler (1976) developed their own medium for this purpose (Part 1, page 382). Protocorms were produced directly on shoot tips cultured on **AZ** medium augmented with 1.9 mg/l NAA and 1.9 mg/l kinetin. Explants on the same medium to which 1.9 mg/l NAA and 0.01 mg/l kinetin had been added, gave rise to callus, which could be maintained with 5.6 mg/l NAA and 0.01 mg/l kinetin, or induced to form shoots on a medium incorporating 0.09–0.9 mg/l NAA and 1.9 mg/l

kinetin. Shoots were rooted on the same medium with 2.8 mg/l NAA plus 0.09 mg/l kinetin.

In the reports by Yam *et al.* (1990 a,b,c), buds were placed on ½**MS** salts (30 g/l sucrose) with ¹⁄₁₀ the normal concentration of **MS** microelements and with 0.5 mg/l thiamine, 20 mg/l glycine and 20 ml/l taro extract (TE), supplemented with 5 mg/l NAA and 5 mg/l BAP

> Potato extract had the same effect as taro extract. The latter was prepared by boiling 600 g of 1 cm3 tuber cubes for 5 minutes in 1 litre water, and then simmering the mixture for 1 hour. The liquor obtained after filtering through a Whatman No. 1 paper was used immediately, or frozen.

Shoots were regenerated on the same medium without growth regulators, but still containing TE.

Araceae

Amorphophallus   (Elephant yam, konjaku)

Corms of *A. rivieri* (Konjaku), *A. titanum* and *A. campanulatus* (Elephant yam) are eaten as a vegetables. *A. campanulatus*, which has very large foetid flowers, is sometimes also grown as an ornamental.

Shoots can be regenerated from callus derived from corm sections or lateral buds (Table 230). Corm tissue of *A. rivieri* gave rise to callus and adventitious shoots on **MS** medium with added 0.09 mg/l NAA and 0.01 mg/l kinetin (Irawati *et al.*, 1986), or on ½**MS** medium with only 200 mg/l ammonium nitrate, to which 0.1–0.3 mg/l NAA and 4–8 mg/l BAP had been added (Asoka *et al.*, 1984c).

Morphogenic callus has also been obtained from sections of young *A. rivieri* leaves which include the midvein. The latter were grown by Kohlenbach and Becht (1988) on the modified **Bourgin and Nitsch (1967)** medium used by Geier for *Anthurium* (page 839), except that 100mg/l ascorbic acid and 500 mg/l casein hydrolysate were added. Callus was grown in the same way as *Anthurium* callus, *i.e.* initiated in the dark, and then transferred to the light for plantlet development.

On this medium, shoot formation from *A. titanum* was somewhat unpredictable. It was most reliably achieved by the following sequence of growth regulator treatments:

1.	Callus initiation	2.5 mg/l 2,4–D + 0.5 mg/l kinetin	(Dark, 25°C)
2.	Shoot formation	0.3 mg/l NAA + 3 mg/l zeatin + 0.01 mg/l GA₃	(25°C, Light 16 h 19–38 µmol m^{-2} s^{-1})
3.	Shoot growth	0.2 mg/l BAP	(Light 16 h 19–38 µmol m^{-2} s^{-1})
4.	Rooting	No regulants	[on **Bourgin & Nitsch (1967)**]

Callus and shoot formation in *A. rivieri* similarly involved several transfers (Kohlenbach and Becht, 1988):

1.	Initiation	0.5 mg/l 2,4–D + 1.0 mg/l BAP	(Dark)
2.	Callus growth	0.1 mg/l 2,4–D + 5 mg/l BAP	(light)
3.	Shoot formation	0.1 mg/l 2,4–D + 5 mg/l BAP	
4.	Shoot growth	3 mg/l zeatin + 0.03 mg/l NAA + 0.01 GA₃,	
5.	Root induction	0.5 mg/l NAA	[on **Bourgin & Nitsch (1967)**]
6.	Rooting	No regulants	[on **Bourgin & Nitsch (1967)**]

Araceae
Xanthosoma (Cocoyams)

The several species of *Xanthosoma* which are cultivated for their edible corms, are called cocoyams. Plants are taller than those of taro and grow on drier ground.

Shoot culture. Fierro (1976) showed that shoots of *Xanthosoma* could be cultured from meristem tips on **MS** medium (100 g/l sucrose) in which the concentration of *myo*–inositol was increased to 200 mg/l. Shoots grew most strongly when the medium contained 1 mg/l NAA and 0.03 mg/l kinetin and produced plantlets which developed roots and a small corm in long days. Rapid plantlet multiplication of *X. caracu* was achieved by Asokan *et al.* (1984b). Elongated shoots with roots were formed when shoot tips were incubated in agitated liquid **MS** medium supplemented with 100 mg/l ascorbic acid (no regulants). When transferred to agar–solidified **Asokan *et al.* (1984b) 1**. medium (listed in Table 47, Part 1, page 382) containing 0.5 mg/l IAA and 2 mg/l BAP, these plantlets formed axillary shoots which could be divided and rooted.

Callus cultures. Callus which forms adventitious shoots is formed when shoot tips of *Xanthosoma* are incubated on **LS** medium to which 0.1 mg/l IAA and 1 mg/l kinetin (Strauss and Arditti (1980), or 5 mg/l NAA, 2 mg/l kinetin and 10% coconut milk (Gupta, 1985), has been added. An alternative technique, effective with *X. violaceum* and *X. saggittifolium*, was to induce callus growth on **Abo El–Nil and Zettler (1976) AZ** medium containing 2 mg/l NAA, and then transfer the callus to **MS** medium augmented with 0.2–2 mg/l NAA and 2 mg/l kinetin (Gupta, 1985). Plants regenerated from callus cultures were virus free, but 18% of the *X. saggittifolium* plants had a morphology different from the norm. As a group, these variants had a compact growth habit and more leaves than usual, the leaves themselves being narrow with pointed basal lobes.

Chenopodiaceae
Beta vulgaris (Sugar beet)

In modern classifications, the species *Beta vulgaris* is divided into several subspecies, *Beta vulgaris* ssp. *vulgaris* including sugar beet; the vegetable, beetroot; and forage beets. *Beta vulgaris* ssp. *vulgaris* is thought to be derived by selection from *Beta vulgaris* ssp. *maritima*. It can be crossed with other subspecies and with other wild species to transfer genes *e.g.* those conveying disease resistance.

Sugar beet is widely grown as an agricultural crop in temperate climates for its roots which are harvested in autumn and winter for sugar production. The plant is a biennial which produces its fleshy tap root during the first year. Flowering is induced by exposure to cold. Some cultivars require only a short exposure to cold temperatures, but the roots of others must have a long cold treatment before flowering occurs. In plant breeding, methods to induce early flowering are important for reducing the interval between seed sowing and crossing.

Beta vulgaris is naturally cross pollinated but self compatibility can be genetically introduced so that selfing can be used to produce inbred lines. These are used extensively by breeders to obtain hybrids. Flowers normally occur in clusters and their ovaries become embedded in a receptacle which is common to a group of flowers. This results in aggregated fruits which are commonly termed 'multigerm seeds'. Germination of fruit aggregates results in more than one seedling arising in close proximity. 'Monogerm seeds' (which arise when flowers occur singly) can be achieved through plant breeding, and are preferred agriculturally as they give better plant spacings.

Hybrid cultivars are usually produced by crossing a male sterile parent with a pollinator. Selected self–sterile genotypes are often maintained by vegetative propagation. This can be done using pieces of mature root or leaf cuttings (Meidema *et al.*, 1980), but results are not always satisfactory and much faster rates of multiplication can now be obtained through micropropagation. Methods appear to be applicable across a wide range of genotypes (providing growth regulator treatments are specifically modified) and the final plants can be induced to flower with no reduction in fertility (Coumans–Gilles *et al.*, 1981; Saunders, 1982b).

Shoot culture

Media. The following media (listed on page 383 *et seq.*) are often used for culture of *Beta vulgaris*:

> **MS**, or media containing **MS** salts
> (Harms *et al.*, 1983); Saunders, 1982a; Saunders and Daub, 1984); Konwar and Coutts, 1990);
>
> Media containing ½**MS** salts
> (Hussey and Hepher, 1978a,b);
>
> **De Greef and Jacobs (1979) PGoB** medium
> (Coumans *et al.*, 1982); Coumans–Gillès *et al.*, 1981);
>
> **Margara (1977; 1978) N30K**
> (Margara, 1977b).

Shoot cultures can be commenced from the apices of mature plants and from seedling shoot apices. Explants give rise to axillary shoots, but often also produce an organogenic callus. Adventitious shoots may also arise on leaf petioles (Harms *et al.*, 1983). Saunders and Daub (1984) found that callus was especially likely to be initiated if temperatures in the growth room reached 30°C.

Seedling shoot apices. Seedlings provide convenient explants, but axenic material can be difficult to obtain because bacteria and fungi are usually harboured by the seed integuments. Konwar and Coutts (1990) exposed seeds to 9.5% NaOCl for 15 minutes on 2 consecutive occasions before rinsing them in distilled water, and Powling and Hussey (1981) obtained some control over persistent organisms by soaking seeds for 20 minutes in ethyl mercuric phosphate (40 g/l) solution. Seeds were afterwards germinated on a nutrient agar and seedlings only selected as a source of explant material if they emerged from uncontaminated seeds (detected by the absence of a surrounding halo in the medium).

In the experiments of Hussey and co–workers, axillary shoots which could be subcultured, were produced on a modified ½**MS** or full strength **MS** medium (Powling and Hussey, 1981) containing 0.12–0.25 mg/l BAP. This technique was repeated by Coumans *et al.* (1982) and Atanassov (1980), who found that as little as 0.08 mg/l BAP would promote shoot proliferation if the seedlings were kept in the cold at 3°C for one week before their apices were excised. Adding 0.01 mg/l GA₃ to the medium enhanced the rate of shoot multiplication from subcultured shoots.

Inflorescence explants. Shoot cultures can also be initiated from apical and sub–apical segments (5 mm long) excised from immature inflorescences 10–15 cm in length (Coumans–Gillès *et al.*, 1981; Coumans *et al.*, 1982). On the medium of **De Greef and Jacobs (1979)** with 0.1 mg/l IBA and 1.1 BAP, up to 50 axillary shoots

were produced per explant in 4 months, through the growth of floral axillary buds released from apical dominance. On subculture onto the same medium (but additionally containing 0.09–0.9 mg/l NAA), each shoot was able to develop up to 20 more axillary shoots. The resulting 1 cm long shoots were rooted in about 15 days on basal medium and were then successfully transferred to soil.

Adventitious shoot formation

Direct formation of adventitious shoots. Adventitious shoots commonly arise directly from leaf petioles and leaves in shoot cultures, especially when these organs touch the medium (Hussey and Hepher, 1978a,b; Saunders, 1982b; Harms *et al.*, 1983). Adventitious shoots also arise directly on petiole and leaf sections, and on shoot tip explants, particularly those excised from shoots which have developed *in vitro*.

Shoots can be induced to form on **De Greef and Jacobs (1979) PGoB** or **MS** medium supplemented with 0.25–1.1 mg/l BAP, with or without 0.1 mg/l IBA and 1–2 mg/l GA₃. Freytag *et al.* (1988) found that the number of shoots regenerated from petiole explants was greatest if **MS** salts were supplemented with a wide range of vitamins (mg/l):

> 0.5 mg/l thiamine HCl; 0.5 mg/l pyridoxine HCl; 0.5 nicotinic acid; 0.4 D–pantothenic acid; 0.015 riboflavin; 0.015 folic acid; 0.2 choline chloride; 0.00025 D–biotin; 0.2 *p*–aminobenzoic acid; 0.4 ascorbic acid (no inositol):

and the following amino acids (mg/l):

> 40 L–arginine; 40 L–asparagine (anhydrous); 20 glycine; 60 L–glutamine; 20 L–phenylalanine; 40 L–tryptophan.

MS medium containing these supplements was called **RV** medium.

Indirect shoot formation. Organogenic callus is readily initiated from the same kinds of explants as those which give rise to shoots directly. Immature embryos, or seedling cotyledons and hypocotyls are also effective explant sources. Often, direct shoot formation and callus initiation occur simultaneously. Callus can be induced on a range of media, **MS** (or **LS**), **B5** and **PGoB** have been used most frequently. **MS** medium has sometimes been amended by the addition of different vitamins. Catlin (1990) found that more shoots were regenerated from cotyledon callus initiated on a slightly modified* **Freytag** *et al.* **(1988) RV** medium (see above) than on **MS**.

Some examples of successful protocols are shown in Table 227. In most of these, callus has been induced which gave rise to shoots on the same medium. However, in the method used by Abe *et al.* (1991), regeneration only

---

*   Catlin (1990) added 100 mg/l *myo*–inositol and 100 mg/l MES

Table 227. Protocols which have resulted in the regeneration of shoots from callus of *Beta vulgaris*.
The medium used in each case is shown in square brackets; sucrose concentrations (%) are given in rounded brackets.

Explants	Callus induction medium (growth regulators in mg/l)	References
Cotyledons	[MS] (4) no vitamins or amino acids 5 BAP + 0.5 TIBA	Hooker and Nabors (1977)
Seedling leaves	[MS†] (3) 0.7–2 BAP	Yu (1989)
Petioles ex i.v. shoots	0.3–3 BAP	Saunders (1982b)
Leaf discs (1 yr-old plants)	[MS‡] (3) None or 1 BAP	Doley and Saunders (1989)
Leaf sections	[PGoB] (3) 1 IAA + 0.1 kin	De Greef and Jacobs (1979)
Leaf discs ex i.v. shoots	[RV§] (3) + 1 BAP (Shoots and embryos to PGR–free PGoB medium for growth)	Owens and Eberts (1992)
Germinated seeds	[MS] or [B5] (3) 0.37 NAA + 1.1 BAP Shoots regenerated when callus moved to [MS] + 1.1 BAP and 1 TIBA	Abe *et al.* (1991)

† MS salts plus 2 mg/l thiamine HCl; 1 mg/l nicotinic acid; 1 mg/l pyridoxone HCl; 100 mg/l inositol.

‡ MS salts plus the vitamins of Mullin et al. 1974) B (see p. 412).

§ MSRV medium, and a modification are given above. Less embryos and shoots were formed when the medium was gelled with agar than with 0.3%Gelrite.

occurred when the callus was moved to a second medium containing different growth regulators and de Greef and Jacobs (1979) obtained shoot formation by storing callus for 3–9 weeks at 4°C on a medium containing 1 mg/l kinetin and 0.2 mg/l GA₃ before incubating the cultures at 24°C. Adventitious shoots and somatic embryos were obtained by Owens and Eberts (1992). These were moved to a growth regulator–free medium for growth.

Habituated callus Several authors have discovered that callus which is habituated for auxin (and often cytokinin also), is readily obtained from sugar beet explants. Such callus has sometimes been directly isolated from a proportion of explants by incubating them on medium devoid of growth regulators (Saunders, 1982b). On other occasions it has been obtained by transferring callus, induced to form in the presence of auxin, onto medium in which the concentration of auxin is reduced at each subculture (Van Geyt and Jacobs, 1985). Habituated callus can be organogenic or non–organogenic (De Greef and Jacobs, 1979; Kevers *et al.*, 1981a,b). Callus newly–initiated from the leaves of the plants regenerated from such shoot forming callus was again habituated and highly regenerative (Coumans *et al.*, 1982).

Rooting

Sugar beet shoots can be rooted *in vitro* without difficulty and have most frequently been placed into semi–solid **MS** medium to which NAA (0.4–3 mg/l) has been added. Owens and Eberts (1992) gelled **MS** medium with 0.2% Gelrite: in other papers, agar has been used. Rooting was also reported by Konwar and Coutts (1990)on **MS** medium containing 0.5 mg/l kinetin as the sole regulant.

Rooting on media other than **MS** may be equally effective. Catlin (1990) rooted shoots on agar–solidified **B5** medium (10 g/l sucrose) supplemented with 0.2 g/l AC and 3 mg/l IBA and Coumans-Gillès *et al.* (1981) found that shoots rooted on **PGoB** medium, without regulants.

Convolvulaceae
Ipomoea batatas   (Sweet potato)

Sweet potato is widely grown in the wet tropics and subtropics where its tubers, which have a high starch content, are eaten as a vegetable. Plants are vegetatively propagated, either from leafy stem cuttings, called slips, or in more temperate regions from shoots produced on stored tubers.

Because of the nature of propagation, *Ipomoea batatas* cultivars are prone to virus diseases. Tissue culture is therefore most useful for producing and maintaining virus–free stocks and for the maintenance of germplasm collections. Meristem culture is often coupled with heat treatment of stock plants (*e.g.* 14 days at 36°C) for virus removal (Chandler and Haque, 1984).

Meristem culture

Although other media can be used (Nielsen, 1960), sweet potato meristems can be cultured satisfactorily on **MS** medium (30 g/l sucrose). Some workers have thought it advisable to use **MS** salts with a wider range of vitamins, or to employ the same vitamins at a higher concentration. For example, Chandler and Haque (*loc. cit.*) added double the normal concentration of **MS** organics.

Love and Rhodes (1985) found that more explants survived transfer to culture if the pH of **MS** was adjusted to 5.2 (instead of 5.7) and if the medium contained 50 (rather than 30) g/l sucrose.

Growth regulator additions to meristem culture media have included:

0.2 mg/l IAA + 0.5 mg/l BAP + 80 AdS dihydrate	Chandler and Haque (1984)
1–5 mg/l IAA or NAA + 1–5 mg/l BAP	Kartha (1982b)
0.03 mg/l NAA + 0.3 BAP	Love and Rhodes (1985)
1 mg/l IAA	Elliott (1969)
0.1 mg/l NAA + 0.1 mg/l kin + 1 mg/l GA$_3$	Rey and Mroginski (1985)

Node cultures

Elongated shoots are produced when nodal segments of *Ipomoea batatas* are cultured on growth regulator–free **MS** medium and incubated at 25–28°C in a 16 h photoperiod (15–60 μmol m^{-2} s^{-1}). Shoots are re–divided into nodal sections for subculture. Jarrett and Gawel (1991a) discovered that if 10 mg/l ABA is added to **MS** medium, the growth of axillary shoots is completely inhibited. However, explants remained viable for periods of up to one year and were able to produce shoots when transferred to a regulant–free medium.

Dioscoreaceae
Dioscorea spp.   (Yams)

Of the many species of climbing plants in the genus *Dioscorea*, 10–12 are grown in the tropics as food sources, particularly in the Caribbean, West Africa and south–east Asia. Plants, and their edible tubers are called yams (although confusingly, this term is sometimes used colloquially to describe the roots or tubers of other tropical plants, especially those of sweet potato).

Yam crops are usually grown on small farms or in gardens for local consumption. Plants are trained to climb up stakes and require a large amount of manual labour during their cultivation. This has led to a decline in production in many areas in favour of alternative crops, such as manioc, sweet potato and potato.

Apart from the edible species of *Dioscorea*, some other wild species are important sources of the steroid diosgenin, a precursor of drugs such as cortisone and progesterone. Tubers have been largely collected from the wild for this purpose and in some countries this has led to a depletion of natural populations leading to interest in the cultivation of some species, particularly *D. floribunda* (see page 1208).

Micropropagation. Plant are normally grown from small tubers, or the top (crown) of large ones, and many species can also be increased from nodal cuttings, should the need arise. Even though the edible species of *Dioscorea* are vegetatively propagated, species are extremely variable, so that micropropagation has been thought to have a role in multiplying high yielding, disease–free strains for distribution to farmers. It may be an aid to breeding in those species which set viable seed.

Shoot and node culture

The application of heat therapy to stock plants, combined with meristem tip culture, has been used to free plants from virus diseases (Mantell *et al.*, 1980; Chandler and Haque, 1984). Meristem tips are usually cultured on **MS**. This medium is also suitable for shoot and single node cultures initiated from shoot tips or nodal cuttings, although there may be an advantage in using a medium containing the macronutrients of **White (1954)**. Mantell and Hugo (1989) used **White (1954)** macronutrients combined with **Heller (1953)** micronutrients but 25 mg/l Fe$_2$SO$_4$ (no EDTA mentioned), and 10 mg/l thiamine HCl [this formulation was called medium **T**, Table 228]. To propagate *D. floribunda*, Chaturvedi (1975) and Chaturvedi and Sinha (1979b) used the medium **2** in Table 228 with 20 g/l sucrose.

Chaturvedi and Sinha (1979b) initiated cultures of *D. floribunda* from single nodes of shoot apex cuttings (consisting of the apex and several young leaves). These were placed on just the mineral salts and sucrose of medium **2**, which was supplemented with 200 mg/l casein hydrolysate to accelerate detection of bacterial or fungal infection. Infection–free nodal explants transferred to medium **2** augmented with 0.1 mg/l NAA and 15 mg/l adenine sulphate produced a swelling from the site of the axillary bud, representing the formation of tuberous tissue from which roots and then shoots were formed. Shoot apex cuttings produced roots from each node, but retained apical dominance and grew into elogated shoots.

Other authors have found that if no growth regulators are added to the medium, cultures commenced from nodal segments (excised with accompanying internode tissue) give rise to single shoots which grow from the lateral bud on each explant. These can be cut into fresh single node segments to initiate new cultures. Mantell *et al.* (1978) could obtain 65 000 plantlets from a single node in one year by culturing explants on **MS** salts supplemented with 20 g/l sucrose 10 mg/l inositol and 1 mg/l thiamine HCl (27°C; 16 h *ca.* 15–17.5 μmol m^{-2} s^{-1}).

The same method of propagation can be used for cultures started from meristem or shoot tips or from small nodal segments, but with these kinds of explant it is necessary

Table 228. Two media which, in addition to **MS** medium, have been used for *Dioscorea* cultures.

Components	Mantell and Hugo (1989) T ①	Chaturvedi and Sinha (1979b) ②
Macronutrients (meq/l)		
NO_3^-	3.33	33.58
PO_4^{3-}	0.36	3.31
SO_4^{2-}	8.66	2.92
Cl^-	0.87	5.44
K^+	1.66	15.94
Ca^{2+}	2.54	5.44
Na^+	2.94	—
Mg^{2+}	5.84	2.92
NH_4^+	—	18.74
Microelements (mg/l)		
$MnSO_4.4H_2O$	0.1	26.4
$ZnSO_4.7H_2O$	1.0	8.0
H_3BO_3	1.0	6.0
KI	0.01	0.8
$CuSO_4.5H_2O$	0.03	0.02
$Na_2MoO_4.2H_2O$	—	0.2
$CoCl_2.6H_2O$	—	0.02
$AlCl_3$	0.03	—
$NiCl_2$	0.03	—
NaFeEDTA (mM)	0.125†	0.1
Vitamins (mg/l)		
myo–Inositol	—	100.0
Thiamine HCl	10.0	0.2
Nicotinic acid	—	0.1
Pyridoxine HCl	—	0.1
Folic acid	—	0.1
Amino acids (mg/l)		
Glycine	—	3.0

† The paper says that 25.0 mg/l $Fe_2(SO_4)_3$ was added to the medium. There is no mention of a chelating agent.

to add auxin and cytokinin to the Stage I medium (*e.g.* 0.02 mg/l NAA and 2.2 zeatin, or 0.5 mg/l NAA and 0.2 mg/l kinetin). Lateral buds are more likely to develop into shoots *in vitro* if nodal segments are excised from young actively growing plants which have been kept in long days.

Typical shoot cultures are also obtained if explants are cultured with higher concentrations of cytokinin (*e.g.* 2 mg/l BAP), for in these circumstances multiple axillary shoots are produced.

The formation of miniature tubers

All species of edible yams naturally produce tubers beneath the soil, but *D. bulbifera* also forms tubers above ground on the stem, and it is the aerial tubers of this species which are edible.

Miniature tubers of yams are formed during *in vitro* culture when conditions are optimised. Small aerial tubers are formed directly on stem node explants of *D. bulbifera* if they are cultured on **MS** medium containing 0.02 mg/l NAA (Uduebo, 1971; Ammirato, 1984), and in flasks of *D. alata* and *D. bulbifera* single node cultures grown for 4–5 months in continuous light (Ammirato, 1982; 1984).

However, Mantell and Hugo (1989) only obtained tuber formation of *D. alata* when cultures were grown in a photoperiod of 8 hours and, although *D. alata* produced tubers in a 16 h photoperiod providing kinetin was present, tuber formation was greatest when light was only provided for 8 h each day. Maximum tuber formation in these species occurred on different media:

- for *D. alata*, medium **T** (above) supplemented with 2% sucrose and 0.54 mg/l kinetin;

- for *D. bulbifera*, **MS** medium containing 4% sucrose and 0.54 mg/l kinetin.

Euphorbiaceae
Manihot esculenta

(Cassava, manioc, tapioca)

Manihot esculenta Crantz. (*M. utilissima* Pohl.) is a woody shrub which can grow to 3 m. Its swollen tuberous roots are a source of edible starch, but have a very low protein content. After reaching maturity, many varieties can be left unattended for one or two years, without deterioration in the quality of the tubers.

Cassava is an important carbohydrate food crop in many tropical areas of the world, but roots have to be heated or fermented before consumption to remove toxic cyanogens. Cassava starch is cheap, has many industrial applications, and is now utilised extensively by developed countries as a carbohydrate component of compounded animal feeds. It has been suggested that the crop could provide a source of fermentable carbohydrate to provide renewable energy supplies (Goldemburg, 1979).

Plants of cassava are vegetatively propagated from stem cuttings, and up to 30 suitable stem sections (*ca.* 25 cm in length) can be obtained from a mature plant. Multiplication is therefore easily accomplished but, although relatively immune from pests and fungal diseases, plants are liable to virus diseases, particularly mosaic, which can severely limit yield in some parts of Africa. The chief use for tissue culture is therefore to obtain, and then propagate, virus–free stocks, and to maintain healthy germplasm collections. It could also be used for the rapid multiplication and distribution of new cultivars.

Production of virus–tested plants

Although cassava can be highly productive even without the use of fertilisers or crop protection chemicals, yields can be greatly reduced by cassava mosaic disease, particularly in Africa and India. The causal virus (Bock and Guthrie, 1978; Bock *et al.* 1978; Sequeira and Harrison, 1982) is transmitted by a white fly, *Bemesia tabaci* and further spread by the use of infected cuttings. Cassava plants can be freed from virus infection by meristem tip culture alone, or meristem tip culture combined with heat treatment (Kaiser and Teemba, 1979; Kartha and Gamborg, 1979; Adejare and Coutts, 1981). The plantlets so obtained could be multiplied by *in vitro* techniques, but propagation of virus–tested plants is most economically carried out by means of cuttings (Howland, 1976).

Kartha and Gamborg (1979) suggested that the incidence of cassava mosaic could be reduced by the production and distribution of large numbers of virus–free plants, so that the inoculum in a given locality is diluted. However, control of the white fly vector of cassava mosaic is difficult because of its wide host range. Long–term breeding programmes for virus control should perhaps concentrate on varieties that do not favour white fly development (Leuschner, 1976), or on the discovery of virus resistance.

Meristem tip culture. Explants are generally taken from sprouted shoots on stem cuttings (stakes), because a greater proportion survives and grows in culture than when tips are excised from mature plants (Kartha *et al.*, 1974c; Bajaj, 1978a; Kartha, 1981a; Adejare and Coutts, 1981). To obtain virus elimination, excised tips should be no longer than 0.4 mm (Kartha, 1981a), because explants of less than 0.2 mm tend to give rise to callus or callus with roots (Kartha and Gamborg, 1975b). Media for meristem tip and other kinds of cassava culture have usually been based on **Murashige and Skoog (1962)** medium. During culture initiation, Kartha and co–workers supplemented **MS** salts with the vitamins of **Gamborg (1966) PRL–4–C** (the vitamins in **B5** medium — page 407). Meristem cultures are usually initiated on media containing 20–30 g/l sucrose and 0.02–0.2 mg/l NAA, 0.02–0.1 mg/l BAP, and 0.03 mg/l GA$_3$. Shoots grow and elongate on this medium and can be rooted in **MS** medium (without gibberellic acid) containing 0.02–0.2 mg/l NAA

(sometimes 0.1 mg/l BAP is also included in the root induction medium).

If required, shoots can be transferred, before rooting, to a second medium in which there is slightly less auxin [0.01 mg/l NAA and a greater concentration of BAP (0.6–1.1 mg/l)], to induce the formation of multiple shoots.

Shoot and node cultures

Shoot cultures of cassava can be initiated from nodal explants. Smith *et al.* (1986) showed that node cultures can be grown on ½**MS** (30 g/l sucrose) to which 0.5 mg/l IBA is added. Single shoots which root *in vitro* are obtained on this medium and can be sectioned and subcultured if required. Alternatively, multiple shoots can be obtained by placing the nodal sections on ½**MS** containing 0.05 mg/l NAA and 0.2 mg/l BAP. These shoots do not form roots in the presence of BAP, but do so if divided and transferred to the initiation medium.

Solanaceae
Solanum tuberosum   (Potato)

Amongst the many species in the genus *Solanum*, approximately 150 produce tubers, several of which (and some interspecific hybrids) are cultivated as food plants. *Solanum tuberosum* has two subspecies, *tuberosum* and *andigena*. The former (to which the remainder of these notes refer) is heavy cropping, early maturing and produces tubers which are relatively smooth with shallow eyes, and is very widely grown throughout the world. Subspecies *andigena* is cultivated at high elevations in South America and produces narrow, late–maturing tubers which are irregular in shape and have deep eyes. Of the cultivated potato species apart from *S. tuberosum*, *S. phureja* is prominent. It is grown in mountain valleys of South America.

S. tuberosum subsp. *tuberosum* is tetraploid and, like other tuberous solanums, is easily propagated vegetatively.

Breeding objectives. The breeding of improved potato varieties is potentially complex, because there is a large number of other species from which genetic traits might be transferred, and many of these are diploid and self–incompatible. However tetraploid offspring are often produced in crosses of diploids with tetraploids, because most diploids produce some unreduced gametes. Dihaploids of *S. tuberosum* can be obtained through crosses with *S. phureja*, and through the use of *in vitro* anther culture. These are useful for crosses with other diploid species and for the formation of autotetraploid

Table 230. Published reports on tissue culture of ROOT AND TUBER CROPS.

	Species name	Type of Culture	Source of explant	Results		References
Araceae						
❖	Amorphophallus paeoniifolius (Dennst.) Nicols. = A. campanulatus (Elephant yam)	Callus	Lateral bud plus corm piece	Shoot regeneration. Rooted plants	—	Irawati et al. (1986)
	Amorphophallus rivieri Durieu. (Konjaku)	Callus	Cubes (6 cm) of corm tissue	30–50 shoots regenerated per explant	—	Asokan et al. (1984c)
❖	Amorphophallus rivieri	Callus/Direct	Midvein explants ex young leaves	Adventitious shoots. Rooted plants	Y	Kohlenbach & Becht (1988)
	Amorphophallus rivieri	Direct/Callus	Tuber pieces	Direct and indirect adventitious shoots	Y	Morel & Wetmore (1951a)
	Amorphophallus rivieri	Shoot	Shoots renerated from callus	Axillary shoot proliferation. Shoots rooted	YY	Asokan et al. (1984c)
	Amorphophallus titanum Becc.	Callus/Direct	Midvein explants from young leaves	Adventitious shoots. Rooted plants	Y	Kohlenbach & Becht (1988)
	Colocasia esculenta L. Schott. (Taro)	Callus	Shoot tips	Adventitious shoots. Rooted to give plantlets	—	Abo El-Nil & Zettler (1976)
	Colocasia esculenta	Callus	Shoot tips	Adventitious shoots, rooted. Virus-free plants	—	Hartman (1974)
	Colocasia esculenta	Callus	Seeds	Adventitious shoots	—	Jackson et al. (1977a)
	Colocasia esculenta	Callus	Stem sections	Adventitious shoots. Rooted plants	—	Jackson et al. (1977b)
	Colocasia esculenta	Callus	Unknown	Adventitious shoots. Shoots then rooted	—	Nyman & Arditti (1984)
	Colocasia esculenta	Callus	Shoot tips	Two types of callus. Adv. shoots, rooted plantlets	—	Nyman et al. (1983 a,b)
	Colocasia esculenta var. esculenta	Callus	Axillary buds ex petiole bases	Adventitious shoots & roots. Plants	—	Yam et al. (1990 a,b,c)
	Colocasia esculenta	Direct	Shoot tips	Protocorm-like bodies with shoots & roots	Y	Abo El-Nil & Zettler (1976)
	Colocasia esculenta	Direct	Seeds	Germination & multiple shoot formation	Y	Jackson et al. (1977a)
	Colocasia esculenta	Embryo	Seed embryos plus endosperm tiss.	Viable plantlets (depended on presence of endosperm)	Y	Nyman et al. (1987)
	Colocasia esculenta	Shoot	Shoot tips & axillary buds	Mutiple shoots. Rooted plants	YY	Jackson et al. (1977b)
	Colocasia esculenta	Shoot	Shoot tips (not axillary buds)	Shoots. Most plants were virus-free	Y	Jackson et al. (1977b)
	Colocasia esculenta	Storage	Shoots ex in vitro cultures	Storage conditions optimized	—	Bessembinder et al. (1993)
	Colocasia esculenta	Embryo	Immature embryos	Seedling germination. Plants	Y	Abraham & Ramachandran (1960)
❖	Xanthosoma caracu (Coco-yam)	Callus	Shoot tips with incisions	Adventitious shoots, if not subcultured	—	Strauss & Arditti (1980)
	Xanthosoma caracu	Shoot	Shoot tips (1–1.2 cm)	Shoot elongation, rooting. Rooted shoots proliferated	YY	Asokan et al. (1984b)
	Xanthosoma sagittifolium (L.) Schott. (Tannia)	Callus	Apical meristem (0.35–0.5 mm) 2–3 leaf primordia	Adventitious shoots with roots. Plants	—	Gupta (1985)
	Xanthosoma sagittifolium	Callus	Shoot tips	Plants via callus	—	Hartman (1974)
	Xanthosoma sagittifolium	Meristem	Apical meristem	Rooted plantlet	Y	Fierro (1976)
	Xanthosoma violaceum Schott. (Blue taro)	Callus	Apical meristem (0.35–0.5 mm) 2–3 leaf primordia	Adventitious shoots with roots. Plants	—	Gupta (1985)
	Xanthosoma violaceum	Direct	Shoot meristem from tuber bud	Corm-like bodies, proliferated. Plantlets with roots	Y	Quynh & Uyen (1987)
Chenopodiaceae						
	Beta spp. [various genotypes] (Sugarbeet)	Callus	Seeds, germinated in vitro	Shoots regenerated and rooted	—	Abe et al. (1991)
*	Beta vulgaris L. [3 cvs.]	Callus	Proximal half of cotyledons	Adventitious shoots. Rooted plants	—	Catlin (1990)
	Beta vulgaris cv.' Prima Hill'	Callus	Shoot tips	Adventitious shoots ex organised callus	Y	Chandler et al. (1988)

Species name	Type of Culture	Source of explant	Results		References
Beta vulgaris	Callus	Callus from base of *in vitro* shoot	Adventitious shoots (highly regenerative callus)	—	De Greef & Jacobs (1979)
Beta vulgaris	Callus	Leaf pieces (3 × 5 mm)	Adventitious buds. Plantlet with callus at base	—	De Greef & Jacobs (1979)
Beta vulgaris [16 populations] (Sugarbeet)	Callus	Leaf discs ex 1 yr.old plants	Shoots and/or roots	—	Doley & Saunders (1989)
Beta vulgaris	Callus	Cotyls, hypocots, & damaged embryos	Adventitious shoots	—	Hooker & Nabors (1977)
Beta vulgaris	Callus	Leaf pieces	Habituated organogenic callus. Adventitious shoots	—	Kevers *et al.* (1981 a,b) &
Beta vulgaris	Callus	Floral buds pre-anthesis	Adventitious shoots on primary & subcultured callus	—	Margara (1970)
Beta vulgaris	Callus	Young flower buds	Adventitious shoots from basal callus. Rooted	—	Margara (1977a)
Beta vulgaris clone REL-1	Callus	Leaf discs ex shoot cults.	Embryos & shoots, rooted	—	Owens & Eberts (1992)
Beta vulgaris	Callus	Callus from bases of shoot cultures	Adventitious shoots. Rooted	—	Saunders & Daub (1984)
Beta vulgaris	Callus	Petiole segment (ex *in vitro* shoot)	Adventitious shoots	—	Saunders (1982b)
Beta vulgaris [several lines]	Callus	Callus from base of primary shoot	Habituated callus forming adventitious shoots. Plants	—	Van Geyt & Jacobs (1985)
Beta vulgaris [lines H10 & 3584]	Callus	Young seedling leaves	Adventitious shoots. Rooted plants	—	Yu (1989)
Beta vulgaris L. [several varieties]	Cryopreservation	Inflorescence meristems	Shoot growth. Plants	Y	Braun (1988)
Beta vulgaris	Direct	Floral buds (pre-flowering)	Adventitious buds	Y	Atanassov (1980)
Beta vulgaris	Direct	Seedling stem apices & cotyledons	Adventitious buds, further increased & rooted	Y	Atanassov (1980)
Beta vulgaris	Direct	Leaves of *in vitro* shoots	Adventitious shoot formation	Y	Coumans *et al.* (1982)
Beta vulgaris	Direct	Petiole sections (2–3 mm)	Adventitious shoots. Rooted	Y	Saunders (1982a)
Beta vulgaris [6 cvs.]	Direct or via callus	Petioles of *in vitro* seedlings	High rate of shoot regeneration. Embryogenesis. Plants	—	Freytag *et al.* (1988)
Beta vulgaris cv. 'Prima Hill'	Direct/Callus	Leaves ex shoot cultures	Adventitious shoots. Rooted	—	Chandler *et al.* (1988)
Beta vulgaris line 86C92-0	Direct/Callus	Petioles ex *in vitro* shoot cultures	Salt-tolerant shoots regenerated & rooted	—	Freytag *et al.* (1990)
Beta vulgaris cv. 'Bella'	Direct/Callus	Petiole & leaf sections	Adv. shoots from petiole & ex callus on cut surfaces	—	Konwar & Coutts (1990)
Beta vulgaris [5 male sterile lines]	Ovule/Embryo	Unfertilized ovules	Viable embryos developed into plants, 81% haploid	Y	Doctrinal *et al.* (1989)
Beta vulgaris	Shoot	Seedling shoot tips	Axillary shoots proliferated	YY	Coumans *et al.* (1982)
Beta vulgaris	Shoot	Inflorescence segments	Shoots from flower initials, multiplied & rooted	YY	Coumans-Gillès *et al.* (1981)&
Beta vulgaris cv. 'Bella'	Shoot	Shoot tips of aseptic seedlings	Growth & detection of contamination	—	Konwar & Coutts (1990)
Beta vulgaris	Shoot	Shoot tips	Shoot proliferation. Shoots rooted.	YY	Margara (1977a)
Beta vulgaris	Shoot	Seedling shoot tips	Shoot proliferation (basal callus)	Y	Saunders & Daub (1984)
Beta vulgaris [several lines]	Shoot	Seedling shoot tips	Shoot growth (& multiplication?)	Y	Van Geyt & Jacobs (1985)
Beta vulgaris cv. 'Bella'	Shoot/Callus	Shoot tips	Axillary shoots & adventitious shoots from callus	Y	Konwar & Coutts (1990)
Beta vulgaris (Red beet)	Shoot/Direct	Shoot tips of axenic seedlings	Adventitious & axillary shoots. Rooted	Y	Harms *et al.* (1983)
Beta vulgaris	Shoot/Direct	Axenic seedlings & leaves thereof	Axillary & adventitious shoots. Rooted plantlets	Y	Hussey & Hepher (1978 a,b)
Beta vulgaris	Shoot/direct	Lateral buds (5–15 mm)	Multiple axillary & adventitious shoots. Rooted	Y	Saunders (1982a)
Compositae — Asteraceae					
❖ *Helianthus tuberosus* L. cv. 'Silver skin' (Jerusalem artichoke)	Callus	Sections of tuber (3 × 0.6 mm)	Studied tracheary element formation	—	Phillips (1987)
Convolulaceae					
* *Ipomoea batatas* (L.) Poir. cv. 'White Star' (Sweet potato)	Callus	Shoot meristem tips	Embryogenesis (maintained over many subcultures)	—	Chee & Cantliffe (1988)
Ipomoea batatas	Callus	Shoot apices	Embryogenesis (from meristem callus)	—	Dewald & Cantliffe (1988)

Leguminosae (Fabaceae)
Pisum sativum (Pea)

The genus *Pisum* is now regarded as being monospecific, and the several other species which were once recognised are now regarded as varieties or ecotypes. The garden pea (*P. sativum* var. *macrocarpon*) is widely grown as a vegetable. Seeds of the related form *P. sativum* var. *arvense* (the field pea) are used as animal feed, while haulms are harvested for animal fodder or used as green manure.

Adventitious shoot formation

Indirect formation. Callus capable of giving rise to adventitious shoots can be initiated from seedling epicotyls or plumules by culture on **MS** medium containing 2 mg/l NAA and 0.5 mg/l NAA (De and Roy, 1985), or **Ziv et al. (1970)** medium (page 388) supplemented with 2.8 mg/l NAA (or 0.5–2 mg/l 2,4–D) and 1 mg/l BAP (Hussey and Gunn, 1984). Shoot regeneration occurred when the callus was transferred to medium with 0.25 mg/l IBA and 1 mg/l BAP.

Gamborg *et al.* (1974) found that regenerative callus could be obtained by incubating seedling shoot apices on either **B5** (20 g/l sucrose), or **MS** (30 g/l sucrose) together with 0.2 mg/l NAA and 0.05–1.1 mg/l BAP. However, larger and more vigorous shoots were produced on **B5** than on **MS**, and the frequency of shoot regeneration from callus and the size and vigour of shoots were improved even further by adding 30 g/l sucrose and extra nitrogen to **B5** medium. Best results were obtained using medium **2** in Table 233.

A highly regenerative callus obtained by Hussey and Gunn (*loc. cit.*) from cv. 'Paget' had the characteristics of a calloid with superficial meristems. The tissue could be subcultured, once large shoots had been removed, by being chopped into a slurry. On agar–solified, or shaken liquid medium containing 0.25 mg/l IBA and 1 mg/l BAP, shoots were produced from it over many years.

Direct shoot formation. Direct shoot formation from immature embryos (Davies and Bedford, 1981), plumes (Hussey and Gunn, 1984), and epicotyl segments (Gosal and Bajaj *in* Bajaj and Gosal, 1982) of *Pisum* has been obtained on **MS** medium, in the latter case augmented with 1 mg/l NAA, 3 mg/l BAP and 7% coconut milk.

Adventitious shoots were regenerated with the minimum of callus formation when segments of 3 day–old leaves were cultured on **MS** medium containing **B5** vitamins [the medium of **Kartha et al. (1974a)** — see Table 233 and page 385] to which had been added 0.2 mg/l NAA and 2.2 mg/l BAP, or 2 mg/l IAA and 2 mg/l kinetin (Mroginski and Kartha, 1981b). Rubluo *et al.* (1984) obtained very simi-

lar results and showed that **Kartha *et al.* (1974a)** was better than either **MS** or **B5** medium for obtaining callus with morphogenic competence. Leaves which were 15 days old failed to give rise to plantlets. Shoots were formed with the minimum of callus growth and without transferring the explants to a second medium, by adding 2.2 mg/l BAP plus either 1.9 mg/l NAA, 2 mg/l IBA or 1.8 mg/l IAA, and incubating the cultures in the light. No shoots were initiated in total darkness, where only roots were formed (Rubluo *et al.*, 1982).

Nauerby *et al.* (1991) floated thin layered sections excised from seedling nodes on liquid half strength medium **3** (Table 233) to which were added 500 mg/l casein hydrolysate, 250 mg/l xylose and 15 g/l glucose, and the growth regulators IBA (0.01 mg/l) and dihydrozeatin (1.1 mg/l) (incubation in continuous light of 50 μmol m^{-2} s^{-1} at 22°C). Shoots were produced when explants were subcultured to the same medium without growth regulators.

Meristem and shoot culture

Kartha *et al.* (1974b) were able to grow meristem tips of peas into individual shoots on **Gamborg *et al.* (1968) B5** medium plus BAP (0.1 mg/l) alone or with the further addition of 0.2 mg/l NAA. Shoots were rooted on half strength **B5** plus 0.2 mg/l NAA. It was suggested that this technique would enable the elimination of some legume viruses which can be seed transmitted.

Shoot culture of *Pisum sativum* was successfully carried out by Griga *et al.* (1986). Shoot apices or lateral buds of seedlings produced multiple shoots on **MS** medium (containing **B5** vitamins) supplemented with 4.5 mg/l BAP and 0.2 mg/l NAA. Shoots were rooted on the same medium in which there was 0.93 mg/l NAA and no BAP.

Leguminosae (Fabaceae)
Trifolium spp. (Clovers)

Clover plants are grown extensively as pasture crops, or for the production of hay, frequently in mixtures with grasses. There is a very large number of species in the genus, but only a few are cultivated and most of these are cross–pollinated and perennial. Crimson clover (*Trifolium incarnatum*) is an annual. In the improvement of outbreeding species, genotypes selected for further experimental crosses, or for the first stages of the production of commercial seed lots, are maintained by vegetative propagation. Plants established from cuttings and grown in pots are, however, liable to become infected with fungal and viral diseases and may be lost. These problems can be solved by using *in vitro* techniques for propagation and for storing valuable material with minimal mainte-

Table 234. Protocols which have led to callus and indirect adventitious shoot formation in *Trifolium*.
Media numbered in square brackets are listed in Table 235.

No.	Explant	Callus/adventitious shoot induction (growth regulators in mg/l)	Callus subculture/ Shoot regeneration (growth regulators in mg/l)	Shoot regeneration/ shoot growth (growth regulators in mg/l)	References
1	Young seedlings	[3] 5 2,4,5–T + 0.1 Kin	[4] 0.5 2,4–D + 0.1 kin	[5] 0.1 2,4–D + 1 kin	Oswald *et al.* (1977c)
2	Seedling hypocotyls	[1] 1 NAA + 1.5 kin	[1] 2 NAA + 0.1 2–iP	[1] 0.5 NAA + 0.5 kin	Mokhtarzadeh and Constantin (1978)
3	Sdlg. hypocotyls	[2] 2 NAA + 2.2 2,4–D 2.2 kinetin		[2†] 2 NAA + 2 adenine	Beach and Smith (1979)
4	Sdlg. shoot apices	[6] 0.06 picloram + 0.1–10 BAP		[6] + 2 2,4–D 0.5 pCPA + 2 BAP	Phillips and Collins (1979a)
5	Sdlg. root or stem sections	[7 or 8] 0.8–2 2,4–D + 0.01–0.5 kin	[8] 0.09 IAA + 0.4 2–iP Got callus with green nodules	[9] 0.4 2–iP	Gresshoff (1980)
6	Sdlg. cotyledons or shoots	[1 or 2] (3) 0.5 NAA + 0.5 BAP (Callus and adventitious shoots on same medium)			Webb *et al.* (1987)
7	Sdlg. hypocotyls	[2] + 2 NAA + 2 2,4–D + 2 kin		[6] + 0.002 pic + 0.2 BAP	McClean and Novak (1989)

† Double the normal **B5** level of thiamine.

nance. Tissue culture techniques are also of interest for increasing the range of useful genetic variation, because little or no transfer of genes between sections of the genus has been possible by conventional crossing techniques.

Meristem and shoot culture

Barnett *et al.* (1975) and Phillips and Collins (1979b) have shown meristem tip culture to be an effective method of eliminating virus infections from *T. repens* and *T. pratense*. The plants obtained can be propagated rapidly and efficiently by shoot culture. Similar techniques can be used for clovers, alfalfa, and birdsfoot trefoil (Table 237). Cheyne and Dale (1980) found that **Miller (1961a)** medium gave the highest rate of shoot 'regeneration' (*sic*) from shoot tips when equal amounts (0.2 mg/l) of IAA and 2–iP were included in the medium. Whether shoots had an axillary or adventitious origin was not stated, but Bhojwani (1981) obtained proliferating shoot cultures of *T. repens* on **MS** medium containing 0.2 mg/l BAP and 3% sucrose. Axillary shoot proliferation was also obtained by Collins *et al.* (1982) and Parrott and Collins (1983) from shoot tips of eight species of *Trifolium*. Cheyne and Dale, and Bhojwani (*loc. cit.*) showed that cultured shoots could be stored at low temperatures (2–6°C) in darkness or low illumination (300 lux).

Caulogenesis

As in *Medicago sativa*, morphogenesis in clovers is found to be strongly dependent on genotype and can be improved by selection (Keyes *et al.*, 1980), but successful plant regeneration is difficult to achieve. For example, Maclean and Nowak (1989) managed to regenerate plan-

tlets from hypocotyl callus of only 3 out of 642 genotypes of *Trifolium pratense*.

Reports of shoot regeneration in *Trifolium* species seem to be confined to explants of seedling origin. Examples of protocols leading to indirect shoot formation are shown in Table 234 and the media employed are listed in Table 235.

Embryogenesis

Somatic embryos can be regenerated directly on *Trifolium* explants, and can also be induced indirectly from previously initiated callus. It is possible that the regeneration of shoots from callus, described above, could in some instances have occurred through somatic embryogenesis. Phillips and Collins (1980) obtained plantlets from buds within callus cultures of red clover but deduced that they arose through embryogenesis because firstly, there was sometimes simultaneous root and shoot formation, and secondly, buds developed a pair of cotyledons before growing normal trifoliate leaves.

Two protocols which have been successful for inducing embryo formation from *Trifolium* callus are shown in Table 236. Once callus has been initiated, cell volume can be increased in suspension cultures before a treatment to initiate embryo formation is applied. Phillips and Collins (1984) initiated and maintained suspensions from seedling explants, or from previously initiated callus, cultured on liquid **L2** medium containing 0.6 mg/l picloram and 0.1 mg/l BAP. Callus from which embryos could be obtained, was recovered by culturing cells on the combination of medium and growth regulators shown in the second stage of protocol **1** in Table 236.

Table 235. Media used for the culture of *Trifolium* species.

Components	MS	Gamborg et al. (1968) B5	Oswald et al. (1977c) C	Oswald et al. (1977c) F	Oswald et al. (1977c) H	Phillips and Collins (1979a) L2	Gresshoff (1980) A	Gresshoff (1980) C	Gresshoff (1980) D	Maheswaran and Williams (1984) EC6
	①	②	③	④	⑤	⑥	⑦	⑧	⑨	⑩
Macronutrients (meq/l)										
NO_3^-	39.4	24.72	26.61	26.61	26.61	33.26	24.72	39.4	19.7	16.89
PO_4^{3-}	3.74	3.26	6.61	6.61	6.61	9.01	3.26	3.0	1.87	3.75
SO_4^{2-}	3.0	4.05	0.28	0.28	0.28	3.52	4.05	3.0	1.5	1.5
Cl^-	5.98	2.04	0.87	0.87	0.87	8.16	2.04	5.98	2.99	2.99
K^+	20.04	24.72	12.96	12.96	12.96	23.15	24.72	20.04	10.02	10.65
Ca^{2+}	5.98	2.04	4.23	4.23	4.23	8.16	2.04	5.98	2.99	2.99
Na^+	—	1.08	—	—	—	0.61	1.08	—	—	—
Mg^{2+}	3.0	2.02	0.28	0.28	0.28	3.52	2.20	3.0	1.5	1.5
NH_4^+	20.61	2.02	12.49	12.49	12.49	12.49	2.02	20.61	10.31	7.5
Microelements (mg/l)										
$MnSO_4.4H_2O$	22.3	13.2	5.81	5.81	5.81	19.8	13.2	13.2	13.2	2.23
$ZnSO_4.7H_2O$	8.6	2.0	1.5	1.5	1.5	5.0	3.0	3.0	3.0	0.86
H_3BO_3	6.2	3.0	1.6	1.6	1.6	5.0	3.0	3.0	3.0	0.62
KI	0.83	1.0	0.75	0.75	0.75	1.0	0.75	0.75	0.75	0.083
$CuSO_4.5H_2O$	0.025	0.025	—	—	0.025	0.1	0.25	0.25	0.25	0.0025
$Na_2MoO_4.2H_2O$	0.25	0.25	—	—	—	0.4	0.25	0.25	0.25	0.025
$CoCl_2.6H_2O$	0.025	0.025	0.036	0.036	0.036	0.1	0.25	0.25	0.25	0.0025
NaFeEDTA (mM)	0.1	0.1†	0.36	0.07	0.07	0.09	0.1	0.1	0.1	0.009
Vitamins (mg/l)										
myo-Inositol	100.0	100.0	100.0	100.0	100.0	250.0	100.0	100.0	100.0	—
Thiamine HCl	0.1	10.0	0.1	0.1	0.1	2.0	10.0	10.0	10.0	—
Nicotinic acid	0.5	1.0	0.5	0.5	0.5	—	1.0	1.0	1.0	—
Pyridoxine HCl	0.5	1.0	0.1	0.1	0.1	0.5	1.0	1.0	1.0	—
Ca pantothenate	—	—	6.0	6.0	6.0	—	—	—	—	—
Biotin	—	—	0.2	0.2	0.2	—	2.0	2.0	2.0	—
Vitamin E (acetate)	—	—	1.0	—	—	—	—	—	—	—
Amino acids and amides (mg/l)										
Glycine	2.0	—	2.0	2.0	2.0	—	—	—	—	—
Casein hydrolysate	—	—	—	—	—	—	1000.0	—	—	—
Other additives (mg/l)										
Yeast extract	—	—	—	—	—	—	—	—	—	1000.0

† **B5** medium was originally formulated with 0.5 mM Fe chelated with DTPA (Sequestrene). It is now commonly used with 0.1 mM NaFeEDTA.

Table 236. Protocols which have been successful for inducing embryo formation from *Trifolium* callus.
Media numbered in square brackets are listed in Table 235.

No.	Explants	Callus/embryo induction (growth regulators in mg/l)	Somatic embryo induction/differentiation (growth regulators in mg/l)	Embryo differentiation/growth (growth regulators in mg/l)	References
1	Parts of seedlings	[6] 0.06 pic + 0.1 BAP § (and subcultures on the same)	[6] 0.01 2,4–D + 6 adenine	[6] 0.001 pic + 0.15 BAP	Phillips and Collins (1984)
2	Sdlg. hypocotyls	[2] 1.25 2,4–D + 0.5 NAA + 0.5 kin †		[2] None	Pederson (1986)
		[6] 0.06 pic + 0.1 BAP‡			

§   *T. pratense*   †   *T.vesiculosum* and *T. repens.*

‡   *T. incarnatum* and *T ambiguum.*

Phillips and Collins (1980, 1984) found that, after induction, embryos were formed on **L2** medium containing 0.01 mg/l 2,4–D and 6 mg/l adenine sulphate (dihydrate). Some embryos germinated to give both shoots and roots on this medium, but often only root growth was promoted. Embryos which did not develop fully therefore needed to be moved singly or in clusters to the third medium shown in protocol **1** in Table 234, on which shoot growth occurred.

Genetic stability. Although most plants regenerated from callus and suspension cultures have been reported to be of normal appearance and to have retained the ploidy of the parent plant (Gresshoff, 1980; Maheswaran and Williams, 1987), some somaclonal variants have been reported (Phillips and Collins, 1980). The likelihood of variation amongst regenerated plants increases if there is prolonged callus or suspension culture before embryo differentiation (Wang and Holl, 1988).

Indirect embryogenesis. Maheswaran and Williams (1984, 1985, 1986a,b; Williams and Maheswaran, 1986) have shown that somatic embryos can be initiated directly on immature zygotic embryos of several *Trifolium*

species, if such explants are incubated on **Maheswaran and Williams (1984) EC6** (medium **10** in Table 235) supplemented with 0.05 mg/l BAP. The inclusion of 1 g/l yeast extract in the medium was critical to somatic embryo initiation, for without it the zygotic embryos germinated precociously, or grew abnormally, and no plantlets were obtained. Secondary embryos were formed when the primary somatic embryos were transferred to **EC6** medium (with 0.25–1 g/l yeast extract) and 2 mg/l BAP (Williams and Maheswaran, 1985). Rooted plantlets formed on unsupplemented **EC6**.

Embryogenic callus can be initiated on a variety of media but the most effective formulation may depend on genotype. Pederson (1986) induced embryogenic callus from hypocotyl sections of *T. ambiguum* and *T. incarnatum* on medium **6** in Table 235 supplemented with 0.06 mg/l picloram and 0.1 mg/l BAP, and of *T. repens* and *T. vesiculosum* on medium **2** (Table 235) containing 1.25 mg/l 2,4–D, 0.5 mg/l NAA and 0.5 mg/l kinetin. Plantlets formed on these media were moved to **B5** medium for hardening and additional root growth.

Table 237. Published reports on tissue culture in FORAGE LEGUMES.

Species name	Type of Culture	Source of explant	Results		References
Leguminosae					
Coronilla varia L. (Crown vetch)	Callus	Peeled leaflets	Embryogenesis. Embryoid germination & plantlets	—	Mariotti & Arcioni (1983)&
Coronilla varia	Callus	Hypocotyls	Embryogenesis	—	Moyer & Giustine (1984)
Hedysarum coronarium L. (French honeysuckle)	Callus	Hypocotyls	Adventitious shoots. Some shoots rooted	—	Arcioni et al. (1985)
Hedysarum coronarium	Protoplast	Cotyledons	Callus, adventitious shoots. 20% shoots rooted	—	Arcioni et al. (1985)
Lathyrus sativus L. Jarosse cv. P24	Callus	Root segments ex in vitro seedlings	Shoots regenerated. Rooted	—	Roy et al. (1992)
Lathyrus sativus	Suspension	Callus ex germinating seeds	Embryogenesis	—	Bhatt & Bhatt (1986)
Lathyrus sativus	Callus	Tips of apical and activ. lat. shoots	Adventitious shoots. Some rooted plants	—	Gharyal & Maheshwari (1980)
Lathyrus sativus	Callus	Shoot tips	Adventitious shoots, not rooted	—	Mukhopadhyay & Bhojwani (1978)
Lathyrus sativus	Callus	Internodes of axenic seedlings	Adventitious shoots, rooted in vitro	—	Sinha et al. (1983)
Lotononis bainesii Paker	Callus	Mature leaves & cotyledons	Multiple adventitious shoots. Rooted	—	Bovo et al. (1986)
Lotus corniculatus	Callus	Peeled leaflets	Embryogenesis. Plantlets	—	Arcioni & Mariotti (1982)
Lotus corniculatus	Callus	Not given	Adventitious shoots and roots in liquid medium	—	Howarth et al. (1983)
Lotus corniculatus L. (Birdsfoot trefoil)	Callus/Suspension	Internode segments	Callus ex susp. cultured cells gave adv. shoots, plants	—	Orshinski et al. (1983)
Lotus corniculatus	Direct	Immature zygotic embryos	Multiple shoot formation	Y	Williams & Maheswaran (1985)
Lotus corniculatus	Direct	Immature zygotic embryos	Somatic embryogenesis	Y	Williams & Maheswaran (1985)
Lotus corniculatus [intersp. crosses]	Embryo	Immature embryos	Hybrid seedlings	Y	Grant et al. (1962)
Lotus corniculatus	Embryo	Immature zygotic embryos	Seedling growth	—	Keim (1953)
Lotus corniculatus	Protoplast	Seedling roots, hypocots. cotyls.	Callus. Adventitious shoots, plants	—	Ahuja et al. (1983)
Lotus corniculatus	Shoot	Stem nodes	Axillary shoot proliferation	Y	Tomes (1979)
Lotus uliginosus Schkuhr = (L. pedunculatus) × L. tenuis	Embryo	Young hybrid embryos	Embryo growth; some seedlings	—	De Lautour et al. (1978)
Lotus tenuis Wald. & Kit. ex Willd. (Narrowleaf trefoil)	Protoplast	Cotyledons, roots	Callus. Plants regenerated	—	Piccirilli et al. (1988)
Macrotyloma uniflorus (Lam.) Verdc. (Horse gram)	Direct	Sdlg. cotyledons and nodal segs.	Adventitious shoots	Y	Mohan Ram et al. (1982)
Medicago arborea (L.) (Moon trefoil)	Protoplast	Seedling roots or leaves	Callus colonies and adventitious shoots	—	Mariotti et al. (1984)
Medicago blancheana & spp.	Organ/Embryo	Young pods	Viable seeds	—	Wang J.W. et al. (1984)
Medicago falcata (L.) Arcang. cvs. 39, 47, 49	Callus	Cotyledons or hypocotyls	Embryogenesis. Rooted plantlets	—	Atanassov & Vlachova (1985)
Medicago falcata Line 47/1–5	Direct embryogen.	Homogenized young leaves ex i.v. plantlets	Plant regeneration from embryos	Y	Denchev et al. (1993)
Medicago media [several genotypes]	Callus	Seedling roots or hypocotyls	Embryogenesis. Plants	—	Nagarajan et al. (1986)
* Medicago sativa L. cvs. 'Rangelander;' 74RS; 'Furez'	Callus	Cotyledons or hypocotyls	Embryogenesis. Rooted plantlets	—	Atanassov & Vlachova (1985)
Medicago sativa (Alfalfa, Lucerne)	Callus	Hypocotyl sections	Plantlet regeneration	—	Bingham et al. (1975)
Medicago sativa [several varieties]	Callus	Cotyledon, hypocotyl, root	Embryogenesis & plants (depended on cv.)	—	Brown (1988).
Medicago sativa [line 'Regen-S']	Callus	Cotyledons	Callus frozen for 1 year in liquid N. Plant regeneration	—	Finkle et al. (1985)
Medicago sativa [9 vars.]	Callus	Seedling explants	Low frequency somatic embryogen.	—	Fuentes et al. (1993)
Medicago sativa [2 heterozygous genotypes]	Callus	Seedling hypocotyl segments	High proportion of variant plants regenerated	—	Groose & Bingham (1984)
Medicago sativa	Callus	Ovaries or cotyledons	Indirect embryogenesis. Plants resistant to fungus	—	Hartman et al. (1984)

Species name	Type of Culture	Source of explant	Results		References
Medicago sativa cv. 'Regen S'	Callus	Seedling root border cells	Roots formed in 10—15% of calli	—	Hawes et al. (1991)
Medicago sativa	Callus	Hypocotyl or cotyledon	Shoot induction & plantlet regeneration	—	Hemphill & Olson (1981)
Medicago sativa cv. 'Europe'	Callus	Peeled leaves	Plants regenerated. Somaclonal variation	—	Latunde-Dada & Lucas (1988)
Medicago sativa	Callus	Hypocotyl	Embryoid proliferation. Plantlets regenerated	—	Lupotto (1983)
Medicago sativa [3 lines]	Callus	Immature ovules	Plant regeneration. Disease resistance studied	—	Mould et al. (1992)
Medicago sativa	Callus	Petioles	Embryogenesis. High prop. of normal embryos converted	—	Nichol et al. (1991)
Medicago sativa	Callus	Petiole best for regeneration	Indirect embryogenesis. Plantlets from embryoids	—	Novák & Konecna (1982)
Medicago sativa	Callus	Immature ovaries	Formation of adventitious buds	—	Saunders & Bingham (1975)
Medicago sativa cv 'Regen S' [line W75RS]	Callus	Selected NaCl tolerant callus	Limited plant regeneration	—	Smith and McComb (1983).
Medicago sativa	Callus	Long-term cotyledon calli	Shoot bud regeneration & elongation. Shoots rooted	—	Stavarek et al. (1980)
Medicago sativa	Callus	Immature ovaries	Shoot &/or root formation	—	Walker et al. (1978)
Medicago sativa	Callus	Immature ovaries	Shoot or root formation	—	Walker et al. (1979)
Medicago sativa F1 populations & selfs	Callus	Petioles of young leaves	Embryogenesis & organogenesis. Plants	—	Wan et al. (1988)
Medicago sativa [several genotypes]	Callus	Young leaf petioles	Embryogenesis. Studied inheritance of regenerability	—	Wan et al. (1988)
Medicago sativa [clone HG2]	Callus	Immature ovaries	Salt tolerance assessed	—	Winicov et al. (1989)
Medicago sativa 'KS 10-3' '1st SC-197'	Direct	Leaf protoplasts	Somatic embryo formation. Plants	—	Song et al. (1990)
Medicago sativa	Direct	Immature zygotic embryos	Somatic embryogenesis	Y	Williams & Maheswaran (1985)
Medicago sativa	Direct embryogen.	Single somatic embryo	Direct adventive embryos	Y	Lupotto (1986)
Medicago sativa	Direct embryogen.	Embryos (0.4-0.8 mm)	Direct embryogenesis	Y	Maheswaran & Williams (1984)
Medicago sativa 'Georgia-TE'	Direct embryogen.	Somatic embryos ex callus cult.	Repeated somatic embryogen.	Y	Parrott & Bailey (1993)
Medicago sativa	Embryo	Immature embryos	Seedlings	Y	Fridriksson & Bolton (1963)
Medicago sativa [line RA-3]	Embryogenic callus	Petiole tissue (?)	Embryo growth, germination. Plantlets	—	Stuart et al. (1988)
Medicago sativa	Protoplast	Callus ex sdlg. explant or leaf segs	Callus colonies, embryogenesis. Plantlets obtained	—	Atanassov & Brown (1984)
Medicago sativa cv 'Rangelander'	Protoplast	Leaf mesophyll	Direct embryogenesis	—	Dijak & Simmonds (1988)
Medicago sativa [Clones of 2 cvs.]	Protoplast	Young mature leaves	Electroporation. Direct somatic embryo formation	—	Dijak et al. (1986)
Medicago sativa	Protoplast	Leaf mesophyll	Callus with green areas. Embryogenesis, plantlets	—	Dos Santos et al. (1980)
Medicago sativa	Protoplast	Leaves	Callus colonies, embryogenesis. Plantlets	—	Johnson et al. (1981)
Medicago sativa	Protoplast	Peeled leaves	Embryogenic callus. Embryo growth	—	Kao & Michayluk (1980)
Medicago sativa	Protoplast	Green seedling cotyledons	Callus. Adventitious shoots, plantlets	—	Lu D.Y. et al. (1982a)
Medicago sativa	Protoplast	Sdling. leaves, cotyledons or roots	Callus. Somatic embryos and adv. shoots. Plantlets	—	Lu et al. (1982 b; 1983)
Medicago sativa	Protoplast	Seedling root sections	Callus colonies, adventitious shoots	—	Xu et al. (1982b)
Medicago sativa	Root	Root tips	Isolated root culture	—	Bonner (1940b)
Medicago sativa	Root	Root tips	Isolated root culture	—	White (1938a)
Medicago sativa	Shoot	Shoot tips (2-4 mm)	Rooted plantlets	Y	Cheyne & Dale (1980)
Medicago sativa	Suspension	Callus derived from shoot tip segs.	Embryoid formation	—	Kao & Michayluk (1981)
Medicago sativa	Suspension	Callus from immature ovaries	Shoots, & indirect adventitious embryos	—	McCoy & Bingham (1977)
Medicago sativa	Suspension	Callus	Studied growth & nutrient utilization	—	McDonald & Jackman (1989)

Species name	Type of Culture	Source of explant	Results		References
Medicago sativa	Suspension	Callus derived from petiole sects.	Indirect embryogenesis. Plantlet regeneration	—	Stuart & Strickland (1984 a,b)
Medicago sativa	Suspension	Callus from ovary or petiole tissue	Indirect embryogenesis. Plantlets from embryos	—	Walker & Sato (1981)
Medicago sativa Genotype A70-34	Suspension	Callus derived from young petioles	High frequency embryogenesis in fungus-treated cultures	—	Yu et al. (1990)
Medicago sp.	Callus	Cotyl. or hypocotyl ex i.v. sdlg.	Indirect embryogenesis. Plantlets from somatic embryos	—	Brown & Atanassov (1985)
Medicago sp.	Direct	Epicotyls ex *in vitro* seedlings	Rooted plantlets	Y	Brown & Atanassov (1985)
Melilotus [interspecific cross]	Embryo	Immature embryos	Seedling plants	Y	Schlosser-Szigat (1962)
Melilotus alba Medik. (Sweet clover)	Root	Root tips	Isolated root culture	—	White (1938a)
Melilotus alba × M.officinalis (L.) Pallas.	Embryo	Hybrid embryos	Small number of seedlings	Y	Webster (1955)
Onobrychis viciifolia Scop. (Sainfoin)	Callus	Peeled leaflets	Shoot regeneration. Shoots rooted	—	Arcioni & Mariotti (1982 ; 1983)
Onobrychis viciifolia	Callus	Seedling shoots & roots	Embryogenesis. Complete plants from embryos	—	Gu (1987)
Onobrychis viciifolia	Protoplast	Leaf mesophyll	Callus. Adventitious shoots	—	Ahuja et al. (1983)
Onobrychis viciifolia	Protoplast	Suspensions ex hypocotyl callus	Colonies streptomycin stressed. Resistant plants	—	Hamill et al. (1986)
Ornithopus intersp. F1 selfed	Embryo	Young hybrid embryos	Seedlings transplanted	Y	Williams & de Lautour (1980) &
Ornithopus interspecific crosses	Embryo	Young hybrid embryos	Seedlings transplanted	Y	Williams & de Lautour (1980) &
Ornithopus interspecific F2/F3 selfs	Embryo	Young hybrid embryos	Seedlings transplanted	Y	Williams & de Lautour (1980) &
Stylosanthes biflora	Callus	Caryopsis	Adventitious shoots	—	Torres et al. (1986)
Stylosanthes guianensis (Aubl.) SW. [2 varieties]	Protoplast	Leaf mesophyll & cell suspensions	Cell colonies. Adv. shoots, rooted. Plantlets	—	Szabados & Roca (1986)
Stylosanthes guyanensis (Stylo)	Callus	Hypocotyl & root sections	Adventitious shoot formation. Shoots rooted	—	Meijer & Broughton (1981) &
Stylosanthes guyanensis	Callus	Mature or juvenile leaflets	Shoot regeneration. Shoots rooted	—	Mroginski & Kartha (1981a)
Stylosanthes guyanensis . cv. 'Cook'	Suspension	Hypocotyl (& leaf) callus	Adventitious shoots. Rooted plantlets	—	Meijer & Steinbiss (1983)
Stylosanthes guyanensis cv. 'Cook'	Suspension/Protopl.	Hypocotyl & leaf callus	Callus. Plant regeneration	—	Meijer & Steinbiss (1983)
Stylosanthes hamata (Caribbean stylo)	Callus/Suspension	Callus derived from scarified seed	Shoot formation & growth	—	Scowcroft & Adamson (1976)
Stylosanthes humilis Rich. ex Hemsl. cv. 'Paterson'	Callus	Leaf sections (transformed Agrob.)	Transgenic plants regenerated	—	Manners (1988)
Stylosanthes humilis (Townsville stylo)	Callus	Seedling leaf or hypocotyl	Shoot induction. Rooting & shoot elongation	—	Meijer (1982b)
Trifolium africanum	Direct	Cotyledons	Adventitious shoots	Y	Webb et al. (1987)
Trifolium alexandrinum (Berseem clover)	Callus	Seedling hypocotyls	Shoot induction. Shoots rooted	—	Mokhtarzadeh & C'stantin (1978)
Trifolium alexandrinum	Suspension	Callus ex seedling hypocotyls	Adventitious shoots	—	Mokhtarzadeh & C'stantin (1978)
Trifolium amabile Kunth. & many other species	Direct	Seedling shoots	Adventitious shoots	Y	Webb et al. (1987)
Trifolium ambiguum Bieb.	Callus	Hypocotyl sections	Pro-embryos or somatic embryos	—	Pederson (1986)
Trifolium ambiguum crosses	Embryo	Young hybrid embryos	Hybrid seedlings. Seedlings hardened	Y	Williams & de Lautour (1980) &
Trifolium batmanicum & several other species	Direct	Cotyledons & seedling shoots	Adventitious shoots	Y	Webb et al. (1987)
Trifolium hybrids	Embryo	Immature embryos	Embryo growth & germination. Shoot growth	Y	Phillips & Collins (1984)
Trifolium hybrids	Embryo	Advanced hybrid embryos	Seedling growth	Y	Williams & de Lautour (1980) &
Trifolium incarnatum L. (Crimson clover)	Callus	Hypocotyl or whole pistils	Plant regeneration from callus	—	Beach & Smith (1979)
Trifolium incarnatum	Callus	Hypocotyl sections	Embryogenesis. Normal fertile diploid plants	—	Pederson (1986)
Trifolium medium L. (Zigzag clover)	Direct/Callus	Petiole segments	Direct shoots. Embryogenesis from callus. Plants	Y	Choo (1988)
Trifolium nanum Torr.	Direct	Sdlg. shts, hypocots, cotyls, roots	Adventitious shoots	Y	Webb et al. (1987)

Species name	Type of Culture	Source of explant	Results		References
Trifolium nigrescens Vis.	Direct	Seedling shoots & hypocotyls	Adventitious shoots	Y	Webb *et al.* (1987)
Trifolium pratense L. (Red clover)	Callus	Hypocotyl or whole pistil	Shoot regeneration. Shoots rooted	–	Beach & Smith (1979)
Trifolium pratense [random crosses]	Callus	Hypocotyl sections	Embryogenesis. Plantlets	–	Keyes *et al.* (1980)
Trifolium pratense [various cvs.]	Callus	Seedling hypocotyl segments	Low frequency plantlet regeneration	–	MacLean & Nowak (1989)
Trifolium pratense	Callus	Vegetative + reproductive tissue	Shoot initiation. Shoots rooted	–	Phillips & Collins (1979a)
Trifolium pratense	Callus	Meristem tips	Shoot proliferation. Shoots rooted	–	Phillips & Collins (1979b)
Trifolium pratense cvs. 'Altaswede,' 'Norseman'	Callus	Seedling hypocotyl segments	Embryogenic calli. Plants regenerated	–	Wang & Holl (1988)
Trifolium pratense	Callus/Suspension.	Callus derived from various explants	Embryoids & shoots (some with roots). Plantlet growth	–	Phillips & Collins (1984)
Trifolium pratense	Direct	Immature zygotic embryos	Somatic embryogenesis	Y	Williams & Maheswaran (1985)
Trifolium pratense	Direct embryogen.	Embryos (0.4–0.8 mm)	Direct embryogenesis	Y	Maheswaran & Williams (1984)
Trifolium pratense	Direct/Callus	Immature zygotic embryos	Embryogenesis. Plants	–	Maheswaran & Williams (1986)
Trifolium pratense	Embryogenic callus	Suspensions from seedling tissues	Somatic embryos which germinated. Rooted plants	Y	Phillips & Collins (1980)
Trifolium pratense	Meristem	Meristem tips	Shoot growth. Rooted to give virus–free plants	Y	Phillips & Collins (1979b)
Trifolium pratense	Meristem	Meristem tips	One or more shoots. Shoots rooted	Y	Phillips & Collins (1984)
Trifolium pratense	Root	Root tips	Isolated root culture	–	White (1938a)
Trifolium pratense	Shoot	Crown buds (4–6 mm)	Shoot tip culture	Y	Campbell & Tomes (1984)
Trifolium pratense	Shoot	Shoots or crown buds	Multiple axillary shoots. Shoots rooted	YY	Phillips & Collins (1984)
Trifolium pratense cvs. 'Altaswede,' 'Norseman'	Shoot	Shoot tips	Multiple shoots. Rooted plants	YY	Wang & Holl (1988)
Trifolium radiosum & 3 other species	Direct	Sdling shoots, hypocotyls, cotyls.	Adventitious shoots	Y	Webb *et al.* (1987)
Trifolium repens L. (White clover)	Callus	Imbibed seeds	Green shoot bud clusters. Multiple buds & plantlets	–	Gresshoff (1980)
Trifolium repens	Callus	Root or stem sections ex *i.v.* sdlgs	Green shoot bud clusters. Multiple buds & plantlets	–	Gresshoff (1980)
Trifolium repens	Callus	Hypocotyl sections	Pro–embryos or somatic embryos	–	Pederson (1986)
Trifolium repens 'Huia S' & 'Sonja 31'	Direct	Crown explants	Glass beads aassessed as a support system	–	MacLeod & Nowak (1990)
Trifolium repens	Direct	Immature zygotic embryos	Adventitious somatic embryos	Y	Maheswaran & Williams (1985)
Trifolium repens	Direct	Immature zygotic embryos	Primary & secondary embryogenesis	–	Williams & Maheswaran (1985)
Trifolium repens	Direct embryogen.	Embryos (0.4–0.8 mm)	Rooted plantlets from germinated primary embryoids	Y	Maheswaran & Williams (1984)
Trifolium repens	Direct embryogen.	Immature zygotic embryos	Rooted plantlets from embryoids formed from hypocotyl	Y	Maheswaran & Williams (1986)
Trifolium repens	Direct/callus	Petioles (ex *in vitro* shoots)	Embryogenesis	–	Cui *et al.* (1988)
Trifolium repens [interspecific crosses]	Embryo	Isolated immature embryos	Hybrid seedlings	Y	Evans (1962)
Trifolium repens	Meristem	Meristem tips	Virus–free plants	Y	Barnett *et al.* (1975)
Trifolium repens	Protoplast	Leaf mesophyll	Callus. Abnormal shoots. Plantlets	–	Ahuja *et al.* (1983)
Trifolium repens	Protoplast	Peeled leaves	Callus colonies. Adventitious shoots but only one plant	–	Bhojwani & White (1982)
Trifolium repens	Shoot	Cold–stored shoot tip	2–6 shoots/explant. Rooted. Nearly 100% established	YY	Bhojwani (1981)
Trifolium repens	Suspension	Callus ex young *in vitro* sdlgs.	Adventitious shoots	–	Oswald *et al.* (1977 c)
Trifolium repens × *T. ambiguum*	Embryo	Young hybrid embryos	Hybrid seedlings obtained	Y	Williams (1978)
Trifolium repens × *T. uniflorum*	Embryo	Young hybrid embryos	Seedlings obtained & hardened	Y	Williams & de Lautour (1980) &
Trifolium resupinatum L. (Persian clover)	Direct	Immature zygotic embryos	Embryogenesis. Plants	–	Maheswaran & Williams (1986)

Table 240. Protocols used by Carron and co–workers to obtain embryogenic callus from the inner integuments of *Hevea* seeds.
Media numbered in square brackets are those listed in Table 239: Sucrose concentrations (%) are shown in round brackets.

Stage			Medium (Growth regulators in mg/l)	Conditions
Carron and Enjalric (1985)				
	1.	Culture initiation	[2] (8) 0.3 2,4–D + 1 IAA ± 1–5 BAP	Dark, 27°C, 3 weeks
	2.	Callus proliferation and induction of embryogenesis (in 20–40 days)	[3] (8) 0.3 2,4–D + 1 IAA ± 1–5 BAP	27°C, 12h 50 μmol m^{-2} s^{-1}
	3.	Embryo formation (Embryos seen by eye in 5–months)	[3] (2) 0.5 NAA + 0.5 BAP	Light, several subcultures
	4.	Plantlet formation (formation of root pole and cotyledons)	[3] + 5 g/l AC + 12 IBA	
Michaux–Ferrière and Carron (1989)				
	1.	Induction of embryogenesis (Essential to subculture once to fresh medium after 20–30 days)	[2] (8) 2 3,4–D† + 2 BAP	Dark, 27°C. (Moved to second stage 10–15 days after subculture)
	2.	Embryo formation	[3] (2) 0.5 NOA + 0.5 BAP	12h 50 μmol m^{-2} s^{-1}
Auboiron *et al.* (1990)				
	1.	Induction of embryogenesis	[2] (8) 2 2,4–D + 2 BAP + 5.9–58.8 μM AgNO₃	Dark, 28°C (40 days)
	2.	Embryo formation	[3] (2) 0.44 2,4–D + 0.45 BAP	Dark, 28°C
Montoro *et al.* (1993)				
	1.	Induction of embryogenesis	[2‡] (8) 1 3,4–D† + 1 kin + 30 μM AgNO₃	Dark, 27°C (25 days)
	2.	Embryo formation	[2‡] (8) 0.3 3,4–D† + 0.3 BAP + 50 μM spermidine	Dark, 27°C (25 days)

† Note that in the marked papers, 3,4–D was said to be employed. The merit of using this, rather than 2,4–D was not explained.

‡ Increasing the calcium concentration in the medium to 12 mM enhanced callus friability in one clone ('PB 260').

recent years by establishing nurseries from stem cuttings which have been treated in hot water.

There would normally be little use for micropropagation, unless possibly it were to be employed for the rapid multiplication of a new selection during the course of a breeding programme, or to provide a greater source of planting material before the release of a new commercial cultivar. However, *in vitro* techniques are valuable for the storage and exchange of germplasm. Waterworth and Kahn (1978) suggested that shoot cultures, initiated from buds of heat treated stalks, should be used for the distribution of virus–free cultivars between countries.

Plants regenerated from callus cultures of cloned varieties have been found to show marked genetic variation in many characteristics, including those of economic importance such as disease resistance (Krishnamurthi and Tlaskal, 1974; Heinz *et al.*, 1977; Liu, 1981; Larkin and Scowcroft, 1981); yield associated characters (Liu and Chen, 1976, 1978) and sugar content (Liu, 1981; Krishnamurthi, 1982). This has prompted experiments at some research stations on the production of plantlets from callus cultures, expressly for the purpose of being able to select new varieties of potential economic value. As would be expected, most of the somaclonal variants ob-

tained in this way have been inferior to the clones from which tissues had originally been derived, and only a few have had advantageous characteristics (Liu and Chen, 1978). Nevertheless some varieties have resulted which have potential value as parents for crosses or as commercial cultivars.

Plants from callus cultures

Callus cultures are readily obtained from explants excised from young tissues, such as portions of young expanding leaves, immature inflorescences, young roots and sections of the stem near the growing point. **MS** medium, or minor modifications of it, have usually been employed. Heinz *et al.* (1977) used **MS** without organic components (except *myo*–inositol) for callus induction, and complete **MS**, for plantlet development and growth. The callus initiation **MS** medium used by the Taiwan Sugar Research Institute contained *myo*–inositol (100 mg/l) and thiamine–HCl (1 gm/l). Casein hydrolysate (400 mg/l) was also added to this formulation for shoot regeneration (Liu, 1981; 1984). Krishnamurthi and Tlaskal (1974) on the other hand, recommended supplementing **MS** medium with extra organic compounds.

Table 241. Examples of protocols which, in sugar cane, have resulted in indirect embryogenesis or apparent indirect adventitious shoot formation
The medium used at each stage is shown in square brackets: the concentration of sucrose added to the medium (%) is given in round brackets.

Callus initiation (growth regulators in mg/l)	Suspension cultures (growth regulators in mg/l)	Shoot/embryo formation (growth regulators in mg/l)	Embryo growth/Rooting (growth regulators in mg/l)	References
Somatic embryogenesis				
[MS] (3) + 0.5–2,4–D	[MS †] (6) + 2–3 2,4–D + 5% CM (proembryoids when 2,4–D lowered to 0.1–1)	[MS †] (3) + 0.25–2 2,4–D + 5% CM	[MS] + 1% AC [plantlets to ½MS (6)]	Ho and Vasil (1983)
[MS ‡] (3) + 2.8 2,4–D	—	[MS ‡] (3) + 2.8 2,4–D	[MS or N6 §] + 1 2,4–D	Fitch and Moore (1993)
[MS ‡] (3) + 3 2,4–D + 10% CM (Calli with embryogenesis after several 3–4 week transfers)	[MS ‡] (3) + 3 2,4–D + 10% CM (transferred to ½MS + 0.5 2,4–D where embryogenesis was observed)	[MS] (60) + 10% CM	[½MS] (3) None	Ahloowalia and Maretzki (1983)
[MS ¶] + 7 2,4–D (dark) Subcultures of nodular calli on [MS ¶] + 1 2,4–D (dark)	—	[MS ¶] None	—	Guiderdoni and Demarly (1988)
Apparent shoot regeneration				
[MS *] (2) + 3 mg/l 2,4–D and 10% coconut milk	—	[MS *] (2) None	—	Heinz and Mee (1969)
[MS *] (2) + 3 mg/l 2,4–D and 10–15% coconut milk	—	[MS] (2)	—	Heinz et al. (1977)
[MS ‡‡] (2) + 4 2,4–D	—	[MS ‡‡] (2) None	[MS ‡‡] (2) + 2 IBA (Shoots rooted)	Irvine (1984)
[MS *] (2) + 3 2,4–D + 10% CM	—	[MS §§] (2) + 1 NAA + 1 kinetin + 10% CM	[SH ¶¶] (2) + 10% CM (Shoots rooted)	Lui et al. (1982) Lui (1984)

†   Plus 500 mg/l casein hydrolysate
‡   But with thiamine HCl increased to 0.4 mg/l
§   **Chu et al. (1976) N6** plus 90 mM proline
¶   But with the vitamins of **Fujii (1970)**
*   With 100 mg/l myo–inositol and 1 mg/l thiamine HCl as the only organic components.
††   Declared to be the medium used by Heinz and Mee (1969) above, but 1 mg/l thiamine HCl omitted in a listing of ingredients.
‡‡   No organic components except 100 mg/l myo–inositol
§§   As callus induction medium plus 7 mM $NH_4H_2PO_4$ and 400 mg/l casein hydrolysate
¶¶   **Schenk and Hildebrant (1972)** with altered micronutrients.

Embryogenesis or organogenesis? Embryogenic callus and cell suspensions can be initiated from sugar cane explants, especially very young leaf explants. The importance of leaf age is shown in the figure on page 15 of Part 1, which is drawn from the results of Guiderdoni and Demarly (1988). Although callus could be initiated from the bases of leaves 1, 2, 3 and 4, nodular embryogenic callus was only obtained from the bases of leaves 1 and 2. Embryogenesis is the principal method of regeneration in callus and cell cultures of Gramineae and it seems likely that this could be the general method in sugar cane. Thus, even though adventitious shoots, which needed to be rooted, have been obtained from many callus cultures initiated in the presence of 2,4–D (Lui, 1984), as discussed on page 1093, they may have originated from somatic embryos which germinated prematurely before the development of root axes.

Examples of protocols which have led to somatic embryo formation, or to the production of shoots, are shown in Table 241. It will be seen that the media and growth regulator treatments for both outcomes are very similar. When shoots have been obtained without roots, they have been rooted in aerated water (Heinz *et al.*, 1977; Krishnamurthi, 1982); or on an agar–solidified medium containing coconut milk [**Schenk and Hildebrandt (1972)** (but 0.1 mM NaFeEDTA) plus 10% coconut milk — (Liu, 1981)] or IBA [**Heinz and Mee (1969)** (page 384) plus 2 mg/l IBA — Irvine (1984)].

Direct shoot formation

Shoots were initiated directly, or after the formation of only a small amount of primary callus, when immature leaf tissues of several genotypes were incubated on the medium of **Heinz and Mee (1969)** containing 5 mg/l NAA and 2 mg/l kinetin (Irvine and Benda, 1985).

The origin of variability

The genetic variability found in callus–derived sugar cane plants doubtless has its origins in many of the factors discussed in Chapter 3. Commercial sugar cane cultivars are interspecific hybrids with highly polyploid chromosome complements, and callus cultures become composed of cells having variable chromosome numbers. Most of this variation undoubtedly arises during culture (especially where there is a long interval between callus initiation and plant regeneration), but has also been thought to result from mixoploidy within parental cultivars. The former explanation seems most probable as immature inflorescence callus, which regenerates shoots very soon after it has been initiated (Krishnamurthi, 1982), gives rise to genetically unaltered plants (Liu, 1981). Some changes in phenotype appear to be transitory

or to occur as the result of altered chimeral structure (Irvine, 1984).

Palmae   (Arecaceae)

The family Palmae is large and diverse and includes 198 genera in which there are 2650 species. All are evergreen trees, varying in form from plants with broad single trunks, to plants producing suckers, or slender liane–like stems (the rattans) capable of extending to the canopy of a rain forest. Palms are cold–sensitive, but although they are only common in tropical and subtropical countries, some species can be grown in sheltered locations in temperate climates.

Date palm, oil palm and coconut have become crops of major economic importance, but many other palms are, or have been, providers of sugar, oil, fibers, waxes, and canes for making items such as chairs, baskets and blinds. The dwindling size of native forests from which many of these resources have been harvested means that most products will soon be curiosities unless plants are deliberately cultivated.

Date palm, oil palm, and coconut are crops of major economic importance. Other palms which are grown on a small scale for their produce include:

Species	Common name	Uses
Arenga saccharifera	Sugar palm	Sugar obtained by tapping
Borassus flabellifer	Palmyra palm	Source of sugar and edible nuts
Caryota urens	Toddy palm	Source of sugars
Copernicia cerifera	Brazilian wax palm	Source of carnuba wax
Corypha umbraculifera	Talipot	Hard seeds, worked into buttons and ornaments
Metroxylon (esp. *M. sagu*)	—	Trunks used as source of sago
Phoenix sylvestris	Wild date palm	Grown as a source of sugar in India

The family is probably under–exploited and several of these and other species could be cultivated as sources of fibre, oil and wax (Tisserat, 1984). Palms are commonly planted in the tropics as ornamental and landscape trees and, in cold climates, certain species are popular as decorative pot plants.

In vitro culture

Despite the diverse nature of plants in the family, common principles can be applied to the tissue culture of most palms.

Explant isolations. Many authors have reported that explants taken from the field are difficult to disinfest and need careful sterilisation. Cryptic contaminants are also

Table 242. Media used for the micropropagation of palms.

Components	MS	Nwankwo and Krikorian (1983)	Tisserat (1982) †	Eeuwens (1976) Y3	Booij et al. (1993)	Karunaratne and P. Kaushalya (1989)
	①	②	③	④	⑤	⑥
Macronutrients (meq/l)						
NO_3^-	39.4	19.7	39.41	20.0	25.0	40.0
PO_4^{3-}	3.74	5.57	6.61†	6.0	6.0	6.0
SO_4^{2-}	3.0	1.5	3.00	2.0	4.0	7.3
Cl^-	5.99	2.99	5.99	34.0	—	6.0
K^+	20.04	10.02	20.04	40.0	16.84	20.0
Ca^{2+}	5.99	2.99	5.99	4.0	4.17	6.0
Na^+	—	1.23	1.91	2.0	—	3.3
Mg^{2+}	3.0	1.50	3.0	2.0	4.0	6.0
NH_4^+	20.61	10.31	20.61	10.0	6.0	20.0
Microelements (mg/l)						
$MnSO_4.4H_2O$	22.3	11.2	22.3	11.2	75.1	22.3
$ZnSO_4.7H_2O$	8.6	4.3	8.6	7.2	9.21	11.5
H_3BO_3	6.2	3.1	6.2	6.2	12.4	9.3
KI	0.83	0.42	0.30	8.3	0.015	0.83
$CuSO_4.5H_2O$	0.025	0.012	0.025	0.25	0.25	0.37
$Na_2MoO_4.2H_2O$	0.25	0.12	0.25	0.24	0.5	0.24
$CoCl_2.6H_2O$	0.025	0.012	0.025	0.24	0.25	0.24
$NiCl_2.6H_2O$	—	—	—	0.024	—	—
NaFeEDTA (mM)	0.1	0.05	0.2	0.05‡	0.1	0.1
Vitamins (mg/l)						
myo–Inositol	100.0	100.0	83.3 †	100.0	—	108.1
Thiamine HCl	0.1	0.04	0.4	1.0	3.0	13.49
Nicotinic acid	0.5	—	—	1.0	1.0	4.92
Pyridoxine HCl	0.5	—	—	1.0	0.1	1.23
Calcium pantothenate	—	—	—	—	—	2.38
Biotin	—	—	—	—	—	0.24
Riboflavin	—	—	—	—	—	3.76
Ascorbic acid	—	—	—	—	75.0	1.76
Amino acids (mg/l)						
Glycine	2.0	—	—	—	—	3.74
Casein hydrolysate	—	500.0	—	—	—	—
L–arginine	—	—	—	100.0	—	—
L–asparagine	—	—	—	100.0	—	—
L–cysteine HCl	—	—	—	—	—	18.9
L–asparagine	—	—	—	100.0	—	—
L–glutamine	—	—	—	100.0	200.0	—
Other supplements (g/l)						
Adenine sulphate dihydrate	—	0.04	—	—	0.04	—
PVP	—	—	—	—	2.0	—
Sugars (g/l)						
Sucrose (g/l)	30.0	30.0	30.0	68.5	40.0	30.0

†   See the footnote on page 1157.

often located within tissues to be discovered after a long period of culture. Tisserat (1979, 1984a) found that the proportion of explants freed from surface contamination was greatly increased if, after the use of hypochlorite during preparation, explants were dipped again briefly (5 seconds) into hypochlorite solution after excision, and then transferred to medium without further rinsing. It can be advisable to wrap delicate explants in paper or cheese-cloth during sterilisation to prevent loss and injury (Tisserat, 1984a).

Cryptic contaminants can be more troublesome to elimi-nate and can make the culture of some palms difficult. Techniques described on page 138 *et seq.* might be tried. The use of antibiotics has been most generally advocated, but may not always prove to be effective. Guerra and Handro (1988) placed fruits of *Euterpe edulis* in NaOCl plus 0.15% streptomycin and 0.01% merthiolate (12 h shaker).

Blackening or browning. Tissues of palms commonly become discoloured with growth–inhibiting oxidation products during excision and initial culture. The extent of the problem depends on the origin of the selected tissue, and is increased if explants are excessively injured. Pre-ventative measures have included ensuring that excision is conducted rapidly and that explants are placed onto a medium without delay (Guerra and Handro, 1988); plac-ing explants into a citric acid : ascorbic acid solution (page 648) after excision and before a final dip into hypochlorite solution (Tisserat, 1979; Tisserat *et al.*, 1979b); and adding 2 g/l caffeine, 1 g/l diethyldithiocar-bamate and 1 g/l PVP to the water used to rinse date palm explants between dips into hypochlorite solution (Poulain *et al.*, 1979).

The blackening of palm explants *in vitro* is most effec-tively avoided by the addition of activated charcoal (1–3 g/l) to the medium, especially if explants are also trans-ferred frequently (*e.g.* at weekly intervals) to fresh me-dium (Nwankwo and Krikorian, 1983; Zaid, 1987). In the presence of activated charcoal, which is found to absorb growth regulators, it is necessary to add abnormally high concentrations of auxin to media, particularly to induce callus formation and embryogenesis (see below).

Tisserat (1979a,b) found that PVP was ineffective in preventing blackening when added to media, but several other workers have routinely included it, instead of acti-vated charcoal (*e.g.* Poulain *et al.*, 1979; Bala–Sarin *et al.*, 1986; Booij *et al.*, 1993). Blackening of coconut palm explants was reduced, and callus growth increased, by including 8.3 mg/l (50 μM) potassium iodide in **Eeuwens (1976) Y3** medium. This provides 10 times the concentra-tion of I⁻ present in **MS** medium.

Media. Half– or full–strength **MS** salts, with or without additional phosphate have been most commonly used in palm tissue culture media. Phosphate supplements result in enhanced callus growth and have been provided in many recent papers by the addition of 0.87–1.23 mM NaH_2PO_4. Instead of using this compound, Srinivasan *et al.* (1985) doubled the concentration of KH_2PO_4 in **MS** medium. One typical enhanced–phosphate formulation, that of **Tisserat (1982)**, is listed in Table 242 (Medium **3**) in comparison with **MS** medium (**1**), and ½**MS** medium with extra phosphate (**2**).

In studying the nutritional requirements of coconut tis-sues, Eeuwens (1976, 1978) developed a medium [**Eeu-wens (1976) Y3** — Medium **4** in Table 242] on which the initiation and growth of callus from stem, leaf and inflo-rescence explants was more rapid than on **MS**. Although the ratio of NO_3^- to NH_4^+ in **MS** salts was found to be correct, optimum growth occurred when the concentra-tion of each ion was halved (*i.e.* 20 mM NO_3^- and 10 mM NH_4^+ — ratio 67:33). Further improvements in growth occurred when the concentrations of PO_4^{3-} of and K^+ were increased. The macronutrients of **Eeuwens (1976) Y3** me-dium are thus very similar to those in **Nwankwo and Krikorian (1983)** (Medium **2** — ½**MS** plus added phos-phate), except that in **Y3** there is a much higher concen-tration of K^+ and Cl^- (the latter not provided intentionally but resulting from the use of KCl as a source of K^+).

Although some workers have added more complex ad-denda, many kinds of palm cultures have been conducted satisfactorily using the organic substances of **Linsmaier and Skoog (1965)** medium.† Media are gener-ally supplemented with 30 g/l sucrose, but Eeuwens (1978) showed that *Cocos* callus grew at a faster rate when 0.2 M (36 g/l) fructose was added to the medium instead of 0.2 M (68 g/l) sucrose.

Types of culture

The kinds of culture which have been possible with palms have been limited. Embryo culture, which is sometimes

---

† Except that Tisserat (*e.g.* 1984a), and some others repeating his experiments, have used 100 mg/l *myo*–inositol dihydrate (*i.e.* 0.46 mM inositol instead of the customary 0.56 mM). Eeuwens (1978) found that during a 6 week incubation period, vitamins had little effect on the growth of coconut or date palm callus, but supposed they might be needed for long–term cultures. The inclusion of 3 amino acids in **Y3** medium increased the growth of *Cocos* callus, even in the presence of inorganic ammonium ions, but only had an effect on *Phoenix* callus when ammonium ions were deficient.

useful for obtaining progeny from difficult crosses, has been widely achieved. Embryos excised from seeds can be germinated on **LS** medium (containing activated charcoal) without growth regulators. Primary roots form in this medium, but adventitious roots will usually be produced more freely if young seedlings are moved to medium containing 0.1 mg/l NAA (Tisserat, 1984a).

In some species it is possible to culture excised shoot tips or lateral buds (from offshoots or tree apices) so that a single shoot is produced from each explant. Shoots are subsequently rooted by transfer to a medium containing auxin. Shoots have also occasionally been obtained by culturing immature inflorescences. In just a few instances (*e.g.* in date palm — see below, and *Chamaedorea costericana* — Reynolds, 1981), axillary shoots have been obtained from shoot cultures.

Successful micropropagation of most palms has only been possible through somatic embryogenesis. The methodology is similar in many genera.

Non–crop species

Embryogenic callus has been initiated from zygotic embryos, immature flower buds and shoot tips of several kinds of ornamental palm. Callus has been initiated on **MS** medium (*e.g.* in *Chamaedorea costericana* and *Howea forsteriana* — Reynolds, 1979; 1981; Reynolds and Murashige, 1979), on Medium **2** (*e.g. Pritchardia kaalae* — El Shiaty *et al.*, 1991) or on Medium **2** to which 400 mg/l glutamine has been added (in *Veitchia merillii* — Srinivasan *et al.*, 1985).

In these instances cultures have been initiated in the presence of 100 mg/l 2,4–D (when 1.5–3 g/l activated charcoal was added to the medium), or (in the absence of charcoal) with 1–5 mg/l 2,4–D, either with or without 1–3 mg/l 2–iP. Callus has been subcultured on the same medium, but may grow more rapidly when the auxin concentration is reduced and the cytokinin concentration increased (El Shiaty *et al.*, 1991). Somatic embryos are produced when callus is transferred to a medium lacking growth regulators, or to one containing a low concentration of gibberellic acid. Activated charcoal is usually omitted at this stage.

Palmae
Cocos nucifera   (Coconut)

As coconut palms are propagated from fruits, and plants are cross pollinated and heterozygous, there is much variation in yield and disease resistance between individual trees. Breeding programmes can make only slow progress towards crop improvement because plants take at least four years to reach sexual maturity, and several more years elapse before productivity can be assessed. If it were possible to clone selected trees through micropropagation, crop improvement would be facilitated (Davis, 1969). The widespread planting of superior clones would result in greatly increased fruit yields.

As only very limited vegetative macropropagation is normally possible (Sudasrip *et al.*, 1978), several public sector and some private sector laboratories have devoted resources towards trying to devise an *in vitro* method of multiplication, but this has proved to be difficult.

Embryo culture

Embryos excised from fruits can be grown *in vitro* to produced plantlets, but results have been variable. Plantlets have been obtained from mature embryos on some occasions but have not always been established successfully in the field.

Gupta *et al.* (1984) placed embryos on liquid **Eeuwens (1976) Y3** medium containing 5% sucrose, 10% coconut milk, 1 mg/l BAP and 0.05 mg/l NAA. When, after 11–12 weeks, embryos were moved to liquid **Y3** medium without growth regulators, their roots elongated and plantlets developed. Other have found that embryos from mature nuts grow well on agar–solidified media containing **MS** salts providing that activated charcoal is added to prevent browning. Iyer (1982), Assy–Bah (1986) and Assy–Bah and Engelmann (1993) found that it was unnecessary to add growth regulators. Iyer (*loc. cit.*) rooted plantlets on filter paper platforms above liquid medium and encouraged the growth of lateral roots by decapitating the first large root which emerged from the sprouted embryo. Assy Bah (1986) preferred to add 20 mg/l NAA to the medium at this stage.

Zygotic embryos of coconut may be useful for germplasm storage and can be used to ship plant material. Excised embryos have been germinated successful after having been dispatched through the post (Blake, 1990). Embryo culture has been useful to increase the 'makapuno' variety of coconut, the endosperm of which is atypically jelly–like and not filled with milky fluid (Balaga and de Guzman, 1971; del Rosario and de Guzman, 1978).

Callus cultures

Embryogenesis. Embryogenic callus has been obtained by culturing different kinds of explant. There have been several reports of callus capable of producing putative pro–embryos or embryo–like structures, but:

- further development has not occurred (Apavatjrut and Blake, 1977; De Guzman *et al.*, 1978a; Pannetier and Buffard–Morel, 1982; Branton and Blake, 1983);

- small shoot–like appendages with roots have been obtained (D'Souza, 1982; Gupta *et al.*, 1984), but these have not developed into plantlets; or

- embryos have germinated to produced small shoots which could not be grown on (Karunaratne and P. Kaushalya, 1989).

Two plants which resulted from the growth of somatic embryos have been successfully transplanted to the field. One was reported by Smith (1986) (photograph in Blake, 1990) and the other by Verdeil *et al.* (1989).

In most of the reports mentioned above, callus was initiated on media containing **Y3** salts (Medium **4**), but various organic and growth regulator supplements were added. Callus initiated from 6–7 month old zygotic embryos on Medium **6** (30 g/l sucrose) containing 2.7–4.4 mg/l (12–20 µM) 2,4–D, could be maintained on the same medium, and formed somatic embryos when the 2,4–D concentration was reduced to 1.8 mg/l (Karunaratne and P. Kaushalya, 1989).

Plants from adventitious shoots. Shoots, and eventually plantlets, were regenerated from callus which originated from young zygotic embryos (Bhalla–Sarin *et al.*, 1986). The callus in these experiments was initiated on **Gamborg *et al.* (1968) B5** medium containing 2 mg/l each of the IAA conjugates, IAA–asparagine and IAA–alanine. Shoots and roots were initiated when the callus was transferred to **B5** containing 2 mg/l NAA and 2 mg/l kinetin and 3 complete plantlets were obtained on further subculture to **B5** with 0.5 mg/l NAA and 2 mg/l BAP, but they had an inadequate root system and could not be established.

Shoot culture

A close approach to *in vitro* propagation was reported by Eeuwens and Blake (1977) who experimented with the culture of immature coconut inflorescences. Depending on stage of development, potential flower bud meristems gave rise to spike–like projections in culture, 'shootlets' bearing leaves and bracts, or recognisable perianth parts. Presumably shoots arose by reversion of floral meristems to a vegetative state? Optimum growth occurred on **Eeuwens (1976) Y3** medium containing 1.1 mg/l BAP. Although the shootlets could be excised, subcultured and rooted, they could not be grown into plantlets (Blake and Eeuwens, 1982).

Shoots were obtained directly from immature inflorescences of *Chamaedorea* by Reynolds (1981).

Palmae
Phoenix dactylifera   (Date Palm)

The date palm is a crop of dry sub–tropical areas and is widely cultivated under irrigation in countries bordering the Mediterranean, and in India, California and Arizona. It is typically grown in desert oases. Plants can be raised from seed, but are then variable and half their number become unproductive males, but cannot be recognised as such until they have been grown in the field for several years. Date palm plantations are therefore established by vegetative propagation and plantations normally consist of one or more clones of mainly female trees, satisfactory pollination being obtained by the presence of only 1 male amongst 50–100 females. Trees have been traditionally propagated from rooted offsets or suckers which are produced from the base of young trees. On average a total of only 20 offshoots are produced per plant during its first 5 years in the field, and this has proved inadequate to both extend date palm cultivation and to replace aging plantations, or those destroyed by Bayoud disease (causal agent *Fusarium oxysporum* f. sp. *albedinis*) (Booij *et al.*, 1993).

Micropropagation is assisting in making more plants available to growers. The highly heterozygous nature of date palms and their perennial habit, has meant that only slow progress can be made in breeding programmes, so that micropropagation should also be useful to speed the increase of genotypes for field evaluation and for making new cultivars more readily available. Two methods are available for *in vitro* multiplication — shoot culture and somatic embryogenesis.

Shoot culture. *Phoenix dactylifera* is unusual in that it is one of the few palms in which multiplication by shoot culture has been successful. Possibly this is due to the fact that plants have a natural tendency to produce axillary shoots?

Shoot culture using a supplemented **MS** medium was first described by Poulain *et al.* (1979). Tisserat (1984b) showed that shoot tips established on agar–solidified **LS** medium with 10 mg/l NAA (3 g/l activated charcoal) would produce axillary shoots if subcultured to a liquid medium of the same composition. Vessels were placed on a rotary shaker and the medium (lacking charcoal) was supplemented with 0.1 mg/l NAA and 10 mg/l BAP. Shoots could be rooted by subculture to agar–solidified **LS** medium (no charcoal) containing 0.1 mg/l NAA.

Booij *et al.* (1993) initiated cultures from shoot tips, or axillary buds, of offshoots. On Medium **5** (Table 242), supplemented with 40 mg/l adenine sulphate dihydrate, 0.5 mg/l IAA and 1 mg/l 2–iP (cv. 'Nobout Seif'), or 3 mg/l 2–iP ('Bou Sthammi'), shoots multiplied and could be subcultured every 6 weeks. Explants were kept each in an individual 2.5 × 15 cm tube.

Commercial micropropagation. Several micropropagation laboratories have been established during the last few years with the especial aim of meeting the demand for trees, particularly for new plantations. Shoot culture is the preferred method of multiplication (Ferry *et al.*, 1987; Booij *et al.*, 1993).

Somatic embryogenesis. Callus capable of regenerating somatic embryos can be obtained by culturing immature or mature zygotic embryos (Reuveni *et al.*, 1972; Reuveni, 1979; Reynolds and Murashige, 1979) or other organs containing meristematic tissues such as immature inflorescences, lateral buds, shoot tips and lateral buds (Tisserat, 1979a,b). Clearly explants from adult tissues, rather than zygotic embryos or seedlings, are required when the aim is to clone designated genotypes.

Medium 3 ($\frac{1}{2}$**MS** salts with added phosphate) has been widely used for callus induction, although Reuveni used $\frac{1}{2}$**MS** medium supplemented with 250 mg/l casein hydrolysate (which would help to relieve any phosphate deficiency in the medium — Part 1, pages 287 and 290). Activated charcoal is added to these media, which have been supplemented with (mg/l):

5 kinetin + 2 IBA + 2 NAA + 0.5 2,4–D	Reuveni (1979)
100 2,4–D + 3 mg/l 2–iP	Tisserat (1979b; 1984)
100 2,4–D + 2 kinetin	Omar *et al.* (1990).

Callus formed in darkness (25–28°C) after 2–3 passages can be subcultured on medium containing 10 mg/l 2,4–D, and will exhibit embryogenesis and plantlet formation on transfer to a growth regulator–free medium (still with added charcoal) in the light. Reuveni (*loc. cit.*) cultured young plantlets in medium containing 30 g/l sucrose, 5 g/l activated charcoal and 0.1 mg/l NAA and 0.1 mg/l kinetin. Young seedlings develop adventitious roots more effectively if moved to a medium lacking charcoal but containing 0.1 mg/l NAA.

Palmae
Elaeis guineensis   (Oil Palm)

E. guineensis is an important source of vegetable oil and is now grown in many parts of the tropics, usually as a plantation crop. Several fruiting forms of the plant are known:—

— *dura* (thick shell) has seeds protected by a thick stony endocarp or shell;

— *pisifera* does not have a hard endocarp and is known as shell–less. Some *pisifera* plants have sterile female flowers and provide a useful pollen source for the production of plants of the third type:

— *tenera*, a hybrid between the two previous forms with intermediate characteristics. Plants of this kind are now widely used for commercial oil production (Nwanko and Krikorian, 1983).

Breeding oil palm for increased yield is slow and difficult because plants are naturally outcrossing and because fruit yield and oil content can only be assessed after 6–10 years when seedlings commence flowering. Vegetative propagation is not possible by conventional means and seedling populations are variable. Within the family of trees resulting from a cross, the best ones can produce up to 60% more than the average (Noiret, 1981). Micropropagation therefore seemed to provide an ideal means of cloning desirable genotypes and during the 1970's research programmes were set up to discover appropriate commercial techniques. These were primarily in France in collaboration with the Institut de Recherches pour les Huiles et Oleagineux, and at the laboratories of Unilever PLC in England, and had the objective of cloning selected elite trees. The difficulty of selecting superior genotypes when each is represented by only a single tree in a mixed population, is similar to that experienced in forest tree breeding (page 970).

Embryogenesis. That tissue culture might provide a method for mass propagation of oil palms, became apparent from the work of Jones (1974c,d). Somatic embryos were noted to be formed in callus derived from the shoot apices of seedlings germinated *in vitro* from seed embryos. Zygotic embryos can also be used as explants (Nwankwo and Krikorian, 1983), but embryogenesis is more conveniently obtained in callus obtained from vegetative explants, such as root pieces, the youngest leaves of shoot apices and immature inflorescences (Rabéchault and Martin, 1976; Paranjothy and Othman, 1982). Immature leaves and inflorescences are most practical, as they can be obtained from axillary shoots, with little contamination and without destroying the stock plant.

In nearly all published protocols, oil palm embryogenesis has been obtained after callus has been initiated and subcultured several times. It is possible to induce embryogenic callus directly on explanted tissue, but Pannetier *et al.* (1981) and Hanower and Pannetier (1982) found that the proportion of primary calluses producing somatic embryos was small.

In the method described by Ahée *et al.* (1981), primary callus was formed on leaf fragments near vascular bundles. Such callus was typically not embryogenic, grew slowly during successive subcultures, and usually became composed of very small nodules. Culture of the nodular callus eventually led to the formation of a fast growing friable callus which could again be subcultured, but which was capable of differentiating somatic embryos in new conditions.

Callus can be induced on leaf fragments by culture on a medium containing the salts of full strength **MS** (medium **1** in Table 242), full strength **MS** with added phosphate (medium **3**), or $\frac{1}{2}$**MS** with added phosphate (medium **2**). Rabéchault and Martin (1976) used **MS** salts with the organic components of Dulieu (1963, 1966):

100 mg/l *myo*–inositol; 1 mg/l Ca pantothenate; 1 mg/l nicotinic acid; 1 mg/l pyridoxine; 1 mg/l thiamine HCl; 0.01 mg/l biotin; 10 mg/l cysteine HCl; 500 mg/l casein hydrolysate; and 40 g/l sucrose.

No activated charcoal was added to prevent browning, but the cysteine would have had an antioxidant effect. Browning was said to be less severe when very young leaves were used as explants.

Primary callus may take 2–3 months to appear on leaf segments. That induced to form on explants in the dark on Rabéchault and Martin's medium supplemented with 2–10 mg/l 2,4–D, was slow growing and required from 5 months to 2 years to become established and have an organogenic capacity. Somatic embryos were then induced to differentiate by transferring the callus to the same medium, lacking 2,4–D but containing 0.5 mg/l NAA, and 2 mg/l each of kinetin, BAP and 2–iP.

Callus initiated in the light (2500–3000 lux) from dormant zygotic embryos on Medium **2** (containing activated charcoal) supplemented with up to 70 mg/l NAA or 2,4–D, needed to be subcultured at 14 day intervals to prevent it becoming brown and necrotic. When transferred to a lower concentration of auxin (*e.g.* 20 mg/l NAA), the callus usually grew more rapidly and produced nodules. Somatic embryos were formed on the same medium, but nodular callus proliferated on medium without growth regulators, and only became organogenic when returned to a low concentration of auxin (Nwankwo and Krikorian, 1983).

Shoot growth is promoted by adding a low concentration of NAA or IBA to the medium together with cytokinins, and root growth is obtained by placing shoots into liquid medium after a brief exposure to NAA (Paranjothy and Othman, 1982).

Field plantings. The first micropropagated palms arising from somatic embryos were field planted in 1977 (Corley, 1977; Corley *et al.*, 1977, 1979) and by 1982 there were 140 ha of field trials in Malaysia and further trials in the Ivory Coast, established with clones of many different genotypes (Wooi *et al.*, 1982a).

Palm clones were first reported to be uniform, of an almost entirely normal appearance (Jones *et al.*, 1982; Wooi *et al.*, 1982a,b), and to yield more than plantings derived from seedlings (Anon, 1981b). In this context, the increased cost of planting material obtained by tissue culture was thought to be of little significance, as the usual field density for oil palms is only *ca.* 145 trees/ha and the life of a plantation is about 25 years (Lioret and Ollagnier, 1981).

Although each oil palm normally bears separate male and female inflorescences, both kinds arise from organs which are initially hermaphrodite. During normal development, female parts become vestigial in male inflorescences, and male organs do not form properly in female inflorescences. Large–scale micropropagation of oil palm clones was interrupted in 1986, when it was discovered that the inflorescences on many micropropagated trees were uncharacteristically effeminate (Part 1, page 247 and page 750 in this volume).

The effeminacy resulting from tissue culture propagation has been found to vary in severity. Mild symptoms which result in one or two supplementary carpels being produced in female flowers are acceptable, but if a large number of carpels are formed from the androecium (which would normally abort in female flowers), there is loss of crop.

Current research is aimed at trying to identify the cause of these abnormalities, which have been found to vary in severity between clones. In those which are resistant, only 1% of trees may be affected, while in other clones yield potential has been been considerably reduced. As the symptoms are common amongst many clones which are otherwise phenotypically normal, it seems unlikely that they are due to changes in nuclear genes.

Once embryogenic callus has been obtained from a selected individual tree, it has tended to be subcultured for several years so that a large number of somatic embryos can be obtained from it. The extent of feminisation within a clone has tended to vary according to the time during the life of the callus when plants were regenerated, being less the shorter the callus incubation period has been. Laboratory experiments (with which there is a delay of at least 6 years before field results become available) have shown that the medium and growth regulators used for callus initiation and subculture, influence the subsequent frequency of abnormality in the field, and that it is possible to predict 'high risk' and 'low risk' protocols for micropropagation.

In consequence of these results, micropropagation of oil palm has had to be scaled back considerably. Laboratories are still producing plants for field planting, but the ambition of completely replacing seedling trees by clones produced by micropropagation has been postponed.

Rubiaceae
Coffea spp.   (Coffee)

Coffee beans are obtained from the fruits of several species of *Coffea*, each of which differs in flavour and quality. Milled coffee and instant coffee granules and powders are often prepared from blends of coffees of different origin.

By far the most important *Coffea* species, in terms of international coffee production, are:

- *C. arabica* L.(Arabian or arabica coffee), which accounts for approximately 70 per cent of the world coffee supply; and

- *C. canephora* Pierre ex Frohner (*C. robusta* Lind. — robusta coffee). The quality of robusta coffee is less than that of arabica, but the area planted with it has been increasing steadily in recent years since the advent of 'instant coffee'. Robusta coffee has a high soluble solid content and it is now responsible for about 26 per cent of total world coffee production.

Other *Coffea* species are cultivated in some regions but generally produce coffee of inferior quality, which is not traded internationally. *C. liberica* yields a bitter flavoured coffee which is sometimes added to blends of robusta.

Coffee plants grow as large shrubs or small trees and can reach up to 5–7 m in height, but in cultivation they are regularly pruned to encourage regular cropping and to ensure that they stay at a height which can be reached by pickers.

Branching habit.   Like cocoa, coffee plants produce both orthotropic and plagiotropic shoots. Young seedling shoots are orthotropic and the two axillary buds at each node (the leaves are opposite) are only able to produce orthotropic shoots until they have about 10–12 nodes. After this, besides dormant orthotropic buds, in each axil there is also a bud with the potential to produce a plagiotropic shoot. In *C. arabica* successive leaf pairs on orthotropic shoots are arranged in a gentle spiral ($\frac{1}{4}$ phyllotaxy) but those on plagiotropic shoots are all inserted in the same plane.

Flowers are only produced on plagiotropic branches, and here leaf axils subtend several buds which normally develop into flowers, one of which sometimes become vegetative and gives rise to another plagiotropic branch. Orthotropic buds are not formed in the axils of plagiotropic shoots.

Methods of propagation

C. arabica is tetraploid and self pollinated so that cultivars have been established as pure bred lines which can be propagated from seeds to give uniform offspring. Other *Coffea* species, including *C. canephora*, are diploid and cross pollinated so that seeds give rise to heterogeneous plant populations. However, *C. canephora* can be propagated from rooted cuttings, although to obtain plants with a normal growth habit, cuttings of must be taken from orthotropic shoots. Rooting is not easy and does not take place unless leaves are present on the cutting. The proportion of shoots which are rooted successfully varies throughout the year (Söndahl and Sharp, 1979). Thus micropropagation of selected genotypes of *C. canephora* and other diploid *Coffea* species would be useful, but whether tissue culture techniques would be more successful and cheaper than conventional vegetative propagation has yet to be demonstrated.

Shoot culture

Shoot cultures can be established from shoot or meristem tips of axenic seedlings, and will produce axillary shoots which can be subcultured in a conventional manner on **MS** (Medium **1** in Table 243), or a modified **MS** medium (Table 244).

Cultures can also be initiated by incubating nodal sections of orthotropic shoots from seedlings or mature plants, but explants from greenhouse and field–grown plants can be heavily contaminated and may also blacken when first isolated, so that a high proportion may be lost. As the leaf axils of the orthotropic shoots of coffee contain several dormant buds capable of orthotropic growth, many shoots can be obtained by culturing nodal explants, even without shoot subculture. Söndahl *et al.* (1984) preferred to use the modified **B5** medium shown in Table 243 (medium **2**) for explants derived from orthotropic shoots. The growth of dormant buds was stimulated by the addition of BAP and IAA (Table 244). If, after axillary shoots had been excised, the original explants were recultured on the same medium, yet more dormant orthotropic buds were stimulated to grow, yielding a further crop of shoots.

Explants from plagiotropic shoots.   Söndahl *et al.* (*loc cit.*) also used axillary buds from plagiotropic shoots as explants. When excised before flower induction and cultured as shown in Table 244, single shoots were produced which grew upwards until they were rooted, but then a plagiotropic habit of growth was observed.

Storage of shoot cultures.   Bertrand–Desbunais *et al.* (1991, 1992) investigated whether various *Coffea* species and cultivars could be stored as cultures initiated from seedling shoot tips. Cultures were initiated on **MS** medium [medium **1** in Table 244 but with the vitamins of

Table 247. Published reports on the tissue culture of TROPICAL AND SUBTROPICAL FIELD CROPS.

Species name	Type of Culture	Source of explant	Results		References
Agavaceae					
Agave cantala Robx.	Node/Shoot	Stem sections from young shoots	Multiple shoots. Slight callusing. Rooted plantlets	YY	Binh et al. (1990)
Agave fourcroydes Lem.	Node/Shoot	Stem sections from young shoots	Multiple shoots. Slight callusing. Rooted plants	YY	Binh et al. (1990)
Agave sisalana Perring. (Sisal)	Direct	Rhizome sections	Multiple adventitious shoots. Rooted	YY	Das (1992)
Agave sisalana	Shoot/Node	Stem sections from young shoots	Multiple shoots. Slight callusing. Shoots rooted	YY	Binh et al. (1990)
Agave spp.	Callus	Stem sections	Shoot formation & multiplication. Shoots rooted	—	Madrigal-Lugo et al. (1990)
Agave spp. See also Herbaceous Ornamentals table.	Shoot	Lateral buds	Shoot multiplication. Shoots rooted	YY	Madrigal-Lugo et al. (1990)
Agave tequilana Weber	Direct/Callus	Stem segments	Multiple shoots, vitrescent at high water potential	—	Castro-Concha et al. (1990)
Furcraea foetida (L.) Haw. = F. gigantea (Mauritius hemp)	Callus	Leaf bases	Adventitious shoots which rooted directly	—	Lakshmanan & Janardhanan (1977a)
Furcraea foetida	Direct	Pieces of apomictic bulbils	Adventitious shoots. Plantlet formation	—	Lakshmanan & Janardhanan (1977b)
Amaranthaceae					
Amaranthus cruentus L.	Direct	Leaf discs	Embryoids from surface & veins	—	Flores et al. (1981)
Asclepiadaceae					
Calotropis gigantea (L.) Ait. f.	Callus	Immature zygotic embryos	Multiple shoots, rooted	—	Roy & De (1990)
Compositae — Asteraceae					
Guizotia abyssinica (L. f.) Cass. cv. 'Ootacamund'	Callus	Seedling cotyledon pieces	Multiple shoots. Rooted	—	Sarvesh et al. (1993a)
Guizotia abyssinica cv. 'Sahyadri'	Direct	Sdlg. hypocot., root & cotyl. sects.	Multiple shoots. Rooted	YY	Nikam & Shitole (1993)
Guizotia abyssinica cv. 'Ootacomund'	Direct	Seedling cotyledon pieces	Multiple shoots	Y	Sarvesh et al. (1993a)
Guizotia abyssinica cv. 'Ootacomund'	Embryogenic callus	Seedling cotyledon pieces	Embryos matured and germinated	—	Sarvesh et al. (1993a)
Parthenium argentatum A.Gray cv. W19 (Guayule)	Callus	Young stem segments	Studied effect of support system on browning	—	Trautmann & Visser (1989)
Parthenium argentatum	Direct	Stem segments	Direct adventitious shoots	Y	Dastoor et al. (1981)
Parthenium argentatum	Direct/Callus	Pretreated seeds	Multiple shoots. Rooted plants	Y	Finnie et al. (1989)
Parthenium argentatum	Direct/Callus/Node	Nodes (0.5–0.8 mm long)	Multiple shoots, rooted	—	Dhar et al. (1989)
Parthenium argentatum	Shoot	Germinated seeds	Shoot growth. Rooted. Shoots regenerated from roots	Y	Staba & Nygaard (1983)
Parthenium argentatum	Shoot/Direct	Apical/axill. bud sects ex i. v. sdlgs	Axillary & adventitious shoots. Shoots rooted	YY	Smith M.K. (1983)
Euphorbiaceae					
* Hevea brasiliensis (A.Juss.) Muell. Arg. (Rubber tree)	Callus	Integument slices ex imm. seeds	Somatic embryogen. promoted by ethylene inhibitors	—	Auboiron et al. (1990)
Hevea brasiliensis	Callus	Leaf or seed tissue	Embryogenesis	—	Carron & Enjalric (1982)
Hevea brasiliensis	Callus	Internal integument of seed	Embryogenesis. Embryos multiplied. Plantlets	—	Carron & Enjalric (1985)
Hevea brasiliensis	Callus	Thin sects. of inner seed tegument	Somatic embryogenesis. Studied timing of subculture	—	Michaux-Ferrière & Carron (1989)
Hevea brasiliensis [5 clones]	Callus	Inner integument ex imm. seeds	Embryogen. Callus structure studied & modified	—	Montoro et al. (1993)
Hevea brasiliensis	Callus	Anther wall	Embryogenesis. Plantlets	—	Paranjothy & Ghandimathi (1975)

Species name	Type of Culture	Source of explant	Results		References
Hevea brasiliensis	Direct	Shoot segments	Adventitious shoots. Rooted to give plants	Y	Mascarenhas *et al.* (1982a)
Hevea brasiliensis	Embryo	Seed embryos	Embryo germination & plants	—	Toruan & Suryatmana (1976)
Hevea brasiliensis	Node	Nodes ex greenhouse grown plants	Single shoots, rooted *in vitro*	Y	Carron & Enjalric (1982)
Hevea brasiliensis	Shoot	Seedling shoot apices	Single shoots rooted	—	Paranjothy & Ghandimathi (1975)
Hevea brasiliensis	Single node	Seedling stem segments	Shoots from axillary buds	Y	Chen Z. (1984)
Ricinus communis L. Line 48-1 (Castor oil)	Direct/Callus	Seedling hypocotyls & shoot tips	Adventitious shoots. No plants	—	Reddy *et al.* (1987)
Ricinus communis	Callus	Seed embryos	Embryogenesis	—	Satsangi & Mohan Ram (1965)
Gramineae					
Saccharum cv. 'F164'	Protoplast	Suspension from leaf base callus	Callus colonies. Organogenesis. Plants	—	Chen *et al.* (1988)
Saccharum hybrid cv. R 574	Callus	Virus infected leaf sections	Virus symptoms passed on to few regenerants	—	Peros *et al.* (1990)
Saccharum hybrid cv. R 574	Node	Virus infected nodes	Virus symptoms passed on to most regenerants	—	Peros *et al.* (1990)
Saccharum hybrid [various cvs.]	Shoot	Apical buds	Multiple shoots, rooted. Plant storage studied	YY	Taylor & Dukic (1993)
Saccharum officinarum L. cv. 'Branchue'	Callus	Sections of apical spindle	96% regenerated plants free from SCM virus Strain E	—	Dean (1982)
Saccharum officinarum [17 clones]	Callus	Young leaves	Somatic embryogen. Plantlets. Longterm cult.	—	Fitch & Moore (1993)
Saccharum officinarum cv. IJ 76—316	Embryogenic callus	Young leaves & meristematic tiss.	Embryos germinated into plantlets	—	Ahloowalia & Maretzki (1983)
Saccharum sp.	Callus	Shoot tips	Adventitious shoots	—	Heinz & Mee (1969)
Saccharum sp.	Callus	Leaf roll slices	Shoot regeneration. Shoots rooted	—	Irvine (1984)
Saccharum sp.	Callus	Young leaf base	Shoot formation from primordia. Shoots rooted	—	Larkin (1982)
Saccharum sp.	Callus	Shoot apex, rolled leaf	Shoot regeneration	—	Liu *et al.* (1972) &
Saccharum sp.	Callus	Shoot apex, rolled leaf	Adventitious shoots, rooted plants	—	Liu (1971 ; 1981 ; 1984)
Saccharum sp.	Callus	Shoot tips	Adventitious shoots. Shoots rooted	—	Nadar & Heinz (1977)
Saccharum sp.	Callus	Embryo leaf sheath	Embryogenesis or shoot regeneration	—	Nadar *et al.* (1978)
Saccharum sp.	Callus	Apical stem sections	Adventitious shoot formation	—	Narayana & Srinivasan (1971)
Saccharum sp. [interspecific hybrids]	Direct/Callus	Sections of shoot apex	Adventitious shoot regeneration	—	Chagvardieff *et al.* (1981)
Saccharum sp. [3 interspecific hybrids] (Sugarcane)	Direct/Callus	Young leaf tissue near apex	Adv. shoots. Some plants freed from mosaic virus	—	Irvine & Benda (1985)
Saccharum sp.	Meristem	Apical meristems	Plants (90% virus-free)	Y	Hendre *et al.* (1975)
Saccharum sp. var. Q75	Shoot	Axillary buds	Shoot growth. Tillers repropagated. Rooted plants	YY	Sauvaire & Galzy (1981)
Saccharum sp. [several cvs.]	Shoot	Lateral buds ex heat-treated stalks	Plants free from SCM virus	—	Waterworth & Kahn (1978)
Saccharum sp.	Suspension	Callus from young leaves	Embryogenesis. Plantlets from germinated embryoids	—	Ho & Vasil (1983)
Saccharum sp. × *Ripidium arundinaceum*	Callus	Not given	Plants regenerated varying in chromosome no.	—	Maretzki (1987)
Saccharum spp. [hybrids & wild types]	Suspens. or callus	Green callus from culm discs	Plants regenerated from longterm cultures	—	Fitch & Moore (1990)
Saccharum × *Zea*	Callus	Expanding leaf	Shoots, roots, plants	—	Sreenivasan & Jalaja (1982)
Malvaceae					
Gossypium Interspecific crosses	Ovule/Embryo	Ovules or embryos	Some plantlets obtained	—	Altman (1988)
Gossypium barbadense L. [hybrids] (Sea Island cotton)	Embryo	Seed embryos	Seedling hybrids plants	—	Beasley (1940)
Gossypium barbadense	Protoplast	Cotyledons	Microcalli (no growth beyond 5–8 cells)	—	Firoozabady & De Boer (1986)

Species name	Type of Culture	Source of explant	Results	References
Gossypium hirsutum L. (Upland cotton)	Callus	Seedling cotyledons	Embryogenesis. Embryos, plants	Davidonis & Hamilton (1983)
Gossypium hirsutum	Callus	Cotyledon pieces	Embryogenesis from one callus strain. Plantlets	Davidonis & Hamilton (1983)
Gossypium hirsutum [2 strains]	Callus	Petioles & leaf discs	Embryogenesis. Low frequency of plant regeneration	Gawel et al. (1986)
Gossypium hirsutum cvs. 'Coker 201' & '315'	Callus	Hypocotyls ex *in vitro* seedlings	Embryogenesis. Embryo germination. Plants	Shoemaker et al. (1986)
Gossypium hirsutum	Callus	Hypocotyls inoc. with Agrobact.	Embryogenesis. Somatic embryos, plants	Srivastava et al. (1991)
Gossypium hirsutum	Callus	Various sdlg. & mature explants	Improved embryogenesis. Plant regeneration	Trolinder & Goodin (1988 a,b)
Gossypium hirsutum	Callus	Hypocotyl sections	Embryogenesis. Somatic embryo, plants	Umbeck et al. (1987)
Gossypium hirsutum 'Coker 312' & 'T25'	Callus/Suspension	Petiole sections	Somatic embryogenesis, best in liquid media	Gawel & Robacker (1990)
Gossypium hirsutum	Callus/Suspension	Hypocotyl segments	Embryogenesis. Plants regenerated	Trolinder & Goodin (1987)
Gossypium hirsutum	Callus/Suspension	Hypocotyl segments	Embryogenesis. Plants regenerated	Trolinder & Goodin (1987)
Gossypium hirsutum	Embryo	27 day-old embryos	Plantlet development	Lofland (1950)
Gossypium hirsutum	Embryo	Heart stage embryos (12–14 d old)	Survival of 75% embryos to maturity	Mauney et al. (1967)
Gossypium hirsutum cv. 'Hancock'	Embryo	Ovules containing embryos	Mature embryos. Precocious germination. Plants	Steward & Hsu (1977)
Gossypium hirsutum	Protoplast	Hypocotyl callus	Multicelled colonies but no regeneration	Bhojwani et al. (1977)
Gossypium hirsutum	Protoplast	Cotyledons	Microcalli (no growth beyond 2–3 cells)	Firoozabady & DeBoer (1986)
Gossypium hirsutum cv. 'Coker 310'	Suspension	Cotyledon callus	Embryogenesis, embryo growth. Plants	Finer (1988b)
Gossypium hirsutum × *G. barbadense*	Ovule	*In vitro* fertilized ovule	Ovule culture. Embryos and plantlets	Refaat et al. (1984)
Gossypium hirsutum × *G. arboreum*	Ovule/Embryo	Fertilized ovules	56% hybrid embryos rescued. Plantlets	Thengane et al. (1986)
Gossypium klotzschianum	Callus	Seedling hypocotyls	Callus and green suspensions. Embryogenesis	Price & Smith (1979)
Gossypium klotzschianum	Protoplast	Stem & petiole sections	Callus and suspensions. Globular and torpedo embryos	Finer & Smith (1982 ; 1984)
Gossypium sp.	Embryo	Pro- and heart-stage embryos	Embryo growth. Seedlings obtained	Mauney (1961)
Gossypium sp.	Root	Root tips	Isolated root culture	Bonner (1940b)
Gossypium sp.	Root	Root tips	Isolated root culture	Robbins (1922a)
Gossypium spp. [various cvs.]	Callus	Hypocotyl sects. ex germin. seeds	Embryogenesis. Studied genotype specificity	Trolinder & Xhixian (1989)

Musaceae

Species name	Type of Culture	Source of explant	Results	References
❖ *Musa textilis* Née (Abaca)	Shoot & Direct	Meristem tip slices	Adventitious & axillary shoot proliferation. Rooted	Mante & Tepper (1983)

Palmae

Species name	Type of Culture	Source of explant	Results	References
Brahea edulis Wendl. ex Wats. = *Erythea edulis*	Shoot & Direct	Seedling shoot tips (3 mm)	Shoot elongation & rooting	Gabr & Tisserat (1985)
Brahea edulis (Guadalupe palm)	Shoot & Direct	Seedling shoot tips (3 mm)	Shoot elongation & rooting	Gabr & Tisserat (1985)
Chamaedorea costaricana Ørst.	Callus	Immature inflorescence pieces	Embryogenesis. A few plants regenerated.	Reynolds & Murashige (1979)
Chamaedorea costaricana	Callus	Panicles from imm. inflorescences	Adv. shoots & roots (Embryogenesis?)	Reynolds (1981)
Chamaedorea costaricana	Direct	Immature inflorescence buds	Shoots from flower bud meristems	Reynolds (1981)
Chamaedorea costaricana	Direct/Shoot	Immature inflorescences	Shoots from flower meristem. Axill. shoots	Reynolds (1981)
Chamaedorea costaricana	Embryogenic callus	Ovules (plus embryo)	Somatic embryos	Reynolds & Murashige (1979)
Chamaedorea costaricana	Embryogenic callus	Immature inflorescence buds	Somatic embryos. Plants regenerated	Reynolds (1981)
Cocos nucifera L. (Coconut)	Callus	Young zygotic embryos	Adventitious shoots & roots. Plants	Bhalla-Sarin et al. (1986)

	Species name	Type of Culture	Source of explant	Results		References
	Cocos nucifera cv. 'Malayan Dwarf'	Callus	Sections of sdlg. stem: rachillae of young inflorescence	Nodular structures (with haustoria?). Embryogenesis?	—	Branton & Blake (1983)
	Cocos nucifera	Callus	Embryos	Protocorm-like outgrowths. Adv. shoots with roots	—	D'Souza (1982)
	Cocos nucifera	Callus	Zygotic embryos (cotyl. sheath)	Adventitious shoot primordia & embryo-like structures	—	De Guzman et al. (1978a)
	Cocos nucifera	Direct	Juvenile rachillae sections	Multiple ''shootlets'	Y	Eeuwens & Blake (1977)
	Cocos nucifera	Embryo	Excised embryos	Some embryo growth	—	Cutter & Wilson (1954)
	Cocos nucifera	Embryo	Immature embryos	Seedling growth	Y	Fisher & Tsai (1978)
	Cocos nucifera var. 'West Coast Tall'	Embryo	Zygotic embryos from mature nuts	Germination. Complete plantlets	Y	Gupta et al. (1984)
	Cocos nucifera	Embryo	Seed embryos	Embryos grew to seedlings	Y	Nuria-Toruan (1978)
	Cocos nucifera [Bali × Nias hybrid]	Embryogenesis?	Cotyl. slices ex cultured embryos	Nodular outgrowths. Shoot-like primordia, roots	—	Tahardi (1987)
	Cocos nucifera var. 'West Coast Tall'	Embryogenic callus	Sections sub apical stem. Young rachilla	Embryo-like structs. Roots & shoots ex rachilla callus	Y	Gupta et al. (1984)
*	*Elaeis guineensis* Jacq. (Oil palm)	Callus	Young leaf fragments	Plantlet regeneration, via embryoids	Y	Rabechault & Martin (1976)
	Elaeis guineensis	Embryo	Seed embryos	Seedling plants	Y	Rabechault et al. (1967, 1969)
	Elaeis guineensis pisifera	Callus	Seed embryos	Plantlet regeneration, via embryoids.	Y	Nwankwo & Krikorian (1983)
	Elaeis guineensis var. 'dura Becc.'	Callus	Zygotic embryos	Embryogenesis. Embryoids formed.	—	Rabechault et al. (1970)
	Elaeis guineensis	Embryo	Cryopreserved embryos	Seedling growth. Plants	Y	Grout et al. (1983)
	Euterpe edulis Mart. (Assai palm)	Direct	Embryos ex mature & imm. fruits	Embryogenesis. Embryo germination; seedlings	YY	Guerra & Handro (1988)
	Howea forsteriana (C.Moore & F.Muell.) Becc.	Embryo	Embryos ex immature fruit	Plantlets	Y	Moura & Carneiro (1992)
	Howea forsteriana (Sentry palm)	Callus	Ovule (plus embryo)	Somatic embryogenesis	—	Reynolds & Murashige (1979)
	Howea forsteriana	Embrygenic callus	Ovule (plus embryo)	Somatic embryos	—	Reynolds & Murashige (1979)
	Metroxylon sp.	Embryogenic callus	Seedling shoot tips (3 mm)	Somatic embryos. Plants	—	Gabr & Tisserat (1985)
	Phoenix canariensis hort. ex Chabaud.	Callus	Seedling shoot tips (3 mm)	Embryoids via callus	—	Gabr & Tisserat (1985)
*	*Phoenix dactylifera* L. (Date palm)	Callus	Base young leaf petiole	Roots only	—	Eeuwens (1978)
	Phoenix dactylifera	Callus	Seedling shoot tips (3 mm)	Embryoids via callus	—	Gabr & Tisserat (1985)
	Phoenix dactylifera	Callus	Ovule segments	Somatic embryogenesis. Plant regeneration	—	Omar & Novak (1990)
	Phoenix dactylifera	Callus	Soft leaf base or rachis	Shoot regeneration. Shoots rooted	—	Poulain et al. (1979)
	Phoenix dactylifera	Callus	Seed embryos, meristele	Embryogenesis. Plantlets regenerated	—	Tisserat et al. (1979)
	Phoenix dactylifera	Callus	Embryo, buds, shoot tips	Embryogenesis. Seedlings obtained. Enhanced root growth	—	Tisserat (1984a)
	Phoenix dactylifera var. 'Allig.'	Direct	Female flower primordia	Reversion to adventitious shoots. Rooted plants	Y	Drira & Benbadis (1985)
	Phoenix dactylifera	Direct & Shoot	*I.v.* plantlet ex embryogenic callus	Adventitious roots & ax. branching. Ax. shoots rooted	Y	Tisserat (1982)
	Phoenix dactylifera	Embryogenic callus	Ovule (plus embryo)	Somatic embryos	—	Reynolds & Murashige (1979)
	Phoenix dactylifera	Embryogenic callus	Shoot tips, floral buds	Plantlet regeneration	—	Tisserat et al. (1979)
	Phoenix dactylifera	Embryogenic callus	Lateral bud	Plantlets regenerated	—	Tisserat (1982)
	Phoenix dactylifera	Shoot	Not given	Shoot multiplication	YY	Booij et al. (1993)
	Phoenix dactylifera	Shoot	Seedling shoot tips (3 mm)	Shoots elongate & root	Y	Gabr & Tisserat (1985)
	Phoenix dactylifera	Shoot	Adv. shoots from lateral bud callus	Axillary shoots on 40% explants	—	Tisserat & De Mason (1985)

Species name	Type of Culture	Source of explant	Results		References
Phoenix dactylifera	Shoot	Shoot tips or plantlets ex embryos	Some axillary shoots. Inflorescences on outgrowths	–	Tisserat & De Mason (1985)
Phoenix dactylifera	Shoot	Shoot tip	Shoot growth. Infrequent rooting	–	Tisserat et al. (1979)
Phoenix dactylifera	Shoot	Shoot tips	Shoot growth. Rooted. Enhanced root growth	Y	Tisserat (1984a)
Phoenix dactylifera	Shoot	Shoot tips (0.5 mm)	Axillary bud proliferation. Shoots rooted	YY	Tisserat (1984b)
Phoenix roebelenii O'Brien.	Embryogenic callus	Seedling shoot tip (3 mm)	Somatic embryos	Y	Gabr & Tisserat (1985)
Pritchardia kaalae Rock. (Ornamental palm)	Callus	Shoot tips 3–4 mm	Embryogenesis	–	El Shiaty et al. (1991)
Veitchia merrillii (Becc.) H.E.Moore. (Manila palm)	Embryogenic callus	Mature embryos	Embryoid maturation & germination to plantlets	–	Srinivasan et al. (1985)
Washingtonia filifera H.A.Wendl. (Cotton palm)	Shoot/Direct	Seedling shoot tips (3 mm)	Shoot elongation & rooting	Y	Gabr & Tisserat (1985)
Washingtonia robusta H.A.Wendl. (Mexican Washingtonia)	Shoot/Direct	Seedling shoot tips (3 mm)	Shoot elongation & rooting	Y	Gabr & Tisserat (1985)

Pedaliaceae

Species name	Type of Culture	Source of explant	Results		References
Sesamum indicum L. cv. 'PT Sesame'	Callus	Seedling hypocotyls	Embryo-like structures	–	George et al. (1987)
Sesamum indicum cv. 'PT Sesame'	Shoot	Shoot tips of seedlings	Multiple shoots. Rooted plants	YY	George et al. (1987)

Polygonaceae

Species name	Type of Culture	Source of explant	Results		References
❖ Polygonum fagopyrum L. = Fagopyrum esculentum (Buckwheat)	Callus	Cotyledon	Shoot regeneration. Direct rooting	–	Srejovic & Neskovic (1981)
Polygonum fagopyrum	Root	Root tips	Isolated root culture	–	White (1938 a; 1943a)

Rubiaceae

Species name	Type of Culture	Source of explant	Results		References
Coffea [no sp. given] (Coffee)	Shoot	Terminal or axillary shoot tips	Shoot multiplication. No rooting reported	–	Moses & Sullivan (1985)
* Coffea arabica L.	Callus	Leaf blade segments	Adventious roots & shoots. Shoots rooted	–	Herman & Haas (1975)
Coffea arabica	Callus	Leaf segments	Embryogenesis	–	Sondahl & Sharp (1977)
Coffea arabica [e.g. cv. 'Bourbon]	Callus	Mature leaf pieces or cotyl. leaves	Embryogenesis in secondary cultures. Plants	Y	Sondahl et al. (1985)
Coffea arabica	Callus/Direct	Leaf	Embryogenesis	–	Sondahl et al. (1984)
Coffea arabica	Embryo	Zygotic embryos	Seedling growth	Y	Sondahl et al. (1979 ; 1984)
Coffea arabica var. 'Typica'	Embryogenic callus	Young leaves (ca. 5 cm)	Embryogenesis. Embryoid germination. Plants	–	Yasuda et al. (1985)
Coffea arabica	Embryogenic callus	Young leaf slices	Somatic embryos. Plantlets	–	Yasuda et al. (1986)
Coffea arabica	Meristem	Seedling shoot meristems	Single shoots (without roots). Rooted later	Y	Kartha et al. (1981)
Coffea arabica	Meristem	Apical meristem (0.3 mm)	Shoot development, rooted plantlets	Y	Sondahl et al. (1984)
Coffea arabica cvs. 'Mundo Nova', 'Catuai'	Meristem	Apex of 3 month old plant	Rooted single shoots	Y	Sondahl et al. (1985)
Coffea arabica	Shoot	Seedling shoot meristems	Multiple shoots with basal callus. Rooted plants	YY	Kartha et al. (1981)
Coffea arabica	Shoot	Young stem nodes	Multiple axillary shoots. Rooted plants	YY	Sondahl et al. (1984)
Coffea arabica cvs. 'Mundo Novo' & others	Shoot	Nodes from orthotropic shoots	Multiple shoots (esp. in subcultures). Rooted plants	YY	Sondahl et al. (1985)
Coffea arabica	Single node/Shoot	Nodal sects. ex 3 month i. v. shts.	At least two shoots per node. Rooted plants	YY	Sondahl et al. (1985)
Coffea arabica & hybrid [3 accessions]	Storage	In vitro shoots	Effect of temperature & sucrose concentration studied	–	Bertrand-Desbrunais et al. (1992)
Coffea canephora Pierre ex Fröhner (Robusta coffee)	Callus	Soft, green internode	Embryogenesis in compact callus	–	Staritsky (1970)
Coffea canephora	Embryo	Zygotic embryos	Seedlings obtained	Y	Colonna et al. (1971)
Coffea excelsa	Embryo	Zygotic embryos	Seedling growth	Y	Colonna et al. (1971)
Coffea spp.	Shoot & direct	Seedling shoot tips	Limited growth (for germplasm storage)	–	Bertrand-Desbrunais et al. (1991)

Simmondsiaceae

	Species name	Type of Culture	Source of explant	Results		References
*	Simmondsia chinensis (Link) Schneid. (Jojoba)	Direct	Epicotyls of axenic seedlings	Many adventitious shoots. Rooted shoots	–	Scaramuzzi & D'Ambrosio (1988)
	Simmondsia chinensis	Direct embryogen.	Embryos (2mm)	Plantlets from germinated somatic embryos	Y	Lee & Thomas (1985c)
	Simmondsia chinensis	Shoot	Shoot tips	Shoot growth & axillary branching	Y	Kenny & Palzkill (1988)
	Simmondsia chinensis	Shoot	Shoot tips	Shoot proliferation. Pretreated shoots rooted	YY	Rost & Hinchee (1980)
	Simmondsia chinensis cv. 'California'	Shoot	Single node leafy cuttings	Shoot multiplication & subculture	Y	Jacoboni & Standardi (1987)
	Simmondsia chinensis	Shoot	Apical & axillary buds	Basal callus then multiple shoots. Rooted in vitro.	Y	Scaramuzzi & D'Ambrosio (1988)

Solanaceae

	Species name	Type of Culture	Source of explant	Results		References
	Nicotiana repanda Willd. × N. tabacum L.	Callus	Leaf of sdlg. from ovule culture	Shoot regenerated. One aneuploid plant	–	Iwai et al. (1985)
	Nicotiana rustica L.	Callus	Shoot tips	Shoot initiation & growth	–	Walkey & Woolfitt (1968)
	Nicotiana rustica	Direct	Pistils from immature flower buds	Diploid adventitious shoots. Rooted plants	–	Basaran et al. (1991)
*	Nicotiana sp.	Meristem	Meristem tips	Shoot proliferation	Y	Shahde-Moses & Murashige (1979)
*	Nicotiana tabacum L. (Tobacco)	Callus	Stem pith callus	Shoot-forming callus	–	Brown & Thorpe (1980)
	Nicotiana tabacum	Callus	Stem pith callus	Shoot-forming callus	–	Brown et al. (1979)
	Nicotiana tabacum GR-Xin No 1	Callus	Leaves	Callus growth and maintenance	–	Chen et al. (1992)
	Nicotiana tabacum cv. 'McNair 944'	Callus	Leaf sections	Adv. shoots (regeneration enhanced by phenolic compounds)	–	Compton & Preece (1988)
	Nicotiana tabacum	Callus	Leaf discs	Indirect morphogenesis. Plantlet regeneration	–	Devreux et al. (1971)
	Nicotiana tabacum	Callus	Callus (source not given)	Adv. shoots. Budding tissue maintained. Shoot formation	–	Engelke et al. (1973)
	Nicotiana tabacum var. 'virginica'	Callus	Hypocotyls	Shoot form. Electric potentials measured	–	Goldsworthy & Lago (1992)
	Nicotiana tabacum	Callus	Sub-epidermal cells	Bud differentiation & shoot growth	–	Ha Ngoc & Tran Thanh Van (1979)
	Nicotiana tabacum	Callus	Wound callus culture described in Bergmann (1964)	Embryogenesis	–	Haccius & Lakshmanan (1965)
	Nicotiana tabacum cv. 'Wisconsin 38'	Callus	Stem pith segments	Studied sucrose inhibition of caulogenesis	–	Hammersley-Straw & Thorpe (1988)
	Nicotiana tabacum	Callus	Stem pith & stem sections	Adventitious buds	–	Helgeson (1979)
	Nicotiana tabacum	Callus	Stem pith	Plant regeneration	–	Hughes (1986)
	Nicotiana tabacum cv. 'Wisconsin 38'	Callus	Stem pith segments	Callus growth & morphogenesis enhanced by ascorbic acid	–	Joy IV et al. (1988)
	Nicotiana tabacum	Callus	Stem pith	Adventitious shoots	–	Kaul & Sabharwal (1971)
	Nicotiana tabacum Su/Su and su/su	Callus	Suspensions from hypocotyl callus	Regenerated some chimeras from mixed callus cultures	–	Marcotrigiano & Gouin (1984a)
	Nicotiana tabacum	Callus	Stem segments	Adventitious shoot formation	–	Miller & Skoog (1953)
	Nicotiana tabacum	Callus	Stem	Shoot formation from wild-type cells. Shoots rooted	–	Müller & Grafe (1978)
	Nicotiana tabacum cv. 'Wisconsin 38'	Callus	Stem pith	Adventitious shoots ex 2n & 4n cell lines	–	Murashige & Nakano (1967)
	Nicotiana tabacum	Callus	Pith	Adventitious shoot formation	–	Nadar et al. (1978)
	Nicotiana tabacum	Callus	Stem sections of haploid plants	Shoots. Rooted, with or without prior gamma–irradiation	–	Nitsch et al. (1969 a,b)
	Nicotiana tabacum W-38	Callus	Pith discs or roots	Shoot regeneration	–	Ogura & Tsuji (1977)
	Nicotiana tabacum cv. 'Wisconsin 38'	Callus	Pith-phloem tissue	Adventitious shoots (studied effect of sodium sulphate)	–	Pua et al. (1985)
	Nicotiana tabacum	Callus	Leaf discs	Shoot differentiation. Studied inhibitors	–	Sethi et al. (1990)
	Nicotiana tabacum cv. ' Wisconsin 38'	Callus	Long-term callus cultures	Embryogenesis. Somatic embryos germinated. Plants	–	Simpson (1985)

embryos were regenerated when the callus was transferred to a medium without auxin which included 1.1 mg/l kinetin. The presence of 0.3 mg/l ABA increased the density of embryos in one *A. cepa* variety.

Allium cepa Agrigatum group   (Shallot)

Varieties of *Allium* which produce a cluster of small lateral bulbs instead of one large one are known as shallots. Those cultivated in Europe were classified as *A. ascalonicum*, but are now generally considered to be a variety of *A. cepa*.

Seo and Kim (1988) obtained adventitious shoots with varying chromosome numbers from callus cultures of *A. wakegi*. As the species is amphidiploid and sterile it has only been multiplied vegetatively, but one of the regenerated plants was tetraploid and fertile, giving the possibility of propagation from seeds.

Allium sativum   (Garlic)   (see Table 257)

Meristem culture. Nearly all genotypes of garlic are sexually sterile and are normally vegetatively propagated from cloves and bulbils (see Novák and Havranek, 1975). In consequence of this, commercial garlic varieties are liable to be virus infected (Havranek, 1973; McBeath and Lee, 1975). An advantage in using tissue culture for propagation therefore lies in the possibility of producing and maintaining virus–free stocks.

Several papers describe the successful use of meristem tip culture to eliminate virus diseases (Table 257), thereby improving yield and crop quality. For small explants **LS** medium containing 0.1 mg/l NAA (Bovo and Mroginski, 1985), 0.01 mg/l NAA and 0.01 mg/l BAP (Matsubara and Chen, 1989), or no regulants is suitable, but the addition of 1 mg/l IAA and 1mg/l BAP causes the production of basal adventitious buds, which assists multiplication at a later stage (Nagakubo *et al.*, 1993). Larger explants from heat–treated cloves have been grown on **B5** medium (Peña–Inglesias and Ayuso, 1982b).

Shoot culture. Shoot culture is useful for multiplying virus indexed stock rapidly to provide adequate planting material. Bhojwani (1978) propagated *A. sativum* from axillary and adventitious shoots derived from 5–8 mm shoot apices isolated from cloves. Shoot proliferation was satisfactory on **B5** medium which contained 2% sucrose and 0.5 mg/l 2–iP and 0.1 mg/l NAA. Bhojwani rooted shoots by transferring to the same medium in which there was 0.01 mg/l 2–iP and 0.2 mg/l NAA, but Matsubara and Chen (1989) found that bulb formation occurred on shoots subcultured to a medium with 0.1 mg/l NAA and 0.1 mg/l BAP. Once bulblets had started to form, plants could be transferred to Rockwool cubes.

An improved version of this technique has been developed by Nagakubo *et al.* (1993). Having initiated cultures from clove meristems (above), shoots were multiplied on **LS** medium from which NH_4NO_3 was eliminated, 187.3 mg/l (3.5 mM) NH_4Cl added, and the concentration of KNO_3 increased to 5712.2 mg/l (56.5 mM). On this medium there was good shoot multiplication in the presence of 5 mg/l NAA and 10 mg/l BAP, but less hyperhydricity than on **LS** medium. Shoots elongated when moved to **LS** medium without regulants and produced bulblets when incubated at 25°C for 2 months on **LS** medium with 60 g/l sucrose, providing cultures consisting of separated plants had first been stored at 5°C for 6 months. As the bulblets formed, the plant leaves senesced and died. Dried bulblets were found to be dormant but could be stimulated to resume active growth by manipulation of the storage temperature. One of the most effective treatments was 2 weeks at 35°C, followed by 2 weeks at 20°C and 4 weeks at 5°C.

Callus culture. Callus cultures of leaf and shoot apex explants have been successfully induced to regenerate plants on **MS** or **Abo El–Nil and Zettler (1976) AZ** media (Table 47, page 382). Abo El–Nil (1977) supplemented **AZ** medium with 1.8 mg/l IAA and 0.2 mg/l kinetin; and Nagasawa and Finer (1988) the medium of **Kartha *et al.* (1974a)** (page 385) with 1 mg/l NAA and 2 mg/l BAP.

Abo El–Nil obtained shoot differentiation when callus fragments were moved to **AZ** medium supplemented with a further 15 mM ammonium nitrate and 1.8 mg/l IAA and 2.2 mg/l kinetin, but the experiment of Nagasawa and Finer (*loc. cit.*) resulted in a nodular (organised) callus which could be multiplied in liquid culture and from which shoots developed on a semi–solid medium without regulants.

Some *A. sativum* plants obtained through callus culture have been found to be genetically abnormal (Novák, 1974), but as sexual recombination does not occur in the species, it may be possible to exploit such variation for the selection of superior genotypes (Novák, 1980b; Novák *et al.*, 1982).

Embryogenesis. Embryogenesis, leading to the regeneration of plants, was first reported by Abo El–Nil (1977) in the callus cultures mentioned above. Somatic embryo formation took place when the Stage II medium contained 1.8 mg/l IAA and 4.3 mg/l kinetin. Embryos and the plantlets which grew from them, were thought to be devoid of filamentous virus particles, whereas the callus cultures in which the somatic embryos formed, were not virus–free.

Allium porrum   (Leek)

Leek plants have an elongated cylindrical bulb. Slow vegetative multiplication can be carried out from the production of bulbils on the inflorescence after cutting away the flowers, or by planting offshoots which occasionally arise from the base of bulbs.

Direct shoot formation. Novák and Havel (1981) obtained shoots directly from pieces of flower head receptacle on **Dunstan and Short (1977a) BDS** medium supplemented with BAP alone or with the further addition of NAA. White flower primordia from receptacles also became a source of adventitious shoots after a period of teratomatous growth.

Regeneration from callus. Debergh and Standaert–de–Metsenaere (1976) induced bulblet formation from the callus which was produced from basal plate explants. The culture medium for both callus initiation and bulblet differentiation consisted of $\frac{1}{2}$**MS** major elements and FeEDTA, with the minor elements and organic additions of **Nitsch and Nitsch (1965)** (page 386). Callus was produced in the dark at 24°C and bulbil production took place in a 17 h photoperiod (4000 lx) at 22°C. Roots and shoots were initiated in the callus, but only inconsistently. Similar results were obtained by Hunault (1976) with seedling–derived callus.

Dunstan and Short (1979b) were able to obtain large numbers of shoots from callus derived from leaf meristematic tissue excised from the bases of leaves, close to the stem apex. The medium used was **BDS** (Dunstan and Short, 1977a,b), with an optimal hormone range of 6.0–8.0 mg/l 2–iP and 1.0–2.0 mg/l NAA. Shoots were rooted and plantlets successfully transferred to greenhouse conditions.

Embryogenesis. Callus which produced somatic embryos and adventitious shoots was obtained from zygotic embryo explants by Van der Valk *et al.* (1992). The method is the same as that described for *A. cepa* above.

Malvaceae
Abelmoschus esculentus
(*Hibiscus esculentus*)

(Okra, Ladies Fingers)

This is an annual crop grown in the tropics and subtropics for its edible pods. Plants are easily raised from seeds, and so there is no interest in micropropagation. There has however been some research on tissue culture methods (Table 255). *Abelmoschus* is one of the few plants in which gibberellic acid has been shown to synergise auxin in promoting adventitious root formation on cuttings (Bhattacharya *et al.*, 1978) (see Part 1, page 448).

Polygonaceae
Rheum rhaponticum   (Rhubarb)

Concealed virus infections, which reduce the vigour of rhubarb plants, can be removed effectively by meristem tip culture (Walkey, 1968). Shoot tip culture can be used to propagate virus–tested stocks. Walkey and Matthews (1979) placed shoot tip or lateral bud explants at Stage I onto filter paper bridges above **MS** medium containing 8 mg/l IAA and 2.6 mg/l kinetin. When established, the explants were moved to an **MS** agar medium with 13 mg/l kinetin for multiple shoot growth. Separated shoots were rooted at Stage IIIb in a medium containing only auxin.

Solanaceae

The fruits of several species in this family are eaten fresh in salads, or as cooked vegetables or food flavourings. Plants are readily propagated from seeds and there is little practical interest in micropropagation, except in connection with plant breeding or genetic manipulation. As in other members of this family, such as *Nicotiana tabacum* (page 1165) and *Solanum tuberosum* (page 1120), cultures of most kinds can be grown on **MS** medium, or media based on **MS** salts. Behki and Lesley (1980) found that, providing there was 60 mM total nitrogen in the medium, the ratio of NO_3^- to NH_4^+ in **MS** could be varied from 67:33 to 87:13 without affecting callus growth or caulogenesis in *Lycopersicon esculentum*, but in *Solanum melongena*, although embryogenesis would occur when the ratio was between 33:67 and 80:20, it reached an optimum when the total nitogen concentration was 60 mM and the ratio of NO_3^- to NH_4^+, 67:33 (*i.e.* as in **MS** medium) (Gleddie *et al.*, 1982). A medium with only 36 mM total nitrogen and a NO_3^- to NH_4^+ ratio of 67:33, was most suitable for root formation (Behki and Lesney, *loc. cit.*). The significance of the NO_3^- / NH_4^+ ratio is discussed in Part 1, page 281).

Solanaceae
Capsicum **spp.**   (Peppers and chillies)

Capsicum annuum (sweet pepper) fruits are eaten in salads and used in pickles or as food flavourings. The plant is an annual and needs a warm climate for fruits to set and mature. Both unripe (green) and ripe (red or yellow) fruits are sold.

The fruits of *Capsicum frutescens* range widely in size and shape, but are generally smaller than those of *C. annuum*. They are pungent and are used in food flavourings, condiments, pickles and hot sauces.

Capsicum annuum F$_1$ hybrids are generally vigorous, early cropping and very productive. However, the cost of hybrid seed is high. Production requires manual pollination as peppers are normally cross–pollinated. An efficient method of micropropagation would be very useful to pepper breeders for the maintenance of inbred breeding lines. Even though the cost of hybrid seed is high (page 791), the vegetative propagation of hybrid peppers for direct field planting is unlikely to be cost effective.

Shoot culture

Sultanbawa and Phatak (1991) described the shoot culture of a sterile ornamental pepper. Shoots were cultured on ½**MS** containing 2 mg/l BAP and rooted on the same medium without growth regulators.

Direct and indirect shoot regeneration

Adventitious shoots are formed directly when *C. annuum* explants (such as zygotic embryos; seedling hypocotyl, cotyledon, shoot tip and root sections; or stem and leaf sections from young plants) are cultured on **MS** medium supplemented with:

5 mg/l BAP	Agrawal *et al.* (1989)
2.5 mg/l BAP + 1 mg/l BAP	Maraffa and Lineberger (1981)
2 mg/l BA + 1 mg/l IAA	Fári and Czakó (1981)
50 mg/l BA + 0.05 mg/l IAA	Phillips and Hubstenberger (1985)

Phillips and Hubstenberger (above) found that shoots were only regenerated from leaf discs incubated at 25°C in a 16 hour photoperiod (160 μmol m^{-2} s^{-1}) if **MS** medium was supplemented with 30 g/l glucose. No shoots were produced in the presence of sucrose. In continuous light shoots were obtained using either sugar, but glucose was still superior.

Callus culture. In the experiments of Gunay and Rao (1978), callus initiated from seedling hypocotyls and cotyledons of *C. annuum* and *C. frutescens* cultured with NAA or IAA, regenerated the greatest number of shoots when transferred to **MS** medium supplemented with 30 g/l sucrose and 2 mg/l BAP and 1 mg/l IAA.

Solanaceae
Lycopersicon esculentum (Tomato)

Like tobacco, the tomato plant has been used as a model for many tissue culture experiments, and there are many reports describing all kinds of *in vitro* culture. However, there is little interest in tissue culture for practical purposes, except perhaps in plant breeding and for genetic manipulation experiments.

Many million tons of tomatoes are produced each year throughout the world, from inumerable cultivars, each selected to be suitable to different climatic conditions and to have a wide range of fruit qualities. It is thus not surprising, considering the diversity of the species, that there is variation in the enviroments which have been found to be most suitable for tissue culture of different genotypes, particularly with regard to growth regulator ammendments to the medium.

Root cultures

Tomato roots were used in many early experiments on isolated root culture. Root tips grow best on a liquid, low salts medium, such as **White (1954)**, to which has been added NaFeEDTA (Sheat *et al.*, 1959) and 15–20 g/l sucrose (Street and McGregor, 1952).

Embryo cultures

Seedlings can often be obtained from interspecfic crosses of *Lycopersicon* by culturing immature embryos which would otherwise abort before reaching maturity. The technique is therefore helpful where it is desired to introduce traits from wild species into the cultivated tomato. Smith (1944) obtained plantlets from embryos cultured on an early medium of White (1934a), but found it necessary to increase the concentration of macronutrients and vitamins (yeast extract). **White (1954)** medium supplemented with **MS** micronutrients and vitamins, might be a suitable substitute. However, Neal and Topoleski (1983) found that a highly suitable medium comprised the HIGH salts and LOW vitamins of **De Fossard *et al.* (1974a)**, combined with 60 g/l sucrose. This level of sucrose was especially essential if lower concentrations of salts were used, suggesting that embryos require to be grown in a medium of low water potential.

A different approach was adopted by Thomas and Pratt (1981) who, by culturing immature hybrid embryos on **Heinz and Mee (1969)**† medium (30 g/l sucrose), supplemented with 2 mg/l 2,4–D, 1 mg/l 2–iP and 10% coconut milk, induced callus formation. Shoots were regenerated when the callus was transferred to **Mullin *et al.* (1974) B**† containing 2 mg/l zeatin and 20 g/l sucrose.

† The composition of these media is given in Part 1, pages 384 and 386 *et seq.*

Meristem tip and shoot cultures

Tomato is a systemic host for many plant viruses, some of which (*e.g.* Tomato Mosaic Virus) can be transmitted through seed tissues or carried on the seed coat to reinfect seedlings. Meristem tip culture can therefore be useful to obtain virus–free stock for seed production.

MS medium (20–30 g/l sucrose) has been found to be suitable for meristem tip and shoot cultures of *Lycoper-*

Table 253. Examples of media and growth regulators which have been employed to obtain direct shoot formation (or shoot formation from primary callus without transfer) on explants of *Lycopersicon esculentum* and its relatives.
Media are indicated with square brackets and sucrose concentrations (%) within rounded brackets.

Species	Explant	Medium (Growth regulators in mg/l unless indicated otherwise)	References
Direct shoot formation			
L. esculentum (many cvs.)	Thin cell layers ex pedicel and peduncle	[**HM** †] (3) 2.2 kin + 0.18 µg/l IAA or NAA	Compton and Veilleux (1988; 1991)
L. peruvianum	Internode segments	[**MS** ‡] (2) 2 IAA + 0.22 kin + 2.2 zeatin + 15% CM	Sree Ramulu *et al.* (1976a)
L. esculentum L. glandulosum L. peruvianum	Cotyledons ex seedlings	[**MS** §] (3) 0.5 IAA + 2 BAP	Ammati *et al.* (1984)
L. esculentum cv. 'Alice'	Cotyledons	[**MS**] (3) 3.5 IAA ¶ + 0.7 µM zeatin riboside	Branca *et al.* (1990)
L. esculentum	Decapitated seedlings	[**MS**] (3) None	Fári *et al.* (1991)
Shoots from primary callus			
L. esculentum	Leaf discs ex 4 week–old plants	[**K** ††] (3) 1.1–2.3 BAP ± 0.02–1.8 IAA, or 0.22–1.1 zeatin ± 0.18–1.8 IAA	Kartha *et al.* (1976)
L. esculentum 'GCRI–26'	Leaf discs ex 4 week–old plants	[**MS**] (3) 3.0 BAP ± 0.3 IAA	Barden *et al.* (1976)
L. esculentum	Seedling hypocotyl and cotyledon sections	[**MS** ‡‡] (3) 2 BAP or 2 kinetin, or 0.5 BAP + 0.5 IAA	Gunay and Rao (1980)
L. esculentum var. 'Porphyre'	Hypocotyl segments	[**MS** §§] (3) 0.57 IAA + 0.2–1 2–iP	Ohki *et al.* (1978)
L. esculentum var. 'Apédice'		[**MS** §§] (3) 0.88 IAA + 0.6–1.0 2–iP	
L. esculentum var. '63–5A'		[**MS** §§] (3) 0.18 IAA + 1 2–iP 0.6–1.0 2–iP	
L. esculentum var. '63–5B'		[**MS** §§] (3) 0.18–1.8 IAA + 0.5–1.0 2–iP	

† **Heinz and Mee (1969)** medium (see Part 1, page 384)

‡ But with 2 mg/l glycine

§ But with **White (1954)** vitamins and 100 mg/l *myo*–inositol; solidified with 2 g/l Gelrite.

¶ Also found that 2–20 µM of a synthetic auxin (1,2–benzisothiazole–3–acetic acid) was very effective.

†† **Kartha *et al.* (1974a)** — see Part 1, page 385)

‡‡ MS medium said to be modified, but modifications not given.

§§ MS macronutrients with **Bourgin and Nitsch (1967) H** micronutrients (page 407); **Nitsch and Nitsch (1965) K & S** vitamins (page 416) and 5 mg/l glycine.

sicon, although some authors [*e.g.* Kartha *et al.* (1977) and Novak and Maskova (1979)] have chosen to increase the concentration of the vitamin component (*e.g.* to use the vitamins of **Gamborg (1966) PRL–4–C**). The growth of unbranched shoots from meristem tip, and shoot tip and nodal explants of *L. esculentum* and related species, is assisted by the addition of 0.5–1.75 mg/l IAA (filter sterilised) (Kartha *et al.*, 1977; Turner *et al.*, 1987). The shoots also root spontaneously. Axillary shoot formation was promoted in cv. 'Fantastic' by the presence of 5 mg/l BAP (without auxin) (Schnapp and Preece, 1986), and in several F$_2$ selections by 2 mg/l 2–iP together with 0.35 mg/l IAA (Ohki *et al.*, 1988).

Direct shoot regeneration

Lycopersicon, Nicotiana and some other Solanaceae, have become popular subjects for tissue culture experiments because plantlets are readily regenerated. In *Ly-*

copersicon, adventitious shoots are frequently produced directly on explants or on primary callus. Examples of the media and growth regulators which have been employed successfully in some experiments are shown in Table 253. It will be seen that concentrations of growth regulators need to be adjusted according to the nature of the cultivar being cultured and the particular auxin and/or cytokinin being employed. The numbers of shoots formed on an explant and the time required for morphogenesis to occur, also vary (Zapata *et al.*, 1981; Ancora and Sree–Ramulu, 1981; Padmanabhan *et al.*, 1974; Novák and Mašková, 1979; Cassells, 1979; Preece and Read, 1980).

Unusually, for plantlets regenerated either directly, or from primary callus, Barden *et al.* (1986) obtained somaclonal variants of a TMV virus–susceptible line, 'GCRI–26', which were virus–free and apparently virus–resistant.

Flower formation. The formation of flower buds has been noticed following treatments which would normally be expected to lead to direct shoot formation (Compton and Veilleux, 1988; 1991) (Table 253). Adventitious shoots were transformed into flowers directly on tomato leaf segments, when these explants were incubated on **MS** medium to which 5 g/l sodium chloride and 2 mg/l zeatin had been added (Liu *et al.*, 1989).

Indirect shoot formation

Explants cultured with slightly higher concentrations of auxin than shown in Table 253 give rise to undifferentiated callus, or callus from which roots are differentiated. A suitable medium for callus initiation is **MS** (with thiamine HCl increased to 1 mg/l and no glycine) supplemented with, for example, 2 mg/l NAA and 1 mg/l BAP (Meredith 1979; Handley and Sink, 1985a). Culturing explants with media containing 2,4–D tends to produce large friable non–morphogenic calluses (Garcia–Reina and Luque, 1988).

Subculture of unorganised callus to a medium in which the ratio of cytokinin to auxin is increased, or in which there is only cytokinin, leads to shoot differentiation, although the most effective compounds and concentrations are found to differ with genotype. Zeatin and 2–iP (1–5 mg/l) are specially effective cytokinins.

Variations in chromosome numbers are common in callus–derived tomato plants, especially those obtained from old or de–differentiated callus.

Rooting

Lycopersicon shoots from shoot cultures, or those obtained adventitiously, can be rooted in **MS** or $\frac{1}{2}$**MS** medium (30 g/l sucrose) with no growth regulators, or with the addition of a low concentration of auxin (*e.g.* 0.01–0.1 mg/l NAA, 0.5 mg/l IAA).

Embryogenesis

Plants have almost invariably been regenerated from *Lycopersicon* callus and cell suspensions through the formation of adventitious shoots, although early stage somatic embryos have been observed in meristematic nodules (Cassells, 1979). Uddin and Berry (1988) successfully initiated embryogenic callus from immature embryos of *L. esculentum* 'Ohio 7870' on **MS** to which 120 g/l sucrose and 2 mg/l dicamba had been added. A suspension culture was obtained from this callus on liquid **MS** containing 30 g/l sucrose and 1 mg/l 2,4–D, but fully developed embryos were not obtained.

Solanaceae
Solanum melongena

(Egg plant, aubergine, brinjal)

Solanum melongena is a perennial plant, usually grown as an annual, cultivated in warm countries for its fruits which are eaten cooked as vegetables.

There is little interest in micropropagation, but as a member of the Solanaceae, the plant has received attention in research laboratories.

Embryo culture

Hydrid embryos form the cross *S. melongena* × *S. khasianum* formed rooted plantlets when cultured on **Bourgin and Nitsch (1967) H** medium, without growth regulators. The addition of 0.1 mg/l IAA to the medium at a later stage assisted plantlet growth (Sharma *et al.*, 1980a).

Shoot culture

Raj Bhansali and Ramawat (1993) cultured plants of *S. melongena* infected with a mycoplasma–like organism by shoot culture and found that the organism was not eliminated *in vitro*. Shoot proliferation was obtained by placing axillary buds with 10–15 mm of stem onto **Lloyd and McCown (1981) WPM** medium containing 0.1 mg/l IAA and 1.0 mg/l BAP. Shoots were subcultured on the same medium or rooted on regulant–free medium, or medium supplemented with 0.1 mg/l NAA.

Adventitious shoots

Adventitious shoots are readily regenerated from *S. melongena* and, as in *Lycopersicon esculentum*, are frequently formed directly on explants or on primary callus, without the need to transfer explants to a second medium. Examples of successful protocols are shown in Table 254. As in tomato, there is variation in the most suitable combination of growth regulators for different genotypes. Fourteen commercial cultivars were shown by Matsuoka and Hinata (1979) to have different growth regulator requirements for adventitious shoot induction or embryogenesis.

In the cultivar 'Pusa Kranti', a high number of shoots were regenerasted from leaf pieces if 44 mM (7.9 g/l) fructose or glucose was added to **MS** medium. The optimum concentration of sucrose (which allowed fewer shoots to be formed than when glucose or fructose were present) was 11–22 mM (3.76–7.53 g/l). However, if 22 mM mannitol was added to 22 mM sucrose, there was a significant increase in shoot formation (Mukerjee *et al.*, 1991).

Table 254. Examples of media and growth regulators which have been employed to obtain direct shoot formation (or shoot formation from primary callus without transfer) on explants of *Solanum melongena*.
Media are indicated with square brackets and sucrose concentrations (%) within rounded brackets.

Explant	Medium (Growth regulators in mg/l)	References
Hypocotyl sections of 4 week–old seedlings	[MS †] (2) 1 IAA + 1 BAP	Kamat and Rao (1978)
Hypocotyl sections of 4 week–old seedlings F₁ hybrids	[MS †] 0.5 IAA + 1 kin	Kamat and Rao (1978)
Hypocotyl sections	[MS ‡] (2) 0.23 BAP + 10 AdS	Matsuoka and Hinata (1979)
Seedling leaf sections	[MS] (0.79 §) + 2 kinetin	Mukherjee *et al.*. (1991)
Leaf secions of F₁ hybrid	[MS] (3) 1–10 IBA + 5 kin or 5 IAA (with no cytokinin)	Macchia *et al.* (1983)

†   Modified micronutrients and more complex and concentrated vitamins than normally in **MS**.

‡   Concentrations of the following compounds were altered: thiamine HCl modified to 0.25 mg/l; pyridoxine HCl to 0.25 mg/l; nicotinic acid to 1.25 mg/l; and glycine to 7.5 mg/l.

§   Glucose or fructose — see text.

Cultures are normally incubated in the light. Leaf segments incubated in the dark on **MS** medium containing 1–10 mg/l IBA produced only callus and roots, but shoots were formed when the dark–grown callus was moved to the light (Macchia *et al.*, 1983). When explants were kept in the light, the growth regulator treatments shown in Table 254 resulted in caulogenic green callus.

Embryogenesis

Either directly, or indirectly, aubergine explants give rise to somatic embryos fairly readily, although some cultivars are more responsive than others. Embryos have been produced directly on seedling cotyledons incubated on **MS** medium [containing the vitamins of **Gamborg (1966) PRL–4–C**] with 2.5–5.0 mg/l NAA (Fobert and Webb, 1988). In these experiments, higher concentrations of auxin caused the formation of friable callus from which shoots were regenerated, but Gleddie *et al.* (1982) and Matsuoka and Hinata (1979), using leaf and hypocotyl explants, found 8–10 mg/l NAA to be required.

Unlike what is usually observed, in the experiments of Gleddie *et al.* (1982), the presence of auxin did not inhibit embryo maturation, and all stages of embryo development were observed in the callus. Embryogenesis was also shown to be light dependent and was inhibited at sucrose concentrations above or below 20.5 g/l (0.06 M).

Umbelliferae (Apiaceae)
Daucus carota   (Carrot)

As regeneration of adventitious shoots and somatic embryos from carrot callus and suspension cultures has proved to be especially easy, carrot has been used as another model system for studying *in vitro* morphogenesis. There are in consequence a great many papers on the subject and it has been impossible to record them all in Table 255.

There is little interest in the vegetative propagation of carrot, but it is a cross pollinated outbreeding crop, and so micropropagation could be of value for multiplying and maintaining inbred varieties intended as parents in the production of F₁ hybrid seed.

Embryogenesis

Callus can be initiated from a variety of explants and on media of many different compositions. It is usually obtained using **MS** containing 20–30 g/l sucrose, but growth will also occur, for example, on **Schenk and Hildebrandt (1972)** (Krul, 1993), **Lin and Staba (1961)** (Halperin, 1964), or on **White (1954)** medium (Sung *et al.*, 1988). The organic components of **MS** medium are occasionally modified.

Callus is usually induced to form by the addition of 0.1–10 mg/l 2,4–D plus a cytokinin, such as 0.1–2 mg/l BAP, 0.2 mg/l kinetin, 2 mg/l adenine, or 10% coconut milk. Callus can be subcultured on the same medium (usually supplemented with 0.1–1 mg/l 2,4–D plus 0.1 mg/l BAP) or used to intitate a suspension culture.

For many purposes, plant propagation is best effected through somatic embryogenesis which is the most common form of morphogenesis in carrot tissue cultures. Somatic embryos are formed when callus or suspension cultured cells are transferred to medium in which there is no auxin. Smith and Street (1974) and Sengupta and Raghavan (1980a) used the following procedure:

Species name	Type of Culture	Source of explant	Results		References
Asparagus officinalis	Protoplast	Suspn. ex sdlg. shoot tissue callus	Culture in buoyant membrane. Plant regeneration	—	Kong & Chin (1988)
Asparagus officinalis [male & female lines]	Protoplast	Callus from spear sections	Callus & shoot regeneration. Plants	—	Sink et al. (1990)
Asparagus officinalis cv. 'Limburgin Nunhems'	Shoot	*In vitro* plantlets	Aerial plantlets with rhizome buds	YY	Aynsley & Marson (1975)
Asparagus officinalis cv. 'Limburgin Nunhems'	Shoot	Axillary buds from shoot tips	Rooted plantlets (lacking rhizome buds)	Y	Aynsley & Marson (1975)
Asparagus officinalis [male clone MD 22-8]	Shoot	Shoot tips	Shoot multiplication. Rooting improved	YY	Cheetham et al. (1992)
Asparagus officinalis	Shoot	Single nodes	Shoot growth. Shoots all rooted.	Y	Chin (1982)
Asparagus officinalis cv. 'Viking KB3'	Shoot	Virus-infected shoot tips	Studied effect of virus on rooting & survival	—	De Vries-Paterson et al (1992)
Asparagus officinalis	Shoot	Stem sections (minus cladodes)	One or more shoots with roots	Y	Doré (1975)
Asparagus officinalis	Shoot	Shoot tips	Axillary shoots. Rooted plants	Y	Greiner (1974)
Asparagus officinalis	Shoot	Shoot tips	Single shoot. (First ever shoot tip culture?)	Y	Loo (1945 ; 1946)
Asparagus officinalis	Shoot	Shoot meristems	Rooted shoots	Y	Tendille & Lecerf (1974)
Asparagus officinalis	Shoot	Basal lateral buds from spears	Axillary shoot growth. Rooted plants	YY	Yang & Clore (1973 ; 1974 a,b)
Asparagus officinalis	Shoot	Lateral buds (1-bud segments later)	Shoot growth. Multiple shoots: rooted	YY	Yang (1977)
Asparagus officinalis	Shoot (meristem)	Shoot tips (1–3 leaf primordia)	Virus-free plantlets	Y	Yang & Clore (1976)
Asparagus officinalis	Shoot (meristem)	Stem tips & apical meristems	Virus-free shoots grown and rooted	Y	Yang (1978)
Asparagus officinalis [2 selections]	Single node	Nodal sections of branched shoots	Shoots. Rooting enhanced with ancymidol & sucrose	Y	Desjardins et al. (1987)
Asparagus officinalis M.S.U. male 88-10	Suspension	Stem-derived callus	Somatic embryos. Plantlets	—	Levi & Sink (1992)
Asparagus officinalis	Suspension	Callus ex shoots & buds, rooted *i.v.*	Embryogenesis. Plantlets obtained	—	Levi et al. (1986)
Malvaceae					
Abelmoschus [interspecific hybrids]	Ovule/embryo	Ovules and immature embryos	Seedlings obtained	Y	Gadwal et al. (1968)
Abelmoschus esculentus (L.) Moench. cv. 'Green Velvet' (Okra)	Callus	Cotyledon, hypocotyl	Embryogenesis. Pro-embryos only	—	Reynolds et al. (1981a,b)
Abelmoschus esculentus cv. 'Parkins Mammoth Longpod'	Direct	Seedling cotyl. or cotyledon. node	Adventitious shoots; rooted plants	Y	Mangat & Roy (1986)
Abelmoschus esculentus	Embryo	27 day-old zygotic embryos	Rapid seedling growth	Y	Patil (1966)
Abelmoschus esculentus var. 'Pusa sawani'	Ovule	Ovules	Embryo growth	—	Bajaj (1965)
Abelmoschus tuberculatus hybrid	Embryo	Immature embryos	Embryo growth to seedlings	Y	Gadwal et al. (1968)
Polygonaceae					
Rheum × cultorum Thors. & Reis. = *R. rhaponticum*	Meristem	Meristem tips	Virus-free plantlets	Y	Walkey (1968)
Rheum × cultorum (Rhubarb)	Shoot	Dormant bud tip (0.2–0.5 mm)	Axillary shoot proliferation. 96% rooting	YY	Roggemans & Claes (1979)
Rheum × cultorum	Shoot	Shoot tips	Multiple shoots. Shoots rooted	YY	Walkey & Matthews (1979)
Smilacaceae — See Medicinal Plants Table					
Solanaceae					
* *Capsicum annuum* L. cv. 'Mathania' (Sweet pepper)	Direct	Various	Multiple shoots, best from cotyledon explants. Rooted	YY	Agrawal et al. (1989)
* *Capsicum annuum* L. cv. 'T. Hatvani'	Direct	Apical section of sdlg. hypocotyl	Shoot formation. Plantlets	Y	Fari & Czako (1981)
Capsicum annuum	Direct	Cotyledon nodal sections	Adventitious buds. Shoot rooted	Y	Phillips & Hubstenberger (1984 ; 85)
Capsicum annuum G4	Direct	Cotyl. & hypocot. ex seed embryos	Adventitious shoots. Plants	—	Subhash et al. (1986)
Capsicum annuum G4	Direct	Roots regenerated from embryos	Adventitious shoots. Plants	—	Subhash et al. (1986)
Capsicum annuum cvs. 'Pimento', 'California Wonder'	Direct/Callus	Seedling cotyledons, hypocotyls	Plantlets regenerated	—	Gunay & Rao (1978)
Capsicum annuum var. 'Dulce Italiano'	Protoplast	Leaves from axenic shoot cults.	Plant regeneration	—	Diaz et al. (1988)

	Species name	Type of Culture	Source of explant	Results		References
	Capsicum annuum cv. 'Californian Wonder'	Protoplast	In vitro shoot tips	Shoot, and then plantlet, regeneration	—	Saxena et al. (1981)
	Capsicum sp.	Shoot	Shoot tips	Shoot formation followed by rooting	Y	Sultanbawa & Phatak (1991)
	Lycopersicon cheesmanii	Direct/Callus	Leaf fragments with some midrib	Adventitious shoots, plantlets	—	Maraffa & Lineberger (1980)
	Lycopersicon chmielewskii	Callus	Leaf sections	Adventitious shoots	—	Kut & Evans (1982)
*	Lycopersicon esculentum Mill. (Tomato)	Callus	Leaf sections	Adventitious shoots	—	Behki & Lesley (1980)
	Lycopersicon esculentum [4 cvs.]	Callus	Seedling stem internode	Adventitious shoots. Rooted plants	—	De Langhe & De Bruijne (1976)
	Lycopersicon esculentum [3 land races, 1 cv.]	Callus	Sdling. cotyl, shoot apex, hypocot.	Shoot regeneration	—	Garcia-Reina & Luque (1988)
	Lycopersicon esculentum	Callus	Seedling hypocotyls & cotyledons	Adventitious shoots, rooted in vitro	—	Gunay & Rao (1980)
	Lycopersicon esculentum	Callus	Leaf fragments	Adventitious shoots, proliferated in vitro	—	Herman & Haas (1978)
	Lycopersicon esculentum	Callus	Leaf discs	Adventitious shoots, rooted in vitro	—	Kartha et al. (1976)
	Lycopersicon esculentum var. 'Porphyre'	Callus	Hypocotyl segments	Shoots on callus at cut ends of explants	—	Ohki et al. (1978)
	Lycopersicon esculentum	Callus	Young leaves	Adventitious shoots grown and elongated	—	Padmanabhan et al. (1974)
	Lycopersicon esculentum	Callus	Leaf sections	Adventitious shoots	—	Tal et al. (1977)
	Lycopersicon esculentum hybrid	Callus	Embryo	Adventitious shoots, rooted in vitro	—	Thomas & Pratt (1981) &
	Lycopersicon esculentum	Callus/Direct	Stem sections	Direct and indirect adv. shoots, rooed in vermiculite	—	Cassells (1979)
	Lycopersicon esculentum	Direct	Seedling cotyledons	Adventitious shoots, rooted in vitro	Y	Ammati et al. (1984)
	Lycopersicon esculentum cv. 'Alice'	Direct	Cotyledon segs. ex germin. seeds	Shoot regeneration — auxin dependent	Y	Branca et al. (1990)
	Lycopersicon esculentum [11 cvs.]	Direct	Pedicel and peduncle tissue	Multiple shoot formation	Y	Compton & Veilleux (1991)
	Lycopersicon esculentum	Direct	Decapitated seedlings	Adventitious shoots without PGR tmt.	—	Fari et al. (1991)
	Lycopersicon esculentum flammatum Lehm.	Direct	Cotyledons of 14 d.-old seedlings	Adv. shoots (usually rooted spontaneously). Plants	Y	Koblitz & Koblitz (1983)
	Lycopersicon esculentum [chloronerva mutant]	Direct	Cotyledons of 14 d.-old seedlings	Adv. shoots. Some spontaneous rooting. Plants	Y	Koblitz & Koblitz (1983)
	Lycopersicon esculentum	Direct	Discs cut from seedling leaves	Adventitious shoots	—	Pence & Caruso (1984)
	Lycopersicon esculentum cv. 'Tropic'	Direct or via callus?	Leaf segments	Adventitious shoot regeneration	—	Read et al. (1983).
	Lycopersicon esculentum [susceptible, line GCRI-26]	Direct/Callus	Leaf discs (4 week-old plant)	Adventitious shoots. Virus resistant plants selected	—	Barden et al. (1986)
	Lycopersicon esculentum	Direct/Callus	Seedling hypocotyls	Adventitious shoots	—	Bigot et al. (1977)
	Lycopersicon esculentum 'Alice'	Direct/Callus	Seedling cotyledon segs.	Shoot, root &/or callus form. auxin-dependent	—	Branca et al. (1991)
	Lycopersicon esculentum [5 cvs.]	Direct/Callus	Cotyledons	Adventitious shoots (mainly via callus)	—	Lipucci di Paola et al. (1983)
	Lycopersicon esculentum Commune, pyriforme	Direct/Callus	Leaf segments with part of midvein	Flower formation & regenerated shoots	—	Liu et al. (1989)
	Lycopersicon esculentum cv. 'Vendor'	Embryo	Immature zygotic embryos	Germination and seedling growth	Y	Neal & Topoleski (1983)
	Lycopersicon esculentum hybrid	Embryo	Immature seed embryos	Plantlets obtained	—	Smith (1944)
	Lycopersicon esculentum cv. 'Ohio'	Embryogenic callus	Immature embryo	Embryogenic suspension cultures	—	Uddin & Berry (1988)
	Lycopersicon esculentum	Meristem	Shoot meristem tips	Virus free plantlets	—	Kartha et al. (1977)
	Lycopersicon esculentum hybrid	Organ	Unfertilised flowers	Parthenocarpic fruit development	—	Asahira & Hosoki (1977)
	Lycopersicon esculentum	Organ	Fertilised ovaries	Fruits grown and ripened	—	Nitsch (1949 : 1951)
	Lycopersicon esculentum	Ovary	Ovary 4–10 days post anthesis	Viable seeds	—	Uralets (1980)
	Lycopersicon esculentum [chloronerva mutant]	Protoplast	Leaf mesophyll	Plants regenerated (shoots eventually grafted)	—	Koblitz & Koblitz (1983)
	Lycopersicon esculentum	Protoplast	Leaves of 4 week-old plants	Cell colonies, adventitious shoots. Shoots rooted i.v.	—	Niedz et al. (1985)
	Lycopersicon esculentum	Protoplast	Seedling leaf pieces	Callus formation. Adventitious shoots, rooted in vitro	—	Shahin (1985)

Species name	Type of Culture	Source of explant	Results		References
Lycopersicon esculentum	Protoplast	Young leaves	Callus colonies. Adventitious shoots	—	Zapata et al. (1977 ; 1981)
Lycopersicon esculentum	Root	Excised root tips	Isolated root culture	—	Boll & Street (1951)
Lycopersicon esculentum	Root	Root tips	Isolated root culture	—	Bonner & Devirian (1939)
Lycopersicon esculentum	Root	Root tips	Isolated root culture	—	Bonner (1940 b; 1943)
Lycopersicon esculentum	Root	Root tips	Isolated root culture	—	Butcher & Ingram (1976)
Lycopersicon esculentum	Root	Excised roots	Isolated root culture	—	Chin et al. (1981)
Lycopersicon esculentum	Root	Root tips	Isolated root culture	—	Dodds & Roberts (1982)
Lycopersicon esculentum	Root	Root tips (10 mm)	Isolated root culture	—	Neales (1964)
Lycopersicon esculentum	Root	Root tips	Isolated root culture	—	Robbins & Schmidt (1939)
Lycopersicon esculentum	Root	Seedling root tips	Continued root culture during 11 years (237 passages)	—	Robbins (1940 ; 1942 ; 1946)
Lycopersicon esculentum	Root	Primary root tip	Isolated root culture	—	Said & Murashige (1979)
Lycopersicon esculentum	Root	Root tips	Isolated root cultures	—	Sheat et al. (1959)
Lycopersicon esculentum	Root	Root tips	Isolated root culture	—	Street & McGregor (1952)
Lycopersicon esculentum	Root	Root tips (10 mm)	Isolated roots grown and subcultured	—	White (1934 a; 1937 a,b,c; 1938b)
Lycopersicon esculentum	Root	Root tips	Isolated root culture	—	White (1939 b; 1940 b; 1943a)
Lycopersicon esculentum [F2 selection]	Shoot	Nodal sections	Shoots multiplied/rooted	YY	Ohki et al. (1988)
Lycopersicon esculentum	Shoot	Shoot tips	Axillary shoot proliferation	Y	Schnapp & Preece (1986)
Lycopersicon esculentum 'Red Alert'	Thin cell layers	Pedicel & peduncle	Roots, shoots & denovo inflorescences	Y	Compton & Veilleux (1988)
Lycopersicon esculentum [8 commercial cvs.]	Transf. (Agrobacterium)	Leaf discs	Primary callus. Adventitious shoots. Plants	—	McCormick et al. (1986)
Lycopersicon esculentum × L. peruvianum	Callus	Glyphosate-resistant callus	Abnormal shoots regenerated	—	Smith et al. (1986)
Lycopersicon esculentum × L. peruvianum	Embryo	Immature embryos	Seedling plants	Y	Choudhury (1955 a,b,c)
Lycopersicon glandifolium	Callus	Leaf sections	Adventitious shoots	—	Kut & Evans (1982)
Lycopersicon hirsutum	Callus	Leaf sections	Adventitious shoots	—	Kut & Evans (1982)
Lycopersicon hirsutum LA/353, LA/223	Shoot/Single node	Shoot tips of axenic seedlings	Shoot growth. Subculture of single node pieces	Y	Turner et al. (1987)
Lycopersicon bycopersicoides	Callus	Leaf sections	Adventitious shoots	—	Kut & Evans (1982)
Lycopersicon parviflorum	Callus	Leaf sections	Adventitious shoots	—	Kut & Evans (1982)
Lycopersicon pennellii	Callus	Leaf sections	Adventitious shoots	—	Kut & Evans (1982)
Lycopersicon peruvianum (L.) Mill. (Wild tomato)	Callus	Stripped stem internode	Globular calli, adventitious shoots, rooted in vitro	—	Ancora & Sree Ramulu (1981)
Lycopersicon peruvianum	Callus	Seedling stem internode	Adventitious shoots. Rooted plants	—	De Langhe & De Bruijne (1976)
Lycopersicon peruvianum	Callus	Leaf segments	Adventitious shoots	—	Tal et al. (1977)
Lycopersicon peruvianum	Direct	Stem internode	Adventitious shoots, rooted in vitro	Y	Sree Ramulu et al. (1976a)
Lycopersicon peruvianum	Direct	Immature zygotic embryos	Multiple shoot formation	Y	Williams & Maheswaran (1985)
Lycopersicon peruvianum	Direct/Callus	Leaf fragments with some midrib	Adventitious shoots	—	Maraffa & Lineberger (1980)
Lycopersicon peruvianum	Protoplast	Leaves ex shoot cultures	Fused with L. pennelli ppsts. Cybrid plants	—	Adams & Quiros (1985)
Lycopersicon peruvianum	Protoplast	Leaf mesophyll	Plants regenerated	—	Adams & Townsend (1983)
Lycopersicon peruvianum × L. pennelii	Protoplast	Leaf mesophyll	Predominantly tetraploid plants regenerated	—	O'Connell et al. (1986)
Lycopersicon peruvianum	Shoot cultures	Shoot tips	Shoot growth	Y	Adams & Townsend (1983)

Species name	Type of Culture	Source of explant	Results		References
Lycopersicon peruvianum [3 lines]	Shoot/Single node	Shoot tips of axenic seedlings	Shoot growth. Subculture of single node pieces	Y	Turner *et al.* (1987)
Lycopersicon pimpinellifolium (Jusl.) Mill. (Currant tomato)	Callus	Leaf sections	Adventitious shoots	–	Kut & Evans (1982)
Lycopersicon pimpinellifolium LA722	Shoot/Single node	Shoot tips of axenic seedlings	Shoot growth. Subculture of single node pieces	Y	Turner *et al.* (1987)
Solanum melongena L. (Eggplant)	Callus	Leaf pieces	Shoot organogenesis. Shoots rooted	–	Gleddie *et al.* (1982)
Solanum melongena F₁ hybrid	Callus	Leaf segments	Adventitious shoots. Rooted plants	–	Macchia *et al.* (1983)
Solanum melongena	Callus	Hypocotyl pieces	Shoot, root, or embryoid formation	–	Matsuoka & Hinata (1979)
Solanum melongena	Callus	Seed embryos	Embryogenesis after 18 months. Plantlets from embryos.	–	Yamada *et al.* (1967)
Solanum melongena	Callus	Seed embryos	Shoot buds via embryogenesis	–	Yamada *et al.* (1967)
Solanum melongena	Callus/Suspension	Callus derived from leaf pieces	Embryoid formation. Plantlets from germinated embryoids	–	Gleddie *et al.* (1982)
Solanum melongena	Direct	Decapitated seedlings	Adventitious shoots without PGR tmt.	–	Fari *et al.* (1991)
Solanum melongena cv. 'Imperial Black Beauty'	Direct	Cotyledons	Embryogenesis	–	Fobert & Webb (1988)
Solanum melongena	Direct	Isolated root cultures	Adventitious shoots	Y	Zelcer *et al.* (1983)
Solanum melongena cv. 'Pusa Kranti'	Direct/Callus	Seedling leaf pieces	Multiple shoots, rooted	–	Mukherjee *et al.* (1991)
Solanum melongena L. × *S. khasianum* C.B.Clark	Embryo	Immature embryos	Hybrid plants	–	Sharma *et al.* (1980)
Solanum melongena	Embryogenic callus	Seed embryos	Plantlets from germinated somatic embryos.	–	Yamada *et al.* (1967)
Solanum melongena cv. 'Pusa Kranti'	Node	Axillary buds + 10–15mm stem, ex infected plants	Infected axillary shoot proliferation. Rooted	Y	Raj Bhansali & Ramawat (1993)
Solanum melongena cv. 'Dourga'	Protoplast	Seedling lamina, stem, petioles	Callus. Embryo-like structures. Some plantlets	–	Sihachakr & Ducreux (1987)
Solanum melongena F₁ hybrid	Shoot	Axillary buds	Single shoots with basal callus. Rooted	–	Macchia *et al.* (1983)
Solanum melongena	Suspension	Callus derived from stem pith (5 × 10 mm)	Shoot regeneration. Rooted to give tetraploid plants	–	Fassuliotis *et al.* (1981)
Umbelliferae					
Apium graveolens var. *dulce* (Mill.) Pers. (Celery)	Callus	Petiole (*Agrobacterium*-transformed)	Shoot regeneration	–	Catlin *et al.* (1988)
Apium graveolens L.	Callus	3–5 cm sections of young petioles	Sporadic shoots; embryogenesis & normal plantlets	–	Chen (1976)
Apium graveolens cv. 'Utah Improved 15'	Callus	Leaf blade explants	Embryogenesis	–	Kim & Janick (1989c)
Apium graveolens cv. 'Utah Improved 15'	Callus	Leaf sects. of plants at 4 leaf stage	Embryogenesis. Embryos germinated	–	Kim & Janick (1990)
Apium graveolens [hybrid with marker loci]	Callus	Immature petiole segments	Embryogenesis. Some genetically abnormal plants	–	Orton (1985)
Apium graveolens cv. SB12	Callus	Leaf	Somatic embryo production. Plant regeneration	–	Saranga & Janick (1991)
Apium graveolens 'Utah improved 15' 'G. Pascal'	Callus/Suspension	Seedling leaf pieces	Somatic embryos. Desiccation tolerance studied	–	Kim & Janick (1991)
Apium graveolens	Callus/Suspension	Axillary buds (& callus from same)	Plantlets from somatic embryos	–	Rappaport *et al.* (1980)
Apium graveolens	Callus/Suspension	Petioles	Embryogenic callus. Embryo germination, plantlets	–	Williams & Collin (1976)&
Apium graveolens	Direct	Petiole sections	Embryoids from cortical cells. Plantlets	Y	Zee & Wu (1979)
Apium graveolens	Root	Root tips	Isolated root culture	–	White (1938a)
Apium graveolens	Suspension	Petiole callus	Embryogenesis. Embryo germination, plantlets	–	Al-Abta & Collin (1978)
Apium graveolens var. *rapaceum* (Mill.) Gaudich. [2 lines]	Suspension	Callus ex petioles of young plants	Plants with aneuploid cells	–	Browers & Orton (1982)
Apium graveolens SB12	Suspension	Petiole & leaf callus	Plantlets recovered from embryogenic suspensions	–	Nadel *et al.* (1989)
Apium graveolens	Suspension	Petiole-derived callus from regenerated plants	Increased efficiency of somatic embryogenesis	–	Nadel *et al.* (1990)
Apium graveolens line 1026-2	Suspension	Leaf-derived callus	Embryogenesis. Embryos used in synthetic seeds	–	Onishi *et al.* (1992)
Daucus carota L. cv. 'Kinkoh-yonsun' (Carrot)	Callus	Not given	Shoot & root formation		Fukuda & Kurata (1992)

Species name	Type of Culture	Source of explant	Results		References
Daucus carota var. 'Chantenay red'	Callus	Hypocotyls	Embryoids. Electric potentials measured	—	Goldsworthy & Lago (1992)
Daucus carota	Callus	Root phloem	Embryogenesis	—	Halperin & Wetherell (1965)
Daucus carota	Callus	Petiole segments	Embryogenesis. Embryoid formation	—	Halperin (1964 ; 1966)
Daucus carota [9 cvs.]	Callus	Cells ex cold-treated roots	Somatic embryogen. enhanced by cold pretreatment	—	Krul (1993)
Daucus carota	Callus	Unknown	Embryogenesis. Embryoid germination, plantlets	—	Reinert (1963)
Daucus carota	Callus	Petioles	Embryogenesis	—	Sung *et al.* (1988)
Daucus carota cv. US-Harumakigosun	Callus/Suspension	Seedling hypocotyl sections	Embryogenesis. Studied effect of N source	—	Kamada & Harada (1979b)
Daucus carota	Callus/Suspension	Root segments	Embryogenesis	—	Smith & Street (1974)
Daucus carota	Cell	Single susp. cells (microinjected)	Somatic embryos from 50% cells	—	Nomura & Komamine (1986)
Daucus carota	Direct	Stem sections	Adventitious shoots. Rooted plants	—	Smith & Murashige (1970)
Daucus carota	Embryo	Mature & immature embryos	Embryo growth	Y	Zenkteler *et al.* (1961)
Daucus carota	Meristem	Apical domes ex microprop. plants	Single rooted shoots	Y	Smith & Murashige (1970)
Daucus carota	Protoplast	Suspension cultures	Callus colonies. Embryogenesis, plantlets	—	Dudits *et al.* (1976a)
Daucus carota	Protoplast	Zygotic embryos	Callus and pro-embryos	—	Rubos (1985)
Daucus carota	Suspension	Diploid cell line	Synchronous embryogenesis	—	Bradley *et al.* (1984)
Daucus carota	Suspension	Hypocotyls	Embryos develop ex meristematic cell clusters	—	Coutos-Thevenot *et al.* (1990)
Daucus carota	Suspension	Root phloem callus	Embryogenesis	—	Fridborg *et al.* (1978)
Daucus carota	Suspension	Callus stock cultures	Synchronous embryogenesis	—	Fujimura & Komamine (1975 ; 1979 a,b)
Daucus carota	Suspension	Stem callus	Embryogenesis in low density suspensions	—	Hari (1980)
Daucus carota (Wild Carrot)	Suspension	10 year-old cell line (no embryogenic capacity)	Embryogenesis (4 passage in corn syrup medium)	—	Kinnersley & Henderson (1988)
Daucus carota cv. 'Kinkoh-yonsun'	Suspension	Callus from seedling hypocotyls	Somatic embryogenesis. Germination	—	Liyanage & Kurata (1992)
Daucus carota	Suspension	Stock culture cells	Examined RNA/DNA in embryogenic cultures	—	Masuda *et al.* (1984)
Daucus carota	Suspension	Hypocotyl callus	Highly embryogenic cell clumps (ex 1 cell or many)	—	Nomura & Komamine (1985 ; 1986)
Daucus carota	Suspension	Hypocotyl callus	Embryogenesis	—	Nomura *et al.* (1982)
Daucus carota	Suspension	Seedling hypocotyl callus	Embryogenesis	—	Nuti Ronchi *et al.* (1984)
Daucus carota cv. 'Royal Chantenay'	Suspension	Callus from seedling hypocotyls	Torpedo embryos purified & concentrated by filter	—	Rodriguez *et al.* (1990)
Daucus carota var. 'Chantenay'	Suspension	Hypocotyls	Embryogen. Studied effects of Ni & Co.	—	Roustan *et al.* (1989)
Daucus carota cv. 'T-gou sangun'	Suspension	Seedling hypocotyl-derived callus	Embryogenesis. Plantlet regeneration	—	Tsuji *et al.* (1992)
Daucus carota	Suspension	Long-term (12 y) callus ex petioles	High rate of embryogenesis	—	Wetherell & Dougall (1976)
Daucus carota	Suspension	Cells ex hypocotyl callus	High level of embryogenesis	—	Wetherell (1984)
Daucus carota	Suuspension	Root phloem tissue	Embryogenesis. Embryoid germination	—	Jones (1974 a,b)
Daucus carota + *D. carota* (CMS) X-irradiated	Protoplast fusion	Suspension cultures	Cybrid male sterile plants	—	Ichikawa *et al.* (1988)
Daucus carota ssp. *sativus*	Direct	Mericarp 'seed' coat	Embryogenesis. Secondary embryogenesis on embryos	—	Smith & Krikorian (1988)
Oenanthe javanica DC. (Mal.) (Chinese celery)	Callus	Leaf segments	Embryogenesis. Plantlets	—	Zee & Wu (1980)
Oenanthe javanica	Callus/Direct	Petiole sections	Embryoids from cortical cells. Plantlets	Y	Zee & Wu (1979)

PLANTS GROWN FOR THEIR SECONDARY (MEDICINAL) PRODUCTS

Plants contain a very wide variety of chemicals that are not directly concerned with primary metabolic processes. These compounds are usually termed secondary metabolites or *secondary products*. Those of a particular chemical class are often characteristic of certain genera or families of plants. The function of secondary products within plants is not always clear. Some are known to:

- have regulatory roles in growth and development;

- provide protection to the plant against attack of fungi or bacteria;

- make the plant unpalatable to browsing animals;

- act as insect repellents or insecticides.

Bell (1980) suggested that millions of secondary products have been produced by plants during the course of evolution, and that when a particular compound has conveyed some selective advantage to the plant, the chances of the plant (and the product) surviving will have been increased. Similarly, once derived as a consequence of a metabolic process, a secondary product may persist from generation to generation if it conveys no disadvantage to reproduction or multiplication.

Practical uses for secondary products

Some secondary products are highly priced commodities and of considerable economic value. When extracted from plants they are used as food additives and flavourings, vitamins, food flavourings, insecticides, cosmetic and perfumery ingredients, essences, or other fine chemicals. In addition, a wide variety of compounds of potential medicinal value is found within the plant kingdom, and plants and plant extracts have featured prominently in traditional cures. Approximately half the drugs in current use throughout the world, still originate from plants. Species from which medicinal products can be derived, that have been used in micropropagation experiments, are listed in Table 256. Many of these plants will also have been the subject of extensive experimentation aimed at trying to produce and extract active medicinal principles from cultures, rather than from the intact plant.

In vitro **production**

Although for many years there has been interest in extracting chemicals from tissue cultured plant cells, several difficulties have become apparent:

- Many secondary products are only found in differentiated tissues and are not produced by callus or cell suspensions.

Where products do occur in undifferentiated cells:

- they are usually not produced in significant quantity during periods when the culture is actively growing;

- they often occur in relatively low concentrations;

- they are usually stored intracellularly, and only low concentrations are excreted into the medium;

- unorganised plant cells are very liable to display somaclonal variation, so that the maintenance of high yielding cell lines may require continuous selection (Luckner and Diettrich, 1990);

- industrial production can be hampered because the large scale culture of plants cells in suspension is difficult.

Nevertheless a few compounds have been produced on a commercial scale from undifferentiated cells, notably shikonin (from *Lithospermum erythrorhizon*), berberine (from *Coptis japonica*) and sanguinarine (from *Papaver*).

Possible methods of production

Various strategies have been devised to increase the yield of valuable chemicals.

Immobilized cells. Instead of being grown in suspension cultures, cells can be entrapped, or *immobilised*, within a matrix, or upon an inert supporting material. This can have a number of advantages. Cells are protected from the shearing forces normally found in bioreactors and can be grown in high densities. Usually, immobilised cells are able to synthesize chemicals over longer periods than in suspensions so that continuous, rather than batch, production become a possiblity. Immobilisation laso keeps cells away from the interface of the medium with air, where coagulation, frothing and sometimes chemical deactivation can occur.

Stimulating chemical production. The relatively low yield of many secondary products from undifferentiated plant tissues has prevented tissue cultures being used for commercial extraction. Product yield may be increased by feeding cells with a precursor of a series of biosynthetic reactions. Thus feeding putrescine to root cultures of *Nicotiana rustica*, increases their production of nicotine (Hamill *et al.*, 1990). However the compound supplied must usually be a fairly immediate precursor of the requisite final product, otherwise it will tend to be utilised in alternative synthetic pathways (Yeoman *et al.*, 1980).

Certain chemicals called *elicitors*, normally produced by fungi, are known to stimulate the production of secondary metabolites in plant cell walls, thereby helping to protect the plant against attack by a pathogen. The same compounds added to cell cultures can increase the production of some secondary products, although unfortunately the effect is usually only transitory.

The low yield of some secondary products may be due to feed–back inhibition of the enzymes responsible for synthesis. In these cases there is some hope that genetic engineering may enable less sensitive enzymes to be substituted.

Bio–conversion. A vast range of enzymes is produced within the plant kingdom so that cell cultures can often be employed to carry out reactions which are difficult or impossible synthetically. Cultures fed with chemicals can often 'bio–transform' or *bio–convert* them into more valuable products which are then of use as pharmaceuticals or fine chemicals (Pras, 1990). A large number of bioconversions which have been achieved by feeding plant cultures with essential oil precursors are listed by Mulder–Krieger *et al.* (1988). The β–hydroxylation of digitoxin by *Digitalis lanata* is probably the most well known bioconversion as it has been used to obtain a commercially valuable product (Kreis and Reinhard, 1986; 1989).

Semi–synthetic production. It may be possible to obtain a chemical precursor of a required fine chemical from tissue cultures and complete its preparation by a chemical procedure. An excellent example of this approach has been provided by Fujita *et al.* (1990) who succeeded in preparing vinblastine from catharanthine, obtained from cell suspension cultures of *Catharanthus roseus* (Smith *et al.*, 1987). Catharanthine was combined with vindoline, extracted from whole plants, in a chemical reaction catalysed by Fe^{3+}.

The culture of differentiated organs. Another approach to increased yields, is to culture roots or shoots which are able to produce compounds not found in undifferentiated cells, or are capable of synthesizing greater quantities. Root cultures have been found to be highly suitable for the production of certain chemicals, but are slow growing. Root cultures of plants transformed by *Agrobacterium rhizogenes* (causing hairy root disease, see page 694) grow more rapidly than normal root cultures and offer new prospects for producing compounds *in vitro*, because genes responsible for biosynthesis can be introduced into the plant (along with the *Agrobacterium* t–DNA) in a reconstructed plasmid. Special techniques may be required to grow root cultures on a large

scale. Roots have been anchored in a large vessel filled with liquid medium, aerated by a sparger at the base (Yamada and Hashimota, 1990); or grown in vessels in which the medium was supplied by sprays or droplets (Wilson *et al.*, 1990).

Although certain secondary products are formed preferentially in stems or leaves, the large scale culture of shoots *in vitro* is difficult because they cannot be grown submerged in liquid medium. However, they too could be grown in a nutrient mist (see Chapter 16). The use of tissues transformed by *Agrobacterium tumefasciens* has been suggested by Spencer *et al.* (1990). These can give rise to teratomatous shoots *in vitro* which are capable of synthesizing the same compounds as would normally be produced in leaf tissue.

Zeldin *et al.* (1988) devised a novel system for recovering essential oils by passing humidified air over shoot cultures. Volatiles from fennel, mint and basil were collected on a column and subsequently eluted.

Reviews

There is a large and specialised literature on the formation of secondary products by cultured plant cells and organs, and many review articles and conference proceedings have been published. For information covering some of the recent developments in the science, readers might consult the books edited by Fiechter (1986), Charlwood and Rhodes (1990) and Nijkamp *et al.* (1990).

MICROPROPAGATION

While investigations continue on the production of plant metabolites in bioreactors, tissue culture can also be used to multiply some species which give rise to these compounds. Micropropagation can provide plants to be field–planted for later chemical extraction, and/or plants for use in trials aimed at selecting varieties with improved yields. Medicinal plants have not usually been the subject of conventional breeding programmes, but even in their absence, much improvement could often be made by using the variation:

- occurring naturally between plants within the species. Varieties with high natural levels of secondary product, could be propagated preferentially;

- induced in tissue cultures by mutagenic treatments;

- found between somaclones regenerated from callus cultures.

Abour–Mandour *et al.* (1979) found that some *Catharanthus roseus* plants regenerated from callus, contained twice as much of the alkaloids serpentine and raubasine, as the mother plants.

Dioscoreaceae
Dioscorea **spp.**   (Yams)

The annual world demand for steroid–based drugs has risen dramatically through the prescription of oral contraceptives. A common precursor for drug synthesis is the steroid diosgenin, which is extracted from *Dioscorea* tubers. Although some yams (e.g. *Dioscorea alata* and *D. bulbifera*) have always been grown as vegetables, large scale cultivation has not been common, and to satisfy the demands of drug companies, wild plants have been collected for steroid extraction, resulting in their depletion. Chaturvedi and Sinha (1979b) calculated that the Indian diosgenin requirement could be met by cultivating *D. floribunda* on about 2,500 acres. Propagation from seed or by conventional vegetative multiplication would be far too slow to supply the plants which would be necessary for such a planting programme.

Some entries for *Dioscorea* have been included in Table 256. Other reports on the culture of plants in this genus will be found in Table 230, and a description of propagation techniques is given on page 1118.

Compositae
Tanacetum (Chrysanthemum) **spp.**
(Plants grown for the production of pyrethrin).

The insecticidal powder pyrethrum has in the past been prepared from the dried flowers and flower buds of *Tanacetum coccineum* Willd., *T. carneum* Bieb., *T. roseum* and especially *T. cinerariifolium* (Trev.) Schultz–Bip., and the compound pyrethrin has more recently been extracted from *Tanacetum* plants for production of synthetic pyrethroid insecticides. *T. cinerariifolium* plants intended for field cultivation (for pyrethrum extraction) have been produced in Ecuador using shoot culture (Levy, 1981).

Methods for propagating the pyrethrum plant (*Tanacetum cinerariifolium*) by shoot culture were described by Grewal and Sharma (1978) and Wambugu and Rangan

(1981) (Table 256). Axillary shoot proliferation can be obtained by adding 0.2 mg/l BAP to **MS** medium, although Staba *et al.* (1984) describe using the much higher BAP concentration of 20 mg/l for shoot cultures grown for direct pyrethrin extraction. Zieg *et al.* (1983) obtained 340 mg pyrethrin per 100 g of dried tissue harvested from shoot cultures.

As in *Dendranthema* × *grandiflorum* (= *C. morifolium*), direct shoot formation in *T. cinerariifolium* and other *Tanacetum* species, can be obtained from explants such as shoot tips (Grewal and Sharma, 1978), the capitulum (Roest and Bokelmann (1973), or achene and petal sections (Fujii and Shimizu, 1990).

Plants producing essential oils

Several oils and essences extracted from plants have uses in industry, as foodstuffs and flavourings, or as components of cosmetics and fragrances (see the very comprehensive review by Mulder–Krieger *et al.*, 1988). For example, the oil from safflower seeds is used in cooking and in the manufacture of pigments for paints and dyes. Lavender and patchouli oils are used in perfumes, soaps and air fresheners, as are the citronella oils produced by the aromatic grasses (*Cymbopogon* spp.), and oils from ornamentals such as rose, geranium and jasmine. Oil of patchouli is distilled from leaves of the shrub *Pogostemon cablin* which seldom flowers and is normally replanted from cuttings after about 2 years growth. *Cymbopogon* is also propagated vegetatively. Tissue culture techniques may therefore have a role in multiplying high yielding selections.

Many oils extracted from plants have medicinal propertied, *e.g.* clove oil (*Eugenia caryophyllus*), cajaput oil (*Melaleuca cajuputi*), eucalyptus oil (*Eucalyptus*), and wintergreen oil (*Betula lenta*). Caster oil is not only used in medicines but in industry as the basal component of lubricants.

Reports on the plants which produce essential oils are distributed in several tables in this book, for example:

Cymbopogon	the grasses table (page 1110);
Lavandula	the woody ornamental table (page 955);
Pogostemon	the table on the following page (1209);
Ricinus	the tropical crops table (page 1169);
Jojoba	the tropical crops table (page 1169).

Table 256. Published reports on the tissue culture of MEDICINAL PLANTS.

Species name	Type of Culture	Source of explant	Results		References
Agavaceae					
❖ Yucca glauca Nutt. ex J.Fraser.	Direct	Rhizome or flower tissue	Shoot initiation	Y	Bentz & Parliman (1985)
Yucca glauca [several genotypes]	Shoot (direct)	Shoot tips	Shoot proliferation (adv. shoots). Rooted plants	Y	Bentz et al. (1988)
Amaranthaceae					
Gomphrena officinalis Mart.	Callus	Leaf & stem sections ex in vitro seedlings	Multiple shoots, rooted	—	Mercier et al. (1992)
Gomphrena officinalis	Node	Stem internodes ex in vitro seedlings	Multiple shoots, rooted	YY	Mercier et al. (1992)
Apocynaceae					
Mandevilla velutina Mart. ex Stadelm R.E.	Callus	Young leaf & stem. Root sections	Many adventitious shoots. Rooted plants	—	Handro et al. (1988)
Rauvolfia serpentina (L.) Kurze.	Callus	Stem tissue	Adventitious shoots. Diploid plants in the field	—	Akram et al. (1986)
Rauvolfia serpentina	Callus	Leaf segments	Embryogenesis, roots & shoots. Entire plants	—	Mitra & Chaturvedi (1970)
Rauvolfia serpentina	Direct	Stem pieces	Stems rooted	Y	Mitra & Kaul (1964)
Rauvolfia serpentina	Shoot	Axillary meristem (field plants)	Multiple shoots	Y	Roja et al. (1985)
Thevetia peruviana (Pers.) Schum. (Yellow oleander).	Callus	Young leaf discs	Somatic embryogenesis. Plantlets	—	Kumar (1992)
Araceae					
Pinellia ternata (Thunb.) Breitenb.	Direct	Bulbil top halves	Adventitious buds & PLBs. Buds rooted	YY	Tsay et al. (1989)
Araliaceae					
Eleutherococcus senticosus Rupr. & Maxim. = Acanthopanax senticosus (Siberian ginseng)	Direct	Mature zygotic embryos	Somatic embryos. Secondary embryos. Plants	—	Gui et al. (1991)
* Panax ginseng C.A.Mey. (Ginseng)	Callus	Leaf, stem & root tissue	Adventitious shoots, embryogenesis	—	Butenko et al. (1968)
Panax ginseng	Callus	Various	Rhizoids and/or somatic embryos	—	Cellárová et al. (1992)
Panax ginseng	Callus	Pith from mature root	Embryogenesis. Plantlets which flowered in vitro	—	Chang & Hsing (1980)
Panax ginseng	Callus	Root, & cotyledons	Embryoid & shoot formation	—	Choi et al. (1982)
Panax ginseng	Callus	Leaf, stem and root tissue	Adventitious shoots. Rooted plantlets	—	Jhang et al. (1974)
Panax ginseng	Callus	Young flower buds	Somatic embryogenesis. Plantlet regeneration	—	Kishira et al. (1992)
Panax ginseng	Direct	Leaf cuttings	Profuse root regeneration	—	Choi et al. (1982)
Panax ginseng	Direct/Callus	Mature zygotic embryos	Somatic embryos. Plantlets which flowered in vitro	—	Lee et al. (1990)
Panax ginseng	Embryogenic callus	Immature zygotic embryos	Embryos. Direct form. of second. embryos. Plantlets	—	Arya et al. (1993)
Panax ginseng	Embryogenic callus	Young flower buds	Somatic embryos; shoot formation	—	Shoyama et al. (1988)
Panax ginseng	Shoot	Shoots ex somatic embryos	Multiple shoots. Shoots rooted	YY	Shoyama et al. (1988)
Panax quinquefolius L. (American ginseng)	Callus	Root pith	Embryogenesis. Plantlets	—	Wang (1990)
Asclepiadaceae					
Asclepias curassavica L. (Blood flower)	Direct (Callus)	Nodal sections	Adv. shoots. Plants with variable chromosome numbers	—	Pramanik & Datta (1986)
Asclepias tuberosa L. (Pleurisy root)	Suspension	Callus ex zygotic embryos	Embryogenesis and plantlet development	—	Groet & Kidd (1980)

Species name	Type of Culture	Source of explant	Results		References
Cynanchum nigrum (Swallow's wort)	Direct	Unpollinated ovaries	Embryogenesis. Nucellar plantlets	Y	Haccius & Hausner (1976)
Cynanchum vincetoxium	Embryogenic callus	Unpollinated ovaries	Embryogenesis. Embryo germination, plantlets	—	Haccius & Hausner (1976)
Tylophora indica (Burm.f.) Merr. (Antamul)	Callus	Stem internode (5mm)	Embryogenesis. Plantlets from germinated embryoids		Rao & Narayanaswami (1972)
Tylophora indica	Callus	Twining stem segments	Shoot buds; rooted. Embryoids; germinated	—	Rao et al. (1970)
Tylophora indica	Node	Single nodes	Shoot multiplication. Rooted	YY	Sharma & Chandel (1992)
Cannabidaceae					
Cannabis sativa L. (Hemp)	Callus	Leaves	Adventitious shoots	—	Verzar-Petri et al. (1982)
Celastraceae					
Catha edulis (Vahl) Forssk. ex Endl. (Khat)	Shoot	Shoot tips	Shoot proliferation. Rooted plants	YY	Elhag (1991)
Compositae — Asteraceae					
❖ Artemisia annua L. (Sweet wormwood)	Callus	Seedling petioles	No friable calli. Adv. shoots, rooted i.v.	—	Mäthé & Laszloffy (1991)
Artemisia annua	Shoot	Seedling shoot tips	Shoot growth. No multiplication. Rooting i.v.	—	Mäthé & Laszloffy (1991)
Artemisia pallens	Callus	In vitro germinated seedlings	Plantlet regeneration. Terpenoid production studied	—	Benjamin et al. (1990)
Atractylodes lancea (Thunb.) DC.	Shoot	Flower buds	One vegetative shoot/bud (then multiple shoots). Rooted	YY	Hiraoka et al. (1984)
Atractylodes lancea	Shoot	In vitro shoots (Colchicine treated)	Shoots rooted. Tetraploid plants	—	Hiraoka (1986)
Flaveria trinervia (Sprengel) C.Mohr.	Callus	Leaf segments	Adventitious shoots. Rooted	—	Sudarshana & Shanthamma (1991)
Gaillardia pulchella Foug. (Indian blanket)	Callus	Wounded stem & leaf sections	Shoots regenerated. Rooted in soil	—	Bourque et al. (1989)
Geigeria aspera	Callus	Leaf segments (5 cm)	Adventitious shoots. Plants	—	Meyer & Van Staden (1986)
Pentanema indica = Vicoa indica Cass. (Banjauri)	Callus	Leaf & stem segs. ex i.v. shoot cult	Shoot primordia. Shoot development & rooting	—	Thulaseedharan & Valdyanathan (1990)
Saussurea costus (Falc.) Lipsch. = S. lappa (Costus/Kuth)	Callus	Cotyled. leaves/in vitro seedlings	Multiple adventitious shoots, rooted	—	Arora & Bhojwani (1989)
Tanacetum cinerariifolium (Trev.) Schultz-Bip. = Chrysanthemum cinerariaefolium (Pyrethrum)	Direct	Capitulum	Direct shoot formation. Shoots rooted	Y	Roest & Bokelmann (1973)
Tanacetum cinerariifolium	Shoot	Shoot tips (0.5 mm)	Shoot proliferation	Y	Grewal & Sharma (1978)
Tanacetum cinerariifolium	Shoot	Shoot tips	Shoot multiplication. Rooted plants	—	Levy (1981)
Tanacetum cinerariifolium	Shoot	Shoot tips	Shoot proliferation	Y	Staba et al. (1984)
Tanacetum cinerariifolium	Shoot	Shoot tips	Axillary bud proliferation. Shoots rooted	YY	Wambugu & Rangan (1981)
Costaceae — See Zingiberaceae					
Crassulaceae					
Sempervivum tectorum L.	Callus	Leaf & shoot segs. ex 30d-old seedlings	Adv. shoots	—	Dobos et al. (1994)
Dioscoreaceae					
Dioscorea composita Hemsl. (Yam)	Callus	Zygotic embryos	Adventitious shoots and/or roots. Shoots multiplied	—	Viana & Mantell (1989)
Dioscorea composita	Node	Stem nodes	Single rooted plantlet	Y	Ammirato (1982)
Dioscorea deltoidea Wall.	Callus	Seedling hypocotyl	Root and Shoot formation	—	Grewal & Atal (1976)
Dioscorea deltoidea	Callus	Leaf or tuber	Shoot formation, followed by rooting	—	Mascarenhas et al. (1976)
Dioscorea deltoidea	Callus	Tuber pieces	Shoot formation and embryogenesis	—	Singh (1978)
Dioscorea deltoidea	Shoot	Shoot tips from tissue-cult. shoots	Shoot proliferation, followed by rooting	YY	Grewal & Atal (1976)
Dioscorea floribunda Mart. & Gal.	Callus	Seed embryo	Embryoids produced from suspended callus. Regeneration	—	Ammirato (1984)

Species name	Type of Culture	Source of explant	Results		References
Dioscorea floribunda	Callus	Node or internode 6-8mm	Shoot formation and proliferation, followed by rooting	—	Sengupta *et al.* (1984)
Dioscorea floribunda	Direct	Leaves	Shoot formation, followed by rooting	Y	Chaturvedi & Sinha (1979b)
Dioscorea floribunda	Node	Single nodes	Multiple shoot formation, followed by rooting	YY	Chaturvedi & Sinha (1979b)
Dioscorea floribunda	Node	Single node	Plantlet regeneration	Y	Lakshmi-Sita *et al.* (1976)
Dioscorea floribunda	Node	Nodal stem	Multiple shoot formation, followed by rooting	YY	Sengupta *et al.* (1984)
Dioscorea floribunda	Root	Shoot apices	Plantlet formation. Production of multibranched plants	Y	Chaturvedi & Sinha (1979b)
Droseraceae					
❖ *Drosera natalensis* Diels.	Direct	Leaves/leaf segments	Multiple shoots, rooted. Plumbagin content measured	YY	Crouch *et al.* (1990)
Ericaceae					
❖ *Arctostaphylos uva-ursi* (L.) A.Gray. (Bearberry)	Node	Nodes ex greenhouse plants	Shoot proliferation. Rooted	YY	M'Kada *et al.* (1991)
Arctostaphylos uva-ursi	Shoot	Shoot tips	Axillary shoot proliferation	Y	Harris & Mason (1983)
Euphorbiaceae					
❖ *Croton sublyratus* Kurz	Callus	Young leaf segments	Used to study plaunotol accumulation	—	Morimoto & Murai (1989)
❖ *Euphorbia antisyphilitica* Zucc. (Candelilla)	Shoot	Shoot tips ex greenhouse plants	Axillary shoot proliferation. Rooted plants	YY	Jakobek *et al.* (1986)
Gentianaceae					
❖ *Gentiana kurroo* Royle (Indian gentian)	Shoot & Node	Shoot tips, nodes	Multiple shoots, rooted	YY	Sharma *et al.* (1993)
Guttiferae					
Calophyllum inophyllum (Alexandrian laurel)	Shoot	Seedling nodal segments	Axillary shoot proliferation. Rooted plants	YY	Lee & Rao (1982)
Hypoxidaceae					
Hypoxis rooperi S. Moore	Direct	Cambial corm pieces	Adventitious shoots, rooted planlets	Y	Page & Van Staden (1984)
Labiatae					
❖ *Mentha pulegium* L. [BRA 000094] (Pennyroyal)	Shoot	Single node segments	Prolific axillary shoots with roots. Plants	YY	Rech & Pires (1986)
Pogostemon cablin (Blanco.) Benth. (Patchouli)	Direct/Callus	Various, especially petioles	Shoots, direct or via callus. Shoots rooted	Y	Hart *et al.* (1970)
Pogostemon cablin	Shoot	Nodes ex mature plants	Multiple shoots. Plants	Y	Posa *et al.* (1987)
Sideritis angustifolia Lag.	Callus	Seedling hypocotyls	Embryogenic calli. Embryoids, shoots, plantlets	—	Sanchez-Gras & Segura (1988a)
Sideritis angustifolia	Callus	Single cells ex hypocotyl calli	Embryogenesis. Adventitious shoots, rooted plants	—	Sanchez-Gras & Segura (1988b)
Lauraceae					
Sassafras albidium (Nutt.) Nees. (Sassafras)	Shoot	Shoot tips	Multiple shoots	Y	Einsett (1987)
Liliacaea					
Aloe vera (L.) Burm. f. = *A. barbadensis* (Aloe)	Callus	Leaf base explants	Callus & adv. shoots (from few explants). Plants	—	Sanchez *et al.* (1988)
Aloe vera	Meristem	Meristem tips (no leaf primordia)	Multiple shoots. 100% rooting	YY	Natali *et al.* (1990)
Aloe vera	Node and direct	Decapitated shoots	Multiple axil. & adv. shoots. 100% rooting	YY	Meyer & Van Staden (1991)
Aloe vera	Shoot	Shoot apices	Multiple shoots	Y	Sanchez *et al.* (1988)
❖ *Asparagus racemosus* Willd. (Satawar)	Callus/Shoot	Stem discs (4—6 mm)	Shoots regenerated and multiplied. Rooted plants	—	Kar & Sen (1985)
Urginea indica Kunth (Indian squill)	Callus	Scales & basal disc	Bulbous plantlets, some rooted. Unrooted ones rooted	—	Jha *et al.* (1984)
Urginea indica	Callus	Bulb or inflorescence segments	Bulbous plants via organogenesis or embryogenesis	—	Jha *et al.* (1991)

Species name	Type of Culture	Source of explant	Results		References
Limnanthaceae					
Limnanthes alba Hartweg. ex Benth. var *foamore*	Embryogenic callus	Embryos ex immature seeds	Somatic embryogenesis	—	Southworth & Kwiatkowski (1991)
Linaceae					
❖ *Linum flavum* L. (Golden flax)	Callus or Susp.	Callus ex sdlg. leaves, stems, roots	Untransferable plantlets. 5-MPT levels assessed	—	Wichers *et al.* (1990)
Papaveraceae					
Argemone mexicana L. (Mexican poppy)	Ovule/Fertilization	Placenta segments with ovules	Ovules pollinated & fertilized	—	Kanta & Maheshwari (1963)
Papaver bracteatum Lindl.	Callus	Seedlings	Shoot regeneration. Shoots rooted	—	Day *et al.* (1986)
Papaver bracteatum	Callus	Seedling root sections (with tip)	Embryogenesis. Somatic embryos, plants	—	Palta (1986)
Papaver bracteatum	Direct	Seedling root sections	Multiple shoots	—	Palta (1986)
Papaver bracteatum var. *Arya II*	Suspension	Callus from germinated seeds	Embryogenesis	—	Kutchan *et al.* (1983)
Papaver somniferum L. [many genotypes] (Opium poppy)	Callus	Anthers from cold-treated buds	Embryogenesis. Plants, mostly diploid	—	Dieu & Dunwell (1988)
Papaver somniferum	Callus	Seedlings germinated *in vitro*	Adventitious shoots (not rooted)	—	Ilahi & Jabeen (1987)
Papaver somniferum	Callus	Hypocotyl sections	Meristemoid induction, then shoot or root formation	—	Nessler & Mahlberg (1979)
Papaver somniferum	Callus	Aseptic seedlings	Embryogenesis	—	Schuchmann & Wellman (1983)
Papaver somniferum	Callus	Seedling hypocotyls	Embryogenesis. Plants all diploid	—	Wakhlu & Bajwa (1986)
Papaver somniferum "Ikkanshu"	Callus	Seedling hypocotyls	Green buds & shoots (embryogen?) Plants (fl.i.v.)	—	Yoshikawa & Furuya (1983)
Papaver somniferum	Fertilisation/Ovule	Unpollinated ovules	Ovules pollinated. Fertilisation and embryo growth	—	Kanta *et al.* (1962)
Papaver somniferum	Fertilisation/Ovule	Placenta plus ovules	Ovules pollinated & fertilised. Seedlings	—	Kanta & Maheshwari (1963)
Papaver somniferum	Suspension	Callus from seedling hypocotyls	Immobilized cells used to study biotransformations	—	Corchete & Yeoman (1989)
Papaver somniferum	Suspension	Callus from hypocotyl explants	Alkaloid production assessed	—	Songstad *et al.* (1989)
Phytolaccaceae					
Phytolacca dodecandra L'Herit (Pokeweed, endod)	Shoot	Shoot tips or nodes	Shoot multiplication. Rooted *in vitro*	YY	Demeke & Hughes (1990)
Plantaginaceae					
Plantago ovata Forsk. cv. G1-2 Isubgol	Callus	Seedling hypocotyls	Shoot regeneration. Shoots rooted	—	Wakhlu & Barna (1989)
Plantago ovata Isubgol	Shoot	Seedling shoot apices	Multiple axillary shoots. Plants	YY	Barna & Wakhlu (1988)
Podophyllaceae					
Podophyllum hexandrum Royle. (Indian podophyllum)	Suspension	Callus from *in vitro* seedling roots	Studied production of podophyllotoxin	—	Van Uden *et al.* (1989)
Polygonaceae					
Rheum australe D.Don = *R. emodi* (Himalayan rhubarb)	Direct	*In vitro* leaf explants	Multiple shoots, rooted	YY	Lal & Ahuja (1989)
Rheum australe	Shoot	Rhizome shoot tips (0.5—1 cm)	Multiple shoots, rooted	YY	Lal & Ahuja (1989)
Rheum australe	Shoot	Shoots ex in vitro cult.	Shoots multiplied, rooted. Best results in shake cult.	YY	Lal & Ahuja (1993)
Ranunculaceae					
Aconitum heterophyllum Wall. ex Royle.	Callus	Leaf and petiole sects. i.v. cults.	Somatic embryogen. Plantlets	—	Giri *et al.* (1993)
Coptis japonica (Thumb.) Mak.	Callus/Suspension	Flower pedicel	Embryogenesis. Germination of embryoids in susps.	—	Nakagawa *et al.* (1982)
Coptis japonica	Embryogenic callus	Petiole segments (5 mm)	Embryogenesis. Embryoid germination	—	Syono & Furuya (1972)
Coptis teeta Wall.	Callus	Hypocotyl sects. ex germin. seeds	Multiple shoots. Rooted	—	Tandon & Rathore (1992)

Species name	Type of Culture	Source of explant	Results		References
Rubiaceae					
Psychotria ipecacuanha (Brot.) Stokes. = *Cephaelis ipecacuanha* (Ipecac)	Direct	Internode segments ex shoot cults.	Adventitious shoots. Rooted	Y	Yoshimatsu & Shimomura (1991)
Psychotria ipecacuanha	Node	Seedling nodes (0.2—0.4 cm)	Multiple axillary shoots. Shoots rooted	YY	Jha & Jha (1989)
Psychotria ipecacuanha	Shoot	Shoot tips	Shoot proliferation. Rooted	YY	Ideda *et al.* (1988)
❖ *Cinchona officinalis* L. 'Ledgeriana' = *C. calisaya* 'Ledgeriana' = *C. ledgeriana*	Shoot	Shoot tips (15 mm) of seedlings	Shoot growth & axillary shoots	Y	Hunter (1979)
Cinchona officinalis 'Ledgeriana'	Shoot	Seedling shoot tips	Shoot proliferation. Rooted	YY	Koblitz et al. (1983).
Cinchona officinalis 'Ledgeriana'	Node	Nodes ex in vitro seedlings	Alkaloid contents of cultures studied	—	Kilby *et al.* (1992)
Cinchona officinalis 'Ledgeriana'	Shoot	Aseptic seedlings	Shoot growth?	—	Anderson et al. (1982)
Cinchona officinalis 'Ledgeriana'	Shoot	Shoot tips & single nodes	Multiple shoots. Rooted plantlets	YY	Krikorian *et al.* (1982)
Cinchona pubescens Vahl. 'Succirubra' = *C. succirubra* (Red bark quinine)	Shoot	Seedling shoot tips	Shoot proliferation. Rooted	YY	Koblitz *et al.* (1983).
Scrophulariaceae					
Digitalis cariensis	Callus	Hypocotyl	Adventitious shoots and plantlets	—	Tewes *et al.* (1982)
* *Digitalis lanata* Ehrh. (Grecian foxglove)	Callus	Anther filaments	Permanently embryogenic callus	—	Tewes *et al.* (1982)
Digitalis lanata	Callus	Seedlings with cotyledons	Leafy cultures	—	Lui and Staba (1979)
Digitalis lanata	Protoplast	Peeled leaves	Cell colonies. Adventitious shoots and leaves	—	Li (1981)
Digitalis lanata	Shoot	Meristems (0.5—1mm) ex ax. buds	Shoot growth & multiplication. Rooted plants	YY	Schoner & Reinhard (1982)
Digitalis lanata	Shoot	Axillary bud meristems	Multiple axillary shoots. Rooted	YY	Schoner & Reinhard (1986)
Digitalis lanata	Suspension	Stem	Embryoid formation	—	Garve *et al.* (1980)
Digitalis lanata	Suspension/Callus	Stat. phase susp. ex callus	Improved embryogenesis. Plants	—	Kranz (1988)
Digitalis lutea L.	Callus/Suspension	Seedling hypocotyls	Embryogenesis. Plants from globular structures	—	Tewes *et al.* (1982)
Digitalis × mertonensis Buxton & C.Darl.	Callus	Hypocotyls	Adventitious shoots & plantlets	—	Tewes *et al.* (1982)
Digitalis purpurea L. (Common foxglove)	Callus	Flower stalk segments	Shoot formation	—	Dollfus & Nicolas-Prat (1969)
Digitalis purpurea	Callus	Seedlings & leaves	Root and shoot formation	—	Hirotani & Furuya (1977)
Digitalis purpurea	Direct	Leaf segments	Shoot bud formation and proliferation	Y	Rücker *et al.* (1981)
Digitalis purpurea	Direct	Leaf segments	Shoot bud formation	Y	Rücker (1982 a.b)
Digitalis thapsi L.	Callus	Hypocotyl, root & leaf segs. ex 30d seedlings	Multiple shoots &/or roots. Shoots rooted	—	Cacho *et al.* (1991)
Digitalis thapsi	Shoot	Seedling shoot tips	Shoots multiplied & rooted spontaneously	YY	Herrera *et al.* (1990)
Picrorhiza kurroa Royle ex Benth. (Kutki)	Shoot	Shoot tips	Shoot proliferation. Rooted	YY	Lal *et al.* (1988)
Rehmannia glutinosa Libosch. f. *hueichingensis*	Direct	*In vitro* leaves	Multiple adventitious shoots	Y	Xu & Davey (1983)
Rehmannia glutinosa	Protoplast	*In vitro* leaves	Shoots regenerated. Rooted	—	Xu & Davey (1983)
Rehmannia glutinosa	Shoot	*In vitro* seedlings	Multiple shoots	YY	Xu & Davey (1983)
Smilacaceae — Liliaceae					
Smilax oldhami Miq. (Shiode)	Callus	Root segment	Embryogen. & shoot formation. Shoots rooted	—	Yamamoto & Oda (1992)
Smilax oldhami	Callus & direct	Shoot internode	Embryogenesis via callus. Plantlets regenerated	—	Yamamoto & Oda (1992)
Smilax oldhami	Direct	Petiole	Multipl. bud formation & development. Shoots rooted	YY	Yamamoto & Oda (1992)

Species name	Type of Culture	Source of explant	Results		References
Smilax oldhami	Direct	Leaf segment	Direct somatic embryogenesis. Germination	YY	Yamamoto & Oda (1992)
Smilax oldhami	Node	Nodal segment	Shoot formation. Shoots rooted	Y	Yamamoto & Oda (1992)
Solanaceae					
Atropa belladonna L. (Deadly nightshade)	Callus	Leaf segments of n & 2n plants	Adventitious shoot formation	–	Eapen *et al.* (1978)
Atropa belladonna	Callus/Suspension	Cultured roots	Caulogenesis; embryogenesis (in callus & suspension)	–	Thomas & Street (1972),&
Atropa belladonna	Protoplast	Suspension cultures ex stem callus	Callus colonies, embryogenesis. Plants regenerated	–	Gosch *et al.* (1975)
Atropa belladonna	Protoplast	Leaves from shoot cultures	Callus colonies, adventitious shoots. Rooted	–	Lörz & Potrykus (1979)
Atropa belladonna	Root	Root tips	Indefinite root culture	–	Thomas & Street (1972),&
Atropa belladonna	Shoot	Shoot tips	Shoot multiplication	YY	Lörz & Potrykus (1979)
Atropa belladonna	Suspensions	Suspensions ex root callus	Cell aggregates with shoots & then somatic embryos	–	Thomas & Street (1970)
Datura candida hybrid	Direct/Callus	Infected *in vitro* plantlets	Transformed hairy root cults. Studied alkaloid prodn.	–	Christen *et al.* (1989)
Datura innoxia Mill.	Callus	Leaf discs	Shoot differentiation. Studied inhibitors	–	Sethi *et al.* (1990)
Datura innoxia	Embryo	Immature zygotic embryos	Seedling growth	Y	Sanders & Burkholder (1948)
Datura innoxia [haploid plant]	Shoot	Shoot tips	Multiple shoots	Y	Furner *et al.* (1978)
Datura insignis Barb. Rodr.	Node	Stem nodes	Plantlets. Normal & vitreous leaf structure studied	Y	Miguens *et al.* (1993)
Datura insignis	Node	Single node segments	Multiple shoots, rooted	YY	Dos Santos *et al.* (1990)
Datura spp.	Direct	Zygotic embryos	Adventitious embryos	–	Sanders (1950)
Datura stramonium L. = *D. tatula*	Embryo	Young embryos (to 0.2—0.3 mm)	Embryo growth	–	Matsubara (1962 ; 1964)
Duboisia myoporoides R.Br.	Callus	Stem sections	Adventitious shoots. Rooted. Plantlets	–	Kitamura *et al.* (1980 ; 1985 ; 1988)
Duboisia myoporoides	Shoot	Single node with axillary bud	Shoot elongation, multiple shoots. Rooted plants	YY	Kukreja & Mathur (1985)
Duboisia myoporoides	Shoot	2-3 cm stem + node & petiole base	Shoot multiplication. Rooted plants in field	YY	Kukreja & Mathur (1985)
Hyoscyamus muticus	Protoplast	Young leaf pieces	Callus colonies; adventitious shoots	–	Hanold (1983)
Hyoscyamus muticus	Protoplast	Leaves of somatic embryos ex anther cultures	Callus growth, shoots regenerated and rooted	–	Wernicke *et al.* (1979)
Hyoscyamus niger L. (Henbane)	Embryogenic callus	Petioles, unpollinated ovaries, germinated seeds	Somatic embryos. Plantlets	–	Cheng & Raghavan (1985)
❖ *Solanum dulcamara*	Callus	Leaves ex 10 (& 15) week plants	Adventitious shoots & flowers (Shoots only)	–	Bhatt *et al.* (1979)
Solanum dulcamara L. (Bittersweet)	Callus	Seedling hypocotyl/stem segments	Adventitious shoots	–	Emke & Eilert (1986)
Solanum dulcamara	Direct	*In vitro* seedling leaf (2.5cm)	Plants via direct adventitious shoots	Y	Zenkteler (1972b)
Solanum dulcamara	Protoplast	Leaves from shoot cultures	Callus colonies. Adventitious shoots, rooted *in vitro*	–	Binding & Nehls (1977)
Solanum dulcamara	Shoot	Shoot tips	Axillary shoots	Y	Binding & Nehls (1977)
Solanum elaeagnifolium Cav. var *leprosum*	Callus	Seedling hypocotyls	Studied production of solasodine	–	Nigra *et al.* (1989)
Solanum khasianum	Callus	Leaves ex 10 (& 15) week plants	Aventitious shoots & flowers (Shoots only)	–	Bhatt *et al.* (1979)
Solanum laciniatum Ait. (Kangaroo apple)	Callus	Leaf discs	Shoot regeneration	–	Chandler *et al.* (1982)
Solanum laciniatum	Callus	Mature leaf discs (5mm)	Adventitious shoots. Shoots rooted	–	Davies & Dale (1979)
Solanum laciniatum	Direct	Leaf segments	Direct shoot bud formation. Shoots rooted	Y	Conner & Conner (1984)
Withania somnifera (L.) Dunal.	Shoot	Shoot tips ex *in vitro* seedlings	Shoot multiplication, rooted	YY	Sen & Sharma (1991)
Withania somnifera	Shoot	Seeds	Multiple shoots, multiplied & elongated	Y	Sen & Sharma (1991)

Species name		Type of Culture	Source of explant	Results		References
Umbelliferae						
	Angelica acutiloba (Sieb. & Zucc.) Kitag. var. 'Ohbuka'	Callus/Suspension	Cut pieces of floral buds	Embryogenesis. Embryo germination. Plants	—	Miura *et al.* (1988)
	Angelica acutiloba	Callus/Suspension	Flower pedicel	Embryogenesis. Plantlets	—	Nakagawa *et al.* (1982)
Valerianaceae						
	Nardostachys grandiflora DC. = *N. jatamansi* (Spikenard)	Callus	Petioles ex young leaves	Somatic embryogen. Plantlets	—	Mathur (1993)
Verbenaceae						
	Lippia dulcis Trev.	Shoot	Nodal segments (1cm)	Shoot multiplication	Y	Sauerwein *et al.* (1991)
Vitidaceae						
	Cayratia japonica (Thunb.). Gagnep.	Callus	Unpollinated ovaries	Embryogenesis. Plantlets	—	Zhou *et al.* (1994)
Zingiberaceae						
❖	*Costus speciosus* (J.G.Koenig.) Sm. (Malay ginger)	Callus	Rhizome tissue	Root & then shoot regeneration. Shoots rooted	—	Jain & Chaturvedi (1985)
	Costus speciosus	Callus	1.5 mm seed embryos	Adventitious shoots (could not be transferred)	—	Pal & Sharma (1982)
	Costus speciosus	Shoot	Rhizome shoot tips (5 mm)	Shoot proliferation. Rooted plants	YY	Chaturvedi *et al.* (1984)
*	*Curcuma zedoaria* (Christm.) Roscoe (Zedoary)	Shoot	Axillary & shoot apex buds	Multiple shoot formation	YY	Yasuda *et al.* (1988)
❖	*Kaempferia galanga* L.	Shoot	Rhizome buds	Shoot multiplication & direct rooting	YY	Vincent *et al.* (1992)

PLANTS GROWN AS SPICES AND FOOD FLAVOURINGS

As is shown in Table 257, methods have been published for the tissue culture and micropropagation of several plants which provide spices, condiments, food flavourings and essences. The market for most products of this type is relatively small, but nevertheless trade in such products is important to the economy of some countries.

Yapabandara (1995) describes work in Sri Lanka aimed at the micropropagation of spices such as cardamon, cinnamon, clove and nutmeg, together with plants producing aromatic oils, such as citronella and lemon grass.

Meristem tip culture could possibly be useful for producing virus–free stock of some perennial species. The use of tissue culture methods for umbelliferous spice plants was reviewed by Jha *et al.* (1982). The propagation of *Allium* and *Brassica* has been reviewed in the section on vegetable crops (page 1177).

Table 257. Published reports on the tissue culture of HERBS AND SPICES.

	Species name	Type of Culture	Source of explant	Results		References
Alliaceae						
*	Allium sativum L. (Garlic)	Callus	Various	Adventitious shoots and bulblets, or embryogenesis	—	Abo El-Nil (1977)
	Allium sativum	Callus	Leaf base tissue	Adventitious shoots, rooted	—	Havranek & Novák (1976)
	Allium sativum	Callus/Direct	Leaf discs	Low frequency of shoot regeneration	—	Rauber & Grunewaldt (1988)
	Allium sativum	Meristem	Shoot apices	Shoots. Virus-free plants	Y	Ayuso & Peña-Inglesias (1980)
	Allium sativum [5 cvs.]	Meristem	Apical meristems	Shoot growth. Plants	Y	Bovo & Mroginski (1985)
	Allium sativum	Meristem	Meristem tips	Virus-free plants	Y	Havranek (1972)
	Allium sativum [several varieties]	Shoot	Shoot buds (5—8mm) from cloves	Axillary & adventitious shoots. Rooted diploid plants	YY	Bhojwani (1978)
	Allium sativum 'Kate'	Shoot	Shoot apices from bulbs	Bulblets. Rooted plants	YY	Matsubara & Chen (1989)
	Allium sativum	Shoot	Shoot tips	Shoot proliferation. Bulblets formed after cold tmt.	YY	Nagakubo et al. (1993)
	Allium sativum [many cvs.]	Shoot	Shoot buds ex heat-treated cloves	Shoots, bulblets. Virus-free plants	Y	Peña-Inglesias & Ayuso (1982)
	Allium sativum cv. Howaito-Roppen'	Suspension	Callus ex shoot meristems	Regeneration from semi-organised cell clumps. Plants	—	Nagasawa & Finer (1988)
	Allium schoenoprasum L. (Chive)	Callus/Direct	Leaf discs	Low frequency of shoot regeneration	—	Rauber & Grunewaldt (1988)
Boraginaceae						
	Borago officinalis L. (Borage)	Direct/Callus	Immature zygotic embryos	Embryogenesis	Y	Janick et al. (1987)
	Borago officinalis	Embryogenic callus	Immature zygotic embryos	Somatic embryogenesis. Fatty acid content analysed	—	Quinn et al. (1989a)
	Borago officinalis	Shoot	Shoot tips from field grown plants & embryo culture	Shoot proliferation. Rooted plants	Y	Janick et al. (1987)
Compositae — Asteraceae						
*	Artemisia dracunculus L. var. sativa (Tarragon)	Shoot	Shoot tips (1.5 cm)	Shoot proliferation. Rooted plants	YY	MacKay & Kitto (1988)
	Artemisia dracunculus sativa	Direct	Leaf pieces	Plantlet regeneration from petiole. Shoots rooted	Y	Garland & Stoltz (1980)
	Artemisia dracunculus sativa	Shoot	Shoot tips	Axillary shoot proliferation	YY	Mackay & Kitto (1986)
*	Stevia rebaudiana Bertoni	Callus/Direct	Young leaves of adult plants	Adventitious shoots from primary callus. Rooted plants	—	Ferreira & Handro (1988a)
	Stevia rebaudiana	Callus	Leaf pieces	Shoot & root cultures. Stevioside synthesis studied	—	Swanson et al. (1992)
	Stevia rebaudiana	Direct	Shoot tip domes (1—2 leaf prim.)	Formation of multiple shoot primordia. Plants	YY	Miyagawa et al. (1986)
	Stevia rebaudiana	Direct	Shoot tips + 2-4 leaf primordia	Multiple adventitious shoots, ex leaves touching medium	Y	Tamara et al. (1984)
	Stevia rebaudiana	Direct	Leaflets ex in vitro seedlings	Multiple adventitious shoots	Y	Yang & Chang (1979)
	Stevia rebaudiana	Shoot	Stem segments & shoot tips	Multiple axillary shoots. Rooted plants	YY	Miyagawa et al. (1984)
	Stevia rebaudiana	Shoot	Shoot tips + 2-4 leaf primordia	Multiple shoots on 80% of explants. 100% rooting	YY	Tamara et al. (1984)
	Stevia rebaudiana	Suspension	Leaf disc callus	Plant regeneration from callus ex plated cells	—	Ferreira & Handro (1988b)
Cruciferae						
*	Armoracia rusticana Gaertn., Mey. & Scherb. = Cochlearia armoracia L. (Horse-radish)	Direct	Leaf sections	Shoot formation. Rooted plantlets, virus-free	Y	Meyer & Milbrath (1977 a,b)
	Armoracia rusticana	Direct	Root sections	Adv. shoots	Y	Wurm (1960)
	Armoracia rusticana	Direct/Shoot	1 cm segs. of 3—4 week-old leaves	Adv. shoots. Shoot multiplic. on subculture. Plants	YY	Górecka (1987)

Species name	Type of Culture	Source of explant	Results		References
Brassica hirta Moench. = Sinapis alba (White mustard)	Callus	Hypocotyl	Rhizogenesis, or shoots & embryoids	—	Bajaj & Bopp (1972)
Brassica hirta [strain UC]	Direct	Cotyledons	Adventitious shoot regeneration	—	Murata & Orton (1987)
Brassica juncea (L.) Czern. (Indian mustard)	Callus	Cotyledons ex 8-day old seedlings	Shoot regeneration	—	Fazekas et al. (1986)
Brassica juncea	Callus	Cotyledons ex axenic seedlings	Adventitious shoots. Rooted	—	George & Rao (1980 ; 1983)
Brassica juncea	Callus	Hypocots. ex abnorm. anther sdlgs.	Shoot regeneration. Haploid & diploid plants	—	George & Rao (1982)
Brassica juncea cvs. RH-30, 'Varuna'	Callus	Cotyledons	Light callus, then shoot formation. Plants	—	Jain et al. (1988)
Brassica juncea	Callus	Protoplasts from sdlg. hypocotyls	Plantlet regen. via embryogen. or organogen.	—	Kirti & Chopra (1990)
Brassica juncea [strains UC-142, UV-1339]	Callus	Hypocotyls (cotyledons)	Very low frequency shoot regeneration	—	Murata & Orton (1987)
Brassica juncea (2 cvs.)	Direct	Seedling cotyledons & hypocotyl	Adv. shoot form. increased by ethylene inhibitors	—	Chi et al. (1990)
Brassica juncea Strain UC-142	Direct	Cotydons	Adventitious shoot regeneration	—	Murata & Orton (1987)
Brassica juncea	Direct	Seedling cotyledons or hypocotyls	Adventitious shoots. Plants from 94% explants	Y	Zee et al. (1980)
Brassica juncea cv. RH36	Direct?	Cotyledons	Shoot bud formation	—	Narasimhulu & Chopra (1988)
Brassica juncea cv. R1K-81-1	Direct?	Seedling cotyledons	Multiple shoots or roots from petiole end	Y	Sharma et al. (1991)
Brassica juncea	Shoot	Shoots of anther-culture seedlings	Multiple shoots	Y	Sharma & Bhojwani (1985)
Brassica nigra (L.) Koch (Black mustard)	Callus	Young hypocotyl	Callus: on transfer shoots on 1% calli in 2 months	—	Dietert et al. (1982)
Brassica nigra [strain UC-1202]	Callus	Hypocotyls (cotyledons)	Very low frequency shoot regeneration	—	Murata & Orton (1987)
Brassica nigra [strain UC-1199]	Direct	Cotyledons	Adventitious shoot regeneration	Y	Murata & Orton (1987)
Brassica nigra cv. IC 257	Direct ?	Cotyledons of 6-day-old seedlings	Shoot bud formation	Y	Narasimhulu et al. (1988)
Brassica nigra cv. IC257	Direct?	Cotyledons	Shoot bud formation	—	Narasimhulu & Chopra (1988)
Brassica nigra cv. IC257	Direct?	Cotyledons of 6 day-old seedlings	Shoot bud formation	Y	Narasimhulu et al. (1988)
Brassica nigra	Embryogenic callus	Seedling hypocotyl sections	Somatic embryos. Plants	—	Gupta et al. (1990)
Brassica nigra	Suspension	Callus ex thin cell layers	Embryogenesis. Plantlets ex adv. shoots on embryos	—	Klimaszewska & Keller (1986)
Brassica nigra × B. oleracea var broccoli	Direct?	Cotyledons of 6-d-old sdlgs.	Shoot bud formation	Y	Narasimhulu et al. (1988)

Iridaceae

	Species name	Type of Culture	Source of explant	Results		References
*	Crocus sativus L. (Saffron crocus)	Direct	Corm fragments	Minicorm formation & proliferation on subculture	Y	Homes et al. (1987)
	Crocus sativus	Direct/Callus	Ovaries,intact or less stig. & style	Stigma-like structures produced. Saffron assessed	—	Sarma et al. (1991)
	Crocus sativus	Shoot	Ethylene pretreated & sectioned corm apical buds	Multiple sprouting buds. Developed into corms	Y	Plessner et al. (1990)

Labiatae

	Species name	Type of Culture	Source of explant	Results		References
❖	Mentha arvensis L. (BRA 000060: 000078) (Corn mint)	Shoot	Single node segments	Axillary shoots with roots. Plants	YY	Rech & Pires (1986)
	Mentha citrata Ehrh. (Orange mint)	Callus	Leaf discs	Adventitious shoots, plants	—	Van Eck & Kitto (1988)
	Mentha citrata	Callus	Leaf discs	Multiple shoots, rooted	—	Van Eck & Kitto (1992)
	Mentha × piperita L. (Peppermint)	Callus	Mature or immature embryos	Adventitious shoots. Rooted plants	—	Van Eck & Kitto (1990)
	Mentha × piperita cv. 'Black Mitcham'	Callus	Leaf discs	Multiple shoots, rooted	—	Van Eck & Kitto (1992)
	Mentha × piperita, M.spicata	Callus	Stem	Shoots & roots	—	Lin & Staba (1961)
	Mentha × piperita	Callus	Seeds	Plant regeneration	—	Van Eck & Kitto (1988)
	Mentha × piperita 'BRA 000086'	Shoot	Single node segments	Prolific axillary shoots with roots. Plants	YY	Rech & Pires (1986)

Species name	Type of Culture	Source of explant	Results		References
Mentha × piperita	Shoot	Axillary & terminal buds	Multiple shoots. Rooted plants	Y	Venkataraman & Ravishankar (1986)
Mentha sp.	Callus	Leaf discs	Adventitious shoots, plants	—	Van Eck & Kitto (1988)
Mentha spicata L.= *M. viridis* (Spearmint) 'BRA 000105'	Shoot	Single node segments	Axillary shoots with roots. Plants	YY	Rech & Pires (1986)
Mentha spicata 'BRA 000124'	Shoot	Single node segments	Prolific axill. shoots with roots. Plants	YY	Rech & Pires (1986)
❖ *Rosemarinus officinalis* L. cv. 'Lockwood de Forest'	Callus	Shoot tips & leaf segments	Studied effect of sucrose & calcium	—	Tawfik *et al.* (1992)
Rosmarinus officinalis (Rosemary)	Callus	Stem material	Adventitious shoots from 2-year old cultures	—	Webb *et al.* (1984)
Rosmarinus officinalis	Node	Single-node stem segments	Axillary shoots	Y	Misra & Chaturvedi (1984)
Rosmarinus officinalis	Shoot	Shoot tips (10mm)	Shoot proliferation & growth. Shoots rooted	YY	Misra & Chaturvedi (1984)
See also *Lavandula* (WOODY ORNAMENTALS table)					
Lauraceae					
Cinnamomum zeylanicum Bl. (Cinnamon)	Callus	Cotyls, hypocotyls, stem segments	Multiple adventitious shoots. Rooted plants	—	Jagadish Chandra & Rai (1986)
Cinnamomum zeylanicum	Direct	Seeds	Multiple shoots. Rooted plants	—	Jagadish Chandra & Rai (1986)
Leguminosae					
Glycyrrhiza glabra L. (Liquorice)	Node	Stem node segments	Shoot & axillary bud growth. Shoots rooted	YY	Shah & Dalal (1980 ; 1982)
Trigonella foenum-graecum L. (Fenugreek)	Protoplast	Primary leaves	Plant regeneration	—	Shekhawat and Galston (1983).
Myrtaceae					
Syzygium aromaticum (L.) Merr. & Perry (Clove)	Callus	Cotyledons, hypocotyls, stem segs.	Multiple adventitious shoots. Rooted plants	—	Jagadish Chandra & Rai (1986)
Syzygium aromaticum	Direct	Seeds	Multiple shoots. Rooted plants	—	Jagadish Chandra & Rai (1986)
Orchidaceae					
Vanilla planifolia Andrews. (Vanilla)	Direct	7mm swollen aerial root apices	Multiple plants from 90% tips	Y	Philip & Nainar (1986)
Vanilla planifolia	Direct	Nodal stem (3mm)	10-15 plants in 30% explants	Y	Philip & Nainar (1986)
Vanilla planifolia	Direct	Tips of aerial roots	After cap lysis, shoot meristem from quiescent centre	—	Philip & Nainar (1988)
Vanilla planifolia	Node	Single node	Proliferated shoots & roots	YY	Kononowicz & Janick (1984a)
Vanilla planifolia	Shoot	Axillary buds	Axillary shoots. Rooted plantlets	Y	Cervera & Madrigal (1981)
Vanilla planifolia	Shoot	Axillary buds	5 shoots per bud in 6 weeks. Shoots rooted	YY	Cervera & Madrigal (1981)
Ranunculaceae					
Nigella sativa L. (Black cumin)	Callus	Stem	Shoot regeneration	—	Banerjee & Gupta (1975a)
Nigella sativa	Callus	Leaf	5% plantlet regeneration	—	Banerjee & Gupta (1975a)
Nigella sativa	Callus	Roots ex callus	Embryogenesis. 50% embryoids give 2n plants	—	Banerjee & Gupta (1975b)
Nigella sativa	Callus	Roots from long-term cultures	Embryogenesis & adventitious shoots. Plants	—	Bhattacharya & Gupta (1987)
Nigella sativa	Callus	Leaf segments	Shoot formation. Shoots flowered	—	Chand & Roy (1981)
Nigella sativa	Root	Root tips	Long-term isolated root cultures	—	Bhattacharya & Gupta (1987)
Solanaceae					
❖ *Capsicum frutescens* L. cv. Bharath (Red chilli pepper)	Direct/Callus	Seedling cotyledons, hypocotyls	Adventitious shoots. Plantlet regeneration	—	Gunay & Rao (1978)
Umbelliferae					
Anethum graveolens L. (Dill)	Callus	Seedling hypocotyls and cotyls.	Embryogenesis. Plants (flowered *in vitro*)	—	Ratnamba & Chopra (1974)
Anethum graveolens	Callus	Young inflorescences	Embryogenesis. Embryos germinated: plants	—	Sehgal (1978)

Species name	Type of Culture	Source of explant	Results		References
Anethum graveolens	Embryo	Single embryos & polyembr. mass	Single seedlings or multiple shoots	—	Johri & Sehgal (1963 a,b)
Anethum graveolens	Ovary	Young ovaries	Flower opened, pollination. Single & multiple embryos	—	Johri & Sehgal (1963 a,b)
Anethum graveolens	Ovary	Pollinated ovaries	Polyembrony and then multiple shoots	—	Johri & Sehgal (1966)
Anethum graveolens	Callus	Mericarps (seeds)	Somatic embryos. Plants regenerated	Y	Wakhlu *et al.* (1990)
Bunium persicum Boiss. (Kala Zira)	Suspension	Petiole segment callus	Embryogenesis. Embryo uniformity improved with ABA.	Y	Ammirato (1974)
Carum carvi L. (Caraway)	Shoot & callus	Seedling-derived shoots	Adv. & axil. shoots. Maturation & rejuv. studied	—	Kataeva & Popowich (1993)
Coriandrum sativum L. (Coriander)	Callus	Hypocotyl/leaf	Adventitious shoots. Rooted plantlets flowered	—	Jha *et al.* (1983)
Cuminum cyminum L. (Cumin)	Embryogenic callus	Nodal segs. from *in vitro* plants	Callus & suspensions. Somatic embryos, plantlets	—	Theiler-Hedtrich & Kagi (1991)
* *Foeniculum vulgare* Mill. [2 breeding lines] (Fennel)	Protoplast	Suspens. (ex e' gen. petiole callus)	Direct embryoid formation. Plantlets	—	Miura & Tabata (1986)
Foeniculum vulgare	Shoot	Shoot tips (1-2cm)	Shoot multiplication. Direct rooting of 92% of shoots	YY	Du Manoir *et al.* (1985)
Foeniculum vulgare [2 breeding lines]	Shoot	Axillary and apical buds	Shoot growth & multipl. Rooted plants	YY	Theiler-Hedtrich & Kagi (1991)
Foeniculum vulgare	Suspension	Callus from *in vitro* stem or petiole	Indirect embryogenesis. Plantlets regen. from embryoids	—	Hunault (1984)
Foeniculum vulgare	Suspension	Leaf petioles	Embryogenesis. Plants (very uniform in field)	—	Miura *et al.* (1986)
Foeniculum vulgare	Suspension	Embryogenic callus ex petioles	Embryoids grown into plants (chemically uniform)	—	Miura *et al.* (1987 a,b)
Foeniculum vulgare	Callus	Petiole	Adventitious roots & shoots, or embryoid formation	—	Vasil & Hildebrandt (1966 b,c)
Petroselinum crispum (Mill.) A.W. Hill (Parsley) = *P. hortense*	Suspension	Hypocotyl callus	Embryogenesis	—	Kudielka & Theimer (1983)
Pimpinella anisum L. (Anise)	Callus	Unknown	Adventitious shoots from 2-year old cultures	—	Becker (1970)
Pimpinella anisum					
Trachyspermum ammi (L.) Sprague.	²Callus	Hypocotyls ex *in vitro* seedlings	Somatic embryogenesis. Seedlings	—	Jastrai *et al.* (1992)

Zingiberaceae

Species name	Type of Culture	Source of explant	Results		References
❖ *Alpinia purpurata* (Vieill.) Schum. [Grinoza hybrid no. 5]	Node	Bract axis sect.+ dorm. bud ex infl.	Multiple axillary shoots. Shoots rooted	YY	Chang & Criley (1993)
❖ *Curcuma longa* L. (Turmeric)	Shoot	Vegetative buds from rhizomes	Shoot growth. Elongated shoots rooted	Y	Nadgauda *et al.* (1978)
Curcuma spp.	Shoot	Rhizome buds	Multiple axillary shoots with roots	YY	Balachandran *et al.* (1990)
Elettaria cardamomum (L.) Maton (Cardamon)	Callus	Not given	Adventitious shoots	—	Priyadarshan & Zachariah (1986)
Elettaria cardamomum	Node	Single nodes	Axillary shoots. Rooted plants	Y	Priyadarshan & Zachariah (1986)
Zingiber officinale Roscoe (Ginger)	Direct	Pseudostems & crown sections ex *i.v.* plants	Adventitious shoots, plantlets	Y	Ikeda & Tanabe (1989)
Zingiber officinale cv. 'Maran'	Callus	Young leaf sections	Multiple shoots. Rooted	—	Babu *et al.* (1992)
Zingiber officinale cv. 'Eruthupetta'	Embryogenic callus	Young leaf segs. ex *in vitro* shoots	Embryo development & germination. Plantlets	—	Kackar *et al.* (1993)
Zingiber officinale var. Wyrad	Meristem/shoot	Meristem tips	Multiple shoots. Rooted	YY	Bhagyalakshmi & Singh (1988)
Zingiber officinale	Shoot	Rhizome buds	Multiple axillary shoots with roots	YY	Balachandran *et al.* (1990)
Zingiber officinale	Shoot	Shoot tips	Shoot proliferation. Rooted	YY	Sakamura *et al.* (1987)
Zingiber officinale	Shoot/Direct	Buds ex stored rhizomes	Multiple adventitious shoots with roots	Y	Hosoki & Sagawa (1977)

The following plant species are also being micropropagated in European laboratories:
Capparis spinosa; *Curcuma colorata*, *C. elata*, *C. ferruginea*.

CONSERVATION OF WILD SPECIES

Several kinds of plants which do not fit into any of our crop categories, have also been the subject of micropropagation experiments. We have listed them in Table 258 because the experience gained in each case may be applicable to cultivated plants of the same genus. Some of the so–called weeds (*e.g. Arabidopsis thaliana, Brachycome dichromosomatica, Heloniopsis orientalis*) are also valuable 'model' plants for physiological and genetical experiments, and methods to grow, propagate and manipulate them *in vitro* are of obvious value in research.

Endangered species

There is another aspect to the tissue culture studies of plants of no economic importance. It is, distressingly, that the wild habitats of many are threatened by the pressures of modern human activities so that, unless deliberate conservation measures are taken, plants are liable to become extinct.

Several botanic gardens now have micropropagation laboratories devoted to the conservation of endangered species. Work on native orchids mentioned on page 919 has largely been conducted under their aegis.

Novel latex producers

Plants of the genera *Araujia, Asclepias, Euphorbia, Ficus* and *Parthenium* produce hydrocarbons (notably latexes) as secondary products and in some countries there is interest in growing them in plantations as a source of rubber. The most important of these, *Parthenium argentatum*, was grown in the U.S.A. as an emergency source of rubber during World War II. This and several of latex–producing plants are drought–tolerant and might therefore become economic crops in otherwise unproductive territories (Tideman and Hawker, 1982).

Tissue culture could not only be used for mass propagation, but also to facilitate genetic manipulation (Dastoor *et al.*, 1981; Misawa *et al.*, 1982), for studying the biochemistry of secondary product synthesis (Wickham *et al.*, 1980), and for looking at effects of various chemicals on latex production (Arreguin and Bonner, 1950).

Some of the above species have been listed in the present table, others have been mentioned in previous sections (*e.g. Asclepias*, several species of which are cultivated as ornamentals, or are regarded as having medicinal properties, and are listed in Tables 174 and 256).

Table 258. Published reports on tissue culture of PLANTS FROM THE WILD.

Species name	Type of Culture	Source of explant		Results	References
Agavaceae					
❖ Agave arizonica Gent. & Weber	Callus	Bulbil basal leaf segments	—	Multiple adventitious shoots. Rooted	Powers & Backhaus (1989)
Aizoaceae					
Sesuvium verrucosum (Halophyte)	Shoot	Shoot tips	Y	Multiple shoot formation	Glenn et al. (1984)
Alliaceae					
❖ Allium altaicum Pall.	Embryogenic callus	Umbels	Y	Somatic embryoids, germination. Plantlets	Phillips & Hubstenberger (1987)
Allium altaicum	Shoot	Umbels	YY	Shoot multiplication	Phillips & Hubstenberger (1987)
Allium roylei Steam	Embryogenic callus	Seedling shoot tips + basal plate	—	Low rate of plantlet regen. from embryoids	Phillips & Hubstenberger (1987)
Allium roylei	Shoot	Seedling shoot tips + basal plate	Y	Low rate of shoot multiplication	Phillips & Hubstenberger (1987)
Allium senescens L. var. 'minor' (German garlic)	Callus	Flower cuds	—	Multiple shoots, rooted	Ashalatha & Bong Bo (1993)
Amaranthaceae					
Aerva tomentosa Forssk.	Ovary/Ovule	Ovaries, flowers & inflorescences	—	Ovules matured into seeds	Puri (1963)
Amaranthus retroflexus L. (Pigweed)	Shoot	Shoot tips	Y	Shoots flowered in vitro and produced seeds	Tisserat and Galleta (1988).
Amaranthus viridis L.	Shoot	Shoot tips	Y	Shoots flowered in vitro	Tisserat and Galleta (1988).
Araceae					
Cryptocoryne lucens De Witt (Aquatic)	Shoot	Shoot tips	YY	Multiple shoots. Rooted extra vitrum	Kane et al. (1990)
Asclepiadaceae					
Araujia sericofera Brot. (Cruel plant)	Direct/Callus	Transverse leaf slices	Y	Adventitious shoots; rooted plantlets	Tideman & Hawker (1982)
Araujia sericofera	Direct/Callus	Immature seeds	—	Somatic embryos. Plantlets	Torné et al. (1992)
Araujia sericofera	Shoot/Callus	Stem node	Y	Some callus. Axillary (?) shoots, rooted in vitro	Tideman & Hawker (1982)
Asclepias rotundifolia (Latex producing plant)	Shoot	Stem node	YY	Axillary shoot proliferation. Shoots rooted	Tideman & Hawker (1982)
Asclepias rotundifolia	Shoot	Fragmented shoot apices	YY	Shoot growth & axill. shoot proliferation. Rooted	Tideman & Hawker (1982)
Asclepias syriaca L. (Common Milkweed)	Callus	Mature embryos	—	Callus from hypocotyl. Embryogenesis. Plantlets	Singh (1984)
Asclepias syriaca	Callus	Stems of seedlings from embryo culture	—	Adventitious shoots and embryogenesis	Wilson & Mahlberg (1977)
Asclepias syriaca	Protoplast	Hypocotyl pieces	—	Cell colonies. Shoot regeneration	Singh (1984)
Asclepias syriaca	Suspension	Callus from zygotic embryos	—	Embryogenesis. Plantlet development	Groet & Kidd (1980)
Asclepias syriaca	Suspension/Callus	Hypocotyl callus	—	Adventitious shoots. Rooted plantlets	Singh (1984)
Telosma cordata (Burm. f.) Merr. = Pergularia minor Anders.	Callus	5 mm segments of twining stem	—	Embryogenesis. Plantlets from germinated embryoids	Prabhudesai & N'yanaswmy (1974)
Boraginaceae					
Symphytum officinale L. (Comfrey)	Callus	Leaf, petiole, ovary, anther, root	—	Adventitious shoots. Plant regeneration	Abou-Mandour et al. (1987)
Symphytum officinale	Callus	Petioles	—	Shoot initiation. Shoots rooted	Huizing et al. (1983)
Symphytum officinale.	Suspension	Callus derived from root sections	—	Shoots, then roots & plantlets	Huizing et al. (1983)
Brassicaceae					
Coronopus navasii Pau.	Direct	Cotyl. & root segs. ex i.v. sdlgs.	YY	Multiple adventitious shoots. Rooted	Iriondo & Perez (1990)

Species name	Type of Culture	Source of explant	Results		References
Caryophyllaceae					
Lychnis candida =Viscaria candida	Shoot	Veg. apices (1mm) + 1-2 leaf prim.	Shoot growth. Shoots flowered in long days	—	Blake (1966)
Lychnis cardinalis	Shoot	Veg. apices (1mm) + 1-2 leaf prim.	Shoot growth. Shoots flowered in vitro	—	Blake (1966)
Stellaria media (L.) Vill. (Chick weed)	Shoot	Shoot tips	Mass of proliferating shoots	Y	Walkey & Cooper (1976)
Stellaria media	Shoot	Shoot tips	Shoots with flower primordia	Y	White (1933)
Chenopodiaceae					
Atriplex canescens (Pursh) Nutt.	Shoot	Seedling shoot tips (4 mm)	Shoot multiplication. Rooted plantlets	YY	Wochok & Sluis (1980b)
❖ Beta macrocarpa Guss. SP 733009 (Wild beet)	Callus	Young seedling leaves	Adventitious shoots. Rooted plants	—	Yu (1989)
Salicornia bigelovii Torr. (Halophyte)	Shoot	Shoot tips	Shoot, and some root, formation	Y	Lee et al. (1992)
Compositae — Asteraceae					
Achillea ptarmica L. (Sneezewort)	Callus	Leaves	Shoots then roots & plantlets	—	Cellárová et al. (1982)
Anthemis arvensis L. (Corn Chamomile)	Direct	Capitulum	Direct shoot formation. Shoots rooted extra vitrum	Y	Roest & Bokelmann (1973)
❖ Brachycome dichromosomatica [2n]	Callus	Leaf segments	Adventitious shoots and rooted plantlets	—	Gould (1979)
Brachycome lineariloba [2n]	Callus	Leaves & buds	Adventitious shoots, embryogenesis. Rooted plants	Y	Gould (1978)
Chrysanthemum segetum L. (Corn marigold)	Direct	Capitulum	Direct shoot formation. Shoots rooted	Y	Roest & Bokelmann (1973)
Chrysothamnus nauseosus albicaulis (Pallas.) Britton.	Shoot	Axillary shoots or nodal sections	Multiple axillary shoots. Rooted plants	YY	Upadhyaya et al. (1985)
Crepis capillaris (L.) Wallr. (Smooth hawksbeard)	Callus	Stem, leaf or meristem	Adventitious shoots	—	Sobko (1978)
Crepis capillaris	Shoot/Callus	Mature fruit	Plantlets and adventitious flowers on callus	—	Jayakar (1971)
Crepis falconeri = Pterotheca falconeri	Callus	Shoot apex, leaf	Callus, shoots, roots, & embryoids. Shoots rooted	—	Mehra & Mehra (1971)
❖ Gerbera aurantiaca Schultz-Bip. (Transvaal daisy)	Shoot/Callus	Seedling shoot apex	Axillary shoots. Buds from morphogenic basal callus	YY	Meyer & Van Staden (1988)
Gerbera piloselloides L. Cass.	Callus	Leaves ex in vitro cultures	Adventitious shoots, rooted	—	Reynoird et al. (1993)
Gerbera viridifolia (DC.) Schultz-Bip.	Callus	Leaves ex in vitro cultures	Adventitious shoots, rooted	—	Reynoird et al. (1993)
❖ Helianthus annuus L. × H. tuberosus L.	Callus	Tubers & immature embryos	Adventitious shoots. Rooted plants	—	Witrzens et al. (1988)
Helianthus bolanderi A.Gray = H. scaberrimus	Shoot	Shoot tips	Shoot cultures	Y	Bohorowa et al. (1986)
Helianthus pauciflorus Nutt. = H. rigidus	Shoot	Shoot tips	Shoot cultures	Y	Bohorowa et al. (1986)
Helianthus praecox	Shoot	Shoot tips	Shoot cultures	Y	Bohorowa et al. (1986)
Hypochoeris radicata L. (Cat's ear)	Direct	Capitulum	Direct shoot formation. Shoots rooted	Y	Roest & Bokelmann (1973)
❖ Lactuca saligna L. (Least lettuce)	Callus/Suspension	Leaf sections	Adventitious shoots on callus. Shoots rooted in vitro	—	Alconero (1983)
Lactuca serriola L. (Prickly lettuce)	Callus/Suspension	Leaf sections	Adv. shoots (some rooted spontaneously, rest rooted i.v.)	—	Alconero (1983)
Leontodon autumnalis L. (Autumn hawkbit)	Direct	Capitulum	Direct shoot formation. Shoots rooted	Y	Roest & Bokelmann (1973)
Leucanthemum vulgare Lam. = Chrysanthemum leucanthemum L. (Ox-eyed daisy)	Direct	Capitulum	Direct shoot formation. Shoots rooted	Y	Roest & Bokelmann (1973)
Matricaria recutita L. = M. chamomilla (Chamomile)	Callus	Top of receptacle	Plantlet regeneration	—	Cellárová et al. (1982)
Olearia microdisca J.M. Black	Node	Nodal segments	Shoot multiplication. Tried to reduce vitrescence	Y	Williams & Taji (1991)
Parthenium hysterophorus L.	Callus	Stem segments	Root & shoot formation	—	Subramanian & Subba Rao (1980)
Parthenium hysterophorus	Callus	Stem, leaf blade, petiole	A few shoot primordia	—	Wickham et al. (1980)
Parthenium hysterophorus	Suspension	Callus derived from leaf segments	Root formation	—	Subramanian & Subba Rao (1980)
Psiadia coronopus (Lam.) Benth.	Node	2-node segments	Shoots multiplied and rooted	YY	Kroestrup & Norgaard (1991)

	Species name	Type of Culture	Source of explant	Results		References
❖	*Senecio jacobaea* L.	Protoplast	Shoot tip, leaf	Callus, adventitious shoots	—	Binding *et al.* (1981)
	Senecio sylvaticus L.	Protoplast	Shoot tip, leaf	Callus colonies. Adventitious shoots	—	Binding *et al.* (1981)
	Senecio vernalis	Protoplast	Shoot tip, leaf	Callus colonies. Adventitious shoots	—	Binding *et al.* (1981)
	Senecio viscosus	Protoplast	Shoot tip, leaf	Callus colonies. Adventitious shoots	—	Binding *et al.* (1981)
	Senecio vulgaris L. (Groundsel)	Protoplast	Leaf callus	Callus colonies. Adventitious shoots which flowered *in vitro*	—	Binding & Nehls (1980)
	Senecio vulgaris	Shoot	Shoot tips	Single & multiple shoots. Shoots rooted	YY	Walkey & Cooper (1976)
	Senecio vulgaris	Direct	Capitulum	Direct shoot formation. Shoots rooted	Y	Roest & Bokelmann (1973)
	Tanacetum parthenium (L.) Schultz-Bip. (Fever-few) = *Chrysanthemum parthenium*					
	Taraxacum officinale [T sect. Ruderalia sp.] (Dandelion)	Callus	Root sections	Shoot & root formation	—	Booth & Satchuthananthi (1974)
	Taraxacum officinale	Callus	Secondary root segment	Roots & leafy structures	—	Bowes (1970)
	Taraxacum officinale	Callus	Leaf lamina disc (12mm)	Shoot buds or roots via callus	—	Slabnik *et al.* (1986)
	Taraxacum officinale	Direct	Root sections	Direct shoot regeneration	Y	Booth & Satchuthananthavale (1974)
	Tripleurospermum inodorum (L.) Schultz-Bip. (Scentless mayweed) = *Matricaria inodorum*	Callus	Flowers, receptacles & stems	Shoot formation	—	Cellárová *et al.* (1982)
	Tripleurospermum maritima (L.) Koch.. (Sea mayweed) = *Matricaria maritima*	Direct	Capitulum	Direct shoot formation. Shoots rooted	Y	Roest & Bokelmann (1973)
	Xanthium pennsylvanicum (Cockle-burr)	Shoot	Large shoot tips	Rapid shoot growth. Shoot flowered in short days	—	Jacobs & Suthers (1971)
Convolvulaceae						
	Convolvulus sp.	Direct	Root segments	Adventitious shoots & roots	Y	Robbins & Torrey (1965)
	Convolvulus arvensis L. [several genotypes] (Field bindweed)	Callus	Young expanded leaves	Shoot regeneration. Studied inhibitors thereof.	—	Christianson & Warnick (1984)
	Convolvulus arvensis	Callus	Stem pieces	Adventitious shoots	—	Hill (1967)
	Convolvulus arvensis	Direct	Roots formed on callus cultures	Adventitious shoots, plants	—	Earle & Torrey (1965a)
	Convolvulus arvensis	Root/Direct	Seedling root tips, root sections	Adventitious shoot & root buds on roots/root sections	Y	Bonnett & Torrey (1965 : 1966)&
	Convolvulus arvensis	Root/Direct	Seedling root tips	Root cultures. Adventitious shoots on roots	Y	Torrey (1958)
	Convolvulus arvensis	Suspension	Callus ex root sections	Callus, adventitious buds & shoots	—	Earle & Torrey (1965a)
	Cuscuta arvensis L.	Shoot	Shoot tips	Shoot cultures	Y	Binding *et al.* (1981)
	Cuscuta campestris (Dodder)	Shoot	Shoot tips from axenic seedlings	Shoot growth over 5 transfers	Y	Loo (1946)
	Cuscuta reflexa	Embryogenic callus	Young embryos	Somatic embryos. Adventive embryos and seedlings	—	Maheshwari & Baldev (1961)
	Cuscuta reflexa	Shoot	Vegetative stem apices	Shoots (which flowered in the dark)	Y	Baldev (1962)
	Cuscuta reflexa	Shoot	Shoot tips	Shoots & 'protocorms'	Y	Binding *et al.* (1981)
Cruciferae						
*	*Arabidopsis thaliana* (L.) Heynh. (Thale cress)	Callus	Various parts of seedlings	Green nodules then adventitious shoots	—	Acedo (1986)
	Arabidopsis thaliana [various ecotypes]	Callus	Various	Shoot regeneration. Shoots rooted	—	Chaudhury & Signer (1989)
	Arabidopsis thaliana	Callus	Seedling hypocotyls	Clumps of adventitious shoots. Plantlets	—	Chu Huang & Yeoman (1984)
	Arabidopsis thaliana	Callus	Stem, seed and leaf pieces	Adventitious shoots. Shoot growth & root formation	—	Negrutiu *et al.* (1975)
	Arabidopsis thaliana [2 races]	Direct/Callus	Stem and leaf explants	Adventitious shoots	Y	Feldmann (1986)
	Arabidopsis thaliana	Protoplast	*In vitro* shoot apex	Callus and plant regeneration	—	Binding *et al.* (1981)
	Arabidopsis thaliana	Protoplast	Leaf mesophyll	Cell Colonies. Plantlet regeneration.	—	Gleba (1978)

Species name	Type of Culture	Source of explant	Results		References
Arabidopsis thaliana	Protoplast	Suspension culture cells	Cell colonies, adventitious shoots. Rooted	—	Le Thi Xuan & Menzel (1980)
Arabidopsis thaliana 'Columbia'	Suspension	Leaf or hypocotyl-derived callus (ex seedling)	Shoot regeneration. Shoots rooted	—	Gleddie (1989)
Arabidopsis thaliana [genotype C24 & other ecotypes]	Transf. (Agrob.)	Leaf discs & expanded cotyls.	Shoot regeneration. Transformed plants	—	Schmidt & Willmitzer (1988)
Capsella bursa-pastoris (L.) Medik. (Shepherd's purse)	Embryo	Glob., heart-shaped zyg. embryos	Embryo growth, germination. Seedlings	Y	Monnier (1976 : 1978 : 1984)
Capsella bursa-pastoris	Embryo	Globular embryos	Embryo growth. Viable plants	Y	Raghavan & Torrey (1963 : 1664a)
Capsella bursa-pastoris	Ovule/Embryo	Ovules (0.74 mm)	Embryo development	—	Monnier & Lagriffol (1986)
Capsella bursa-pastoris	Shoot	Shoot tips	Single shoots. Rooted	Y	Walkey & Cooper (1976)
Cardamine pratensis L. (Ladies smock)	Callus	Stem pieces	Adventitious shoots. Rooted plantlets	—	Henry *et al.* (1979)
Isatis tinctoria L. (Woad)	Root/Direct	Root pieces	Shoots ex cut surfaces and ex roots after 16th passage	Y	Danckwardt-Lilliestrom (1957)
Sisymbrium irio L. (London rocket)	Callus	Stem segments	Shoot buds & embryoids. Shoot buds rooted	—	Pareek & Chandra (1978b)

Cuscutaceae — See Convolvulaceae

Cyperaceae

Species name	Type of Culture	Source of explant	Results		References
Carex flacca Schreb. (Glaucous sedge)	Shoot	Vegetative shoot apices	Some shoot growth & axillary buds	—	Smith D.L. (1968)
Carex turida	Embryo	Zygotic embryos	Plantlets obtained	Y	Lee (1952)
Carex scoparia	Embryo	Zygotic embryos	Plantlets obtained	Y	Lee (1952)
Carex stipata	Embryo	Zygotic embryos	Germination. Plantlets obtained	Y	Lee (1952)
Caustis dioica R.Br. (Chinese puzzle)	Embryo	Zygotic embryos	Shoots multiplied & rooted	Y	Rossetto *et al.* (1992)

Dennstaedtiaceae

Species name	Type of Culture	Source of explant	Results		References
Pteridium aquilinum (L.) Kuhn (Bracken fern)	Callus	Gametophytes ex germin. spores	Haploid apogamous sporophytes. Plants	—	Breznovits & Mohay (1987)
Pteridium aquilinum	Prothallus	Prothalli	Apogamous sporophytes formed	—	Whittier & Steeves (1960)
Pteridium aquilinum ssp. 'latiusculum'	Prothallus	Pieces of gametophytic colony	Apogamous sporophytes formed	—	Whittier (1964)
Pteridium aquilinum	Prothallus/Callus	Spores	Prothallus, filamantous callus, prothallus regen.	—	Steeves *et al.* (1955)

Droceraceae

Species name	Type of Culture	Source of explant	Results		References
❖ *Drosera* [20 unnamed spp.] (Insectivorous plants)	Germination/Shoot	Seeds	Propagated plants from axillary rosettes	YY	Kukulczanka & Czastka (1988)
Drosophyllum lusitanicum (L.) Link (Portuguese sundew)	Callus	Seed embryos	Root and shoot formation	—	Doré Swamy & Mohan Ram (1967)
Drosophyllum lusitanicum	Embryo	Seed embryos	Seedlings produced	—	Doré Swamy & Mohan Ram (1967)
Drosophyllum lusitanicum	Shoot/node	Seedling shoots	Some adventitious shoots. Nodes recultured	—	Woodward *et al.* (1991)

Elaeagnaceae

Species name	Type of Culture	Source of explant	Results		References
Hippophae rhamnoides L. (Sea-buckthorn)	Shoot	Seedling shoot tips	Axillary shoots. Plants (soil-inoc. with Frankia)	YY	Montpetit & Lalonde (1988)

Epacridaceae

Species name	Type of Culture	Source of explant	Results		References
Leucopogon obtectus Benth. (Hidden beard heath)	Shoot	Shoot tips (6 mm long)	Shoot multiplication. 70% rooting	YY	Bunn *et al.* (1989)

Equisetaceae

Species name	Type of Culture	Source of explant	Results		References
Equisetum hyemale L.	Shoot	Shoot apex	Shoot growth	—	Wetmore (1954)

Euphorbiaceae

Species name	Type of Culture	Source of explant	Results		References
❖ *Euphorbia esula* L. (Leafy spurge)	Suspension	Stem callus	Plant regeneration	—	Davis *et al.* (1988)
Euphorbia lathyris L. (Caper spurge)	Callus	Apical shoot tips	Adventitious shoots via callus. Etiolated shoots rooted	—	Ripley & Preece (1986)

Species name	Type of Culture	Source of explant	Results		References
Euphorbia lathyris	Node	Stem node	Axillary shoot proliferation. Rooted	YY	Tideman & Hawker (1982)
Euphorbia lathyris	Shoot	Apical shoot tips	Axillary shoot proliferation. Etiolated shoots rooted	YY	Ripley & Preece (1986)
Euphorbia lathyris	Shoot	Stem node	Axillary shoot proliferation. Rooted	YY	Tideman & Hawker (1982)
Euphorbia peplus (peplis L.?) (Latex producing plant)	Callus	Stem internode	Adventitious shoot formation. Rooted	—	Tideman & Hawker (1982)
Euphorbia peplus	Shoot/Callus	Stem node	Profuse callus. (Axillary?) shoots. Rooted *in vitro*	Y	Tideman & Hawker (1982)
Euphorbia tannensis ssp. *eremophila* (A. Cunn.)	Shoot/Callus	Stem node	Axillary shoots (some callus). Rooted *in vitro*	Y	Tideman & Hawker (1982)
Goodeniaceae					
Lechenaultia formosa	Shoot	Shoot tips	Shoot formation & multiplication, possibly rooting	—	Williams *et al.* (1992)
Guttiferae					
❖ *Hypericum perforatum* L. (St.John's wort)	Direct	Capitulum	Direct shoot formation. Shoots rooted.	Y	Roest & Bokelmann (1973)
Hydrocharitaceae					
Thalassia testidunum Banks ex Koenig. (Seagrass)	Germination	Seeds	Seedlings, plants	—	Moffler & Durako (1984)
Vallisneria spiralis L. (Submerged aquatic)	Seed germination	Seeds	Plants. Flowered *in vitro*	—	Uma & Mohan Ram (1972)
Lauraceae					
Cassytha filiformis L.	Embryo/Germinat.	Adult seed embryos	Germination & seedling growth	Y	Rangan & Rangaswamy (1969)
Leguminosae					
Alhagi camelorum (Camel thorn)	Callus/Direct	Root, stem, leaf or hypocotyl	Direct shoots & shoot proliferation from callus. Plants	Y	Bharal & Rashid (1981)
Arachis paraguariensis Chod. & Hassl. (Wild peanut)	Callus	Young anthers	Adventitious shoots which flowered	—	Still *et al.* (1985)
Arachis paraguariensis	Callus	Stamens	Adventitious shoots. Grafted onto A.hypogaea rootstocks	—	Still *et al.* (1986)
Arachis paraguariensis	Suspension	Morphogenic callus from anthers	Adventitious shoots (very low rooting frequency)	—	Still *et al.* (1985)
Aspalathus linearis (Burm. f.) Dahlgr. (Rooibos)	Node	Nodes ex *in vitro* seedlings	Multiple axillary shoots, rooted	YY	Le Roux *et al.* (1992)
Glycine canescens [4 lines]	Callus	Various explants	Adventitious shoot formation. Plants	—	Hammatt *et al.* (1987)
Glycine canescens G1171 (Wild soybean)	Callus	Infected hypocot bases ex i.v. sdlgs	Transformed adv. roots leading to plantlet recovery	—	Rech *et al.* (1989)
Glycine canescens	Callus	Cotyledon & hypocotyl	Adventitious shoots, not rooted	—	Widholm & Rick (1983)
Glycine canescens	Suspension	Callus from young leaves ex *in vitro* seedling	Shoot regeneration	—	Myers *et al.* (1989)
Glycine clandestina Wendle. [one accession]	Direct	Leaf sections. Cotyledon, hypocotyl	Adventitious shoots. Fertile plants	Y	Hymowitz *et al.* (1986)
Glycine clandestina (Wild glycine spp.)	Suspension	Callus from young leaves ex *in vitro* seedling	Shoot regeneration	—	Myers *et al.* (1989)
Glycine falcata Lines G1153, G1155	Callus	Leaf joint & lamina	Adventitious shoots. Plants	—	Hammatt *et al.* (1987)
Glycine falcata Lines G1153, G1155	Shoot	Cotyledon & epicotyl nodes	Shoot proliferation	YY	Hammatt *et al.* (1987)
Glycine latrobeama [3 lines]	Callus	Leaf joint, lamina, petiole	Adventitious shoot formation. Plants	—	Hammatt *et al.* (1987)
Glycine tomentella Line G1300	Callus	Leaf lamina	Low frequency of adventitious shoot formation	—	Hammatt *et al.* (1987)
Indigofera enneaphylla	Callus	Hypocotyl or cotyledon	Adventitious shoots, rooted *in vitro*	—	Bharal & Rashid (1979)
Lathyrus articulatus & hybrids	Embryo	0.5 and 2 mm embryos from ovules	Embryo germination	—	Pecket & Selim (1965)
Lotus tenuis Wald. & Kit. ex Willd. (Narrowleaf trefoil)	Callus	Cotyls., leaves, roots, hypocotyls	Shoots regenerated. Rooted diploid plants	—	Piccirilli *et al.* (1988)
❖ *Medicago coerulea*	Protoplast	Peeled leaflets	Callus colonies, embryogenesis, plantlets	—	Arcioni *et al.* (1982)
Medicago glutinosa	Protoplast	Peeled leaves	Callus colonies, embryogenesis, plantlets	—	Arcioni *et al.* (1982)

Page	Table	No.	Medium	KNO_3	$NaNO_3$	NH_4NO_3	$Ca(NO_3)_2\cdot4H_2O$	$CaCl_2\cdot2H_2O$	$MgSO_4\cdot7H_2O$	KCl	KH_2PO_4	$NaH_2PO_4\cdot H_2O$	K_2SO_4	$(NH_4)_2SO_4$	See notes
	161	2	Harvais (1982)	200		1400	400		200	100	200				
	161	3	Arditti et al.(1985)			220	350		260		120				
	161	4	Van Waes & Debergh (1986)						100		300				
	161	5	Muir & Mitchell (1989)	100			400		100	50	100				
952	174	1	Samartin (1989) mod. MS	MS macronutrients. See Part 1 page 395											
	174	2	—	½MS macronutrients											
	174	3	Berretta & Eccher (1987)	1200		1000		75	75		270				
	174	4	Vieitez et al.(1985a) H + SO₄		600			75	250	750		125		132.2	
	174	5	Vieitez et al.(1984) H + SO₄ (2N)		1200			75	250	750		125		264.3	
	174	6	Vieitez et al.(1989a)		750			94	312.5	937.5		156.3		132.2	
	174	7	Lloyd & McCown (1981)	WPM macronutrients. See Part 1 page 394											
952	174	8	Samartin (1992)	B5 macronutrients. See Part 1 page 394											
975	175	1	McCown & Amos (1979)	Gamborg (1966) PRL-4-C macronutrients. See Part 1 page 394											
	175	2	Chalupa (1981a) BTM	190		165	640	44	370		170		860	240	
	175	3	Lloyd & McCown (1981)	WPM macronutrients. See Part 1 page 394											
976	176	1	Gupta & Mascarenhas (1987)	MS macronutrients											
	176	2	Gupta & Mascarenhas (1987)	½MS medium (macronutrients)											
	176	3	Burger (1987)	½MS macronutrients											
	176	4	Das & Mitra (1990)	1900		1650		146	370		170				
	176	5	Lakshmi Sita & Shobha Rani (1985)	1900		1650		440	370		170				
979	179	2	Whitehead & Giles (1977)	MS macronutrients. See Part 1 page 395											
	179	4	Welander et al.(1989)	Chu et al. (1975) N6 macronutrients. See Part 1 page 393											
	179	6	Nadel et al. (1992)	500		500	250		17.5	32.5	150				5
	179	7	Driver & Kuniyuki (1984)			1417	1960	147	740		259		1560		
	179	8	Thompson & Gordon (1977)	Murashige et al.(1972b) macronutrients. See Part 1 page 395											
	79	9	Coleman & Ernst (1989)			1650	2000	96	370		170				6
998	184	2	Cheng (1977, 1978)	950		825		220	185		85				
	184	3	Litvay et al.(1981) LM	1900		1650		22	1850		340				
	184	4	Gresshoff & Doy (1972) 1.	Gamborg (1966) PRL-4-C macronutrients. See Part 1 page 394											
	184	5	Sommer et al. (1975) GD	Gamborg (1966) PRL-4-C macronutrients. See Part 1 page 394											
	184	6	Reilly & Washer (1977) GD	Gamborg (1966) PRL-4-C macronutrients. See Part 1 page 394											
	184	7	Horgan & Aitken (1981)	Gamborg (1966) PRL-4-C macronutrients. See Part 1 page 394											
	184	8	Campbell & Durzan (1975)	340		800	980		370	65	170				
	184	9	Schenk and Hildebrandt (1972)	See Part 1 page 395											
999	184	10	Horgan & Aitken (1981) SH mod.	Schenk & Hildebrandt (1972) macronutrients. See Part 1 page 395											
	184	11	Reilly & Washer (1977) SH	Schenk & Hildebrandt (1972) macronutrients. See Part 1 page 395											
	184	12	Von Arnold and Eriksson (1981) LPm	See Part 1 page 396											
	184	14	David et al. (1982a)	Margara (1977, 1978) N30K macronutrients. See Part 1 page 394											
	184	15	Bornman (1983) MCM	2022			472		247	149	272			397	7
	184	16	Aitken Christie (1984) LP	1800		400	1200		360		270				
	184	17	Gupta & Durzan (1985) DCR	340		400	556	85	370		170				
	184	18	Amerson et al. (1988) BLG	101.1				440	370	745.5	170				
1008	190	1	Von Arnold & Eriksson (1981) LPm	see Part 1, page 396											
	190	2	Von Arnold & Hakman (1988b)	950		1200		90	185		170				
	190	3	Lainé and David (1990)	950		1200		90	185		170				
	190	4	Norgaard & Krogstrup (1990)	½MS macronutrients.											
	190	5	Litvay et al. (1981) LM	1900		1650		22	1850		340				
	190	6	Verhagen & Wann (1989) ½ BLG	50				220	160	372	85				
	190	7	Verhagen & Wann (1989) HM	1900		1200		180	370		340				
	190	8	Krogstrup (1986) BMI-S	2335.4		272.2		220	185		85				
	190	9	Finer et al. (1989)	340		400	556	85	370		170				
1019	193	1	Standardi & Catalano (1985) Stage 1	1800		400	1200		360		270				
	193	2	Standardi & Catalano (1985) Stage 2	1800		400	1200		360		270				
	193	3	Standardi & Catalano (1985) Stage 3	900		200	600		180		135				
1023	196	2	Murashige & Tucker (1969)	MS macronutrients.											
	196	3	Cohen & Cooper (1982)	Knop (1865) macronutrients. See Part 1 page 394											
	196	4	Mondal et al. (1990)	MS macronutrients											

Page	Table	No.	Medium	KNO_3	$NaNO_3$	NH_4NO_3	$Ca(NO_3)_2 \cdot 4H_2O$	$CaCl_2 \cdot 2H_2O$	$MgSO_4 \cdot 7H_2O$	KCl	KH_2PO_4	$NaH_2PO_4 \cdot H_2O$	K_2SO_4	$(NH_4)_2SO_4$	See notes
	196	5	Drew & Smith (1986)	2022		1601		294.1	739.5			138.01			
	196	6	Drew & Miller (1989)	1011		800.5		294.1	369.8			138.01			
1027	199	1	Anderson (1975)	950		2000		440	370		170	170			
	199	2	Anderson (1978a; 1980b))	480		400		440	370			380			
	199	3	Lyrene (1980)	190			1140		370		170				
	199	4	Zimmerman & Broome (1980) Z-2	202		160	708		370		408			198	
	199	5	Lloyd & McCown (1981)	WPM macronutrients. See Part 1 page 394											
	199	6	Economou & Read (1984)	See Part 1 page 393											
	199	7	Eccher et al.(1986)	See Part 1 page 393											
1030	201	2	Driver and Kuniyuki (1984) DKW			1417	1960	147	740		259		1560		
	201	3	Gruselle and Boxus (1990) A	1516.5		600.4		220	185		85				
	201	4	Gruselle and Boxus (1990) B	3033		1200.8		440	370		170				
1035	203	1	Rugini (1984) OM	1100		412	600	440	1500	500	340				
1037	204	1	Adams (1972)	MS macronutrients.											
	204	2	Jones & Vine (1968) Med C	Knop (1865) macronutrients. See Part 1 page 394											
	204	3	Van Hoof (1974) M	373	240	165	805.9	169.6	150	305		575.1		79	8
	204	4	Van Hoof (1974) T	373	240	165	805.9	169.6	150	305		575.1		79	8
	204	5	Mullin et al. (1974) A	Knop (1865) macronutrients. See Part 1 page 394											
	204	6	Mullin et al. (1974) B	Knop (1865) macronutrients. See Part 1 page 394											
	204	7	Boxus (1974a) Meristems	Knop (1865) macronutrients. See Part 1 page 394											
	204	8	Boxus (1974a) Rooting	Knop (1865) macronutrients. See Part 1 page 394											
1038	205	1	Boxus (1974a)	Knop (1865) macronutrients. See Part 1 page 394											
1043	—	—	Tabachnik and Kester (1977)	200			1140		839		200				9
1044/5	209	1	Reeves et al. (1983)	950		825		220	185		85	170			
	209	2	Jona and Vigliocco (1985, 1987)	1820		400.3	1181		370		544.4				
	209	4	Marino (1991)	1900		825		440	370		510.3				
	209	5	Righetti et al. (1988)	1900		825		440	370		170				
	209	6	Ranjit et al. (1988a)	950		825		220	370		170				
	209	7	Tchernets et al. (1987)	700		1650		440	370		170				
	209	8	Tchernets et al. (1987)	1900		2200		440	370		170				
1050	211	1	Rodriguez et al. (1991)	950		825		880	740		170				
	211	2	Quoirin and Lepoivre (1977)	1800		400	200		3600		2700				10
	211	2	Q and L (1977) [ammended]	1800		400	1200		360		270				
1051	212	2	Anderson (1978a, 1980b)	480		400		440	370			380			
	212	3	Pyott & Converse (1981)	475		412.5		110	92.5		42.5	170			
	212	4	Wellander (1985c)	950		825		440	370		170				
1056	213	2	Webb and Street (1977) CI	340		800	980		370	65	170				
	213	3	Harris and Stevenson (1982) A	1425		1238		330	278		128	170			
	213	4	Stevenson and Monette (1983) I	1425		1238		330	278		128	128			
	213	5	Murashige (1974)	1900		1650		440	370		170	170			
	213	6	Miller and Murashige (1976) II	1900		1650		440	370		170	170			
	213	7	Troncoso et al. (1988)	480		400	719.5	440	370			380		300	
1059	215	1	Galzy and Compan (1988)	131.4		160.1	495.9		123.3		122.5				
	215	2	Moriguchi and Yamaki (1989)	1900·		99		440	370		170				
1088	218	3	Paterson & Everett (1985)HaR	6900		1650		440	370		170				
	218	4	Witrzens et al. (1981) 1.	¾MS macronutrients.											
	218	5	Witrzens et al. (1981) 2.	½MS macronutrients.											
	218	6	Freyssinet & Freyssinet (1988)	MS macronutrients.											
1094	221	2	Green (1982)	MS macronutrients.											
	221	3	Carman et al.(1988a)	2 × macronutrients.											
	221	4	Armstrong & Green (1985)	2830				166	185		400			463	
1097	223	2	Norstog (1973) Barley II					740	740	750	910				
	223	3	Jensen (1977) C-17	300		200		250	325	150	150		100		
1119	228	1	Mantell and Hugo (1989) T	80			300		720	65	16.5				11
	228	2	Chaturvedi and Sinha (1979b)	1500		1500		400	360		150				
1135	232	2	Schenk & Hildebrandt (1972)	2500				200	400						12

Page	Table	No.	Medium	KNO_3	$NaNO_3$	NH_4NO_3	$Ca(NO_3)_2.4H_2O$	$CaCl_2.2H_2O$	$MgSO_4.7H_2O$	KCl	KH_2PO_4	$NaH_2PO_4.H_2O$	K_2SO_4	$(NH_4)_2SO_4$	See notes
	232	3	Walker et al.(1978) BI2Y	1000		1000	500		35	65	300				
	232	4	Saunders & Bingham (1972) BOi2Y	Blaydes (1966) Version 2 macronutrients. See Part 1 page 393											
	232	5	Bingham et al. (1975) BII	Blaydes (1966) Version 2 macronutrients. See Part 1 page 393											
	232	6	Stuart & Strickland (1984b)	2500					200	400		359.9		1651.9	
	232	8	Atanassov & Vlachova (1985)	Gamborg et al. (1968) B5 macronutrients. See Part 1 page 394											
	232	9	Atanassov & Brown (1984B5h	3000					1020	500		150		134	
1136	233	1	Kartha et al. (1974a)	MS macronutrients.											
	233	2	Gamborg et al. (1974) B5N	3538.5					150	250		150		792.9	
	233	3	Nauerby et al. (1991)	2500	250				300	250		150		134	
1139	235	3	Oswald et al. (1977c) C	1000		1000	500		35	65	300				
	235	4	Oswald et al. (1977c) F	1000		1000	500		35	65	300				
	235	5	Oswald et al. (1977c) H	1000		1000	500		35	65	300				
	235	6	Phillips & Collins (1979a) L2	2100		1000		600	435		325	85			
	235	7	Gresshoff (1980) A	Gamborg et al. (1968) B5 macronutrients. See Part 1 page 394											
	235	8	Gresshoff (1980) C	MS macronutrients.											
1139	235	9	Gresshoff (1980) D	½MS macronutrients.											
	235	10	Maheswaran & Williams (1984) EC6	950		600			220	185	170				
1152	239	1	Chen Z. (1984)	424.6			708		123.3		125.2				
	239	2	Carron & Enjalric (1985) MH1	2022		1601			441.1	739		276			13
	239	3	Carron & Enjalric (1985) MH2	950		825			582.9	739		680			14
1156	242	2	Nwankwo & Krikorian (1983)	950		825			220	185	85	170			
	242	3	Tisserat (1982)	Murashige et al.(1972b) macronutrients. See Part 1 page 395											
	242	4	Eeuwens (1976) Y3	See Part 1 page 393											
	242	5	Booij et al. (1993)	1500		480	492		492		272				
	242	6	Karunaratne and P. Kaushalya (1989)	2022		1601			441.1	739.5		276			15
1163	243	2	Sondahl et al. (1984) 1.	Gamborg et al. (1968) B5 macronutrients. See Part 1 page 394											
	243	3	Sondahl et al. (1984) 2.	MS macronutrients											
	243	4	Sondahl et al. (1984) Pre–incubation	½ MS macronutrients											
	243	5	Sondahl and Sharp (1977a) 2.	3800		825			220	185	85				
	243	6	Yasuda et al. (1985)	475		412.5			110	92.5	85				

Notes.

1. Na_2SO_4 22.0 mg/l;

2. K_2HPO_4 200 mg/l:

3. K_2HPO_4 300 mg/l: NaCl 100 mg/l

4. NaCl 100: mg/l

5. Ca gluconic acid 3mM:

6. K_2SO_4 990 mg/l

7. Urea 150 mg/l:

8. Na_2SO_4 450 mg/l:

9. Mg originally given as 410 mg/l $MgSO_4$ (no hydrate):

10. This composition is as printed in the 1977 paper, but was almost certainly misprinted. We think the correct composition (given by authors such as Jona and Viglocco, 1985; Boxus et al., 1991) is as given on the line below.

11. Na_2SO_4 200 mg/l

12. $NH_4H_2PO_4$ 300 mg/l:

13. Na_2SO_4 92.4 mg/l:

14. Na_2SO_4 92.4 mg/l.

15. Na_2SO_4 92.3 mg/l (0.65 mM).

NOTES ADDED IN PROOF

Flowering and juvenility.

Articles appearing in Nature while Part 2 has been in proof, have raised interesting points regarding flowering and juvenility.

In *Arabidopsis*, the commitment of apical and lateral shoot meristems to form flowers instead of shoots has been shown to be controlled by the combined, but overlapping, functions of the genes LEAFY (LFY), APETALA1 (AP1), and CAULIFLOWER. These loci are normally transcriptionally activated by flower promoting signals such as plant age and daylength and are then only expreesed in young flower meristems. However, transgenic plants of *Arabidopsis* produced by introducing LFY (Weigel and Nilsson, 1995), or AP1 (Mandel and Yanofsky, 1995) attached to the cauliflower mosaic virus 35S promoter, are expressed in every cell (constitutively). In these circumstances both genes have been found to cause lateral meristems to be converted to floral buds, and to cause the transgenic plants to flower well in advance of normal.

Of outstanding interest has been the demonstration that in transgenic aspen (*Populus tremula* × *P. temuloides*)[†], and transgenic *Nicotiana tabacum*, the constitutive expression of LFY causes precocious flower formation (Weigel and Nilsson, 1995). Aspen trees do not normally commence flowering until they are at least 8 years old: the transgenic plants flowered *in vitro* after 5 months, or if rooted and moved to the greenhouse, after 7 months.

Implications

Plants which flower before they have grown to a satisfactory size will not normally be of value, but accelerated flowering which permits the time between successive generations to be shortened, would be of considerable value in some plant breeding programmes.

As it is possible to induce flowering by attaching genes to a promoter which ensures transcription, will it soon be possible to prevent flowering and retain or initiate a permanently juvenile condition by preventing the expression of appropriate genes? Maintenance of the high growth rates and habit associated with juvenility could be of great advantage in trees grown for timber production.

In some plants (*e.g.* sunflower and bamboo), *in vitro* culture can result in premature flowering (Chapter 17). By analogy with the results in *Arabidopsis,* it would appear that, in these species, one or more factors of the *in vitro* environment leads to premature transcription of flower promoting genes.

In vitro culture also leads to rejuvenation, particularly of woody plants. One might conjecture that here too, genes which facilitate such phenomena as root initiation either become expressed or are no longer repressed so that they can be transcribed in the presence of a suitable stimulus (auxin?). Or does the cultural environment prevent the expression of genes which normally determine the mature state?

Hyperhydricity

The suggestion that agar may contain substances which can prevent hyperhydricity was mentioned on pages 339 and 664. Nairn (1995, reported by Aitken–Christie *et al.*, 1995) has announced the identification of a sulphonated galactan in agar, which is able to prevent the symptoms of hyperhydricity when added back to semi–solid or liquid media. This active principle can be used at every cultural stage except rooting.

---

†   Obtained by transformation of stem segments, and the subsequent *in vitro* regeneration of plantlets

Bibliography

To economise in space, references which were included in Part 1, have been excluded from the following list.

Search the Part 1 Bibliography too !

ABBOTT A.J. 1978 Practice and promise of micropropagation in woody species. Acta Hort., **79**, 113–127.

ABBOTT A.J. & WHITELEY E. 1976 Culture of *Malus* tissues *in vitro*. 1. Multiplication of apple plants from isolated shoot apices. Scientia Hort., **4**, 183–189.

ABDULLAH A.A., GRACE J. & YEOMAN M.M. 1989 Rooting and establishment of Calabrian pine plantlets propagated *in vitro*: influence of growth substances, rooting medium and origin of explant. New Phytol., **113**, 193–202.

ABDULLAH A.A., YEOMAN M.M. & GRACE J. 1985 *In vitro* adventitious shoot formation from embryonic and cotyledonary tissues of *Pinus brutia* Ten. Plant Cell Tiss. Organ Cult., **5**, 35–44.

ABDULLAH A.A., YEOMAN M.M. & GRACE J. 1987 Micropropagation of mature Calabrian pine (*Pinus brutia* Ten.) from fascicular buds. Tree Physiol., **3**, 123–136.

ABE J., NAKASHIMA H., MITOUI K., MIKAMI T. & SHIMAMOTO Y. 1991 Tissue culture response of *Beta* germplasm: callus induction and plant regeneration. Plant Cell Tiss. Organ Cult., **27**, 123–127.

ABE T. & FUTSUHARA Y. 1985 Efficient plant regeneration by somatic embryogenesis from root callus tissues of rice (*Oryza sativa* L.). J. Plant Physiol., **121**, 111–118.

ABO EL–NIL M.M. 1977 Organogenesis and embryogenesis in callus cultures of garlic (*Allium sativum* L.). Plant Sci. Lett., **9**, 259–264.

ABO EL–NIL M.M. 1979 Genetic heterogeneity of *in vitro* shoot initiation in conifers. In Vitro, **15**, 210 (Abst.194).

ABO EL–NIL M. 1987 Tissue culture of Douglas fir and Western North American conifers. pp. 80–100 in Bonga and Durzan (eds.) 1987 (*q.v.*).

ABO EL–NIL M.M. & HILDEBRANDT A.C. 1871a In Vitro, **6**, 399 (Abst. 103).

ABOU–MANDOUR A. 1977a Ein Standardnahrmedium fur die Anzucht von Kalluskulturen einiger Arzneipflanzen. Z. Pflanzenphysiol., **85**, 273–277.

ABOU–MANDOUR A.A. & HARTUNG W. 1980 The effect of abscisic acid on growth and development of intact seedlings, root and callus cultures and stem and root segments of *Phaseolus coccineus*. Z. Pflanzenphysiol., 100, 25–33.

ABOU–MANDOUR A.A., CZYGAN F.–C., HAASS D. & FRANZ G. 1987 Fructan synthesis in tissue cultures of *Symphytum officinale* L. initiation, differentiation and metabolic activity. Planta Med., **53**, 482–487.

ABOU–MANDOUR A., FISCHER S. & CZYGAN F.-C. 1979 Regeneration von intakten Pflanzen aus diploiden und haploiden von *Catharanthus roseus*. Z. Pflanzenphysiol., **91**, 83–88.

ABOU–ZEID A. 1972 Embryoachseukultur von kirschen in flussiger nahrlosung. Gartenbauwiss., 37, 273–280.

ABOU–ZEID A. & GRUPPE W. 1972 Das wachstum von kirschenembryonen verschiedener arten und sorten in abhangigheit von dem grad der embryoentwicklung, temperaturbehandlung und nahrmedian. Gartenbauwiss., 37, 225–238.

ABRAHAM H. & RAMACHANDRAN K. 1960 Growing *Colocasia* embryos in culture. Current Sci., 29, 342–343.

ABU–QAOUD H., SKIRVIN R.M. & BELOW F.E. 1991 Influence of nitrogen form and NH$_4^+$–N/NO$_3^-$–N ratios on adventitious shoot formation from pear (*Pyrus communis*) leaf explants *in vitro*. Plant Cell Tiss. Organ Cult., 27, 315–319.

ABURKHES M., FAAMI N., BENHMEDA A., NAFFATI M. & ZIGLAM A. 1991 Virus free potatoes by tissue culture in Libya. Acta Hort., **289**, 77–79.

ACEDO G.N. 1986 Regeneration of *Arabidopsis* callus *in vitro*. Plant Cell Tiss. Organ Cult., 6, 109–114.

ADACHI T., YAMAGUCHI A., MIIKE Y. & HOFFMANN F. 1989 Plant regeneration from protoplasts of common buckwheat (*Fagopyrum esculentum*). Plant Cell Rep., **8**, 247–250.

ADAMS R.M., KOENIGSBERG S.S. & LANGHANS R.W. 1979a *In vitro* propagation of *Cephalotus follicularis* (Australian pitcher plant). HortScience, **14**, 512–513.

ADAMS R.M., KOENIGSBERG S.S. & LANGHANS R.W. 1979b *In vitro* propagation of the butterwort *Pinguicula moranensis* H.B.K. HortScience, 14, 701–702.

ADAMSON W.C. & O'BRYAN J.E. 1981 Plant differentiation of *Hibiscus hierianus* from callus grown from embryo explants. Env. Exp. Bot., **21**, 434–435.

ADEJARE G.O. & COUTTS R.H.A. 1981 Eradication of cassava mosaic disease from Nigerian cassava (*Manihot esculenta*) clones by meristem–tip culture. Plant Cell Tiss. Organ Cult., **1**, 25–32.

ADUAYI E.A. & EDOWU E.O. 1981 The response of Okra *Abelmoschus–esculentus* cultivar Emerald to Molybdenum in sand culture. Commun.Soil Sci.Plant Anal., **12**, (10) 965–978.

AERTS J. 1977 The importance of virus–free planting material for glasshouse strawberry culture. Med. Fac. Landbouwwet. Rijksuniv. Gent, **42**, 1135–1139 (HA 48 6377).

AFELE J.C. & DE LANGHE E. 1991 Increasing *in vitro* germination of *Musa balbisiana* seed. Plant Cell Tiss. Organ Cult., **27**, 33–36.

AGARWAL B., SINGH U. & BANERJEE M. 1992 *In vitro* clonal propagation of tea *Camellia sinensis* (L.) O. Kuntze. Plant Cell Tiss. Organ Cult., **30**, 1–5.

AGGARWAL R. K., SHARMA D. R. & SINGH R. K. 1982 Isolation and culture of mesophyll protoplasts of a few *Brassica* species. pp. 593–594 in Fujiwara (ed.) 1982 (*q.v.*)

AGHION D. & BEAUCHESNE G. 1960 Utilisation de la technique de la culture stérile d'organes pour obtenir des clones d'ananas. Fruits, **15**, 444–446.

AGNIHOTRI A., LAKSHMIKUMARAN M., SHIVANNA K.R. & JAGANNATHAN V. 1990 Embryo rescue of interspecific hybrids of *Brassica spinescens* × *Brassica campestris* and DNA analysis. pp. 270–274 in Nijkamp *et al.* (eds.) 1990 (*q.v.*).

AGRAWAL S., CHANDRA N. & KOTHARI S.L. 1989 Plant regeneration in tissue cultures of pepper (*Capsicum annuum* L.) cv. mathania. Plant Cell Tiss. Organ Cult., **16**, 47–55.

AGUETTAZ P., PAFFEN A., DEL VALLEE I., VAN DER LINDE P. & DE KLERK G.–J. 1990 The development of dormancy in bulblets of *Lilium* speciosum generated *in vitro*. 1. The effects of culture conditions. Plant Cell Tiss. Organ Cult., **22**, 167–172.

AHLOOWALIA B. S. 1978 Novel ryegrass genotypes regenerated from embryo–callus culture. p. 515 in Thorpe (ed.) *Frontiers of Plant Tissue Culture*. Calgary, Canada: University of Calgary.

AHLOOWALIA B.S. 1982 Plant regeneration from callus culture in wheat. Crop Sci., **22**, 405–410.

AHMED H.A. & ANDREA M. 1987 Effect of heat treatment on acceleration of *Chrysanthemum* multiplication by meristem–tip culture. Acta Hort., **212**, 99–106.

AHN B.J., HUANG F.H. & KING J.W. 1984 Callus growth and plant regeneration in Bermudagrass tissue culture. In Vitro, **20**, 277–278.

AHN B.J., HUANG F.H. & KING J.W. 1985 Somatic embryogenesis in common bermudagrass. pp. 299–300 in Henke *et al.* (eds.) 1985 (*q.v.*).

AHN C.S. & HARTMAN R.W. 1978 Interspecific hybridization between rice bean *Vigna umbellata* (Thunb.) Ohwi & Ohashi and Adzuki bean *V. angularis* (Willd.) Ohwi & Ohashi. J. Am. Soc. Hort. Sci., **103**, 435–438.

AHUJA M.R. 1984 A commercially feasible micropropagation method for aspen. Silvae Genetica, **33**, 174–176.

AHUJA M.R. 1984 *In vitro* induction of organogenesis in juvenile and mature beech. Silvae Genetica, **33**, 241–242.

AHUJA P.S., HADIUZZAMAN S., DAVEY M.R. & COCKING E.C. 1983 Prolific plant regeneration from protoplast–derived tissues of *Lotus corniculatus* L. (Birdsfoot trefoil). Plant Cell Rep., **2**, 101–104.

AHUJA P.S., LU D.Y., COCKING E.C. & DAVEY M.R. 1983 An assessment of the cultural capabilities of *Trifolium repens* L. (white clover) and *Onobrychis viciifolia* Scop. (Sainfoin) mesophyll protoplasts. Plant Cell Rep., **2**, 269–272.

AHUJA P.S., PENTAL D. & COCKING E.C. 1982 Plant regeneration from leaf base callus and cell suspensions of *Triticum aestivum*. Z. Pflanzenzuchtg., **89**, 139–144.

AIDID S.B. & THAIN J.F. 1980a Comparative studies of leaf tissue and isolated mesophyll cells of *Antirrhinum majus* L. I. O_2 exchange and CO_2 fixation. J. Exp. Bot., **31**, 1035–1042.

AIDID S.B. & THAIN J.F. 1980b Comparative studies of leaf tissue and isolated mesophyll cells of *Antirrhinum majus* L. J. Exp. Bot., **31**, 1043–1049.

AIRD E.L.H., HAMILL J.D. & RHODES M.J.C. 1988 Cytogenetic analysis of hairy root cultures from a number of plant species transformed by *Agrobacterium rhizogenes*. Plant Cell Tiss. Organ Cult., **15**, 47–57.

AITKEN J. & THORPE T.A. 1979 Histological & histochemical studies of adventitious shoot formation from embryonic tissues of Radiata pine. In Vitro, **15**, 191 (Abst.112).

AITKEN–CHRISTIE J. 1991 Automation. pp. 363–388 in Debergh and Zimmerman (eds.) 1991 (*q.v.*).

AITKEN–CHRISTIE J. & DAVIES H.E. 1988 Development of a semi–automated micropropagation system. Acta Hort., **230**, 81–87.

AITKEN–CHRISTIE J., DAVIES H.E., HOLLAND L., KUBOTA C. & FUJIWARA K. 1992 Effect of nutrient media composition on sugar–free growth and chlorophyll fluorescence of *Pinus radiata* shoots *in vitro*. Acta Hort., **319**, 125–130.

AITKEN–CHRISTIE J., DAVIES H.E., SIVITER J. & NAIRN B. 1989 Automation in the micropropagation of Radiata pine. In Vitro Cell Dev. Biol., **25**, (3) 22A.

AITKEN–CHRISTIE J., SIGLEY M. & WILLIAMS N. 1995 Highlights of the 11th Biennial Conf. of the New Zealand IAPTC, 12-15th February 1995. Plant Tiss. Cult. & Biotech. **1**, 95–100.

AITKEN–CHRISTIE J., SINGH A. P., HORGAN K. J. & THORPE T. A. 1982 pp. 175–176 in Fujiwara (ed.) 1982 (*q.v.*)

AITKEN–CHRISTIE J., SINGH A.P. & DAVIES H. 1988 Multiplication of meristematic tissue: a new culture system for radiata pine. pp. 413–432 in Hanover and Keathley (eds.) 1988 (*q.v.*).

AKE S. & LAMBERT C. 1987 *In vitro* culture of *Platanus acerifolia* in relation with canker stain disease induced by *Ceratocystis fimbriata*. Acta Hort., **212**, 539–542.

AKRAM M., ILAHI I. & MIRZA M.A. 1986 Acclimatization of *in vitro* raised plants of *Rauwolfia serpentina* Benth. p. 29 in Somers et al. (eds.) 1986 (*q.v.*).

AL MAARRI K., ARNAUD Y. & MIGINIAC E. 1986 *In vitro* micropropagation of quince (*Cydonia oblonga* Mill). Scientia Hort., **28**, 315–321.

AL MEHDI A.A. & PARFITT D.E. 1986 *In vitro* propagation of peach: 1. Propagation of 'Lovell' and 'Nemaguard' peach rootstocks. Fruit Var. J., **40**, 12–17.

AL WAREH H., TROLINDER N.L. & GOODIN J.R. 1989a Callus initiation, shoot regeneration, and micropropagation of three potato cultivars. HortScience, **24**, 680–682.

AL WAREH H., TROLINDER N.L. & GOODIN J.R. 1989b *In vitro* flowering of potato. HortScience, **24**, 827–829.

AL–ABTA S. & COLLIN H.A. 1978a Control of embryoid development in tissue cultures of celery. Ann. Bot., **42**, 773–782.

AL–ABTA S. & COLLIN H.A. 1978b Cell differentiation in embryoids and plantlets of celery tissue cultures. New Phytol., **80**, 517–521.

AL–ABTA S. & COLLIN H.A. 1979 Endogenous auxin and cytokinin changes during embryoid development in celery tissue cultures. New Phytol., **82**, 29–35.

AL–ABTA S., GALPIN I.J. & COLLIN H.A. 1979 Flavour compounds in tissue cultures of celery. Plant Sci. Lett., **16**, 129–134.

AL–ATABEE J.S., MULLIGAN B.J. O POWER J.B. 1990 Interspecific somatic hybrids of *Rudbeckia hirta* and *R. laciniata* (Compositae). Plant Cell Rep., **8**, 517–520.

AL–JUBOORY K., SKIRVIN R.M. & WILLIAMS D.J. 1991b Improved flowering of cotyledon–derived shoots of 'Burpless Hyrid' cucumber *in vitro*. HortScience, **26**, 1085.

AL–JUBOORY K.H., WILLIAMS D.J. & SKIRVIN R.M. 1991a Growth regulators influence root and shoot development of micro– propagated Algerian ivy. Hort-Science, **26**, 1079–1080.

AL–KHAYRI J.M., HANG F.H., MORELOCK T.E. & BUSHARAR T.A. 1992 Spinach tissue culture improved with coconut water. HortScience, **27**, 357–358.

AL–KHAYRI J.M., HUANG F.H. & MORELOCK T.E. 1991 Regeneration of Spinach from leaf callus. HortScience, **26**, 913–914.

AL–KHAYRI J.M., HUANG F.H., MOREL.CK T.E. & BUSHARAR T.A. 1992 Stimulation of shoot regeneration in spinach callus by gibberellic acid. HortScience, **27**, 1046.

AL–KHAYRI J.M., HUANG F.H., MORELOCK T.E. & LANE F.E. 1991 *In vitro* flowering in regenerated shoots of spinach. HortScience, **26**, 1422.

AL–MEHDI A. & HOGAN L. 1976 Tissue culture of *Carica papya*. HortScience, **11**, 311 (Abst. 158).

AL–MEHDI A.A. & HOGAN L. 1979 *In vitro* growth and development of Papaya (*Carica papaya* L.) and date palm (*Phoenix dactylifera* L.). Plant Physiol., **63**, 5 (Abst. 553).

ALBERS M.R.J. & KUNNEMAN B.P.A.M. 1992 Micropropagation of *Paeonia*. Acta Hort., **314**, 85–92.

ALBRECHT C. & KOHLENBACH H.W. 1989 Induction of somatic embryogenesis in leaf–derived callus of *Vicia narbonensis* L. Plant Cell Rep., **8**, 267–269.

ALCONERO R. 1983 Regeneration of plants from cell suspensions of *Lactuca saligna, Lactuca sativa* and *L. serriola*. HortScience, **18**, 305–307.

ALDERSON P.G. & TAEB A.G. 1990b Effect of bulb storage on shoot regeneration from floral stems of tulip *in vitro*. J. Hort. Sci., **65**, 65–70.

ALDERSON P.G., RICE R.D. & WRIGHT N.A. 1983 Towards the propagation of tulip *in vitro*. Acta Hort., **131**, 39–47.

ALDRUFEU A., PAGES M., MASSEGUER J. & MELE E. 1983 *In vitro* rhizogenesis of *Rosa* sp. in different substrates. Acta Hort., **150**, 315–323.

ALDWINCKLE H.S. & BUTURAC I. 1981 *In vitro* culture of grapevine for study of obligate pathogens. Env. Exp. Bot., **21**, 439 (Abst.).

ALDWINKLE S., GUSTAFSON H.L. & BUTURAC I. 1981 *In vitro* propagation of 'Poorman' gooseberry. Env. Exp. Bot., **21**, 440 (Abst.).

ALEXANDER M.P. & RAO T.C.R. 1968 *In vitro* culture of bamboo embryos. Current Sci., **37**, 415–416.

ALFERMANN A.W. & REINHARD E. (eds.) 1978 *Production of Natural Compounds by Cell Culture Methods*. Proc. Int. Symp. on Plant Cell Culture. Tubingen, 1977.

ALFERMANN A.W. & REINHARD E. (eds.) 1980 Biotransformation by plant tissue cultures. pp. 399–410 in Sala et al. (eds.) 1980 (*q.v.*).

ALFONSO A. & CAPOTE A. 1980 Culture of sugar cane tissues; their establishment and the subsequent regeneration of plants *in vitro*. (In Spanish). Ciencias de la Agricultura (1980), **6**, 29–34.

ALI N., SKIRVIN R., SPLITTS TOESSER W.E. & GEORGE W.L. 1991 Germination and regeneration of plants from old cucumber seed. HortScience, **26**, 917–918.

ALLARD J.M., BLAKE J., GRIFFIN D.P. & HUTCHINSON M. 1991 Method for micropropation of seed potatoes and harvesting microtubers – plants grown in containers and planted in gel cut and transferred by gravity or air–flow to second container filled with gel and replanted. World Patent Applic. No. 9115110.

ALLAVENA A. 1984 Chapter 6 — Beans (*Phaseolus*). pp. 137–168 in Sharp *et al.* (eds.) 1984 (*q.v.*).

ALLAVENA A. & ROSSETTI L. 1983 Efforts in somatic embryogenesis of *Phaseolus vulgaris* L. Acta Hort., **131**, 239–246.

BARUAH A. & BORDOLOI D.N. 1989 High frequency plant regeneration of *Cymbopogon martinii* (Roxb.) Wats. by somatic embryogenesis and organogenesis. Plant Cell Rep., **8**, 483–485.

BARUCH E.R. & QUAK F. 1966 Virus–free plants of Iris 'Wedgewood' obtained by meristem culture. Neth. J. Plant Path., **72**, 270–273.

BARWALE U.B. & WIDHOLM J.M. 1990 Whole plant regeneration via organogenesis and somaclonal variation in *Glycine* species. U.S. Patent No. 4857465.

BARZ W., REINHARD E. & ZENK M. H. 1977 *Plant Tissue Culture and its Bio–technological Application.* Springer–Verlag. Berlin, Heidelberg, New York.

BASARAN D., COLAK G., NAMLI O., ONAY A. & YUCEL S. 1991 Recherches sur l'obtention des plantes diploid en *in vitro* à partir des pistils de *Nicotiana rustica* L. Acta Hort., **289**, 215–216.

BASKIN J.M. & BASKIN C.C. 1971 Effect of chilling and gibberellic acid on growth potential of excised embryos of *Ruellia humilis*. Planta, **100**, 365–369.

BASS A. & HUGHES W. 1984 Conditions for isolation and regeneration of viable protoplasts of oil palm (*Elaeis guineensis*). Plant Cell Rep., **3**, 169–171.

BASS P., CLOG E. & WALTER B. 1988 Improvements in apex culture in *Vitis* species. Acta Hort., **227**, 485–488.

BASSI G. & COSSIO F. 1991 *In vitro* shoot regeneration of 'Bluefire' and 'Susina di Dro' prune cultivars (*Prunus domestica* L.). Acta Hort., **289**, 81–82.

BATES G.W. 1985 Optimization of electrofusion for the formation and culture of protoplast heterokaryons. pp. 304–305 in Henke *et al.* (eds) 1985 *(q.v.)*.

BATES S., PREECE J.E., NAVARETTE N.E., VAN SAMBEEK J.W. & GAFFNEY G.R. 1992 Thidiazuron stimulates shoot organogenesis and somatic embryogenesis in white ash (*Fraxinus americana* L.). Plant Cell Tiss. Organ Cult., **31**, 21–29.

BATEY J.W. 1977 Callus growth and organogenesis in cultures of *Zea mays* L. root tissue. Plant Physiol., **59 Supp.**, 2 (Abst. 4).

BAUBAULT C., LANOY V., BAUDIER F. & DUCOMMUN C. 1991 *In vitro* preservation of *Rhododendron* during multiplication and rhizogenesis stages. Acta Hort., **298**, 355–358.

BAUSHER M.G. & YELENOSKY G. 1988 Immunoblotting to detect a soluble glycoprotein from trifoliate orange in a citrus hybrid. HortScience, **23**, 768–770.

BAWA K.S. & STETTLER R.F. 1972 Organ culture with black cottonwood: morphogenetic response of female catkin primordia. Can. J. Bot., **50**, 1627–1631.

BAYLEY A.D. & VAN STADEN J. 1987 Propagation of *Gasteria croucheri* Bak. from shoot producing callus. Plant Cell Tiss. Organ Cult., **11**, 227–231.

BEACH K.H. & GRESSHOFF P.M. 1988 Characterization and culture of *Agrobacterium rhizogenes* transformed roots of forage legumes. Plant Science, **57**, 73–81.

BEASLEY C.A. 1977 Ovule culture: fundamental and pragmatic research for the cotton industry. pp. 160–178 in Reinert and Bajaj (eds.) 1977 *(q.v.)*.

BEASLEY C.A. & TING I.P. 1971 Axenic culture of cotton (*Gossypium hirsutum* L.) ovules. Am. J. Bot., 58, 475.

BEAUCHESNE G. 1974 Obtention de clone de *Pelargonium* en culture *in vitro* à partir de méristèmes. Proc. Int. Hort. Cong., **19**, (1A) 64.

BEAUJARD F., VIEMONT J.D. & LABAUME M.P. 1988 Discontinuous growth of twigs of two Ericaceae grown *in vitro*. Acta Hort., **227**, 408–410.

BECK M.J. & CAMPER N.D. 1991 Shoot regeneration from petunia leaf discs as a function of explant size, configuration and benzyladenine exposure. Plant Cell Tiss. Organ Cult., **26**, 101–106.

BECK M.J. & CAPONETTI J.D. 1983 The effects of kinetin and naphaleneacetic acid on *in vitro* shoot multiplication and rooting in the fishtail fern. Am. J. Bot., **70**, 1–7.

BECKER U. & REUTHER G. 1986 pp. 425–428 in Horn W. *et al.* (eds.) *Genetic Manipulation in Plant Breeding.* Walter de Gruyter & Co., Berlin, New York.

BECKER–ZENS R. 1983 Anther and embryo culture in *Pelargonium zonale* hybrids. Acta Hort., **131**, 209–213.

BECKER–ZENS R. & GRUNEWALDT J. 1984 Breeding research in kohlrabi (*Brassica oleracea* L. var. Gongylodes) Gartenbauwiss., **49**, 158–161.

BECWAR M.R., NOLAND T.L. & WANN S.R. 1986 Genotypic differences in somatic embryo development from Norway spruce embryogenic callus. p. 137 in Somers *et al.* (eds.) 1986 *(q.v.)*.

BECWAR M.R., WANN S.R., JOHNSON M.A., VERHAGEN S.A., FEIRER R.P. & NAGMANI R. 1987 Development and characterization of *in vitro* embryogenic systems in conifers. Tech. Paper Ser., Inst. Paper Chem., Appleton, WI, U.S.A. No. 258, 1–17.

BEEBE J.D. 1980 Morphogenetic responses of seedlings and adventitious buds of the carnivorous plant *Dionaea muscipula* in aseptic culture. Bot. Gaz., **141**, 396–400.

BEECH M.G., CRISP C.M., SIMPSON S.E. & ATKINSON D. 1988 The effect of *in vitro* cytokinin concentration on the fruiting and growth of conventionally propagated strawberry runner progeny. J. Hort. Sci., **63**, 77–81.

BEECHEY C.N. 1970 Propagation of orchids from aerial roots. Am. Orchid Soc. Bull., **39**, 1085–1088.

BEHKI R.M. & LESLEY S.M. 1976 *In vitro* plant regeneration from leaf explants of *Lycopersicum esculentum* (tomato). Can.J.Bot. 54 2409–2414.,

BEHNKE M. 1975 Regeneration in Gewebekulturen einiger dihaploider *Solanum tuberosum* Klone. Z. Pflanzenzucht., **75** , 262

BEJOY M. & HARIHARAN M. 1992 *In vitro* plantlet differentiation in *Annona muricata*. Plant Cell Tiss. Organ Cult., **31**, 245–247.

BELAIZI M., PAUL H., SANGWAN R.S. & SANGWAN–NORREEL B.S. 1990 Direct organogenesis from internodal segments of *in vitro* grown shoots of apple cv. Golden Delicious. Plant Cell Rep., **9** , 471–474.

BELAIZI M., PAUL H., SANGWAN R.S., BOXUS Ph. & SANGWAN–NORREEL B.S. 1991 *In vitro* regeneration of adventitious shoots from internodal segments of apple cv. Golden Delicious. Acta Hort., **289**, 83–84.

BELAY S.M. 1985 The culture of *Eragrostis tef in vitro*. p. 306 in Henke *et al.* (eds.) 1985 *(q.v.)*.

BELIVANIS T. & DORE C. 1986 Interspecific hybridization of *Phaseolus vulgaris* L. and *Phaseolus angustissimus* A. Gray using *in vitro* embryo culture. Plant Cell Rep., **5**, 329–331.

BELKENGREN R.O. & MILLER P.W. 1962 Culture of apical meristems of *Fragaria vesca* strawberry plants as a method of excluding latent virus. Plant Dis. Rep., **46**, 119–121.

BELL E.A. 1980 The possible significance of secondary compounds in plants. pp. 11–21 in Bell & Charlwood (eds.) 1980 *Secondary Plant Products. Encyclopedia of Plant Physiology* New Series Vol.8. Springer-Verlag, Berlin, Heidelberg, New York. ISBN 3-540-09461-X.

BELLATO C.M., BRAGIN A., CHEN Z., LIU S., SEREDUK T.B. & SONDAHL M.R. 1993 Somatic embryogenesis and plant regeneration of cacao plantlets – allows regeneration of somatic embryos from zygotic or non–zygotic tissue and plantlet regeneration from somatic embryos. World Patent Applic. No. 9312645.

BELOUALY N. 1991 Plant regeneration from callus culture of three *Citrus* rootstocks. Plant Cell Tiss. Organ Cult., **24** , 29–34.

BEN–JAACOV J. & LANGHANS R.W. 1972a A tissue culture technique for the rapid multiplication of *Chrysanthemum morifolium*. Proc. Int. Hort. Cong. 1970, **18**, (1) 211.

BENEDICIC D. RAVNIKAR M. & GOGALA N. 1991 The influence of jasmonic acid on the development of *Phaaseolus vulgaris* shoot culture. Acta Hort., **289**, 85–86.

BENJAMIN B.D., HEBLE M.R. & CHADHA M.S. 1979 Alkaloid synthesis in tissue cultures and regenerated plants of *Tylophora indica* (Asclepiadaceae). Z. Pflanzenphysiol., **92**, 77–84.

BENJAMIN B.D., SIPAHIMALANI A.T. & HEBLE M.R. 1990 Tissue cultures of *Artemisia pallens:* organogenesis, terpenoid production. Plant Cell Tiss. Organ Cult., **21**, 159–164.

BENNETT L.K. & DAVIES F.T. 1984a *In vitro* propagation of *Ungnadia speciosa* Endl. HortScience, **19**, 556.

BENNETT L.K. & DAVIES F.T. 1985 Micropropagation of *Cercis*. HortScience, **20**, 592.

BENTZ S.E. & PARLIMAN B.J. 1985 Source of explants for *in vitro* propagation of *Yucca glauca* Nutt. HortScience, **20**, 540.

BERETTA D., VANOLI M. & ECCHER T. 1988 The influence of glucose, vitamins and IBA on rooting of *Camellia* shoots *in vitro*. Acta Hort., **227**, 473–475.

BERG L.A. & BUSTAMANTE M. 1974 Heat treatment and meristem culture for the production of virus–free bananas. Phytopath., **64**, 320–322.

BERGERVOET J.H.W., VAN DER MARK F. & CLUSTERS J.B.M. 1989 Organogenesis versus embryogenesis from long–term suspension cultures of cucumber (*Cucumis sativus* L.). Plant Cell Rep., **8**, 116–119.

BERGMAN L., VON ARNOLD S. & ERIKSSON T. 1985 Effect of N6–benzyladenine on shoots of five willow clones (*Salix* spp.) cultured *in vitro*. Plant Cell Tiss. Organ Cult., **4**, 135–144.

BERGMANN L. 1964 Der Einfluss von Kinetin auf die Ligninbildung und Differenzierung in Gewebekulturen von *Nicotiana tabacum.* Planta, **62**, 221–254.

BERGONON S., SODINA C., BASTIDA J., VILADOMAT F. & MELE E. 1992 The shake liquid culture as an alternative way to the multiplication of *Narcissus* plants. Acta Hort., **325**, 447–452.

BERRIOS J.G. & ECONOMOU A.S. 1991 Study of the efficiency of gardenia shoot formation *in vitro.* Acta Hort., **300**, 51–57.

BERROS B., ASTORGA R., REY M., PENUELA R. & RODRIGUEZ R. 1993 Rooting studies on *in vitro* walnut tissues aging effect. Acta Hort., **311**, 105–116.

BERRY L.J. & NORRIS W.E. Jr. 1949 Studies of onion root respiration. I. Velocity of oxygen consumption in different segments of root at different temperatures as a function of partial pressure of oxygen. Biochim. Biophys. Acta, **3**, 593–606.

BERRY S. 1978 The effect of auxins, vitamins and light on *Peperomia caperata* tissue cultures. p. 247 in Hughes *et al.* (eds.) 1978 *(q.v.).*

BERRY S.F., LU D.Y., PENTAL D. & COCKING E.C. 1982 Regeneration of plants from protoplasts of *Lactuca sativa* L. Z. Pflanzenphysiol., **108**, 31–38.

BERTACCINI A., DAVIS R.E. & LEE I.M. 1992 *In vitro* micropropagation for maintenance of mycoplasma–like organisms in infected plant tissues. HortScience, **27**, 1041–1043.

BERTRAND L.J. & LALONDE M. 1985 *In vitro* propagation and nodulation by Frankia of actinorhizal Russian olive (*Elaeagnus angustifolia* L.) Plant & Soil, **87**, 143–152.

BERTRAND–DESBRUNAIS A., NOIROT M. & CHARRIER A. 1991 Minimal growth *in vitro* conservation of coffee (*Coffea* spp.). 1. Influence of low concentrations of 6–benzyladenine. Plant Cell Tiss. Organ Cult., **27**, 333–339.

BERTRAND–DESBRUNAIS A., NOIROT M. & CHARRIER A. 1992 Slow growth *in vitro* conservation of coffee (*Coffea* spp.). 2. Influences of reduced concentrations of sucrose and low temperature. Plant Cell Tiss. Organ Cult., **31**, 105–110.

BERTSCH W. 1967 A new frontier: Orchid propagation by meristem culture. Am. Orchid Soc. Bull., **36**, 32–37.

BERUTO M. & DEBERGH P. 1992 Somatic embryogenesis in *Ranunculus asiaticus* L. hybr. *thalamus* cultivated *in vitro.* Plant Cell Tiss. Organ Cult., **29**, 161–165.

BERUTO M. & DEBERGH P.C. 1991 Differences in availability of water to *in vitro* cultures using different brands of agar. Acta Hort., **289**, 331–333.

BESSEMBINDER J.J.E., STARITSKY G. & ZANDVOORT E.A. 1993 Long–term *in vitro* storage of *Colocasia esculenta* under minimal growth conditions. Plant Cell Tiss. Organ Cult., **33**, 121–127.

BEVERSDORF W.D. 1990 Micropropagation in crop species., pp. 3–12 in Nijkamp *et al.* (eds.) 1990 *(q.v.).*

BEVERSDORF W.D. & BINGHAM E.T. 1977 Degrees of differentiation obtained in tissue cultures of *Glycine* species. Crop Sci., **17**, 307–311.

BEVERSDORF W.D., WEISS–LERMAN J., ERICKSON L.R. & SOUZA MACHADO V. 1980 Transfer of cytoplasmically-inherited triazine resistance from bird's rape to cultivated oilseed rape (*Brassica campestris* and *B. napus*). Can.J.Genet.Cytol., **22**, 167–172.

BEWLEY J.D., BOWLEY S., BROWN D.C.W., McKERSIE B.D. & SENARATNA T. 1993 Inducing desiccation tolerance in somatic embryos – by inducing or applying abscisic acid at early stage of development then gradually drying. European Patent No. 300730.

BEYL C.A. & MITCHELL C.A. 1982 *In vitro* protection of indoleacetic acid during thin layer chromatography. HortScience **17**, 187–188.

BHAGYALAKSHMI & SINGH N.S. 1988 Meristem culture and microproagation of a variety of ginger (*Zingiber officinale* Rosc.) with a high yield of oleoresin. J. Hort. Sci., **63**, 321–327.

BHALA–SARIN N., BAGGA S., SOPORY S.K. & GUHA–MUKHERJEE S. 1986 Induction and differentiation of callus from embryos of *Cocos nucifera* L. by IAA–conjugates. Plant Cell Rep., **5**, 322–324.

BHARAL S. & RASHID A. 1979 Regeneration of plants from tissue cultures of the legume *Indigofera enneaphylla* Linn. Z. Pflanzenphysiol., **92**, 443–447.

BHARAL S. & RASHID A. 1981 Tissue culture of *Alhagi camelorum* – a legume of high regenerative capacity. Physiol. Plant., **53**, 497–500.

BHARGAVA S. & CHANDRA N. 1983 *In vitro* differentiation in callus cultures of moth bean, *Vigna aconitifolia* (Jacq) Marechal. Plant Cell Rep., **2**, 47–50.

BHAT R. & CHANDEL K.P.S. 1993 *In vitro* conservation of *Musa* germplasm: effects of mannitol and temperature on growth and storage. J. Hort. Sci., **68**, 841–846.

BHAT S.R., CHITRALEKHA P. & CHANDEL K.P.S. 1992 Regeneration of plants from long–term root culture of lime, *Citrus aurantifolia* (Christm.) Swing. Plant Cell Tiss. Organ Cult., **29**, 19–25.

BHATNAGAR S.P. & SINGH M.N. 1984 Organogenesis in the cultured female gametophyte of *Ephedra foliata.* J. Exp. Bot., **35**, 268–278.

BHATT B.P. & FASSULIOTIS G. 1981 Plant regeneration from mesophyll protoplasts of eggplant. Z. Pflanzenphysiol., **104**, 81–89.

BHATT D.P. & BHATT P.N. 1986 Production of a neurotoxic amino acid and somatic embryos in the cell suspension culture of a hardy legume, *Lathyrus sativus.* p. 64 in Somers *et al.* (eds.) 1986 *(q.v.).*

BHATT P.N., BHATT D.P. & SUSSEX I.M. 1979 Organ regeneration from leaf discs of *Solanum nigrum, S. dulcamara* and *S. khasianum.* Z. Pflanzenphysiol., **95**, 355–362.

BHATTACHARYA N.M. & SEN S.K. 1980 Production of plantlets through somatic embryogenesis in *Brassica campestris.* Z. Pflanzenphysiol., **99**, 357–366.

BHATTACHARYA P. & SEN S.K. 1980 Potentiality of leaf sheath cells for regeneration of rice (*Oryza sativa* L.) plants. Theor. Appl. Genet., **58**, 87–90.

BHATTACHARYA P., DEY S., DAS N. & BHATTACHARYA B. 1990 Rapid mass propagating of *Chrysanthemum morifolium* by callus derived from stem and leaf explants. Plant Cell Rep., **9**, 439–442.

BHATTACHARYA S. & GUPTA S. 1987 Growth and regenerating potentiality of roots of *Nigella sativa* L. in long term culture. Phytomorph., **37**, 303–306.

BHOJWANI S.S. 1966 Morphogenetic behaviour of mature endosperm of *Croton bonplandianum* Baill. in culture. Phytomorph., **16**, 349–353.

BHOJWANI S.S. 1978 *In vitro* propagation of garlic by shoot proliferation. Scientia Hort., **13**, 47–52.

BHOJWANI S.S. 1980 Micropropagation method for a hybrid willow (*Salix matsudana × alba* NZ – 1002). N. Z. J. Bot., **18** , 209–214.

BHOJWANI S.S. & JOHRI B.M. 1970 Cytokinin–induced shoot bud differentiation in mature endosperm of *Scurrula pulverulenta.* Z. Pflanzenphysiol., **63**, 269–275.

BHOJWANI S.S. & WHITE D.W.R. 1982 Mesophyll protoplasts of white clover: isolation culture and organogenesis. Plant Sci. Lett., **26**, 265–271.

BHOJWANI S.S., EVANS P.K. & COCKING E.C. 1977 Isolation, culture and division of cotton callus protoplasts. Plant Sci. Lett., **8**, 85–89.

BHOJWANI S.S., MULLINS K. & COHEN D. 1984 *In vitro* propagation of *Pyrus pyrifolia.* Scientia Hort., **23**, 247–254.

BIDNEY D., BURRUS M., GARNAAT V.W. & HEATON T. 1992 New sunflower plants of variety PTO24 able to regenerate fertile plants for use in research or commercial seed production. European Patent No. 490600.

BIDNEY D.L. & SHEPARD J.F. 1980 Colony development from sweet potato petiole protoplasts and mesophyll cells. Plant Sci. Lett., **18**, 335–342.

BIGGS B.J., SMITH M.K. & SCOTT K.J. 1986 The use of embryo culture for the recovery of plants from cassava (*Manihot esculenta* Crantz) seeds. Plant Cell Tiss. Organ Cult., **6**, 229–234.

BIGOT C. 1974a Comparaison des aptitudes pour le bourgeonnement de tissus profonds, cultivés *in vitro.* Cas de la tige d'un lis hybride, cv. 'Enchantment'. Compt. Rend. Acad. Sci. Paris, **278D**, 1027–1030.

BIGOT C. 1974b Entire plants derived from floral peduncles of *Gloxinia hybrida* cultivated *in vitro.* Z. Pflanzenphysiol., **73**, 178–183.

BIGOT C. 1975 Multiplication végétative de *Gloxinia hybrida* à partir d'organes cultivés *in vitro.* Ann.Amelior.Plantes, **25**, 337–351.

BIGOT C. 1981a Multiplication végétative *in vitro* de *Begonia × hiemalis* ('Rieger' et 'Schwabenland') I. Méthodologie. Agronomie, **1**, 433–440.

BIGOT C. 1981b Multiplication végétative *in vitro* de *Begonia × hiemalis* (Rieger et Schwabenland). II. Conformité des plantes élevées en serre. Agronomie, **1**, 441–447.

BIGOT C. & ENGELMANN F. 1987 Vegetative propagation *in vitro* of *Cunninghamia lanceolata* (Lamb.) Hook. pp. 114–127 in Bonga & Durzan (eds.) 1987c *(q.v.).*

BILDERBACK D.E. 1972 The effects of hormones upon the development of excised floral buds of *Aquilegia.* Am. J. Bot., **59**, 525–529.

BILDERBACK D.E., KARPOFF A.J. & TEPFER S.S. 1968 Development of excised floral buds of *Aquilegia*: The coconut milk problem. Am. J. Bot., **55**, 1042–1046.

BILKEY P.C. & COCKING E.C. 1981 Increased plant vigour by *in vitro* propagation of *Saintpaulia ionantha* Wendl. from sub–epidermal tissue. HortScience 16 643–644.

BILKEY P.C., McCOWN B.H. & HILDEBRANDT A.C. 1978 Micropropagation of African violet from petiole cross–sections. HortScience, **13**, 37–38.

BILLINGTON W.P. & BROWN F.R. 1991 Gripper for plant tissue – has pair of cantilevered rollers projecting from pair of supports. World Patent Applic. No. 9100167.

BILLINGTON W.P. & GRUNDON P.M. 1991 Cutter for micropropagation – has tabular cutter movable downwardly to tip cut a portion of plant. World Patent Applic. No. 9118499.

BILLINGTON W.P. & GRUNDON P.M. 1992 Robotic end tool for use in micro–propagation of plants – tool holder has shaped resilient spring steel fingers which can be splayed open by plate which has blade to cut plant section. World Patent Applic. No. 9201369.

BINDING H. 1974a Cell cluster formation by leaf protoplasts from axenic cultures of haploid *Petunia hybrida* L. Plant Sci. Lett., **2**, 185–188.

BINDING H. 1974b Regeneration von haploiden und diploiden pflanzen aus protoplasten von *Petunia hybrida* L. Z. Pflanzenphysiol., **74**, 327–356.

BINDING H. 1974c Reproducibly high plating efficiencies of isolated mesophyll protoplasts from shoot cultures of tobacco. Physiol. Plant., **35**, 225–227.

BINDING H. & NEHLS R. 1977 Regeneration of isolated protoplasts to plants in *Solanum dulcamera* L. Z. Pflanzenphysiol., **85**, 279–280.

BINDING H. & NEHLS R. 1978 Regeneration of isolated protoplasts of *Vicia faba* L. Z. Pflanzenphysiol., **88**, 327–332.

BINDING H. & NEHLS R. 1980 Protoplast regeneration to plants in *Senecio vulgaris* L. Z. Pflanzenphysiol., **99**, 183–185.

BINDING H. & NEHLS R. 1980b Transfer of genetic information in higher plants via protoplast fusion. pp. 315–319 in Ferenczy & Farkas (eds.) 1980 *(q.v.)*

BINDING H., NEHLS R., KOCK R., FINGER J. & MORDHORST G. 1981 Comparative studies on protoplast regeneration in herbaceous species of the Dicotyledoneae class. Z. Pflanzenphysiol., **101**, 119–130.

BINH D.Q., HESZKY L.E., GYULAI G. & CSILLAG A. 1992 Plant regeneration of NaCl–pretreated cells from long–term suspension culture of rice (*Oryza sativa* L.) in high saline conditions. Plant Cell Tiss. Organ Cult., **29**, 75–82.

BINH D.Q., HESZKY L.E., GYULAI G., KISS E. & CSILLAG A. 1989 Plant regeneration from callus of *Puccinellia distans* (L.) Parl. Plant Cell Tiss. Organ Cult., **18**, 195–200.

BINH L.T., MUOI L.T., OANH H.T.K., THANG T.D. & PHONG D.T. 1990 Rapid propagation of *Agave* by *in vitro* tissue culture. Plant Cell Tiss. Organ Cult., **23**, 67–70.

BIONDI S. & THORPE T.A. 1982b Clonal propagation of forest tree species. pp. 197–204 in Rao A.N. (ed.) 1982 *(q.v.)*.

BIRNBAUM E. 1978 *Simmondsia chinensis*: studies by tissue culture. pp. 243–251 in Alfermann & Reinhard (eds.) 1978 *(q.v.)* .

BIVINS J.L. & HACKETT W.P. 1969 Effect of medium & wounding techniques on aseptic culture of *Cymbidium* orchids from shoot apices. Plant Propagator 15 9–14.

BLACKMON W.J., REYNOLDS B.D. & POSTEK C.E. 1980 Regeneration of plantlets from winged bean explants. HortScience, **15**, 417 (Abst.324).

BLAIR L.C., CHASTAIN C.J. & WIDHOLM J.M. 1988 Initiation and characterization of a cotton (*Gossypium hirsutum* L.) photoautotrophic cell suspension culture. Plant Cell Rep., **7**, 266–269.

BLAKE J. 1990 Coconut (*Cocos nucifera* L.); Micropropagation. pp. 538–554 in Bajaj Y.P.S. (ed.) 1990 *(q.v.)*.

BLAKESLEE A.F. & SATINA S. 1944 New hybrids from incompatible crosses in *Datura* through culture of excised embryos on malt media. Science, **99**, 331–334.

BLANKE M.M. & BELCHER A.R. 1989 Stomata of apple leaves cultured *in vitro*. Plant Cell Tiss. Organ Cult., **19**, 85–89.

BLAZICH F.A. & NOVITZKY R.T. 1984 *In vitro* propagation of *Sansevieria trifasciata*. HortScience, **19**, 122–123.

BLAZINA I., RAVNIKAR M., ZOLNIR M., KOROSEC–KORUZA Z. & GOGALA N. 1991 Regeneration of GFLV–free grapevines and synchronization of micropropagation *in vitro*. Acta Hort., **289**, 87–88.

BLEECKER A.B., ROSE–JOHN S. & KENDE H. 1987 An evaluation of 2,5–norbornadiene as a reversible inhibitor of ethylene action in deepwater rice. Plant Physiol., **84**, 395–398.

BLOKSBERG L.N. & SALTVEIT M.E. 1985 Regenerating plants from axillary buds of field–grown iceberg lettuce hearts. HortScience, **20**, 540.

BOCK K.R. & GUTHRIE E.J. 1978 Transmission of African Cassava Mosaic by mechanical inoculation. Plant Dis. Rep., **62**, 580–581.

BOCK K.R., GUTHRIE E.J. & MEREDITH G. 1978 Distribution, host range, properties and purification of Cassava Latent Virus, a geminii virus. Ann. Appl. Biol., **90**, 361–367.

BOESHORE M.L., LIFSHITZ I., HANSON M.R. & IZHAR S. 1983 Novel composition of mitochondrial genomes in *Petunia* somatic hybrids derived from cytoplasmic male sterile and fertile plants. Mol. Gen. Genet., **190** , 459–467.

BOHNKE E., DORFNER M. & SONNEBORN H.–H. 1983 Micropropagation of *Crossandra infundibuliformis*. Acta Hort., **131** , 71–74.

BOHOROWA N.E., COCKING E.C. & POWER J.B. 1986 Isolation, culture and callus regeneration of protoplast of wild and cultivated *Helianthus* species. Plant Cell Rep., **5**, 256–258.

BOIS F. 1992 The influence of some natural cell–wall derived precursors on organogenesis and differentiation of wild strawberry (*Fragaria vesca* L.) callus cultures. Plant Cell Tiss. Organ Cult., **28**, 91–96.

BOISSOT N., VALDEZ M. & GUIDERDONI E. 1990 Plant regeneration from leaf and seed–derived calli and suspension cultures of the African perennial wild rice, *Oryza longistaminata*. Plant Cell Rep., **9**, 447–450.

BOKELMANN G.S. & ROEST S. 1983 Plant regeneration from protoplasts of potato (*Solanum tuberosum* cv. Bintje). Z. Pflanzenphysiol., **109**, 259–265.

BOMMINENI V.R., WALDEN D.B. & GREYSON R.I. 1989 Recovery of fertile plants from isolated cultured maize shoot apices. Plant Cell Tiss. Organ Cult., **19**, 225–234.

BON M.–C., GENDRAUD M. & FRANCLET A. 1988 Roles of phenolic compounds on micropropagation of juvenile and mature clones of *Sequoiadendron giganteum*: influence of activated charcoal. Scientia Hort., **34**, 283–291.

BOND S. & ALDERSON P.G. 1993a The effect of explant density, temperature and light on rhizome growth *in vitro* of *Alstroemeria*. J. Hort. Sci., **68**, 855–859.

BOND S. & ALDERSON P.G. 1993b The influence of apical dominance on the *in vitro* multiplication of the rhizome of *Alstroemeria*. J. Hort. Sci., **68**, 905–910.

BONGA J. 1974 *In vitro* culture of microsporophytes & megagametophyte tissue of Pinus. In Vitro, **9**, 270–277.

BONGA J.M. 1965 *Arcenthobium pusillum* Peck: collection of seeds and *in vitro* culture of the early seedling stage. Can. J. Bot., **43**, 1307–1308.

BONGA J.M. 1971 Formation of holdfasts, callus, embryoids & haustorial cells in the *in vitro* cultures of dwarf mistletoe *Areuthobium pusillum*. Phytomorph., **21**, 140–153.

BONGA J.M. 1977a Organogenesis in *in vitro* cultures of embryonic shoots of *Abies balsamea* (Balsam fir). In Vitro, **13**, 41–48.

BONGA J.M. 1977b Applications of tissue culture in forestry. pp 93–108 in Reinert & Bajaj (eds.) 1977 *(q.v.)*

BONGA J.M. 1981 Organogenesis *in vitro* of tissues from mature conifers. In Vitro, **17**, 511–518.

BONGA J.M. 1982b Vegetative propagation of mature trees by tissue culture. pp. 191–196 in Rao A.N. (ed.) 1982 *(q.v.)*.

BONGA J.M. 1982c Shoot formation in callus from the stalks of young female strobili of *Larix decidua*. Can. J. Bot., **60**, 1357–1359.

BONGA J.M. 1987 Clonal propagation of mature trees: problems and possible solutions. pp. 249–271 in Bonga and Durzan (eds.) 1987a *(q.v.)*.

BONGA J.M. & DURZAN D.J. (eds.) 1982 *Tissue culture in Forestry*. Martinus Nijhoff/Dr. W. Junk Publ., The Hague.

BONGA J.M. & DURZAN D.J. (eds.) 1987a *Cell and Tissue Culture in Forestry*. Vol. 1. *General Principles and Biotechnology*. Martinus Nijhoff Publishers. Dordrecht, Boston, Lancaster.

BONGA J.M. & DURZAN D.J. (eds.) 1987b *Cell and Tissue Culture in Forestry* Vol. 2. Martinus Nijhoff Publishers. Dordrecht, Boston, Lancaster. ISBN 90–247–3431–2.

BONGA J.M. & DURZAN D.J. (eds.) 1987c *Cell and Tissue Culture in Forestry* Vol. 3. *Case Histories: Gymnosperms, Angiosperms and Palms*. Martinus Nijhoff Publishers, Dordrecht, Boston, Lancaster. ISBN 90–247–3432–0

BONGA J.M. & FOWLER D.P. 1970 Growth and differentiation in gametophytes of *Pinus resinosa* cultured *in vitro*. Can. J. Bot., **48**, 2205–2207.

BONGA J.M. & POND S.E. 1991 Adventitious shoot formation in cultures of 30–year–old *Larix decidua, L. leptolepis, L. eurolepis* and *L. laricina* trees. Plant Cell Tiss. Organ Cult., **26**, 45–51.

BOOIJ T., MONFORT S. & MACHEIX J.J. 1993 Relationships between peroxidases and budding in date palm tissues cultured *in vitro*. Plant Cell Tiss. Organ Cult., **35**, 165–171.

BORGAN A.K. & NAESS S.K. 1987 Hormogeneity and plant quality of *in vitro* propagated *Nephrolepis exaltata* Bostoniensis. Acta Hort., **212** , 433–438.

BORGMAN C.A. & MUDGE K.W. 1986 Factors affecting the establishment and maintenance of 'Titan' red raspberry root organ cultures. Plant Cell Tiss. Organ Cult., **6**, 127–137.

BORKOWSKA B. & SZCZERBA J. 1990 Micropropagation of sour cherry cultivars and nursery/orchard behaviour of trees received by this technique. Acta Hort., **285**, 187.

BORNMAN C.H. 1981 *In vitro* regeneration potential of the conifer phyllomorph. pp. 43–56 in Eriksson G.& Lundkvist K. (eds.) 1981 Symposium on Clonal Forestry, Swed. Univ. Agric. Sci., Dept. Forestry Genetics, Upsala, Sweden. Res. Notes 32.

BORNMAN C.H. 1983 Possibilities and contraints in the regeneration of trees from cotyledonary needles of *Picea abies in vitro*. Physiol. Plant., **57**, 5–16.

BORNMAN C.H. 1985 Regeneration *in vitro* of economically important crop plants in the Nordic countries. Heriditas, Suppl.3, 7–13.

BORNMAN C.H. 1987 *Picea abies*. pp. 2–29 in Bonga and Durzan (eds.) 1987c (*q.v.*).

BORNMAN BOSE T.K. & MUKHERJEE T.P. 1974 Effect of growth substances on seedling growth and differentiation from callus of *Vanda in vitro* culture. Orchid Rev., **82**, 148–149.

BOTT J.C. 1980 Tissue culture of Delphiniums: preliminary experiments with *D. elatum* and University hybrids. Plantsman, **2**, 169–171.

BOTTINO P.J., MAIRE C.E. & GOFF L.M. 1979 Tissue culture and organogenesis in the winged bean. Can. J. Bot., **57**, 1773–1776.

BOULAY M. 1986 *In vitro* propagation of forest tree species. p. 9 in Somers et al. (eds.) 1986 (*q.v.*).

BOULAY M. 1979 Propagation *in vitro* du Douglas par micropropagation de germination aseptique et culture de bourgeons dormants. AFOCEL Etud. Rech. **12**, 67–75.

BOULAY M. 1987a Conifer micropropagation: applied research and commercial aspects. pp. 185–206 in Bonga and Durzan (eds.) 1987c (*q.v.*).

BOULAY M. & FRANCLET A. 1977 Recherches sur la propagation végétative du Douglas: *Pseudotsuga menziesii* (Mirb.) Franco. Possibilités d'obtention de plantes viable à partir de la culture *in vitro* de bourgeons de pieds–mères/juvéniles. Compt. Rend. Acad. Sci. Paris, **284D**, 1405–1407.

BOULTER D. & CROCOMO O.J. 1977 Plant cell culture implications: Legumes. pp. 615–631 in Sharp *et al.* (eds.) 1977 (*q.v.*).

BOURGIN J.–P. & NITSCH J.P. 1967 Production of haploid *Nicotiana* from excised stamens. Ann. Physiol. Veg., **9**, 377–382.

BOURGIN J.–P., CHUPEAU Y. & MOREL G. 1972 Obtention et culture *in vitro* de protoplastes multinuclées de mésophylle de Tabac (*Nicotiana tabacum* L.). Compt. Rend. Acad. Sci. Paris **274D**, 3545–3548.

BOURGIN J.–P., MISSONIER C. & CHUPEAU Y. 1976 Culture de protoplastes de mésophylle de *Nicotiana sylvestris* Spegazzini et Comes haploide. Compt. Rend. Acad. Sci. Paris, **282D**, 1853–1856.

BOURGKARD F. & FAVRE J.M. 1988 Somatic embryos from callus of *Sequoia sempervirens*. Plant Cell Rep., **7**, 445–448.

BOURIQUET G. 1948 Les engrais chimique et le vanillier. Agron. Tropicale, **3**, 498.

BOURQUE J.E., TANNER S. & MABRY T.J. 1989 *In vitro* regeneration of *Gaillardia pulchella* Foug. Plant Cell Tiss. Organ Cult., **16**, 67–72.

BOUZA L., SOTTA B., BONNET M., JAQUES M. & ARNAUD Y. 1992 Hormone content and meristematic activity of *Paeonia suffruticosa* Andr. cv. Madame de Vatry vitro plants during *in vitro* rooting. Acta Hort., **320** , 213–216.

BOUZID S. 1975 Quelques traits du comportement de boutures de *Citrus* en culture *in vitro*. Compt. Rend. Acad. Sci. Paris **280D**, 1689–1692.

BOUZID S. 1986 *In vitro* micropropagation of mature citrus. p. 147 in Somers *et al.* (eds.) 1986 (*q.v.*).

BOVO O.A. & MROGINSKI L.A. 1985 Obtencion de plantas de ajo (*Allium sativum* L.) por cultivo *in vitro* de meristemas. Phyton., **45**, 159–163.

BOWDEN A. 1985 Transferring tissue–cultured plants—in particular *Grevilleas*—to the nursery environment. Comb. Proc. Int. Plant Prop. Soc. 1984, **34**, 76–78.

BOWER B.K., CARLSON W.C. & HARTLE J.E. 1992 Analogues of plant embryos encapsulated with gel and preferably the outer shell have improved germination properties due to oxygenation using perfluorocarbon gel. World Patent Applic. No. 9207457.

BOWER J.P. & FRASER C. 1982 Shoot tip culture of Williams bananas. Subtropica, **3**, 13–14.

BOWES B.G. 1970 Preliminary observations on organogenesis in *Taraxacum officinale* tissue cultures. Protoplasma, **71**, 197–202.

BOWES B.G. 1971 The occurrence of shoot ceratomata in tissue cultures of *Taraxacum officinale*. Planta, **100**, 272–276.

BOWES B.G. 1975 Morphology of Teratomous organs in tissue cultures. Cellule 71 19–29 (BA 62 4627).,

BOXUS Ph. 1973 The production of healthy strawberry plants. Acta Hort., **30**, 187–191.

BOXUS Ph. 1975 La culture de meristemes de *Prunus* pour l'obtention de plants sains. Acta Hort., **44**, 43–46.

BOXUS Ph. 1976 Rapid production of virus–free strawberry by *in vitro* cultures. Acta Hort., **66**, 35–38.

BOXUS Ph. 1987a L'acclimatation des arbres fruitiers. pp. 108–111 in Ducaté *et al.* (eds.) 1987 (*q.v.*).

BOXUS Ph. & LARVOR P. (eds.) 1987 Workshop on strawberry plants issued from tissue culture. The European Communities Biol. Series.

BOXUS Ph. & PAQUES M. 1986 Propagation of woody plants in culture medium containing hydrolyzed agar to prevent vitrification. Belgium Patent No. 904661.

BOXUS Ph. & PAQUES M. 1990 Micropropagation of woody plants – in a medium containing hydrolysed agar to prevent vitrification. European Patent No. 247018.

BOXUS Ph. & QUOIRIN M. 1974 La culture de méristèmes apicaux de quelques espèces de *Prunus*. Bull. Soc. Roy. Bot. Belg., **107** , 91–101.

BOXUS Ph., DAMIANO C. & BRASSEUR E. 1984 Chapter 17 — Strawberry. pp. 453–486 in Ammirato *et al.* (eds.) 1984 (*q.v.*).

BOXUS Ph., TERZI J.M., LIEVENS C.H., PYLYSER M., NGABOYAMAHINA P. & DUHEM K. 1991 Improvement and perspectives of micropropagation techniques applied to some hot climate plants. Acta Hort., **289** , 55–64.

BOYES C.J. & SINK K.C. 1981a Morphogenetic responses of *Salpiglossis sinuata* leaf explants & callus. Scientia Hort., **15**, 53–60.

BOYES C.J. & SINK K.C. 1981b Regeneration of plants from callus–derived protoplasts of *Salpiglossis*. J. Am. Soc. Hort. Sci., **106** , 42–46.

BOYES C.J. & VASIL I.K. 1984 Plant regeneration by somatic embryogenesis from cultured young inflorescences of *Sorghum arundinaceum* (Desv.) Stapf. var. Sudanense (Sudan Grass). Plant Sci. Lett., **35**, 153–157.

BOYES C.J., ZAPATA F.J. & SINK K.C. 1980 Isolation, culture and regeneration to plants of callus protoplasts of *Salpiglossis sinuata* L. Z. Pflanzenphysiol., **99**, 471–474.

BRADLEY P.M., EL–FIKI F. & GILES K.L. 1984 Polyamines and arginine affect somatic embryogenesis of *Daucus carota*. Plant Sci. Lett., **34**, 397–401.

BRADLEY P.M., EL–FIKI F. & GILES K.L. 1985 The effects of putrescine on somatic embryogenesis of *Daucus carota* as examined by two–dimensional electrophoresis. pp. 307–308 in Henke *et al.* (eds.) 1985 (*q.v.*).

BRAGDO–AAS M. 1977 Regeneration of plants from callus of potato tubers. Acta Hort., **78**, 133–137.

BRAINERD K.E. & FUCHIGAMI L.H. 1981 Acclimatization of aseptically cultured apple plants to low relative humidity. J. Am. Soc. Hort. Sci., **106**, 515–518.

BRAINERD K.E., FUCHIGAMI L.H., KWIATKOWSKI S. & CLARK C.S. 1981 Leaf anatomy and water stress of aseptically cultured 'Pixy' plum grown under different environments. Hort Science, **16**, 173–175.

BRANCA C., BUCCI G., DOMIANO P., RICCI A., TORELLI A. & BASSI M. 1991 Auxin structure and activity on tomato morphogenesis *in vitro* and pea stem elongation. Plant Cell Tiss. Organ Cult., **24**, 105–114.

BRANCA C., TORELLI A. & BASSI M. 1990 Effects of benzisoxazole and benzy-isothiazole on tomato plant regeneration *in vitro*. Plant Cell Tiss. Organ Cult., **21**, 17–19.

CHOI K–T., KIM M–W. & SHIN H–S. 1982 Root and shoot formation from callus and leaflet cultures of ginseng (*Panax ginseng* C. A. Meyer). pp. 171–172 in Fujiwara (ed.) 1982 (*q.v.*)

CHOINSKI J.S.Jr., TRELEASE R.N. & DOMAN D.C. 1981 Control of enzyme activities in cotton *Gossypium hirsutum* cotyledons during maturation and germination. 3. *In vitro* embryo development in the presence of abscisic acid. Planta, **152**, 428–435.

CHOMCHALOW N. & SAHAVACHARIN O. 1982 The role of tissue culture in the development of medicinal plants and spices. pp. 162–166 in Rao A.N. (ed.) 1982 (*q.v.*)

CHOO T.M. 1988 Plant regeneration in zigzag clover (*Trifolium medium* L.). Plant Cell Rep., **7**, 246–248.

CHOPRA R.N. & RATNAMBA S.P. 1975 Morphogenetic studies on stem segments of *Lobularia maritima.* Phytomorph., **25**, 490–492.

CHOUDHURY B. 1955c Embryo culture technique. III. Growth of hybrid embryos (*Lycopersicon esculentum* × *Lycopersicon peruvianum*) in culture medium. Ind. J. Agric., **12**, 155–156.

CHOUDHURY B. 1955a Embryo culture technique. I. The growth of immature tomato embryos *in vitro.* Ind. J. Agric., **12**, 143–151.

CHOUDHURY B. 1955b Embryo culture technique II. Embryo factors and immature tomato embryo. Ind. J. Agric., **12**, 152–154.

CHOUREY P.S. & ZURAWSKI D.B. 1981 Callus formation from protoplasts of a maize cell culture. Theor. Appl. Genet., **59**, 341–344.

CHOUREY P.S., SMITH H.H. & COMBATTI N.C. 1973 Effects of X irradiation and indoleacetic acid on specific peroxidase isozymes in pith tissue of a *Nicotiana* amphiploid. Am. J. Bot., **60**, 853–857.

CHOVEAUX N.A. & VAN STADEN J. 1981 The effect of 1- Naphthaleneacetic acid in the endogenous cytokinin content of aseptically cultured bark segments of *Salix babylonica.* Plant & Cell Physiol., **22**, 1207–1214.

CHOW Y.N., HARVEY B.M.R. & SELBY C. 1990 An improved method for callus proliferation and regeneration of *Fuchsia hybrida.* Plant Cell Tiss. Organ Cult., **22**, 17–20.

CHOW Y.N., SELBY C. & HARVEY B.M.R. 1992a A simple method for maintaining high multiplication of *Narcissus* shoot cultures *in vitro.* Plant Cell Tiss. Organ Cult., **30**, 227–230.

CHOW Y.N., SELBY C. & HARVEY B.M.R. 1992b Stimulation by sucrose of *Narcissus* bulbil formation *in vitro.* J. Hort. Sci., **67**, 289–293.

CHOWDHRY C.N., TYAGI A.K., MAHESHWARI N. & MAHESHWARI S.C. 1993 Effect of L–proline and L–tryptophan on somatic embryogenesis and plantlet regeneration of rice (*Oryza sativa* L. cv. Pusa 169). Plant Cell Tiss. Organ Cult., **32**, 357–361.

CHRISTEY M.C. & EARLE E.D. 1991 Regeneration of *Brassica oleracea* from peduncle explants. HortScience, **26**, 1069–1072.

CHRISTIANSEN J. & FONNESBECH M. 1975 Prevention by polyvinylpyrrolidone of growth inhibition of *Hamamelis* shoot tips grown *in vitro* and of browning of the agar medium. Acta Hort., **54**, 101–104.

CHRISTIANSON M., WARNICK D.A. & CARLSON P.S. 1986 Plant generation by cell culture. U.S. Patent No. 4548901.

CHRISTIANSON M.L. & WARNICK D.A. 1983 Competence and determination in the process of *in vitro* shoot organogenesis. Dev. Biol., **95**, 288–293.

CHRISTIANSON M.L., WARNICK D.A. & CARLSON P.S. 1983 A morphologically competent soybean suspension culture. Science, **222**, 632–634.

CHRISTIE C.B. 1978 Rapid propagation of aspens and silver poplars using tissue culture techniques. Comb. Proc. Int. Plant Prop. Soc., **28**, 255–260.

CHU C.Y., KNIGHT S.L. & SMITH M.A.L. 1993 Effect of liquid culture on the growth and development of miniature rose (*Rosa chinensis* Jacq. 'Minima'). Plant Cell Tiss. Organ Cult., **32**, 329–334.

CHU HUANG B. & YEOMAN M.M. 1984 Callus proliferation and morphogenesis in tissue cultures of *Arabidopsis thaliana* L. Plant Sci. Lett., **33**, 353–363.

CHU I.Y.E. 1986 The application of tissue culture to plant improvement and propagation in the ornamental horticulture industry. pp. 15–32 in Zimmerman *et al.* (eds.) 1986 (*q.v.*).

CHU I.Y.E. & KURTZ S.L. 1990 Commercialization of plant micropropagation. pp. 126–164 in Ammirato *et al.* (eds.) 1990 (*q.v.*).

CHU W–H., CHANG Y–L., LI H–L. & CHENG K–T. 1981 Preliminary studies on tissue culture of *Panax ginseng.* pp. 491–499 in Anon 1981a (*q.v.*).

CHUONG P.V., PAULS K.P. & BEVERSDORF W.D. 1985 A simple culture method for *Brassica* hypocotyl protoplasts. Plant Cell Rep., **4**, 4–6.

CHUPEAU Y., BOURGIN J–P., MISSONIER C., DORION N. & MOREL G. 1974 Preparation et culture de protoplastes de divers *Nicotiana.* Compt. Rend. Acad. Sci. Paris, **278D**, 1565–1568.

CHURCHILL M.E., BALL E.A. & ARDITTI J. 1970 Production of orchid plants from seedling leaf tips. Orchid Dig., **34**, 271.

CHURCHILL M.E., BALL E.A. & ARDITTI J. 1972 Tissue culture of orchids. II.Methods for root tips. Am. Orchid Soc. Bull., **41**, 726–730.

CLARE M.V. & COLLIN H.A. 1973 Meristem culture of Brussels sprouts. Hort. Res., **13**, 111–118.

CLAYTON P.W., HUBSTENBERGER J.F., PHILLIPS G.C. & BUTLER–NANCE S.A. 1990 Micropropagation of members of the Cactaceae subtribe Cactinae. J. Am. Soc. Hort. Sci., **15**, 337–343.

CLEMENTS M.A. & ELLYARD R.K. 1979 The symbiotic germination of Australian terrestrial orchids. Am. Orchid Soc. Bull., **48**, 810–816.

CLEMENTS M.A., MUIRI H. & CRIBB P.J. 1986 A preliminary report on the symbiotic germination of European terrestrial orchids. Kew Bulletin, **41**, 437–445.

CLOG E., BASS P. & WALTER B. 1990 Plant regeneration by organogenesis in *Vitis* rootstock species. Plant Cell Rep., **8**, 726–728.

CLORE W.J. & YANG H.–J. 1975 Using tissue culture for vegetatively propagating and improving asparagus production and quality. Comb. Proc. Int. Plant Prop. Soc., **25**, 119–122.

CLOSE K.R. 1986 Process for regenerating corn by culturing tissue on media containing mineral salts, vitamin(s), sucrose and hormone. European Patent Applic. No. 177738.

CLOSE K.R. 1987a Process for regenerating corn. U.S. Patent No. 4665030.

CLOSE K.R. 1987b Regenerating maize plants from cells and tissue – by callus formation on medium containing dihalobenzoic acid hormone, then generating of roots and shoots. European Patent Applic. No. 246527.

CLOSE K.R. 1988 Process for regenerating corn. U.S. Patent No. 4830966.

CLOSS T. & PEFFLEY E.B. 1988 Micropropagation of *Leucophyllum candidum* "Silver Cloud'. HortScience, **23**, 759.

COBB B.G., HOLE D.J., SMITH J.D. & KENT M.W. 1988 The effects of modifying sucrose concentration on the development of maize kernels grown *in vitro.* Ann. Bot., **62**, 265–270.

COBB B.G., VANDERZEE D., LOESCHER W.H. & KENNEDY R.A. 1985 Evidence for plantlet regeneration via somatic embryogenesis in the grasses *Echinochloa muricata* and *E. crus–galli* var. oryzicola. Plant Science, **40**, 121–127.

COBIANCHI D., DE SALVADOR F.R., FAEDI W., INSERO O., LIVERANI A., RIVALTA L., MINGUZZI A. & MARENI M. 1988 Preliminary field observations on *in vitro* propagated trees. Acta Hort., **227**, 514–516.

COCKREL A.D., McDANIEL G.L. & GRAHAM E.T. 1986 *In vitro* propagation of florists' Cineraria. HortScience, **21**, 139–140.

COHEN D. 1977 Thermotherapy & meristem–tip culture of some ornamental plants. Acta Hort., **78**, 381–388.

COHEN D. 1981 Application of micropropagation methods for blueberries and tamarillos. Comb. Proc. Int. Plant Prop. Soc. 1980, **30**, 144–146.

COHEN D. 1982 Micropropagation of *Zantedeschia* hybrids. Comb. Proc. Int. Plant Prop. Soc. 1981, **31**, 312–316.

COHEN D. & ELLIOTT D. 1979 Micropropagation methods for blueberries and tamarillos. Comb. Proc. Int. Plant Prop. Soc., **29**, 177–179.

COHEN D. & LE GAL P.M. 1976 Micropropagation of *Daphne* × *burkwoodii* Turriel. Comb. Proc. Int. Plant Prop. Soc., **26**, 330–333.

COHEN D., LADIZINSKY G., ZIV M. & MUEHLBAUER F.J. 1984 Rescue of interspecific *Lens* hybrids by means of embryo culture. Plant Cell Tiss. Organ Cult., **3**, 343–347.

COHEN D., MILNE K.S. & HYLAND M.J. 1985 *In vitro* manipulation of virus concentrations in hybrid lilies. Acta Hort., **164**, 314–319.

COLEMAN G.D. & ERNST S.G. 1989 *In vitro* shoot regeneration of *Populus deltoides:* effect of cytokinin and genotype. Plant Cell Rep., **8**, 459–462.

COLEMAN G.D. & ERNST S.G. 1990 Axillary shoot proliferation and growth of *Populus deltoides* shoot cultures. Plant Cell Rep., **9**, 165–167.

COLEMAN W. & THORPE T.A. 1976 Induction of buds in tissue cultures of four different conifers. Plant Physiol., **57**, (5 Suppl.) 67.

COLEMAN W.K. & THORPE T.A. 1977b Induction of microsporangiate strobili from mature vegetative shoot tips of *Thuja plicata* cultured *in vitro*. Plant Physiol., **59**, (6 Suppl.) 3.

COLIJN C.M., KOOL A.J. & NIJKAMP H.J.J. 1979b Induction of root and shoot formation from root meristems of *Petunia hybrida*. Protoplasma, **99**, 335–340.

COLIJN–HOOYMANS C.M., BOUWER B., ORCZYK W. & DONS J.J.M. 1988b Plant regeneration from cucumber (*Cucumis sativus*) protoplasts. Plant Science, **57**, 63–71.

COLLET G.F. 1988 Improvement to induce rooting of fruit trees *in vitro*. Acta Hort., **227**, 318–323.

COLLI S. & KERBAUY G.B. 1993 Direct root tip conversion of *Catasetum* into protocorm–like bodies. Effects of auxin and cytokinin. Plant Cell Tiss. Organ Cult., **33**, 39–44.

COLLINS G.B. & SUNDERLAND N. 1974 Pollen–derived haploids of *Nicotiana knightiana, N. raimondii* and *N. attenuata*. J. Exp. Bot., **25** , 1030–1033.

COLLINS G.B., HILDEBRAND D.F., LAZZERI P.A., ADAMS T.R., PARROTT W.A. & HARTWECK L.M. 1988 Somatic embryogenesis of *Glycine* plant species – by culturing excised cotyledon tissue from immature embryos on medium containing auxin of alpha–nephthalene acetic acid family. European Patent Applic. No. 256751.

COLLINS G.B., LEGG P.D. & KASPERBAUER M.J. 1972 Chromosome numbers in anther–derived haploids of two *Nicotiana* species. J. Hered., **63**, 113–118.

COLLINS G.B., TAYLOR N.L. & PARROTT W.A. 1982 *In vitro* culture and plant regeneration in *Trifolium* species. pp. 705–706 in Fujiwara (ed.) 1982 (*q.v.*).

COLOMAS J. 1971 Obtention de cultures de tissus à partir de fragments de tiges de *Pachycereus pringlei*. Compt. Rend. Acad. Sci. Paris, **272D**, 1380–1382.

COLONNA J.P., CAS G. & RABECHAULT H. 1971 Mise au point d'une méthode de culture *in vitro* d'embryons de caféiers. Application a deux variété de caféiers cultivés. Compt. Rend. Acad. Sci. Paris, **272D**, 60–63.

COMAN T., BOTEZ M., GHENA N. & ZAMBROWICZ E. 1977 The behaviour of some strawberry cultivars during the process of obtaining planting material free from the main viruses. Lucrarile Stiintife ale Institutulai de Cercetari pentru Pomicultura, **5**, 397–403.

COMPTON M.E. & PREECE J.E. 1986 Exudation and explant establishment. I.A.P.T.C. Newsletter, **50**, 9–18.

COMPTON M.E. & PREECE J.E. 1988b Response of tobacco callus to shoot tip exudation from five species. HortScience, **23**, 208–210.

COMPTON M.E. & VEILLEUX R.E. 1988 Morphogenesis in tomato thin cell layers. HortScience, **23**, 754.

COMPTON M.E. & VEILLEUX R.E. 1991 Shoot, root and flower morphogenesis on tomato inflorescence explants. Plant Cell Tiss. Organ Cult., **24**, 223–231.

COMPTON M.E., GRAY D.J. & ELMSTROM G.W. 1993 A simple protocol for micropropagating diploid and tetraploid watermelon using shoot–tip explants. Plant Cell Tiss. Organ Cult., **33**, 211–217.

CONGER B.V. (ed.) 1981a *Cloning Agricultural Plants via in vitro Techniques*. CRC Press Inc., Boca Raton, Florida.

CONGER B.V. 1981b Agronomic crops. pp. 165–215 in Conger B.V. (ed.) 1981a (*q.v.*).

CONGER B.V. & McDONNELL R.E. 1983 Plantlet formation from cultured inflorescences of *Dactylis glomerata* L. Plant Cell Tiss. Organ Cult., **2**, 191–197.

CONGER B.V., HANNING G.E., GRAY D.J. & McDANIEL J.K. 1983 Direct embryogenesis from mesophyll cells of orchard grass. Science, **221**, 850–851.

CONNER A.J. & FALLOON P.G. 1990 Osmotic versus nutrition effects when rooting asparagus minicrowns on high sucrose media. Acta Hort., **271**, 100.

CONNER A.J. & THOMAS M.B. 1982 Re–establishing plantlets from tissue culture: a review. Comb. Proc. Int. Plant Prop. Soc. 1981, **31** , 342–357.

CONNER L.N. & CONNER A.J. 1984 Comparative water loss from leaves of *Solanum laciniatum* plants cultured *in vitro* and *in vivo*. Plant Sci. Lett., **36**, 241–246.

CONOVER C.A. & POOLE R.T. 1984 Acclimatization of indoor foliage plants. Hort. Rev., **6**, 119–154.

CONSTABEL F., RAMBOLD S., CHATSON K.B., KURZ W.G.M. & KUTNEY J.P. 1982 Alkaloid production in *Catharanthus roseus* L. G.Don. VI. Variation in alkaloid spectra of cell lines derived from one single leaf. Plant Cell Rep., **1**, 3–5.

CONSTABEL F., RAMBOLD S., SHYLUK J.P., LETOURNEAU D., KURZ W.G.W. & KUTNEY J.P. 1981 Alkaloid production in *Catharanthus roseus* cell cultures. Z. Pflanzenphysiol., **105**, 53–58.

CONSTANTIN M.J., HENKE R.R., HUGHES K.W. & CONGER B.V. 1981 *Propagation of Higher Plants through Tissue Culture: Emerging Technologies and Strategies*. Permagon Press, Oxford, New York, Toronto, Sydney, Paris, Frankfurt ISSN 0098–8472.

CONSTANTINE D.R. & ABBOTT A.J. 1977 Microvegetative propagation and modification of *Prunus* spp. Long Ashton Ann. Rep. 1977, 63–64.

CONTI L., FRANGI P., TOSCA A. & VERGA P. 1991 Breeding clones of *Gerbera jamesonii* hybr. suitable to micropropagation and pot cultivation. Acta Hort., **300**, 103–106.

COOK D.A., DECKER D.M. & GALLAGHER J.L. 1989 Regeneration of *Kosteletzkya virginica* (L.) Presl. (seashore mallow) from callus cultures. Plant Cell Tiss. Organ Cult., **17**, 111–119.

COOK S.K., ADAMS H., HEDLEY C.L., AMBROSE M.J. & WANG T.L. 1988 An analysis of seed development in *Pisum sativum*. VII. Embryo development and precocious germination *in vitro*. Plant Cell Tiss. Organ Cult., **14**, 89–101.

COOKE R.C. 1977 Tissue culture propagation of African violets. HortScience, **12**, 549.

COOLEY G. & WILCOX A. 1984 Sunflower regeneration through embryogenesis and organogenesis. U.S. Patent No. 4670391.

COOLEY G.L. & WILCOX A.S. 1989a Regeneration of sunflower plants from tissue culture by three stage culture in media containing hormones ensuring callus, shoot and root formation. European Patent No. 170904.

COOLEY G.L. & WILCOX A.S. 1989b Sunflower plant regeneration by a four stage process using culture media containing specified plant hormone mixtures. European Patent No. 171593.

COOLEY G.L. & WILCOX A.S. 1989c Sunflower regeneration through embryo generation using media containing mineral salts, vitamin(s), amino acid(s), sucrose and hormone. European Patent No. 172377.

COOPER A. 1987 Hygiene and the use of tissue cultures in the nursery industry. Comb. Proc. Int. Plant Prop. Soc. 1986, **36**, 216–220.

COOPER P.A. & COHEN D. 1983 *Caladium* — a candidate for micropropagation? Comb. Proc. Int. Plant Prop. Soc. 1982, **32**, 363–367.

COOPER P.A. & COHEN D. 1985 Micropropagation of Japanese persimmon (*Diospyros kaki*). Comb. Proc. Int. Plant Prop. Soc. 1984, **34**, 118–124.

CORCOS A. 1973 Redifferentiation of *Arabidopsis thaliana* from callus culture. Am. J. Bot., **60**, 5.

CORLEY R.H.V. 1977 First clonal oil palms planted in the field. Planter, **53**, 331–332.

CORLEY R.H.V., BARRETT J.N. & JONES L.H. 1977 Vegetative propagation of oil palm via tissue culture. Oil Palm News, **22**, 2–7.

CORNEANU M. & CORNEANU G.C. 1991 The genotype, explant, type and medium composition influence on *in vitro* multiplication in *Pelargonium* sp. Acta Hort., **289**, 101–102.

CORNU D. & CHAIX C. 1981 Multiplication par culture *in vitro* de merisiers adult (*Prunus avium*). Application à un large éventail de clones. pp. 71–79 in *Colloque international sur la culture in vitro* des essences forestières. International United Research Organisation.

CORNU D. & GEOFFRION C. 1990 Aspects de l'embryogenèse somatique chez le mélèze. Euk. Soc. Bot. Fr. **137**, 25–34.

CORONA N.V. & YANEZ L.L. 1984 Propagacion de *Cephalocereus senilis* mediante cultivos de tejidos. Cat. Suc. Mex., **29**, 3–7.

CORTE–OLIVARES J., PHILLIPS G.C. & BUTLER–NANCE S.A. 1990 Somatic embryogenesis from pecan zygotic embryo explants. HortScience, **25**, 983.

COSSIO F. 1981a Moltiplicazione *in vitro* di quattro cultivar di ciliegio acido. Frutticoltura, **43**, (10–11), 19–24.

COSSIO F. 1981b *In vitro* propagation of *Aeschynanthus lobbiana* Hook. Riv.Ortoflorofrutt.Ital., **65**, 149–157.

COSSIO F. & MARINO G. 1983 Indagini preliminari sull'isolamento e la coltura dei protoplasti di *Actinidia chinensis*. Riv. Ortoflorofrutt. Ital., **67**, 455–464.

COSSIO F. & MENIN G. 1982 Micropropagazione della fragola. Frutticoltura, **44**, 54–57.

DREW R.A., SIMPSON B.W. & OSBORNE W.J. 1991 Degradation of exogenous indole–3–butyric acid and riboflavin and their influence on rooting response of papaya *in vitro*. Plant Cell Tiss. Organ Cult., **26**, 29–34.

DREW R.A., SMITH M.K. & ANDERSON D.W. 1992 Field evaluation of micropropagated bananas derived from plants containing banana bunchy–top virus. Plant Cell Tiss. Organ Cult., **28**, 203–205.

DREW R.L.K. & FELLOWS J.R. 1986 Generation of seakale (*Crambe maritima* L.) plantlets by tissue culture. Ann. Bot., **58**, 179–181.

DRISS–ECOLE D. 1981 Fasciation d'extrémités caulinaires du *Celosia cristata* (Amarantaceae) cultivées *in vitro*. Can. J. Bot., **59**, 1367–1372.

DRIVER J.A. 1987 Propagating plant tissue culture shoots by multiplying shoots pretreating and planting root–induce propagules prior to root emergence. European Patent Applic. No. 248131.

DRIVER J.A. & KUNIYUKI A.H. 1984 *In vitro* propagation of Paradox walnut rootstock. HortScience, **19**, 507–509.

DRUART P. 1980 Plantlet regeneration from root callus of different *Prunus* species. Scientia Hort., **12**, 339–342.

DRUART Ph. 1991 Potentialities of the *in vitro* culture to improve plum tree breeding. Acta Hort., **283**, 199–286.

DRUART Ph. & BOXUS Ph. 1987 Comportement au champ de *Malus domestica* Borkh. cv. 'Golden Delicious' issu de micropropagation. pp. 185–189 in Ducaté *et al.* (eds.) 1987 (*q.v.*).

DU MANOIR J., DESMAREST P. & SAUSSAY R. 1985 *In vitro* propagation of fennel (*Foeniculum vulgare* Miller). Scientia Hort., **27**, 15–19.

DUBEY K.C. & RISHI N. 1976 Studies on the nucellar embryos of some cultivated citrus. Hort. Res., **15**, 49–52.

DUBLIN P. 1984 Chapter 20 — Cacao. pp. 541–563 in Ammirato *et al.* (eds.) 1984 (*q.v.*)

DUBOIS L.A.M. & DE VRIES P.P. 1988 Comparison of the plant habit of pot roses propagated *in vitro* and by cuttings. Acta Hort., **226**, 611–613.

DUBOIS L.A.M., ROGGEMANS J., SOYEURT G. & DE VRIES D.P. 1988 Comparison of the growth and development of dwarf rose cultivars propagated *in vitro* and *in vivo* by softwood cuttings. Scientia Hort., **35**, 293–299.

DUCATE G., JACOBS M. & SIMEON A. (eds.) 1987 *Plant Micropropagation in Horticultural Industries — Preparation, Hardening and Acclimatization Processes*., Symposium of the Belgium Plant Tissue Culture Group. Florizel 87, Arlon, Belgium.

DUCREUX G., ROSSIGNOL L. & SIHACHAKR D. 1991 Exploitation of genetic and physiological variability in Solanaceae: the examples of potato and eggplant. Acta Hort., **289**, 65–75.

DUDITS D., HADLACZKY G., BAJSZAR G.Y., KONCZ C., LAZAR G. & HORVATH G. 1979 Plant regeneration from intergeneric cell hybrids. Plant Sci. Lett., **15**, 101–112.

DUDITS D., KAO K.N., CONSTABEL F. & GAMBORG O.L. 1976a Embryogenesis and formation of tetraploid and hexaploid plants from carrot protoplasts. Can. J. Bot., **54**, 1063–1067.

DUFOUR M. 1990 Improving yield of adventitious shoots in apple. Acta Hort., **280**, 51–58.

DUHOUX E. & DAVIES D. 1985 Caulogenèse à partir des bourgeons cotyledonaires d'*Acacia albida* et influence du saccharose sur la rhyzogenèse. J.Plant Physiol., **121**, 175–180.

DUHOUX E., SOUGOUFARA B. & DOMMERGUES Y. 1986 Propagation of *Casuarina equisetifolia* through axillary buds of immature female inflorescences cultured *in vitro*. Plant Cell Rep., **5**, 161–164.

DULIEU H.-L. 1963 Sur la fécondation *in vitro* chez le *Nicotiana tabacum* L. Compt. Rend. Acad. Sci. Paris **256**, 3344–3346.

DULIEU H.-L. 1966 Pollination of excised ovaries and culture of ovules of *Nicotiana tabacum* L. Phytomorph., **16**, 69–75.

DUNBAR K.B. & STEPHENS C.T. 1989 Shoot regeneration of hybrid seed geranium (*Pelargonium × hortorum*) and regal geranium (*Pelargonium × domesticum*) from primary callus cultures. Plant Cell Tiss. Organ Cult., **19**, 13–21.

DUNCAN D.R., SINGLETARY G.W., BELOW F.E. & WIDHOLM J.M. 1989 Increased induction of regenerable callus cultures from cultured kernals of the maize inbred FR27 rhm. Plant Cell Rep., **8**, 350–353.

DUNSTAN D.E., TURNER K.E. & LAZAROFF W.R. 1985 Propagation *in vitro* of the apple rootstock M4: effect of phytohormones on shoot quality. Plant Cell Tiss. Organ Cult., **4**, 55–60.

DUNSTAN D.I. & SHORT K.C. 1979b Shoot production from cultured *Allium porrum* tissues. Scientia Hort., **11**, 37–43.

DUNSTON S. & SUTTER E. 1982 Effects of greenhouse acclimatization and various light intensities *in vitro* on the anatomy of tissue cultured plants. HortScience, **17**, 532 (Abst. 427).

DUNSTON S. & SUTTER E. 1984 *In vitro* propagation of prayer plants. HortScience, **19**, 511–512.

DUNWELL J.M. 1975a *In vitro* micropropagation of *Brassica oleracea* var. *gemmifera* (Brussels sprout). Ann. Rep. John Innes Inst. 1975 pp. 63–64.

DUNWELL J.M. & CORNISH M. 1978a Induction of adventitious shoots on leaf discs of *Brassica campestris*. Ann. Rep. John Innes Inst. 1977 p. 50.

DUNWELL J.M. & CORNISH M. 1978b Regeneration of adventitious plants from leaf discs of *Brassica oleracea* on hormone–free media. Ann. Rep. John Innes Inst. 1977 p. 51.

DUNWELL J.M. & CORNISH M. 1983 Ann. Rep. John Innes Inst. 1981–1982 pp. 136–137.

DURAN–VILA N., GOGORCENA Y., ORTEGA V., ORTIZ J. & NAVARRO L. 1992 Morphogenesis and tissue culture of sweet orange (*Citrus sinensis* L. Osb.): effect of temperature and photosynthetic radiation. Plant Cell Tiss. Organ Cult., **29**, 11–18.

DURAN–VILA N., ORTEGA V. & NAVARRO L. 1989 Morphogenesis and tissue culture of three citrus species. Plant Cell Tiss. Organ Cult., **16**, 123–133.

DURAND J., POTRYKUS I. & DONN G. 1973 Plants from protoplasts of *Petunia*. Z. Pflanzenphysiol., **69**, 26–34.

DURAND R. & DURAND B. 1984 Sexual differentiation in higher plants. Physiol. Plant., **60**, 267–274.

DURAND–CRESSWELL R., BOULAY M. & FRANCLET A. 1985 Vegetative propagation of *Eucalyptus*. pp. 15–181 in Bonga and Durzan (eds.) 1985 (*q.v.*).

DURBIN R. D. (ed.) 1979 *Nicotiana*: Procedures for experimental use. U.S. Dept. Agric. Technical Bulletin 1586.

DURON M. 1984 *In vitro* propagation of the ornamental INRA *Malus × perpetu* 'Evereste'. Scientia Hort., **22**, 133–137.

DURZAN D. 1982b Somatic embryogenesis and sphaeroblasts in conifer cell suspensions. pp. 113–114 in Fujiwara (ed.) 1982 (*q.v.*).

DURZAN D.J. & LOPUSHANSKI S.M. 1975 Propagation of American elm via cell suspension cultures. Can. J. For. Res., **5**, 273–277.

DURZAN D.J., EINSPHAR D., JOHNSON M.A. & VERMA D. 1979 Morphogenesis in suspension cultures of conifers. In Vitro **15**, 209–210.

DUTCHER R.D. & POWELL L.E. 1972 Culture of apple shoots from buds *in vitro*. J. Am. Soc. Hort. Sci., **97**, 511–514.

DWEIKAT I.M. & LYRENE P.M. 1988 Adventitious shoot production from leaves of Blueberry cultured *in vitro*. HortScience, **23**, 629.

DYER A.F. 1979 The culture of fern gametophytes for experimental investigation. pp. 251–305 in Dyer A.F. (ed.) 1979 The experimental biology of ferns. Academic Press, London, New York.

DYKEMAN B.W. & CUMMING B.G. 1985 *in vitro* propagation of the ostrich fern (*Matteuccia struthiopteris*). Can. J. Plant Sci., **65**, 1025–1032.

EAPEN S. & GEORGE L. 1990 Influence of phytohormones, carbohydrates, aminoacids, growth supplements and antibiotics on somatic embryogenesis and plant differentiation in finger millet. Plant Cell Tiss. Organ Cult., **22**, 87–93.

EAPEN S. & RAO P.S. 1982 Callus induction and plant regeneration from immature embryos of rye *Triticale*. Plant Cell Tiss. Organ Cult., **1**, 221–227.

ECONOMOU A. & READ P.E. 1981 Improving the efficiency of *Petunia* propagation from leaf segments cultured *in vitro*. HortScience, **16**, 406.

ECONOMOU A.S. 1991 Ethylene and shoot formation *in vitro*. Acta Hort., **300**, 35–43.

ECONOMOU A.S. & READ P.E. 1982 Effect of NAA on shoot production *in vitro* from BA–treated *Petunia* leaf explants. J. Am. Soc. Hort. Sci., **107**, 504–506.

ECONOMOU A.S. & READ P.E. 1986b Microcutting production from sequential reculturing of hardy deciduous azalea shoot tips. HortScience, **21**, 137–139.

ECONOMOU A.S. & SPANOUDAKI M.J. 1985 *In vitro* propagation of gardenia. HortScience, **20**, 213.

ECONOMOU A.S. & SPANOUDAKI M.J. 1986 The influence of cytokinins and giberellic acid on *Gardenia* tissue cultures. Scientia Hort., **29**, 155–161.

ECONOMOU A.S., READ P.E. & PELLETT H.M. 1981 Micropropagation of hardy deciduous azaleas. HortScience **16**, 452.

ECONOMOU A.S., READ P.E. & PELLETT H.M. 1982 Reculture of *in vitro*-derived shoots of hardy deciduous azaleas for microcutting production. HortScience, **17**, 33.

ECONOMOU A.S., READ P.E. & SPANOUDAKI M.J. 1988 Azalea regeneration from callus culture. Acta Hort., **226**, 209–216.

EEUWENS C.J. 1978 Effects of organic nutrients and hormones on growth and development of tissue explants from coconut (*Cocos nucifera*) and date (*Phoenix dactylifera*) palms cultured *in vitro*. Physiol. Plant., **42**, 173–178.

EGEA J., BURGOS L., ZOROA N. & EGEA L. 1992 Influence of temperature on the *in vitro* germination of pollen of apricot (*Prunus armeniaca* L.). J. Hort. Sci., **67**, 247–250.

EINSET J.W. 1986c Role of cytokinin in woody plant micropropagation. Comb. Proc. Int. Plant Prop. Soc., **35**, 608–615.

EINSET J.W. 1987 Cytokinin consumption by micropropagated shoots. Comb. Proc. Int. Plant Prop. Soc., **36**, 635–640.

EIZENGA G.C. & DAHLEEN L.S. 1990 Callus production, regeneration and evaluation of plants from cultured inflorescences of tall fescue (*Festuca arundinacea* Schreb.). Plant Cell Tiss. Organ Cult., **22**, 7–15.

EL HASAN ANAS A. & DEBERGH P. 1987 Regeneration, multiplication and tuberization of virus–free plantlets from virus–infected tubers of *Solanum tuberosum* L. pp. 154–159 in Ducaté *et al.* (eds.) 1987 (*q.v.*).

EL SHIATY O., STINO G. & ABOU EL DAHAB A. 1991 Callus initiation promotion and plantlet regeneration from different parts of the shoot tip of *Pritchardia* ornamental palms grown *in vitro*. Acta Hort., **300**, 281–286.

EL–SHERBINI N., SWARTZ H.J., GOUIN F., STUTTE G. & BORS R. 1988 Paclobutrazol–assisted rooting. HortScience, **23**, 756.

ELHAG H.M. 1991 *In vitro* propagation of *Catha edulis*. HortScience, **26**, 212.

ELLIOTT G.C., SMITH M.A. & BRIDGEN M.B. 1993 Growth response of *Alstroemeria* 'Parigo Pink' to phosphate supply *in vitro*. Plant Cell Tiss. Organ Cult., **92**, 199–204.

ELLIOTT R.F. 1969 Growth of excised meristem–tips of *Rumara, Ipomoea batatas* (Linn.) Poir in axenic culture. N. Z. J. Bot., **7**, 158–166.

ELLIOTT R.F. 1972 Axenic culture of shoot apices of apple. N. Z. J. Bot., **10**, 254–258.

ELLIS D.D. & JUDD R.C. 1987 SDS – PAGE analysis of bud–forming cotyledons of *Pinus ponderosa*. Plant Cell Tiss. Organ Cult., **11**, 57–65.

ELLIS D.D., BARCZYNSKA H., McCOWN B.H. & NELSON N. 1991 A comparison of BA, zeatin and thidiazuron for adventitious bud formation from *Picea glauca* embryos and epicotyl explants. Plant Cell Tiss. Organ Cult., **27**, 281–287.

ELLYARD R.K. 1978a *In vitro* propagation of *Anigozanthos manglesii, A. flavidus* and *Macropidia fulginosa*. HortScience, **13**, 662–663.

ELLYARD R.K. 1978b Tissue culture propagation of *Anigozanthos manglesii, Anigozanthos flavidus* and *Macropidia fulginosa*. Proc. Int. Hort. Cong., **20**, Abst. 1887.

ELMER W.H., BALL T., VOLOKITA M., STEPHENS C.T. & SINK K.C. 1989 Plant regeneration from callus–derived protoplasts of asparagus. J. Am. Soc. Hort. Sci., **114**, 1019–1024.

ELMHEUSER H., NEUMAN K.K. & SCHUSTER W. 1978 The effects of various phytohormones on growth and development of tissue cultures of some rape varieties (*Brassica napus* L. ssp. oleifera). Ober. Naturwiss. Z., **44**, 5–11.

ELMORE H.W., SAMPLES B., SHARMA S. & HARRISON M. 1990 Influence of cultural and physiochemical factors on ascorbate stability in plant tissue culture media. Plant Cell Tiss. Organ Cult., **20**, 131–135.

EMADIAN S.F. & NEWTON R.J. 1989 Growth enhancement of loblolly pine (*Pinus taeda* L.) seedlings by silicon. J. Plant Physiol., **134**, 98–103.

EMKE A. & EILERT U. 1986 Steroidal alkaloids in tissue cultures and regenerated plants of *Solanum dulcamera*. Plant Cell Rep., **5**, 31–34.

EMSWELLER S.L., ASEN S. & UHRING J. 1962 *Lilium speciosum* × *Lilium auratum*. Lily Yb. N. Am. Lily Soc., **15**, 7–15.

ENDO T., GOODBODY A. & MISAWA M. 1987 Alkaloid production in root and shoot cultures of *Catharanthus roseus*. Planta Med., **53**, 479–482.

ENGELMANN F. 1991 *In vitro* conservation of horticultural species. Acta Hort., **298**, 327–334.

ENGLER D.E. & GROGAN R.G. 1983 Isolation, culture and regeneration of lettuce leaf mesophyll protoplasts. Plant Sci. Lett., **28**, 223–229.

EPSTEIN E., KOCHBA J. & NEUMANN H. 1977 Metabolism of indoleacetic acid by embryogenic and non–embryogenic callus lines of Shamouti orange (*Citrus sinensis* Osb.). Z. Pflanzenphysiol., **85**, 263–268.

ERNST R. 1975 Studies in asymbiotic culture of orchids. Am. Orchid Soc. Bull., **44**, 12–18.

ERNST R., BALL E.A. & ARDITTI J. 1982 Biological effects of surfactants. V. Growth and anthocyanin production by callus cultures of *Dimorphotheca*. Am. J. Bot., **69**, 1340–1345.

ESCOBA A.H.A., VILLALOBOS A.V.M. & VILLEGAS M.A. 1986 *Opuntia* micropropagation by axillary proliferation. Plant Cell Tiss. Organ Cult., **7**, 269–277.

ESPINASSE A., LAY C. & VOLIN J. 1989 Effects of growth regulator concentrations and explant size on shoot organogenesis from callus derived from zygotic embryos of sunflower (*Helianthus annuus* L.). Plant Cell Tiss. Organ Cult., **17**, 171–181.

ESTRADA R., MANYA W., PULACHE C., SANCHEZ H.& YONAMINE T. 1986b Maintenance micropropagation and seed producetiong of the Andean tuber crops. p. 103 in Somers *et al.* (eds.) 1986 (*q.v.*).

ETTINGER T.L. & PREECE J.E. 1985 Aseptic micropropagation of *Rhododendron* P.J.M. hybrids. J. Hort. Sci., **60**, 269–274.

ETTINGER–PALTIN R., IZHAR S., SWARTZBERG D. & TABIB Y. 1984 Growth hormones as a selection tool for somatic hybridization in *Petunia*. Plant Sci. Lett., **35**, 231–235.

EVANS D.A. & MORRISON R. 1988 Tomato anther culture. U.S. Patent No. 4835339.

EVANS D.A. & SHARP W.R. 1988 Tissue cultures of *Lycopersicon* spp. U.S. Patent No. 4734369.

EVANS D.A., FLICK C. & SHARP W.R. 1988a Generation of somaclonal non-Mendelian variants. U.S. Patent No. 4818699.

EVANS D.A., FLICK C. & SHARP W.R. 1988b Generation of somaclonal non-Mendelian variants. U.S. Patent No. 4827079.

EVANS D.A., ELGI J.E., KUT S.A., SHARP W.R. & FLICK C.E. 1981b *In vitro* regeneration of the ornamental tobacco *Nicotiana alata*. HortScience, **16**, 425 (Abs. 195).

EVANS D.A., SHARP W.R. & PADDOCK E.F. 1977 Chemical and physical regulation of growth and differentiation in tissue cultures of *Glycine max*. Plant Physiol., **59**, (6 Suppl.) 1.

EVANS D.A., SHARP W.R., AMMIRATO P.V. & YAMADA Y. (eds.) 1983 *Handbook of Plant Cell Culture*. Vol. 1. *Techniques for Propagation and Breeding*. Macmillan Publishing Co., New York, London.

EVELEENS L.A. 1992 Forcing hydrangea plants into bloom all year round – using tissue culture plants which are lignified and possess flower buds after cold storage. European Patent No. 325816.

EVERETT N.P. 1986 Plant growth medium. U.S. Patent No. 4552844.

FACCIOTTI D. & PILET P.–E. 1979 Plants and embryoids from haploid *Nicotiana sylvestris* protoplasts. Plant Sci. Lett., **15**, 1–6.

FAEDI W., TURCI O., SIROLI M., D'ERCOLE N. & BAZZOCCHI C. 1989 Effect of different propagation systems on strawberry plant performance. Acta Hort., **265**, 321–326.

FAKHRAI F. & EVANS P.K. 1989 Morphogenic potential of cultured explants of *Crocus chrysanthus* Herbert cv. E.P. Bowles. J. Exp. Bot., **40**, 809–812.

FALAVIGNA A. & HUSSEY G. 1979 Origin of adventitious shoots from *Allium cepa* and the effect of daylength. Ann. Rep. John Innes Inst. 1978, 52.

FAN M.L. & HU T.–W. 1976 Plantlets from *Paulownia* tissue cultures., Bull. No. 286, Taiwan For. Res. Inst.

FANIZZA G. & RICCIARDI L. 1988 The response of a range of genotypes of *Vitis vinifera* to sequential shoot tip cultures at high temperatures. Euphytica, **39**, 19–23.

FANIZZA G., RICCARDI L., SILVESTRONI O. & BOSCIA D. 1988 The influence of high temperatures and benzyladenine on root induction during *in vitro* shoot tip culture in *Vitis vinifera* L. Acta Hort., **227**, 479–481.

FANIZZA G., TANZARELLA O.A., CARROZZO G. & GRECO B. 1984 Influence of *Vitis* source on *in vitro* shoot apex culture. Ann. Appl. Biol., **104**, 577–578.

FARI M. 1988 System for sterile micropropagation of plants – carries out feed, mixing, filling and closure in aseptic environment. World Patent Applic. No. 8806618.

FARI M., BANKI–PEREDI A. & TOTH–CSANYI M. 1991 Highly efficient *in vitro* shoot regeneration system in tomato and egg plant via seedling decapitation method (SDM). Acta Hort., **289**, 111.

FARI M., MANNINGER S., HAJAS J., KOVACS S., ANDRASFALVY A. & LAZLO M. 1987 Propamatic: A new, semi–automated plant micropropagation technology. pp. 67 in Ducaté *et al.* (eds.) 1987 (*q.v.*).

FARKAS T., VIGH L.H.I. (nee NAGY V.A.F.F.), MESZAROS A., TOTH I. & HUNGARY S. 1985a Plant tissue cultivation process. U.S. Patent No. 4554252.

FARKAS T., VIGH L.H.I. (nee NAGY V.A.F.F.), MESZAROS A., TOTH I. & HUNGARY S. 1985b Improving survival rate of *in vitro* multiplied plants by incorporating acetyl or chloro acetyl amide. British Patent Applic. No. 2112413.

FARNHAM M.W. & NELSON B.V. 1993 Ability of *in vitro* propagation for field–grown broccoli: effect of genotype and growing season. HortScience, **28**, 655–656.

FARQUHARSON L.I. 1957 Hybridization of *Tripsacum* and *Zea*. J. Hered., **48**, 295–299.

FARRELL M.A. 1987 Liquid medium system for plant propagation. Moet–Hennesy Conf. on Electronics and Management of Living Plants, Monaco.

FASOLO F., ZIMMERMAN R.H. & FORDHAM I. 1989 Adventitious shoot formation on excised leaves of *in vitro* grown shoots of apple cultivars. Plant Cell Tiss. Organ Cult., **16**, 75–87.

FASOLO FABBRI MALAVASI F. & PREDIERI S. 1988 *In vivo* rooting of GF 655–2 peach rootstock and kiwi cv. 'Hayward' microcuttings. Acta Hort., **227**, 500–503.

FASSULIOTIS G. 1975 Regeneration of whole plants from isolated stem parenchyma cells of *Solanum sisymbriifolium*. J. Am. Soc. Hort. Sci., **100**, 636–638.

FASSULIOTIS G., NELSON B.V. & BHATT D.P. 1981 Organogenesis in tissue culture of *Solanum melongena* cv. Florida market. Plant Sci. Lett., **22**, 119–125.

FAST G. 1973 The propagation of *Oncidium papilio* by shoot tip culture and a discussion of some nutrient media. Orchidee, **24**, 240–246.

FAULKS L. & MUDGE K.W. 1988 Optimization of environmental conditions of stage IV micropropagated grapes. HortScience, **23**, 757.

FAZEKAS G.A., SEDMACH P.A. & PALMER M.V. 1986 Genetic and environmental effects on *in vitro* shoot regeneration from cotyledon explants of *Brassica juncea*. Plant Cell Tiss. Organ Cult., **6**, 177–180.

FELDMANN K.A. 1986 Rapid and efficient regeneration of *Arabidopsis thaliana*. p. 36 in in Somers et al. (eds.) 1986 (*q.v.*).

FELICIANO A.J. & DE ASSIS M. 1983 *In vitro* rooting of shoots from embryo–cultured peach seedlings. HortScience, **18**, 705–706.

FELLENBERG G. 1963 Uber die Organbildung an *in vitro* kultiviertem Knollenewebe von *Solanum tuberosum*. Z. Bot., **51**, 113–141.

FERENCZY L. & FARKAS G.L. (eds.) 1980 *Advances in Protoplast Research*. Proc. 5th Int. Protoplast Symposium, Szeged, Hungary 1979. Permagon Press. Oxford, New York, Toronto.

FERNANDEZ G.E. & CLARK J.R. 1991 *In vitro* propagation of the Great Thornless 'Novaho' blackberry. HortScience, **26**, 1219.

FERNANDEZ H., BERTRAND A. & SANCHEZ TAMES R. 1991 Micropropagation of *Asplenium nidus–avis*. Acta Hort., **289**, 113–114.

FERNANDEZ L. & SANCHEZ DE JIMENEZ E. 1982 *In vitro* culture of *Bouvardia ternifolia*. Can. J. Bot., **60**, 917–921.

FERREIRA A.G. & HU C.–Y. 1989 Light–mediated inhibition of *in vitro* late embryogeny of *Ilex*. J. Am. Soc. Hort. Sci., **114**, 819–823.

FERREIRA C.M. & HANDRO W. 1988b Production, maintenance and plant regeneration from cell suspension cultures of *Stevia rebaudiana* (Bert.) Bertoni. Plant Cell Rep., **7**, 123–126.

FERRY M., LOUVET J., LOUVET J.M., MONFORT S. & TOUTAIN G. 1987 The specific character of the research into *in vitro* propagation and mass production of date palm. Acta Hort., **212**, 576.

FERSING G. & LUTZ A. 1977 Études comparative de la multiplication végétative *in vitro* de deux espèces horticoles d'*Anthurium: A. andreanum* et *A. Scherzerianum*. Compt. Rend. Acad. Sci. Paris, **284D**, 2231–2233.

FEUCHT W. & DAUSEND B. 1976 Root induction *in vitro* of easy–to–root *Prunus pseudocerasus* and difficult–to–root *Prunus avium*. Scientia Hort., **4**, 49–54.

FIECHTER A. (ed.) 1980 *Advances in Biochemical Engineering*. 18. Springer–Verlag, Berlin, Heidelberg, N.York.

FIECHTER A. (ed.) 1986 *Bioproducts. Advances in Biochemical Engineering/biotechnology* 33. Springer-Verlag, Berlin, Heidelberg, New York, Tokyo.

FIERRO C.A. 1976 *In vitro* cormel development in *Xanthosoma* explants. Plant Physiol., **57**, 81 (Abst.423).

FIGUEIRA A., WHIPKEY A. & JANICK J. 1991 Increased CO_2 and light promote *in vitro* shoot growth and development of *Theobroma cacao*. J. Am. Soc. Hort. Sci., **116**, 585–589.

FILLATTI J. & COMAI L. 1988 Transformation and foreign gene expression with woody species. U.S. Patent No. 4795855.

FINCH R.P., BASET A., SLAMET I.H. & COCKING E.C. 1992 *In vitro* shoot culture of wild *Oryza* and other grass species. Plant Cell Tiss. Organ Cult., **30**, 31–39.

FINER J. 1992 Propagation of cotton plants by tissue culture – using suspension culture to produce pro–embryonic cell masses. European Patent Applic. No. 317512.

FINER J.J. 1987 Direct somatic embryogenesis and plant regeneration from immature embryos of hybrid sunflower (*Helianthus annuus* L.) on a high sucrose–containing medium. Plant Cell Rep., **6**, 372–374.

FINER J.J. 1988a Apical proliferation of embryogenic tissue of soybean *Glycine max* (L.) Merrill . Plant Cell Rep., **7**, 238–241.

FINER J.J. & SMITH R.H. 1982 Isolation and culture of protoplasts from cotton (*Gossypium klotzschianum* Anderss.) callus cultures. Plant Sci. Lett., **26**, 147–151.

FINER J.J. & SMITH R.H. 1982b *Gossypium klotzschianum* protoplast isolation and callus formation. In Vitro **18**, 276 (Abst.5).

FINER J.J. & SMITH R.H. 1984 Initiation of callus & somatic embryos from explants of mature cotton (*Gossypium klotzschianum* Anderss.). Plant Cell Rep., **3**, 41–43.

FINER J.J., KRIEBEL H.B. & BECWAR M.R. 1989 Initiation of embryogenic callus and suspension cultures of eastern white pine (*Pinus strobus* L.). Plant Cell Rep., **8**, 203–206.

FINNIE J.F. & VAN STADEN J. 1987 Multiplication of the tree fern *Cyathea dregei*. HortScience, **22** , 665.

FINNIE J.F. & VAN STADEN J. 1989 *In vitro* propagation of *Sandersonia* and *Gloriosa*. Plant Cell Tiss. Organ Cult., **19**, 151–158.

FINNIE J.F., ACKERMANN C. & VAN STADEN J. 1989 *In vitro* culture of guayule using pre–treated seeds. HortScience, **24**, 836–837.

FIOLA J.A., HASSAN M.A., SWARTZ H.J., BORS R.H. & McNICOLS R. 1990 Effect of thidiazuron, light fluence rates and karomycin on *in vitro* shoot organogenesis from excised *Rubus* cotyledons and leaves. Plant Cell Tiss Organ Cult., **20**, 223–228.

FIORINO F. & LEVA A.R.. 1986 Investigation on the micropropagation of the olive (*Olea europaea* L.). Influence of some mineral elements of the proliferation and rooting of explants. Olea, **17**, 101–104.

FIORINO P. & LEVA A.R. 1983 Propagation of apple cultivars. Acta Hort., **131**, 95–99.

FIRN R.D., WILLIS D. & ORTON P. 1989 Plant tissue culture process – with a liquid culture medium provided to contact each individual piece of plant. British Patent Applic. No. 2211714.

FIROOZABADY E. 1986 Rapid plant regeneration from *Nicotiana mesophyll* protoplasts. Plant Science, **46**, 127–131.

FIROOZABADY E. & DE BOER D.L. 1986 Isolation, culture, and cell division in cotyledon protoplasts of cotton (*Gossypium hirsutum* and *G. barbadense*). Plant Cell Rep., **5**, 127–131.

FIROOZABADY E., NORIEGA C., ROBINSON K. & SONDAHL M.R. 1992 Somatic embryos and young plant production – from mature rose plant material by culturing in callus induction and regeneration media for herbicide and pesticide resistance. World Patent Applic. No. 9200371.

FISCHER G. & ZIMMER K. 1988 Regeneration of germinating seeds *in vitro*. Acta Hort., **226**, 615–618.

FISHER J.B. & TSAI J.H. 1978 *In vitro* growth of embryos and callus of coconut palm. In Vitro **14**, 307–311.

FITCH M.M.M. 1993 High frequency somatic embryogenesis and plant regeneration from papaya hypocotyl callus. Plant Cell Tiss. Organ Cult., **32** , 205–212.

FITCH M.M.M. & HINCHEE M. 1982 Androgenic callus production from *Saccharum spontaneum* L. Plant Physiol. **69**, 31 (Abst. 172).

FITCH M.M.M. & MANSHARDT R.M. 1990 Somatic embryogenesis and plant regeneration from immature zygotic embryos of papaya (*Carica papaya* L.). Plant Cell Rep., **9**, 320–324.

FITCH M.M.M. & MOORE P.H. 1990 Comparison of 2,4–D and picloram for selection of long–term totipotent green callus cultures of sugarcane. Plant Cell Tiss. Organ Cult., **20**, 157–163.

FITCH M.M.M. & MOORE P.H. 1993 Long–term culture of embryogenic sugarcane callus. Plant Cell Tiss. Organ Cult., **32**, 335–343.

FITCHET M. 1990a Clonal propagation of Queen and Smooth Cayenne pineapples. Acta Hort., **275**, 261–266.

FITCHET M. 1990b Induction of embryogenic callus from flower shoot tips of dwarf Cavendish banana. Acta Hort., **275**, 275–284.

FITCHET M. 1990c Organogenesis in callus cultures of pineapple (*Ananas comosus* (L.) Merr. Acta Hort., **275**, 267–274.

FLADUNG M. & HESSELBACH J. 1986 Callus induction and plant regeneration in *Panicum bisulcatum* and *Panicum milioides*. Plant Cell Rep., **5**, 169–173.

FLAMEE M. 1978 Influence of selected media and supplements on the germination and growth of *Paphiopedilum* seedlings. Am. Orchid Soc. Bull., **47**, 419–423.

FLICK C.E., SHARP W.R. & EVANS D.A. 1981b Isolation, culture and fusion of protoplasts from the ornamental tobacco *Nicotiana alata*. HortScience, **16**, 425–426 (Abst.196).

FLORES H.E. & NAZARIO V.E. 1977 *In vitro* organogenesis of *Gloxinia* leaf tissue. Plant Physiol., **59**, (Suppl.) 3 (Abst. 13).

FLORES H.E., THIER A. & GALSTON A.W. 1981 Tissue culture of *Amaranthus*. Env. Exp. Bot., **21**, 437–438 (Abst.).

FLORES H.E., THIER A. & GALSTON A.W. 1982 *In vitro* culture of grain and vegetable amaranths (*Amaranthus* spp.). Am. J. Bot., **69**, 1049–1054.

FLYNN W.P., GLICENSTEIN L.J. & FRITZ P.J. 1990 *Theobroma cacao* L.: an axillary bud *in vitro* propagation procedure. Plant Cell Tiss. Organ Cult., **20**, 111–117.

FOEGLEIN F. 1993 Method for adaptation of plants increased by tissue culture for direct planting out — involves growing plants in one or more stages in fertile soil, the osmotic pressure of which corresponds to 0.1–0.4 M saccharose content. European Patent Applic. No. 563423.

FOGLEIN F., OSVATH Z. & BALOGH J. 1988b *In vitro* production of potato minitubers – by *in vitro* tuber formation, greenhouse plating and tuber development while inhibiting haulm growth, and re–planting in soil. World Patent Applic. No. 8804137.

FOGLEIN F., SUM I., OLEAR G., MAGYAR M., MESZAROS A. & SZEGEDI M. 1988a Viroid and virus–free potato propagation material production – comprises plant tissue culture of cells of potato shoot apex tissue, induction of mini–tubers etc. World Patent Applic. No. 8802213.

FONNESBECH A. & FONNESBECH M. 1980 *In vitro* propagation of *Monstera deliciosa*. HortScience, **15**, 740–741.

FONNESBECH M. 1972a Growth hormones and propagation of *Cymbidium in vitro*. Physiol. Plant., **27**, 310–316.

FONNESBECH M. 1974b Temperature effects on shoot & root development from *Begonia* × *cheimantha* petiole segments grown *in vitro*. Physiol. Plant., **32**, 282–286.

FONNESBECH M. 1975 Cultivation of *Asparagus plumosus* shoot tips *in vitro* with special reference to vegetative propagation. Acta Hort., **54**, 93–94.

FONNESBECH M. & FONNESBECH A. 1979 *In vitro* propagation of *Spathiphyllum*. Scientia Hort., **10**, 21–25.

FORD J.L. & SINK K.C. 1982 Protoplast isolation and culture from cell suspension and callus cultures of *Petunia alpicola*. HortScience, **17**, 532 (Abst.424).

FORD–LOGAN J. & SINK K.C. 1988 Plantlet regeneration from protoplasts of *Petunia alpicola*. HortScience, **23**, 293–395.

FORDHAM I., STIMART D.P. & ZIMMERMAN R.H. 1982 Axillary and adventitious shoot proliferation of Exbury azaleas *in vitro*. HortScience, **17**, 738–739.

FORSYTH C. & VAN STADEN J. 1982 An improved method of *in vitro* propagation of *Dioscorea bulbifera*. Plant Cell Tiss. Organ Cult., **1**, 275–281.

FORTI E., MANDOLINO G. & RANALLI P. 1991 *In vitro* tuber induction: influence of the variety and of the media. Acta Hort., **300**, 127–132.

FOULETIER B. 1974 Conditions favorisant la néoformation de cals haploides à partir d'anthères de riz cultivées *in vitro*. Compt. Rend. Acad. Sci. Paris, **278D**, 2917–2920.

FOURNIOUX J.C. & BESSIS R. 1993 Use of carbon dioxide enrichment to obtain adult morphology of grapevine *in vitro*. Plant Cell Tiss. Organ Cult., **33**, 51–57.

FOX J.E. 1963 Growth factor requirements and chromosome number in tobacco tissue cultures. Plant Physiol., **16**, 793–803.

FRANCLET A. 1979 Réjeunissement des arbres adultes en vue de leur propagation végétative. pp. 1–18 in *Micropropagation d'Arbres Forestiers*. AFOCEL, Études et Recherches No. 12.

FRANCLET A. 1991 Biotechnology in 'rejuvenation': hope for the micropropagation of difficult woody plants. Acta Hort., **289**, 273–282.

FRANCLET A. & BOULAY M. 1982 Micropropagation of frost resistant *Eucalyptus* clones. Aust. J. For. Res., **13**, 83–89.

FRANCLET A., BOULAY M., BEKKAOUI F., FOURET Y., VERSCHOORE–MAR-TOUZET B. & WALKER N. 1987 Rejuvenation., pp. 232–248 in Bonga and Durzan (eds.) 1987 (*q.v.*).

FRANKLIN C.I., MOTT R.L. & VUKE T.M. 1989 Stable ploidy levels in long–term callus cultures of loblolly pine. Plant Cell Rep., **8**, 101–104.

FRANKLIN C.I., TRIEU T.N. & GONZALES R.A. 1990 Plant regeneration through somatic embryogenesis in the forage grass Caucasian bluestem (*Bothriochloa caucasica*). Plant Cell Rep., **9**, 443–446.

FRANKLIN C.I., TRIEU T.N., GONZALES R.A. & DIXON R.A. 1991 Plant regeneration from seedling explants of green bean (*Phaseolus vulgaris* L.) via organogenesis. Plant Cell Tiss. Organ Cult., **24**, 199–206.

FRANSZ P.F., DE RUIJTER N.C.A. & SCHEL J.H.N. 1989 Isozymes as biochemical and cytochemical markers in embryogenic callus cultures of maize (*Zea mays* L.). Plant Cell Rep., **8**, 67–70.

FRASER L.G., HARVEY C.F. & KENT J. 1991 Ploidy manipulations of kiwi fruit in tissue culture. Acta Hort., **297**, 109–114.

FREARSON E.M., POWER J.B. & COCKING E.G. 1973 The isolation, culture and regeneration of *Petunia* leaf protoplasts. Develop. Biol., **33**, 130–137.

FREEBERG J.A. & WETMORE R.H. 1957 Gametophytes of *Lycopodium* as grown *in vitro*. Phytomorph., **7**, 204–217.

FRETT J.J. & DIRR M.A. 1983 Tissue culture propagation of *Liriope muscari* and *Ophiopogon jaburan*. HortScience, **18**, 431–432.

FREY L. & JANICK J. 1991 Organogenesis in carnation. J. Am. Soc. Hort. Sci., **116**, 1108–1112.

FREY L., SARANGA Y. & JANICK J. 1992 Somatic embryogenesis in carnation. HortScience, **27**, 63–65.

FREYSSINET G. & FREYSSINET M. 1991a Regenerating sunflower cultivars by somatic embryogenesis – by forming embryos from tissue cells then germination, using similar growth media containing cytokinin hormone. European Patent No. 266287.

FREYSSINET G. & FREYSSINET M. 1991b Process for regenerating sunflowers by embryogenesis. U.S. Patent No. 5017491.

FREYTAG A.H., RAO–ARELLI A.P., ANAND S.C., WRATHER J.A. & OWENS L.D. 1989 Somaclonal variation in soybean plants regenerated from tissue culture. Plant Cell Rep., **8**, 199–202.

FRIDBORG G. 1971 Growth and organogenesis in tissue cultures of *Allium cepa* var. proliferum. Physiol. Plant., **25**, 436–440.

FRIDRIKSSON S. & BOLTON J.L. 1963 Preliminary report on the culture of alfalfa embryos. Can. J. Bot., **41**, 439–440.

FRISCH C.H. & CAMPER N.D. 1985 *In vitro* culture of *Camellia sinensis*. pp. 320–321 in Henke *et al.* (eds.) 1985 (*q.v.*).

FU F.M.L. 1978 Studies on the tissue culture of orchids. 1. Clonal propagation of *Phalaenopsis* by lateral buds from flower stems. Orchid Rev., **86**, 308–310.

FU F.M.L. 1979 Studies on the tissue culture of orchids. II. Clonal propagation of *Aranda, Ascocenda* and *Cattleya* by leaf tissue culture. Orchid Rev., **87**, 343–346.

FUENTES S.I., SUAREZ R., VILLEGAS T., ACERO L.C. & HERIVANDEZ G. 1993 Embryogenic response of Mexican alfalfa (*Medicago sativa*) varieties. Plant Cell Tiss. Organ Cult., **34**, 299–302.

FUERNKRANZ H. & MAYNARD C.A. 1986 Improved rooting of axillary shoots of mature *Prunus serotina in vitro*. p. 110 in Somers *et al.* (eds.) 1986 (*q.v.*).

FUJII J.A., SLADE D. & REDENBAUGH M.K. 1990 Method of plant somatic embryo production – in tissue culture for planting in growth chamber, greenhouse or as a true seed. World Patent Applic. No. 9000002.

FUJII T. 1970 Callus formation in wheat anthers. Wheat Information Serv. **31**, 1–2.

development medium containing adsorbent reducing acid concentration over time. World Patent Applic. No. 9105854.

GUPTA P.K., SHAW D. & DURZAN D.J. 1987 Loblolly pine: Micropropagation, somatic embryogenesis and encapsulation. pp. 101–108 in Bonga & Durzan (eds.) 1987 (*q.v.*).

GUPTA P.P. 1986a Eradication of mosaic disease and rapid clonal multiplication of bananas and plantains through meristem tip culture. Plant Cell Tiss. Organ Cult., **6**, 33–39.

GUPTA P.P. 1986b Regeneration of plants from mesophyll protoplasts of ground–cherry (*Physalis minima* L.). Plant Science, **43**, 151–154.

GUPTA S.C. & BABBAR S.B. 1980 Enhancement of plantlet formation in anther cultures of *Datura metel* L. by pre–chilling of buds. Z. Pflanzenphysiol.,**96**, 465–470.

GUPTA V., AGNIHOTRI A. & JAGANNATHAN V. 1990 Plant regeneration from callus and protoplasts of *Brassica nigra* (IC 257) through somatic embryogenesis. Plant Cell Rep., **9**, 427–430.

GUPTON C.L. 1986 Production of non–chimeral colchiploids in *Rubus* spp. by tissue culture HortScience, **21**, 734 (Abst.).

GURI A. & SINK K.C. 1988 Organelle composition in somatic hybrids between an atrazine resistant biotype of *Solanum nigrum* and *Solanum melongena*. Plant Science, **58**, 51–58.

GUY A.L., HEINIS J.L. & PANCHOLY S.K. 1978 Induction and biochemical parameters of callus growth from three peanut cultivars. Peanut Sci., **5**, 78–82.

HA NGOC K.A. & TRAN THANH VAN M. 1979 Bud formation capacity of callus formed from thin cell epidermal cell layers excised from floral branches of *N. tabacum* cultivar Wisconsin 38. Physiol. Plant., **40**, 203–207.

HAAGEN–SMIT A.J., SIU R. & WILSON G. 1945 A method for the culturing of excised, immature corn embryos *in vitro*. Science, **101**, 234.

HABERLACH G.T. & HELGESON J.P. 1981 Shoots from potato mesophyll proto-plasts: procedures for improving the frequency of regeneration. Plant Physiol., **67**, (Suppl.) 26 (Abst.140).

HACHEY J.E., SHARMA K.K. & MOLONEY M.M. 1991 Efficient shoot regeneration of *Brassica campestris* using cotyledon explants cultured *in vitro*. Plant Cell Rep., **9**, 549–554.

HACKETT W.P. & MURRAY J.R. 1992 Maturation and rejuvenation in woody plants. Acta Hort., **314**, 195–203.

HACKETT W.P., GENEVE R.L. & MOKHTARI M. 1988 Use of leaf petioles of *Hedera helix* to study regulation of adventitious root initiation. pp. 139–148 in Hanover & Keathley (eds.) 1988 (*q.v.*).

HACKETT W.P., TSE A. & SMITH R.J. 1972 Adventitious bud formation on *Phalaenopsis* nodes as a propagation method. Plant Propagator, **18**, 4–5.

HADDON L. & NORTHCOTE D.H. 1976 The effect of growth conditions and origin of tissue on the ploidy and morphogenetic potential of tissue cultures of bean (*Phaseolus vulgaris*). J. Exp. Bot., **27**, 1031–1051.

HADLEY G. & HARVAIS G. 1968 The effect of certain growth substances on asymbiotic germination and development of *Orchis purpurella*. New Phytol., **67**, 441–445.

HAGEN S.R., MUNETA P., AUGUSTIN J. & LE TOURNEAU D. 1991 Stability and utilization of picloram, vitamins and sucrose in a tissue culture medium. Plant Cell Tiss. Organ Cult., **25**, 45–48.

HAHN J. 1970 Die vermehrung der orchideen durch meristemkultur. Zierpflan-zenbau, **10**, 508–516.

HAHNE B., LORZ H. & HAHNE G. 1990 Oat mesophyll protoplasts: their response to various feeder cultures. Plant Cell Rep., **8**, 590–593.

HAIBOU T. K. & KOVOOR A. 1982 Regeneration of callus from coconut proto-plasts. pp. 149–151 in Rao A. N. (ed.) 1982 (*q.v.*).

HAISSIG B.E. 1986 Metabolic processes in adventitious rooting of cuttings. pp. 141–189 in Jackson M.B. (ed.) 1986 (*q.v.*).

HAJELA R.K., HAJELA N., BOLYARD M.G., BARNES W.M. & STICKLEN M.B. 1993 A simple transformation system using adventitious shoot multiplication of June-berry. HortScience, **28**, 330–332.

HAKKAART F.A. & HARTEL G. 1979 Virus eradication from some *Pelargonium zonale* cultivars by meristem tip culture. Neth. J. Plant Path., **85**, 39–46.

HAKKAART F.A. & VERSLUIJS J.M.A. 1983a Control of leaf curl and *Xantho-monas begoniae* in *Begonia* 'Elatior' by meristem culture and an isolation test. Acta Hort., **131**, 299–301.

HAKMAN I. & VON ARNOLD S. 1985 Plantlet regeneration through somatic embryogenesis in *Picea abies* (Norway spruce). J.Plant Physiol., **121**, 149–158.

HAKMAN I., FOWKE L.C., VON ARNOLD S. & ERIKSSON T. 1985 The develop-ment of somatic embryos in tissue cultures initiated from immature embryos of *Picea abies* (Norway spruce). Plant Science, **38**, 53–59.

HAKMAN I.C. & VON ARNOLD S. 1983 Isolation and growth of protoplasts from cell suspensions of *Pinus contorta* Dougl. ex Loud. Plant Cell Rep., **2**, 92–94.

HALDER T. & GADGIL V. N. 1982 Morphogenesis in some plant species of the family Cucurbitaceae. pp. 98–103 in Rao A. N. (ed.) 1982 (*q.v.*)

HALE S.A., YOUNG R.E., ADELBERG J.W., KEESE R.J. & CAMPER N.D. 1992 Bioreactor development for continual–flow, liquid plant tissue culture. Acta Hort., **319**, 107–112.

HALL C.B. 1948 Culture of *Solanum nigrum* embryos. Proc. Am. Soc. Hort. Sci., **52**, 343–346.

HALL T.R.H. & COLLIN H.A. 1975 Initiation and growth of tissue cultures of *Theobroma cacao*. Ann. Bot., **39**, 555–570.

HALOS S.C. & GO N.E. 1993 Micropropagation of *Pinus caribaea* Morelet. Plant Cell Tiss. Organ Cult., **32**, 47–53.

HALPERIN W. 1964 Morphogenetic studies with partially synchronized cultures of carrot embryos. Science, **146**, 408–410.

HAMA I. 1986 Artificial seeds. Japanese Patent Application no. 40708/1986.

HAMALAINEN J.J., KURTEN U., KAUPPINEN V. & HEILALA J. 1992 Automated classification of somatic plant embryos. Acta Hort., **319**, 601–606.

HAMDORF G. 1976 Propagation of *Pelargonium* varieties by stem–tip culture. Acta Hort., **59**, 143–151.

HAMILL J.D. & RHODES J.C. 1988 A spontaneous, light independent and prolific plant regeneration response from hairy roots of *Nicotiana hesperis* transformed by *Agrobacterium rhizogenes*. J. Plant Physiol. **133**, 506–509.

HAMILL J.D., ROBBINS R.J., PARR A.J., EVANS D.M., FURZE J.M., BENT E.G. & RHODES M.J.C. 1990 The effects of over- expressing the yeast ornithine decar-boxylase gene upon the nicotine and polyamine levels in transformed roots of *Nicotiana rustica*. pp. 732–737 in Nijkamp *et al.* (eds.) 1990 (*q.v.*).

HAMILL S.D., SHARROCK S.L. & SMITH M.K. 1993 Comparison of decontamina-tion methods used in initiation of banana tissue cultures from field–collected suckers. Plant Cell Tiss. Organ Cult., **33**, 343–346.

HAMMATT N. & DAVEY M. 1987 Somatic embryogenesis and plant regeneration from cultured zygotic embryos of soybean (*Glycine max* L. Merr.). J. Plant Physiol., **128**, 219–226.

HAMMATT N. & EVANS P.K. 1985 The *in vitro* propagation of an endangered species: *Centaurea junoniana* Svent. (Compositae). J. Hort. Sci., **60**, 93–97.

HAMMATT N. & RIDOUT M.S. 1992 Micropropagation of common ash (*Fraxinus excelsior*). Plant Cell Tiss. Organ Cult., **31**, 67–74.

HAMMER P.A. 1976 Tissue culture propagation of *Hosta decorata* Bailey. Hort-Science, **11**, 309 (Abst.138).

HAMMERSCHLAG F. 1981b *In vitro* propagation of Myrobalan plum (*Prunus cerasifera*). HortScience, **16**, 283 (Abst.).

HAMMERSCHLAG F.A. 1990 Resistance responses of plants regenerated from peach callus cultures to *Xanthomonas campestris* pv. *pruni*. J. Am. Soc. Hort. Sci., **115**, 1034–1037.

HAMMERSCHLAG F.A. & SCORZA R. 1991 Field performance of micropropa-gated, own–rooted peach trees. J. Am. Soc. Hort. Sci., **116**, 1089–1091.

HAMMERSCHLAG F.A., OWENS L.D. & SMIGOCKI A.C. 1989 *Agrobacterium*–mediated transformation of peach cells derived from mature plants that were propagated *in vitro*. J. Am. Soc. Hort. Sci., **114**, 508–510.

HAN K. & STEPHENS L.C. 1992 Carbohydrate and nitrogen sources affect respectively *in vitro* germination of immature ovules and early seedling growth of *Impatiens platypetala* Lindl. Plant Cell Tiss. Organ Cult., **31**, 211–214.

HANDRO W. 1977 Structural aspects of the neo- formation of floral buds on leaf discs of *Streptocarpus nobilis* cultured *in vitro*. Ann. Bot., **41**, 303–305.

HANDRO W. 1991 Commercial micropropagation in South and Central America. pp. 199–203 in Debergh and Zimmerman (eds.) 1991 (*q.v.*).

HANDRO W., FLOH E.I.S., FERREIRA C.M. & GUERRA M.P. 1988 Tissue, cell culture and micropropagation of *Mandevilla velutina*, a natural source of a bradykinin antagonist. Plant Cell Rep., **7**, 564–566.

HANDRO W., RAO P.S. & HARADA H. 1972 Controle hormonal de la formation de cals, bourgeons, racines et embryons sur les explantats de feuilles et de tiges de *Petunia* cultivés *in vitro*. Compt. Rend. Acad. Sci. Paris, **275D**, 2861–2863.

HANNAPEL D.J., DIRR M.A. & SOMMER H.E. 1981 Micropropagation of native *Rhododendron* species. HortScience, **16**, 452 (Abst.391).

HANNING G.E. & CONGER B.V. 1982 Embryoid and plantlet formation from leaf segments of *Dactylis glomerata*. Theor. Appl. Genet., **63**, 155–159.

HANOVER J.W. & KEATHLEY D.E. (eds.) 1988 *Genetic Manipulation of Woody Plants*. Plenum Press, New York, London. ISBN 0–306–42815–6

HANOWER J. & PANNETIER C. 1982 *In vitro* vegetative propagation of the oil palm *Elaeis guineensis* Jacq. pp. 745–746 in Fujiwara (ed.) 1982 (*q.v.*)

HANSCHE P.E. & BERES W. 1980 Genetic remodeling of fruit and nut trees to facilitate cultivar improvement. HortScience **15**, 710–715.

HANSELER K. 1992 Automatic plant dividing machine for use in micropropagation – has conveyor to transport tray containing plant standing upright and harvesting mechanism. World Patent Applic. No. 9203913.

HANSEN K.C. & LAZARTE J.E. 1982 *In vitro* propagation of Pecan (*Carya illinoinensis*). HortScience, **17**, 487 (Abst.109). 3

HANSMAN D. & OWENS Y. & DE NOVOA C. 1986 Micropropagation of temperate nut trees. Hort. Abs., **56**, 403–416.

HANSON M. R. 1982 Cell and tissue culture of *Lycopersicon*. pp. 193–194 in Fujiwara (ed.) 1982 (*q.v.*)

HAQUE M.M., DAS BITHEE, HADIUZZAMAN S., ISLAM A.S. & RAHMAN M.H. 1986 Regeneration of multiple shoots from explants of germinating seeds of *Corchorus*. p. 30 in Somers et al. (eds.) 1986 (*q.v.*).

HARA M. & KOZAI T. 1992 Mathematical methods to maximize the overall multiplication ratio of micropropagation in a determined period. Acta Hort., **319**, 625–630.

HARADA H. 1967 Flower induction in excised shoot apices of *Pharbitis* and *Chrysanthemum* cultured *in vitro*. Nature, **214**, 1027–1028.

HARADA H. 1975 *In vitro* organ culture of *Actinidia chinensis* as a technique for vegetative multiplication. J. Hort. Sci., **50**, 81–83.

HARAZY A., LESHEM B., COHEN A. & RABINOWITCH H.D. 1985 *In vitro* propagation of statice as an aid to breeding. HortScience, **20**, 361–362.

HARBAGE J.F. & STIMART D.P. 1987 Adventitious shoot regeneration from *in vitro* subcultured callus of *Rhododendron* Exbury hybrid. HortScience, **22**, 1324–1325.

HARBAOUI Y. & DEBERGH P. 1980 pp. 1–7 in *Application de la Culture* in vitro *à l'amelioration des Plantes otagères*. Eucarpia meeting, Versailles, France.

HARBERD D.J. 1969 A simple effective embryo culture technique for *Brassica*. Euphytica, **18**, 425–429.

HARMS C.T., BAKTIR I. & OERTLI J.J. 1983 Clonal propagation *in vitro* of red beet (*Beta vulgaris* ssp.) by multiple adventitious shoot formation. Plant Cell Tiss. Organ Cult., **2**, 93–102.

HARMS C.T., LORZ H. & POTRYKUS I. 1976 Regeneration of plantlets from callus cultures of *Zea mays* L. Z. Pflanzenzuchtg., **77**, 347–351.

HARRELL R.C., HOOD C.F., MOLTO E., MUNILLA R., BIENIEK M. & CANTLIFFE D.J. 1992 Automatic identification and separation of somatic embryos *in vitro*. Acta Hort., **319**, 595–600.

HARRIS G.P. 1959 Amino acids as nitrogen sources for the growth of excised roots of red clover. New Phytol., **58**, 330.

HARRIS R., WRIGHT M., BYRNE M., VARNUM J., BRIGHTWELL B. & SCHUBERT K. 1988 Callus formation and plantlet regeneration from protoplasts derived from suspension cultures of wheat (*Triticum aestivum* L.). Plant Cell Rep., **7**, 337–340.

HARRIS R.A. & MANTELL S.H. 1991 Effects of Stage II subculture durations on the multiplication rate and rooting capacity of micropropagated shoots of tree paeony (*Paeonia suffruticosa* Andr.). J. Hort. Sci., **66**, 95–102.

HARRIS R.E. & STEVENSON J.H. 1982 *In vitro* propagation of *Vitis*. Vitis, **21**, 22–32.

HARRISON C.R. 1970 A simple method for flasking orchid seeds. Am. Orchid Soc. Bull., **39**, 715–716.

HARRISON C.R. & ARDITTI J. 1970 Growing orchids from seed. Orchid Dig., **34**, 199–204.

HART J.W., WOODCOCK G.J. & WILSON L. 1970 Culture and sesquiterpene analyses of cells and regenerated plantlets of *Pogostemon cablin* (Patchouli). Ann. Bot., **34**, 789–798.

HARTMAN C.L., McCOY T.J. & KNOUS T.R. 1984 Selection of alfalfa (*Medicago sativa*) cell lines and regeneration of plants resistant to the toxin(s) produced by *Fusarium oxysporum* f.sp. *medicaginis*. Plant Sci. Lett., **34**, 183–194.

HARTMAN R.D. 1974 Dasheen mosaic virus and other phytopathogens eliminated from *Caladium*, taro and cocoyam by culture of shoot tips. Phytopath., **64**, 237–240.

HARTMAN R.D. 1985 How tissue culture makes better crops. pp. 165–172 in V. Ball (ed.) *Ball Redbook* 14th ed. Reston Publishing, Reston, Virginia.

HARTNEY V.J. 1983 Tissue culture of *Eucalyptus*. Comb. Proc. Int. Plant Prop. Soc. 1982, **32**, 98–109.

HARTNEY V.J. 1986 Commercial aspects of micropropagating eucalypts. p. 14 in Somers *et al.* (eds.) 1986 (*q.v.*).

HARTUNG W. & ABOU–MANDOUR A.A. 1980 Abscisic acid in root cultures of *Phaseolus coccineus* L. Z. Pflanzenphysiol., **97**, 265–269.

HARTWECK L.M., LAZZERI P.A., MYERS J.R., HILDEBRANDT D.F. & COLLINS G.B. 1986 Soybean somatic embryogenesis — a morphological and histological evaluation of initiation and development. p.160 in Somers *et al.* (eds.) 1986 (*q.v.*).

HARVEY A. E. & GRASHAM J. L. 1977 Callus proliferation & differentiation of *Ribes* spp. *in vitro*. U.S.D.A. Forest Research Note, Intermountain For. & Range Exp. Stat., No. INT–222.

HARVEY A.E. 1967 Tissue culture of *Pinus monticola* on a chemically defined medium. Can. J. Bot., **45**, 1783–1787.

HARVEY A.E. & GRASHAM J.L. 1969 Procedures and media for obtaining tissue cultures of twelve conifer species. Can. J. Bot., **47**, 547–549.

HARVEY B.M.R., CROTHERS S.H., EVANS N.E. & SELBY C. 1991 The use of growth retardants to improve microtuber formation by potato (*Solanum tuberosum*). Plant Cell Tiss. Organ Cult., **27**, 59–64.

HASEGAWA A. 1991 Occurrence of variegation in the shoot of variegated *Cymbidium* multiplied by shoot tip culture. Acta Hort., **300**, 353–356.

HASEGAWA A., OHASHI H. & GOI M. 1985 Effects of BA, rhizome length, mechanical treatment and liquid shaking culture on the shoot formation from rhizome in *Cymbidium faberi* Rolfe. Acta Hort., **166**, 25–40.

HASEGAWA P.M. 1980 Factors affecting shoot & root initiation from cultured rose shoot tips J. Am. Soc. Hort. Sci., **105**, 216–220.

HASHIM Z.N., CAMPBELL W.F. & CARMAN J.G. 1990 Morphological analyses of spring wheat (CIMMYT cv. PCYT–10) somaclones. Plant Cell Tiss. Organ Cult., **20**, 95–99.

HASKINS R.H.F., CONSTABEL L.N. & GAMBORG O.L. 1971 Plastid development in albino plants obtained from brome grass cell cultures by embryogenesis. Am. J. Bot., **58**, 452.

HASSABALLA I.A., EL–GINDY F.A. & POWER J.B. 1988b Plants regenerated from etiolated cotyledon protoplasts of Volkamer lime seedlings (*Citrus volkameriana* L.). HortScience, **23**, 757.

HASSANPOUR–ESTAHBANATI A. & DEMARLY Y. 1985 Plant regeneration from protoplasts of *Solanum pennellii*: effect of photoperiod applied to donor plants. J. Plant Physiol., **121**, 171–174.

HAVEL L. & KOLAR Z. 1983 Micro–explants isolation from Cactaceae. Plant Cell Tiss. Organ Cult., **2**, 349–353.

HAVEL L. & NOVAK F.J. 1981 *In vitro* pollination of maize (*Zea mays* L.) – proof of double fertilization. Plant Cell Rep., **1**, 26–28.

HAVEL L. & NOVAK F.J. 1985 Meristem–tip culture of *Allium cepa* L. Scientia Hort., **27**, 209–214.

HAVRANEK P. 1972 Virus–free garlic clones obtained from meristem cultures. Ochrana Rostlin, **8**, 291–298.

HAVRANEK P. & NOVAK F.J. 1976 The bud formation in the callus cultures of *Allium sativum*. Z. Pflanzenphysiol., **68**, 308–318.

HAWES M.C., SMITH L.Y. & STEPHENSON M. 1991 Root organogenesis from single cells released from the root cap of *Medicago* sp. Plant Cell Tiss. Organ Cult., **27**, 303–308.

HAWKER J.J., DOWNTON W.J.S., WISKICH D. & MULLINS M.G. 1973 Callus and cell culture from grape berries. HortScience, **8**, 398–399.

HAWKES H.Y. & WAINWRIGHT H. 1987 *In vitro* organogenesis of *Cyclamen persicum* Mill. seedling tissue. Acta Hort., **212**, 711–714.

HAYASHI M., FUJITA N., KITAYA Y. & KOZAI T. 1992 Effect of sideward lighting on the growth of potato plantlets *in vitro*. Acta Hort., **319**, 163–166.

HAYASHI Y. & SHIMAMOTO K. 1988 Wheat protoplast culture: embryogenic colony formation from protoplasts. Plant Cell Rep., **7**, 414–417.

HAYDU Z. & VASIL I.K. 1981 Somatic embryogenesis and plant regeneration from leaf tissues of *Pennisetum purpureum* Schum. Theor. Appl. Genet., **59**, 26–273.

HAYNES F.L. 1954 Potato embryo culture. Am.Pot.J., **31**, 282–288.

HAYWARD C. & POWER J.B. 1975 Plant production from leaf protoplasts of *Petunia parodii*. Plant Sci. Lett., **4**, 407–410.

HAYWARD J.L., SKIRVIN R.M., NANCARROW J. & KNIGHT S.L. 1988 Acclimatization of tissue culture–derived rose shoots to the greenhouse environment. HortScience, **23**, 781.

HE D–G. & OUYANG J–W. 1984 Callus and plantlet formation from cultured wheat anthers at different developmental stages. Plant Sci. Lett., **33**, 71–79.

HE D.–G., YANG Y.–M. & SCOTT K.J. 1991 Zinc deficiency and the formation of white structures in immature embryo cultures of wheat (*Triticum aestivum* L.). Plant Cell Tiss. Organ Cult., **24**, 9–12.

HEARNE D.A. 1983 Preliminary report on a technique which provides a 'maturity factor' for trees grown in tissue culture. Comb. Proc. Int. Plant Prop. Soc. 1982, **32**, 109–113.

HEDTRICH C.M. 1979 Regeneration of shoots from leaves, and propagation of *Gerbera jamesonii*. Gartenbauwiss., **44**, 1–3.

HEIDE O.M. 1965a Photoperiodic effects on the regeneration ability of *Begonia* leaf cuttings. Physiol. Plant., **18**, 185–190.

HEILE–SUDHOLT C., HUETTEMAN C.A., PREECE J.E., VAN SAMBEEK J.W. & GAFFNEY G.R. 1986 *In vitro* embryonic axis and seedling shoot tip culture of *Juglans nigra*. Plant Cell Tiss. Organ Cult., **6**, 189–197.

HEIMAN P.J. & PREECE J.E. 1983 Aseptic micropropagation of *Fraxinus pennsylvanica* Marsh and *Fraxinus americana* L. utilizing shoot tip explants. HortScience, **18**, 616 (Abst.).

HEIRWEGH K.M.G., BANERJEE N., VAN NERUM K. & DE LANGHE E. 1985 Somatic embryogenesis and plant regeneration in *Cichorium intybus* L. (Witloof, Compositae). Plant Cell Rep., **4**, 108–111.

HELGESON J.P., COHEN B.A., HENDRICKS N.R., TOWILL L.E. & HABERLACH G.T. 1982 Isolation and culture of protoplasts from *Solanum* species. Plant Physiol., **69**, (Suppl.) 72 (Abst.403).

HEMPEL M. 1979 Studies on *in vitro* multiplication of carnation. 1. The influence of some cytokinins on the differentiation of shoot apices. Acta Hort., **91**, 317–321.

HEMPEL M. 1985 The influence of micropropagation on progeny plants. Acta Hort., **167**, 263–272.

HEMPEL M. & DEBERGH P.C. 1991 Commercial production in Poland and other Eastern European countries. pp. 167–171 in Debergh and Zimmerman (eds.) 1991 (*q.v.*).

HEMPHILL J.K. & EIKENBERRY E.J. 1986 Regeneration of soybeans by a four–stage process using growth media containing specific mixtures of growth hormones. European Patent Applic. No. 171679.

HEMPHILL J.K. & EIKENBERRY E.J. 1987 Process for regenerating soybeans. U.S. Patent No. 4684612.

HEMPHILL J.K. & OLSON A.C. 1981 Alfalfa plantlet regeneration. Plant Physiol., **67**, (Suppl) 118 (Abst.666).

HENDERSON J. H. M., PHILLS B. R. & WHATLEY B. T. 1984 Chapter 11 — Sweet potato. pp. 302–326 in Sharp *et al.* (eds.) 1984 (*q.v.*).

HENDERSON J.H.M., DURELL M.E. & BONNER J. 1952 The culture of normal sunflower stem callus. Am. J. Bot., **39**, 467–473.

HENDRE R.R., MASCARENHAS A.L., NADGIR A.L., PATHAK M. & JAGANNATHAN V.J. 1976 Growth of mosaic virus–free sugarcane plants from apical meristems. Indian Phytopath., **28**, 175–178.

HENDRIX R.C., LITZ R.E. & KIRCHOFF B.K. 1987 *In vitro* organogenesis and plant regeneration from leaves of *Solanum candidum* Lindl., *S. quitoense* Lam. (Onaranjilla) and *S. sessiliflorum* Dunal. Plant Cell Tiss. Organ Cult., **11**, 67–73.

HENKE R. R., MANSUR M. A. & CONSTANTIN M. J. 1978a Effect of 2–iP on organogenesis in rice cultures. p. 255 in Hughes *et al.* (eds.) 1978 (*q.v.*)

HENKE R.R., HUGHES K.W., CONSTANTIN M.J., HOLLAENDER A. & WILSON C.M. (eds.) 1985 *Tissue culture in Forestry and Agriculture*. Plenum Press. New York, London.

HENKE R.R., MANSUR M.A. & CONSTANTIN M.J. 1978b Organogenesis and plantlet formation from organ– and seedling–derived calli of rice (*Oryza sativa*). Physiol. Plant., **44**, 11–14.

HENNY R.J. 1978 *In vitro* propagation of *Peperomia* Red Ripple from leaf discs. HortScience, **13**, 150–151.

HENNY R.J. & FOOSHEE W.C. 1990 Thidiazuron stimulates basal bud and shoot formation in *Alocasia* × *chantrieri* Andre. HortScience, **25**, 124.

HENRY M., MARIE B. & GUIGNARD J.–L. 1979 La regeneration de plantes entières à partir de culture de cellules in vitro chez *Cheiranthus cheiri* L. et *Cardamine pratensis* L. Bull. Soc. Bot. Fr., **126**, 143–148.

HEPPER C.M. & MOSSE B. 1980 Vesicular–arbuscular mycorrhiza in root organ cultures. pp. 167–171 in Ingram & Helgeson (eds.) 1980 (*q.v.*).

HERMAN E.B. & HAAS G.J. 1975 Clonal propagation of *Coffea arabica* L. from callus culture. HortScience, **10**, 588–589.

HERMESEN J.G.Th., RAMMANA M.S., ROEST S. & BOKELMANN G.S. 1981 Chromosome doubling through adventitious shoot formation on *in vitro* cultivated leaf explants from diploid interspecific potato hybrids. Euphytica, **30**, 239–246.

HERRERA M.T., CACHO M., CORCHETE M.P. & FERNANDEZ–TARRAGO J. 1990 One step shoot tip multiplication and rooting of *Digitalis thapsi* L. Plant Cell Tiss. Organ Cult., **22**, 179–182.

HERRINGTON E. & McPHERSON J.C. 1993 Light quality growth promotion of *Spiraea nipponica*: the influence of a low photon fluence rate and transfer time to a higher fluence rate. Plant Cell Tiss. Organ Cult., **32**, 161–167.

HESS E. & LEIPOLDT G. 1979 Regeneration of shoots and roots from isolated mesophyll protoplasts of *Nemesia strumosa*. Biochem. Physiol. Pflanzen., **174**, 411–417.

HESZKY L.E., BINH D.G., KISS E. & GYULAI G. 1989 Increase of green plant regeneration efficiency by callus selection in *Puccinellia limosa* (Schur.) Holmbg. Plant Cell Rep., **8**, 174–177

HEUSER C.W. 1976 Tissue culture propagation of *Hemerocallis*. HortScience, **11**, 321 (Abst. 244).

HEUSER C.W. 1982 Tissue culture propagation of *Lythrum salicaria*. HoreScience, **17**, 488 (Abst.118).

HEUSER C.W. & APPS D.A. 1976 *In vitro* plantlet formation from flower petal explants of *Hemerocallis* cv. Chipper Cherry. Can. J. Bot., **54**, 616–618.

HEUSER C.W. & HARKAR J. 1976 Tissue culture propagation of daylilies. Comb. Proc. Int. Plant Prop. Soc., **26**, 269–272.

HEYSER J.W. & MOTT R.L. 1980 The relationship between the production of phenolic compounds and the decline in growth of Loblolly pine cultures. Plant Physiol., **65**, (Suppl) 90 (Abst.492).

HEYSER J.W. & NABORS M.W. 1981 The maintenance of totipotency in cereal tissue cultures through the cultivation of green spots. Plant Physiol., **67**, (Suppl) 118 (Abst.664).

HEYSER J.W. & NABORS M.W. 1982a Long–term plant regeneration, somatic embryogenesis and green spot formation in secondary oat (*Avena sativa*) callus. Z. Pflanzenphysiol., **107**, 153–160.

HEYSER J.W. & NABORS M.W. 1982b Regeneration of Proso millet from embryogenic calli derived from various plant parts. Crop Sci., **22**, 1070–1074.

HICKS G. & VON ADERKAS P. 1986 A tissue culture of the ostrich fern *Matteuccia struthiopteris* (L.) Todaro. Plant Cell Tiss. Organ Cult., **5**, 199–204.

HIGGINS W.S. & STIMART D.P. 1990 Influence of *in vitro* generation temperature and post–*in vitro* cold storage duration on growth response of *Lilium longiflorum* bulblets. J. Am. Soc. Hort. Sci., **115**, 930–933.

HIGUCHI H., AMAKI W. & SUZUKI S. 1987 *In vitro* propagation of *Nephrolepis cordifolia* Prsel. Scientia Hort., **32**, 105–113.

HILL D.W. 1988 Fundamentals of rooting tissue–cultured cuttings. Comb. Proc. Int. Plant Prop. Soc. 1987, **37**, 90–92.

HILL G.P. 1967 Morphogenesis in stem–callus cultures of *Convolvulus arvensis* L. Ann. Bot., **31**, 437–446.

HILL G.P. 1967b Morphogenesis of short primordia in cultured stem tissue of a garden rose. Nature, **216**, 596–597.

HILL G.P. 1968 Shoot formation in tissue cultures of *Chrysanthemum* 'Bronze Pride'. Physiol. Plant., **21**, 386–389.

HILL M. 1988 The specifications for Neo Plants' new propagation unit. Comb. Proc. Int. Plant Prop. Soc. 1987, **37**, 306–313.

HILL R.A., TUSKAN G.A. & BOE A.A. 1989 *In vitro* propagation of *Hosta sieboldiana* using excised ovaries from immature florets. Plant Cell Tiss. Organ Cult., **17**, 71–75.

HIRABAYASHI T. & AKIHAMA T. 1982 *In vitro* embryogenesis and plant regeneration from the anther-derived callus of *Vitis*. pp. 547–548 in Fujiwara A. (ed.) 1982 (*q.v.*).

HIRABAYASHI T., KOZAKI I. & AKIHAMA T. 1976 *In vitro* differentiation of shoots from anther callus in *Vitis*. HortScience, **11**, 511–512.

HIRAOKA N. 1986 Formation and propagation of tetraploid *Atractylodes lancea in vitro*. p. 36 in Somers et al. (eds.) 1986 (*q.v.*).

HIRAOKA N. & KODAMA T. 1984 Effects of non–frozen cold storage on the growth, organogenesis and secondary metabolism of callus cultures. Plant Cell Tiss. Organ Cult., **3**, 349–357.

HIRAOKA N. & OYANAGI M. 1988 *In vitro* propagation of *Glehnia littoralis* from shoot tips. Plant Cell Rep., **7**, 39–42.

HIRAOKA N. & TOMITA Y. 1990 Botanical and chemical evaluation of *Atractylodes lancea* plants propagated *in vitro* and by division of the rhizome. Plant Cell Rep., **9**, 332–334.

HIRAOKA N., KODAMA T., OYANAGI M., NAKANO S., TOMITA Y., YAMADA N., IIDA O. & SATAKE M. 1986 Characteristics of *Bupleurum falcatum* plants propagated through somatic embryogenesis of callus cultures. Plant Cell Rep., **5**, 319–321.

HIRAOKA N., YAMADA N., KODAMA T. & TOMITA Y. 1984 *In vitro* propagation of *Atractylodes lancea*. Plant Cell Rep., **3**, 85–87.

HIRATA Y., KAWARABAYASHI W., MATSUBARA K., SHIRANE Y., TAKAHASHI S., YAMAGATA H. & YOSHIOKA T. 1992 Culture tank for plant material – includes cutting device for cutting cultured plant bodies. European Patent No. 298722.

HIRATA Y., KAWARBAYASHI W., MAUBARA K., MOTOYAMA Y., SHIRANE Y., TAKAHASHI S. & YAMAGATA H. 1989 Preparation of inoculum sections for plant tissue culture – by cutting multiple slices from sterilised or uncontaminated plant material. World Patent Applic. No. 8905090.

HIRATA Y., TAKAHASHI S., MORIWAKI R. & KOYAMA A. 1990 Multiplying plant belonging to the genus *Asparagus* – by culturing tissue or callus of plant, to form a tuber–like tissue or crown. European Patent Applic. No. 375218.

HIRIMBUREGAMA K. & WIJESINGHE L.P.J. 1992 *In vitro* growth of *Ananas comosus* L Merr. (pineapple) shoot apices on different media. Acta Hort., **319**, 203–208.

HIROTANI M. & FURUYA T. 1977 Restoration of cardenolide–synthesis in redifferentiated shoots from callus cultures of *Digitalis purpurea*. Phytochem., **16**, 610–611.

HIRSCH A.M. 1975 The effect of sucrose on the differentiation of excised fern leaf tissues into either gametophytes or sporophytes. Plant Physiol., **56**, 390–393.

HIRSCH A.M., FORTUNE D., XIAO X.G. & BLANCHET P. 1991 Somaclonal variations related to kiwi fruit micropropagation, study of fruitful male plants and use of peroxidase as a sex marker. Acta Hort., **297**, 123–131.

HISHINUMA K., MATSUNAGA T., ONO M., UMETSU H. & WAKE H. 1990 Plant tissue culture using extract of photosynthetic prokaryote – promotes adventitious embryo formation and plant regeneration. World Patent Applic. No. 9000855.

HO R.H. 1987 Embryo culture. pp. 137–167 in Bonga and Durzan (eds.) 1987b (*q.v.*).

HODDS H., HILL R.P., DEMAUREX L., BONNET J. & VELUZ S. 1988 Micropropagation of plant and cell cultures – using an absorbent plug with a retaining sleeve or chemical coating. European Patent Applic. No. 287284.

HOL G.M.G.M. & VAN DER LINDE P.C.G. 1992 Reduction of contamination in bulb–explant culture of *Narcissus* by a hot–water treatment of parent bulbs. Plant Cell Tiss. Organ Cult., **31**, 75–79.

HOMMA Y. & ASAHIRA T. 1985 New means of *Phalaenopsis* propagation with internode sections of flower stalk. J. Jap. Soc. Hort. Sci., **54**, 379–387.

HONMA S. 1955 A technique for artificial culturing of bean embryos. Proc. Am. Soc. Hort. Sci., **65**, 405–408.

HOOKER B.S. & LEE J.M. 1990 Cultivation of plant cells in aqueous two–phase polymer systems. Plant Cell Rep., **8**, 546–549.

HOOKER M.P. & NABORS M.W. 1977 Callus initiation, growth and organogenesis in sugar beet (*Beta vulgaris*). Z. Pflanzenphysiol., **84**, 237–246.

HOPWOOD P.R., DAVIS P.E. & BRYANT A. 1981 A medium for the aseptic culture of orchid seed. Aust.Orchid Rev., **46**, (1) 41.

HORGAN K. 1987c Pinus radiata. pp. 128–145 in Bonga & Durzan (eds.) 1987 (*q.v.*).

HORN M.E., HARMS C.T. & SHILLITO R.D. 1989 Embryonic cell cultures from sub–family Pooideae – are regenerated after conversion to protoplast(s) and optionally, incorporation of foreign DNA. European Patent No. 332581.

HORN M.E., SHERRARD J.H. & WIDHOLM J.M. 1983 Photoautotrophic growth of soybean cells in suspension culture. 1. Plant Physiol., **72**, 426–429.

HORN M.E., SHILLITO R.D., CONGER B.V. & HARMS C.T. 1988b Transgenic plants of orchardgrass (*Dactylis glomerata* L.) from protoplasts. Plant Cell Rep., **7**, 469–472.

HORN W. 1988 Micropropagation of *Pelargonium × domesticum* (*P. grandiflorum* hybrids). Acta Hort., **226**, 53–58.

HORST R.K. 1990 *Chrysanthemum*. pp. 319–351 in Ammirato et al. (eds.) 1990 (*q.v.*).

HORST R.K.M., SMITH S.H., HORST H.T. & OGLEVEE W.A. 1976 *In vitro* regeneration of shoot and root growth from meristem tips of *Pelargonium × hortorum* Bailey. Acta Hort., **59**, 131–141.

HOSIER M., GARTON S., READ P.E. & FARNHAM R.S. 1981 *In vitro* propagation of *Alnus glutinosa*. HortScience, **16**, 453 (Abst.400).

HOSIER M.A., FLATEBO G. & READ P.E. 1985 *In vitro* propagation of Lingonberry. HortScience, **20**, 364–365.

HOSOKI T. & ASAHIRA T. 1980a *In vitro* propagation of *Narcissus*. HortScience, **15**, 602–603.

HOSOKI T. & ASAHIRA T. 1980b *In vitro* propagation of bromeliads in liquid culture. HortScience, **15**, 603–604.

HOSOKI T. & SAGAWA Y. 1977 Clonal propagation of ginger (*Zingiber officinale* Roscoe) through tissue culture. HortScience, **12**, 451–452.

HOSOKI T. & TAHARA Y. 1993 *In vitro* propagation of *Salvia leucantha* Cav. HortScience, **28**, 226.

HOSOKI T. & YASUFUKU T. 1992 *In vitro* mass propagation of Chinese artichoke (*Stachys sieboldii* Miq.). Acta Hort., **319**, 149–152.

HOSOKI T., ANDO M., KUBARA T., HAMADA M. & ITAMI M. 1989 *In vitro* propagation of herbaceous peony (*Paeonia lactiflora* Pall.) by a longitudinal shoot–split method. Plant Cell Rep., **8**, 243–246.

HOSSAIN M., KARIM M.R., ISLAM R. & JOARDER O.I. 1993 Plant regeneration from nucellar tissues of *Aegle marmelos* through organogenesis. Plant Cell Tiss. Organ Cult., **34**, 199–203.

HOSSAIN M.M., INDEN H.F & ASAHIRA T. 1988 Intergeneric and interspecific hybrids through *in vitro* ovule culture in the Cruciferae. Plant Science, **58**, 121–128.

HOVANESIAN J.C. & TORRES K.C. 1986 Micropropagation of *Uniola paniculata* L. Plant Cell Rep., **5**, 385–386.

HOWARD B. & MARKS T. 1988 Interactions between micropropagation and conventional propagation. Comb. Proc. Int. Plant Prop. Soc., **38**, 247–251.

HOWARD B.H., BASSUK N.L. & KIM Y.–K. 1981 Response to endogenous and applied growth regulators during the propagation and raising of fruit trees. Acta Hort., **120**, 199–210.

HOWARD B.H., JONES O.P. & VASEK J. 1989a Long–term improvement in the rooting of plum cuttings following apparent rejuvenation. J. Hort. Sci., **64**, 147–156.

HOWARD B.H., JONES O.P. & VASEK J. 1989b Growth characteristics of apparently rejuvenated plum shoots. J. Hort. Sci., **64**, 157–162.

HOWARTH M.J., PETERSON R.L. & TOMES D.T. 1983 Cellular differentiation in small clumps of *Lotus corniculatus* callus. Can. J. Bot., **61**, 507–517.

HSU F.C. & OBENDORF R.L. 1982 Compositional analysis of *in vitro* matured soybean seeds. Plant Sci. Lett., **27**, 129–135.

HSU J.Y., YEH C.C., YANG T.P., LIN W.C. & TSAY H.S. 1990 Initiation of cell suspension cultures and plant regeneration from protoplast colonies. Acta Hort., **271**, 135–143.

HU C.–Y. & WANG P.J. 1983 Meristem, shoot tip and bud cultures. pp. 177–227 in Evans et al. (eds.) 1983 (*q.v.*).

HU C.Y. 1975 *In vitro* culture of rudimentary embryos of eleven *Ilex* species. J. Am. Soc. Hort. Sci., **100**, 221–225.

HU N., YANG Z. & LU G. 1990 Peach. pp. 278–299 in Chen et al. (eds.) 1990 (q.v.).

HUANG C., YAN H., YAN Q., ZHU M., YUAN M. & XU A. 1993 Establishment and characterization of embryogenic cell suspension cultures from immature and mature embryos of barley (*Hordeum vulgare* L.). Plant Cell Tiss. Organ Cult., **32**, 19–25.

HUANG H.–S., LING T.–H., TSENG P.–L., SHIEN Y.–L., SHI P., TSENG R.–F. HUANG P.–T. 1981 Studies on medium component in anther culture of *Oryza sativa* subsp. Hsien by mathmatical methods. pp. 244–246 in Anon(1981a) (*q.v.*)

HUANG L.–C. 1984 Alternative media and method for *Cattleya* propagation by tissue culture. Am. Orchid Soc. Bull., **53**, 167–170.

HUANG L.–C., CHEN W.–L. & CHIU D.–S. 1988 *In vitro* graft–enhanced nucellar plant development in the monoembryonic *Citrus grandis* L. J. Hort. Sci., **63**, 705–709.

HUBER J., CONSTABEL F. & HAMBORG O.L. 1978 A cell counting procedure applied to embryogenesis in cell suspension cultures of anise (*Pimpinella anisum* L.). Plant Sci. Lett., **12**, 209–215.

HUETTEMAN C.A. & PREECE J.E. 1993 Thidiazuron: a potent cyutokinin for woody plant tissue culture. Plant Cell Tiss. Organ Cult., **33**, 105–119.

HUGHES H., LAM S. & JANICK J. 1973 *In vitro* culture of *Salpiglossis sinuata* L. HortScience, **8**, 335–336.

HUGHES K. W., HENKE R. & CONSTANTIN M. (eds.) 1978 *Propagation of higher plants through tissue culture*. Technical Inf. Center, U.S. Dept. Energy, Springfield, Va. CONF–7804111.

HUGHES K.W. 1981 *In vitro* ecology: exogenous factors affecting growth and morphogenesis in plant culture systems. Env. Exp. Bot., **21**, 281–288.

HUGHES K.W. 1986 Tissue culture derived crossing barriers. Am. J. Bot., **73**, 323–329.

HUGHES K.W. & BARNI B. 1978 Regeneration of *Kohleria amabilis* (Gesneriaceae) from leaf and petiole explants. pp. 248–249 in Hughes *et al.* (eds.) 1978 (*q.v.*).

HUHTINEN O. 1976 *In vitro culture of haploid tissue of trees*. Proc. IUFRO World Congr., Oslo. 28–30.

HUIZING H.J., PFAUTH E.C., MALINGRE Th.M. & SIETSMA J.M. 1983 Regeneration of plants from tissue– and cell suspension cultures of *Symphytum officinale* L. and effect of *in vitro* culture on pyrrolizidine alkaloid production. Plant Cell Tiss. Organ Cult., **2**, 227–238.

HULME J.S., HIGGINS E.S. & SHIELDS R. 1992 An efficient genotype–independent method for regeneration of potato plants from leaf tissue. Plant Cell Tiss. Organ Cult., **31**, 161–167.

HULSCHER M., KRIJGSHELD H.T. & VAN DER LINDE P.C.G. 1992 Propagation of shoots and bulb growth of tulip *in vitro*. Acta Hort., **325**, 441–446.

HUNAULT G. 1976 Obtention de nouvelles souches de tissus à partir de diverse espèces de Liliacées. Compt. Rend. Acad. Sci. Paris, **283D**, 1401–1404.

HUNAULT G. 1984 *In vitro* culture of fennel tissues (*Foeniculum vulgare* Miller) from cell suspension to mature plant. Scientia Hort., **22**, 55–65.

HUNTER C.P. 1989 Plant generation method. U.S. Patent No. 4840906.

HUNTER S.A., FOXE M.J. & HENNERTY M.J. 1983 The influence of temperature and light intensity on the *in vitro* propagation of the strawberry (*Fragaria* × *ananassa* Duch.) cv. Cambridge Favourite. Acta Hort., **131**, 153–161.

HURWITZ C.D. & AGRIOS G.N. 1984 Isolation and culture of protoplasts from apple callus and cell suspension cultures. J. Am. Soc. Hort. Sci., **109**, 348–350.

HUSEMANN W. 1983 Continuous culture growth of photoautotrophic cell suspensions from *Chenopodium rubrum*. Plant Cell Rep., **2**, 59–62.

HUSSEY G. 1976a Propagation of Dutch iris by tissue culture. Scientia Hort., **4**, 163–165.

HUSSEY G. & HEPHER A. 1978b *In vitro* clonal propagation of sugar beet plants and polyploid formation. Ann. Rep. John Innes Inst. 1977 P. 49.

HUSSEY G. & HILTON J. 1975 Proliferation of *in vitro* monocotyledonous plantlets with cytokinin. Ann. Rep. John Innes Inst. 1975 pp. 53–56.

HUSSEY G. & HILTON J. 1976 *In vitro* propagation of *Gladiolus* by precocious axillary shoot formation. Ann. Rep. John Innes Inst. 1976 pp. 65–67.

HUSSEY G. & HILTON J. 1978b *In vitro* propagation of the onion, *Allium cepa*. Ann. Rep. John Innes Inst. 1977 pp. 46–47.

HUSSEY G. & PERRY M.F. 1979 Formation of adventitious shoot clusters in *Lilium*. Ann. Rep. John Innes Inst. 1978 pp. 50–51.

HUSSEY G. & STACEY N.J. 1983 Formation of mini tubers from potato shoot cultures. Ann. Rep. John Innes Inst. 1981–1982 pp. 129–134.

HUSSEY G. & STACEY N.J. 1984 Factors affecting the formation of *in vitro* tubers of potato (*Solanum tuberosum* L.). Ann. Bot., **53**, 565–578.

HUSSEY G. & TURNER J. 1971 Growth and differentiation in pea callus and suspension cultures. Ann. Rep. John Innes Inst. 1971 p. 39.

HUSSEY G. & WADDY M. 1981 *In vitro* propagation of *Lavandula*. Ann. Rep. John Innes Inst. 1980 pp. 59–60.

HUSSEY G. & WYVILL C. 1972 Propagation of bulbous species by tissue culture. Ann. Rep. John Innes Inst. 1972 pp. 64–66.

HUSSEY G. & WYVILL C. 1973 *In vitro* responses of bulbs and corms. Ann.Rep.John Innes Inst. 1973 pp. 64–67.

HUSSEY G., PERRY M.F. & HILTON J. 1979 *In vitro* propagation of *Narcissus*. Ann. Rep. John Innes Inst. 1978 pp. 49–50.

HUTCHINSON J.F. 1984a *In vitro* propagation of *Dionaea muscipula* Ellis (Venus fly trap). Scientia Hort., **22**, 189–194.

HUTCHINSON J.F. 1984b Factors affecting shoot proliferation and root initiation in organ cultures of the apple 'Northern Spy'. Scientia Hort., **22**, 347–358.

HUTCHINSON J.F. 1985b Micropropagation of 'Northern Spy' apple rootstock. Comb. Proc. Int. Plant Prop. Soc. 1984, **34**, 38–48.

HUTCHINSON J.F. & ZIMMERMAN R.H. 1987 Tissue culture of temperate fruit and nut trees. Hort. Rev., **9**, 273–349.

HUTH W. 1978 Kultur von Apfelpflanzen aus apikalen Meristemen. Gartenbauwiss., **43**, 163–166.

HUTH W. 1979 Culture of raspberry plants from apical meristems. Gartenbauwissen., **44**, 53–55.

HUTNER S. H. 1953 Comparative physiology of heterotrophic growth in plants. pp. 417–446 in Loomis W. E. (ed.) 1953 *Growth and Differentiation in Plants*. Iowa State College Press. Ames, Iowa.

HVOSLEF–EIDE A.K. 1992 Effects of pre–storage conditions on storage of *in vitro* cultures of *Nephrolepis exaltata* (L.) Schott and *Cordyline fruticosa* (L.) A. Chev. Plant Cell Tiss. Organ Cult., **28**, 167–174.

HWANG L.–S., SKIRVIN R.M., CASAYO J. & BOUWKAMP J. 1980 Embryoid formation from sweet potato root discs *in vitro*. HortScience, **15**, 415.

HWANG L.S., SKIRVIN R.M., CASYAO J. & BOUWKAMP J. 1983 Adventitious shoot formation from sections of sweet potato grown *in vitro*. Scientia Hort., **20**, 119–129.

HWANG S.C., CHEN C.L., LIN J.C. & LIN H.L. 1984 Cultivation of banana using plantlets from meristem culture. HortScience, **19**, 231–233.

HYMOWITZ T., CHALMERS N.S., CONSTANZA S.H. & SAAM M.M. 1986 Plant regeneration from leaf explants of *Glycine clandestina* Wendl. Plant Cell Rep., **5**, 192–194.

HYNDMAN S.E., BRESSAN P.H., KIM Y.–J., HASEGAWA P.M. & BRESSAN R.A. 1981 Regulation of shoot multiplication and adventitious root initiation from cultured rose shoot tips. Env. Exp. Bot., **21**, 440–441 (Abst.).

HYNDMAN S.E., HASEGAWA P.M. & BRESSAN R.A. 1982a Stimulation of root initiation from cultured rose shoots through the use of reduced concentrations of mineral salts. HortScience, **17**, 82–83. IAPICHINO G., CHEN T.H.H. & FUCHIGAMI L.H. 1991 Plant regeneration from somatic tissue of *Rhododendron laetum* × *aurigeranum*. Plant Cell Tiss. Organ Cult., **27**, 37–43.

IAPICHINO G., McCULLOCH S. & CHEN T.H.H. 1992 Adventitious shoot formation from leaf explants of *Rhododendron*. Plant Cell Tiss. Organ Cult. **30**, 237–241.

IBARAKI Y., IIDA Y. & KURATA K. 1992 Effects of air currents on gas exchange of culture vessels. Acta Hort., **319**, 221–224.

IBRAHIM F.M., COLLINS J.C. & COLLIN H.A. 1992 Characterization of progeny of *Coleus blumei* following an *in vitro* selection for salt tolerance. Plant Cell Tiss. Organ Cult., **28**, 139–145.

ICHIHARA K. & NODA M. 1981 Lipid synthesis in germinating safflower *Carthamus tinctorius*seeds and protoplasts. Phytochem., **20**, 1023–1030.

IDEDA K., TESHIMA D., AOYAMA T., SATAKE M. & SHIMOMURA K. 1988 Clonal propagation of *Cephaelis ipecacuanha*. Plant Cell Rep., **7**, 288–291.

IHA T.B. & ROY S.C. 1979 Rhizogenesis from *Nigella sativa* protoplasts. Protoplasma **101**, 139–142.

IKEDA L.R. & TANABE M.J. 1989 *In vitro* subculture applications for ginger. HortScience **24**, 142–143.

IKUTA A., SYONO K. & FURUYA T. 1975 Alkaloids in plants regenerated from *Coptis* callus cultures. Phytochem. **14**, 1209–1210.

ILAHI I. 1982 Tissue culture of opium poppy cotyledons. pp. 81–82 in Fujiwara (ed.) 1982 (*q.v.*)

ILAHI I. & JABEEN M. 1987 Callus and plantlet induction in *Papaver somniferum*. Acta Hort., **212**, 697–699.

IMAMURA J. & HARADA H. 1980 Effects of abscisic acid and water stress on the embryo and plantlet formation in anther culture of *Nicotiana tabacum* cv. Samsun. Z. Pflanzenphysiol. **100**, 285–289.

IMAMURA J., OKABE E., KYO M. & HARADA H. 1982 Embryogenesis and plantlet formation through direct culture of isolated pollen in *Nicotiana tabacum* cv. Samsum and *N. rustica* cv. Rustica. Plant & Cell Physiol., **23**, 713–716.

INFANTE R. 1992 *In vitro* axillary shoot proliferation and somatic embryogenesis of yellow pitaya *Mediocactus coccineus* (Salm–Dyck). Plant Cell Tiss. Organ Cult., **31**, 155–159.

INFANTE R., MAGNANINI E. & RIGHETTI B. 1989 The role of light and CO_2 in optimising the conditions for shoot proliferation of *Actinidia deliciosa in vitro*. Physiol. Plant., **77**, 191–195.

INGESTAD T. 1979 Mineral nutrient requirements of *Pinus sylvestris* and *Picea abies* seedlings. Physiol. Plant., **45** , 373–380.

INGRAM D.S. & HELGESON J.P. (eds.) 1980 *Tissue Culture Methods for Plant Pathologists*. Blackwell Scientific Publications.

INNOCENTI A.M. & AVANZI S. 1971 Some cytological aspects of the differentiation of metaxylem in the root of *Allium cepa*. Caryologia, **24**, 283–292.

INOUE K., NAYESHIRO H., INOUYE H. & ZENK M. 1981 Anthraquinones in cell suspension cultures of *Morinda citrifolia* L. Phytochem., **20**, 1693–1700.

INTUWONG O. & SAGAWA Y. 1973 Clonal propagation of sarcanthine orchids by aseptic culture of inflorescences. Am. Orchid Soc. Bull., **42**, 209–215.

INTUWONG O. & SAGAWA Y. 1974 Clonal propagation of *Phalaenopsis* by shoot tip culture. Am. Orchid Soc. Bull., **43**, 893–895.

INTUWONG O. & SAGAWA Y. 1975 Clonal propagation of *Dendrobium* 'Golden Wave' and other nobile types. Am. Orchid Soc. Bull., **44**, 319.

INTUWONG O., KUMISAKI J.T. & SAGAWA Y. 1972 Vegetative propagation of *Phalaenopsis* by flower stalk cuttings. Hawaii Orchid J., **1**, 13–18.

IRAWATI, ARDITTI J. & NYMAN L.P. 1986 *In vitro* propagation of the elephant yam, *Amorphophallus campanulatus* var. *hortensis* Backer (Araceae). Ann. Bot., **57**, 11–17.

IRAWATI, HARJADI S., SUSENO H. & IDRIS S. 1977 Tissue culture of *Aranthera* James Storiei (Storie). Orchid Rev., **85**, 138–142.

IRIKURA Y. 1975 Induction of haploid plants by anther culture in tuber-bearing species and interspecific hybrids of *Solanum*. Potato Res., **18**, 133–140.

IRIONDO J.M. & PEREZ C. 1990 Micropropagation of an endangered plant species: *Coronopus novasii*(Brassicaceae). Plant Cell Rep., **8**, 745–748.

IRVINE J.E. 1984 The frequency of marker changes in sugar cane plant regeneration from callus culture. Plant Cell Tiss. Organ Cult., **3**, 201–209.

IRVINE J.E. & BENDA G.T.A. 1985 Sugarcane mosaic virus in plaetlets regenerated from diseased leaf tissue. Plant Cell Tiss. Organ Cult., **5**, 101–106.

IRVINE J.E., FITCH M. & MOORE P.H. 1983 The induction of callus in sugarcane tissue cultures by selected chemicals. Plant Cell Tiss. Organ Cult., **2**, 141–149.

ISHII C. 1982 Callus induction and shoot differentiation of wheat, oat and barley. pp. 185–186 in Fujiwara (ed.) 1982 (*q.v.*)

ISHII K. & KANAZASHI T. 1992 Three years field performance of *in vitro* propagated Japanese white birch (*Betula platyphylla* var. japonica). Acta Hort., **319**, 167–170.

ISHII M., SHOYAMA Y., UEMOTO S., NISHIOKA I. & FUJIEDA K. 1976 Studies on tissue culture in *Cattleya* species. 1. Separation identification and biological activity of phenolics from *Cattleya*. Sci. Bull. Fac. Agric., Univ. Kyushu, **31**, 99–105.

ISHIOKA N. & TANIMOTO S. 1990 Plant regeneration from Bulgarian rose callus. Plant Cell Tiss. Organ Cult., **22**, 197–199.

ISIKAWA H. 1987 *In vitro* culture of *Cryptomeria* callus and organs. pp. 109–113 in Bonga and Durzan (eds.) 1987c (*q.v.*).

ISLAM A.S. 1964 A rare hybrid combination through application of hormones and embryo culture. Nature, **201**, 320.

ISLAM A.S. 1982 Production of desirable jute plants through tissue culture. pp. 159–161 in Rao A.N. (ed.) 1982 (*q.v.*).

ISLAM A.S., BEGUM H.A. & HAQUE M.M. 1982 Studies on regeneration of *Saccharum officinarum* for disease resistant varieties. pp. 709–710 in Fujiwara (ed.) 1982 (*q.v.*).

ISLAM R., HOSSAIN M., JOARDER O.I. & KARIM M.R. 1993a Adventitious shoot formation on excised leaf explants of *in vitro* grown seedlings of *Aegle marmelos* Corr. J. Hort. Sci., **68**, 495–498.

ISLAM R., ZAMAN A., JOARDER O.I. & BARMAN A.C. 1993b *In vitro* propagation as an aid for cloning of *Morus laevigata* Wall. Plant Cell Tiss. Organ Cult., **33**, 339–341.

IWAI S., KISHI C., NAKATA K. & KAWASHIMA N. 1986 Production of *Nicotiana tabacum* × *Nicotiana acuminata* hybrid by ovule culture. Plant Cell Rep., **5**, 403–404.

IWAI S., KISHI C., NAKATA K. & KUBO S. 1985 Production of a hybrid *Nicotiana repanda* Willd. × *N. tabacum* L. by ovule culture. Plant Science, **41**, 175–178.

IYER R.D. & GOVILA O.P. 1964 Embryo culture of interspecific hybrids in the genus *Oryza*. Ind. J. Genet. Plant Breed., **24**, 116–121.

IZSAK E. & IZHAR S. 1983 Rapid micropropagation of strawberry plantlets from seeds for breeding purposes. Acta Hort., **131**, 101–103.

JACKSON J.A. & DALE P.J. 1989 Somaclonal variation in *Lolium multiflorum* L. and *L. temulentum*L. Plant Cell Rep., **8**, 161–164.

JACKSON M.B. (ed.) 1986 *New Root Formation in Plants and Cuttings*. Martinus Nijhoff Publishers, Dordrecht, Boston, Lancaster. ISBN 90–247–3260–3

JACOB M., DENEE G. & COUMANS M. 1980 La production de *Saintpaulia ionantha in vitro*: aspects economique. Med. Fac. Landbouww. Rijksuniv., Gent, **45**, 335–343.

JACOBONI A. & STANDARDI A. 1982 La moltiplicazione *in vitro* del melo cv. Wellspur. Riv. Ortoflorofrutti. Ital., **66**, 217–229.

JACOBS G., BORNMAN C.H. & ALLAN P. 1968 Tissue culture studies on rose. Use of pith explants. S. Afr. J. Agri. Sci., **11**, 673–678.

JACOBS G., RICHARD M., ALLDERMAN L.A. & THERON K.I. 1992 Direct and indirect organogenesis in tissue cultures of *Nerine bowderii* W. Watts. Acta Hort., **325**, 475–480.

JACOBS W.P. & SUTHERS H.B. 1971 The culture of apical buds of *Xanthium* and their use for flowering activity of ecdysterone. Am. J. Bot., **58**, 836–843.

JACOBSEN E. 1981 Polyploidization in leaf callus tissue and in regenerated plants of dihaploid potato. Plant Cell Tiss. Organ Cult., **1**, 77–84.

JACOBSEN E., VISSER R.G.F. & WIJBRANDI J. 1985 Phenylalanine and tyrosine accumulating cell lines of a dihaploid potato selected by resistance to 5–methyl-tryptophan. Plant Cell Rep., **4**, 151–154.

JACOBSEN H–J. & KYSELY W. 1984 Induction of somatic embryos in pea, *Pisum sativum* L. Plant Cell Tiss. Organ Cult., **3**, 319–324.

JACOBSEN H.–J., INGENSIEP H.W., HERLT M. & KAUL M.L.H. 1980 Tissue culture studies in *Pisum sativum*. pp. 319–324 in Sala *et al.* (eds.) 1980 (*q.v.*).

JACQUIN–DUBREUIL A., CHETRIT S., FLINIAUX M.A., TRINH T.H., COSSON L. & TRAN THANH VAN K. 1991 Study of the alkaloid content of four 'hypohaploids' of *Nicotiana plumbaginifolia*grown *in vitro*. Plant Cell Tiss. Organ Cult. **27**, 1–6.

JACQUIOT C. 1955 Formation d' organes par le tissu cambial d' *Ulmus campestris* L. et de *Betula verrucosa* Gaert. Compt. Rend. Acad. Sci. Paris, **240**, 557–558.

JAGADISH CHANDRA K.S. & RAVISHANKAR RAI V. 1986 *In vitro* propagation of forest trees — *Cinnamomum zeylanicum*and *Syzigium aromaticum*. p. 12 in Somers *et al.* (eds.) 1986 (*q.v.*).

JAGENDORF A.T., BONNER D.M. & NAYLOR A.W. 1952 An atypical growth of cabbage seedling roots. I. Morphology, histology and induction conditions. Bot. Gaz., **113**, 334–347.

JAIN A.K. & DATTA R.K. 1992 Shoot organogenesis and plant regeneration in mulberry (*Morus bombycis* Koidz.): factors influencing morphogenetic potential in callus cultures. Plant Cell Tiss. Organ Cult., **29**, 43–50.

JAIN A.K., DANDIN S.B. & SENGUPTA K. 1990 *In vitro* propagation through axillary bud multiplication in different mulberry genotypes. Plant Cell Rep., **8**, 737–740.

JAIN M. & CHATURVEDI H.C. 1985 Caulogenesis is rhizome callus of *Costus speciosus*. Planta Med., **51**, 462–463.

JAIN S.M., JOKINEN K. & VIRTA U. 1986 Factors effecting shoot regeneration in cultured potato (*Solanum tuberosum*) tuber disks. p. 34 in Somers *et al.* (eds.) 1986 (*q.v.*).

JALAL M.A.F. & COLLIN H.A. 1979 Secondary metabolism in tissue cultures of *Theobroma cacao*. New Phytol., **83**, 343–349.

JAMES D.J. 1983b Adventitious root formation *in vitro* in apple rootstock (*Malus pumila*). II. Uptake and distribution of indol–3yl–acetic acid during the auxin–sensitive phase in M9 and M26. Physiol. Plant., **57**, 154–158.

JAMES D.J., KNIGHT V.H. & THURBON I.J. 1980 Micropropagation of red raspberry and the influence of phloroglucinol. Scientia Hort., **12**, 313–319.

JAMES D.J., PASSEY A.J. & DEEMING D.C. 1984b Adventitious embryogenesis and *in vitro* culture of apple seed parts. J. Plant Physiol., **115**, 217–229.

JANG J.C. & TAINTER F.H. 1990 Hyphal growth of *Phytophtora cinnamomi* on pine callus tissue. Plant Cell Rep., **8**, 741–744.

JANG J.C. & TAINTER F.H. 1991 Micropropagation of shortleaf, Virginia and loblolly × shortleaf pine hybrids via organogenesis. Plant Cell Tiss. Organ Cult. **25**, 61–67.

JANICK J. & KONONOWICZ H.M. 1986 Asexual embryogenesis of callus from *Theobroma cacao* L. U.S. Patent No. 4545147.

JANICK J. & WHIPKEY A. 1986 *In vitro* propagation of *Cuphea wrightii*. HortScience **21**, 135–137.

JANICK J. & WHIPKEY A. 1988 Somatic embryogenesis in *Theobroma grandiflorum*. HortScience **23**, 807.

JANICK J., SIMON J.E. & WHIPKEY A. 1987 *In vitro* propagation of borage. HortScience, **22**, 493–495.

JANSEN M.A.K., BOOIJ H., SCHEL J.H.N. & DE VRIES S.C. 1990 Calcium increases the yield of somatic embryos in carrot embryogenic suspension cultures. Plant Cell Rep., **9**, 221–223.

JANSENS J. & SEPELIE M. 1989 *In vitro* multiplication of *Blechnum*spp. and *Pelaea rotundifolia* (Forst.) Hook. by homogenisation. Scientia Hort., **38**, 161–164.

JANSSENS J. 1987 Homogenization *in vitro* of *Begonia* Ç *hiemalis* for propagation. Meded. Fac. Landbouwwet Rijksuni Gent, **52**, 1501–1503.

JARRET R.L. & GAWEL N. 1991a Abscisic acid–induced growth inhibition of sweet potato (*Ipomoea batatas* L.) *in vitro*. Plant Cell Tiss. Organ Cult., **24**, 13–18.

JARRET R.L. & GAWEL N. 1991b Chemical and environmental growth regulation of sweetpotato (*Ipomoea batatas* (L.) Lam *in vitro*. Plant Cell Tiss. Organ Cult., **25**, 153–159.

JARRET R.L., HASEGAWA P.M. & ERICKSON H.T. 1980b Factors affecting shoot initiation from tuber discs of potato (*Solanum tuberosum*). Physiol. Plant. **49**, 177–184.

JARRET R.L., LITZ R.E. & FISHER J. 1985c Organ formation from callus cultures of banana and plantains. p. 329 in Henke *et al.* (eds.) 1985 (*q.v.*).

JARRET R.L., RODRIGUEZ W. & FERNANDEZ R. 1985a Evaluation, tissue culture propagation and dissemination of 'Saba' and 'Pelipita' plantains in Costa Rica. Scientia Hort. **25**, 137–147.

JARRET R.L., SALAZAR S. & FERNANDEZ R. 1984 Somatic embryogenesis in sweet potato. HortScience **19**, 397–398.

JASRAI Y.T., BAROT S.M. & MEHTA A.R. 1992 Plant regeneration through somatic embryogenesis in hypocotyl explants of *Trachyspermum ammi* (L.) Sprague. Plant Cell Tiss. Organ Cult., **29**, 57–60.

JAVOUHEY M. & MARIONNET J. 1990 Fifty years of asparagus breeding valorized through twelve years of *in vitro* culture. II. Further prospects for micropropagation of the best selected clones. Acta Hort., **271**, 129–133.

JAY–ALLEMAND C., PENG S., CAPELLI P. & CORNU D. 1993 Micropropagation of hybrid walnut trees. Some factors involved in rooting. Acta Hort. **311**, 117–124.

JAYAKAR M. 1971 *In vitro* flowering of *Crepis capillaris*. Phytomorph., **20**, 410–412.

JAYOS–RIOS E. 1985 Effects of different phytohormonal treatments on the organogenesis of callus tissues of *Zea mays* L. Ann. Sci. Nat. Bot. Biol. Veg., **7**, 55–62.

JEAN M. & CAPPADOCIA M. 1991 *In vitro* tuberization in *Diascorea alata* L. 'Brazo fuerte' and 'Florido' and *D. abyssinica* Hoch. Plant Cell Tiss. Organ Cult., **26**, 147–152.

JELASKA S. 1972 Embryoid formation by fragments of cotyledons and hypocotyls in *Cucurbita pepo*. Planta, **103**, 278–280.

JELASKA S. 1974 Embryogenesis and organogenesis in pumpkin explants. Physiol. Plant., **31**, 257–261.

JELASKA S. & LIBBY W.J. 1988 Control of morphogenesis in *Calocedrus decurrens* tissue culture. pp. 377–388 in Hanover & Keathley (eds.) 1988 (*q.v.*).

JELASKA S. & SUTINA R. 1977 Maintained culture of multiple plantlets from carnation shoot tips. Acta Hort., **78**, 333–340.

JELASKA S., JURETIC B., KRSNIK–RASOL M., PAPES D. & BOSNJAK V. 1986 High frequency plant development in long–term embryogenic cell culture of *Cucurbita pepo*. p. 106 in Somers *et al.* (eds.) 1986 (*q.v.*).

JEMMALI A., BOXUS Ph. & KINET J.M. 1992 Are strawberry plantlets arising from adventitious stipule buds also true to type? Acta Hort., **319**, 171–176.

JERZY M. & LUBOMSKI M. 1992 *In vitro* adventitious bud techniques for mutation breeding of *Gerbera jamesonii*. Acta Hort., **314**, 269–274.

JHA S. & JHA T.B. 1989 Micropropagation of *Cephaelis ipecacuanha* Rich. Plant Cell Rep., **8**, 437–439.

JHA S. & SEN S. 1985 *In vitro* regeneration of *Ruscus hypophyllum* L. plants. Plant Cell Tiss. Organ Cult., **5**, 79–87.

JHA S. & SEN S. 1985 Regeneration and rapid multiplication of *Bowiea volubilis* Harv. in tissue culture. Plant Cell Rep., **4**, 12–14.

JHA S., MITRA G.C. & SEN S. 1984 *In vitro* regeneration from bulb explants of Indian squill, *Urginia indica* Kunth. Plant Cell Tiss. Organ Cult., **3**, 91–100.

JHA S., SAHU N.P. & MAHATO S.B. 1991 Callus induction, organogenesis and somatic embryogenesis in three chromosomal races of *Urginea indica* and production of bufadienolides. Plant Cell Tiss. Organ Cult., **25**, 89–90.

JHA T.B. 1986 Morphogenesis in cashew nut — *Anacardium occidentale* L. p. 27 in Somers *et al.* (eds.) 1986 (*q.v.*).

JHA T.B., ROY S. & MITRA G.C. 1982 A brief review of *in vitro* studies on Umbelliferous spice plants. pp. 94–97 in Rao A.N. (ed.) 1982 (*q.v.*).

JHANG J.J., STABA E.J. & KIM J.Y. 1974 American and Korean ginseng tissue cultures: growth, chemical analysis and plantlet production. In Vitro, **9**, 253–259.

JOHANSSON L. & ERIKSSON T. 1977 Induced embryo formation in anther cultures of several *Anemone* species. Physiol. Plant., **40**, 172–174.

JOHNSON B. B. & MITCHELL E. D. Jr. 1978a *In vitro* propagation of broccoli from leaf, stem and rib explants. p. 251 in Hughes *et al.* (eds.) 1978 (*q.v.*).

JOHNSON B.B. 1978b *In vitro* propagation of *Episcia cupreata*. HortScience **13**, 596.

JOHNSON B.B. 1978a *In vitro* propagation of *Gloxinia* from leaf explants. HortScience, **13**, 149–150.

JOHNSON B.B. 1981 Embryo and ovule culture in peanuts (*Arachis hypogaea*L.) cultivar EC–5. Env. Exp. Bot., **21**, 439 (Abst.).

JOHNSON B.B. & MITCHELL E.D. 1978c The effect of temperature on *in vitro* propagation of broccoli from leaf rib and leaf explants. In Vitro, **14**, 334 (Abst. 01).

JOHNSON B.B. & MITCHELL E.D. Jr. 1978b *In vitro* propagation of broccoli from stem, leaf and leaf rib explants. HortScience, **13**, 246–247.

JOHNSON B.B. & WORTHINGTON M. 1987 Establishment of suspension cultures from seeds of plains bluestem (*Bothriochloa ischaemum* L. Keng.) and regeneration of plants via somatic embryogenesis. In Vitro, **23**, 783–788.

JOHNSON J.L. & EMINO E.R. 1977a Tissue culture propagation of *Mammillaria elongata* as influenced by plant growth regulators. HortSci., **12**, 394 (Abst. 107).

JOHNSON J.L. & EMINO E.R. 1977b Propagation of selected cactus species by tissue culture. HortScience, **12**, 404 (Abst. 192).

JOHNSON K.A. 1992 Liquid medium addition to improve shoots elongation of *Blandfordia grandiflora* R. Br. *in vitro*. Acta Hort. **325**, 453–460.

JOHNSON K.A. & BURCHETT M. 1991 *In vitro* propagation of *Blandfordia grandiflora* (Liliaceae). J. Hort. Sci., **66**, 389–394.

JOHNSON L.B., STUTEVILLE D.L., HIGGINS R.K. & SKINNER D.Z. 1981 Regeneration of alfalfa plants from protoplasts of selected Regen S clones. Plant Sci. Lett. **20**, 297–304.

JOHNSON L.B., STUTEVILLE D.L., SCHLARBAUM S.E. & SKINNER D.Z. 1984 Variation in phenotype and chromosome number in alfalfa protoclones regenerated from nonmutagenised calli. Crop Sci. **24**, 948–951.

JOHNSON R.T., KOENIGSBERG S.S. & LANGHANS R.W. 1976 Tissue culture propagation of Christmas & Easter cactus. HortScience, **11** , 303 (Abst.70).

JOHRI B. M. & BAJAJ Y. P. S. 1963 *In vitro* response of the embryo of *Dendrophthoe falcata* (L.f.) Ettings. pp. 292–301 in Maheshwari & Ranga Swamy (eds.) 1963 (*q.v.*).

JOHRI B. M. & SEHGAL C. B. 1963a Growth of ovaries of *Anethum graveolens* L. pp. 245–256 in Maheshwari & Ranga Swamy (eds.) 1963 (*q.v.*).

JOHRI B.M. & BAJAJ Y.P.S. 1962 Behaviour of mature embryo of *Dendrophthoe falcata*(L.f.) Ettings *in vitro*. Nature, **193**, 194–195.

JOHRI B.M. & BAJAJ Y.P.S. 1964 Growth of embryos of *Amyema, Amylotheca* and *Scurrula* on synthetic media. Nature, **204**, 1220–1221.

JOHRI B.M. & BHOJWANI S.S. 1965 Growth responses of mature endosperm in cultures. Nature, **208**, 1345–1347.

JOHRI B.M. & BHOJWANI S.S. 1970 Embryo morphogenesis in the stem parasite *Scurrula pulverulenta*. Ann. Bot., **34**, 685–690.

JOHRI B.M. & NAG K.K. 1970 Endosperm of *Taxillus vestitus* Wall: A system to study the effect of cytokinins *in vitro* in shoot bud formation. Current Sci., **39**, 177–179.

JOHRI B.M. & SEHGAL C.B. 1963b Chemical induction of polyembryony in *Anethum graveolens* L. Naturwissenschaften **50**, 47–48.

JOHRI B.M. & SEHGAL C.B. 1966 Growth responses of ovaries of *Anethum, Foeniculum and Trachyspermum.*Phytomorph., **16**, 364–386.

JOKINEN K., JONASSON D., MANNERI E., PUSKA R. & TORMALA T. 1990 Laser–cutting of plant propagation material – surrounding plant material by e.g. nitrogen shield gas and cutting with either continuous or pulsed laser beam. British Patent No. 2202723.

JONA R. & GRIBAUDO I. 1988a Environmental factors affecting *in vitro* propagation of *Ficus lyrata*. Acta Hort., **226**, 59–64.

JONA R. & GRIBAUDO I. 1988b Intensive propagation procedure of *Ficus lyrata* by *in vitro* culture. Acta Hort., **227**, 390–395.

JONA R. & WEBB K.J. 1978 Callus and axillary–bud culture of *Vitis vinifera* 'Sylvaner Riesling'. Scientia Hort., **9**, 55–60.

JONA R., GRIBAUDO R. & VIGLIOCCO R. 1987 Natural development of ethylene in air tight vessels of GF 677. pp. 61–66 in Ducaté *et al.* (eds.) 1987 (*q.v.*).

JONES C. 1986 Getting started in micropropagation of Tasmanian Blackwood (*Acacia melanoxylon*). Comb. Proc. Int. Plant Prop. Soc., **36**, 477–481.

JONES H., KARP A. & JONES M.G.K. 1989 Isolation, culture and regeneration of plants from potato protoplasts. Plant Cell Rep., **8**, 307–311.

JONES J. 1979 Commercial use of tissue culture for the production of disease-free plants. pp. 441–452 in Sharp *et al.* (eds.) 1979 (*q.v.*).

JONES J.B. 1986 Determining markets and market protential of horticultural crops. pp. 175–182 in Zimmerman *et al.* (eds.) 1986 (*q.v.*).

JONES J.B. 1987 Commercial plant tissue culture in the United States. Acta Hort., **212**, 639–643.

JONES L.H. 1974a Factors influencing embryogenesis in carrot cultures. Ann. Bot., **38**, 1077–1088.

JONES L.H. 1974c Propagation of clonal oil palms by tissue culture. Oil Palm News, **17**, 1–9.

JONES L.H. 1974d Plant cell culture and biochemistry: studies for improved vegetable oil production. pp. 813–833 in Spencer B. (ed.) *Industrial Aspects of Biochemistry* Vol. **30**, Part II. North Holland, Amsterdam, London.

JONES L.H. 1983 The oil palm and its clonal propagation by tissue culture. Biologist, **30**, (4) 181–188.

JONES L.H. 1990 Endogenous cytokinins in oil palm (*Elaeis guineensis* L.) callus, embryoids and regenerant plants measured by radioimmunoassay. Plant Cell Tiss Organ Cult., **20**, 201–209.

JONES L., BARFIELD D., BARRETT J., FLOOK A., POLLOCK K. & ROBINSON P. 1982 Cytology of oil palm cultures and regenerant plants. pp. 727–728 in Fujiwara (ed.) 1982 (*q.v.*).

JONES M.G.K. & DALE P.J. 1982 Reproducible regeneration of callus from suspension culture protoplasts of the grass *Lolium multiflorum*. Z. Pflanzen-physiol. **105**, 267–274.

JONES O.P. 1967 Effect of benzyl adenine on isolated apple shoots. Nature, **215**, 1514.

JONES O.P. 1991 The role of biotechnology in the multiplication and improvement of woody plants. Acta Hort. **289**, 35–44.

JONES O.P. & HADLOW W.C.C. 1989 Juvenile–like character of apple trees produced by grafting scions and rootstocks produced by micropropagation. J. Hort. Sci. **64**, 395–401.

JONES O.P. & VINE S.J. 1968 The culture of gooseberry shoot tips for eliminating virus. J. Hort. Sci., **43**, 289–292.

JONES O.P. & WEBSTER C.A. 1989 Improved rooting from conventional cuttings taken from micropropagated plants of *Pyrus communis* rootstocks. J. Hort. Sci., **64**, 429–434.

JONES O.P., GAYNER J.A. & WATKINS R. 1984 Plant regeneration from callus tissue cultures of the cherry rootstock Colt (*Prunus avium* × *P. pseudocerasus*) and the apple rootstock M.25 (*Malus pumila*). J. Hort. Sci., **59**, 463–467.

JONES R.A.C. 1982 Tests for transmission of four potato viruses through potato true seed. Ann. Appl. Biol., **100**, 315–320.

JONKERS H. & PIERIK R.L.M. 1978 Plantenteelt in kweekbuizen en toepassingen in de fruitteelt. Fruitteelt, **68**, 1216–1220.

JORDAN A.M., CALVO M.C. & SEGURA J. 1990 Morphogenesis in callus and single cell cultures of *Lavendula latifolia* Medicus. J. Hort. Sci., **65**, 49–53.

JORDAN M. 1987 Somatic embryogenesis from cell suspension cultures in *Carica candamarcencis*. Plant Cell Tiss. Organ Cult., **7**, 257–261.

JORDAN M. & OYANEDAL E. 1992 Regeneration of *Pouteria lucuma*(Sapotaceae) plants *in vitro*. Plant Cell Tiss. Organ Cult. **31**, 249–252.

JORDAN M., CORTES I. & MONTENEGRO G. 1983a Regeneration of *Lapageria rosea* plantlets by tissue culture. Gartenbauwiss., **48**, 97–100.

JORDAN M., CORTES I. & MONTENEGRO G. 1983b Regeneration of plantlets by embryogenesis from callus cultures of *Carica candamarcensis*. Plant Sci. Lett., **28**, 321–326.

JORDAN M., ITURRIAGA L. & FEUCHT W. 1982 Effects of nitrogenous bases on root formation of hypocotyls from *Prunus avium* L. 'Mericier' and 'Bing' grown *in vitro*. Gartenbauwiss., **47**, 46–48.

JORDAN M.C. & McHUGHEN A. 1988 a Glyphosate tolerant flax plants from *Agrobacterium* mediated gene transfer. Plant Cell Rep., **7**, 281–284.

JORGENSEN J. 1988 Embryogenesis in *Quercus petraea* and *Fagus sylvatica*. J. Plant Physiol., **132**, 638–640.

JORGENSEN R.B., JENSEN C.J., ANDERSEN B. & VON BOTHMER R. 1986 High capacity of plant regeneration from callus of interspecific hybrids with cultivated barley (*Hordeum vulgare* L.). Plant Cell Tiss. Organ Cult., **6**, 199–207.

JOSEKUTTY P.C., SHAH S. & PRATHAPASENAN G. 1993 Direct and indirect organogenesis in *Coccinia indica*. J. Hort. Sci. **68**, 31–35.

JOURDAN P.S. & EARLE E.D. 1989 Genotypic variability in the frequency of plant regeneration from leaf protoplasts of four *Brassica* spp. and of *Raphanus sativus*. J. Am. Soc. Hort. Sci., **114**, 343–349.

JOY R.W., KUMAR P.P. & THORPE T.A. 1991 Long–term storage of somatic embryogenic white spruce tissue at ambient temperature. Plant Cell Tiss. Organ Cult., **25**, 53–60.

JOYCE P.J. & McCOWN B.H. 1989 Micro–tuber propagation of potatoes – by inducing shoot tip necrosis to form micro–tuber, elongating and tuberisation of the multiple shoot axes. World Patent Applic. No. 8910399.

JUNCKER B. & FAVRE J.M. 1989 Clonal effects in propagating oak trees via *in vitro* culture. Plant Cell Tiss. Organ Cult., **19**, 267–276.

JURETIC B. & JELASKA S. 1991 Plant development in long–term embryogenic callus lines of *Cucurbita pepo*. Plant Cell Rep., **9**, 623–626.

KACHARMAZOV V. & IZVORSKA N. 1974 Strawberry runner tip meristems for the production of virus-free plants. pp. 25–31 in *Virusni Bolesti po Rasteniyata*. Sofia, Bulgaria.

KACKAR A., BHAT S.R., CHANDEL K.P.S. & MALIK S.K. 1993 Plant regeneration via sometic embryogenesis in ginger. Plant Cell Tiss. Organ Cult., **32**, 289–292.

KADDAR G., WATAD A.A., BEN–NOON T. & BEN–JAACOV J. 1992 Propagation of *Phaenocoma prolifera* in *in vitro* culture. Acta Hort., **316**, 47–49.

KADKADE P.G. & JOPSON H. 1978 Influence of light quality on organogenesis from the embryo–derived callus of Douglas fir (*Pseudotsuga menziesii*). Plant Sci. Lett., **13**, 67–73.

KADKADE P.G. & O'CONNOR H.J. 1976 Interactive effects of growth regulators on organogenesis in lettuce tissue culture. Plant Physiol., **57**, Suppl. Abst. 389.

KAHANE R. 1992 Micropropagation of bulbed plants – controlling bulb formation by illumination adjustment. European Patent Applic. No. 485298.

KAHANE R., RANCILLAC M. & TEYSSENDIER DE LA SERVE B. 1992 Long–term multiplication of onion (*Allium cepa* L.) by cyclic shoot regeneration *in vitro*. Plant Cell Tiss. Organ uult., **28**, 281–288.

KAI A.H., SALESSES G. & MOURAS A. 1984 Multiplication *in vitro* du noisetier (*Corylus avellana* L.). Agronomie, **4**, 399–402.

KAISER W.J. & TEEMBA L.R. 1979 Use of tissue culture and thermotherapy to free East African cassava cultivars of African cassava mosaic and cassava brown streak diseases. Plant Dis. Rep., **63**, 780–784.

KAKEHI M. 1979 Studies on the tissue culture of carnation. V. Induction of redifferentiated plants from petal tissue. Bull. Hirosima Agric. Coll., **6**, 159–166.

KAKONIOVA D. & LISKOVA D. 1991 The regeneration ability in long–term spruce cultures. Acta Hort., **289**, 117–118.

KAMADA H. & HARADA H. 1979a Studies on the organogenesis in carrot tissue cultures. I. Effects of growth regulators on somatic embryogenesis and root formation. Z. Pflanzenphysiol., **91**, 255–266.

KAMEYA T. 1982 The method for fusion with dextran. pp. 613–614 in Fujiwara (ed.) 1982 (*q.v.*).

KAMEYA T. & WIDHOLM J. 1981 Plant regeneration from hypocotyl sections of *Glycine* species. Plant Sci. DLett., **21**, 289–294.

KAMO K.K. & HODGES T.K. 1986 Establishment and characterization of long–term embryogenic maize callus and cell suspension cultures. Plant Science, **45**, 111–117.

KANAKIS A.G. & DEMETRIOU K. 1993 *In vitro* shoot regeneration of globe artichoke from shoot apices treated with thidiazuron and from mature zygotic embryos treated with cytokinins. J. Hort. Sci., **68**, 439–445.

KANAZAWA T., YAKUWA T. & ARAKI H. 1992 Plant regeneration from tissue cultured root in *Allium victorialis* L. ssp. *platyphyllum* Hult. Acta Hort., **319**, 209–214.

KANE M. E., SHEEHAN T. J. & FERWERDA F. H. 1988a *In vitro* growth of American Lotus embryos. HortScience, **23**, 611–613.

KANE M.E., GILMAN E.F., JENKS M.A. & SHEEHAN T.J. 1990 Micropropagation of the aquatic plant *Cryptocoryne lucens*. HortScience, **25**, 687–689.

KANE M.E., McCONNELL D.B. & SHEEHAN T. 1988b *In vitro* regneration studies on ornamental aquatic plants: *Myriophyllum aquaticum* and *Limnophila indica*. HortScience, **23**, 780.

KANTA K. & MAHESHWARI P. 1963 Test tube fertilisation in some angiosperms. Phytomorph., **13**, 230–237.

KAO H.M., KELLER W.A., GLEDDIE S. & BROWN G.G. 1990 Efficient plant regeneration from hypocotyl protoplasts of broccoli (*Brassica oleracea* L. ssp. Italica Plenck). Plant Cell Rep., **9**, 311–315.

KAO K.N. & MICHAYLUK M.R. 1980a Plant regeneration from alfalfa mesophyll protoplasts and suspension culture cells. In Vitro, **16**, 216 (Abst.50).

KAO K.N. & MICHAYLUK M.R. 1981 Embryoid formation in alfalfa cell suspension cultures from different plants. In Vitro, **17**, 645–648.

KAO K.N., CONSTABEL F., MICHAYLUK M.R. & GAMBORG O.L. 1974 Plant protoplast fusion and growth of intergeneric hybrid cells. Planta, **120**, 215–227.

KAO K.N., SALEEM M., ABRAMS S., PEDRAS M., HORN D. & MALLARD C. 1991 Culture conditions for induction of green plants from barley microspores by anther culture methods. Plant Cell Rep., **9**, 595–601.

KAPOOR M. 1959 Influence of growth substances on the ovules of *Zephyranthes*. Phytomorph., **9**, 313–315.

KAPOOR S. & GUPTA S.C. 1986 Rapid *in vitro* differentiation of *Lesbania bispinosa* plants — a leguminous shrub. Plant Cell Tiss. Organ Cult., **7**, 263–268.

KAR D.K. & SEN S. 1985 Propagation of *Asparagus racemosus* through tissue culture. Plant Cell Tiss. Organ Cult., **5**, 89–95.

KARATA K., IBARAKI Y. & GOTO E. 1991 System for micropropagation by nutrient mist supply. Am. Soc. Agric. Engineers. **34**, 621–624.

KARASAWA K. 1966 On the media with banana and honey added for seed germination and subsequent growth of orchids. Orchid Rev., **74**, 313–318.

KARESCH H., BILANG R. & POTRYKUS I. 1991 *Arabidopsis thaliana*: protocol for plant regeneration from protoplasts. Plant Cell Rep., **9**, 575–578.

KARHU S.T. & HAKALA K.–L. 1991 Micropropagation of *Berberis thunbergii*. Acta Hort., **289**, 119–120.

KARNOSKY D.F. & DINER A.M. 1986 Techniques for increasing clone sizes in *Larix*. p. 10 in Somers *et al.* (eds.) 1986 (*q.v.*).

KARNOSKY D.F. & DINER A.M. 1987 Method for clonal propagation of coniferous trees. U.S. Patent No. 4607378.

KARNOSKY D.F. & DINERR A.M. 1986 Clonal micropropagation of coniferous trees by germinating surface– sterilised seeds, separating cotyledon and hypocotyl and incubating. World Patent Applic. No. 8607378.

KARP A., RISIOTT R., JONES M.G.K. & BRIGHT S.W.J. 1984 Chromosome doubling in monohaploid and dihaploid potatoes by regeneration from cultured leaf explants. Plant Cell Tiss. Organ Cult., **3**, 363–373.

KARP R. & SINK K.C. 1976 Induction of adventitious shoots on *Kalanchoe* explants *in vitro*. HortScience, **11**, 321.

KARPOFF A.J. 1982 Hormones and early *in vitro* development of epiphyllous propagules on *Bryophyllum calycinum*. Am. J. Bot., **69**, 348–355.

KARTHA K.K. 1982a Organogenesis and embryogenesis. pp. 10–18 in Wetter & Constabel (eds.) 1982 (*q.v.*).

KARTHA K.K. 1982b Meristem culture. pp. 19–24 in Wetter & Constabel (eds.) 1982 (*q.v.*).

KARTHA K.K. (ed.) 1985a *Cryopreservation of plant cells and organs*. CRC Press Inc., Boca Raton, Florida. ISBN 0–8493–6102–8.

KARTHA K.K. & GAMBORG O.L. 1978 Meristem culture techniques in the production of disease–free plants and freeze–preservation of germplasm of tropical tuber crops and grain legumes. pp. 267–283 in Maraite & Meyer (eds.) *Diseases of Tropical Food Crops*. Proc. Int. Symp. Univ. Catholique, Louvaine–la–Neuve, Belgium.

KARTHA K.K. & GAMBORG O.L. 1979 Cassava tissue culture — principles and applications. pp. 711–725 in Sharp *et al.* (eds.) 1979 (*q.v.*).

KARTHA K.K., GAMBORG O.L. & CONSTABEL F. 1974b Regeneration of pea (*Pisum sativum*) plants from shoot apical msristems. Z. Pflanzenphysiol., **72**, 172–176.

KARTHA K.K., GAMBORG O.L., SHYLUK J.P. A CONSTABEL F. 1976 Morphogenetic investigations on *in vitro* leaf culture of tomato *Lycopersicon esculentum*, and high frequency plant regeneration. Z. Pflanzenphysiol., **77**, 292–301.

KARTHA K.K., MICHAYLUK M.R., KAO K.N., GAMBORG O.L. & CONSTABEL F. 1974 e Callus formation and plant regeneration from mesophyll protoplasts of rape plants (*Brassica napus* L. cv. Zephyr). Plant Sci. Lett., **3**, 265–271.

KARUNARATNE S. & PERIYAPPERUMA KAUSHALYA 1989 Culture of immature embryos of coconut, *Cocos nucifera* L.: callus proliferation and somatic embryogenesis. Plant Science, **62**, 247–253.

KARUNARATNE S.M. & SCOTT K.J. 1981 Mitotic activity in protoplasts isolated from *Sorghum bicolor* leaves. Plant Sci. Lett., **23**, 11–16.

KASPERBAUER M.J. & EIZENGA G.C. 1985 Tall fescue doubled haploids via tissue culture and plant regeneration. Crop Sci., **25**, 1091–1095.

KATAEVA N.V. & POPOWICH E.A. 1993 Maturation and rejuvenation of *Coriandrum sativum* shoot clones during micropropagation. Plant Cell Tiss. Organ Cult., **34**, 141–148.

KATAEVA N.V., ALEXANDROVA I.G., BUTENKO R.G. & DRAGAVTCEVA E.V. 1991 Effect of applied and internal hormones on vitrification and apical necrosis of different plants cultured *in vitro*. Plant Cell Tiss. Organ Cult., **27**, 149–154.

KATANO M., ISIHARA A. & SAKAI A. 1983 Survival of dormant apple shoot tips after immersion in liquid nitrogen HortScience, **18**, 707–708.

KATAOKA I. & INOUE H. 1992 Factors influencing *ex vitro* rooting of tissue cultured papaya shoots. Acta Hort., **321**, 589–597.

KATHJU S. & TEWARI M.N. 1973 Development of the root from the cotyledonary callus of *Acacia senegal*. Labdev.J.Sci.Techn. Part B Life Sci., **11**, 84–85.

KATO A. 1982 Kinetic studies of growth and flowering of *Lemna gibba* G3 under continuous light:effects of night interruptions with red and far–red light. Plant Sci. Lett., **27**, 203–212.

KATO M. 1989 Polyploids of *Camellia* through culture of somatic embryos. HortScience, **24**, 1023–1025.

KATO Y. 1975a Adventitious bud formation in etiolated stem segments and leaf callus of *Heloniopsis orientalis* (Liliaceae). Z. Pflanzenphysiol., **75**, 211–216.

KATO Y. 1975b Further studies of regeneration in etiolated *Heloniopsis orientalis*: Organ formation in excised stem segments, isolated leaves and leaf fragments *in vitro*. Phytomorph., **25**, 430–434.

KATO Y. & KAWAHARA S. 1972 Bud formation in leaves, leaf fragments and midrib pieces of *Heloniopsis orientalis* (Liliaceae). Planta, **107**, 111–120.

KATO Y. & YASUTAKE Y. 1977 Plantlet formation and differentiation of epidermal tissues in green callus cultures from excised leaves of *Lilium leichtlinii* var. Maximowiczii. Phytomorph., **27**, 390–396.

KAUL V., MILLER R.M., HUTCHINSON J.F. & RICHARDS D. 1990 Shoot regeneration from stem and leaf explants of *Dendranthema grandiflora* Tzvelev (syn. *Chrysanthemum morifolium* Ramat.). Plant Cell Tiss. Organ Cult., **21**, 21–30.

KAUR–SAWHNEY R. & GALSTON A. W. 1984 Chapter 4 — Oats. pp. 92–107 in Sharp *et al.* (eds.) 1984 (*q.v.*).

KAVANAGH J.M., HUNTER S.A. & CROSSAN P.J. 1987 Micropropagation of Catawba hybrid rhododendrons, 'Nova Zembla', 'Cynthia' and 'Pink Pearl'. Comb. Proc. Int. Plant Frop. Soc. 1986, **36**, 264–272.

KAVATHEKAR A.K. & GANAPATHY P.S. 1973 Embryoid differentiation in *Eschscholzia californica*. Current Sci., **42**, 671–673.

KAVI KISHOR P.B. & REDDY G.M. 1986 Osmotic adjustment and organogenesis in long–term cultures of rice. p. 159 in Somers *et al.* (eds.) 1986 (*q.v.*).

KAWAMURA M. & YAMAZAKI K. 1987 Mass propagation of *Phryma leptostachya* Linne – by culturing plant tissue *in vitro* in a medium containing auxin and/or cytokinin. European Patent Applic. No. 244211.

KAWARABAYASHI W., MATSUBARA K., YOSHIOKA T., YAMAGATA H., TAKAHASHI S., HIRATA Y. & SHIRANE Y. 1991a Culturing apparatus. U.S. Patent No. 4951415.

KAWARABAYASHI W., TAKAHASHI S. & YAMAGATA H. 1991b Method of multiplying bulbous plants – has seedlings multiplied by applying tissue culture to cells of plants. European Patent No. 275682.

KE S., SKIRVIN R.M., McPHEETERS K.D., OTTERBACHER A.G. & GALLETTA G. 1985 *In vitro* germination and growth of *Rubus* seeds and embryos. HortScience, **20**, 1047–1049.

KEHR A.E. & SCHAEFFER G.W. 1976 Tissue culture and differentiation of garlic. HortScience, **11**, 422–423.

KEIM W.F. 1953 An embryo culture technique for forage legumes. Agron.J., **45**, 509–510.

KELLER J. 1990 Haploids from unpollinated ovaries of *Allium cepa* — single plant screening, haploid determination, and long term storage. pp. 275–279 in Nijkamp *et al.* (eds.) 1990 (*q.v.*).

KELLER J. 1991 *In vitro* conservation of haploid and diploid germplasm in *Allium cepa* L. Acta Hort., **289**, 231–232.

KELLER W.A., RAJHATHY T. & LACAPRA J. 1975 *In vitro* production of plants from pollen in *Brassica campestris*. Can.J.Gen.Cytol., **17**, 655–666.

KENNY L. & PALZKILL D.A. 1988 *In vitro* culture of jojoba: Evaluation of modifications of six media. HortScience, **23**, 757.

KENT N. & BRINK R.A. 1947 Growth *in vitro* of immature *Hordeum* embryos. Science, **106**, 547–548.

KERBEL E.L., KADER A.A. & ROMANI R.J. 1990 Respiratory and glycolytic response of suspension–cultured 'Passe Crassane' pear fruit cells to elevated CO_2 concentrations. J. Am. Soc. Hort. Sci., **115**, 111–114.

KERMODE A.R. 1990 Regulatory mechanisms involved in the transition from seed development to germination. CRC Crit. Rev. Plant Sci., **9**, 155–195.

KERNS H.R. & MEYER M.M. 1985 *In vitro* propagation of red–silver hybrid maples. HortScience, **20**, 593.

KERNS H.R., BARWALE U.B., MEYER M.M. Jr. & WIDHOLM J.M. 1986 Correlation of cotyledonary node shoot proliferation and somatic embryoid development in suspension cultures of soybean (*Glycine max* L. Merr.). Plant Cell Rep., **5**, 140–143.

KERNS H.R., BARWALE U.B., MEYER M.M. Jr. & WIDHOLM J.M. 1986 Correlation of cotyledonary node shoot proliferation and somatic embryoid development in suspension cultures of soybean (*Glycine max* L. Merr.). Plant Cell Rep., **5**, 140–143.

KERNS H.R., BARWALE U B., MEYER M M. Jr. & WIDHOLM J.M. 1986 Histological studies of soybean embryoid development from immature zygotic embryos. p. 44 in Somers *et al.* (eds.) 1986 (*q.v.*).

KERTZ M.G. 1989a Integument and method for micropropagation and tissue culturing. U.S. Patent No. 4908315.

KERTZ M.G. 1989b Culturing of living organic material – in cellules made of gas–permeable and liquid– and contaminant–impermeable membrane. World Patent Applic. No. 8912385.

KERTZ M.G. 1990a Organic material culture in chambers – formed between two membrane strips sealed and handled mechanically. Canadian Patent Applic. No. 2004325.

KERTZ M.G. 1990b Container for growing biological production formed of gas–permeable, liquid impermeable membrane with rupturable internal pouches. World Patent Applic. No. 9015527.

KERTZ M.G. 1990c Growing living organic material in atmospheric environment – using gas permeable liquid impermeable membrane chamber sealed about the organic material. World Patent Applic. No. 9015526.

KERTZ M.G. 1990d Automated propagation unit – transports cellules containing growth media to manipulation unit where tissue cuttings are added before sealing, culturing and monitoring. World Patent Applic. No. 9006058.

KESTER D.E. & HESSE C.O. 1955 Embryo culture of peach varieties in relation to season of ripening. Proc. Am. Soc. Hort. Sci., **65**, 265–273.

KESTER D.E., TABACHNIK L. & NEGUEROLES J. 1977 Use of micropropagation and tissue culture to investigate genetic disorders in almond cultivars. Acta Hort., **78**, 95–101.

KEVERS C. & GASPAR Th. 1985a Soluble, membrane and cell wall peroxidases phenylalanine ammonia lyase and lignin changes in relation to vitrification of carnation tissues cultured *in vitro*. J. Plant Physiol., **118**, 41–48.

KEVERS C., PRAT R. & GASPAR Th. 1987 Vitrification of carnation *in vitro*: changes in cell wall mechanical properties, cellulose and lignin content. Plant Growth Reg., **5**, 59–66.

KEVERS CL., COUMANS–GILLES M.F., COUMANS M. & GASPAR Th. 1983 *In vitro* vegetative multiplication of *Fuchsia* hybrids. Scientia Hort., **21**, 67–71.

KEYES G.J., COLLINS G.B., TAYLOR N.L. 1980 Genetic variation in tissue cultures of red clover. Theor. Appl. Genet., **58**, 265–272.

KEYS R.N. & CECH F.C. 1978 Tissue culture of American chestnut, *Castanea dentata* (March) Borkh. p. 259 in Hughes *et al.* (eds.) 1978 (*q.v.*).

KHANNA P. & STABA E.J. 1970 *In vitro* physiology and morphogenesis of *Cheiranthus cheiri* var. Cloth of Gold and *C. cheiri* var. Goliath. Bot. Gaz., **131**, 1–5.

KHASANOV M.M. & BUTENKO R.G. 1979 Cultivation of isolated protoplasts from cotyledons of cotton (*Gossypium hirsutum*). Sov. Plant Physiol., **26**, 77–82.

KHATTAR S. & MOHAN RAM H.Y. 1982 Organogenesis in the cultured tissues of *Sesbania sesban,* a leguminous shrub. Ind. J. Exp. Biol., **20**, 216–219.

KHATTAR S. & MOHAN RAM H.Y. 1983 Organogenesis and plantlet formation *in vitro* in *Lesbania grandiflora* (L) Pers. Ind. J. Exp. Biol., **21**, 251–253.

KHOKHAR J. 1983 Studies on clonal propagation and transplanting physiology of African violet. P. Phil. thesis, NE London Polytechnic, London.

KHOSH–KHUI M. & SINK K.C. 1982b Rooting–enhancement of *Rosa hybrida* for tissue culture propagation. Scientia Hort., **17**, 371–376.

KHOSH–KHUI M., SHEKAFANDEH A. & AZARAKHSH H. 1984 Micropropagation of myrtle. Scientia Hort., **22**, 139–146.

KIERNAN J.N., HENDRIX J.W., STOLTZ L.P. & MARONEK D.M. 1984 Characterization of strawberry plants produced by tissue culture and infected with specific mycorrhizal fungi. HortScience, **19**, 883–885.

KIKUTA Y. & OKAZAWA Y. 1984 Control of root and shoot–bud formation from potato tuber tissue cultured *in vitro*. Physiol. Plant., **61**, 8–12.

KIL SUN YOO, PIKE L.M. & COBB B.G. 1990 Promotion of *in vitro* leaf growth of inner scales excised from dormant onion bulbs. HortScience, **25**, 228–229.

KIM K.K., KUNISAKI J.T. & SAGAWA Y. 1970 Shoot tip culture of dendrobiums. Am. Orchid Soc. Bull., **39**, 1077–1080.

KIM S.–G., CHANG J.–R., CHA H.C. & LEE K.–W. 1988 Callus growth and plant regeneration in diverse cultivars of cucumber (*Cucumis sativus* L.). Plant Cell Tiss. Organ Cult., **12**, 67–84.

KIM S.K., LAGERSTEDT H.B. & DALEY L.S. 1985 Germination responses of filbert pollen to pH, temperature, glucose, fructose and sucrose. HortScience, **20**, 944–946.

KIM Y–J., HASEGAWA P.M. & BRESSAN R.A. 1981 *In vitro* propagation of hyacinth. HortScience, **16**, 645–647.

KIM Y.–H. & JANICK J. 1989c Origin of somatic embryos in celery tissue culture. HortScience, **24**, 671–673.

KIM Y.–H. & JANICK J. 1990 Synthetic seed technology: improving desiccation tolerance of somatic embryos of celery. Acta Hort., **280**, 23–28.

PEVALEK–KOZLINA B. & JELASKA S. 1986 *In vitro* growth and development of oaks (*Quercus robur* and *Quercus petraea*). Acta Bot. Croat., **45**, 55–62.

PFISTER J.M. & WIDHOLM J.M. 1984 Plant regeneration from snapdragon tissue cultures. HortScience, **19**, 852–854.

PHAN C.–T. & CAILLOUX M. 1980 Phenolic compounds of parent and cultured tissue of twigs and vegetative buds of apple–trees. Plant Physiol., **65**, (Suppl.) 92 (Abst. 505).

PHAN C.T. 1991 Vitreous state *in vitro* culture: ethylene versus cytokinin. Plant Cell Rep., **9**, 517–519.

PHILIP V.J. & NAINAR S.A.Z. 1988 *In vitro* transformation of root meristem to shoot and plantlets in *Vanilla planifolia*. Ann. Bot., **61**, 193–199.

PHILLIPS D.A. 1974 Factors affecting the reduction of acetylene by *Rhizobium*–soybean cell associations *in vitro*. Plant. Physiol., **53**, 67–72.

PHILLIPS G. C. & COLLINS G. B. 1984 Chapter 7 — Red clover and other forage legumes. pp. 169–210 in Sharp *et al*. (eds.) 1984 (*q.v.*).

PHILLIPS G.C. & HUBSTENBERGER J.F. 1984 Adventitious budding and organogenesis in tissue cultures of Chile pepper (*Capsicum annuum* L.). In Vitro, **20**, 277.

PHILLIPS G.C., & HUBSTENBERGER J.F. 1987 Plant regeneration *in vitro* of selected *Allium* species and interspecific hybrids. HortScience, **22**, 124–125.

PHILLIPS G.C., COLLINS G.B. & TAYLOR N.L. 1982 Interspecific hybridisation of red clover (*Trifolium pratense* L.) with *T. sarosiense* using *in vitro* embryo rescue. Theor. Appl. Genet., **62**, 17–24.

PHUKAN M.K. & MITRA G.C. 1982 *In vitro* regeneration of *Albizzia odoratissima* Benth., a shade tree for tea plantation of North–East India. Two and a Bud, **30**, 54–58.

PIAGNANI C., ECCHER T. & CASTELLI S. 1986 Micropropagation of *Actinidia chinensis*: effects of growth regulators on proliferation rate. Acta Hort., **179**, 887–890.

PICARD E. 1973 Influence de modifications dans les correlations internes sur le devenir du gametophyte male de *Triticum aestivum* L. in situ et en culture *in vitro*. Compt. Rend. Acad. Sci. Paris, **277D**, 777–780.

PICCIRILLI M., PUPILLI F. & ARCIONI S. 1988 *Lotus tenuis* Wald. & Kit.: *In vitro* conditions for plant regeneration from protoplasts and callus of various explants. Plant Science, **55**, 77–82.

PICCOTINO D., MASSAI R., BARONI G. & BOVO M. 1991 Root system conformation and growth of kiwi fruit as affected by propagation technique. Acta Hort., **297**, 391–401.

PICKERING R.A. 1989 Plant regeneration and variants from calli derived from immature embryos of diploid barley (*Hordeum vulgare* L.) and *H. vulgare* L. × *H. bulbosum* L. crosses. Theor. Appl. Genet., **78**, 105–112.

PIEPER W. & ZIMMER K. 1976a Clonal propagation of *Phalaenopsis in vitro*. Acta Hort., **64**, 21–23.

PIEPER W. & ZIMMER K. 1976b Ein neues System fur die Vermehrung von Geweben *in vitro*. Gartenbauwiss., **41**, 221–224.

PIERIK R.L.M. 1966a The induction and initiation of flower buds *in vitro* in tissues of *Lunaria annua* L. Naturwiss., **53**, 45.

PIERIK R.L.M. 1966b The induction and initiation of flowerbuds *in vitro* in root tissues of *Cichorium intybus* L. Naturwiss., **53**, 387.

PIERIK R.L.M. 1972 Adventitious root formation in isolated petiole segments of *Lunaria annua*. Z. Pflanzénphysiol., **66**, 343–351.

PIERIK R.L.M. 1975a Callus multiplication of *Anthurium andraeanum* Lind. in liquid media. Neth. J. Agric. Sci., **23**, 299–302.

PIERIK R.L.M. 1975b Vegetative propagation of horticultural crops *in vitro* with special attention to trees and shrubs. Acta Hort., **54**, 71–82.

PIERIK R.L.M. 1976a *Anthurium andreanum* plantlets produced from *in vitro* cultivated callus tissues. Physiol. Plant., **37**, 80–82.

PIERIK R.L.M. 1976c Nieuwe methode voor vegetatieve vermeerdering van freesia in kweekbuizen. Vakblad voor de Bloemisterij, **31**, (28) 61.

PIERIK R.L.M. 1988 Handicaps for the large scale commercial application of micropropagation. Acta Hort., **230**, 63–71.

PIERIK R.L.M. 1991a Commercial micropropagation in Western Europe and Israel. pp. 155–165 in Debergh and Zimmerman (eds.) 1991 (*q.v.*).

PIERIK R.L.M. 1991b Micropropagation of ornamental plants. Acta Hort., **289**, 45–53.

PIERIK R.L.M. & IPPEL B.J. 1977 Plantlet formation from excised bulb scale segments of *Nerine*. Acta Hort., **78**, 197–202.

PIERIK R.L.M. & STEEGMANS H.H.M. 1975b Effect of auxins, cytokinins, gibberellins, abscisic acid and ethephon on regeneration and growth of bulblets on excised bulb scale segments of hyacinth. Physiol. Plant., **34**, 14–17.

PIERIK R.L.M. & STEEGMANS H.H.M. 1975d Vegetatieve vermeerdering van freesia in kweekbuizen. Vakblad voor de Bloemisterij, **30**, (24) 18–19.

PIERIK R.L.M. & STEEGMANS H.H.M. 1975e Vegetatieve vermeeridering van *Anthurium scherzerianum in vitro*. Vakblad voor de Bloemisterij, **30**, 21.

PIERIK R.L.M. & STEEGMANS H.H.M. 1976a Vegetative propagation of *Anthurium scherzerianum* shoot through callus cultures. Scientia Hort., **4**, 291–292.

PIERIK R.L.M. & STEEGMANS H.H.M. 1976b Vegetative propagation of *Freesia* through isolation of shoots *in vitro*. Neth. J. Agric. Sci., **24**, 274–277.

PIERIK R.L.M. & WOETS J. 1971 Regeneration of isolated bulb scale segments of hyacinth. Acta Hort., **23**, 423–428.

PIERIK R.L.M., JANSEN J.L.M. & MAASDAM A. 1974c Vegetatieve vermeerdering van gerbera in kweekbuizen. Vakbl. Bloem., **29**, 18–19.

PIERIK R.L.M., JANSEN J.L.M., MAASDAM A. & BINNENDIJK C.M. 1975a Optimalization of *Gerbera* plantlet production from excised capitulum explants. Scientia Hort., **3**, 351–357.

PIERIK R.L.M., STEEGMANS H.H.M. & HENDRIKS J. 1984 The influence of napthaleneacetic acid on the growth of *in vitro* cultivated seedlings of Bromeliaceae. Scientia Hort., **24** , 193–199.

PIERIK R.L.M., STEEGMANS H.H.M. & IPPEL B.J. 1977 Vakblad voor de Bloemisterij, **32**, (50/51) 56–57.

PIERIK R.L.M., STEEGMANS H.H.M. & MARELIS J.J. 1973 *Gerbera* plantlets from *in vitro* cultivated capitulum explants. Scientia Hort., **1**, 117–119.

PIERIK R.L.M., STEEGMANS H.H.M., VAN SCHAIK W. & VAN EYK- BOS G. 1975d With the aid of shaking machines: callus propagation of *Anthurium andreanum*. Vakblad Bloemisterij **30**, 27.

PIERIK R.L.M., STEEGMANS H.H.M., WOUTERS A.N. & VERHAEGH J. 1979a Nieuwe ontwikkelingen vegetatieve vermeerdering gerbera in kweekbuizen. Vakblad voor de Bloemisterij, **34**, (25) 36–37.

PIERIK R.L.M., VAN DER MEYS J.A.J. & STEEGMANS H.H.M. 1974a Vakblad voor de Bloemisterij, **29**, (6) 12–15.

PIERIK R.L.M., VAN LEEUWEN P. & RIGTER G.C.C.M. 1979b Regeneration of leaf explants of *Anthurium andreanum* Lind. *in vitro*. Neth. J. Agric. Sci., **27**, 221–226.

PIERON S., BELAIZI M. & BOXUS Ph. 1992 Scheme for rapid clonal propagation of *Cichorium intybus* L. through nodule culture. Acta Hort., **319**, 285–290.

PIETERSE R.E. 1989 Regeneration of plants from callus and embryos of 'Royal' apricot. Plant Cell Tiss. Organ Cult., **19**, 175–179.

PIETROPAOLO P.A. & REISCH B.I. 1984 Micropropagation of Stanley plum. HortScience, **19**, 535–536.

PIJNACKER L.P., HERMELINK J.H.M. & FERWERDA M.A. 1986 Variability of DNA content and karyotype in cell cultures of an interdihaploid *Solanum tuberosum*. Plant Cell Rep., **5**, 43–46.

PIKE L.M. & YOO K.S. 1990 Asexual propagation of plants of the *Allium* genus by culturing immature flower buds obtained from umbels of plants prior to opening of spathes. World Patent Applic. No. 9010383.

PILET P.E. & BERNASCONI P. 1984 *Rubus hispidus* callus cultured *in vitro* and endogenous lysozyme: growth processes. Plant Sci. Lett., **35**, 147–151.

PILLAI S.K. & HILDEBRANDT A.C. 1968 Geranium plants differentiated *in vitro* from stem tip and callus cultures. Plant Disease Rep., **52**, 600–601.

PILLAI V., DAVEY M.R. & POWER J.B. 1990 Plant regeneration from mesophyll protoplasts of *Centaurea cyanus*, *Senecio × hybridus* and *Callistephus chinensis*. Plant Cell Rep., **9**, 402–405.

PINK D.A.C. & WALKEY D.G.A. 1984 Rapid propagation of *Cucurbita pepo* L. by culture of meristem tips. Scientia Hort., **24**, 107–114.

PINOL M.T., PALAZON J. & SERRANO M. 1984 Growth and nicotine content of tobacco callus cultures without organogenesis. Plant Sci. Lett., **35**, 219.

PITTET H. & MONCOUSIN C. 1981 Multiplication nouvelle du rosier. Rev. Hort. Suisse, **54**, 169–173.

PIUS J., GEORGE L., EAPEN S. & RAO P.S. 1993 Enhanced plant regeneration in pearl millet (*Pennisetum americanum*) by ethylene inhibitors and cefotaxime. Plant Cell Tiss. Organ Cult., **32**, 91–96.

PLANCKAERT F. & WALBOT V. 1989 Transient gene expression after electroporation of protoplasts derived from embryogenic maize callus. Plant Cell Rep., **8**, 144–147.

PLATA E. & VIEITEZ A.M. 1990 *In vitro* regeneration of *Camellia reticulata* by somatic embryogenesis. J. Hort. Sci., **65**, 707–714.

PLESSNER O., ZIV M. & NEGBI M. 1990 *In vitro* corm production in the saffron crocus (*Crocus sativus* L.). Plant Cell Tiss. Organ Cult., **20**, 89–94.

PLIEGO–ALFARO F. & MURASHIGE T. 1988 Somatic embryogenesis in avocado (*Persea americana* Mill.) *in vitro*. Plant Cell Tiss. Organ Cult., **12** , 61–66.

PLUMMER J.A. & DE FOSSARD R.A. 1982 The influence of plant hormones and growth factors on growth of *Eriostemum australasius* Pers. in tissue culture. Comb. Proc. Int. Plant Prop. Soc. 1981, **31**, 295–303.

POCOCK S. 1984 Procedures and problems associated with the transfer of tissue–cultured plants. Comb. Proc. Int. Plant Prop. Soc. 1983, **33**, 316–320.

PODWYSZYNSKA M. & HEMPEL M. 1988 The factors influencing acclimatization of *Rosa hybrida* plants multiplied *in vitro* to greenhouse conditions. Acta Hort., **226**, 639–642.

POGANY M.F. & LINEBERGER R.D. 1990 Phenotypic variation during micropropagation of the chimeral *Rhododendron* 'President Roosevelt'. Plant Cell Tiss. Organ Cult., **21**, 201–209.

POLANCO M.C., PELAEZ M.E. & RUIZ M.L. 1988 Factors affecting callus and shoot formation from *in vitro* cultures of *Lens culinaris* Medik. Plant Cell Tiss. Organ Cult., **15**, 175–182.

POLITO V.S., McGRANAHAN G., PINNEY K. & LESLIE C. 1989 Origin of somatic embryos from repetitively embryogenic cultures of walnut (*Juglans regia* L.): implications for *Agrobacterium*–mediated transformation. Plant Cell Rep., **8**, 219–221.

PONCHIA G. & GARDIMAN M. 1992 Research on *in vitro* propagation of Mulberry (*Morus alba* L.). Acta Hort., **314**, 99–104.

PONCHIA G. & ROSELLI G. 1980 Prove di micropropagazione di due cloni di ciliegio acido (*Prunus cerasus* L.). Riv. Ortoflorofrutti. Ital., **64**, 229–240.

PONSONBY D.J. & MANTELL S.H. 1993 *In vitro* establishment of *Picea pungens* f. *glauca* and *P. sitchensis* seedling root stocks with an assessment of their suitabilities for micrografting with scions of various *Picea* species. J. Hort. Sci., **68**, 463–475.

PONTIKIS C.A. 1984 *In vitro* propagation of *Pistacia terebinthus* L. Plant Propagator, **30**, 14–15.

POOLE H.A. & SHEEHAN T.J. 1977 Effects of media and supplementary micro element fertilization on growth and chemical composition of *Cattleya*. Am. Orchid Soc. Bull., **46**, 155–160.

POOLE R.T. & CONOVER C.A. 1983 Establishment and growth of *in vitro* cultured *Dieffenbachia*. HortScience, **18**, 185–187.

POONSAPAYA P., NABORS M.W., WRIGHT K. & VAJRABHAYA M. 1989 A comparison of methods for callus cultured and plant regeneration of RD 25 rice (*Oryza sativa* L.) in two laboratories. Plant Cell Tiss. Organ Cult., **16**, 175–186.

POPOV Y.G. 1974 Meristem culture of strawberries affected by virus diseases. Sel'skokhozyaistvennaya Biologiya, **9**, 694–697.

POPOV Y.G., VYSOTSKII V.A. & TRUSHECHKIN V.G. 1976 Culture of isolated sour cherry shoot apices. Soviet Plant Physiol., **23**, 513–518.

POSA B.T., CALINAWAN N.M., SIBHAZ D.L. & HALOS S.C. 1987 *In vitro* culture of *Pogostemon cablin* Benth. Acta Hort., **212**, 457–462.

POTLURI S.D.P. & DEVI PRASAD P.V. 1993 Influence of salinity on axillary bud cultures of six lowland tropical varieties of potato (*Solanum tuberosum*). Plant Cell Tiss. Organ Cult., **32**, 185–191.

POULAIN C., RHISS A. & BEAUCHESNE G. 1979 Multiplication végétative en culture *in vitro* du palmier–dattier. Compt. Rend. Acad. Agric. France, **65**, 1151–1154.

POULSEN G.B. & NIELSEN S.V.S. 1989 Regeneration of plants from hypocotyl protoplasts of rapeseed (*Brassica napus* L. var. *oleifera*) cultivars. Plant Cell Tiss. Organ Cult., **17**, 153–158.

POWELL W., BROWN J. & CALIGARI P.D.S. 1989 Variability in response of potato cultivars to micropropagation. II. Subsequent field performance. Ann. Appl. Biol., **115**, 123–128.

POWER C.J. & FIROOZABADY E. 1991 Sunflower regeneration from cotyledons. U.S. Patent No. 5030572.

POWER J.B. & BERRY S.F. 1979 Plant regeneration from protoplasts of *Browallia viscosa*. Z. Pflanzenphysiol., **94**, 469–471.

POWER K.C., FITZGERALD J.B., MEYER G.E. & SCHULTE D.D. 1991 Plant production cost–accounting management system. HortScience, **26**, 201–203.

POWERS D.E. & BACKHAUS R.A. 1989 *In vitro* propagation of *Agave arizonica* Gentry and Weber. Plant Cell Tiss. Organ Cult., **16**, 57–60.

PRABHUDESAI V. & NARAYANASWAMY S. 1974 Organogenesis in tissue cultures of certain asclepiads. Z. Pflanzenphysiol., **71**, 181–185.

PRAKASH L., JOHN P., NAIR G.M. & PRATHAPASENAN G. 1988 Effect of spermidine and methylglyoxal–bis–(guanyl–hydrazone) (MGBG) on *in vitro* pollen germination and tube growth in *Catharanthus roseus*. Ann. Bot., **61**, 373–375.

PRAMANIK T.K. & DATTA S.K. 1986 Plant regeneration and ploidy variation in culture derived plants of *Asclepias curassavica* L. Plant Cell Rep., **5**, 219–222.

PRAS N. 1990 Bioconversion of precursors occurring in plants and of related synthetic compounds. pp. 640–649 in Nijkamp *et al.* (eds.) 1990 (*q.v.*).

PRASAD R.N. & MITRA G.C. 1975 Nutrient requirements for germination of seeds and development of protocorms and seedlings of *Cymbidium* in aseptic cultures. Ind. J. Exp. Biol., **13**, 123–126.

PREDIERI S. & MALAVASI P.F.F. 1989 High–frequency shoot regeneration from leaves of the apple rootstock M26 (*Malus pumila* Mill.). Plant Cell Tiss. Organ Cult., **17**, 133–142.

PREDIERI S., FASOLO FABBRI MALAVASI F. & ANCHERANI M. 1989 Regeneration of plants from strawberry (*Frageria × ananassa* Duch.) unpollinated ovaries and petals. Acta Hort., **265**, 335–342.

PREDIERI S., FASOLO FABBRI MALAVASI F., PASSEY A.J., RIDOUT M.S. & JAMES D.J. 1989 Regeneration from *in vitro* leaves of 'Conference' and other pear cultivars (*Pyrus communis* L.). J. Hort. Sci., **64**, 553–559.

PREECE J.E. 1991 Practical regulation of woody plant growth and development using biotechnology. Acta Hort., **300**, 23–33.

PREECE J.E. 1995 Can nutrient salts partially substitute for plant growth regulators? Plant Tissue Culture and Biotechnology, IAPTC, **1**, 26–37.

PREECE J.E. & READ P.E. 1980 Comparisons between isogenic lines of tomatoes of different branching habits for growth and differentiation on tissue culture media. HortScience, **15**, 416 (Abst. 317).

PREECE J.E., CHRIST P.H., ENSENBERGER L. & ZHAO J.–L. 1988 Micropropagation of ash (*Fraxinus*). Comb. Proc. Int. Plant Prop. Soc. 1987, **37**, 366–372.

PREECE J.E., HUETTEMAN C. A., ASHEY W. C., BRESNAN D. F., & ROTH P. L. 1988 Provenance tests for biomass production using micropropagated Silver Maple. HortScience, **23**, 803.

PREECE J.E., HUETTEMAN C.A., ASHBY W.C. & ROTH P.L. 1991a Micro– and cutting propagation of silver maple. I. Results with adult and juvenile propagules. J. Am. Soc. Hort. Sci., **116**, 142–148.

PREECE J.E., HUETTEMAN C.A., ASHBY W.C. & ROTH P.L. 1991b Micro– and cutting propagation of silver maple. II. Genotype and provenance affect performance. J. Am. Soc. Hort. Sci., **116**, 149–155.

PREECE J.E., ZHAO J.–L. & KUNG F.H. 1989 Callus production and somatic embryogenesis from White Ash. HortScience, **24**, 377–380.

PREIL W. & BECK A. 1991 Somatic embryogenesis in bioreactor culture. Acta Hort., **289**, 179–192.

PREIL W. & ENGELHARDT M. 1977 Meristem culture of azaleas (*Rhododendron simsii*). Acta Hort., **78**, 203–208.

PREIL W., ENGELHARDT M. & WALTHER F. 1983 Breeding of low temperature tolerant poinsettia (*Euphorbia pulcherrima*) and chrysanthemum by means of mutation induction in *in vitro* culture. Acta Hort., **131**, 345–351.

PRESS T.F. 1984 Propagation: fog not mist. Comb. Proc. Int. Plant Prop. Soc. 1983, **33**, 100–109.

PRETOVA A. 1986 Growth of zygotic flax embryos *in vitro* and influence of kinetin. Plant Cell Rep., **5**, 210–211.

PRETOVA A. & WILLIAMS E.G. 1987 Zygotic embryo cloning in oilseed rape (*Brassica napus* L.). Plant Science, **47**, 195–198.

PRICE H. J. & SMITH R.H. 1984 Chapter 18 — Cotton. pp. 487–510 in Ammirato *et al.* (eds.) 1984 (*q.v.*).

PRICE H.J., SMITH R.H. & GRUMBLES R.M. 1977 Callus cultures of six species of cotton (*Gossypium* L.) on defined media. Plant Sci. Lett., **10**, 115–119.

PRINGSHEIM E.G. & PRINGSHEIM O. 1962 Axenic culture of *Utricularia*. Am. J. Bot., **49**, 898–901.

PRIOLI L.M., SILVA W.J. & ARRUDA P. 1985 *In vitro* regeneration capacity of corn and teosinte genotypes. pp. 342–343 in Henke *et al.* (eds.) 1985 (*q.v.*).

PRIYADARSHAN P.M. & ZACHARIAH P.K. 1986 Studies on *in vitro* culture on cardamom (*Elettaria cardamomum* Maton; Zingiberaceae) – progress and limitations. p. 107 in Somers *et al.* (eds.) 1986 (*q.v.*).

PRIYADARSHI S. & SEN S. 1992 A revised scheme for mass propagation of Easter lily. Plant Cell Tiss. Organ Cult., **30**, 193–197.

PROSKAUER J. & BERMAN R. 1970 Agar culture medium modified to approximate soil conditions. Nature, **227**, 1161.

PRUSKI K., NOWAK J. & GRAINGER G. 1990 Micropropagation of four cultivars of Saskatoon berry (*Amelanchier alnifolia* Nutt.). Plant Cell Tiss. Organ Cult., **21**, 103–109.

PRUTPONGSE P. & GAVINLERTVATANA P. 1992 *In vitro* micropropagation of 54 species from 15 genera of bamboo. HortScience, **27**, 453–454.

PUA E.-C., TRINH T.H. & CHUA N.-H. 1989 High frequency plant regeneration from stem explants of *Brassica alboglabra* Bailey *in vitro*. Plant Cell Tiss. Organ Cult., **17**, 143–152.

PUGLIESI C., MEGALE P., CECCONI F. & BARONCELLI S. 1993 Organogenesis and embryogenesis in *Helianthus tuberosus* and in the interspecific hybrid *Helianthus annuus* × *Helianthus tuberosus*. Plant Cell Tiss. Organ Cult., **33**, 187–193.

PUGLIESI C., RABAGLIO M., CECCONI F. & BARONCELLI S. 1992 Plant regeneration from tissue cultures of Persian buttercup (*Ranunculus asiaticus* L.). Plant Cell Tiss. Organ Cult., **28**, 125–128.

PUHLER A., REILAENDER H. & WEBER G. 1988 Nitrogen fixation regulator genes. U.S. Patent No. 4782022.

PUITE K., BROEKE W. & SCHAART J. 1988 Inhibition of cell wall synthesis improved flow cytometric sorting of potato heterofusions resulting in hybrid plants. Plant Science, **56**, 61–68.

PUITE K.J., ROEST S. & PIJNACKER L.P. 1986 Somatic hybrid potato plants after electrofusion of diploid *Solanum tuberosum* and *Solanum phureja*. Plant Cell Rep., **5**, 262–265.

PULLMAN G.S. & GUPTA P. 1991 Method for reproducing coniferous plants by somatic embryogenesis using adsorbent materials in the development stage media. U.S. Patent No. 5034326.

PUNJA Z.K., ABBAS N., SARMENTO G.G. & TANG F.A. 1990a Regeneration of *Cucumis sativus* var. *sativus* and *C. sativus* var. *hardwickii*, *C. melo* and *C. metuliferus* from explants through somatic embryogenesis and organogenesis. Plant Cell Tiss. Organ Cult., **21**, 93–102.

PUNJA Z.K., TANG F.A. & SARMENTO G.G. 1990b Isolation, culture and plantlet regeneration from cotyledon and mesophyll protoplasts of two pickling cucumber (*Cucumis sativus* L.) genotypes. Plant Cell Rep., **9**, 61–64.

PUONTI–KAERLAS J. & ERIKSSON T. 1988 Improved protoplast culture and regeneration of shoots in pea (*Pisum sativum* L.). Plant Cell Rep., **7**, 242–245.

PURI P. 1963 Growth *in vitro* of parthenogenetic embryos of *Aerva tomentosa* Forsk. pp. 281–291 in Maheshwari & Ranga Swamy (eds.) 1963 (*q.v.*).

PURNHAUSER L. & GYULAI G. 1993 Effect of copper on shoot and root regeneration in wheat, triticale, rape and tobacco tissue cultures. Plant Cell Tiss. Organ Cult., **35**, 131–139.

QIAO Y.M. & FALAVIGNA A. 1990 An improved *in vitro* anther culture method for obtaining doubled–haploid clones of asparagus. Acta Hort., **271**, 145–150.

QUAK F. 1957 Meristem cultuur gecombineerd met warmtebehandling voor het verkrijgen van virusvrije anjerplanten. Tijdschr.PlZiekt, **63**, 13.

QUAZI M.H. 1980 *In vitro* multiplication of *Lavandula* spp. Ann. Bot., **45**, 361–362.

QUINN J., SIMON J.E. & JANICK J. 1989a Recovery of λ–linolenic acid from somatic embryos of borage. J. Am. Soc. Hort. Sci., **114**, 511–515.

QUINN J., SIMON J.E. & JANICK J. 1989b Histology of zygotic and somatic embryogenesis in borage. J. Am. Soc. Hort. Sci., **114**, 516–520.

QUINTERO A., BAEZA A. & SORIANO J. 1986 Tomato tissue culture and isolation of metabolically active protoplasts. Phyton., **46**, 61–68.

QUINTERO E. 1990 Yucca. pp.783–799 in Ammirato *et al.* (eds.) 1990 (*q.v.*).

QUOIRIN M., LEPOIVRE P. & BOXUS Ph. 1977 Un premier bilan de 10 annees de recherches sur les cultures de meristemes et la multiplication *in vitro* de fruitiers ligneux., pp. 93–117 in C. R. Rech. 1976–1977 & Rapports de Synthese, Stat. Cult. Fruit. et Maraich., Gembloux.

QURAISHI A., ROSSIGNOL–BANCILHON L. & NOZERAN R. 1979 Effet de l'origine de fragment sur la callogenèse et l'organogenèse *in vitro* chez *Solanum tuberosum* L. var. 'BF15'. Ann.Amelior.Plantes, **29**, 639–663.

QURESHI J.A., KARTHA K.K., ABRAMS S.R. & STEINHAUER L. 1989 Modulation of somatic embryogenesis in early and late–stage embryos of wheat (*Triticum aestivum* L.) under the influence of (F128æ)–abscisic acid and its analogs. Plant Cell Tiss. Organ Cult., **18**, 55–69.

QUYNH N.T. & UYEN N.V. 1987 Aroids propagation by tissue culture: I. Shoot tip culture and propagation of *Xanthosoma violaceum*. HortScience, **22**, 671–672.

RABAKOARIHANTA A., SEKIOKA T.T. & ASANO W.Y. 1982 Embryo development in *Carica papaya* L. HortScience, **17**, 487.

RABECHAULT H. 1967 Relation entre le comportement des embryons de palmier a huile (*Elaeis guineensis* Jacq.) en culture *in vitro* et la teneur en eau des graines. Compt. Rend. Acad. Sci. Paris, **264**, 276–279.

RABECHAULT H. & MARTIN J–P. 1976 Vegetative propagation of oil palm (*Elaeis guineensis*) by means of leaf tissue culture. Compt. Rend. Acad. Sci. Paris, **283D**, 1735–1737.

RABECHAULT H., AHEE J. & GUENIN G. 1969 Developpment *in vitro* des embryons de palmier à huile (*Elaeis guineensis* Jacq. var. Becc.). Estraits de graines dormantes ou non dormantes au cours de leur deshydration naturelle. Compt. Rend. Acad. Sci. Paris, **268**, 1728–1731.

RABECHAULT H., AHEE J. & GUENIN G. 1970 Colonier cellulaires et formes embryoids obtenues *in vitro* à partir de culture d'embryons de palmier à huile (*Elaeis guineensis* Jacq. var. *dura* Becc.). Compt. Rend. Acad. Sci. Paris, **270D**, 3067–3070.

RADOJEVIC L. 1979 Somatic embryos and plantlets from callus cultures of *Paulownia tomentosa* Steud. Z. Pflanzenphysiol., **91**, 57–62.

RADOJEVIC L., DRUART P. & BOXUS P. 1987a Vegetative propagation of androgenus embryos of horse chestnut by meristem culture *in vitro*. Acta Hort., **212**, 531–537.

RADOJEVIC L., VUJICIC R. & NESKOVIC M. 1975 Embryogenesis in tissue culture of *Corylus avellana* L. Z. Pflanzenphysiol., **77**, 33–41.

RADOJEVIC L.J., LANDRE P. & NESKOVIC M. 1980 Isolement de trois souches tissulaires à partir d'embryons immatures d'*Acer negundo* L. Z. Pflanzenphysiol., **99**, 191–198.

RAEMAKERS C.J.J.M., BESSEMBINDER J.J.E., STARITSKY G., JACOBSEN E. & VISSER R.G.F. 1993 Induction, germination and shoot development of somatic embryos in cassava. Plant Cell Tiss. Organ Cult., **33**, 151–156.

RAGHAVAN V. 1986 Variability through wide crosses and embryo rescue. pp. 613–633 in Vasil I.K. (ed.) 1986 *Cell Culture and Somatic Cell Genetics of Plants* Vol. 3. *Plant Regeneration and Genetic Variability*. Academic Press, New York.

RAGHAVAN V. & JACOBS W.P. 1961 Studies on the floral histogenesis and physiology of Perilla. II. Floral induction in cultured apical buds of *P. frutescens*. Am. J. Bot., **48**, 751–760.

RAGHAVAN V. & TORREY J.G. 1963 Growth and morphogenesis of globular and older embryos of *Capsella* in culture. Am. J. Bot., **50**, 540–551.

RAGHAVAN V. & TORREY J.G. 1964a Effect of certain growth substances on the growth and morphogenesis of immature embryos of *Capsella* in culture. Plant Physiol., **39**, 691–699.

RAGHAVAN V. & TORREY J.G. 1964b Inorganic nitrogen nutrition of the seedlings of the orchid *Cattleya*. Am. J. Bot., **51**, 264–274.

RAHARJO S.H.T. & PUNJA Z.K. 1993 Plantlet regeneration from petiole explants of the African horned cucumber *Cucumis metuliferus*. Plant Cell Tiss. Organ Cult., **32**, 169–174.

RAHMAN M.A. 1988 Effect of nutrients on the growth and survival of *in vitro Artocarpus heterophyllus* Lam. plantlets after transfer to *ex vitro* conditions in the glasshouse. J. Hort. Sci., **63**, 329–335.

RAHMAN S.M., HOSSAIN M., BISWAS B.K., JOARDER O.I. & ISLAM R. 1993 Micropropagation of *Caesalpinia pulcherrima* through nodal bud culture of mature tree. Plant Cell Tiss. Organ Cult., **32**, 363–365.

RAI P. P. & SHOK M. 1982 Anthracene derivatives in tissue cultures of *Cassia* species indigenous to Nigeria. pp. 277–278 in Fujiwara (ed.) 1982 (*q.v.*).

RAIKJEL N.V., PALEVITZ B.A. & HAIGLER C.H. 1986 Abscisic acid control of lectin accumulation in wheat seedlings and callus cultures. Plant Physiol., **80**, 167–171.

RAINS D.W., VALENTINE R.C. & HOLLAENDER A. (eds.) 1980 *Genetic Engineering of Osmoregulation.* Plenum Press, New York, London.

RAJ BHANSALI R. & ARYA H.C. 1978 Differentiation in explants of *Citrus paradisi* Macf. (grapefruit) grown in culture. Ind. J. Exp. Biol., **16**, 409–411.

RAJ BHANSALI R. & ARYA H.C. 1979 Organogenesis in *Citrus limettioides* (sweet lime) callus culture. Phytomorph., **29**, 97–100.

RAJ BHANSALI R. & RAMAWAT K.G. 1993 Micropropagation of little leaf diseased eggplants infected with mycoplasma–like organisms. J. Hort. Sci., **68**, 25–30.

RAJ BHANSALI R., DRIVER J. & DURZAN D.J. 1991 Somatic embryogenesis in cell suspension cultures of *Prunus persica* (L.). J. Hort. Sci., **66**, 601–605.

RAJ BHANSALI R., DRIVER J.A. & DURZAN D.J. 1990 Rapid multiplication of adventitious somatic embryos in peach and nectarine by secondary embryogenesis. Plant Cell Rep., **9**, 280–284.

RAJ BHANSALI R., RAMAWAT K.G., KUMAR A. & ARYA H.C. 1978 Callus initiation and organogenesis *in vitro* cultures of *Crotalaria burkia.* Phytomorph., **28**, 98–102.

RAJASEKARAN K. & MULLINS M.G. 1981 Organogenesis in internode explants of grapevine. Vitis, **20**, 218–227.

RAJEEVAN M.S. & PANDEY R.M. 1983 Propagation of papaya through tissue culture. Acta Hort., **131**, 131–139.

RAJEEVAN M.S. & PANDEY R.M. 1986 Lateral bud culture of papaya (*Carica papaya* L.) for clonal propagation. Plant Cell Tiss. Organ Cult., **6**, 181–188.

RAJU C.R., PRAKASH KUMAR P., CHANDRAMOHAN M. & IYER R.D. 1984 Coconut plantlets from leaf tissue cultures. J. Plantation Crops, **12**, 75–81.

RAKOCZY–TROJANOWSKA M. & MALEPSZY S. 1989 A method for increased plant regeneration from immature F_1 and BC_1 embryos of *Cucurbita maxima* Duch. × *C. pepo* L. hybrids. Plant Cell Tiss. Organ Cult., **18**, 191–194.

RAMA P. & PONTIKIS C.A. 1990 *In vitro* propagation of olive (*Olea europea sativa* L.) 'Kalamon'. J. Hort. Sci., **65**, 347–353.

RAMACHANDRA S. & KHATAMIAN H. 1989 Micropropagation of *Peperomia* and *Begonia* species using petiole segments. HortScience, **24**, 153.

RAMAN K. 1977 Rapid multiplication of *Streptocarpus* and *Gloxinia* from *in vitro* cultured pedicel segments. Z. Pflanzenphysiol., **83**, 411–418.

RAMAN K. & NARAYANASWAMY S. 1970 Growth in axenic culture of isolated shoot apices of *Eichhornia crassipes.* Physiol. Plant., **23**, 154–158.

RAMAN K., WALDEN D.B. & GREYSON R.I. 1980 Propagation of *Zea mays* L. by shoot tip culture; a feasibility study. Ann. Bot. **45**, 183–189.

RAMANUJA RAO I. V., MEHTA U. & MOHAN RAM H. Y. 1982 Whole plant regeneration from cotyledonary protoplasts of *Crotalaria juncea.* pp. 595–596 in Fujiwara (ed.) 1982 (*q.v.*).

RAMAWAT K.G. & ARYA H.C. 1976 Growth and morphogenesis in callus cultures of *Ephedra gerardiana.* Phytomorph., **26**, 395–403.

RAMAWAT K.G., BHANSALI R.R. & ARYA H.C. 1978 Shoot formation in *Catharanthus roseus* L. Don. callus cultures. Current Sci., **47**, 93–94.

RAMAWAT K.G., RAJ BHANSALI R. & ARYA H.C. 1977 Differentiation in *Crotalaria* callus cultures. Phytomorph., **27**, 303–307.

RAMIREZ–MALAGON R. & OCHOA–ALEJO N. 1991 Adventitious shoot formation and plant regeneration from tissues of tomatillo (*Physalis ixocarpa* Brot.). Plant Cell Tiss. Organ Cult., **25**, 185–188.

RAMJI M.V. 1975 Histology of growth with regard to embryos and apical meristems in some angiosperms. I. Embryogeny of *Stellaria media.* Phytomorph., **25**, 131–145.

RAMJI M.V. 1976 The histology of growth with regard to embryos and meristems in some angiosperms. II. Differentiation of apical meristems in *Stellaria media.* Phytomorph., **26**, 124–135.

RAMMING D.W. 1985 *In ovulo* embryo culture of early–maturing *Prunus.* HortScience, **20**, 419–420.

RAMMING D.W. & EMERSHAD R.L. 1982 *In–ovulo* embryo culture of seeded and seedless *Vitis vinifera* L. HortScience, **17**, 487 (Abst.111).

RANCH J.P. & BUCHEIM J. 1991 Propagating multiple whole fertile plants from immature leguminous plants. U.S. Patent No. 5008200.

RANCH J.P., OGLESBY L. & ZIELINSKI A.C. 1986 Plant regeneration from tissue cultures of soybean by somatic embryogenesis. pp. 97–109 in Vasil I.K. (ed.) 1986 *Cell Culture and Somatic Cell Genetics of Plants* Vol. 3. Academic Press.

RANCH J.P., OGLESBY L.F & ZIELINSKI A.C. 1985 Plant regeneration from embryo–derived tissue cultures of soybean. In Vitro, **21**, 653–658.

RANCILLAC M. 1979 Mise au point d'une méthode de multiplication végétative *in vitro* du Pin maritime (*Pinus pinaster* Sol.) pour la constitution de clones à partir de semences. AFOCEL, **12**, 41–48.

RANCILLAC M. 1981 Perspectives d'application des cultures d'organes *in vitro* à la multiplication végétative du Pine maritime, *Pinus pinaster* Sol. Ann. Sci. Forest., **38**, 55–69.

RANCILLAC M., FAYE M. & DAVID A. 1982 *In vitro* rooting of cloned shoots in *Pinus pinaster.* Physiol. Plant., **56**, 97–101.

RANCILLAC M., KLINGUER A. & KLINGUER S. 1991 Plant biotechnologies applied to a forest tree, the American red oak (*Quercus rubra* L.). Acta Hort., **289**, 341–342.

RANDOLF L.F. & KHAN R. 1960 Growth response of excised mature embryos of *Iris* and wheat to different culture media. Phytomorph., **10**, 43–49.

RANDOLPH L.F. 1945 Embryo culture of *Iris* seed. Am.Iris Soc.Bull., **98**, 33–45.

RANDOLPH L.F. & COX L.G. 1943 The germination of *Iris* seeds and the relation of inhibition substances. Proc. Am. Soc. Hort. Sci., **43**, 284–300.

RANGAN T.S., MURASHIGE T. & BITTERS W. S. 1969 *In vitro* studies of zygotic and nucellar embryogenesis in *Citrus.* p. 225 in Proc. 1st Int. Citrus Symp. Vol. 1. Univ. of California, Riverside.

RANGAN T.S. 1976 Growth and plantlet regeneration in tissue cultures of some Indian millets: *Paspalum scrobiculatum* L., *Eleusine coracana* Gaert. and *Pennisetum typhoideum* Pers. Z. Pflanzenphysiol., **78**, 208–216.

RANGAN T.S. 1984 Pineapple. pp. 373–382 in Ammirato *et al.* (eds.) 1984 (*q.v.*).

RANGAN T.S. & MATHEWS V.H. 1980 Growth and multiple plantlet formation in lateral bud, leaf explant and callus cultures of pineapple (*Ananas comosus* L. Merr.). pp. 301–304 in Sala *et al.* (eds.) 1980 (*q.v.*).

RANGAN T.S. & RANGASWAMY N.S. 1969 Morphogenic investigations on parasitic angiosperms. III. *Cassytha filiformis* (Lauraceae). Phytomorph., **19**, 292–300.

RANGAN T.S. & VASIL I.K. 1983 Somatic embryogenesis and plant regeneration in tissue cultures of *Panicum miliaceum* L. and *Panicum miliare* Lamk. Z. Pflanzenphysiol., **109**, 49–53.

RANGAN T.S., MURASHIGE T. & BITTERS W.P. 1968 *In vitro* initiation of nucellar embryos in monoembryonic *Citrus.* HortScience, **3**, 226–227.

RANGANATHAN B., MASCARENHAS A. F., SAYAGAUER B. M. & JAGANNATHAN V. 1963 Growth of *Papaver somniferum* tissue *in vitro.* pp. 108–110 in Maheshwari & Ranga Swamy (eds.) 1963 (*q.v.*).

RANGASWAMY N.S. & PROMILA 1972 Morphogenesis of the adult embryo of *Azadirachta indica* A. Juss. Z. Pflanzenphysiol., **67**, 377–379.

RANGASWAMY N.S. & SHIVANNA K.R. 1967 Induction of gamete compatibility and seed formation in axenic cultures of a diploid self–incompatible species of *Petunia.* Nature, **216**, 937–939.

RANJIT M., KESTER D.E. & POLITO V.S. 1988b Micropropagation of cherry rootstocks: III. Correlations between anatomical and physiological parameters and root initiation. J. Am. Soc. Hort. Sci., **113**, 155–159.

RAO A.N. 1963 Organogenesis in callus cultures of orchid seeds. pp. 322–344 in Maheshwari & Ranga Swamy (eds.) 1963 (*q.v.*).

RAO A.N. 1977 Tissue culture in the orchid industry. pp. 44–69 in Reinert and Bajaj (eds.) 1977 (*q.v.*).

RAO A.M., KAVI KISHOR P.B., REDDY L.A. & VAIDYANATH K. 1988 Callus induction and high frequency plant regeneration in Italian millet (*Setaria italica*). Plant Cell Rep., **7**, 557–559.

RAO A.N. 1969 Tissue culture from bulbil of *Dioscorea sansibarensis.* Can. J. Bot., **47**, 565–566.

RAO A.N. (ed.) 1982 *Tissue Culture of Economically Important Plants.* Proc. of the Int. Symp. Singapore 1981. COSTED and ANBS.

RAO A.N., YEOW M.S., KOTHAGODA N. & HUTCHINSON J.F. 1982 Cotyledon tissue culture of some tropical fruit. pp. 124–137 in Rao A.N. (ed.) 1982 (*q.v.*).

RAO I.V.R., NARANG V. & RAO I.U. 1986 Origin and development of embryogenic callus and somatic embryos in the bamboo *Dendrocalmus strictus.* p. 134 in Somers *et al.* (eds.) 1986 (*q.v.*).

STABA E.J. & NYGAARD B.G. 1983 *In vitro* culture of guayule. Z. Pflanzenphysiol., **109**, 371–378.

STABA E.J., NYGAARD B.G. & ZITO S.W. 1984 Light effects on pyrethrum shoot cultures. Plant Cell Tiss. Organ Cult., **3**, 211–214.

STAFFORD A. & DAVIES D.R. 1979 The culture of immature pea embryos. Ann. Bot., **44**, 315–321.

STAMP J.A. 1987 Somatic embryogenesis in cassava: the anatomy and morphology of the regeneration process. Ann. Bot., **59**, 451–459.

STAMP J.A. & HENSHAW G.G. 1987 Somatic embryogenesis from clonal leaf tissues of cassava. Ann. Bot., **59**, 445–450.

STAMP J.A. & MEREDITH C.P. 1988b Somatic embryogenesis from leaves and anthers of grapevine. Scientia Hort., **35**, 235–250.

STAMP J.A., COLBY S.M. & MEREDITH C.P. 1990a Improved shoot organogenesis from leaves of grape. J. Am. Soc. Hort. Sci., **115**, 1038–1042.

STAMP J.A., COLBY S.M. & MEREDITH C.P. 1990b Direct shoot organogenesis and plant regeneration from leaves of grape (*Vitis* spp.). Plant Cell Tiss. Organ Cult., **22**, 127–133.

STANDAERT-DE METSENAERE R.E.A. 1991 Economic considerations. pp. 123–140 in Debergh and Zimmerman (eds.) 1991 (*q.v.*)

STANDARDI A. 1981 Micropropagazione dell'*Actinidia chinensis* Pl. mediante coltura *in vitro* di apici meristematici. Frutticoltura, **43.**, 23–27.

STANDARDI A. 1983 La micropropagazione nelle moltiplicazione dell'actinidia. Frutticoltura, **45**, 17–22.

STANDARDI A. & ROMANI F. 1990 Effects of some antioxidants on *in vitro* rooting of apple shoots. HortScience, **25**, 1435–1436.

STANIS V.A. 1983 Effects of growth regulators on organogenesis in perennial ryegrass tissue culture. Soviet Plant Physiol., **30**, 325–329.

STAPFER R.E. & HEUSER C.W. 1986 Rapid multiplication of *Heuchera sanguinea* Engeln. Rosamundi propagated *in vitro*. HortScience, **21**, 1043–1044.

STAPFER R.E., HEUSER C.W. & DENEKE C.F. 1985 Rapid multiplication of *Veronica* 'Red Fox' propagated *in vitro*. HortScience, **20**, 866–867.

STARITSKY G. 1970 Embryoid formation in callus tissues of coffee. Acta Bot. Neerl., **19**, 509–514.

STARLING R.J. 1985 *In vitro* propagation of *Leuchtenbergia principis*. Cactus & Succulent J., **57**, 114–115.

STARRANTINO A. & CARUSO A. 1988b *In vitro* culture for *Citrus* micropropagation. Acta Hort., **227**, 444–446.

STARRANTINO A. & RUSSO F. 1980 Seedlings from undeveloped ovules of ripe fruits of polyembryonic citrus cultivars. HortScience, **15**, 296–297.

STAVAREK S.J., CROUGHAN T.P. & RAINS D.W. 1980 Regeneration of plants from long–term cultures of alfalfa cells. Plant Sci. Lett., **19**, 253–261.

STEINITZ B., COHEN A., GOLDBERG Z. & KOCHBA M. 1991 Precocious gladiolus corm formation in liquid shake cultures. Plant Cell Tiss. Organ Cult., **26**, 63–70.

STEPHENS L.C., KRELL S.L. & WEIGLE J.L. 1985 *In vitro* propagation of Java, New Guinea, and Java × New Guinea *Impatiens*. HortScience, **20**, 362–363.

STEVENSON J.H., HARRIS R.E. & MONETTE P.L. 1982 A comparison of liquid and semi–solid culture media for the *in vitro* proliferation of *Nicotiana tabacum* cv. Xanthi–nc. Plant Propagator, **28**, 12–14.

STEWARD F. C., SHANTZ E. M., MAPES M. O., KENT A. E. & HOLSTEN R. D. 1964 The growth–promoting substances from the environment of the embryo. 1. The criteria and measurement of growth–promoting activity and the responses induced. pp. 45–58 in Regulateurs naturels de la Croissance végétale. Actes du Coll. Int. C.N.R.S. No.123.

STEWARD F.C. & MAPES M.O. 1971a Morphogenesis in aseptic cell cultures of *Cymbidium*. Bot. Gaz., **132**, 65–70.

STEWARD F.C. & MAPES M.O. 1971b Morphogenesis and plant propagation in aseptic cultures of asparagus. Bot. Gaz., **132**, 70–79.

STEWARD F.C., MAPES M.O. & SMITH J. 1958 Growth and organised development of cultured cells. I. Growth and division of freely suspended cells. Am. J. Bot., **45**, 693–703.

STEWARD J. McD. 1981 *In vitro* fertilization and embryo rescue. Env. Exp. Bot., **21**, 301–315.

STEWARD J.McD. & HSU C.L. 1977 In ovulo embryo culture and seedling development of cotton (*Gossypium hirsutum* L.). Planta, **137**, 113–117.

STEWART J. & BUTTON J. 1975 Tissue culture studies in *Paphiopedilum*. Am. Orchid Soc. Bull., **44**, 591–599.

STEWART J. & MITCHELL R. 1991 Test tube orchids. The Garden, **116**, (1) 32–36.

STEWART J. M. & HSU C. L. 1979 *In ovulo* embryo culture as a means to interspecific *Gossypium*. p. 860 in Sharp *et al.* (eds.) 1979 (*q.v.*)

STEWART J.M. & HSU C.L. 1977 *In ovulo* embryo culture and seedling development of cotton (*Gossypium hirsutum* L.). Planta, **137**, 113–117.

STEWART J.M., NIGAM S.N., RAJU M.V.S. & McCONNELL W.B. 1978 Effect of sodium selenate silenomethyl selenocysteine and methylcysteine on organogenesis in detached leaves of *Echeveria elegans*. Can. J. Bot., **56**, 343–347.

STICHEL E. 1959 Gleichzeeitige Induktion von Sprossen und Wurzein an *in vitro* kultivierten Gewebestucken von *Cyclamen persicum*. Planta, **53**, 293–317.

STICKLEN M.B., DOMIR S.C. & LINEBERGER R.D. 1986 Shoot regeneration from protoplasts of *Ulmus* × 'Pioneer'. Plant Science, **47**, 29–34.

STIFF C.M., BOE A.A., ROBERTS L.W. & STIFF C.T. 1985 *In vitro* culture of mugo pine needle fascicles. HortScience, **20**, 447–448.

STILES W. 1950 *An Introduction to the Principles of Plant Physiology.* Second edition, Methuen & Co. Ltd. London.

STILL D.W., HUBSTENBERGER J.F., PHILLIPS G.C. & HOOKS R.F. 1985 Clonal propagation of *Chilopsis linearis* (Cav.) through tissue culture. pp. 354–355 in Henke *et al.* (eds.) 1985 (*q.v.*).

STILL P.E., CAMPBELL R.J. & NIBLETT C.L. 1986 Shoot regeneration from callus in the genus *Arachis*. p. 39 in Somers *et al.* (eds.) 1986 (*q.v.*).

STILL P.E., PLATA M.I. & NIBLETT C.L. 1985 Highly morphogenic callus of *Arachis paraguariensis* from agar and suspension cultures. p. 356 in Henke *et al.* (eds.) 1985 (*q.v.*).

STIMART D.P. & ASCHER P.D. 1974 Culture medium suitable for growing small excised lily embryos. Lily Yearbook, N. Am. Lily Soc., **27**, 77–84.

STIMART D.P. & ASCHER P.D. 1978b Propagation and stability of diploid *Freesia hybrida* cv. 'Royal' in tissue culture. HortScience, **13**, 382–383.

STIMART D.P. & ASCHER P.D. 1978c Tissue culture of bulb scale sections for asexual propagation of *Lilium longiflorum* Thunb. J. Am. Soc. Hort. Sci., **103**, 182–184.

STIMART D.P. & ASCHER P.D. 1981c *In vitro* germination of *Paphiopedilum* seed on a completely defined medium. Scientia Hort., **14**, 165–170.

STIMART D.P. & HARBAGE J.F. 1989 Shoot proliferation and rooting *in vitro* of *Liatris spicata*. HortScience, **24**, 835–836.

STIMART D.P., ASCHER P.D. & WILKINS H.F. 1982 Overcoming dormancy in *Lilium longiflorum* bulblets produced in tissue culture. J. Am. Soc. Hort. Sci., **107**, 1004–1007.

STOKES M.J. 1981 Current aspects of commercial micropropagation. Comb. Proc. Int. Plant Prop. Soc. 1980, **30**, 255–267.

STOLARZ A. & LORZ H. 1988 Protoplast culture and transformation studies of triticale (× *Triticosecale* Wittmack). Plant Cell Tiss. Organ Cult., **12**, 227–230.

STOLTZ L.P. 1979a *In vitro* propagation of *Acalphya wilkesiana* (Copperleaf). HortScience, **14**, 702–703.

STOLTZ L.P. 1979c Iron nutrition of *Cattleya* orchid grown *in vitro*. J. Am. Soc. Hort. Sci., **104**, 30–310.

STOLTZ L.P. 1984 *In vitro* propagation and growth of *Hydrangea*. HortScience, **19**, 717–719.

STONE E.C. & DUFFIELD J.W. 1950 Hybrids of sugar pine embryo culture. J. Forest, **48**, 200–201.

STOUTAMIRE W. 1974 Terrestrial orchid seedlings. pp. 101–128 in Withner C. L. (ed.) 1974 (*q.v.*).

STOUTAMIRE W.P. 1964 Seeds and seedlings of native orchids. Michigan Botan., **3**, 107–119.

STRAATHOF T.P. & GOLDY R.G. 1987 *In vitro* germination and establishment of some strawberry species. HortScience, **22**, 119–121.

STRAHLHEIM E. & CAILLOUX M. 1981 La propagation des pommiers Ottawa–3 et Malling 9 par la culture de tissus. Colloques Scientifiques No. 15, 511–530.

STRAIN J.R. 1980 Analyzing costs in tissue culture laboratories., Staff paper 167, Food and Resources Economics Dept., Inst. Food & Agric. Sci., Univ. of Florida, Gainesville, Florida.

STRANDBERG J.O. 1993 Meristem culture of *Ophiopogon japonicus* and production of embryo–like structures. Plant Cell Tiss. Organ Cult., **32**, 277–282.

STRAUSS A. & POTRYKUS I. 1980 Callus formation from protoplasts of cell suspension cultures of *Rosa* Paul Scarlet. Physiol. Plant., **48**, 15–20.

STRAUSS M.S. & ARDITTI J. 1980 Plantlet regeneration from shoot tip cultures of *Xanthosoma caracu*. Ann. Bot., **45**, 209–212.

STREET H.E. (ed.) 1977a Plant Tissue and Cell Culture.Bot. Monographs Vol.II Blackwell Scientific Publications.

STRICKLAND S.G., McCALL C.M. NICHOL J.W. & STUART D.A. 1986 Enhanced somatic embryogenesis in *Medicago sativa* and its higher homologs to the culture medium. p. 188 (Abst. 206) in Somers *et al.* (eds.) 1986 (*q.v.*).

STRINGHAM G.R. 1979 Regeneration in leaf callus cultures of haploid rapeseed (*Brassica napus* L.) Z. Pflanzenphysiol., **92**, 459–462.

STROBEL G.A., NACHMIAS A. & HESS W.M. 1988 Improvements in the growth and yield of olive trees by transformation with the Ri plasmid of *Agrobacterium rhizogenes*. Can. J. Bot., **66**, 2581–2585.

STRODE R.E., TRAVERS P.A. & OGLESBY R.P. 1979 Commercial micropropagation of rhododendrons. Comb. Proc. Int. Plant Prop. Soc., **29**, 439–442.

STUART D.A. 1987 Enhancing plant somatic embryogenesis using a plant cell cultured medium containing a selected amino acid. World Patent Applic. No. 8702701.

STUART D.A. & STRICKLAND S.G. 1984a Somatic embryogenesis from cell cultures of *Medicago sativa* L. I. The role of amino acid additions to the regeneration medium. Plant Sci. Lett., **34**, 165–174.

STUART D.A. & STRICKLAND S.G. 1984b Somatic embryogenesis from cell cultures of *Medicago sativa* L. II. The interaction of amino acids with ammonium. Plant Sci. Lett., **34**, 175–181.

STUART D.A. & STRICKLAND S.G. 1987 Methods and media for enhanced somatic embryogenesis. Int. Patent Application No. WO 87/02701.

STUART D.A., McCALL C.M. & SLADE D. 1990 Improved somatic embryogenesis – using induction medium containing synthetic auxin analogues. World Patent Applic. No. 9001058.

STUART D.A., NELSEN J. & NICHOL J.W. 1988 Expression of 7 S and 11 S alfalfa seed storage proteins in somatic embryos. J. Plant Physiol., **132**, 134–139.

STUART D.A., STRICKLAND S.G. & NICHOL J.W. 1986 Enhanced somatic embryogenesis using maltose. U.S. Patent No. 4801545.

STYER D.J. 1985 Bioreactor technology for plant propagation., pp. 117–130 in Henke *et al.* (eds.) 1985 (*q.v.*).

STYER D.J. & CHIN C.K. 1983 Meristem and shoot tip culture for propagation, pathogen elimination and germplasm preservation. Hort. Rev., **5**, 221–277.

SUBBAIAH M.M. & MINOCHA S.C. 1990 Shoot regeneration from stem and leaf callus of *Eucalyptus tereticornis*. Plant Cell Rep., **9**, 370–373.

SUBHASH K., REUBEN C., PROLARAM B. & RAJAM M.V. 1986 *In vitro* regeneration of pepper plants from embryo, cotyledon and hypocotyl cultures from normal and mutagen treated seeds. p. 31 in Somers *et al.* (eds.) 1986 (*q.v.*).

SUBHASHINI U., VENKATESWARLU T. & ANJANI K. 1986 Embryo rescue in Nicotiana hybrids by *in vitro* culture. Plant Science, **43**, 219–222.

SUBRAMANIAN V. & SUBBA RAO P.V. 1980 *In vitro* culture of the allergenic weed *Parthenium hysterophorus* L. Plant Sci. Lett., **17**, 269–277.

SUBRAMANYA R. & SCHWANDES L.P. 1984 *In vitro* propagation of escarole from leaf explants. HortScience, **19**, 234–235.

SUDARSHANA M.S. & SHANTHAMMA C. 1991 *In vitro* regeneration from excised leaves of *Flaveria trinervia* (Sprengel.) C. Mohr. Plant Cell Tiss. Organ Cult., **27**, 297–302.

SUDARSONO & GOLDY R. G. 1988 Effect of some growth regulators on *in vitro* culture of three *Vitis rotundifolia* cultivars. HortScience, **23**, 757.

SUDASRIP H., KAAT H. & DAVIS A. 1978 Clonal propagation of the coconut via the bulbils. Philipp. J. Coconut Studies, **3**, 5–14.

SULAIMAN I.M. & BABU C.R. 1993 *In vitro* regeneration through organogenesis of *Meconopsis simplicifolia* — an endangered ornamental species. Plant Cell Tiss. Organ Cult., **34**, 295–298.

SULAIMAN I.M., RANGASWAMY N.S. & BABU C.R. 1991 Formation of plantlets through somatic embryogeny in the Himalayan blue poppy, *Meconopsis simplicifolia* (Papaveraceae). Plant Cell Rep., **9**, 582–585.

SULKLYAN D.S. & MEHRA P.N. 1977 *In vitro* morphogenetic studies in *Nephrolepis cordifolia*. Phytomorph., **27**, 396–407.

SULTANBAWA F. & PHATAK S.C. 1991 Propagation of sterile ornamental pepper by cuttings and *in vitro* shoot–tip culture. HortScience, **26**, 1078.

SUN C.S. & CHU C.C. 1986 Somatic embryogenesis and plant regeneration from immature inflorescence segments of *Coix lacryma–jobi*. Plant Cell Tiss. Organ Cult., **5**, 175–178.

SUN C.S., PRIOLI L.M. & SONDAHL M.R. 1989 Regeneration of haploid and dihaploid plants from protoplasts of supersweet (sh2sh2) corn. Plant Cell Rep., **8**, 313–316.

SUNDBERG E. & GLIMELIUS K. 1986 A method for production of interspecific hybrids within *Brassica via* somatic hybridization, using resynthesis of *Brassica napus* as a model. Plant Science, **43**, 155–162.

SUPRASANNA P., RAO K.V. & REDDY G.M. 1991 Somatic embryogenesis and plant regeneration in maize. Acta Hort., **289**, 265–266.

SURESH KUMAR A., REDDY T.P. & REDDY G.M. 1983 Plantlet regeneration from different callus cultures of Pigeonpea (*Cajanus cajan* L.). Plant Sci. Lett., **32**, 271–278.

SUTTER E. 1982 Problems posed by microplant morphology. Comb. Proc. Int. Plant Prop. Soc. 1981, **31**, 563–566.

SUTTER E. & LANGHANS R. W. 1978b Micropropagation of *Anemone coronaria* L. pp. 249–250 in Hughes *et al.* (eds.) 1978 (*q.v.*).

SUTTER E. & LANGHANS R.W. 1982 Formation of epicuticular wax and its effect on water loss in cabbage plants regenerated from shoot–tip culture. Can. J. Bot., **60**, 2896–2902.

SUTTER E.G. & BARKER P.B. 1985 *In vitro* propagation of mature *Liquidambar styraciflua*. Plant Cell Tiss. Organ Cult., **5**, 13–21.

SUTTER E.G., FABBRI A. & DUNSTON S. 1985 Morphological adaptation of leaves of strawberry plants grown *in vitro* after removal from culture. p. 358–359 in Henke *et al.* (eds.) 1985 (*q.v.*).

SUTTER E.G., SHACKEL K. & DIAZ J.C. 1992 Acclimatization of tissue cultured plants. Acta Hort., **314**, 115–119.

SUTTON J. 1978 The production of virus free gladioli using meristem culture. XXth Int. Hort. Cong. (Abst. 1888).,

SWANSON E.B. & TOMES D.T. 1983 Evaluation of birdsfoot trefoil regenerated plants and their progeny after *in vitro* selection for 2,4–D. Plant Sci. Lett., **29**, 19–24.

SWARTZ H.J. & LINDSTROM J.T. 1986 Small fruit and grape tissue culture from 1980 to 1985: commercialization of the technique., pp. 201–220 in Zimmerman *et al.* (eds.) 1986 (*q.v.*).

SWARTZ H.J., BORS R., MOHAMED F. & NAESS S.K. 1990 The effect of *in vitro* pretreatments on subsequent shoot organogenesis from excised *Robus* and *Malus* leaves. Plant Cell Tiss. Organ Cult., **21**, 179–184.

SWARTZ H.J., GALLETA G.J. & ZIMMERMAN R.H. 1983 Field performance and phenotypic stability of tissue culture–propagated thornless blackberries. J. Am. Soc. Hort. Sci., **108**, 285–290.

SWARTZ H.J., GALLETTA G.J. & ZIMMERMAN R.H. 1981a Phenotypic stability and field performance of tissue culture propagated thornless blackberry. HortScience, **16**, 418 (Abst. 137).

SWARTZ H.J., GALLETT G.J. & ZIMMERMAN R.H. 1981b Field performance and phenotypic stability of tissue culture–propagated strawberries. J. Am. Soc. Hort. Sci., **106**, 667–673.

SY M.O., MARTINEUI L. & SCIENZA A. 1991 *In vitro* organogenesis and regeneration in cashew (*Anacardium occidentale* L.). Acta Hort., **289**, 267–268.

SZABADOS L. & ROCA W.M. 1986 Regeneration of isolated mesophyll and cell suspension protoplasts to plants in *Stylosanthes guianensis*. A tropical forage legume. Plant Cell Rep., **5**, 174–177.

TABACHNIK L. & KESTER D.E. 1977 Shoot culture for almond and almond–peach clones *in vitro*. HortScience, **12**, 545–547.

TABAEIZADEH Z., PERENNES C. & BERGOUNIOUX C. 1985 Increasing the variability of *Lycopersicon peruvianum* Mill. by protoplast fusion with *Petunia hybrida* L. Plant Cell Rep., **4**, 7–11.

TABAEIZADEH Z., PLOURDE A. & COMEAU A. 1990 Somatic embryogenesis and plant regeneration in *Triticum aestivum* × *Leymus angustus* F$_1$ hybrids and the parental line. Plant Cell Rep., **9**, 204–206.

TAEB A.G. & ALDERSON P.G. 1990a Effect of photoperiod and quality of light on bulbing of tulip shoots regenerated *in vitro*. J. Hort. Sci., **65**, 71–74.

TAEB A.G. & ALDERSON P.G. 1990b Effect of low temperature and sucrose on bulb development and on the carbohydrate status of bulbing shoots of tulip *in vitro*. J. Hort. Sci., **65**, 193–197.

TAEB A.G. & ALDERSON P.G. 1990c Shoot production and bulbing of tulip *in vitro* related to ethylene. J. Hort. Sci., **65**, 198–204.

TAGUCHI T. & KAMEYA T. 1986 Production of somatic hybrid plants between cabbage and Chinese cabbage through protoplast fusion. Jap. J. Breed., **36**, 185–189.

TAHA R.M. & FRANCIS D. 1990 The relationship between polyploidy and organo-genetic potential in embryo– and root–derived tissue cultures of Vicia faba L. Plant Cell Tiss. Organ Cult., **22**, 229–236.

TAHARDI S. 1987 Organogenesis in hybrid coconut embryo culture. Acta Hort., **212**, 567–569.

TAIARIOL V., OAKLEY R. & VENTURA P. 1991 Method for *in vitro* reproduction and growth of cells in culture medium. U.S. Patent 5017490.

TAJI A. & WILLIAMS R.R. 1987 Application of *in–vitro* pollination and embryo culture to Australian native plants. Comb. Proc. Int. Plant Prop. Soc. 1986, **36**, 195–198.

TAJI A.M. & WILLIAMS R.R. 1989 *In vitro* propagation of *Clianthus formosus* (Sturt's desert pea), an Australian native legume. Plant Cell Tiss. Organ Cult., **16**, 61–66.

TAKAHASHI A., SAKURAGI Y., KAMADA H. & ISHIZUKA K. 1984 Plant regeneration through somatic embryogenesis in Barnyardgrass, *Echinochloa oryzicola* Vasing. Plant Sci. Lett., **36**, 161–163.

TAKAHASHI S., MATSUBARA K., YAMAGATA H. & MORIMOTO T. 1992 Micropropagation of virus–free bulblets of *Lilium longiflorum* by tank culture. 1. Development of liquid culture method and large scale propagation. Acta Hort., **319**, 83–88.

TAKAHATA Y., BROWN D.C.W., KELLER W.A. & KAIZUMA N. 1993 Dry artificial seeds and desiccation tolerance induction in microspore–derived embryos of broccoli. Plant Cell Tiss. Organ Cult., **35**, 121–129.

TAKAHATA Y., WAKUI K., KAIZUMA N. & BROWN D.C.W. 1992 A dry artificial seed system for *Brassica* crops. Acta Hort., **319**, 317–322.

TAKAYAMA S. 1990 Begonia. pp. 253–283 in Ammirato *et al.* (eds.) 1990 (*q.v.*).

TAKAYAMA S. & AKITA M. 1988 Tubers production by plant culture in liquid medium – starting with plant almost submerged and reducing proportion submerged as plant grows. European Patent No. 293488; World Patent Applic. No. 8804136.

TAKAYAMA S. & AKITA M. 1991 Method for propagation of potatoes. U.S. Patent No. 5034327.

TAKAYAMA S. & MISAWA M. 1982a Regulation of organ formation by cytokinin and auxin in *Lilium* bulb scales grown *in vitro*. Plant & Cell Physiol., **23**, 67–74.

TAKAYAMA S. & MISAWA M. 1983a The mass propagation of *Lilium in vitro* by stimulation of multiple adventitious bulb–scale formation and by shake culture. Can. J. Bot., **61**, 224–228.

TAKAYAMA S., SWEDLUND B. & MIWA Y. 1991 Automated propagation of microbulbs of lilies. pp. 111–131 in Vasil I.K. (ed.) 1990 (*q.v.*).

TAKENO K., TAYLOR J.S., SRISKANDARAJAH S., PHARIS R.P. & MULLINS M.G. 1983 Endogenous gibberellin– and cytokinin–like substances in cultured shoot tissue of apple *Malus pumila* cv. Jonathan, in relation to adventitious root formation. Plant Growth Reg., **1**, 261–268.

TAL E., BEN–JAACOV J. & WATAD A.A. 1992c Hardening and *in vivo* establishment of micropropagated *Grevillea* and *Leucospermum*. Acta Hort., **316**, 63–67.

TAL E., SOLOMON H., BEN–JAACOV J. & WATAD A.A. 1992b Micropropagation of selected *Leucospermum cordifolium*: effect of antibiotics and GA₃. Acta Hort., **316**, 55–58.

TAL E., STEIN–SNEIDER R., WATAD A.A. & BEN–JAACOV J. 1992a Rooting and weaning of micropropagated *Leucospermum cordifolium*. Acta Hort., **314**, 155–163.

TAL M. & WATTS J.W. 1979 Plant growth conditions and yield of viable protoplasts isolated from leaves of *Lycopersicon esculentum* and *L. peruvianum*. Z. Pflanzenphysiol., **92**, 207–214.

TAL M., DEHAN K. & HEIKIN H. 1977 Morphogenetic potential of cultured leaf sections of cultivated and wild species of tomato. Ann. Bot., **41**, 937–942.

TALIAFERRO C.M., DABO S.M., MITCHELL E.D., JOHNSON B.B. & METZINGER R.D. 1989 Morphologic, cytogenetic and enzymatic variation in tissue culture regenerated plants of apomictic old–world bluestem grasses (*Bothriochloa* sp.). Plant Cell Tiss. Organ Cult., **19**, 257–266.

TAMURA M., TAO R. & SUGIURA A. 1992 Highly stable regeneration from long–term cultures of Japanese Persimmon callus. HortScience, **27**, 1048.

TAMURA Y., NAKAMURA S., FUKUI H. & TABATA M. 1984 Clonal propagation of *Stevia rebaudiana* Bertoni by stem tip culture. Plant Cell Rep., **3**, 183–185.

TANAKA K., FUJIWARA K. & KOZAI T. 1992 Effects of relative humidity in the culture vessel on the transpiration and net photosynthetic rates of potato plantlets *in vitro*. Acta Hort., **319** , 59–64.

TANAKA M. & SAKANISHI Y. 1977 Clonal propagation of *Phalaenopsis* by leaf tissue culture. Am. Orchid Soc. Bull., **46**, 733–737.

TANAKA M. & SAKANISHI Y. 1980 Clonal propagation of *Phalaenopsis* through tissue culture. pp. 215–221 in Proc. 9th World Orchid Conf.

TANAKA M. & SAKANISHI Y. 1985 Regenerative capacity of *in vitro* cultured leaf segments excised from mature *Phalaenopsis* plants. Bull. Univ. Osaka Pref. Ser. B, **37**, 1–4.

TANAKA M., SENDA Y. & HASEGAWA A. 1976 Plantlet formation by root–tip culture in *Phalaenopsis*. Am. Orchid Soc. Bull., **45**, 1022–1024.

TANAKA N., HAYAKAWA M., MANO Y., OHKAWA H. & MATSUI C. 1985 Infection of turnip and radish storage roots with *Agrobacterium rhizogenes*. Plant Cell Rep., **4**, 74–77.

TANDON P. & RATHORE T.S. 1992 Regeneration of plantlets from hypocotyl–derived callus of *Coptis teeta*. Plant Cell Tiss. Organ Cult., **28**, 115–117.

TANG A.F., CAPPADOCIA M. & BYRNE D. 1983 *In vitro* flowering in cassava (*Manihot esculenta* Crantz). Plant Cell Tiss. Organ Cult., **2**, 199–206.

TANIMOTO S. 1988 Increasing production of seedlings by tissue culture – by introducing calmodulin, calcium or both into the cells, stimulating differentiation to buds, etc. European Patent Applic. No. 281374.

TANIMOTO S. & HARADA H. 1981b Chemical factors controlling floral bud formation of *Torenia* stem segments cultured *in vitro*. II. Effects of growth regulators. Plant Cell Physiol., **22**, 543–550.

TANIMOTO S. & HARADA H. 1982a Physiological and hormonal factors influencing organogenesis in *Rudbeckia bicolor* explants cultured *in vitro*. Plant Cell Physiol., **23**, 107—113.

TANIMOTO S. & HARADA H. 1984 Stimulation of adventitious bud initiation by cyclic AMP and traumatic acid in *Torenia* stem segments. Biol. Plant., **26**, 337–341.

TANIMOTO S., HIRATA Y., TAKAHASHI S. & ONO R. 1989 Method for propagating nursery plant – use of single culture medium and single culture tank for regeneration rooting and acclimatisation. European Patent Applic. No. 344992.

TANIMOTO S., SATOH S., FUJII T. & HARADA H. 1984 Inhibition of cytokinin–induced adventitious bud initiation in *Torenia fournieri* stem segments by inhibitors of serine proteases. Plant Cell Physiol., **25**, 1161–1168.

TANZARELLA O.A. & GRECO B. 1985 Clonal propagation of *Triticum durum* Desf. from immature embryos and shoot base explants. Euphytica, **34**, 273–277.

TAO R. & SUGIURA A. 1992 Adventitious bud promotion from callus cultures of Japanese persimmon. HortScience, **27**, 259–261.

TAO R., YONEMORI K. & SUGIURA A. 1991 High frequency plant regeneration from callus cultures derived from primordial leaves of adult Japanese persimmon and protoplast isolation from those callus lines. Acta Hort., **300**, 251–254.

TATICEK R.A., MOO–YOUNG M. & LEGGE R.L. 1991 The scale–up of plant cell culture: Engineering considerations. Plant Cell Tiss. Organ Cult., **24**, 139–158.

TAUTORUS T.E., ATTREE S.M., FOWKE L.C. & DUNSTAN D.I. 1990 Somatic embryogenesis from immature and mature zygotic embryos, and embryo regeneration from protoplasts of black spruce (*Picea mariana* Mill.). Plant Science, **67**, 115–124.

TAVAZZA R. & ANCORA G. 1986 Plant regeneration from mesophyll protoplasts in commercial potato cultivars (Primura, Kennebec, Spunta, Desiree). Plant Cell Rep., **5**, 243–246.

TAVAZZA R., ORDAS R.J. & ANCORA G. 1988 Procedure for the regeneration of plants from cell suspension protoplasts of tetraploid potato (*Solanum tuberosum* L.) cv. Desiree. Plant Science, **58**, 223–230.

TAVAZZA R., TAVAZZA M., ORDAS R.J., ANCORA G. & BENVENUTO E. 1988 Genetic transformation of potato (*Solanum tuberosum*): an efficient method to obtain transgenic plants. Plant Science, **59**, 175–181.

TAWFIK A.A., READ P.E. & CUPPET S.L. 1992 Effect of some nutritional factors on monoterpene synthesis in *Rosemarinus officinalis* cultured *in vitro*. Acta Hort., **319**, 189–194.

TAWFIK A.A.–A., SALAC S.S. & READ P.E. 1988 *In vitro* propagation of *Liatris*. HortScience, **23**, 780.

TAYLOR M.E. & KNAUSS J.F. 1978 Tissue culture multiplication and subsequent handling of known pathogen–free *Dieffenbachia maculata* cultivar Perfection. Proc. Fl. State Hort. Soc., **91**, 233–235.

TAYLOR P.W.J. & DUKIC S. 1993 Development of an *in vitro* culture technique for conservation of *Saccharum* spp. hybrid germplasm. Plant Cell Tiss. Organ Cult., **34**, 217–222.

TCHERNETS A.M., SMIRNOV V.A. & ABRAMENKO N.M. 1987 Study on effect of some nutrient medium factors on the development of cherry and sweet cherry rootstocks *in vitro*. Acta Hort., **212**, 595–598.

TEASDALE R.D. 1992 Aqueous medium for plant tissue culture – comprises reduced nitrogen compound, phosphorus compound chelating agent and iron compound. World Patent Applic. No. 9207460.

TEASDALE R.D. & RUGINI E. 1983 Preparation of viable protoplasts from suspension cultured loblolly pine (*Pinus taeda*) cells and subsequent regeneration to callus. Plant Cell Tiss. Organ Cult., **2**, 253–261.

TEJOVATHI G. & ANWAR S.Y. 1986 *In vitro* plantlet regeneration and capitula induction in safflower (*Carthamus tinctorius*)., p. 28 in Somers *et al.* (eds.) 1986 (*q.v.*).

TEMPLETON K.M. & CLINE M.G. 1979 Flowering of shoot apices of *Pharbitis nil* cultured *in vitro*. In Vitro, **15**, 178 (Abst. 51).

TENDILLE C. & LECERF M. 1974 La multipication végétative de l'asperge (*Asparagus officinalis* L.). Action de divers facteurs, en particulier de la nutrition minérale, sur la développement des méristèmes d'asperge, sur la croissance de plantules issues de ces méristèmes et sur la production de plantes adultes. Ann. Amelior. Plantes, **24**, 269–282.

TENG W.–L., LIN C.–P. & LIU Y.–J. 1993 Regenerating lettuce from suspension culture in a 2–liter bioreactor. HortScience, **28**, 669–671.

TENG W.–L., LIU Y.–J. & SOONG T.–S. 1992 Rapid regeneration of lettuce from suspension culture. HortScience, **27**, 1030–1032.

TEO C.K.H. 1978 Clonal propagation of *Haemaria discolor* by tissue culture. Am. Orchid Soc. Bull., **47**, 1028.

TEO C.K.H. 1992 *In vitro* culture of the mangosteen seed. Acta Hort., **292**, 81–85.

TEO C.K.H. & WONG C.H. 1978 Effects of sucrose on the growth of protocorms of *Holttumara* Loke Tuck Yip. Orchid Rev., **86**, 285–289.

TEO C.K.H., KUNISAKI J.T. & SAGAWA Y. 1973 Clonal propagation of strap–leafed *Vanda* by shoot tip culture. Am. Orchid Soc. Bull., **42**, 402–405.

TEPFER S.S., GREYSON R.I., CRAIG W.R. & HINDMAN J.L. 1963 *In vitro* culture of floral buds of *Aquilegia*. Am. J. Bot., **50**, 1035–1045.

TERRY E. & MACINTYRE R. (eds.) 1976 *The International Exchange and Testing of Cassava* Germplasm in Africa. Proc. of Workshop at IITA, Ibadan, Nigeria 1975.

TEWES A., WAPPLER A., PESCHKE E.–M., GARVE R. & NOVER L. 1982 Morphogenesis and embryogenesis in long–term cultures of *Digitalis*. Z. Pflanzenphysiol., **106**, 311–324.

THAKUR S. 1973 *In vitro* foliar shoot bud formation in *Begonia semperflorens*. Current Sci., **42**, 430–432.

THAKUR S. 1975 Differentiation of shoot buds and roots in petiolar segments of *Begonia picta* Smith. Ind. J. Exp. Biol., **13**, 517–520.

THAKUR S., GANAPATHY P.S. & JOHRI B.M. 1976 Differentiation of abnormal plantlets in *Bacopa monnieri*. Phytomorph., **26**, 422–424.

THEILER–HEDTRICH R. & KAGI A.C. 1991 Cloning *in vitro* and somatic embryogenesis in *Foeniculum vulgare* Mill. (Fennel) of 'Zefa Fino' and 'Zefa Tardo'. Acta Hort., **300**, 287–291.

THEILER–HEDTRICH R. & THEILER–HEDTRICH C.M. 1979 The use of tissue culture for the production of ornamental plants: some economical aspects. Acta Hort., **131**, 179–192.

THEILER–HEDTRICH R. & WOLFENSBERGER H. 1987 Comparison of plant and yield characters of *in vitro* and normal propagated strawberry plants. Acta Hort., **212**, 445–448.

THIES K.L. & GRAVES Jr. C.H. 1992 Meristem micropropagation protocols for *Vitis rotundifolia* Michx. HortScience, **27**, 447–449.

THOMAS B.R. & PRATT D. 1981 Efficient hybridisation between *Lycopersicon esculentum* and *L. peruvianum* via embryo callus. Theor. Appl. Genet., **59**, 215–219.

THOMAS E. 1981 Plant regeneration from shoot culture–derived protoplasts of tetraploid potato (*S. tuberosum* cv. Maris Bard). Plant Sci. Lett., **23**, 81–88.

THOMAS E. & STREET H.E. 1970 Organogenesis in cell suspension cultures of *Atropa belladonna* L. and *Atropa belladonna* cultivar *lutea* Doll. Ann. Bot., **34**, 657–669.

THOMAS E., KING P.J. & POTRYKUS I. 1977 Shoot and embryo–like structure formation from cultured tissues of *Sorghum bicolor*. Naturwiss., **64**, 587.

THOMPSON D. G. & GORDON J. C. 1977 Propagation of poplars by shoot apex culture and nutrient film technique. pp. 77–82 in Tappi Forest Biol. & Wood Chem. Conference 1977.

THOMPSON D.G. 1981 Induction of adventitious buds on cultured embryonic shoots of Douglas fir *Pseudotsuga menziesii* (Mirb.) Franco. Env. Exp. Bot., **21**, 433 (Abst.).

THOMPSON M.R., MURAVSKA L., HARRY I.S., LU C.–Y. & THORPE T.A. 1986 Micropropagation of five Canadian conifer species. p. 108 in Somers *et al.* (eds.) 1986 (*q.v.*).

THOMPSON P.A. 1974a Growing orchids from seed. J.Royal Hort.Soc., **99**, 117–122.

THOMPSON P.A. 1975 Germination of seeds of *Oncidium* and *Odontoglossum* species. Orchid Rev., **83**, 375–379.

THOMPSON P.W. & WOOD L. 1990 Anti–lift fermentor. U.S. Patent No. 4943535.

THORNTON M.K. & KNUTSON K.W. 1986 Effect of transplant container volume and growing season length on field performance of micropropagated potatoes. Am. Pot. J., **63**, 399–410.

THORPE T.A. (ed.) 1978a *Frontiers of Plant Tissue Culture*. Int. Assoc. for Plant Tissue Culture. Distrib. by The Bookstore, Univ. of Calgary, Calgary, Alberta T2N 1N4, Canada.

THORPE T.A. (ed.) 1981 *Plant Tissue Culture. Methods and Applications in Agriculture*. Academic Press. New York, London, Toronto, Sydney.

THORPE T.A. & BIONDI S. 1984 Chapter 16 — Conifers. pp. 435–470 in Sharp *et al.* (eds.) 1984 (*q.v.*)

THULASEEDHARAN A. & VALDYANATHAN C.S. 1990 Induction of callus and plant regeneration in *Vicoa indica*. Plant Cell Tiss. Organ Cult., **23**, 45–48.

TIFFIN L.O. & BROWN J.C. 1961 Selective absorption of iron from iron chelates by soybean plants. Plant Physiol., **36**, 710–714.

TIMMIS M., ABO EL–NIL M. & STONECYPHER R.W. 1987 Potential genetic gain through tissue culture. pp. 198–215 in Bonga and Durzan (eds.) 1987a (*q.v.*).

TING K.C. & GIACOMELLI G.A. 1988 A robot for transplanting plugs. Greenhouse Grower, **6**, 58, 60.

TISSERAT B. 1979a Propagation of date palm (*Phoenix dactylifera* L.) *in vitro*. J. Exp. Bot., **30**, 1275–1283.

TISSERAT B. 1982 Factors involved in the production of plantlets from date palm callus cultures. Euphytica, **31**, 201–214.

TISSERAT B. 1984a Chapter 18 — Date palm. pp. 505–545 in Sharp *et al.* (eds.) 1984 (*q.v.*).

TISSERAT B. 1984b Propagation of date palms by shoot tip cultures. HortScience, **19**, 230–231.

TISSERAT B. & DE MASON D.A. 1985 Occurrence and histological structure of off–shoots and inflorescences produced from *Phoenix dactylifera* L. plantlets *in vitro*. Bull. Torrey Bot. Club, **112**, 35–42.

TISSERAT B. & GALLETA P.D. 1988 *In vitro* flowering in *Amaranthus*. HortScience, **23**, 210–212.

TISSERAT B. & GALLETTA P.D. 1987 *In vitro* culture of lemon juice vesicles. Plant Cell Tiss. Organ Cult., **11**, 81–95.

TISSERAT B. & VANDERCOOK C.E. 1985 Development of an automated plant culture system. Plant Cell Tiss. Organ Cult., **5**, 107–117.

TISSERAT B. & VANDERCOOK C.E. 1986 Computerized long-term tissue culture for orchids. Am. Orchid Soc. Bull., **55**, 35–42.

TISSERAT B., FOSTER G. & DE MASON D. 1979b Plantlet production *in vitro* from *Phoenix dactylifera* L. Date Growers' Inst.Rep., **54**, 19–23.

TOMAR U.K. & GUPTA S.C. 1986 Organogenesis and somatic embryogenesis in Leguminous trees (*Albizia* spp.). p. 41 in Somers *et al.* (eds.) 1986 (*q.v.*).

TOMES D.T. 1991 Plants with increased tissue culture and regeneration potential produced using embryo–generating callus culture on defined medium. European Patent Applic. No. 442175.

TOMES D.T., ELLIS B.E., HARNEY P.M., KASHA K.J. & PETERSON R.L. 1982 *Application of Plant Cell and Tissue Culture to Agriculture and Industry.* Plant Cell Culture Centre, University of Guelph, Ontario, Canada.

TONELLI C. 1982 Effects of D–amino acids and amino acids analogs on embryo cultures of proline requiring nutrients in *Zea mays.* pp. 237–238 in Fujiwara (ed.) 1982 (*q.v.*).

TOPFER R. & STEINBISS H–N. 1985 Plant regeneration from cultured fertilised barley ovules. Plant Science, **41**, 49–54.

TORELLO W.A. & SYMINGTON A.G. 1984 Regeneration from perennial rye grass callus tissue. HortScience, **19**, 56–57.

TORELLO W.A., RUFNER R. & SYMINGTON A.G. 1985 The ontogeny of somatic embryos from long–term callus cultures of red fescue. HortScience, **25**, 938–942.

TORELLO W.A., SYMINGTON A.G. & RUFNER R. 1984 Callus initiation, plant regeneration, and evidence of somatic embryogenesis in Red Fescue. Crop Sci., **24**, 1037–1040.

TORIYAMA K., ARIMOTO Y., UCHIMIYA H. & HINATA K. 1988 Transgenic rice plants after direct gene transfer into protoplasts. Bio/Technology, **6**, 1072–1074.

TORNE J.M., CLAPAROLS I. & SANTOS M.A. 1992 Somatic embryogenesis in *Araujia sericifera.* Plant Cell Tiss. Organ Cult., **29**, 269–274.

TORNE J.M., SANTOS M.A. & BLANCO J.L. 1984 Methods of obtaining maize totipotent tissues. II. Atrophic tissue culture. Plant Sci. Lett., **33**, 317–325.

TORNE J.M., SANTOS M.A., PONS A. & BLANCO M. 1980 Regeneration of plants from mesocotyl tissue cultures of immature embryos of *Zea mays* L. Plant Sci. Lett., **17**, 339–344.

TORRES A.C. & GIORDANO L.B. 1986 Morphogenesis in cultures of flower buds of *Brassica oleracea* L. var. Capitata., p. 31 in Somers *et al.* (eds.) 1986 (*q.v.*).

TORRES K.C. & NATARELLA N.J. 1982 Morphological development and the regeneration of bulblets from scale explants of *Lilium longiflorum* 'Harson' grown *in vitro.* HortScience, **17**, 532 (Abst.425).

TORRES K.C. & NATARELLA N.J. 1984 *In vitro* propagation of *Exacum.* HortScience, **19**, 224–225.

TORRES K.C., TORRES J.S., THRO A.M. & KITCHEN L. 1986 Micropropagation and screening of *Stylosanthes biflora* cultures to various levels of glyphosate. p. 74 in Somers *et al.* (eds.) 1986 (*q.v.*).

TORREY J.G. 1954 The role of vitamins and micronutrient elements in the nutrition of the apical meristem of pea roots. Plant Physiol., **29**, 279–287.

TORREY J.G. 1957 Cell division in isolated single plant cells *in vitro.* Proc. Nat. Acad. Sci. Wash., **43**, 887–891.

TORREY J.G. & FOSKET D.E. 1970 Cell division in relation to cytodifferentiation in cultured pea root segments. Am. J. Bot., **57**, 1072–1080.

TORREY J.G. & SHIGEMURA Y. 1957 Growth and controlled morphogenesis in pea root callus tissue grown in liquid media. Am. J. Bot., **44**, 334–344.

TORUAN N.L. & SURYATMANA N. 1976 Tissue culture of *Hevea brasiliensis* Muell Arg. Int.Rubber Res.Dev.Board Symposium, Bogor, Indonesia 1976., (Abst.11).

TOSAKI C., YAMADA K. & KARIYA M. 1989 Cell or plant tissue culture in full culture vessel rotated about horizontal axis, preferably eccentrically, to reduce cell damage. European Patent No. 164888.

TOSCA A., PANDOLFI R. & MACCHI A. 1992 *In vitro* regeneration of *Camellia* hybr. c.v. 'Debbie' from leaf or stem explants. Acta Hort., **314**, 69–76.

TOUSSAINT A.N., KUMMERT J., MAROQUIN C., LEBRUN A. & ROGGEMANS J. 1993 Use of virazole to eradicate Adantoglossum Ringspot Virus from *in vitro* cultures of *Cymbidium* Sw. Plant Cell Tiss. Organ Cult., **32**, 303–309.

TOUSSAINT A.N., LEBRUN A. & ROGGEMANS J. 1992 Cutting and *in vitro* propagation of *Eugenia smithii* Poir. Acta Hort., **314**, 77–83.

TRAN THANH VAN K. 1992 *In vitro* organogenesis and somatic embryogenesis. Acta Hort., **314**, 27–38.

TRAN THANH VAN K.M. 1981 Control of morphogenesis in *in vitro* cultures. Ann. Rev. Plant Physiol., **32**, 291–311.

TRAN THANH VAN M. & DRIRA A. 1970 Definition of a simple experimental system of directed organogenesis *de novo*: organ neoformation from epidermal tissues of *Nautilocalyx lynchei.* pp. 169–176 in *Les Cultures de Tissus de Plantes.* Coll. Int. C.N.R.S. 193.

TRANVAN H. 1979 *In vitro* adventitious bud formation on isolated seedlings of *Pinus silvestris* L. Plantarum, **21**, 230–233.

TRAUTMANN I.A. & VISSER J.H. 1989 Development of a liquid flow–through system to inhibit browning in callus cultures of guayule (*Porthenium argentatum* Gray). Plant Cell Tiss. Organ Cult., **16**, 39–46.

TRAVERS J.N., STARBUCK C.J. & NATARELLA N.J. 1985 Effects of culture medium on *in vitro* rooting of Antonovka 313 apple. HortScience, **20**, 1051–1052.

TREMBLAY L. & TREMBLAY F.M. 1991 Carbohydrate requirements for the development of black spruce (*Picea mariana* Mill.) and red spruce (*P. rubens* Sarg.) somatic embryos. Plant Cell Tiss. Organ Cult., **27**, 95–103.

TRIFIU M., MEZGHANI S. & MARRAKCHI M. 1981 Multiplication végétative de tournesol *Helianthus annuus* L. par culture *in vitro.* Physiol. Veg., **19**, 99–102.

TRIGIANO R.N., BEATY R.M. & DIETRICH J.T. 1989 Somatic embryogenesis and plantlet regeneration in *Cornus florida.* Plant Cell Rep., **8** , 270–273.

TRIGIANO R.N., BEATY R.M. & GRAHAM E.T. 1988 Somatic embryogenesis from immature embryos of redbud (*Cercis canadensis*). Plant Cell Rep., **7**, 148–150.

TRIPATHI B. K. 1971 Etudes sur la nutrition minérale et la néoformation de racines par les tissus de topinambour cultivés *in vitro.*, **193** pp. 201–208 in *Les Cultures de Tissus de Plantes.* Colloq. Int. C.N.R.S., Paris.

TRIPATHI B.K. 1968 Nutrition minérale et néoformation de racines par les tissus de topinambour cultivés *in vitro.* Compt. Rend. Acad. Sci. Paris, **266**, 1123–1126.

TRIPATHI B.K. & BITAILLON C. 1985 *In vitro* plant regeneration of *Hedychium roxburghii* Blume through rhizome–meristem culture. Plant Cell Tiss. Organ Cult., **4**, 11–17.

TRIPATHI B.K. & SAUSSAY R. 1980 Sur la multiplication végétative de l'*Actinidia chinensis* Planchon, 'Chinese gooseberry' par la culture de racines issues de filets staminaux. Compt. Rend. Acad. Sci. Paris, **291D**, 1067–1069.

TROLINDER N.L. & GOODIN J.R. 1988a Somatic embryogenesis in cotton (*Gossypium*). I. Effect of source of explant and hormone regime. Plant Cell Tiss. Organ Cult., **12**, 31–42.

TROLINDER N.L. & XHIXIAN C. 1989 Genotype specificity of the somatic embryogenesis reponse in cotton, Plant Cell Rep., **8**, 133–136.

TROLINDER N.L., BERLIN J.D. & GOODIN J.R. 1987 Differentiation of cotton fibers from single cells in suspension culture. In Vitro, **23**, 789–794.

TRONCOSO A., CANTOS M., LINAN J., PRIETO J. & SARMIENTO R. 1988 The use of *in vitro* culture and tubular container system to propagate selected grapevine plants for sherry wine production. Acta Hort., **227**, 358–362.

TRULSON A.J. & SHAHEEN E.A. 1988a Regeneration of *Cucumis* sp. plants *in vitro* – from protoplast(s) by induction and development culturing in media containing exogenous hormones. World Patent Applic. No. 8802211.

TRULSON A.J. & SHAHEEN E.A. 1988b Regulation on *Cucumis* sp. plants *in vitro* – by culturing explant tissue in an induction medium containing BAP, 2,4–D and optionally NAA. World Patent Applic. No. 8802399.

TRULSON A.J. & SHAHIN E.A. 1986 *In vitro* plant regeneration in the genus *Cucumis.* Plant Science, **47**, 35–43.

TSAI C.H. & KINSELLA J.E. 1981 Initiation and growth of callus and cell suspensions of *Theobroma cacao.* Ann. Bot., **48**, 549–558.

TSANG E.W.T., DAVID H., DAVID A. & DUNSTAN D.I. 1989 Toxicity of antibiotics on zygotic embryos of white spruce (Picea glauca) cultured *in vitro.* Plant Cell Rep., **8**, 214–216.

TSAY H.S., GAU T.G. & CHEN C.C. 1989 Rapid clonal propagation of *Pinellia ternata* by tissue culture. Plant Cell Rep., **8**, 450–454.

TSUCHIYA I. 1954 Possibility of germination of orchid seeds from immature fruits. Orchids Hawaii, **4**, 11–16.

TSUJI K., NAGAOKA M. & ODA M. 1992 Promotion of the growth of carrot plantlets *in vitro* by controlling environmental conditions in culture vessels. Acta Hort., **319**, 297–302.

TSUKAMOTO Y., KANO K. & KATSUURA T. 1963 Instant media for orchid seed germination. Am. Orchid Soc. Bull., **32**, 354–355.

TUKEY H.B. 1938 Growth patterns of plants developed from immature embryos in artificial culture. Bot. Gaz., **99**, 630–665.

TUKEY H.B. & LEE F.A. 1937 Embryo abortion in the peach in relation to chemical composition and season of fruit ripening. Bot. Gaz., **98**, 586–597.

TULECKE W. 1987 Somatic embryogenesis in woody perennials. pp. 61–91 in Bonga and Durzan (eds.) 1987b (*q.v.*).

TULECKE W., McGRANAHAN G. & AHMADI H. 1988 Regeneration by somatic embryogenesis of triploid plants from endosperm of walnut, *Juglans regia* L. cv. Manregian. Plant Cell Rep., **7**, 301–304.

TUMER N.E. 1990 Virus resistant plants. U.S. Patent No. 4970168.

TUR–KASPA Y., HARTMAN R.D., HORNACEK K.J. & BRENDEL K.J. 1990 Automated plant culture proliferation system. U.S. Patent No. 4910146.

TURNER D.A., COX P.N. & PEEL E. 1987 Micropropagation of some wild species of the genus *Lycopersicon*. Acta Hort., **212**, 667–670.

TURNER S.R. & SINGHA S. 1988a Shoot regeneration from pear cotyledons *in vitro*. HortScience, **23**, 755.

TURNER S.R. & SINGHA S. 1988b Influence of celrite on shoot proliferation and vitrification of crabapple and geum. HortScience, **23**, 780.

TUSA N. & GERACI G. 1988 *In vitro* propagation of some *Citrus* rootstocks. Acta Hort., **227**, 464–466.

TUSA N. DE PASQUALE F. & RADOGNA L. 1979 Research on the technology of micrografting citrus species. pp. 229–234 in Anon 1979 (*q.v.*).

TUSA N., GROSSER J.W. & GMITTER F.G. Jr. 1990 Plant regeneration of 'Valencia' sweet orange, 'Femminello' lemon, and the interspecific somatic hybrid following protoplast fusion. J. Am. Soc. Hort. Sci., **115**, 1043–1046.

TUSA N., RADOGNA L., DAVINO M. & LA ROSA R. 1988 Micrografting technology for recovering three virus–affected 'Femminello' lemon clones. Acta Hort., **227**, 104–106.

TUSKAN G.A., SARGENT W.A., RENSEMA T. & WALLA J.A. 1990 Influence of plant growth regulators, basal media and carbohydrate levels in the *in vitro* development of *Pinus panderosa* (Dougl. ex Law.) cotyledon explants. Plant Cell Tiss. Organ Cult., **20**, 47–52.

TYAGI A.K., RASHID A. & MAHESHWARI S.C. 1980 Enhancement of pollen embryo formation in *Datura innoxia* by charcoal. Physiol. Plant., **49**, 296–298.

TYAGI A.K., RASHID A. & MAHESHWARI S.C. 1981 Promotive effect of polyvenylpolypyrrolidone on pollen embryogenesis in *Datura innoxia*. Physiol. Plant., **53**, 405–406.

TYLER R.T., KURZ W.G.W. & PANCHUK B.D. 1986 Photoautotrophic cell suspension cultures of periwinkle (*Catharanthus roseus* (L) G. Don): Transition from heterotrophic to photoautotrophic growth. Plant Cell Rep., **5**, 195–198.

TYMOSZUK J. & HEMPEL M. 1987 The comparison of the quality of *Kalanchoe blossfeldiana* plants obtained by rooting of microcuttings *in vitro* and *in vivo*. pp. 112–118 in Ducaté *et al.* (eds.) 1987 (*q.v.*).

TYMOSZUK J., SANIEWSKI M. & RUDNICKI R.M. 1979 The physiology of hyacinth bulbs. XV. The effect of gibberellic acid and silver nitrate on dormancy release and growth. Scientia Hort., **11**, 95–99.

UDDIN R. & BERRY S.Z. 1988 Investigations on the somatic embryogenesis in tomato. HortScience, **23**, 755.

UDUEBO A.E. 1971 Effect of external supply of growth substances on axillary proliferation and development in *Dioscorea bulbifera*. Ann. Bot., **35**, 159–163.

UEDA H. & TORIKATA H. 1974 Organogenesis in *Cymbidium* meristem cultures. VII. A study of the extract from mycorrhizomes of *C. goeringii*. J. Jap. Soc. Hort. Sci. **43**, 281–285.

UHRING J. 1983 *In vitro* propagation of *Sedum* and *Myrtus* cultivars. HortScience, **18**, 616 (Abst.).

ULRICH J.M., FINCKLE B.J., MACKEY B.E., SCHAEFFER G.W. & SHARPE F. 1984 Responses of six rice callus cultures to deep–frozen temperatures. Crop Sci., **24**, 82–85.

ULRICH J.M., MICKLER R.A., FINKLE B.J. & KARNOSKY D.F. 1984 Survival and regeneration of American elm callus cultures after being frozen in liquid nitrogen. Can. J. For. Res., **14**, 750–753.

UMA M.C. & MOHAN RAM H.Y. 1972 *In vitro* culture of *Vallisneria spiralis*. Phytomorph., **22**, 121–124.

UOSUKAINEN M. 1987 Establishment of cultures without preconditioning. Acta Hort., **212**, 60.

UPADHYAYA A., DAVIS T.D., SANKHLA D. & SANDHLA N. 1992 Micropropagation of *Lupinus texensis* from cotyledonary node explants. HortScience, **27**, 1222–1223.

UPADHYAYA A., SANKHLA N., DAVIS T.D., WEBER D.J. & SMITH B.N. 1985 *In vitro* propagation of a rubber– producing desert shrub. HortScience, **20**, 864–865.

UPADHYAYA S. & CHANDRA N. 1983 Shoot and plantlet formation in organ and callus cultures of *Albizia lebbek* Benth. Ann. Bot., **52**, 421– 424.

UPFOLD S.J., VAN STADEN J. & EDWARDS T.J. 1992 *In vitro* propagation of *Rhodohypoxis baurii*. HortScience, **27**, 1230.

UPHAM S.K. 1981 *In vitro* propagation of *Pinus strobus* (L.). Env. Exp. Bot., **21**, 433 (Abst.).

URALETS L.I. 1980 *In vitro* culture of tomato ovaries. Fiziol. Biokhim Kult. Rast., **12**, 523–528.

URATA U. & IWANAGA E.T. 1965 The use of Ito–type vials for vegetative propagation of *Phalaenopsis*. Am. Orchid Soc. Bull., **34**, 410–413.

URIGAMI A., SAKAI A. & NAGAI M. 1990 Cryopreservation of dried axillary buds from plantlets of *Asparagus officinalis* L. grown *in vitro*. Plant Cell Rep., **9**, 328–331.

USHA RAO I.,RAMANUJA RAO I.V. & NARASIMHAM M. 1986 Induction of androgenesis in the *in vitro* grown anthers of winged bean (*Psophocarpus tetragonolobus*). Phytomorph., **36**, 111–116.

USPENSKI E.E. & USPENSKAJA W.J. 1925 Reinkultur und ungeschlechtliche fortpflanzung des *Volvox minor* und *Volvox globator* in eine synthetischen Nahrlosung. Zeitschr.Bot., **17**, 273–308.

VAHALA T., STABEL P. & ERIKSSON T. 1989 Genetic tramsformation of willows (*Salix* spp.) by *Agrobacterium tumefaciens*. Plant Cell Rep., **8**, 55–58.

VAIN P., YEAN H. & FLAMENT P. 1989 Enhancement of production and regeneration of embryogenic type II callus in *Zea mays* L. by AgNO₃. Plant Cell Tiss. Organ Cult., **18**, 143–151.

VAINSTEIN A., FISHER M. & ZIV M. 1992 Shoot regeneration from petals as a basis for genetic variation and transformation. Acta Hort., **314**, 39–46.

VAJRABHAYA M. & VAJRABHAYA T. 1970 Tissue culture of *Rhynchostylis gigantea*, a monopodial orchid. Am. Orchid Soc. Bull., **39**, 907–910.

VAJRABHAYA M., THANAPAISAL T. & VAJRABHAYA F. 1989 Development of salt tolerant lines of KDML and LPT rice cultivars through tissue culture. Plant Cell Rep., **8**, 411–414.

VALMAYOR H.L. & SAGAWA Y. 1967 Ovule culture on some orchids. Am. Orchid Soc. Bull., **36**, 766–769.

VALOBRA C.P. & JAMES D.J. 1990 *In vitro* shoot regeneration from leaf discs of *Betula pendula* 'Dalecarlica EM85'. Plant Cell Tiss. Organ Cult., **21**, 51–54.

VAN AARTRIJK J. & BLOM–BARNHOORN G.J. 1979 Some influences of α–naphthylacetic acid on the differentiation of meristems of *Lilium speciosum* 'Rubrum' Nr. 10 *in vitro*. Acta Hort., **91**, 269– 219.

VAN AARTRIJK J. & BLOM–BARNHOORN G.J. 1980 Effect of sucrose, mineral salts and some organic substances on the adventitious regeneration *in vitro* of plantlets from bulb-scale tissue of *Lilium speciosum* 'Rubrum'. Acta Hort., **109**, 297–301.

VAN AARTRIJK J., BLOM–BARNHOORN G.J. & BRUINSMA J. 1982 Interactions between NAA, wounding, temperature, and TIBA in their effects on adventitious sprout formation on Lilium bulb tissue. pp. 131–132 in Fujiwara (ed.) 1982 (*q.v.*).

VAN ALTVORST A.C., BRUINSMA T., KOEHORST H.J.J. & DORVS J.J.M. 1992 Regeneration of carnation (*Dianthus caryophyllus*) using leaf explants. Acta Hort., **307**, 109–116.

VAN ARK H.F., ZAAL M.A.C.M., CREEMERS–MOLENAAR J. & VAN DER VALK P. 1991 Improvement of the tissue culture response of seed–derived callus cultures of *Poa pratensis* L.: Effect of gelling agent and abscisic acid. Plant Cell Tiss. Organ Cult., **27**, 275–280.

VAN DEN ENDE G., CROES A.F., KEMP A., BARENDSE G.W.M. & KROH M. 1984b Floral morphogenesis in thin–layer tissue cultures of *Nicotiana tabacum*. Physiol. Plant., **62**, 83–88.

VAN DER KRIEKEN W.M., BRETELER H. & VISSER M.H.M. 1991 Indolebutyric acid–induced root formation in apple tissue culture. Acta Hort., **289**, 343–345.

VAN DER LINDE P.C.G. 1992 Tissue culture of flower–bulb crops: Theory and Practice. Acta Hort., **325**, 419–428.

VAN DER MEIJS A.J. 1980 Vegetative propagation of horticultural crops by tissue culture. Zaadbelangen, **34**, 62–64.

VAN DER POL P.A. & BREUKELAAR A. 1982 Stenting of roses: a method for quick propagation by simultaneously cutting and grafting. Scientia Hort., **17**, 187–196.

VAN DER VALK P., SCHOLTEN O.E., VERSTAPPEN F., JANSEN R.C. & DONS J.J.M. 1992 High frequency somatic embryogenesis and plant regeneration from zygotic embryo– derived callus cultures of three *Allium* species. Plant Cell Tiss. Organ Cult., **30**, 181–191.

VAN DER VALK P., ZAAL M.A.C.M. & CREEMERS–MOLENAAR J. 1988 Regeneration of albino plantlets from suspension derived protoplasts of *Poa pratensis* L. (Kentucky bluegrass). Euphytica, **Suppl.**, 169–176.

VAN ECK J.M. & KITTO S.L. 1988 Regeneration of mint. HortScience, **23**, 803.

VAN ECK J.M. & KITTO S.L. 1990 Callus initiation and regeneration in *Mentha*. HortScience, **25**, 804–806.

VAN ECK J.M. & KITTO S.L. 1992 Regeneration of peppermint and orange mint from leaf disks. Plant Cell Tiss. Organ Cult., **30**, 41–49.

VAN HOOF P. 1974 Méthode practique de culture de méristèmes de fraisiers. Bull. Soc. Roy. Bot. Belge, **107**, 5–8.

VAN NIEUWKIRK J.P., ZIMMERMAN R.H. & FORDHAM I. 1986 Thidiazuron stimulation of apple shoot proliferation *in vitro*. HortScience, **21**, 516–518.

VAN OEVEREN J.J. 1990 Method of aseptically rooting *in vitro* propagated material – has conical shaped container made from semi–permeable, and translucent membrane. Is used to house spongy artificial substrate. World Patent Applic. No. 9015528.

VAN TELGEN H.–J., ELAGOZ V., VAN MIL A., PAFFEN A. & DE KLERK G.–J. 1992 Role of plant hormones in lateral bud growth of rose and apple *in vitro*. Acta Hort., **319**, 137–142.

VAN TUYL J.M., VAN CREIJ M.G.M. & VAN DIEN M.P. 1992 *In vitro* pollination and ovary culture as a breeding tool in wide hybridization of *Lilium* and *Nerine*. Acta Hort., **325**, 461–466.

VAN WAES J. 1987 Effect of activated charcoal on *in vitro* propagation of Western European orchids. Acta Hort., **212**, 131–138.

VARDI A. 1978 Studies on isolation and regeneration of orange protoplasts. pp. 234–241 in Alfermann & Reinhard (eds.) 1978 (*q.v.*)

VARDI A. & RAVEH D. 1976 Cross–feeder experiments between tobacco and orange protoplasts. Z. Pflanzenphysiol., **78**, 350–359.

VARDI A., HUTCHINSON D.J. & GALUN E. 1986 A protoplast–to–tree system in *Microcitrus* based on protoplasts derived from a sustained embryogenic callus. Plant Cell Rep., **5**, 412–414.

VARGA A., THOMA L.H. & BRUINSMA J. 1988 Effects of auxins and cytokinins on epigenetic instability of callus–propagated *Kalanchoe blossfeldiana* Poelln. Plant Cell Tiss. Organ Cult., **15**, 223–231.

VARGHESE T.M. & KAUR A. 1991 Micropropagation of *Albizia lebbeck* Benth. Acta Hort., **289**, 161–162.

VASIL I.K. (ed.) 1980a *Perspectives in plant cell and tissue culture*. Int. Rev. Cytology Suppl. 11A Academic Press.

VASIL I.K. 1982 Somatic embryogenesis and plant regeneration in cereals and grasses. pp. 101–104 in Fujiwara (ed.) 1982 (*q.v.*).

VASIL I.K. 1985 Somatic embryogenesis and its consequences in the Gramineae. pp. 31–48 in Henke *et al.* (eds.) 1985 (*q.v.*).

VASIL I.K. 1987 Developing cell and tissue culture systems for the improvement of cereal and grass crops. J. Plant Physiol., **128** , 193–218.

VASIL I.K. 1990 The contributions of plant biotechnology and its challenges. Newsletter Int. Ass. Plant Tiss. Cult., **62**, 2–11.

VASIL I.K. (ed.) 1991 *Scale–up and automation in plant propagation. Cell Culture and Somatic Cell Genetics of Plants* Vol. 8. Academic Press Inc., San Diego, New York. ISBN 0– 12–715008–0

VASIL I.K. & VASIL V. 1972 Totipotency and embryogenesis in plant cell and tissue culture. In Vitro, **8**, 117–125.

VASIL I.K. & VASIL V. 1980b Embryogenesis and plantlet formation from protoplasts of pearl millet (*Pennisetum americanum*). pp. 255–259 in Ferenczy & Farkas (eds.) 1980 (*q.v.*).

VASIL I.K. & VASIL V. 1980c Isolation and cultivation of protoplasts. pp. 1–19 in Vasil I. K.(ed.) 1980 (*q.v.*).

VASIL I.K., AHUJA M.R. & VASIL V. 1979 Adv. Genet., **20**, 127–215.

VASIL I.K., HILDEBRANDT A.C. & RIKER A.J. 1964 Plantlets from free suspended cells and cell groups *in vitro*. Science, **146**, 76–77.

VASIL I.K., VASIL V. & REDWAY F. 1990 Plant regeneration from embryogenic calli, cell suspension cultures and protoplasts of *Triticum aestivum* L. (wheat). pp. 33–37 in Nijkamp *et al.* (eds.) 1990 (*q.v.*).

VASIL V. & HILDEBRANDT A.C. 1965 Differentiation of tobacco plants from single isolated cells in microcultures. Science, **150** , 889–982.

VASIL V. & VASIL I.K. 1979 Isolation and culture of cereal protoplasts. I. Callus formation from pearl millet (*Pennisetum americanum*) protoplasts. Z. Pflanzenphysiol., **92**, 379–384.

VASIL V. & VASIL I.K. 1980b Isolation and culture of cereal protoplasts. II. Embryogenesis and plantlet formation from protoplasts of *Pennisetum americanum*. Theor. Appl. Genet., **56**, 97–99.

VASIL V. & VASIL I.K. 1982b Characterization of an embryogenic cell suspension culture derived from cultured inflorescences of *Pennisetum americanum* (pearl millet, Gramineae). Am. J. Bot., **69**, 1441–1449.

VASSEUR J. & ROGER V. 1983 Syntheses d'acides nucleiques et de proteines au cours de l'initiation de bourgeons adventifs sur des explantats de *Cichorium intybus* cultivés *in vitro*. Physiol. Plant., **57**, 485–491.

VATSYA B. & BHASKARAN S. 1981 Production of sub–protoplasts in *Brassica oleracea* var. Capitata — a function of osmolarity of the media. Plant Sci. Lett., **23**, 277–282.

VAZQUEZ A.M. & SHORT K.C. 1978 Morphogenesis in cultured floral parts of African violet. J. Exp. Bot., **29**, 1265–1271.

VAZQUEZ A.M., DAVEY M.R. & SHORT K.C. 1977 Organogenesis in cultures of *Saintpaulia ionantha* (African violet). Acta Hort., **78**, 249–258.

VCELAR R.M., FERREIRA D.I. & NIEDERWIESER J.G. 1992 Elimination of Ornithogalum Mosaic Virus in the *Ornithogalum* cv. Rojel through meristem tip culture and chemotherapy. Plant Cell Tiss. Organ Cult., **29**, 51–55.

VEGA DE ROJAS R. & KITTO S.L. 1991 Regeneration of babaco (*Carica pentagona*) from ovular callus. J. Am. Soc. Hort. Sci., **116**, 747–752.

VENCES F.J., VAQUERO F., VASQUEZ A.M. & PEREZ DE LA VEGA M. 1986 Isozymatic changes during *in vitro* morphogenetic processes in self–pollinated species of *Secale*. J. Plant Physiol., **123** , 31–36.

VENKATARAMAN L.V. & RAVISHANKAR G.A. 1986 Clonal propagation of elite plants of *Mentha piperata* by tissue culture. p.65 in Somer *et al.* (eds.) 1986 (*q.v.*).

VENVERLOO C.J., KOSTER J. & LIBBENGA K.R. 1983 The formation of adventitious organs. IV. The ontogeny of shoots and leaves from epidermis cells of *Nautilocalyx lynchii*. Z. Pflanzenphysiol., **109**, 55–67.

VERDEIL J.L., BUFFARD-MOREL J. & PANNETIER C. 1989 Somatic embryogenesis of coconut (*Cocos nucifera* L.) from leaf and inflorescence tissues: research, results, prospects. Oléagineux, **44**, 403–411.

VERHAGEN S., JOHNSON M., LITVAY J. & FEIRER R. 1982 *In vitro* development of conifer embryos excised from seeds. Plant Physiol., **69**, (Suppl.) 72 (Abst.402).

VERHAGEN S.A. & WANN S.R. 1989 Norway spruce somatic embryogenesis: high frequency initiation from light–cultured mature embryos. Plant Cell Tiss. Organ Cult., **16**, 103–111.

VERMEER E. & EVERS P. 1987a Induction of branching and nutrient replenishment in embryo culture of *Quercus robur*. pp. 260–263 in Ducaté *et al.* (eds.) 1987 (*q.v.*).

VERMEER E., EVERS P.W. & VAN EEDEN S. 1991 Rejuvenation, micropropagation and field testing of *Quercus robur*. Acta Hort., **289** , 345–346.

VERTESY J. 1976 Virus elimination from certain strawberry cultivars by apical meristem culture. Gyümölestermesztés **3**, 153–159.

VERTESY J. 1980 *In vitro* propagation of *Prunus persica* and *P. persico–davidiana* shoot–tips in order to get virus–free plants. Acta Hort., **94**, 261–264.

VESTRI F., SCHIFF S., COI A., SANTADREA G. & BENNICI A. 1991 *In vitro* behaviour of *Alnus*, *Cupressus* and *Castanea* spp. Acta Hort., **289**, 163–164.

VIANA A.M. & MANTELL S.H. 1989 Callus induction and plant regeneration from excised zygotic embryos of the seed–propagated yams *Dioscorea composita* Hemsl. and *D. cayenensis* Lam. Plant Cell Tiss. Organ Cult., **16**, 113–122.

VIEIRA M.L.C., JONES B. & COCKING E.C. 1990 Plant regeneration from protoplasts isolated from seedling cotyledons of *Stylosanthes guianensis, S. macrocephala* and *S. scabra*. Plant Cell Rep., **9**, 289–292.

VIEITEZ A.M. & BARCIELA J. 1990 Somatic embryogenesis and plant regeneration from embryonic tissues of *Camellia japonica* L. Plant Cell Tiss. Organ Cult., **21**, 267–274.

VIEITEZ A.M. & VIEITEZ E. 1980a Plantlet formation from embryonic tissue of chestnut grown *in vitro*. Physiol. Plant., **50**, 127–130.

VIEITEZ A.M. & VIEITEZ M.L. 1983 *Castanea sativa* plantlets proliferated from axillary buds cultivated *in vitro*. Scientia Hort., **18**, 343–351.

VIEITEZ A.M., BALLESTER A., SAN–JOSE M.C. & VIEITEZ E. 1985b Anatomical and chemical studies of vitrified shoots of chestnut regenerated *in vitro*. Physiol. Plant., **65**, 177–184.

VIEITEZ A.M., BALLESTER A., VIEITEZ M.L. & VIEITEZ E. 1983 *In vitro* plantlet regeneration of mature chestnut. J. Hort. Sci., **58**, 457–463.

VIEITEZ A.M., CARMEN SANJOSE M. & BALLESTER A. 1989b Progress towards clonal propagation of *Camellia japonica* cv. Alba Plena by tissue culture techniques. J. Hort. Sci., **64**, 605–610.

VIEITEZ A.M., SAN JOSE C., VIEITEZ F.J. & BALLESTER A. 1991 Somatic embryogenesis from roots of *Camellia japonica* plantlets cultured *in vitro*. J. Am. Soc. Hort. Sci., **116**, 753–757.

VIJ S.P., SOOD A. & PLAHA K.K. 1984 Propagation of *Rhynchostylis retusa* Bl. (Orchidaceae) by direct organogenesis from leaf segment cultures. Bot. Gaz., **145**, 210–214.

VILLALOBOS V. 1981 Floral differentiation in carnation (*Dianthus caryophyllus* L.) from anthers cultivated *in vitro*. Phyton, **41**, 71–75.

VILLALOBOS V.M., LEUNG D.W.M. & THORPE T.A. 1984a Light–cytokinin interaction in shoot formation in cultured cotyledon explants of radiata pine. Physiol. Plant., **61**, 497–504.

VINCENT K.A., MATHEW K.M. & HARIHARAN M. 1992 Micropropagation of *Kaempferia galanga* L. — a medicinal plant. Plant Cell Tiss. Organ Cult., **28**, 229–230.

VINE S.J. 1968 Improved culture of apical tissues for production of virus–free strawberries. J. Hort. Sci., **43**, 293–297.

VINTERHALTER B. & NESKOVIC M. 1992 Factors affecting *in vitro* propagation of quince (*Cydonia oblonga* Mill.). J. Hort. Sci., **67**, 39–43.

VINTERHALTER D. & VINTERHALTER B. 1992 Effect of inorganic nutrition on the formation of lateral roots in *Dracaena fragrans* Ker–Gawl cultured *in vitro*. Plant Cell Tiss. Organ Cult., **28**, 267–274.

VINTERHALTER D., GRUBISIC D., BOJOVIC–CVETIC D. & BUDIMIR S. 1992 Lenticel hypertrophy in shoot cultures of *Ceratonia siliqua* L. Plant Cell Tiss. Organ Cult., **31**, 111–114.

VINTERHALTER D., GRUBISIC D., VINTERHALTER B. & KONJEVIC R. 1990 Light–controlled root elongation in *in vitro* cultures of *Dracaena fragrans* Ker–Gawl. Plant Cell Tiss. Organ Cult., **22**, 1–6.

VINTERHALTER D.V. 1989 *In vitro* propagation of green–foliaged *Dracaena fragrans* Ker. Plant Cell Tiss. Organ Cult., **17**, 13–19.

VITTUM M.T. 1979 Trends in vegetable culture: Past, present and future. HortScience, **14**, 345–349.

VON ADERKAS P. 1986 Enhancement of apospory in liquid culture of *Matteuccia struthiopteris*. Ann. Bot., **57**, 505–510.

VON ADERKAS P., BONGA J.M. & NAGMANI R. 1987 Promotion of embryogenesis in cultured megagametophytes of *Larix decidua*. Can. J. For. Res., **17**, 1293–1297.

VON ARNOLD S. 1982 Factors influencing formation, development and rooting of adventitious shoots from embryos of *Picea abies* L. Karst. Plant Sci. Lett., **27**, 275–287.

VON ARNOLD S. & HAKMAN I. 1986 Effect of sucrose on initiation of embryogenic callus cultures from mature zygotic embryos of *Picea abies* L. Karst. (Norway spruce). J. Plant Physiol., **122**, 261–265.

VON ARNOLD S. & HAKMAN I. 1988a Regulation of somatic embryo development in *Picea abies* by abscisic acid (ABA). J. Plant Physiol., **132**, 164–169.

VON ARNOLD S. & HAKMAN I. 1988b Plant regeneration *in vitro* via adventitious buds and somatic embryos in Norway spruce (*Picea abies*). pp. 199–215 in Hanover & Keathley (eds.) 1988 (*q.v.*).

VON SCHMUDE N.F.H. 1985 Tissue culturing *Phalaenopsis* using leaves and leaf segments. Proc. World Orchid Conf. 1984, **11**, 311.

VOTRUBA R. & KODYTEK K. 1988 Investigation of genetic stability in *Chrysanthemum morifolium* 'Blanche Poitevine Supreme' after meristem culture. Acta Hort., **226**, 311–319.

VUYLSTEKE D. & DE LANGHE E. 1985 Feasibility of *in vitro* propagation of bananas and plantains. Trop. Agric., **62**, 323–328.

WAGER V.T., SONG Y.C., MATTHYS–ROCHON E. & DUMAS C. 1989 Observations on the isolated embryo sac of *Zea mays* L. Plant Science, **59**, 127–132.

WAGNER G. & HESS D. 1973 *In vitro* Befruchtungen bei *Petunia hybrida*. Z. Pflanzenphysiol., **69**, 262–269.

WAINWRIGHT H. & FLEGMANN A.W. 1985a The micropropagation of gooseberry (*Ribes uva–crispa* L.). 1. Establishment *in vitro*. J. Hort. Sci., **60**, 215–221.

WAINWRIGHT H. & FLEGMANN A.W. 1985b The micropropagation of gooseberry (*Ribes uva–crispa* L.). 2. *In vitro* proliferation and *in vivo* establishment. J. Hort. Sci., **60**, 485–491.

WAINWRIGHT H. & HARWOOD A.C. 1985 *In vitro* organogenesis and plant regeneration of *Cyclamen persicum* Mill. using seedling tissue. J. Hort. Sci., **60**, 397–403.

WAINWRIGHT H. & MARSH J. 1986 The micropropagation of watercress (*Rorippa nasturtium–aquaticum* L.). J. Hort. Sci., **61**, 251–256.

WAINWRIGHT H. & SCRACE J. 1989 Influence of *in vitro* preconditioning with carbohydrates during the rooting of microcuttings on *in vivo* establishment. Scientia Hort., **38**, 261–267.

WAKE H., UMETSU H., OZEKI Y., SHIMOMURA K. & MATSUNAGA T. 1991 Extracts of marine cyanobacteria stimulated somatic embryogenesis of *Daucus carota* L. Plant Cell Rep., **9**, 655–658.

WAKHLU A.K. & BARNA K.S. 1989 Callus initiation, growth and plant regeneration in *Plantago ovata* Forsk. cv. G1–2. Plant Cell Tiss. Organ Cult., **17**, 235–241.

WAKHLU A.K., NAGARI S. & BARNA K.S. 1990 Somatic embryogenesis and plant regeneration from callus cultures of *Bunium persicum* Boiss. Plant Cell Rep., **9**, 137–138.

WAKIZUKA T. & YAMAGUCHI T. 1987 The induction of enlarged apical domes *in vitro* and multi–shoot formation from Finger Millet (*Eleusine coracana*). Ann. Bot., **60**, 331–336.

WALDENMAIER S. & BUNEMANN G. 1991 *Ex vitro* effects in micropropagation of *Syringa* L. Acta Hort., **300**, 201–209.

WALE S.J. 1983 The use of micropropagated plants of potato cultivars to determine relative susceptibilities to common scab (*Streptomyces scabies*). Tests of Agrochemicals and cultivars no. 4. (Ann. Appl. Biol. 102, Suppl.) 68–69.

WALKER K.A., WENDELN M.L. & JAWORSKI E.G. 1979 Organogenesis in callus tissue of *Medicago sativa*. The temporal separation of induction processes from differentiation processes. Plant Sci. Lett., **16**, 23–30.

WALKER K.A., YU P.C., SATO S.J. & JAWORSKI E.G. 1978 The hormonal control of organ formation in callus of *Medicago sativa* L. cultured *in vitro*. Am. J. Bot., **65**, 654–659.

WALKEY D.G.A. 1968 The production of virus–free rhubarb by apical tip culture. J. Hort. Sci., **43**, 283–287.

WALKEY D.G.A. 1972 Production of apple plantlets from axillary bud meristems. Can. J. Plant Sci., **52**, 1085–1087.

WALKEY D.G.A. 1985 *Applied Plant Virology*. Heinemann, London. ISBN 0–434–92225–0.

WALKEY D.G.A. & ANTILL D.N. 1989 Agronomic evaluation of virus–free and virus–infected garlic (*Allium sativum* L.). J. Hort. Sci., **64**, 53–60.

WALKEY D.G.A. & MATTHEWS K.A. 1979 Rapid clonal propagation of rhubarb (*Rheum rhaponticum* L.) from meristem tips in tissue culture. Plant Sci. Lett., **14**, 287–290.

WALKEY D.G.A., COOPER V.C. & CRISP P. 1974 The production of virus-free cauliflowers by tissue culture. J. Hort. Sci., **49**, 273–275.

WALKEY D.G.A., NEELEY H.A. & CRISP P. 1980 Rapid propagation of white cabbage by tissue culture. Scientia Hort., **12**, 99–107.

WALL J.R. 1954 Interspecific hybrids of *Cucurbita* obtained by embryo culture. Proc. Am. Soc. Hort. Sci., **63**, 427–430.

WALTERS P.R., MACFARLANE N. & SPENSLEY P.C. 1979 *Jojoba: an assessment of prospects*. Report G128, Tropical Products Inst., London.

WALTERS T.W. & EARLE E.D. 1990 A simple, versatile feeder layer system for *Brassica oleracea* protoplast culture. Plant Cell Rep., **9**, 316–319.

WAMBUGU F.M. & RANGAN T.S. 1981 *In vitro* clonal multiplication of pyrethrum (*Chrysanthemum cinerariaefolium* Vis.) by micropropagation. Plant Sci. Lett., **22**, 219–226.

WAN ABDUL RAHAMAN W.Y., GHANDIMATHI H., ROHANI O. & PARANJOTHY K. 1981 Recent developments in tissue culture of *Hevea*. International Rubber Res. Development Board Symposium, Haadyai, 1981.

WAN ABDUL RAHAMAN W.Y., GHANDIMATHI H., ROHANI O. & PARANJOTHY K. 1982 Recent developments in tissue culture of *Hevea*. pp. 152–158 in Rao A.N. (ed.) 1982 (*q.v.*).

Subject index

This index lists the subjects covered in both Part 1 and Part 2

Part 2 commences with page 575